Geometry

Third Edition

Harcourt Brace Jovanovich

New York Chicago San Francisco Atlanta Dallas *and* London

Printed in the United States of America

Regular Edition: **ISBN 0-15-353926-7**
With Alternate Answers: **ISBN 0-15-353927-5**

Curriculum and Writing

James F. Ulrich
Chairman of Department of Mathematics
Arlington High School
Arlington Heights, Illinois

Fred F. Czarnec
Executive Editor, Secondary Mathematics
Center for Curriculum Development
New York, New York

Dorothy L. Guilbault
Senior Editor, Secondary Mathematics
Center for Curriculum Development
New York, New York

Picture Credits

Cover: Jerry Kresh

KEY: (*t*) top, (*c*) center, (*b*) bottom

p. 34, St. Charles Manufacturing Co.; p. 129, American Telephone and Telegraph Co.; p. 146 (*t*), De Wys, Inc.; (*b*), M. White from Monkmeyer; p. 244, courtesy R. Buckminster Fuller; p. 296 (*c*), Grant Heilman; p. 407, Harbrace Art; p. 511 (*c*), Mt. Wilson and Palomar Observatories, California Institute of Technology Bookstore; (*b*), Bauch and Lomb Optical Co.; p. 533 (*t*), Westinghouse Research and Development Corporation.

Contents

Chapter 3: **Congruent Triangles** 93

Chapter 4: **Parallel Lines** 153

Chapter 1
Introduction to Geometry

1-1 Introduction

You are familiar with sets of points such as lines and angles. **Space** is the set of all points. **Geometry** is the study of sets of points in space.

Model	Name	Description
	Point *A*	Indicates position; has no size. Points are in or on lines and planes.
	Line *BC* or Line *CB*	Extends without end in two opposites directions. Lines are in or on planes.
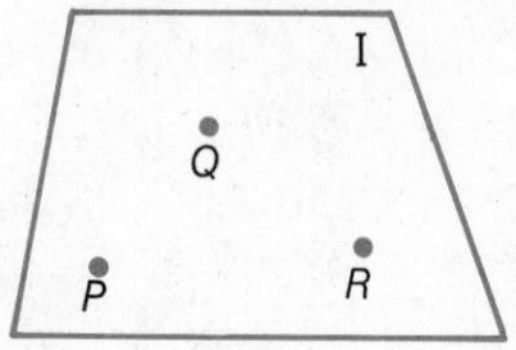	Plane *PQR* or Plane I	A flat surface that extends without end in all directions. A plane is usually represented by a four-sided figure.

Points that are on the same line are **collinear.**

For any three distinct (different) points on a line, one is **between** the other two. Point *E* is between *D* and *F* on line *DE*.

Model	Name	Description
	Segment *GK* or Segment *KG*	Consists of two endpoints, *G* and *K*, and all the points between them.
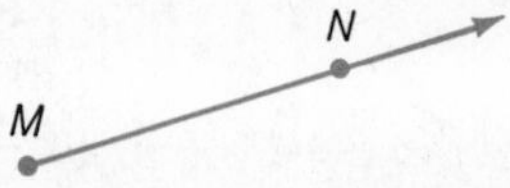	Ray *MN*	Extends without end in one direction from its one endpoint, *M*.

Example

Use symbols and the given line to name:

a. Three distinct segments. **b.** Three distinct rays.
c. The line in three ways.

a. Segments: $\overline{AB}$, $\overline{AC}$, $\overline{BC}$ **b.** Rays: $\overrightarrow{AD}$, $\overrightarrow{DA}$, $\overrightarrow{BD}$ **c.** The line: $\overleftrightarrow{AD}$, $\overleftrightarrow{BC}$, $\overleftrightarrow{BD}$

NOTE: Other answers are possible.

NOTE: $\overline{AD}$ and $\overline{DA}$ are the same segment. However, $\overrightarrow{AD}$ and $\overrightarrow{DA}$ are distinct rays.

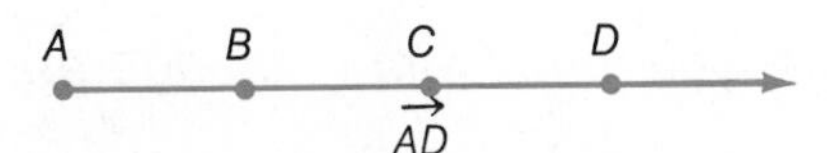

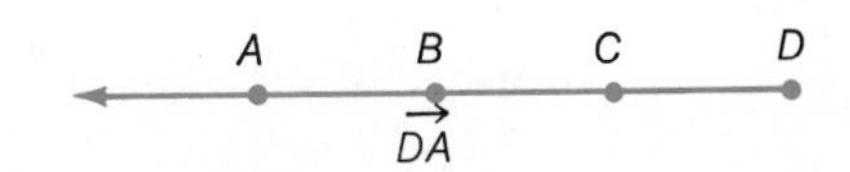

Some familiar geometric figures are made up of segments and rays.

Model	Name	Description
	Angle ABC ($\angle ABC$) or Angle CBA ($\angle CBA$)	$\overrightarrow{BA}$ and $\overrightarrow{BC}$ are the sides of the angle. The common point of the sides is the **vertex** (plural: vertices) of the angle. It is the middle letter in the name.
	Triangle DEF ($\triangle DEF$) or Triangle FDE ($\triangle FDE$) or Triangle FED ($\triangle FED$)	$\overline{DE}$, $\overline{EF}$, and $\overline{FD}$ are the three sides of the triangle. $\angle DEF$, $\angle EFD$, and $\angle FDE$ are the three angles.

Try These

Replace the _?_ with the missing symbol or name.

1. Name: _?_
Symbol: $\overrightarrow{TU}$

2. Name: Triangle HAP
Symbol: _?_

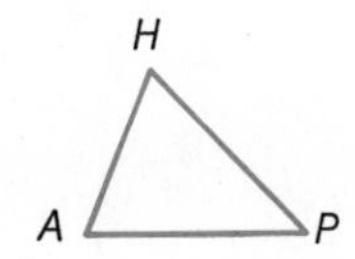

3. Name: _?_
Symbol: $\angle WHY$

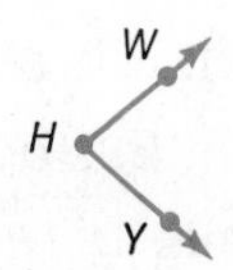

Exercises ***4–7*** *refer to the line below.*

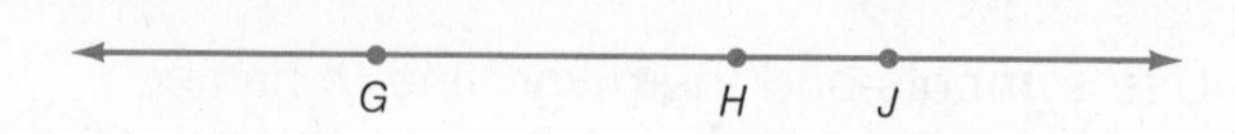

4. Use the point G to name the line in three different ways.

5. Name two rays that have H as an endpoint.

6. Name three segments.

7. Name $\overrightarrow{GJ}$ in a different way.

Exercises

Match one or more names in Column A with each figure in Exercises ***1–6.***

1.

2.

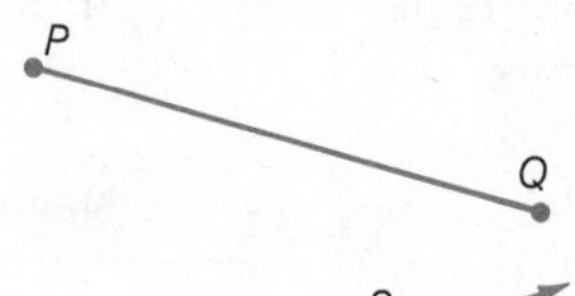

3.

4.

5.

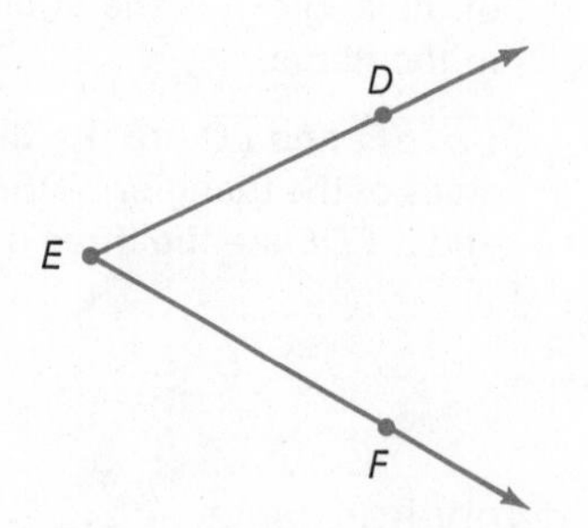

6.

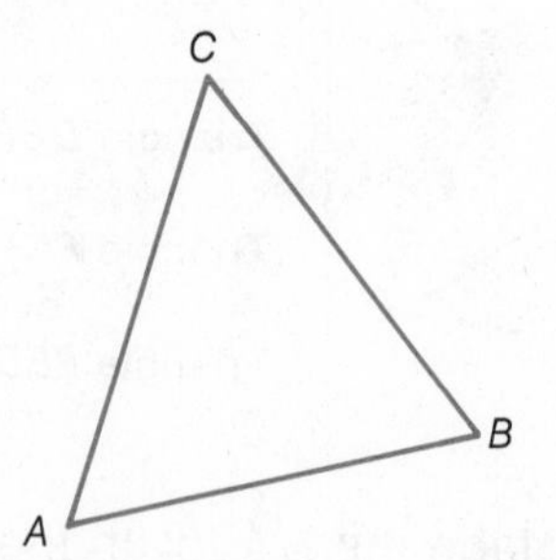

Column A

a. $\triangle BCA$
b. $\overline{PQ}$
c. $\overrightarrow{RT}$
d. $\angle FED$
e. $\triangle ABC$
f. $\overleftrightarrow{XY}$
g. $\angle DEF$
h. $\overline{QP}$
i. $\overrightarrow{NS}$
j. $\triangle CAB$
k. $\angle E$
l. $\overleftrightarrow{YX}$

Classify each statement as *<u>True</u>* *or* *<u>False</u>. Refer to the figure.*

7. Points M, E, and R are collinear.

8. Point E is on $\overleftrightarrow{MR}$.

9. Point E is on $\overleftrightarrow{HK}$.

10. Points M, H, and E are collinear.

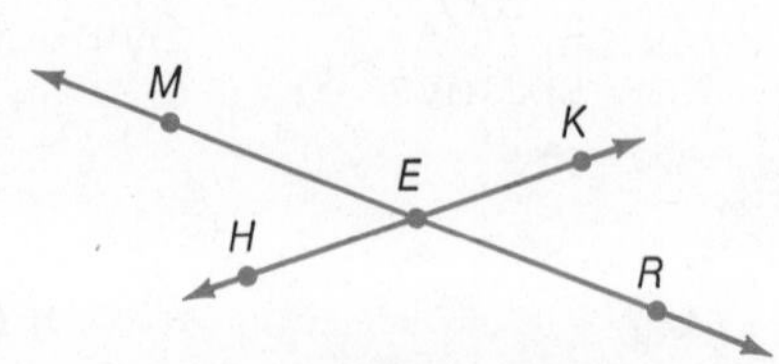

11. $\overline{EM}$ has two endpoints.

12. $\overrightarrow{EM}$ has one endpoint.

13. $\overleftrightarrow{EM}$ has no endpoints.

14. Another name for $\overrightarrow{EM}$ is $\overrightarrow{ME}$.

For Exercises **15–17,** *refer to the figure for Exercises* **7–14.**

15. Name four rays with the same endpoint.

16. Use point K to name $\overleftrightarrow{EH}$ in three different ways.

17. Name six different segments.

Complete the table.

	Number of Rays	Figures	Angles	Number of Angles
18.	2		$\angle X$	?
19.	3		$\angle AXB$, $\angle BXC$, $\angle AXC$	?
20.	4		$\angle AXB$, $\angle BXC$, $\angle CXD$, $\angle AXC$, $\angle BXD$, $\angle$?	?
21.	5		$\angle AXB$, $\angle BXC$, $\angle$?, $\angle$?, $\angle AXC$, $\angle BXD$, $\angle$?, $\angle AXD$, $\angle$? $\angle$?	?

22. Draw six rays with the same endpoint. How many angles are formed? (Do not draw any two rays on the same line.)

23. Suppose you draw seven rays with the same endpoint (no two on the same line). Predict the number of angles formed.

1-2 Segments

A segment has two endpoints and can be measured.

Model	Meaning	Symbol
A B	$\overline{AB}$ is 3 units long.	$AB = 3$
C D	$\overline{CD}$ is 3 units long.	$CD = 3$
E F	$\overline{EF}$ is 5 units long.	$EF = 5$
1 2 3 4 5 6		

NOTE: AB is the measure of $\overline{AB}$. Therefore, AB is a number.

Example 1

Use the figures above to tell whether each statement is True or False.

Statement	True or False?	Reason
$AB = CD$	True	$AB = 3$ and $CD = 3$. Therefore, $AB = CD$.
$\overline{AB} = \overline{CD}$	False	$\overline{AB}$ and $\overline{CD}$ are different segments. Therefore, they are two different sets of points.
$\overline{AB} = \overline{BA}$	True	$\overline{AB}$ and $\overline{BA}$ are the same segment. Therefore, they are the same set of points.
$AB = EF$	False	$AB = 3$ and $EF = 5$; $3 \neq 5$
$\overline{AB} = 3$	False	$\overline{AB}$ is a segment, not a measure.

$\overline{AB}$ and $\overline{CD}$ have the same measure. They are **congruent segments.**

$\overline{AB} \cong \overline{CD}$ ← Read "$\overline{AB}$ is congruent to $\overline{CD}$."

Two segments that have the same measure are congruent.

Example 2

Use the figure at the right to classify each statement as True or False.

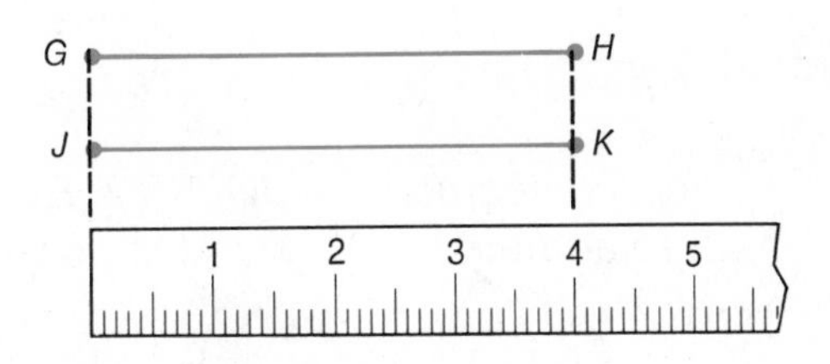

Statement	True or False?	Reason
$GH \cong JK$	False	$\overline{GH} \cong \overline{JK}$; their measures are equal
$GH = JK$	True	$GH = 4$ and $JK = 4$. Therefore, $GH = JK$.
$\overline{GH} \cong \overline{JK}$	True	Segments that have the same measure are congruent.
$\overline{GH} = \overline{JK}$	False	$\overline{GH}$ and $\overline{JK}$ are two different segments. Therefore, they are two different sets of points.
$\overline{GH} = \overline{HG}$	True	$\overline{GH}$ and $\overline{HG}$ are the same segment. Therefore, they are the same set of points.

In $\overline{ST}$, $SR = 2\frac{1}{2}$ and $RT = 2\frac{1}{2}$. Therefore, $\overline{SR} \cong \overline{RT}$. Since R is between S and T and $\overline{SR} \cong \overline{RT}$, R is the midpoint of $\overline{ST}$. The **midpoint** of a segment separates it into two congruent segments.

These marks identify congruent segments.

S R T

1 2 3 4 5

Try These

Classify each statement as True or False.

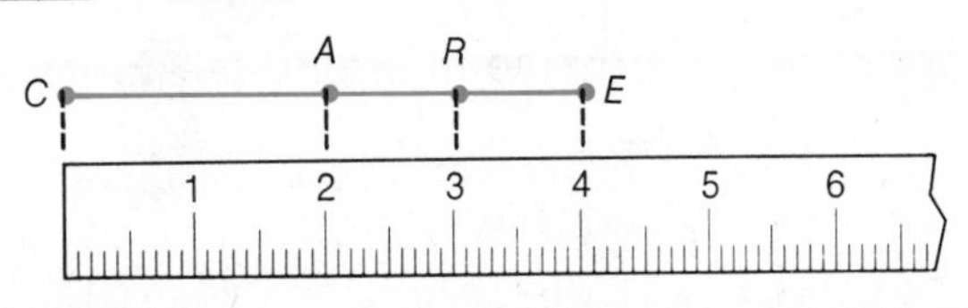

1. $CA = 2$

2. $\overline{CR} = 3$

3. $CA = AR$

4. $CA = AE$

5. $\overline{AR} = \overline{RE}$

6. $\overline{CA} \cong \overline{AE}$

7. A is the midpoint of $\overline{CR}$.

8. A is the midpoint of $\overline{CE}$.

9. R is the midpoint of $\overline{AE}$.

Exercises

For the segment below, $SR = RQ = QT$ and T is the midpoint of $\overline{SM}$. Replace each _?_ with the correct measure.

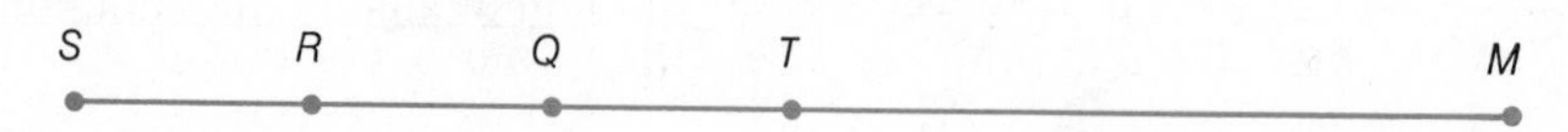

1. If $SR = 15$, then $RQ =$ _?_.
2. If $SQ = 25$, then $SR =$ _?_.
3. If $RQ = 7$, then $ST =$ _?_.
4. If $SR = 3$, then $TM =$ _?_.

Given that $\overline{AE} \cong \overline{EB}$ and $\overline{DE} \cong \overline{EC}$, classify each statement as True or False.

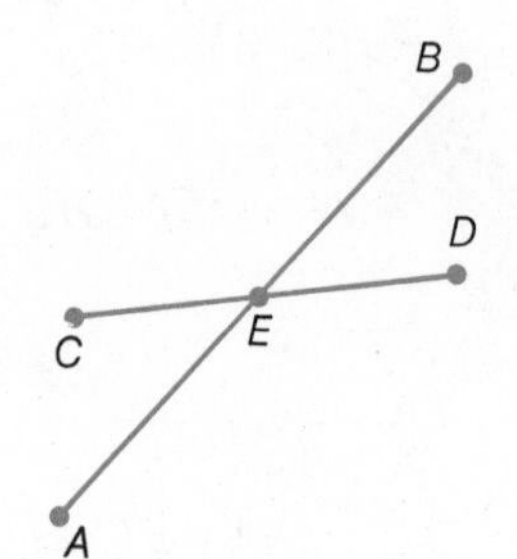

5. $\overline{AE} = \overline{EB}$
6. $DE = EC$
7. E is the midpoint of $\overline{AB}$.
8. E is the midpoint of $\overline{DC}$.
9. If $AB = 38$ and $DC = 30$, then $AE = ED$.
10. If $EC = 3.5$, then $DC = 7$.

*For Exercises **11–26**, use the figure below to name the segment, ray, or line that completes each statement.*

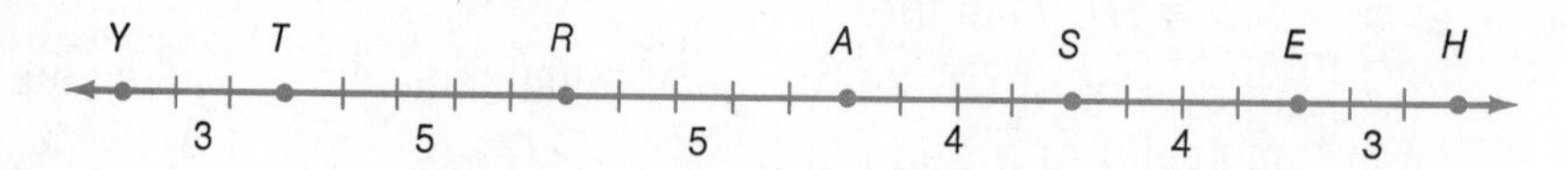

11. $\overline{TR} \cong$ _?_
12. $\overline{YT} \cong$ _?_
13. $\overline{YR} \cong$ _?_
14. _?_ $\cong \overline{ES}$
15. _?_ $\cong \overline{YE}$
16. R is the midpoint of _?_.
17. _?_ is the midpoint of $\overline{AE}$.
18. Another name for $\overrightarrow{RY}$ is _?_.
19. $AH = AE +$ _?_
20. $YA = TA +$ _?_
21. $TE = TR +$ _?_
22. $YT = YR -$ _?_
23. $YA = YS -$ _?_
24. $TH - SH =$ _?_
25. $TR + RA = YT +$ _?_
26. $AS + SE = YT +$ _?_

1-3 Angles

You use a **protractor** to measure an angle. The unit of measure is the **degree,** °. The degree measure of $\angle ABC$ is 1, or $m\angle ABC = 1$.

The measure of an angle is greater than 0 but less than 180.

Example 1

Use a protractor to measure each angle.

a. $\angle RST$ **b.** $\angle XYZ$

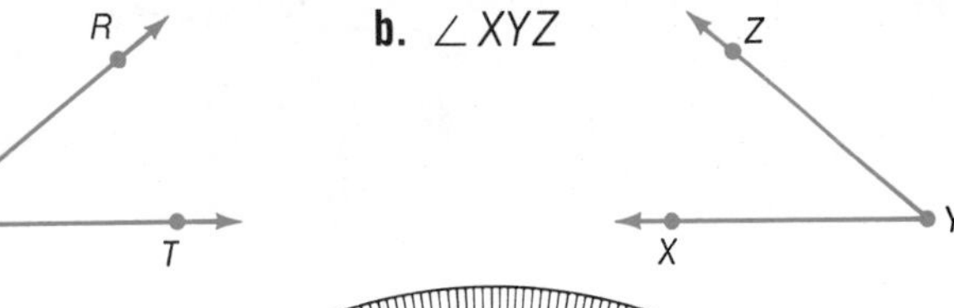

a. 1. Place the center of the protractor on S, the vertex of $\angle RST$. Place the edge of the protractor along $\overrightarrow{ST}$.

2. Since $\overrightarrow{SR}$ intersects the protractor at 40 on the inner scale, the measure of $\angle RST$ is 40, or $m\angle RST = 40$.

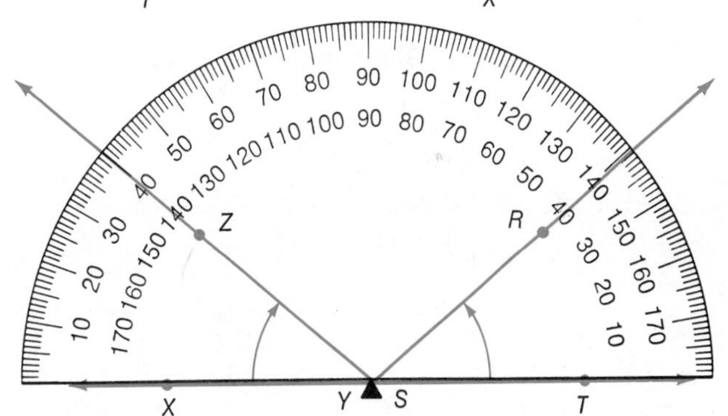

NOTE: $\overrightarrow{SR}$ was extended to intersect the scale of the protractor.

b. 1. Place the center of the protractor on Y with the edge of the protractor along $\overrightarrow{XY}$.

2. $\overrightarrow{YZ}$ intersects the protractor at 40 on the outer scale. Thus, $m\angle XYZ = 40$.

NOTE: $\angle XYZ$ and $\angle RST$ have the same measure. Angles that have the same measure are **congruent angles.**

$\angle XYZ \cong \angle RST$ ⟵ $\angle XYZ$ is congruent to $\angle RST$.

An angle can be named by the letter at its vertex only, as long as there is no confusion.

Example 2

Use these figures to determine whether each statement is True or False.

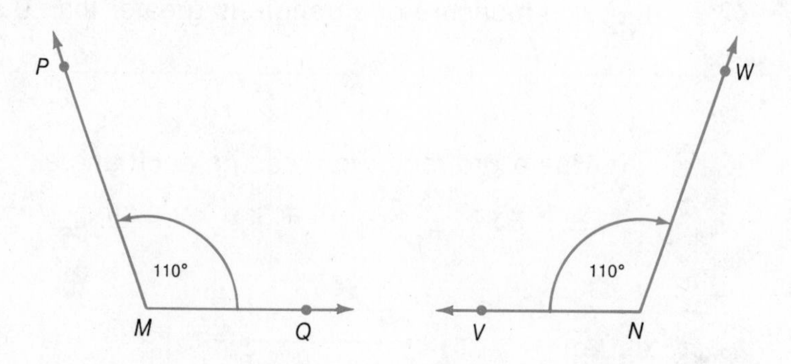

Statement	True or False?	Reason
$\angle M = \angle N$	False	$\angle M$ and $\angle N$ are two different angles. Therefore, they are not the same set of points.
$m\angle M = m\angle N$	True	$m\angle M = 110$ and $m\angle N = 110$. Therefore, $m\angle M = m\angle N$.
$\angle M \cong \angle N$	True	Angles that have the same measure are congruent.
$m\angle M \cong m\angle N$	False	Only geometric figures can be congruent; their measures can be equal.
$\angle M = 110$	False	$\angle M$ is a geometric figure; $m\angle M = 110$.
$m\angle M = 110$	True	The measure of $\angle M$ is 110.

Angles can be classified according to their measures.

Model	Measure	Name	Description
	55	**Acute**	Its measure is greater than 0 and less than 90.
	90	**Right**	Its measure is 90.
	110	**Obtuse**	Its measure is greater than 90 and less than 180.

An angle has an **interior** and an **exterior.**

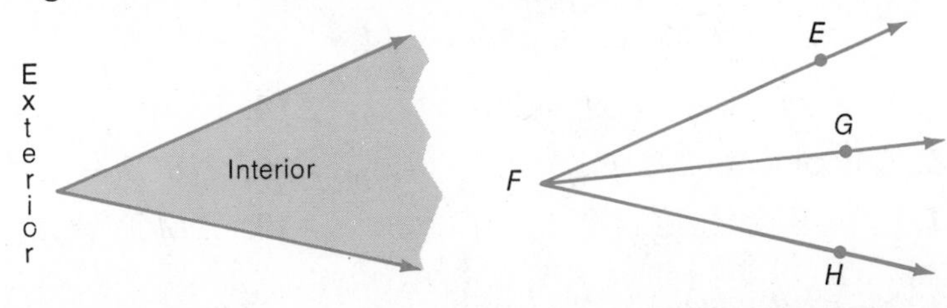

In the figure at the right above, $\overrightarrow{FG}$ lies between $\overrightarrow{FE}$ and $\overrightarrow{FH}$ and $m\angle EFG = m\angle HFG$. Since angles that have the same measure are congruent, $\angle EFG \cong \angle HFG$. Therefore, $\overrightarrow{FG}$ is the **bisector** of $\angle EFH$.

Try These

Classify each angle as acute, right, or obtuse.

1. $\angle EMF$ **2.** $\angle FMO$ **3.** $\angle EMR$

Classify each statement as True or False.

4. $\angle DMO \cong \angle EMF$ **5.** $\angle DMO = \angle RMO$ **6.** $\overrightarrow{ME}$ is the bisector of $\angle RMF$.

7. $m\angle RMF = 125$ **8.** $m\angle EMO = 125$ **9.** E is in the interior of $\angle RMF$.

Exercises

Classify each angle as acute, right, or obtuse.

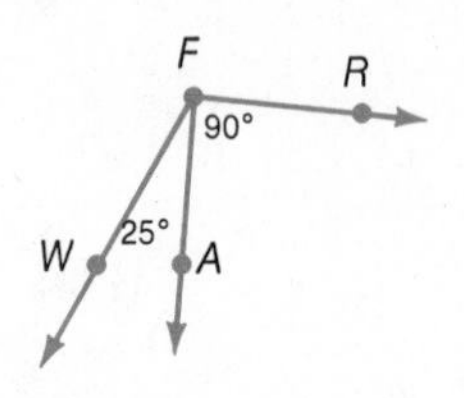

a

1. ∠AFR **2.** ∠AFW **3.** ∠WFR

Use the figure at the right for Exercises ***4–18.***

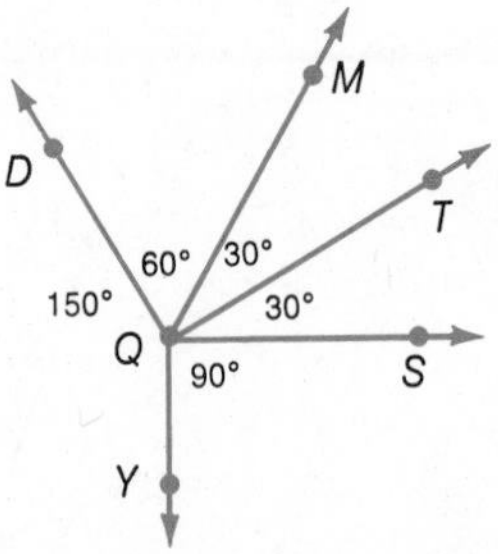

4. m∠DQM = ? **5.** m∠TQS = ?

6. m∠DQY = ? **7.** m∠SQY = ?

8. m∠MQT = ? **9.** m∠DQT = ?

Name the following geometric figures.

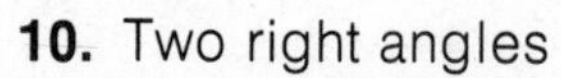

10. Two right angles

11. Two obtuse angles that have $\overrightarrow{QD}$ as a side

12. Three acute angles that have $\overrightarrow{QM}$ as a side

Complete each statement.

13. Ray ? bisects ∠MQS. **14.** Point ? is in the interior of ∠TQY.

15. $\overrightarrow{QM}$ bisects ∠ ?. **16.** ∠SQT ≅ ∠ ?

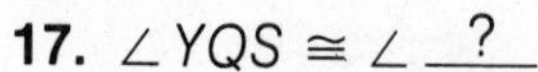

17. ∠YQS ≅ ∠ ? **18.** ∠MQY ≅ ∠ ?

Trace the figures below on your paper. Use your protractor to measure each angle. (Extend the rays as far as necessary.)

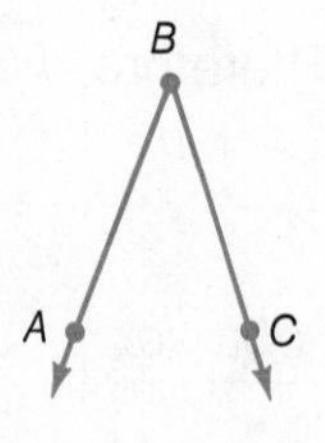

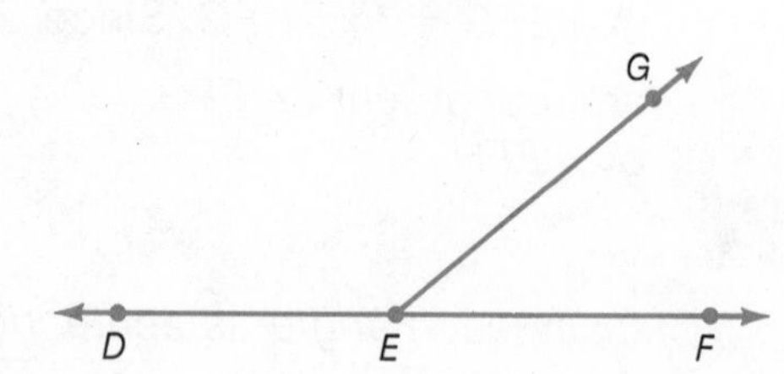

19. m∠ABC = ? **20.** m∠GEF = ? **21.** m∠DEG = ?

Refer to your tracings for Exercises ***19–21.*** *Use your protractor to draw the following rays.*

b

22. Ray BZ, bisecting ∠ABC **23.** Ray EW, bisecting ∠DEG

1-4 Triangles

Triangles can be classified according to the measures of their sides as equilateral, isosceles, or scalene.

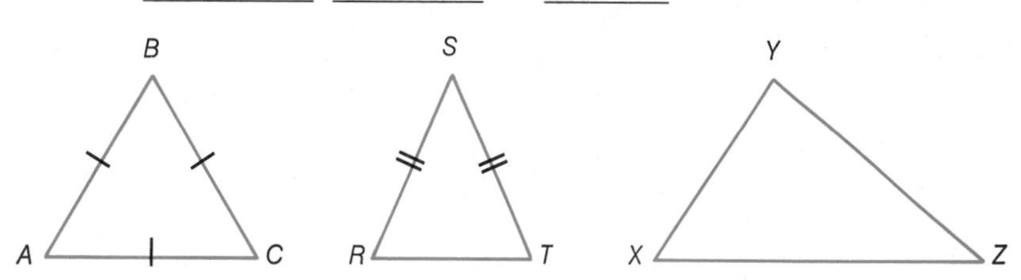

Triangle	Name	Description
$\triangle ABC$	**Equilateral**	All sides are congruent.
$\triangle RST$	**Isosceles**	Two sides are congruent.
$\triangle XYZ$	**Scalene**	No sides are congruent.

The marks on $\triangle ABC$ and $\triangle RST$ indicate the congruent sides.

$$\overline{AB} \cong \overline{BC} \cong \overline{AC}, \text{ so } AB = BC = AC.$$
$$\overline{RS} \cong \overline{ST}, \text{ so } RS = ST.$$

The parts (sides and angles) of an isosceles triangle have special names.

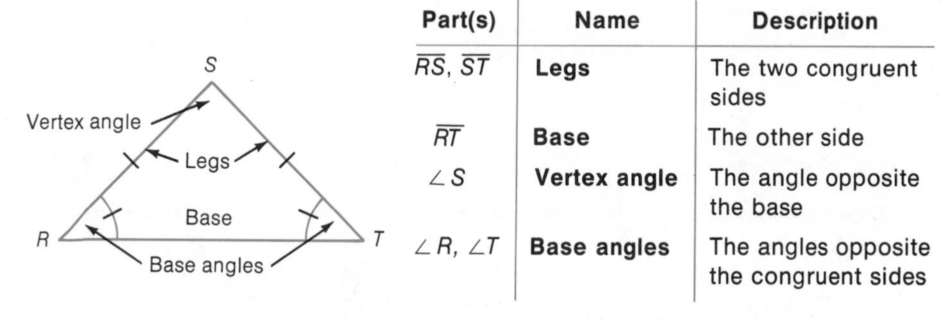

Part(s)	Name	Description
$\overline{RS}$, $\overline{ST}$	**Legs**	The two congruent sides
$\overline{RT}$	**Base**	The other side
$\angle S$	**Vertex angle**	The angle opposite the base
$\angle R$, $\angle T$	**Base angles**	The angles opposite the congruent sides

The marks on $\angle R$ and $\angle T$ indicate that they are congruent. If you use a protractor to measure the base angles of different isosceles triangles, you will find that the base angles are congruent.

If all three angles of a triangle are congruent, the triangle is **equiangular.** If you measure the three sides of any equiangular triangle, you will find that an equiangular triangle is equilateral.

Triangles can also be classified according to the measures of their angles as right, obtuse, or acute.

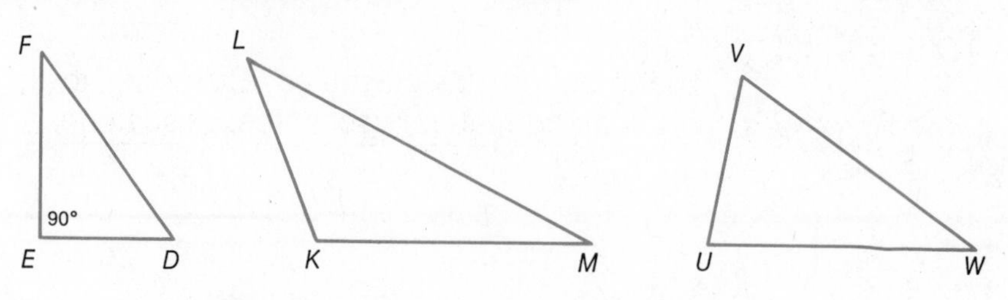

Triangle	Name	Description
$\triangle DEF$	**Right**	One angle is a right angle.
$\triangle KLM$	**Obtuse**	One angle is an obtuse angle.
$\triangle UVW$	**Acute**	All its angles are acute.

In a right triangle, the side opposite the right angle is the **hypotenuse.** The other two sides are **legs** of the triangle. In the figure at the right, the ⌐ indicates a right angle.

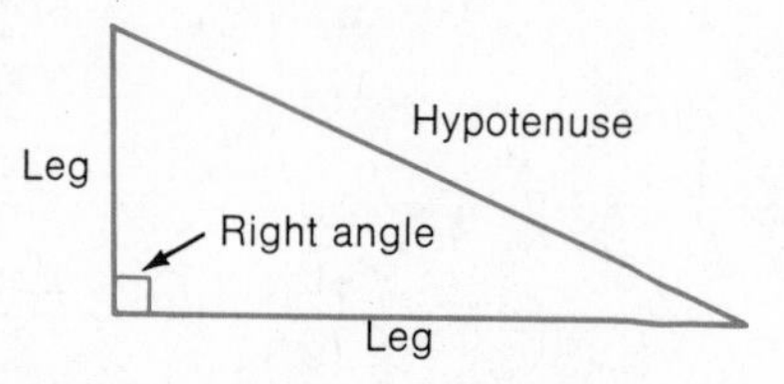

A triangle can be classified according to the measures of its angles and sides.

Example

Classify these triangles according to the measures of their angles and sides.

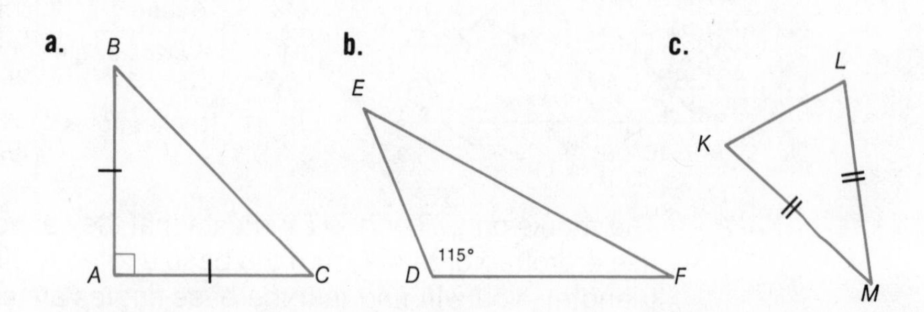

Triangle	Name	Reason
$\triangle ABC$	Right isosceles	$\angle A$ is a right angle; $\overline{AB} \cong \overline{AC}$
$\triangle DEF$	Obtuse scalene	$\angle D$ is obtuse; no sides are congruent.
$\triangle KLM$	Acute isosceles	All angles are acute; $\overline{LM} \cong \overline{KM}$

Try These

Name the following parts for isosceles triangle ABC. Then give each measure.

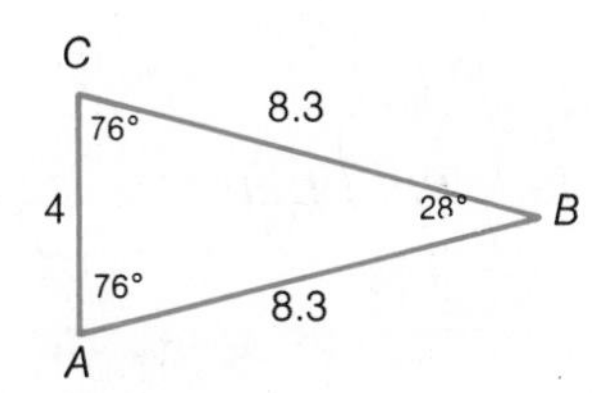

1. The legs
2. The vertex angle
3. The base angles

Name the following parts for right triangle THR. Then give each measure.

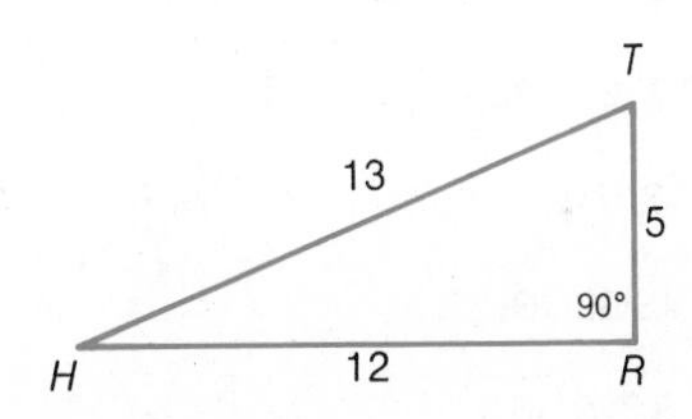

4. The right angle
5. The hypotenuse
6. The legs

For each kind of triangle, tell how many sides are congruent.

7. Isosceles
8. Scalene
9. Equilateral

The angles of a triangle have the measures shown. Classify each triangle as acute, right, or obtuse.

10. 17°, 80°, 83°
11. 44°, 83°, 53°
12. 25°, 65°, 90°

Classify each triangle according to the measures of its angles and sides.

13. $\triangle ABC$ has one right angle and two congruent sides.
14. $\triangle XYZ$ has no obtuse angles and no congruent sides.
15. $\triangle DEF$ has one obtuse angle and two congruent sides.

Exercises

Name the following parts for right triangle EFD below. Then give each measure.

a

1. The right angle **2.** The legs 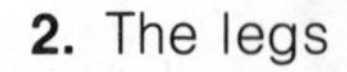 **3.** The hypotenuse

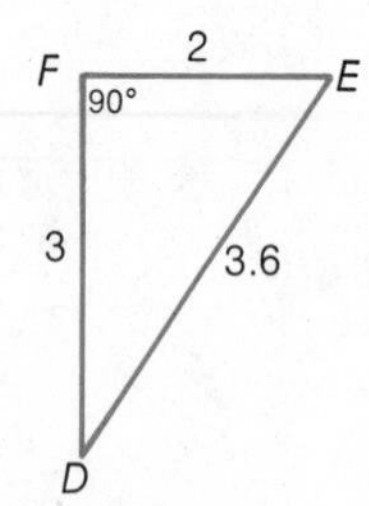

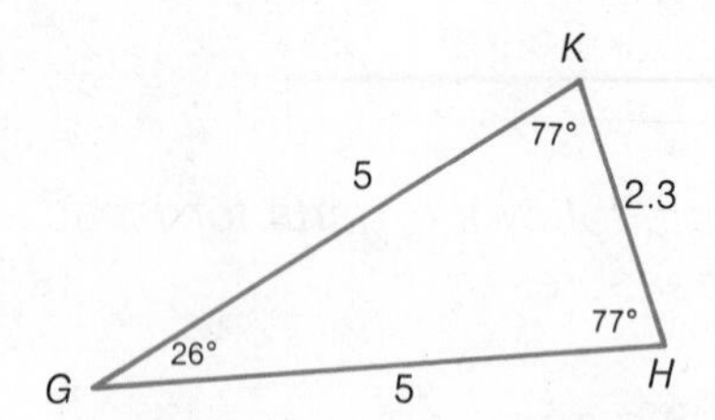

Name the following parts for isosceles triangle GHK above. Then give each measure.

4. The legs **5.** The base angles **6.** The vertex angle

Match each description at the left with one or more triangles on the right.

7. Right isosceles

8. Right scalene

9. Obtuse isosceles

10. Obtuse scalene

11. Acute isosceles

12. Acute scalene

13. Acute equilateral

14. Equiangular

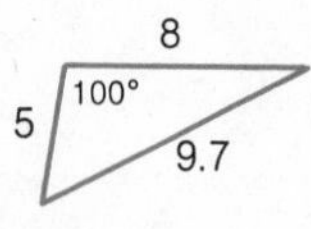

b.

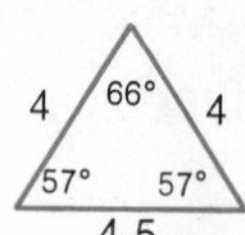

c.

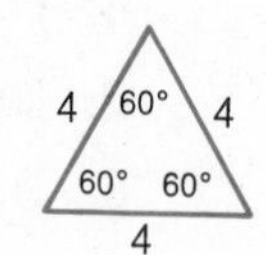

d. 13, 5, 90°, 12

e. 5, 7.1, 90°, 5

f.

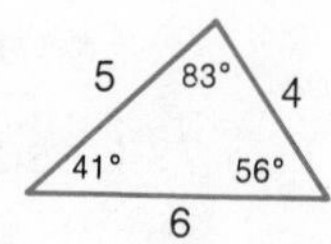

g.

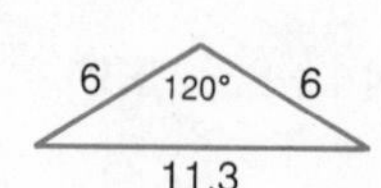

h.

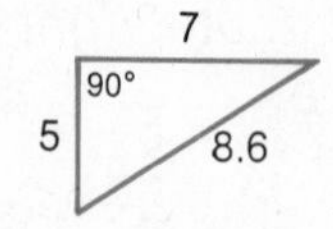

i.

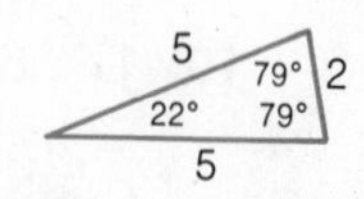

Classify each triangle according to the measures of its angles and sides.

15. $\triangle DEF$ has three congruent angles.

16. $\triangle RST$ has one right angle and no congruent sides.

17. $\triangle XYZ$ has three acute angles and two congruent sides.

18. $\triangle MOQ$ has one obtuse angle and two congruent sides.

Refer to the figure at the right for Exercises ***19–21.***

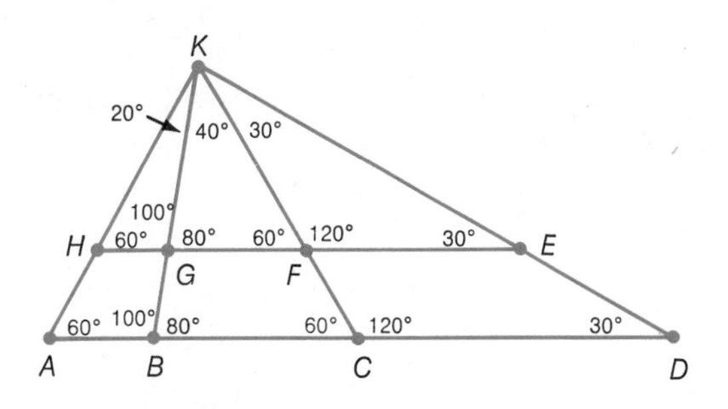

19. Name as many triangles as you can. (There are 12 triangles.)

20. For each triangle listed in answer to Exercise **19,** state whether it is an acute, a right, or an obtuse triangle.

21. Which of the triangles are equiangular?

Refer to the figure at the right for Exercises ***22–24.***

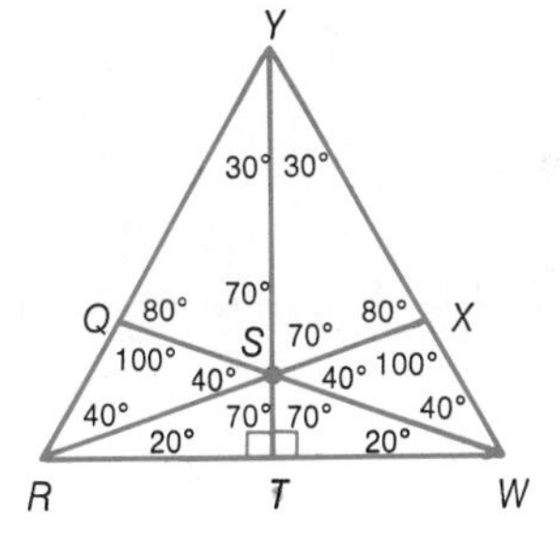

22. Name as many triangles as you can. (There are 16 triangles.)

23. For each triangle listed in answer to Exercise **22,** state whether it is an acute, right, or an obtuse triangle.

24. Which triangle is equiangular?

PUZZLE

An ant is at point A, the upper left corner of a gate. The ant can walk downward only. Thus, the ant can reach point B in two ways, but there is only one way in which it can reach point C.

In how many ways can the ant walk from point A to point D?

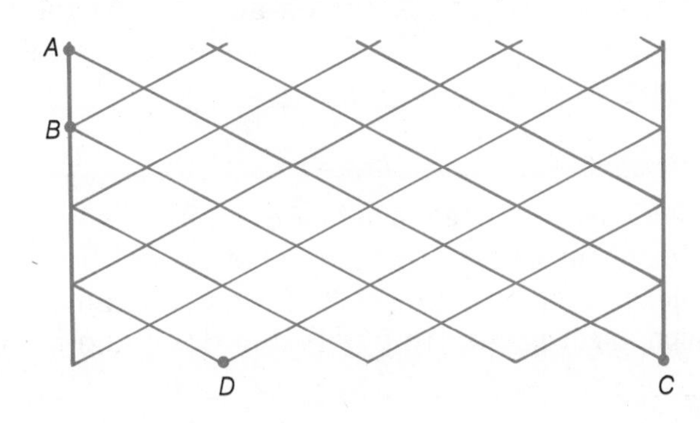

1-5 Definitions

Points are the basic elements that make up each set in geometry.

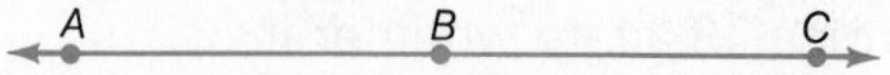

$A \in \overleftrightarrow{AC}$ — A is an element of $\overleftrightarrow{AC}$.

If a first set contains every element of a second set, then the second set is a **subset** of the first set.

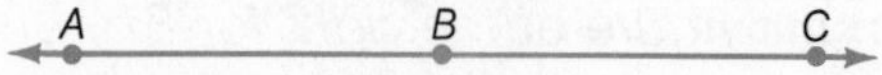

$\overline{AB} \subset \overleftrightarrow{AB}$ — $\overline{AB}$ is a subset of $\overleftrightarrow{AB}$.

The **union** of two sets is the set whose elements belong to either set or to both of them.

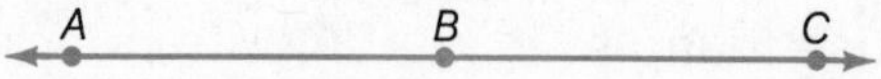

$\overline{AB} \cup \overline{BC} = \overline{AC}$ — The union of $\overline{AB}$ and $\overline{BC}$ is $\overline{AC}$.

The **intersection** of two sets is the set whose elements are common to both sets.

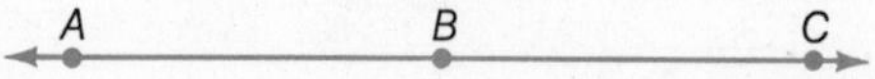

$\overline{AB} \cap \overline{BC} = \{B\}$ — The intersection of $\overline{AB}$ and $\overline{BC}$ *is* $\{B\}$.

In geometry, point, line, and plane are undefined terms. These terms, along with those given above, form the basis for defining other geometric terms. The terms used in Sections 1–4 of this chapter were described but not defined.

Definitions: **Collinear points** are points that lie on the same line.
Noncollinear points are points that do not lie on the same line.
Coplanar points are points that lie in the same plane.
Noncoplanar points are points that do not lie in the same plane.

The definitions at the bottom of page 18 use only undefined terms. A definition must use only undefined terms and terms that have been previously defined.

In the table below, the definitions are given in order of definition. Undefined terms and terms that have been previously defined are underlined.

Definitions	Examples
A **ray** is a subset of a line that contains a given point and all the points on one side of the given point. The given point is the **endpoint** of the ray.	A B C D $\overrightarrow{BD} \subset \overleftrightarrow{AD}$ Endpoint: B $\overrightarrow{BA} \subset \overleftrightarrow{AD}$ Endpoint: B $\overrightarrow{CD} \subset \overleftrightarrow{AD}$ Endpoint: C $\overrightarrow{CA} \subset \overleftrightarrow{AD}$ Endpoint: C
An **angle** is the union of two distinct noncollinear rays with a common endpoint.	D E F $\overrightarrow{ED} \cup \overrightarrow{EF} = \angle DEF$
Opposite rays are rays that have a common endpoint and whose union is a line.	X Y Z Opposite rays: $\overrightarrow{YZ}$ and $\overrightarrow{YX}$

Using between as an undefined term, you can also define line segment, or simply, segment. Then you can use segment to define triangle.

Definitions: A **line segment** is a subset of the points on a line consisting of any two distinct points of the line and all the points between them. The two given points are the **endpoints** of the segment.

A **triangle** is the union of three segments joining three noncollinear points.

Example 1

Arrange the terms in the order in which their definitions should be stated.

a. Isosceles triangle, triangle, base angles of an isosceles triangle.
b. Hypotenuse, triangle, right triangle.

a. Triangle, isosceles triangle, base angles of an isosceles triangle.
b. Triangle, right triangle, hypotenuse.

Every definition is **reversible.** This means that the reversed statement is also true.

Collinear points are points that lie on the same line. ← Definition

Points that lie on the same line are collinear points. ← Reversed statement

Example 2

Reverse each statement. Tell whether the reversed statement is true.

Statement	Reversed Statement	Is the reversed statement true?
A right triangle is a triangle with one right angle.	A triangle with one right angle is a right triangle.	Yes
Right angles are congruent angles	Congruent angles are right angles.	No. Thus, the statement is not a definition.

Try These

Arrange the terms in the order in which their definitions should be stated.

1. Measure of an angle, angle, congruent angles.
2. Legs of an isosceles triangle, isosceles triangle, triangle.

3. Angle, obtuse triangle, obtuse angle.

Reverse each statement. Tell whether the reversed statement is true.

4. An equilateral triangle is a triangle with three congruent sides.
5. In a right triangle, the hypotenuse is the side opposite the right angle.

Exercises

For Exercises **1–6,** arrange the terms in the order in which their definitions *should be stated.*

a

1. Acute triangle, angle, acute angle, triangle
2. Triangle, legs of a right triangle, right triangle
3. Endpoint of a ray, ray, angle
4. Isosceles triangle, triangle, vertex angle of an isosceles triangle
5. Midpoint of a segment, congruent segments, segment
6. Congruent angles, bisector of an angle, angle

Reverse each statement. Tell whether the reversed statement is true.

7. Coplanar lines are lines that lie in the same plane.
8. An isosceles triangle is a triangle with two congruent sides.
9. A right angle is an angle that measures 90°.
10. Points that do not lie on the same line are noncollinear points.
11. A scalene triangle is a triangle with no congruent sides.
12. The legs of an isosceles triangle are the two congruent sides of the triangle.
13. Congruent segments are segments that have the same measure.

For each definition, name the words or phrases that may be taken as undefined or must have been previously defined.

14. An acute triangle is a triangle with three acute angles.
15. Congruent angles are angles that have the same measure.

16. Ray FG is the <u>bisector</u> of $\angle EFH$ if G lies in the interior of $\angle EFH$ and $m\angle EFG = m\angle GFH$.

17. Equal angles are the angles that contain the same points.

18. A right triangle is a triangle with one right angle.

A good definition has several characteristics.

1. The term being defined must be named.
2. The definition must use only accepted undefined terms or previously defined terms.
3. The definition must identify the set to which the term belongs. It should give just enough additional information to distinguish it from other members of that set.
4. The definition must be reversible.

The following statements are not good definitions. Tell why.

b

19. It is when you have two distinct rays with a common endpoint.

20. It measures less than 90.

21. Coplanar points are in the same plane.

22. A triangle is when you have three angles and three sides.

23. Congruent segments are segments that have the same measure and are equal.

24. An angle is a geometric figure.

c

25. Rewrite the statements in Exercises **19–24** so that they are acceptable definitions.

PUZZLE

Five blocks are placed in a row as shown below. Each block is covered with paper showing 6 pictures arranged the same way on each block. If a paper cover is removed and flattened out as shown below on the right, what pictures will appear on the squares numbered 1, 2, and 3?

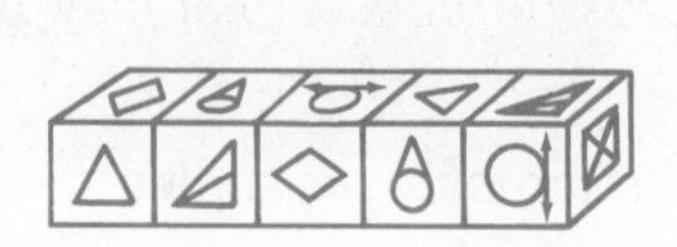

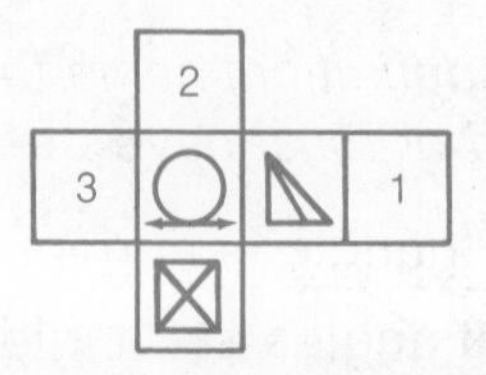

1-6 Postulates and Theorems

In geometry, a **postulate** is a mathematical statement that is accepted without proof.

Postulate 1: Every line contains at least two distinct points.

Postulate 2: Every plane contains at least three distinct noncollinear points.

Postulate 3: Space contains at least four noncoplanar points.

Postulates 1, 2, and 3 establish the least number of points for lines, planes, and space. Clearly, there is an infinite number of points in a line, in a plane, and in space.

Postulate 4: For any two distinct points, there is exactly one line containing them.

Postulate 5: For any three distinct noncollinear points, there is exactly one plane containing them.

Postulates 4 and 5 are often stated as follows.

Two points determine a line. (Postulate 4)

Three noncollinear points determine a plane. (Postulate 5)

Postulate 6: If any two distinct points lie in a plane, the line containing these points lies in the plane.

Postulate 7: If two distinct planes have one point in common, they have at least two points in common.

This figure shows Postulates 4 and 6 taken together. You can draw only one line through R and S, line RS, and line RS lies in plane I.

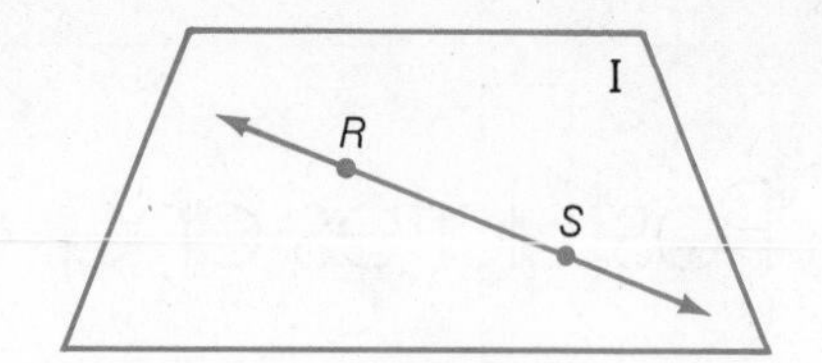

Example

In this figure, planes I and II have one point in common, A. Use the postulates to explain why the intersection of the planes is a line.

There must be a second common point. Call it B. ⟵ **Postulate 7**

A and B determine $\overleftrightarrow{AB}$. ⟵ **Postulate 4**

$\overleftrightarrow{AB}$ lies in plane I. ⟵ **Postulate 6**

$\overleftrightarrow{AB}$ lies in plane II. ⟵ **Postulate 6**

Since $\overleftrightarrow{AB}$ lies in both planes, the intersection of the two planes is a line.

This example is actually a proof of a mathematical statement; it is part of the proof of Theorem 1-1. A **theorem** is a mathematical statement that can be proved.

Theorem 1-1: If two distinct planes intersect, then their intersection is a line.

These figures suggest Theorems 1-2 and 1-3 which involve simple relationships among lines, planes, and points.

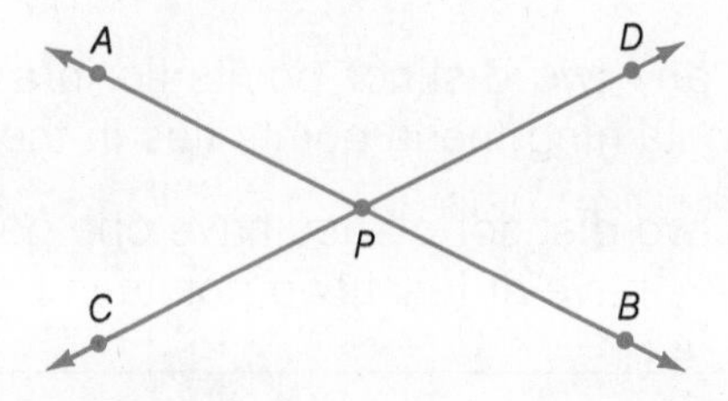

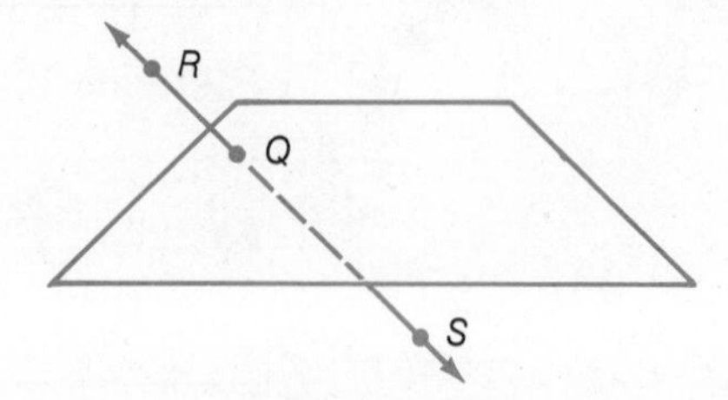

Theorem 1-2: If two distinct lines intersect, then their intersection is a point.

Theorem 1-3: If a line and a plane intersect and the plane does not contain the line, then their intersection is a point.

Try These

Plane I contains point D and collinear points A, B, and C. Point E is not in plane I.

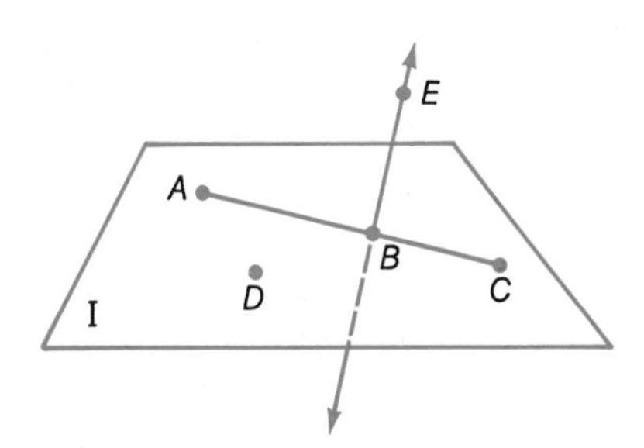

1. What postulate tells you there is exactly one plane containing points E, B, and A?
2. What postulate tells you there is exactly one line containing points D and A?
3. What postulate tells you that if D and C are in plane I, then all points of $\overleftrightarrow{DC}$ are in I?
4. What is the intersection of plane I and the plane determined by E, B, and C?
5. What is the intersection of plane I and $\overleftrightarrow{EB}$?

Exercises

A square pyramid, with square base XYZP, has point W not in the plane containing the square. Give a reason for each statement in Exercises **1–6.** *Use a postulate or theorem.*

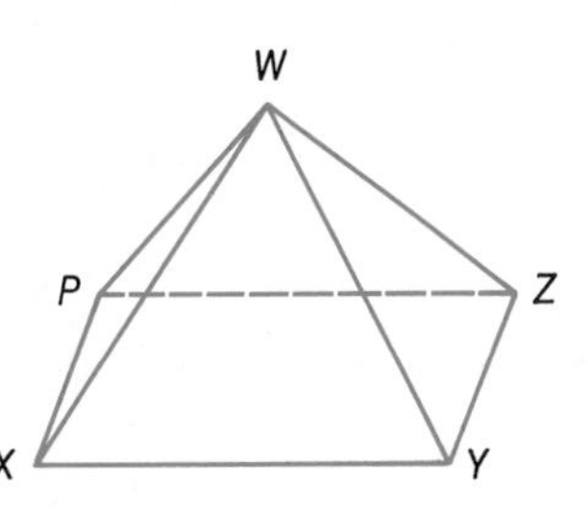

a

1. $\overleftrightarrow{XW}$ and $\overleftrightarrow{YW}$, which intersect in W, have no other point in common.
2. Exactly one plane contains W, X, and Y.
3. Points Z and P determine a line.
4. Any plane containing X and Y must contain $\overleftrightarrow{XY}$.
5. $\overleftrightarrow{ZW}$ intersects the plane determined by W, Y, and X in only one point.
6. The intersection of the plane determined by W, Y, and Z and the plane determined by X, Y, and W is $\overleftrightarrow{WY}$.

In the figure below, points E, B, and D are collinear. Points A and C are not on $\overleftrightarrow{ED}$. Classify each statement as True or False.

7. $\overleftrightarrow{ED}$ and $\overleftrightarrow{AB}$ intersect in B.

8. Points D, B, and C determine a plane.

9. The plane determined by A, B, and E contains D.

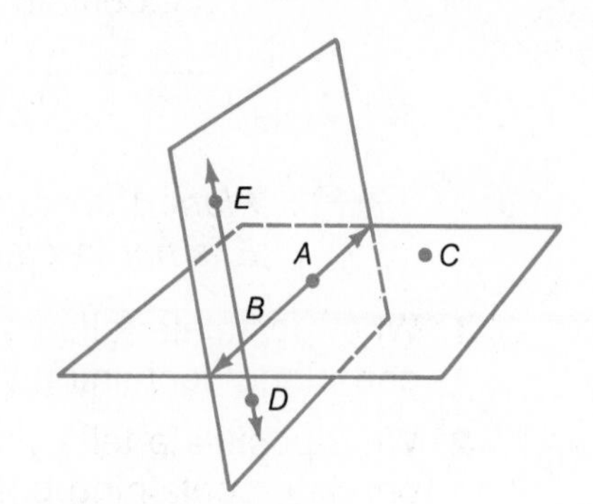

10. Points A and B determine a plane.

11. Only one plane contains E, B, and D.

12. Only one plane contains $\overleftrightarrow{EB}$ and A.

13. Points A, B, C, and D are coplanar.

14. Points A, B, D, and E are coplanar.

15. The intersection of the planes determined by E, D, and A and by A, B, and C is $\overleftrightarrow{AB}$.

For Exercises **16–20,** *choose the answer that best completes each statement.*

16. The intersection of two distinct planes is a __?__. (point, line)

17. A plane does not contain line ST. If $\overleftrightarrow{ST}$ and the plane intersect, their intersection is a __?__. (point, line)

18. Two distinct lines intersect in at most __?__ (1 point, 2 points)

19. A plane is determined by three __?__ points. (collinear, noncollinear)

20. A __?__ is accepted without proof. (postulate, theorem)

21. Show that two distinct intersecting lines determine a plane by giving reasons for each statement below. In the figure, lines m and k intersect at A. (You can use a lower case letter, such as k, to name a line.)

1. Line k contains at least one point other than A. Call it B.
2. Line m contains at least one point other than A. Call it C.
3. Since A, B, and C are not collinear, they determine a plane.

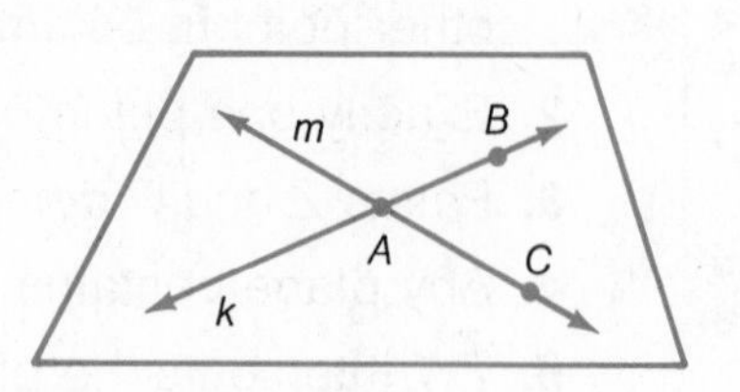

22. Explain why the following statement is true:

If a point is not on a line, then the point and the line determine a plane.

*In Exercises **23–30,** tell how many planes at most can pass through each set of points.*

23. One point

24. Two points

25. One line

26. Three noncollinear points

27. Three collinear points

28. A line and a point not on the line

29. An angle

30. The intersection of two planes

C **31.** What is the greatest number of planes determined by four points, no three of which are collinear?

32. What is the greatest number of planes determined by five points, no three of which are collinear?

1-7 Deductive Reasoning

In mathematics, a statement in the if-then form is a **conditional.** Theorems 1-1, 1-2, and 1-3 are conditionals. In proving a theorem, the "if" part is the **hypothesis.** It tells you the accepted facts. The "then" part is the **conclusion.** It tells you what is to be proved.

Theorem 1-4: If a point is not on a line, then the point and the line determine exactly one plane.

To prove this theorem, first write the hypothesis giving names for the point and the line. Call this the Given. It is helpful to draw a picture of the Given.

Given: Point C is not on line k.

Write the conclusion in a similar way.

Prove: Point C and line k determine exactly one plane.

Given: Point C is not on line k.

Prove: Point C and line k determine exactly one plane.

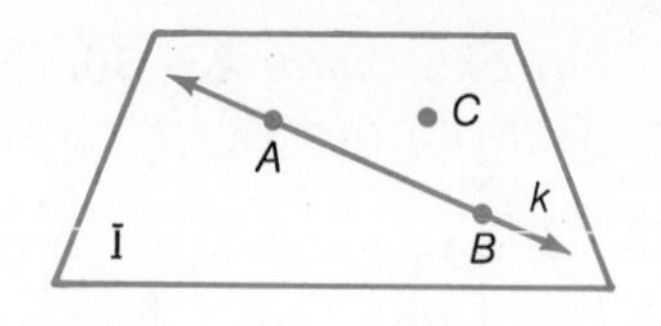

Proof: You are given line k with point C not on k. Line k contains at least two points by Postulate 1. Call the points A and B. Then points A, B, and C determine exactly one plane by Postulate 5. Therefore, point C and line k determine exactly one plane.

Once a theorem is proved, it may be used to prove other theorems. The proof of Theorem 1-4 is written in paragraph form. The proof of Theorem 1-5 is written in two-column form.

Theorem 1-5: If two distinct lines intersect, then they determine exactly one plane.

Given: Lines k and m intersect.

Prove: Lines k and m determine exactly one plane.

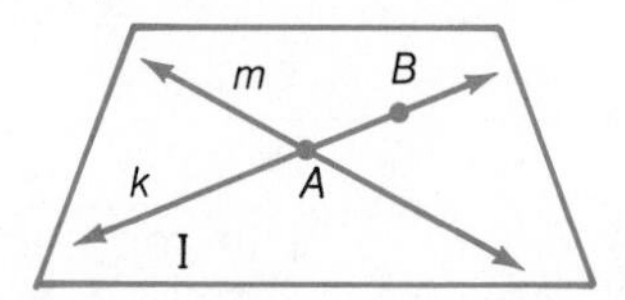

Statements	Reasons
1. Lines k and m intersect.	1. Given
2. Lines k and m intersect at a point. Call it A.	2. If two distinct lines intersect, then their intersection is a point.
3. Line k contains another point B, and B is not on line m.	3. Every line contains at least two distinct points.
4. Point B and line m determine plane I.	4. If a point is not on a line, then the point and the line determine exactly one plane.
5. Therefore, lines k and m determine exactly one plane.	5. Steps 1–4.

The proofs of Theorems 1-4 and 1-5 illustrate **deductive reasoning.**

Steps in Deductive Reasoning

1. You begin with an accepted fact or facts (hypothesis).
2. You then proceed in a step-by-step fashion with statements that are justified by stating the hypothesis, postulates, theorems, or definitions as reasons.
3. Each statement should lead you to another statement until you reach the last statement which is the conclusion.

Example

Arrange the statements in order from general to more specific so that they lead to the given conclusion.

A

C B

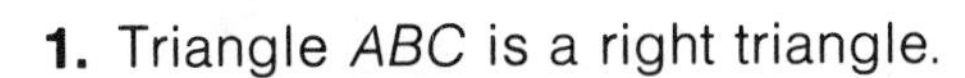

1. Triangle ABC is a right triangle.
2. In a right triangle, one angle is a right angle.

Conclusion: One angle in triangle ABC is a right angle.

Solution: 1. In a right triangle, one angle is a right angle.
2. Triangle ABC is a right triangle.

Try These

In Exercises **1–2,** *first state the hypothesis of the conditional. Then state the conclusion.*

1. If two planes intersect, then their intersection is a line.
2. If the three sides of a triangle are congruent, then the three angles of the triangle are congruent.

The figure at the right represents the statement in Exercise 2. Complete the *Given* *and* *Prove.*

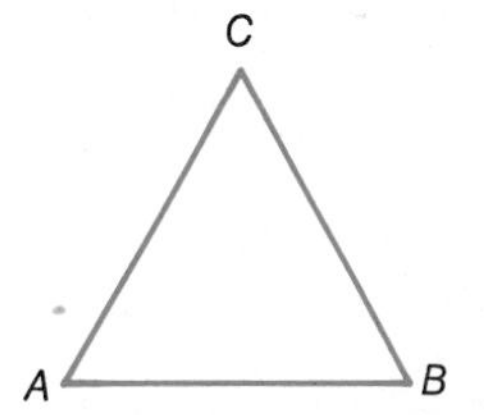

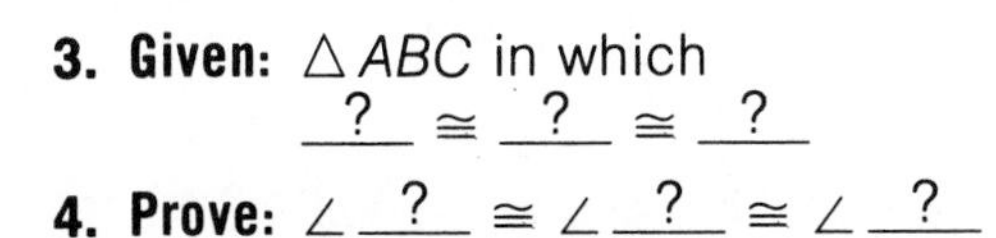

3. **Given:** $\triangle ABC$ in which $\underline{\ ?\ } \cong \underline{\ ?\ } \cong \underline{\ ?\ }$
4. **Prove:** $\angle \underline{\ ?\ } \cong \angle \underline{\ ?\ } \cong \angle \underline{\ ?\ }$

Arrange the statements in order from general to more specific so that they lead to the stated conclusion.

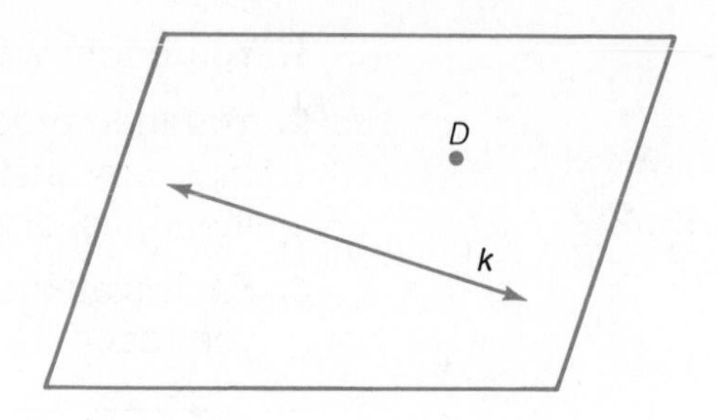

5. **1.** Point D is not on line k.

2. If a point is not on a line, then the point and the line determine exactly one plane.

Conclusion: Point D and line k determine exactly one plane.

Exercises

*In Exercises **1–8,** first state the hypothesis of each conditional. Then state the conclusion.*

a

1. If an angle is acute, then the measure of the angle is less than 90.

2. If two angles each have a measure of 35, then the angles are congruent.

3. If a triangle is isosceles, then it has two congruent sides.

4. If $\overrightarrow{AB}$ bisects $\angle DAC$, then B is in the interior of $\angle DAC$.

5. Points P, Q, and R are collinear if $\overrightarrow{PQ}$ and $\overrightarrow{PR}$ are opposite rays.

6. One angle of $\triangle ABC$ has a measure of 90 if $\triangle ABC$ is a right triangle.

7. $\overleftrightarrow{DE}$, $\overleftrightarrow{EF}$, and $\overleftrightarrow{DF}$ lie in plane W if points D, E, and F lie in plane W.

8. $\overrightarrow{RS}$ has exactly one endpoint if $\overrightarrow{RS}$ is a ray.

*For Exercises **9–11,** a figure is drawn and labeled to represent each statement. Complete the Given and the Prove.*

9. If $\angle ABC$ is obtuse and $m\angle ABD$ is greater than $m\angle ABC$, then $\angle ABD$ is obtuse.

Given: $\angle ABC$ is obtuse and $m\angle ABD$ is greater than $m\angle ABC$.

Prove: ?

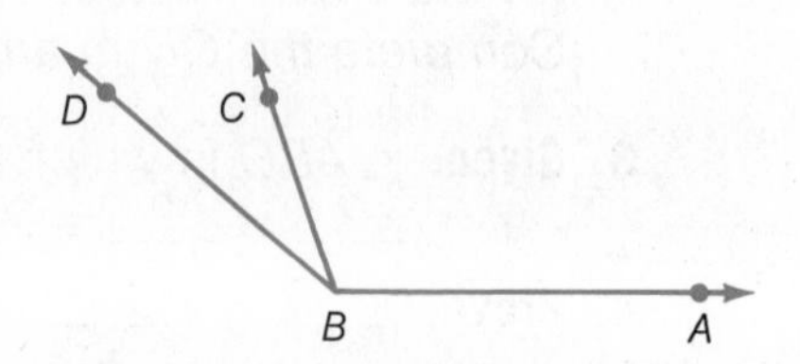

10. If three sides of a triangle are congruent, then the three angles of the triangle are congruent.

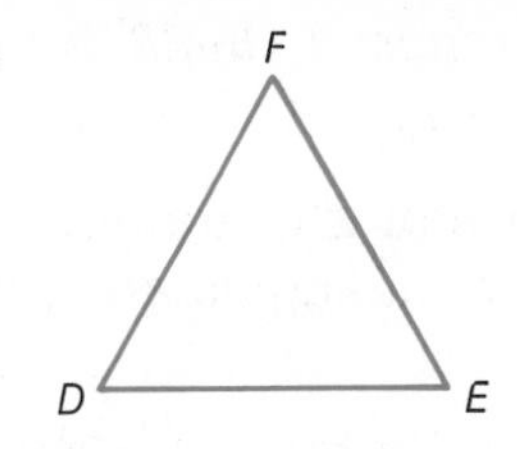

Given: $\triangle DEF$ with $\overline{DE} \cong \overline{EF} \cong$?

Prove: $\angle D \cong \angle$? $\cong \angle$?

11. If points *A*, *B*, and *C* lie in two distinct planes, then the points are collinear.

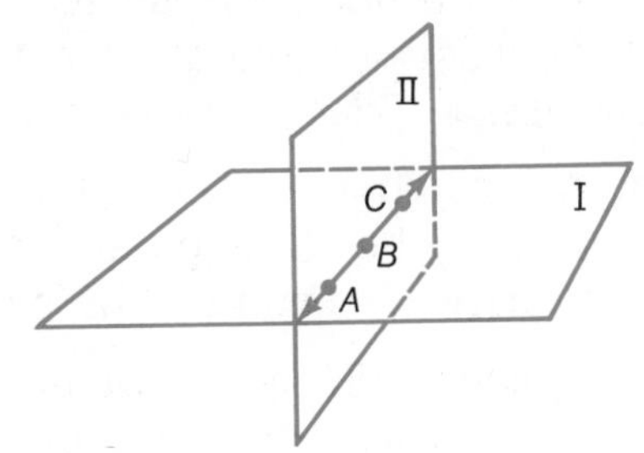

Given: Planes I and II, each containing points *A*, *B*, and *C*

Prove: ?

For Exercises **12–14,** *figures are drawn to represent each statement. Write the Given and the Prove in terms of the figure.*

12. If two angles have the same measure, the angles are congruent.

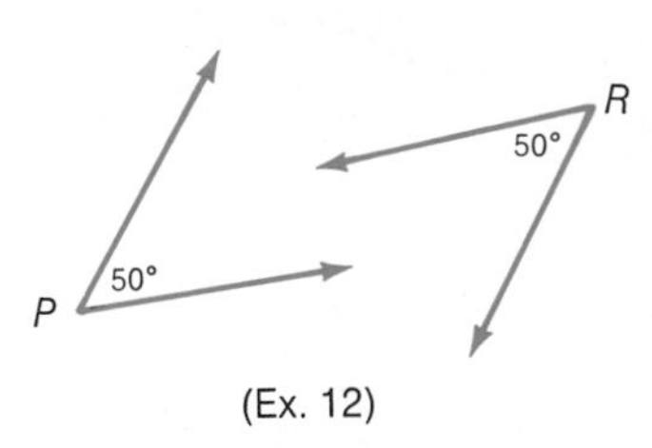

(Ex. 12)

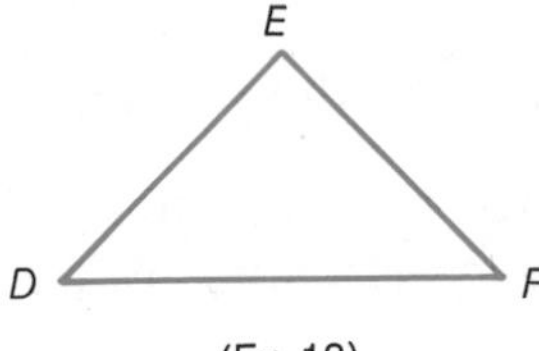

(Ex. 13)

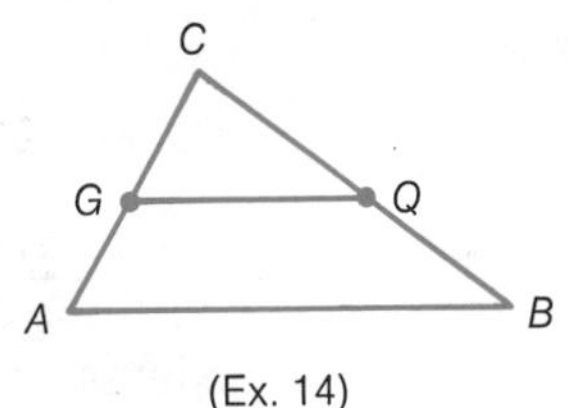

(Ex. 14)

13. If two angles of a triangle are congruent, then the sides opposite the angles are congruent.

14. If a segment joins the midpoints of two sides of a triangle, then the measure of the segment is half the measure of the third side.

For Exercises **15–17,** *draw a figure, and label it. Then state the Given and the Prove in terms of the figure.*

15. If three angles of a triangle are congruent, then the three sides are congruent.

16. If a segment is drawn from the midpoint of the base of an isosceles triangle to the opposite vertex, then the segment forms congruent angles at that vertex.

17. If each of two segments is a radius of a circle, then the segments are congruent.

*For Exercises **18–22**, arrange the first two statements in order from general to more specific so that they lead to the stated conclusion.*

18. **1.** $\angle T$ and $\angle Q$ are right angles.
2. All right angles are congruent.
Conclusion: $\angle T$ and $\angle Q$ are congruent.

19. **1.** Triangle *RSW* is isosceles.
2. An isosceles triangle is not scalene.
Conclusion: Triangle *RSW* is not scalene.

20. **1.** Any number greater than 0 is a positive number.
2. The number 12 is greater than 0.
Conclusion: The number 12 is positive.

21. **1.** Triangle *ABC* is an equilateral triangle.
2. The measure of each angle of an equilateral triangle is 60.
Conclusion: In $\triangle ABC$, $m\angle A = 60$, $m\angle B = 60$, and $m\angle C = 60$.

22. **1.** $\overline{VZ}$ and $\overline{XY}$ are the opposite sides of a rectangle.
2. The opposite sides of a rectangle are congruent.
Conclusion: $\overline{VZ} \cong \overline{XY}$

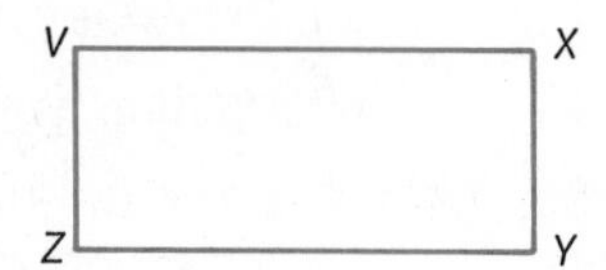

*In Exercises **23–28**, write the correct conclusion.*

23. **1.** The opposite sides of a parallelogram are parallel.
2. $\overline{VX}$ and $\overline{ZY}$ are opposite sides of parallelogram *VXYZ*.
Conclusion: ___?___

24. **1.** Two intersecting lines determine exactly one plane.
2. Lines *p* and *q* intersect.
Conclusion: ___?___

25. **1.** Two coplanar lines either intersect or are parallel.
2. Coplanar lines *p* and *q* do not intersect.
Conclusion: ___?___

26. **1.** Two coplanar lines either intersect or are parallel.
2. Coplanar lines *p* and *q* are not parallel.
Conclusion: ___?___

27. **1.** Distinct intersecting lines have exactly one point in common.
2. Lines *p* and *q* intersect.
Conclusion: ___?___

28. **1.** Three distinct noncollinear points determine a plane.
2. Points *R*, *S*, and *T* are distinct noncollinear points.
Conclusion: ___?___

In Exercises **29–35,** *supply the missing statement.*

29. 1. ___?___
2. Points D and E are distinct points.
Conclusion: Points D and E determine line DE.

30. 1. ___?___
2. Planes I and II intersect.
Conclusion: Planes I and II intersect in a line.

31. 1. A theorem is a mathematical statement that can be proved.
2. "Two planes intersect in a line" is a theorem.
Conclusion: ___?___

32. 1. ___?___
2. Point F is not on line r.
Conclusion: Point F and line r determine a plane.

33. 1. ___?___
2. $m\angle PQR = 105$
Conclusion: $\angle PQR$ is an obtuse angle.

34. 1. ___?___
2. Segments AB and EF have the same measure.
Conclusion: $\overline{AB} \cong \overline{EF}$

35. 1. ___?___
2. Triangle XYZ is a scalene triangle.
Conclusion: Triangle XYZ has no congruent sides.

PUZZLE

The shapes below can be cut from graph paper.

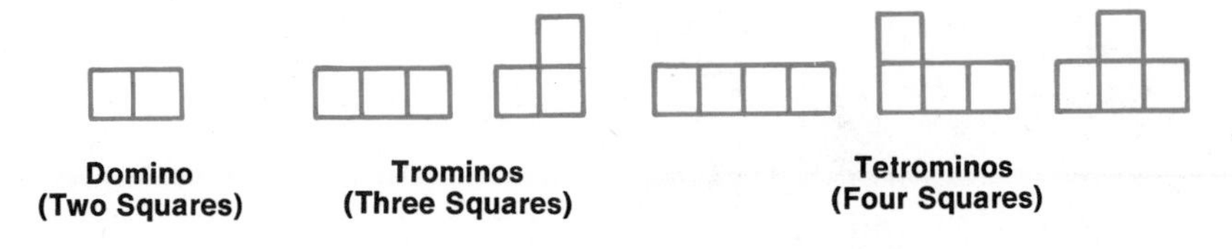

How can you fit four tetrominos of the first shape shown above into a square? Repeat the procedure with each of the other tetrominos.

Five tetrominos can be drawn. Draw the other two.

Mathematics and Architecture

An **architect** is involved with the planning of a wide variety of structures, such as houses, hospitals, office buildings and airports. To be a licensed architect, the general requirements are a bachelor's degree from an accredited architectual school (which usually takes 5 years) plus 3 years of experience in an architect's office. Four years of high school mathematics are required for entrance into most degree programs.

The architect is concerned not only with appearance but also with practicality. For example, in designing a home, the architect has to make decisions regarding the arrangement of the cabinets, sink, refrigerator, stove, and other components of the kitchen in order to make maximum use of the available space and to make an efficient layout.

In some modern kitchens, an important factor is the "triangle of efficiency," which connects the sink (A), the refrigerator (B), and the stove (C). Note the different kinds of triangles used to form this "triangle of efficiency."

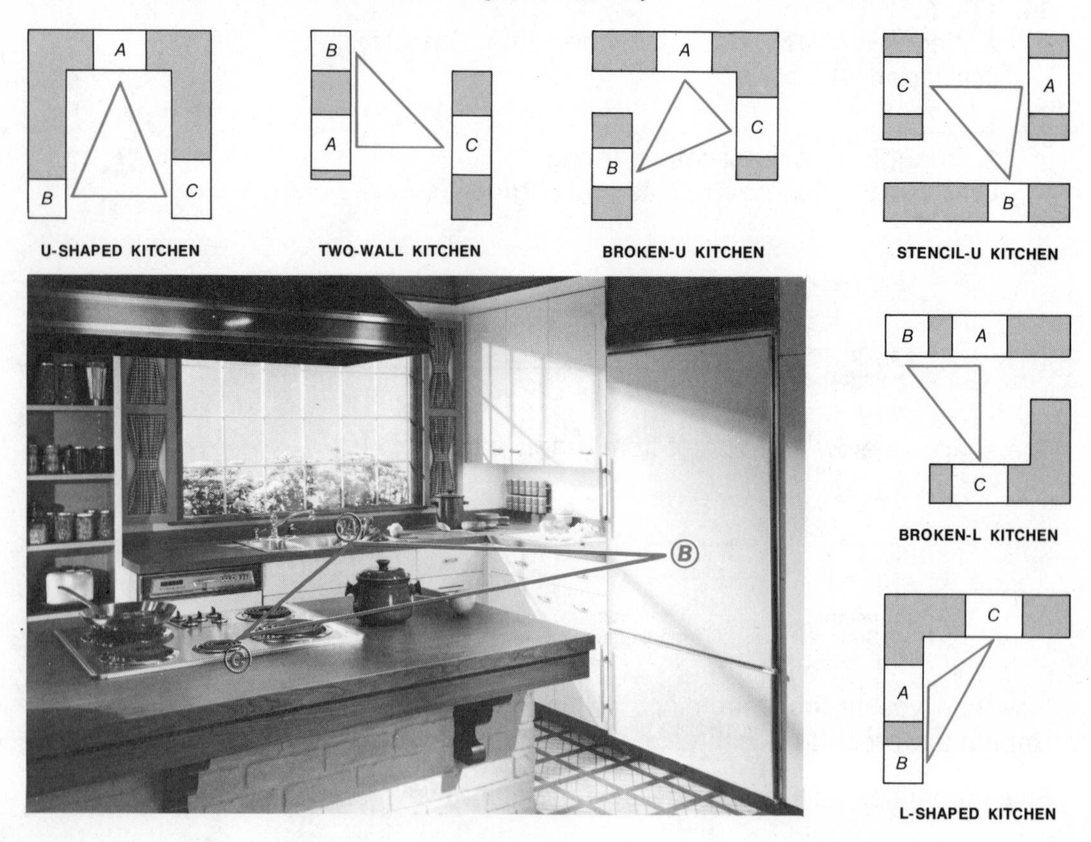

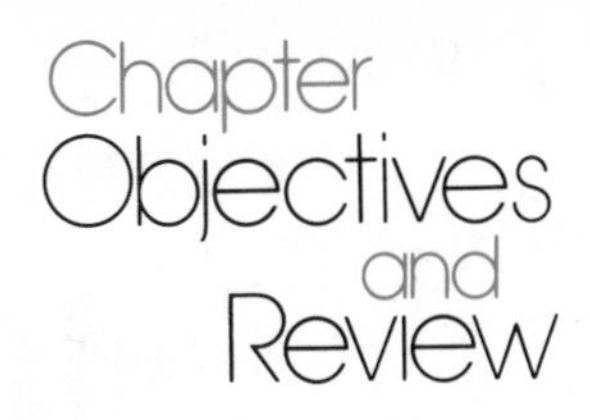

Objective: To recall, and give examples of, the important mathematical terms of the chapter.

1. Be sure that you know the meanings of these mathematical terms used in Chapter 1.

acute angle (p. 11)
acute triangle (p. 14)
angle (p. 19)
base angles (p. 13)
bisector of an angle (p. 11)
collinear points (p. 18)
conclusion (p. 27)
conditional (p. 27)
congruent angles (p. 10)
congruent segments (p. 6)
coplanar points (p. 18)
degree (p. 9)
endpoints (p. 19)
equilateral triangle (p. 13)
hypotenuse (p. 14)
hypothesis (p. 27)
interior of an angle (p. 11)
intersection of two sets (p. 18)
isosceles triangle (p. 13)
legs
  isosceles triangle (p. 13)
  right triangle (p. 14)
line (p. 2)
midpoint (p. 7)
noncollinear points (p. 18)
noncoplanar points (p. 18)
obtuse angle (p. 11)
obtuse triangle (p. 14)
opposite rays (p. 19)
plane (p. 2)
point (p. 2)
postulate (p. 23)
protractor (p. 9)
ray (p. 19)
right angle (p. 11)
right triangle (p. 14)
scalene triangle (p. 13)
segment (p. 19)
space (p. 2)
subset (p. 18)
theorem (p. 24)
union of two sets (p. 18)
vertex angle (p. 13)
vertex of an angle (p. 3)

Objective: To distinguish between line, segment, and ray. (Section 1-1)

Replace each _?_ with line, segment, or ray.

2. A _?_ has two endpoints.

3. A _?_ has no endpoint.

4. A _?_ has one endpoint.

5. A _?_ has a definite length.

Objective: To use symbols for segment, ray, line, angle and triangle. (Section 1-1)

Use symbols to name the following.

6. Line AZ **7.** Ray AZ **8.** Ray ZA

9. Triangle RST **10.** Angle R **11.** Side ST

Classify each statement as True or False.

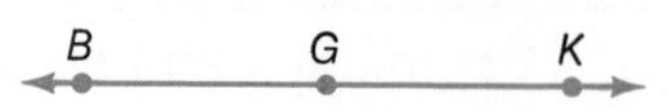

12. $\overline{BG} = \overline{GB}$ **13.** $\overrightarrow{BG} = \overrightarrow{GB}$ **14.** $\overrightarrow{BG} = \overrightarrow{BK}$

15. $\overleftrightarrow{BG} = \overleftrightarrow{GK}$ **16.** $\overrightarrow{GB} = \overrightarrow{GK}$ **17.** $\overleftrightarrow{BG} = \overleftrightarrow{GB}$

Objective: To use symbols for "is congruent to" and "has the same measure." (Section 1-2)

In the figure below at the right, $TR = 12$ and S is the midpoint of $\overline{TR}$. Replace each _?_ with $=$ or $\cong$.

18. $\overline{TS}$ _?_ $\overline{SR}$ **19.** TS _?_ SR

20. TS _?_ 6 **21.** SR _?_ $\frac{1}{2}(TR)$.

T S R

Objective: To use symbols for angle and measure of an angle. (Section 1-3)

Classify each sentence as True or False.

22. $m\angle DEG = 65$ **23.** $\angle DEG = \angle GEF$

24. $m\angle DEG = m\angle GEF$ **25.** $\angle DEG \cong \angle GEF$

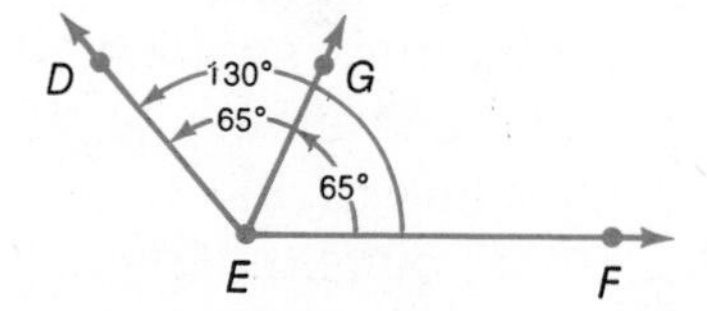

Objective: To classify angles according to their measures. (Section 1-3)

Classify each angle as acute, right, or obtuse.

26. 25° **27.** 99° **28.** 111° **29.** 90°

Objective: To classify a triangle according to the measures of its angles. (Section 1-4)

Classify each triangle below as acute, right, or obtuse.

30.

E
60°
8
8
C
60°
60°
D
8

31.

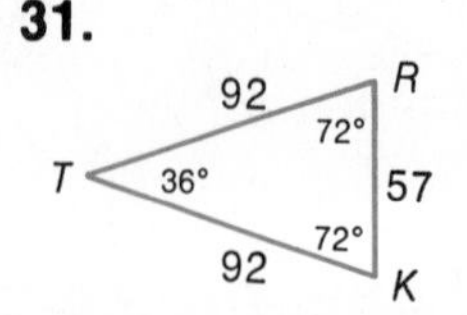

32.

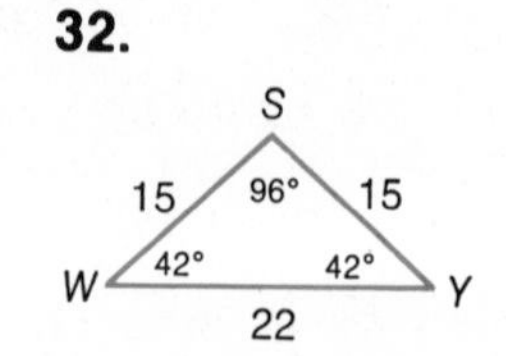

33.

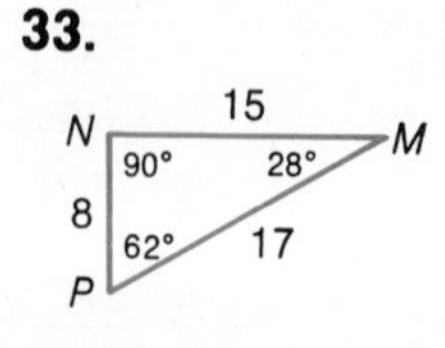

Objective: To classify a triangle according to the measures of its sides. (Section 1-4)

34. Classify each triangle in Exercises **30–33** as equilateral, isosceles, or scalene.

Objective: To recognize that a mathematical definition depends on basic undefined terms and on previously defined terms. (Section 1-5)

35. Tell which of the following words or phrases must be defined before the word angle may be defined.

vertex, ray, acute angle, union of two sets

Objective: To use postulates and theorems to justify statements. (Section 1-6)

Write the postulate or theorem that justifies each conclusion.

36. Points A and B lie in plane I.
Conclusion: All points on line AB lie in plane I.

37. Points P, Q, and R are noncollinear.
Conclusion: Points P, Q, and R determine a plane.

38. Line s and plane I intersect and line s is not in plane I.
Conclusion: Line s and plane I have only one point in common.

39. Lines p and q intersect.
Conclusion: Lines p and q have at least one point in common.

Objectives: To recognize a conditional and to identify its parts. (Section 1-7)

State the hypothesis and conclusion for each conditional.

40. If a triangle is equilateral, then it is equiangular.

41. Two angles are congruent if they have equal measures.

42. For Exercises **40–41,** draw a figure and label it. Then state the Given and Prove in terms of the figure.

Chapter Test

Use symbols to name each geometric figure.

1. Segment DE **2.** Line DE **3.** Ray DE **4.** Triangle WXY

Classify each statement as True *or* False.

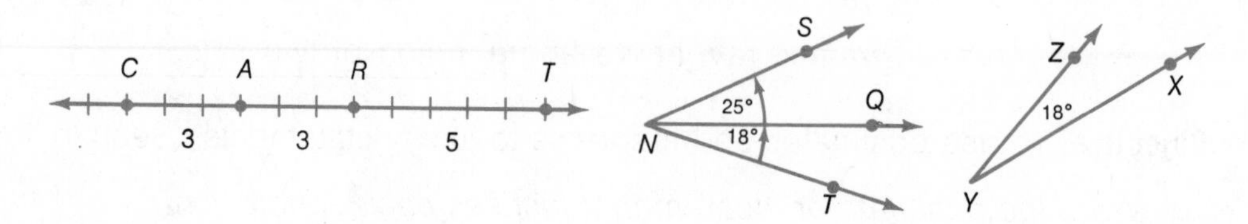

5. $\overrightarrow{AR} = \overrightarrow{AT}$ **6.** $\overline{AR} = \overline{RA}$ **7.** $\overleftrightarrow{CT}$ has two endpoints.

8. $\overleftrightarrow{CA} = \overleftrightarrow{RT}$ **9.** $\overrightarrow{AR} = \overrightarrow{RA}$ **10.** The midpoint of $\overline{CR}$ is A.

11. $CA \cong AR$ **12.** $\angle XYZ = \angle QNT$ **13.** $m\angle QNT = 18$

Identify each triangle as acute isosceles, right scalene, and so on.

14.

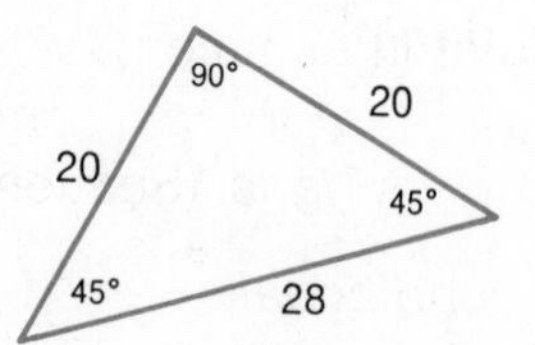

15.

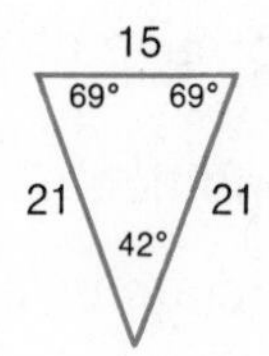

16.

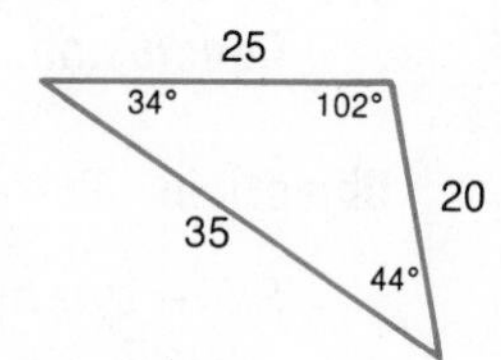

Complete each statement.

17. A __?__ is a mathematical statement that can be proved.

18. For any two distinct points, exactly one __?__ contains them.

19. For any three distinct noncollinear points, exactly one __?__ contains them.

Refer to this conditional for Exercises **20–21:** *If three angles of a triangle are congruent, then the three sides of the triangle are congruent.*

20. State the hypothesis and the conclusion.

21. Draw the figure to represent the conditional and label it. Then write the Given and Prove in terms of the figure.

Chapter 2
Segments and Angles

2-1 Measure of Segments

A number associated with a point on a number line is the **coordinate** of the point. The two points with coordinates 0 and 1 determine the length of one unit on the number line.

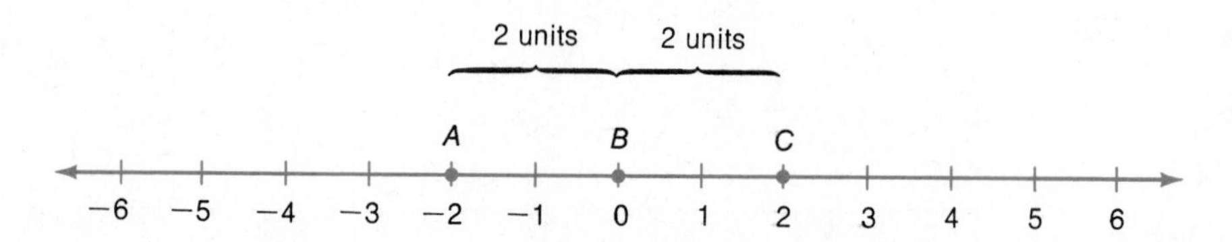

On the number line above, the coordinate of point A is -2. The coordinate of point C is 2. Each is two units from 0. A distance measure is always positive. You use absolute value notation to indicate distance, but not direction, from 0. The symbol for absolute value is $|\ |$. Thus,

$$|-2| = 2 \qquad |2| = 2 \qquad |0| = 0$$

Definition

The absolute value of a real number x is the distance of x from 0. It is written $|x|$.

You use absolute value to find the distance between any two points on the number line.

Definition

The **distance between any two points** on a number line is the absolute value of the difference of the coordinates of the points.

Example 1

Find the distance between each given pair of points.

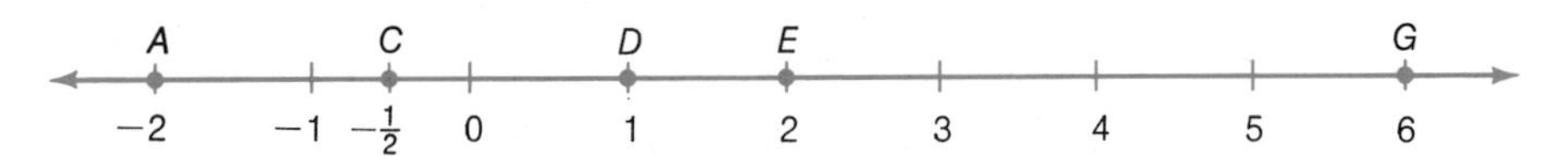

Points	Distance
a. D and E	$\lvert 2-1\rvert = \lvert 1\rvert = 1$ or $\lvert 1-2\rvert = \lvert -1\rvert = 1$
b. E and G	$\lvert 6-2\rvert = \lvert 4\rvert = 4$, or $\lvert 2-6\rvert = \lvert -4\rvert = 4$
c. A and G	$\lvert 6-(-2)\rvert = \lvert 6+2\rvert = \lvert 8\rvert = 8$, or $\lvert -2-6\rvert = \lvert -8\rvert = 8$
d. A and C	$\lvert -\frac{1}{2}-(-2)\rvert = \lvert -\frac{1}{2}+2\rvert = \lvert 1\frac{1}{2}\rvert = 1\frac{1}{2}$, or
	$\lvert -2-(-\frac{1}{2})\rvert = \lvert -2+\frac{1}{2}\rvert = \lvert -1\frac{1}{2}\rvert = 1\frac{1}{2}$

Example 1 suggests the following postulate which has two parts.

Postulate 8: The Ruler Postulate

a. To every distinct pair of points there corresponds exactly one positive number. This number is the distance between the two points.

b. To every real number there corresponds a point on the number line. To every point on the number line there corresponds a real number.

In Example 1, you found that $DE = 1$ and $EG = 4$. Similarly, you could find $DG = 5$. Thus, $DE + EG = DG$.

This leads to a formal definition of betweenness for points.

Definition: For three distinct points A, B, and C, **A is between B and C** if

a. A, B, and C are collinear, and **b.** $BA + AC = BC$.

This definition allows you to add the measures of segments. You may refer to it as the Segment Addition Property.

Now that betweenness for points has been defined, a definition for line segment can be stated. Recall that line segment was defined in Chapter 1 where between was used as an undefined term.

Definition: A **line segment,** or **segment,** is a subset of a line consisting of any two distinct points of the line and all the points between them.

By this definition, the two given points are the endpoints of the segment. Thus, the distance between two points on the number line is the measure of the segment that has these two points as endpoints.

Example 2

In the figure below, E is between D and F, $DF = 12$, and $DE = EF$. Find DE and EF.

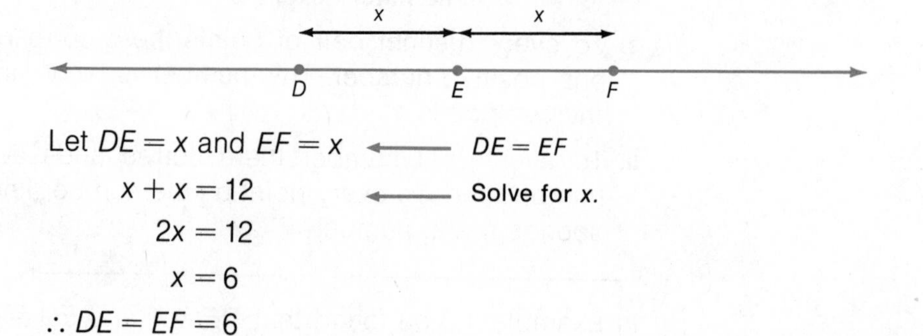

Let $DE = x$ and $EF = x$ ⟵ $DE = EF$

$x + x = 12$ ⟵ Solve for x.

$2x = 12$

$x = 6$

$\therefore DE = EF = 6$

Example 2 suggests that for any segment DF, there is a point E between D and F that is equally distant, or equidistant, from D and F. This point is called the midpoint.

Definition: Point E is the **midpoint** of $\overline{DF}$ if E is between D and F and $DE = EF$.

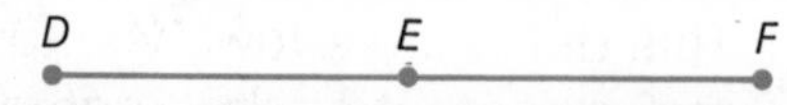

Point E bisects $\overline{DF}$. In geometry, **bisect** means to separate into two parts having the same measure. Segments having the same measure are **congruent segments.**

Theorem 2-1: A segment has exactly one midpoint.

Try These

Complete each statement. Refer to the number line.

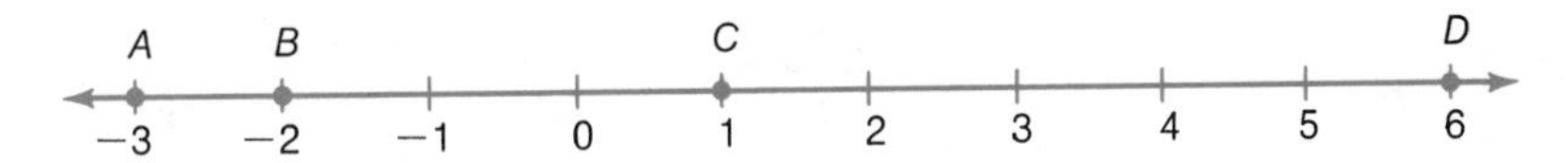

1. The distance from C to D is $|1 - 6|$, or __?__.
2. The distance from C to __?__ is $|1 - (-2)|$.
3. The measure of $\overline{BC}$ is __?__.
4. If $AT + TC = 4$, then T is between __?__ and __?__.
5. If P is the midpoint of $\overline{BD}$, the coordinate of P is __?__.
6. If Q is between C and D, and $BC + CQ = QD$, then Q is the midpoint of __?__.

Exercises

Write the number named by each expression.

a

1. $\lvert 3 \rvert$	**2.** $\lvert -7 \rvert$	**3.** $\lvert -5 - 7 \rvert$	**4.** $\lvert -9 + 8 \rvert$
5. $\lvert 17 + 14 \rvert$	**6.** $\lvert 11 - 17 \rvert$	**7.** $\lvert -7 + 7 \rvert$	**8.** $\lvert -23 + 6 \rvert$
9. $\lvert 8 - (-4) \rvert$	**10.** $\lvert -6 - 3 \rvert$	**11.** $\lvert -12 - (-7) \rvert$	**12.** $\lvert 0 - 2 \rvert$

Two points on a number line have the coordinates given below. In each case, find the distance between the points.

13. 8; 3	**14.** 2; 5	**15.** 7; 0	**16.** 15; 23
17. −3; 10	**18.** 6; −3	**19.** −5; 18	**20.** −11; 9
21. −2; −8	**22.** 0; −9	**23.** −7; −16	**24.** 14; 14

*For Exercises **25–36,** use the number line to find the measure of each segment.*

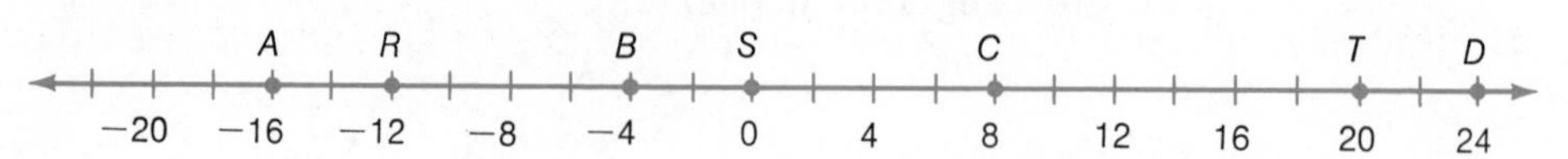

25. $\overline{CS}$ **26.** $\overline{ST}$ **27.** $\overline{CD}$ **28.** $\overline{DC}$

29. $\overline{SB}$ **30.** $\overline{BC}$ **31.** $\overline{TB}$ **32.** $\overline{CR}$

33. $\overline{AD}$ **34.** $\overline{AC}$ **35.** $\overline{RC}$ **36.** $\overline{TR}$

*Use the figures below for Exercises **37–41.***

G H J K
17 22 28 37

V W X Y Z
−19 −13 −9 −3 1

37. Find GH, HJ, and GJ. Does $GH + HJ = GJ$?

38. Find GJ, JK, and GK. Does $GJ + JK = GK$?

39. Show that $|22 - 28| + |28 - 37| = |37 - 22|$. To what three points do these coordinates *refer*? What betweenness relation exists for the three points?

40. Complete each statement in Column A below.

Column A	Column B
1. Y is between V and _?_.	**a.** $|-3+9| + |1+3| = |1+9|$
2. W is between Y and _?_	**b.** $|-9+13| + |-3+9| = |-3+13|$
3. _?_ is between W and Y.	**c.** $|-3+19| + |1+3| = |1+19|$
4. Y is between X and _?_	**d.** $|-13+19| + |-3+13| = |-3+19|$

41. Match an equation in Column B with a statement in Column A. (Use Exercise **40.**)

b

42. Show that $|a + b|$ can be used to find the distance between points with coordinates a and $-b$.

*In Exercises **43–48,** R, S, and T are collinear points with coordinates r, s, and t, respectively.*

43. If $RS = 15$, $r > s$, and $r = 13$, find s.

44. If $r < s < t$, which of R, S, and T is between the other two?

45. $RT = ST = 19$. If $s < r$ and $t = 7$, *find* s and r.

46. $TR = RS = 12$. Find r and t if $s = -14$. (Two answers are possible.)

47. If $r = -12$, $s = 10$, and S is the midpoint of $\overline{RT}$, find t.

48. If $s = 5$, $t = 12$, and T is the midpoint of $\overline{SR}$, find r.

49. Points K, L, and M are collinear and the coordinate of L is greater than the coordinate of K. If $KM = ML = 6$, and the coordinate of M is 3, what are the coordinates of K and L?

50. Point B is the midpoint of $\overline{AC}$, the coordinate of C is 12, and $BC = 8$. Give two possible coordinates for A.

*In Exercises **51–53,** Y is the midpoint of $\overline{XZ}$ and x, y, and z are the coordinates of X, Y, and Z, respectively.*

51. Find y if $x = \frac{2}{21}$ and $z = \frac{3}{21}$. (HINT: Does $\frac{2}{21} = \frac{4}{42}$? Does $\frac{3}{21} = \frac{6}{42}$?)

52. Use a method similar to that of Exercise **51** to find y if $x = \frac{13}{36}$ and $z = \frac{7}{18}$.

53. Find y if $x = \frac{5}{27}$ and $z = \frac{2}{9}$.

*For Exercises **54–56,** assume that points A and X are two points on a number line. The coordinate of A is 3, and the coordinate of X is x. Find x.*

54. $|x - 3| = 7$

55. $|x - 3| = 12$

56. $|x - 3| = 0$

*For Exercises **57–59,** assume that points B and Y have coordinates -9 and y, respectively. Find y.*

57. $|y - (-9)| = 5$

58. $|-9 - y| = 8$

59. $|y + 9| \leq 3$

PUZZLE

Through 2 points you can draw one line.
Through 3 points you can draw three lines.
Through 4 points you can draw six lines.
Through 5 points you can draw ten lines.

How many lines can you draw through 6 points?

(No more than 2 points are collinear.)

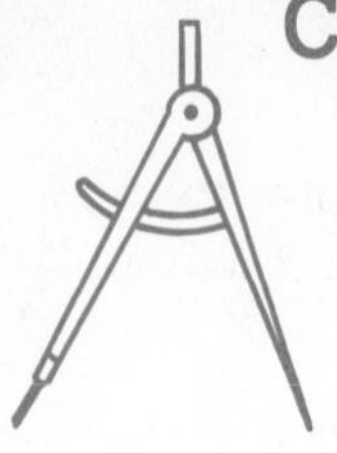

Constructions

Constructing a Segment Congruent to a Given Segment

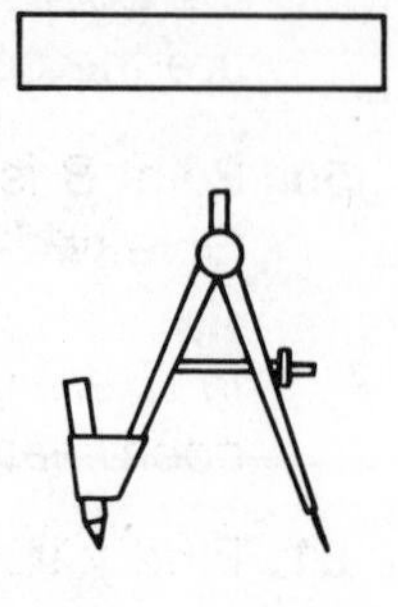

In constructions, a straightedge is used to draw lines, segments, or rays. A straightedge looks like a ruler without measurement marks.

A compass is used in constructions to draw circles or arcs of circles. A **circle** is the set of all points in a plane that are at a given distance from a given point in the plane. The given point is the **center** of the circle and the given distance is the **radius.** All radii (plural of radius) of the same circle have the same measure and are, therefore, congruent. Also, congruent circles have congruent radii. If the radii of two circles have the same measure, then the circles are congruent. An arc of a circle, such as arc *RS* in the figure at the right, is a subset of the circle. You can use these definitions and statements about circles as reasons in the proofs of constructions.

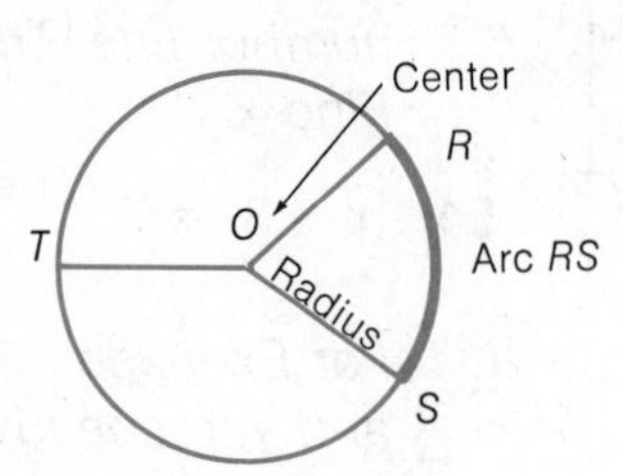

NOTE: The word radius can be used to refer both to the segment and to the length of the segment.

Given: $\overline{XY}$

Required: To construct a segment congruent to $\overline{XY}$.

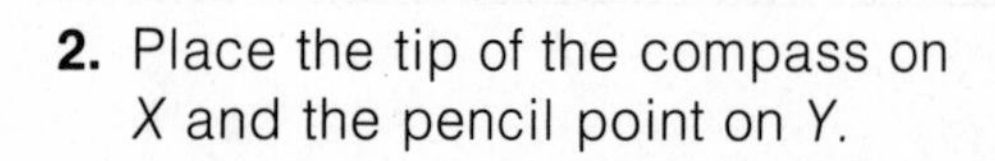

1. Draw any ray *AB*. Extend $\overrightarrow{AB}$ so that it is longer than $\overline{XY}$.

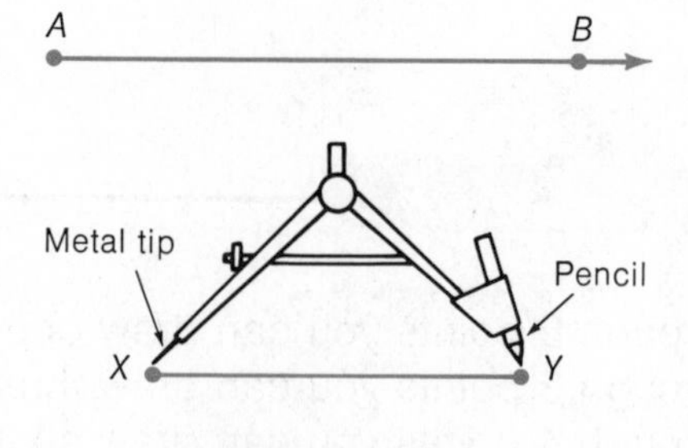

2. Place the tip of the compass on *X* and the pencil point on *Y*.

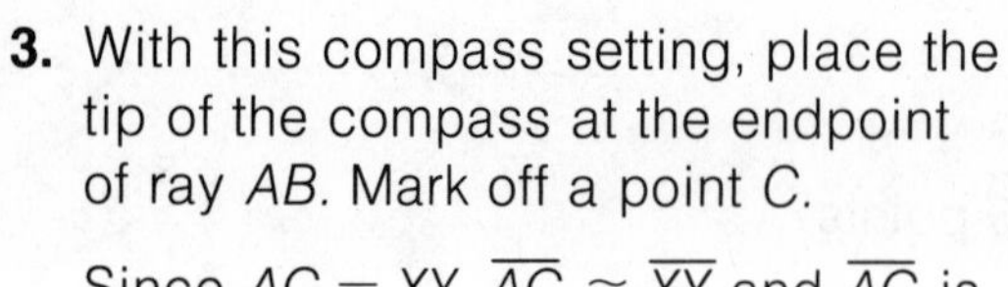

3. With this compass setting, place the tip of the compass at the endpoint of ray *AB*. Mark off a point *C*.

Since $AC = XY$, $\overline{AC} \cong \overline{XY}$ and $\overline{AC}$ is the required segment.

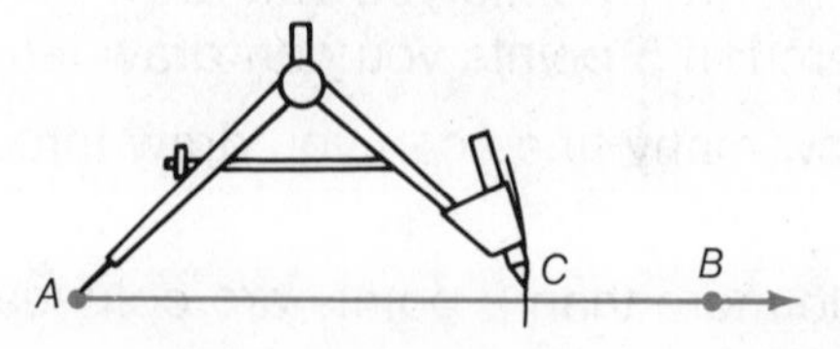

Bisecting a Segment

Given: $\overline{MN}$

M N

Required: To bisect $\overline{MN}$.

1. Open the compass so that the opening is more than half the length of $\overline{MN}$.
2. Place the tip of the compass at M and make an arc above $\overline{MN}$ and another arc below $\overline{MN}$.

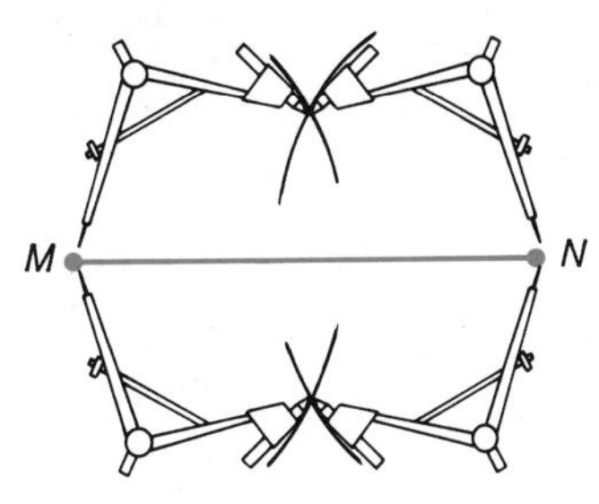

3. Keeping the same radius, place the tip of the compass at N and repeat Step 2.
4. Label the points of intersection of the arcs C and D. Then draw a line through C and D. Point Q on $\overline{MN}$ is the midpoint of $\overline{MN}$.

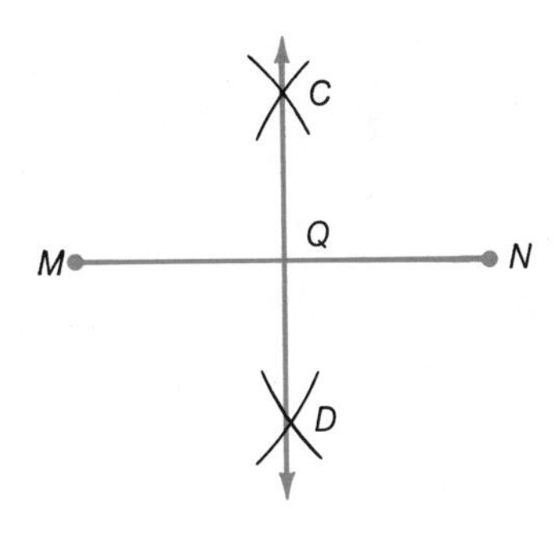

Point Q bisects $\overline{MN}$. Any line, ray, segment, or plane through Q is a **bisector** of $\overline{MN}$. The proof of this construction is given in Example 3 on page 109.

Exercises

1. Use a ruler to draw a segment 7 centimeters long. Then, on ray WK, construct another segment measuring 7 centimeters.
2. Draw a segment, $\overline{AE}$, that is 6 centimeters long. Construct C, the midpoint of $\overline{AE}$. Then construct B, the midpoint of $\overline{AC}$, and construct D, the midpoint of $\overline{CE}$.

For Exercises ***3–10,*** *draw a segment, $\overline{AB}$, that is 2 centimeters long and a segment, $\overline{CD}$, that is 3 centimeters long. Then construct each of the following.*

3. $AB + CD$	**4.** $3AB$	**5.** $AB + 2CD$	**6.** $\frac{1}{2}(3CD)$
7. $\frac{1}{2}(AB + CD)$	**8.** $AB + \frac{1}{2}CD$	**9.** $\frac{5}{2}AB$	**10.** $2AB - CD$

2-2 Measuring Angles

In the figure at the left below, line p separates plane I into three sets of points.

1. The **half-plane** that contains point A
2. The **half-plane** that contains point B
3. Line p itself

Line p is called the **edge** of each half-plane; it does not lie in either half-plane.

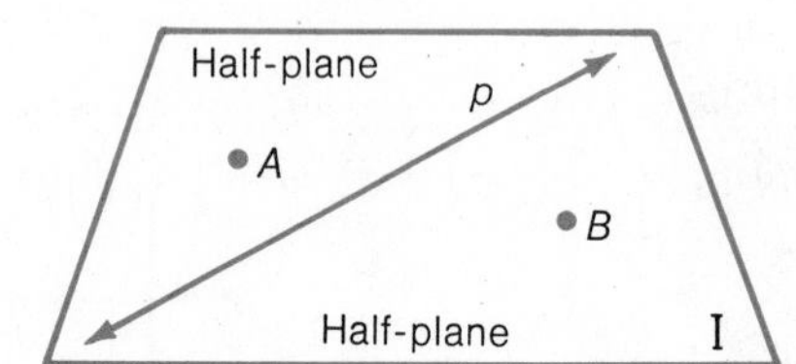

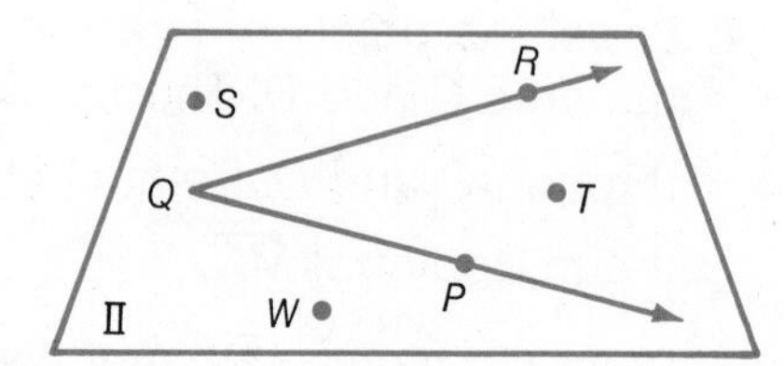

In the figure at the right above, $\angle Q$ separates plane II into three sets of points.

1. The points on $\angle Q$, such as P, Q, and R
2. The points in the interior of $\angle Q$, such as T

   The **interior** of $\angle Q$ is the intersection of two half-planes. The first contains point R and has edge $\overleftrightarrow{QP}$; the second contains point P and has edge $\overleftrightarrow{QR}$.

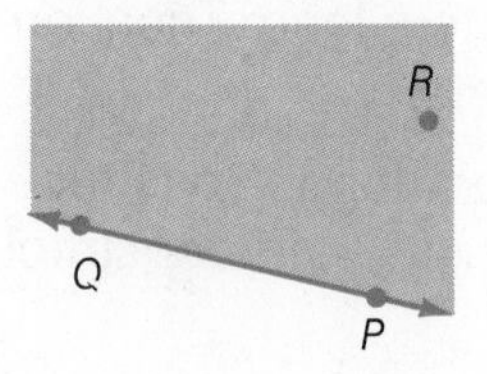

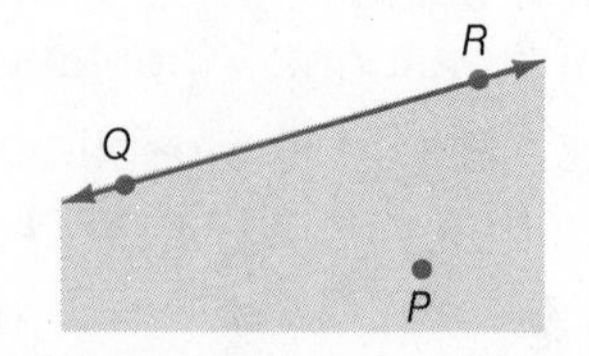

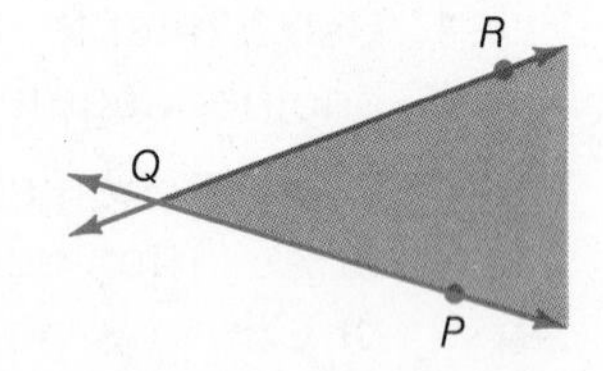

3. The points, such as S and W, that lie neither on $\angle Q$ nor in the interior of $\angle Q$. These points lie in the **exterior** of $\angle Q$.

To measure angles, a coordinate system for rays is used. Each ray is in one-to-one correspondence with a real number between 0 and 180 inclusive.

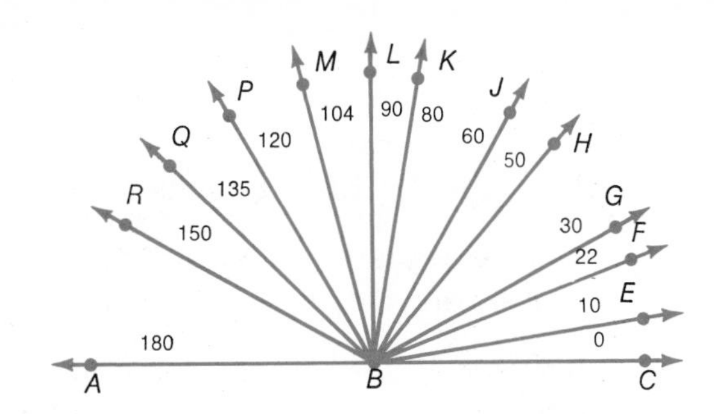

The coordinates of the two rays, $\overrightarrow{BC}$ and $\overrightarrow{BA}$, in the edge, $\overleftrightarrow{AC}$, of the half-plane, are 0 and 180 respectively. However, since these two rays are collinear, they do not determine an angle.

You use absolute value notation to find the measure of an angle.

Definition: The **measure of an angle** is the absolute value of the difference between the coordinates of the rays of the angle.

Because the two rays of an angle are distinct, the measure of an angle cannot equal 0. Since the two rays are noncollinear, the measure of an angle cannot equal 180.

Example 1

Find the measure of each given angle.

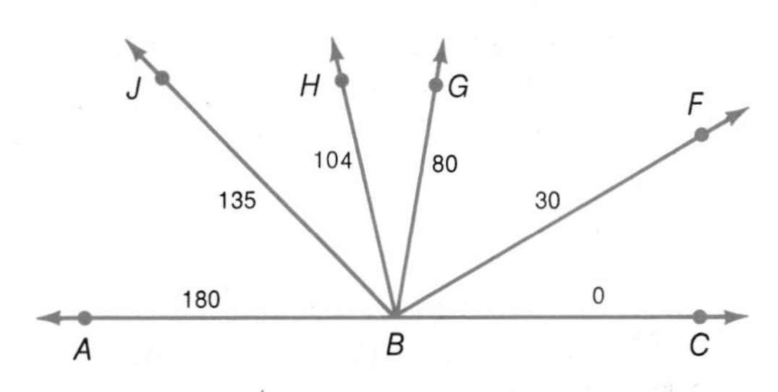

Angle	Measure
a. $\angle FBC$	$\|30 - 0\| = 30$ or $\|0 - 30\| = 30$
b. $\angle FBG$	$\|80 - 30\| = 50$ or $\|30 - 80\| = 50$
c. $\angle HBF$	$\|104 - 30\| = 74$ or $\|30 - 104\| = 74$
d. $\angle GBJ$	$\|135 - 80\| = 55$ or $\|80 - 135\| = 55$

Example 1 is based on the following postulate.

Postulate 9: The Protractor Postulate

a. To every angle there corresponds exactly one real number between 0 and 180. This number is the measure of the angle.

b. For half-plane H and the point Q on its edge, p, the rays in H or p with vertex Q can be placed in one-to-one correspondence with the real numbers n, $0 \leq n \leq 180$, such that a coordinate system for rays is established.

In Example 1, you found $m\angle FBG = 50$ and $m\angle GBJ = 55$. Similarly, you could find $m\angle FBJ = 105$. Thus,

$$m\angle FBG + m\angle GBJ = m\angle FBJ$$

This leads to a formal definition of betweenness for rays.

Definition: For three distinct rays, AX, AY, and AZ, and $\angle XAZ$, **$\overrightarrow{AY}$ is between $\overrightarrow{AX}$ and $\overrightarrow{AZ}$** if

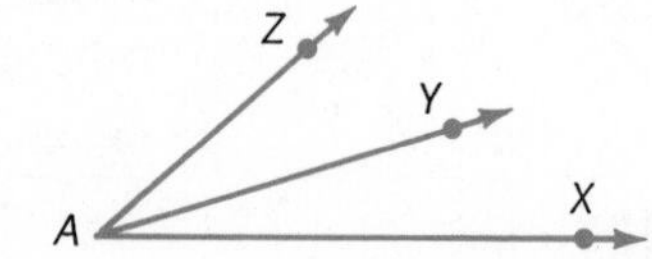

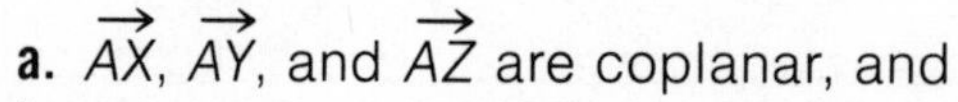

a. $\overrightarrow{AX}$, $\overrightarrow{AY}$, and $\overrightarrow{AZ}$ are coplanar, and
b. $m\angle XAY + m\angle YAZ = m\angle XAZ$.

This definition allows you to add the measures of angles. You may may refer to it as the Angle Addition Property.

Example 2

In $\angle ABC$, $\overrightarrow{BD}$ is between $\overrightarrow{BA}$ and $\overrightarrow{BC}$, $m\angle ABC = 80$, and $m\angle ABD = m\angle DBC$. Find $m\angle ABD$ and $m\angle DBC$.

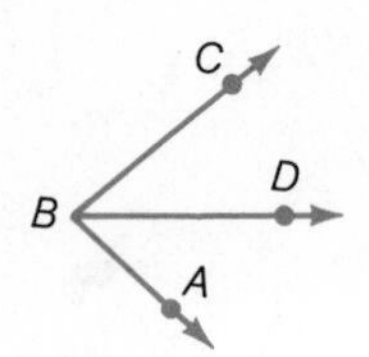

Let $m\angle ABD = x$ and $m\angle DBC = x$. ⟵ $m\angle ABD = m\angle DBC$

$x + x = 80$ ⟵ Solve for x.

$2x = 80$

$x = 40$

$\therefore\ m\angle ABD = m\angle DBC = 40$

Example 2 suggests the definition of angle bisector.

Definition: Ray AY is the **bisector** of $\angle XAZ$ if $\overrightarrow{AY}$ is between $\overrightarrow{AX}$ and $\overrightarrow{AZ}$ and $m\angle XAY = m\angle YAZ$.

In the definition, $\overrightarrow{AY}$ bisects $\angle XAZ$. That is, $m\angle XAY = m\angle YAZ$, and $\angle XAY \cong \angle YAZ$. **Angles** that have the same measure are **congruent**.

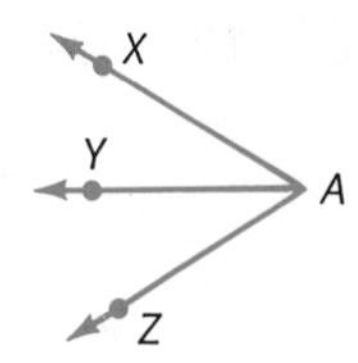

Theorem 2-2: An angle has exactly one bisector.

Try These

Find the measure of each angle.

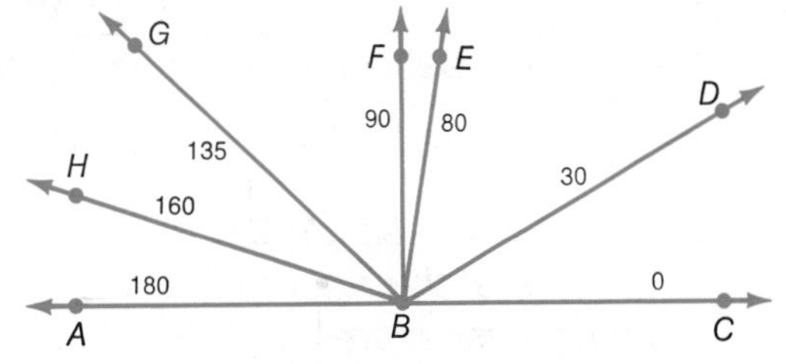

1. $\angle CBD$
2. $\angle DBE$
3. $\angle CBE$
4. $\angle EBG$
5. $\angle FBC$
6. $\angle GBH$
7. $\angle HBA$
8. $\angle GBD$
9. $\overrightarrow{AC}$ is between $\overrightarrow{AB}$ and $\overrightarrow{AD}$, $m\angle BAC = 42$, and $m\angle CAD = 28$. Find $m\angle DAB$.

Exercises

Find the measure of each angle.

a

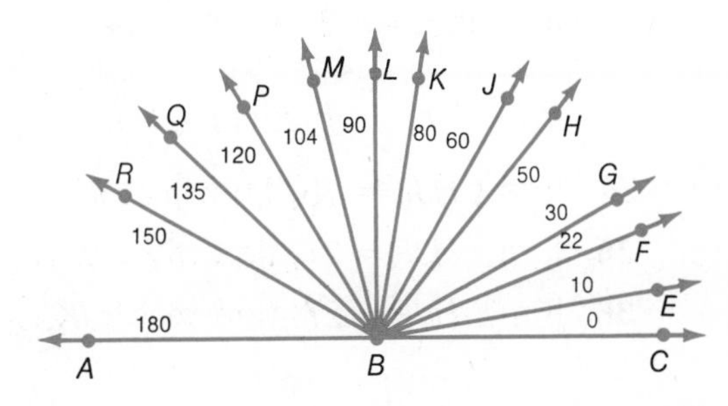

1. $\angle CBF$
2. $\angle CBQ$
3. $\angle FBH$
4. $\angle CBR$
5. $\angle HBL$
6. $\angle KBQ$
7. $\angle LBQ$
8. $\angle MBA$
9. $\angle PBR$
10. $\angle HBM$

Use the figure below to supply the missing angle measures.

	$m\angle RMQ$	$m\angle QMK$	$m\angle RMK$
11.	18	31	?
12.	37	44	?
13.	24	?	58
14.	?	51	70
15.	43	?	82

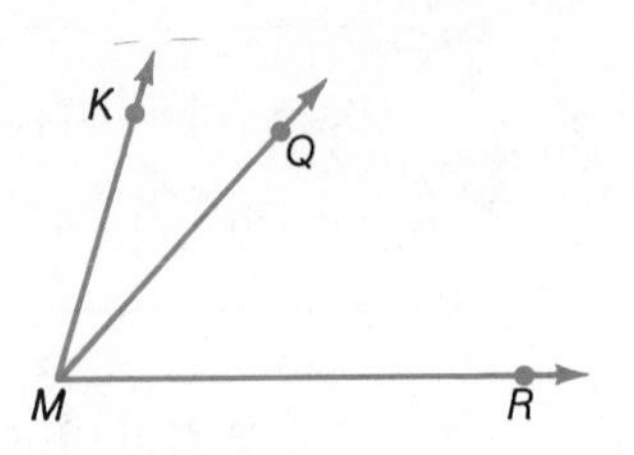

Classify each statement as True *or* False.

16. Any real number can be the measure of an angle.

17. An angle has exactly one bisector.

18. The bisector of an angle forms two congruent angles.

19. The bisector of an acute angle forms two acute angles.

20. The bisector of an obtuse angle forms two obtuse angles.

21. The bisector of a right angle forms two acute angles.

22. The bisector of an obtuse angle forms two right angles.

23. If $\overrightarrow{BD}$ is between $\overrightarrow{BA}$ and $\overrightarrow{BC}$, then $m\angle ABD = m\angle CBD$.

24. If $\overrightarrow{RQ}$ bisects $\angle SRT$ and $\overrightarrow{RA}$ bisects $\angle SRT$, then $\overrightarrow{RQ} = \overrightarrow{RA}$.

For Exercises **25–31,** *use the figure at the right to find the angle measures.*

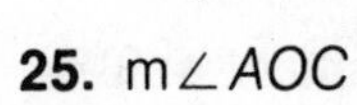

25. $m\angle AOC$ **26.** $m\angle BOD$

27. $m\angle AOD$ **28.** $m\angle 2 + m\angle 3$

29. $m\angle 1 + m\angle 2 + m\angle 3$ **30.** $m\angle AOC - m\angle 2$ **31.** $m\angle AOD - m\angle 3$

32. If $m\angle DAC = 24$, $m\angle DAB = 52$, and $m\angle CAB = 28$, which ray is between the other two?

33. If $m\angle DAC = 24$, $m\angle DAB = 52$, and $m\angle CAB = 76$, which ray is between the other two?

In $\triangle HJK$, $\overrightarrow{JP}$ bisects $\angle HJK$.

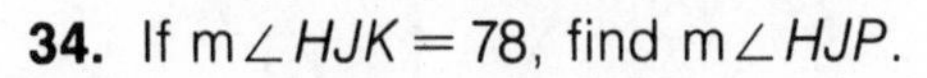

34. If $m\angle HJK = 78$, find $m\angle HJP$.

35. If $m\angle HJP = 27$, find $m\angle KJP$.

36. If $m\angle HJP = 27$, find $m\angle HJK$.

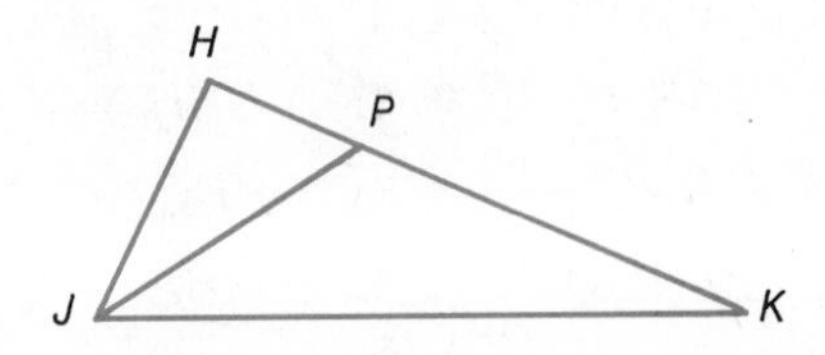

b

37. In the figure at the right, $\overrightarrow{PQ}$ bisects $\angle MPS$ and $\overrightarrow{PO}$ bisects $\angle QPS$. Show that $m\angle OPS = \frac{1}{4}\, m\angle MPS$.

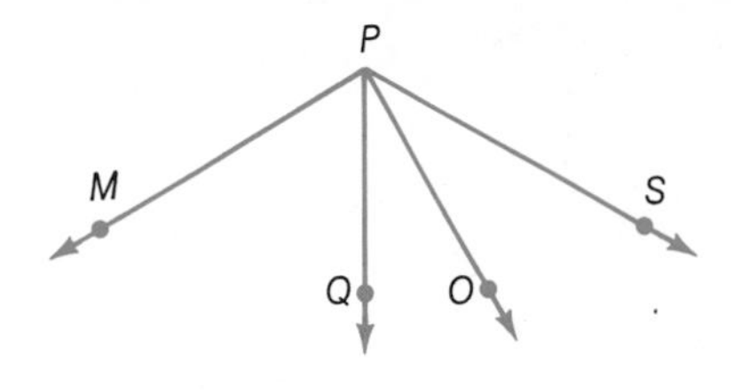

38. If $m\angle A + m\angle B = 147$ and the measure of $\angle B$ is three more than twice the measure of $\angle A$, find $m\angle A$ and $m\angle B$.

39. If $m\angle A + m\angle B = 4x + 7$, $m\angle A = 2x$, and $m\angle B = 3x$, find $m\angle A$ and $m\angle B$.

40. If $m\angle X = a$, $m\angle Y = 2a - 10$, and $m\angle X + m\angle Y = 2a + 10$, find $m\angle X$ and $m\angle Y$.

41. If $m\angle Q = x$, $m\angle P = 6x$, and $m\angle P + m\angle Q = 84$, find $m\angle Q$ and $m\angle P$.

42. If $m\angle T + m\angle R = 2y + 12$, $m\angle R = 2y - 12$, and $m\angle T = y$, find $m\angle R$.

c

43. Give the reason for each statement in the proof.

Given: $\overrightarrow{EG}$ lies between $\overrightarrow{EF}$ and $\overrightarrow{EN}$;
$\overrightarrow{EN}$ lies between $\overrightarrow{EG}$ and $\overrightarrow{ED}$;
$m\angle FEG = m\angle DEN$

Prove: $m\angle FEN = m\angle DEG$

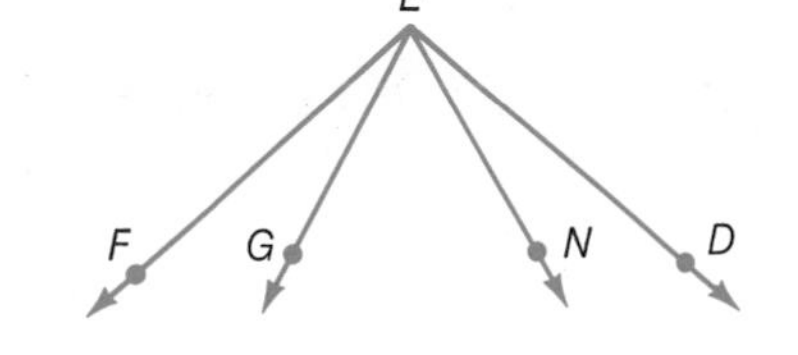

Statements	Reasons
1. $m\angle FEG = m\angle DEN$	1. ?
2. $m\angle GEN = m\angle GEN$	2. ?
3. $m\angle FEG + m\angle GEN = m\angle DEN + m\angle GEN$	3. ?
4. $m\angle FEG + m\angle GEN = m\angle FEN$	4. ?
5. $m\angle DEN + m\angle GEN = m\angle DEG$	5. ?
6. $m\angle FEN = m\angle DEG$	6. ?

44. Rays AR, AS, and AT are in the same half-plane with A on the edge of the half-plane. The rays have coordinates r, s, and t respectively. If $\overrightarrow{AS}$ is between $\overrightarrow{AR}$ and $\overrightarrow{AT}$, what statement can be made about r, s, and t?

45. In a coordinate system for rays, $\overrightarrow{AR}$, $\overrightarrow{AS}$, and $\overline{AT}$ have coordinates r, s, and t respectively. $\overrightarrow{AS}$ bisects $\angle TAR$ and $m\angle TAR = 72$. If $s = 104$, find r and t.

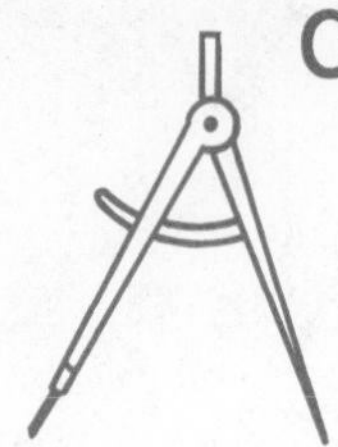

Constructing an Angle Congruent to a Given Angle

Given: $\angle EFG$

Required: To construct an angle congruent to $\angle EFG$.

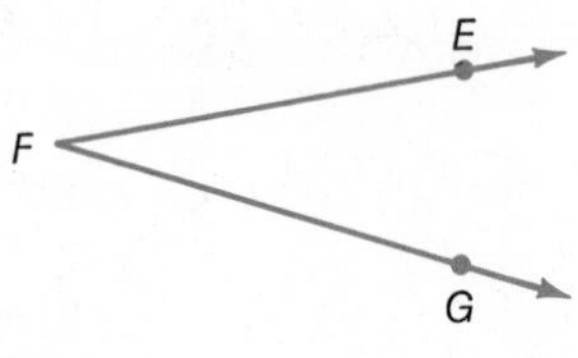

1. Draw any ray, $\overrightarrow{XY}$.

2. Place the tip of the compass at F, the vertex of $\angle EFG$, and make an *arc* that intersects the sides of $\angle EFG$. Call the points of intersection H and K.

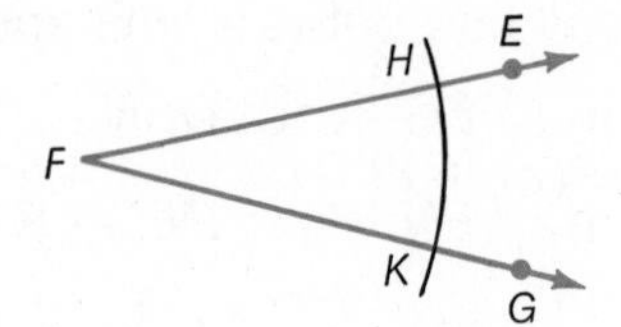

3. With the compass at the same setting as in Step 2, place its tip at X on $\overrightarrow{XY}$ and make an arc intersecting $\overrightarrow{XY}$. Label this point J.

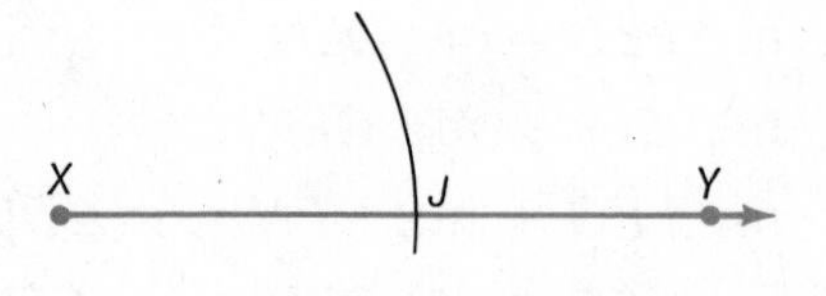

4. On $\angle EFG$, place the tip of the compass at K. Open the compass until the pencil point rests on H.

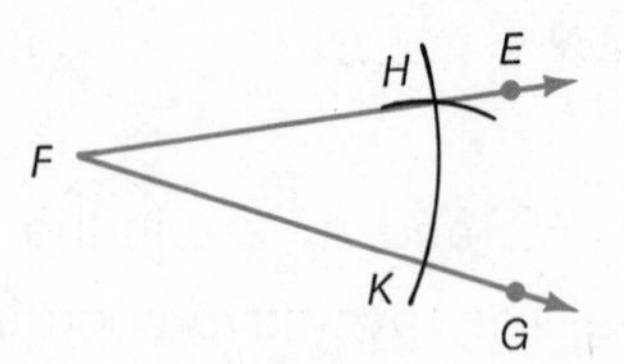

5. With the same setting as in Step 4, place the tip of the compass at J and make an arc that intersects the arc of Step 3. Label this point M.

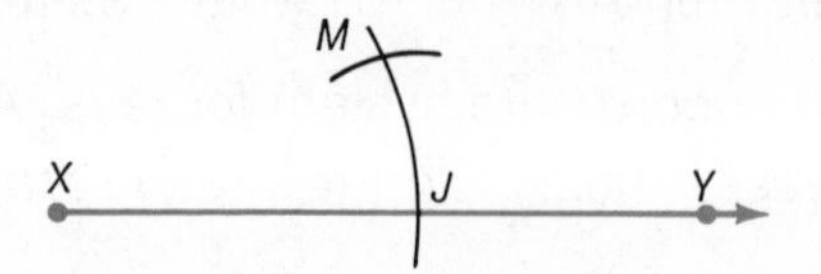

6. Draw $\overrightarrow{XM}$.

$\angle MXJ$ is the required angle. (You will be asked to prove this construction on page 113.)

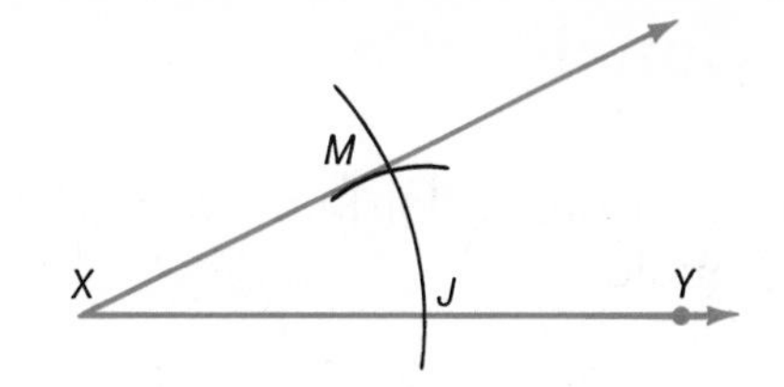

Bisecting an Angle

Given: $\angle ABC$

Required: To bisect $\angle ABC$.

1. To bisect $\angle ABC$, make an arc that intersects the sides of the angle. Call the points of intersection D and E.

2. With the tip of the compass at E and with the compass open more than $\frac{1}{2}DE$, make an arc in the interior of the angle. Repeat this procedure keeping the same setting but with the tip of the compass at D. Label the intersection of the arcs point F.

3. Draw $\overrightarrow{BF}$.
Then $\overrightarrow{BF}$ bisects $\angle ABC$.
(You will be asked to prove this construction on page 113.)

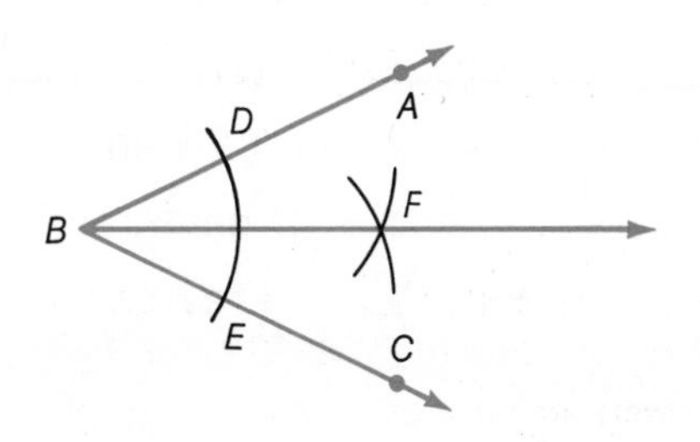

Exercises

1. Use your protractor to draw an angle of 50°. Construct $\angle ABC$ congruent to this angle.
2. Use your protractor to draw an angle of 165°. Construct $\angle DEF$ congruent to this angle.
3. Use your protractor to draw an angle of 90°. Construct $\angle QPR$ congruent to this angle.

Use a protractor to draw an angle of 140°. Label it $\angle ACE$.

4. Construct $\overrightarrow{CB}$ to bisect $\angle ACE$.
5. Construct $\overrightarrow{CD}$ to bisect $\angle BCE$.

Use a protractor to draw $\angle K$, an angle of 35° and $\angle S$, an angle of 70°. Then construct angles having each of the following measures.

6. $m\angle S + m\angle K$
7. $3\ m\angle K$
8. $m\angle S + 2\ m\angle K$
9. $\frac{1}{2}(m\angle S + m\angle K)$
10. $2\ m\angle S$
11. $m\angle S - m\angle K$
12. $\frac{1}{2}\ m\angle S$
13. $\frac{1}{4}\ m\angle S$
14. $\frac{1}{8}\ m\angle S$
15. $\frac{1}{2}(m\angle S - m\angle K)$
16. $3\ m\angle K - m\angle S$
17. $2(m\angle S - \frac{1}{2} m\angle K)$

Remember

Complete each statement.

1. The vertex of $\angle RPS$ is __?__.
2. The sides of $\angle SPQ$ are __?__ and __?__.
3. Ray __?__ lies between $\overrightarrow{PR}$ and $\overrightarrow{PQ}$.
4. Angles RPS and SPQ have ray __?__ in common.
5. $m\angle QPS + m\angle$ __?__ $= m\angle QPR$.

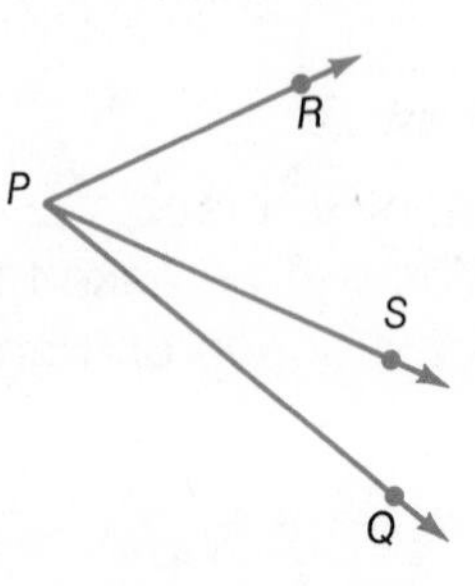

The answers are on page 92. If you need help, see pages 3, 11, and 50.

2-3 Important Angle Pairs

Angle pairs that occur often in geometry are given special names.

Name	Definition	Model
Complementary angles	Two angles whose measures have a sum of 90. Each angle is a <u>complement</u> of the other.	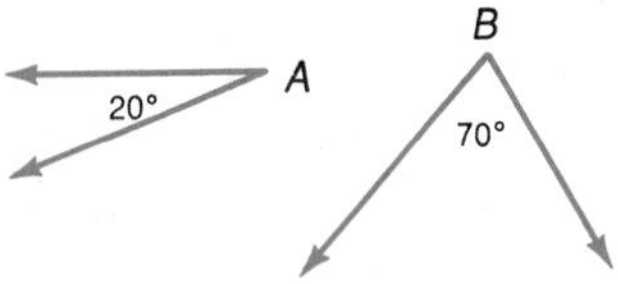 A 20°; B 70°
Supplementary angles	Two angles whose measures have a sum of 180. Each angle is a <u>supplement</u> of the other.	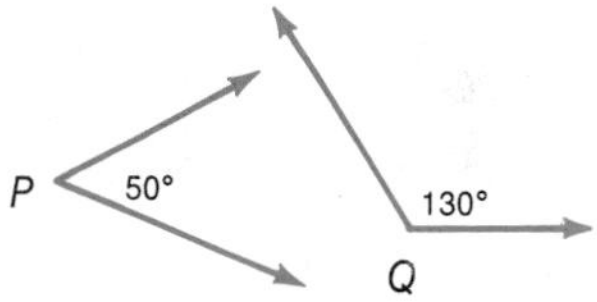 P 50°; Q 130°
Adjacent angles	Two coplanar angles with the same vertex and a common side but no interior points in common.	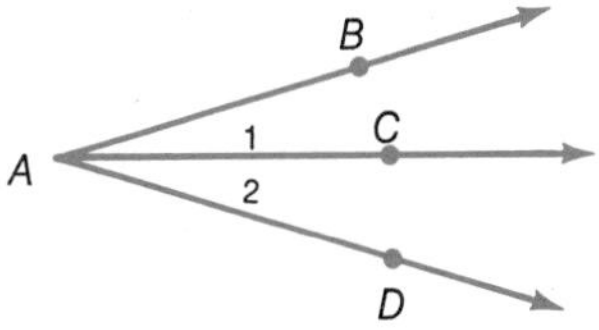 A, B, C, D, 1, 2
Linear pair	Adjacent angles such that two of the rays are opposite rays.	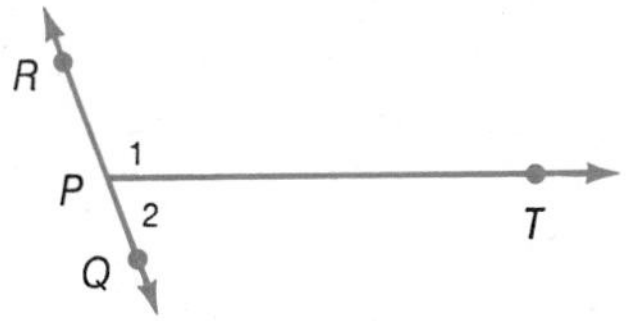 R, P, Q, T, 1, 2
Vertical angles	The nonadjacent angles formed when two lines intersect.	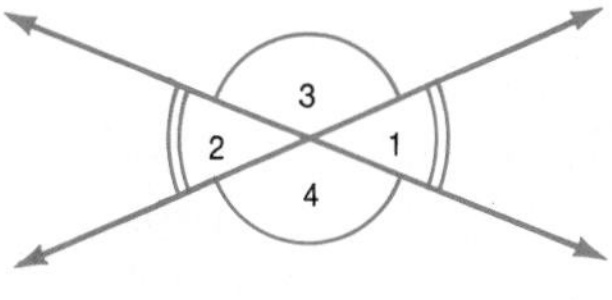 1, 2, 3, 4

Some of these angles pairs are related to each other. For example, two angles that form a linear pair are always supplementary. However, supplementary angles do not always form a linear pair. Example 1 points out some of these relationships.

Example 1

Complete the table for each marked pair of angles.

Angles	Complementary?	Supplementary?	Adjacent?	Linear Pair?	Vertical?
20°, 50°	No	No	Yes	No	No
130°, 130°	No	No	No	No	Yes
90°, 90°	No	Yes	No	No	Yes
90°, 90°	No	Yes	Yes	Yes	No
60°, 30°	Yes	No	No	No	No

The definitions of supplementary angles and linear pair suggest this postulate.

Postulate 10: Linear Pair Postulate

If two angles form a linear pair, then they are supplementary.

Two lines (rays, segments) that form a right angle are **perpendicular** to each other. The symbol for is perpendicular to is $\perp$.

$\overleftrightarrow{AB} \perp \overleftrightarrow{CD}$

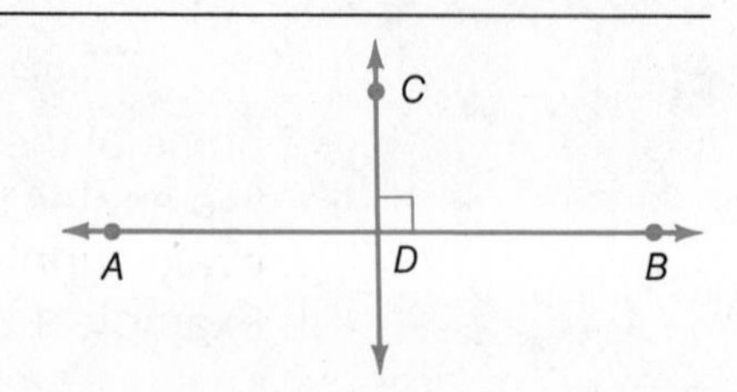

Example 2

Angles AOD and DOC form a linear pair and $m\angle AOD = m\angle DOC$. Explain why $\overrightarrow{OD} \perp \overleftrightarrow{AC}$.

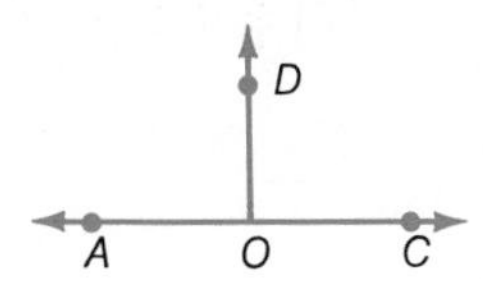

Statement	Reason
Let $x = m\angle AOD = m\angle DOC$.	$m\angle AOD = m\angle DOC$
Angles AOD and DOC are supplementary.	**If two angles form a linear pair, then they are supplementary.**
$m\angle AOD + m\angle DOC = 180$	**Supplementary angles are angles whose measures have a sum of 180.**
$x + x = 180$	
$2x = 180$	
$x = 90$	$m\angle AOD$ and $m\angle DOC$
$\angle DOC$ is a right angle.	**A right angle is an angle whose measure is 90.**
$\overrightarrow{OD} \perp \overleftrightarrow{AC}$	**Two lines that form a right angle are perpendicular to each other.**

The figures below and Example 2 suggest Theorem 2-3.

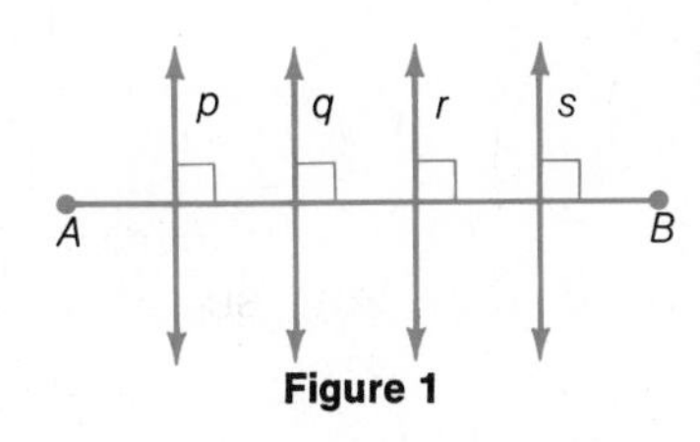

Figure 1

There are many lines perpendicular to a given segment.

A E B

Figure 2

A segment has exactly one midpoint.

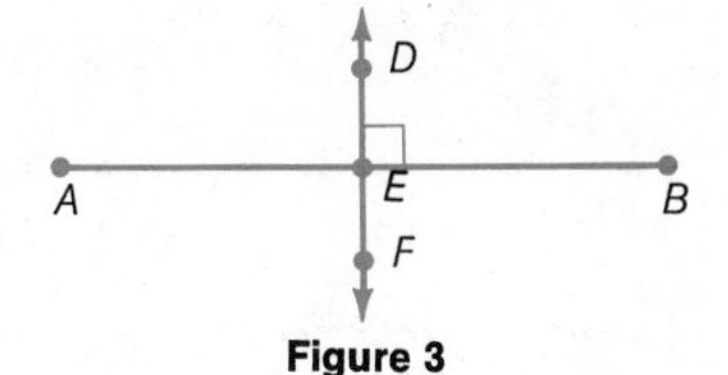

Figure 3

Through the midpoint of a segment, there is exactly one line perpendicular to the segment.

Theorem 2-3: Through a given point on a line in a plane, there is exactly one line in that plane perpendicular to the given line.

In Figure 3, $\overleftrightarrow{DF}$ is the perpendicular bisector of $\overline{AB}$. In a plane, the **perpendicular bisector** of a segment is the line perpendicular to the segment at the midpoint of the segment.

Theorem 2-4: For a given segment in a plane, the segment has exactly one perpendicular bisector in the plane.

Try These

In the figure below, $\overleftrightarrow{AB}$ and $\overleftrightarrow{CD}$ intersect at E, $\overrightarrow{EF} \perp \overleftrightarrow{CD}$, $m\angle AEF = 70$, and $m\angle DEB = 20$. Use this information for Exercises **1–10.**

1. Name a pair of vertical angles.
2. Name two right angles.
3. What is the measure of $\angle FEC$?
4. What is the measure of $\angle AEC$?
5. What angle forms a linear pair with $\angle AEF$?
6. What right angle is adjacent to $\angle DEB$?
7. What angle is complementary to $\angle DEB$?
8. Name two complementary angles that are also adjacent.
9. If an angle is supplementary to $\angle AEF$, what is its measure?
10. Name a supplement of $\angle AEF$.

For each angle measure, find the measure of a supplementary angle.

a

1. 30 **2.** 50 **3.** 132 **4.** 90

For each angle measure, find the measure of a complementary angle.

5. 48 **6.** 42 **7.** 67 **8.** 3

9. $\angle A$ and $\angle B$ are supplementary and $m\angle A = 125$. Which is greater, $m\angle A$ or $m\angle B$?

10. Find the difference between the measure of the supplement and the measure of the complement of an angle of 60°.

11. In the figure at the left below, $m\angle AEC = 90$, $m\angle BED = 90$, and $m\angle AEB = 65$. Find $m\angle 1$ and $m\angle 2$.

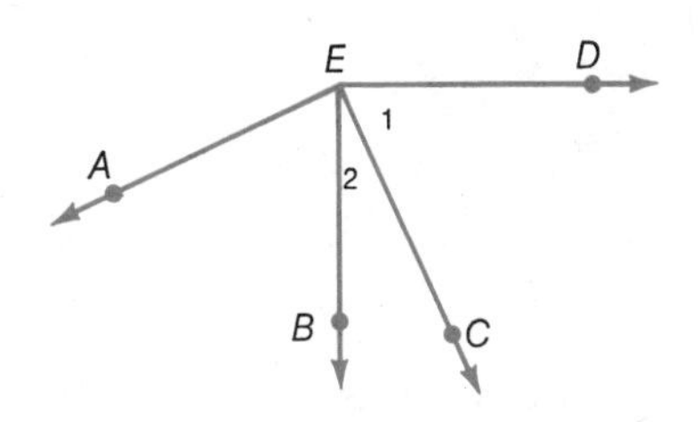

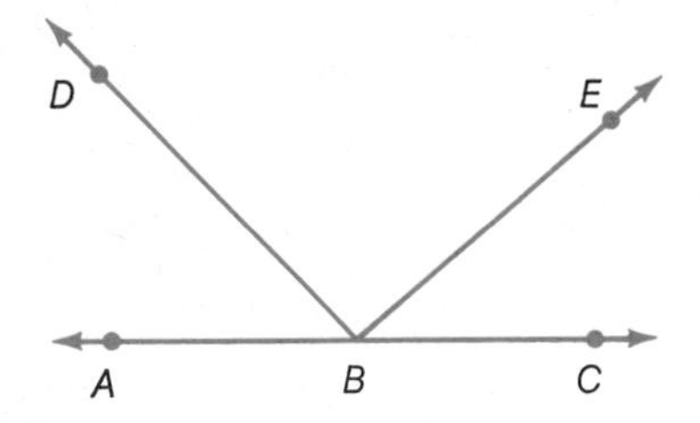

12. In the figure at the right above, point B is between points A and C. Name two pairs of supplementary angles. Which of these are linear pairs?

In polygon ABCD, $\overline{AC}$ and $\overline{BD}$ are diagonals.

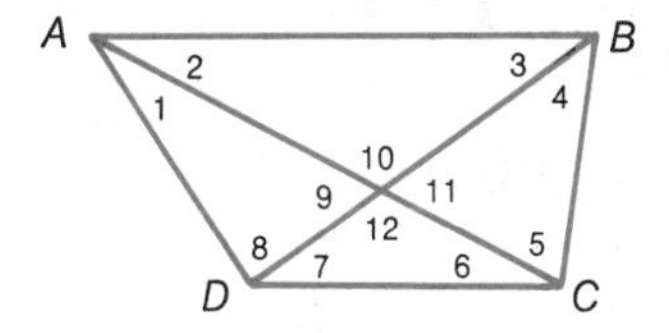

13. Name two pairs of vertical angles.
14. Name four linear pairs.
15. Name eight pairs of adjacent angles.
16. Are the angles of a linear pair also adjacent?

*In Exercises **17–27,** complete each statement. All statements refer to the figure at the right below in which $\overleftrightarrow{AB} \perp \overleftrightarrow{FD}$ at C.*

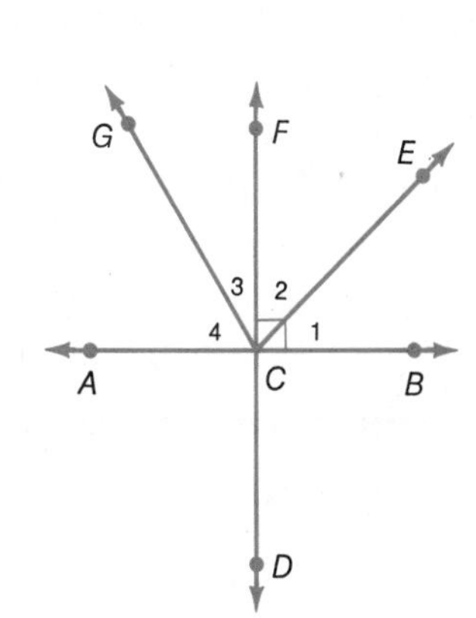

17. The complement of $\angle 4$ is $\angle$ __?__.
18. $\angle 1$ and $\angle$ __?__ are complementary.
19. $\angle GCD$ and $\angle$ __?__ are supplementary.
20. An acute angle adjacent to $\angle 4$ is $\angle$ __?__.
21. Two acute angles adjacent to $\angle 3$ are $\angle$ __?__ and $\angle$ __?__.
22. $\angle ACE$ and $\angle$ __?__ form a linear pair.
23. $\angle GCB$ and $\angle$ __?__ form a linear pair.
24. If $m\angle 1 = 25$, then $m\angle 2 =$ __?__.
25. If $m\angle 1 = 45$, then $m\angle ECD =$ __?__.
26. If $m\angle 1 = 35$, then $m\angle ACE =$ __?__.
27. If $m\angle 1 = m\angle 3 = 40$, then $m\angle GCE =$ __?__.

*For Exercises **28–37**, classify each statement as True or False.*

28. If two adjacent angles are complementary, then their exterior rays are perpendicular to each other.

29. All right angles are congruent.

30. Two vertical angles may also be complementary.

31. Two vertical angles may also be adjacent.

32. If two congruent angles form a linear pair, then each is a right angle.

33. The complement of an acute angle is an obtuse angle.

34. The supplement of an acute angle is an obtuse angle.

35. Two supplementary angles always form a linear pair.

36. If two supplementary angles are congruent, then each has a measure of 90.

37. If two complementary angles are congruent, then each has a measure of 45.

*For Exercises **38–42**, complete each statement.*

b **38.** Angles A and B form a linear pair. If $m\angle A = x$, then $m\angle B =$ _?_. $(90 - x, 90 + x, 180 - x, 180 + x)$

39. Angles C and D are complementary. If $m\angle C = y - 10$, then $m\angle D =$ _?_. $(80 - y, 100 - y, y + 80, y + 100)$

40. If the measure of one angle of a linear pair is five times that of the other, then the measure of the larger angle is _?_. (30, 36, 144, 150)

41. One of two complementary angles measures three times the other. The measure of the smaller angle is _?_. $(22\frac{1}{2}, 30, 45, 60)$

42. Angle A is supplementary to angle B and angle B is supplementary to angle C. If $m\angle A = x$, then $m\angle C =$ _?_. $(90, x, 180 + x, 180 - x)$

c **43.** The measure of an angle is 20 less than the measure of its supplement. Find the measure of the angle, the measure of the supplementary angle, and the measure of the complementary angle.

44. Two angles are complementary. One half the measure of the larger angle exceeds one fourth the measure of the smaller by 30. Find the measure of each angle.

45. Show that the following statement is true:

> *The difference between the measures of the supplement and the complement of an angle is 90.*

(HINT: Let the measure of the given angle be a, its supplement b, and its complement c. Then $a + b = 180$ and $a + c = 90$. Solve the two equations for b and c, respectively; then find $(b - c)$.

2-4 Equivalence Relations

Equality between real numbers is an **equivalence relation** because it has the following properties.

Postulates of Equality

Reflexive Postulate: $a = a$
Symmetric Postulate: If $a = b$, then $b = a$.
Transitive Postulate: If $a = b$ and $b = c$, then $a = c$.

Equivalence relations are also useful in geometry.

Example 1

Determine whether congruence for angles is an equivalence relation.

Property	Model	True or False?
Reflexive	$\angle A \cong \angle A$	True; an angle is congruent to itself.
Symmetric	$\angle A \cong \angle B$ (A, 40°; B, 40°)	True; if $\angle A \cong \angle B$, then $\angle B \cong \angle A$.
Transitive	$\angle A \cong \angle B$ and $\angle B \cong \angle C$ (A, 40°; B, 40°; C, 40°)	True; if $\angle A \cong \angle B$ and $\angle B \cong \angle C$, then $\angle A \cong \angle C$.

Since congruence for angles is reflexive, symmetric, and transitive, it is an equivalence relation.

Example 1 suggests this theorem.

Theorem 2-5: Congruence is an equivalence relation.

By Theorem 2-5, the congruence of geometric figures is reflexive, symmetric, and transitive. In geometry, the reflexive property of congruence is commonly called **identity.**

Example 2

Use the properties of an equivalence relation to give a reason for each statement in the table.

Model	Statement	Reason
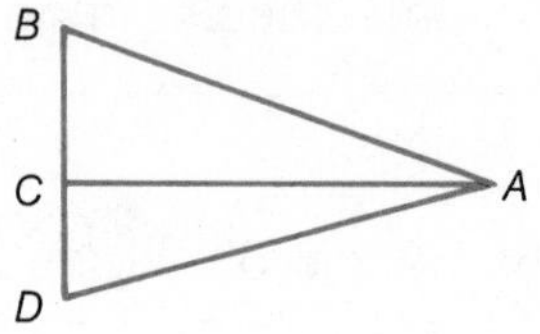	$\overline{AC} \cong \overline{AC}$	Reflexive property of congruence, or identity.
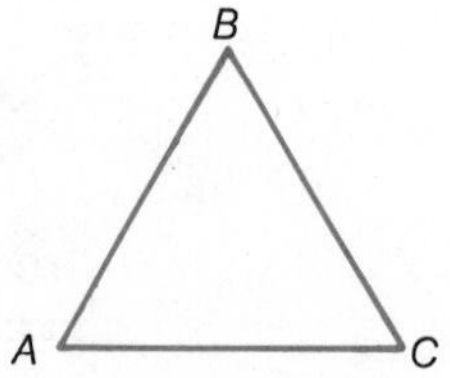 $\overline{AB} \cong \overline{AC}$; $\overline{AC} \cong \overline{CB}$	$\overline{AB} \cong \overline{CB}$	Transitive property of congruence.
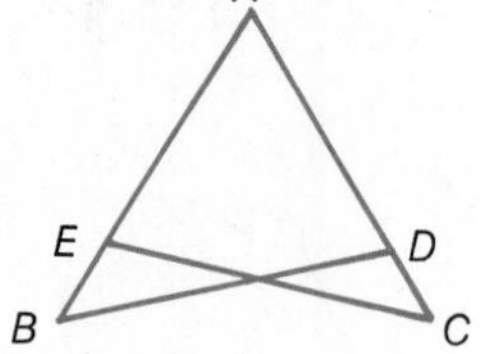 $\angle B \cong \angle C$	$\angle C \cong \angle B$	Symmetric property of congruence.

Other algebraic postulates are also useful in geometry. For these postulates and the Substitution Principle, a, b, c, x, and y are real numbers.

Postulate	Example
Commutative Postulate	
for Addition: $a + b = b + a$	$1.5 + 9.2 = 9.2 + 1.5$
for Multiplication: $a \cdot b = b \cdot a$	$\frac{5}{7} \cdot \frac{1}{2} = \frac{1}{2} \cdot \frac{5}{7}$
Associative Postulate	
for Addition: $a + (b + c) = (a + b) + c$	$5.5 + (6 + 3.1) = (5.5 + 6) + 3.1$
for Multiplication: $a(bc) = (ab)c$	$3(\frac{6}{11} \cdot \frac{5}{9}) = (3 \cdot \frac{6}{11})\frac{5}{9}$
Distributive Postulate Multiplication over Addition	
$a(b + c) = a \cdot b + a \cdot c$	$5(6 + 9) = 5 \cdot 6 + 5 \cdot 9$
Addition Postulate for Equations	
If $x = y$, then $x + a = y + a$.	If $x = 10$, then $x + (-5) = 10 + (-5)$.
Multiplication Postulate for Equations	
If $x = y$, then $ax = ay$ $(a \neq 0)$.	If $x = 5$, then $\frac{1}{5}x = \frac{1}{5}(5)$.

The Substitution Principle is also used in geometry.

Substitution Principle: If $a = b$, then a may be substituted for b in any equation or inequality.

The Substitution Principle and postulates from algebra are used to solve equations that occur in geometry.

Example 3

Solve $6x + (5x + 4) = 180$ for $6x$ and $5x + 4$.

$6x + (5x + 4) = 180$

$(6x + 5x) + 4 = 180$ ← Associative Postulate for Addition

$11x + 4 - 4 = 180 - 4$ ← Addition Postulate for Equations

$11x = 176$

$\frac{1}{11}(11x) = \frac{1}{11}(176)$ ← Multiplication Postulate for Equations

$x = 16$

$6x = 96$ and $5x + 4 = 84$ ← Substitution Principle

Try These

*Each statement in Exercises **1–5** illustrates a property of congruence for segments or angles. Use the property indicated to complete each statement.*

1. Transitive Property: If $\overline{AB}$ is congruent to $\overline{CD}$ and $\overline{CD}$ is congruent to $\overline{EF}$, then $\overline{AB}$ is congruent to __?__.
2. Symmetric Property: If $\overline{RS} \cong \overline{SK}$, then __?__ $\cong \overline{RS}$.
3. Reflexive Property: $\angle A \cong$ __?__.
4. Transitive Property: If $\angle T \cong \angle R$ and $\angle R \cong \angle G$, then __?__ $\cong$ __?__.
5. Transitive Property: If $\overline{MP} \cong \overline{PQ}$ and __?__ $\cong \overline{QR}$, then $\overline{MP} \cong \overline{QR}$.

*For Exercises **6–9,** name the algebraic postulate illustrated. The letters a, b, and c represent real numbers.*

6. $15 + c = c + 15$
7. $3(ab) = (3a)b$
8. $(b + 1) + c = b + (1 + c)$
9. If $a = 3$, then $\frac{1}{2}(a) = \frac{1}{2}(3)$.

Exercises

a

1. Name the three properties of an equivalence relation.

*For Exercises **2–8,** name the Equality Postulate illustrated.*

2. If $m\angle ABC = m\angle 1$ and $m\angle 1 = m\angle GHK$, then $m\angle ABC = m\angle GHK$.
3. If $RS = DW$, then $DW = RS$.
4. The length of segment AC is equal to itself.
5. $m\angle D = m\angle D$.
6. If $m\angle A = m\angle D$ and $m\angle D = m\angle E$, then $m\angle A = m\angle E$.
7. If $CE = BA$ and $BA = \frac{1}{2}(BD)$, then $CE = \frac{1}{2}(BD)$.
8. If $WR = PQ + 2(ST)$, then $PQ + 2(ST) = WR$.

*For exercises **9–11,** state whether each relation is reflexive. Give an example in each case.*

9. Is supplementary to for angles

10. Is perpendicular to for lines

11. Is complementary to for angles

*For Exercises **12–14,** state whether each relation is symmetric. Give an example in each case.*

12. Is supplementary to for angles

13. Is perpendicular to for lines

14. Is complementary to for angles

*For Exercises **15–17,** state whether each relation is transitive. Give an example in each case.*

15. Is supplementary to for angles

16. Is perpendicular to for lines

17. Is complementary to for angles

*Use your answers to Exercises **9–17** to tell whether each of the following is an equivalence relation.*

18. Is supplementary to for angles

19. Is perpendicular to for lines

20. Is complementary to for angles

*For Exercises **21–22,** the solution to each equation is given. Supply the missing reason.*

21.

$90 - x = 2x$

$90 - x + x = 2x + x$ __?__

$90 = 3x$

$\frac{1}{3}(90) = \frac{1}{3}(3x)$ __?__

$30 = x$

$x = 30$ __?__

22.

$\frac{2}{3}x + x = 90$

$\frac{5}{3}x = 90$

$3(\frac{5}{3}x) = 3(90)$ __?__

$5x = 270$

$\frac{1}{5}(5x) = \frac{1}{5}(270)$ __?__

$x = 54$

$\frac{2}{3}x = 36$ __?__

Solve each equation.

23. $y - 9 = 3$
24. $n + 3n = 90$
25. $3x + 2x + 5 = 540$
26. $90 - x = x + 50$
27. $\frac{1}{2}y + y = 180$
28. $-7x = 7.42$
29. $2.7 = 4.8 + t$
30. $8n + 22 = 70$
31. $5x - 17 = 22$
32. $5 - 2y = 15$
33. $4 = 30 - 6n$
34. $4y + 27 = 3$
35. $4\frac{1}{4} = x + 5\frac{1}{2}$
36. $\frac{1}{2}x = 3\frac{1}{2}$
37. $8 = \frac{5}{3}y$
38. $\frac{1}{16}n = 1.06$
39. $5.4 + n = -9.7$
40. $\frac{1}{2}y - \frac{3}{4} = \frac{1}{4} - \frac{1}{2}y$
41. $5 - 7n = 1 - 5n$
42. $\frac{3}{5}n - 7 = 14$
43. $\frac{2}{3}t + 5 = 23$
44. $1.2t + 3.4 = -1.4$
45. $0 = 1.6n - 6.4$
46. $2.1 = 4.3 - 1.1w$
47. $1.6n + 7.0 = 2.2$
48. $\frac{5}{12}t - 12 = 48$
49. $53 + \frac{3}{5}x = 26$

For Exercises **50–54,** *give a reason for each statement.*

50. If $WY = RT$, then $\frac{1}{2}(WY) = \frac{1}{2}(RT)$.
51. If $\frac{1}{2}(WY) = \frac{1}{2}(RT)$, and $RS = \frac{1}{2}(RT)$, and $WS = \frac{1}{2}(WY)$, then $RS = WS$.

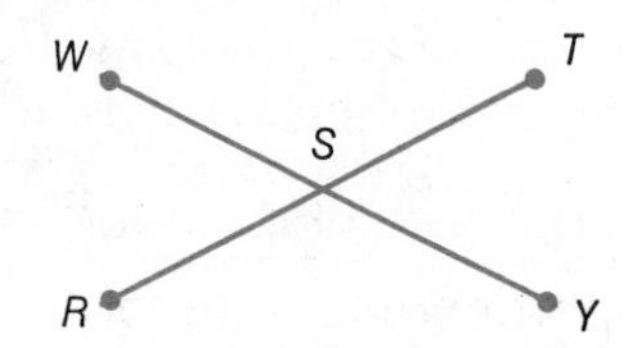

52. $BC = BC$.
53. If $AB = CD$, then $AB + BC = CD + BC$.
54. If $AB + BC = BC + CD$, and $AC = AB + BC$, and $BD = BC + CD$, then $AC = BD$.

think–draw–see

1. Use a ruler and protractor to draw two intersecting lines with $m\angle 1 = 40$.
2. Use your protractor to find $m\angle 2$, $m\angle 3$, and $m\angle 4$.

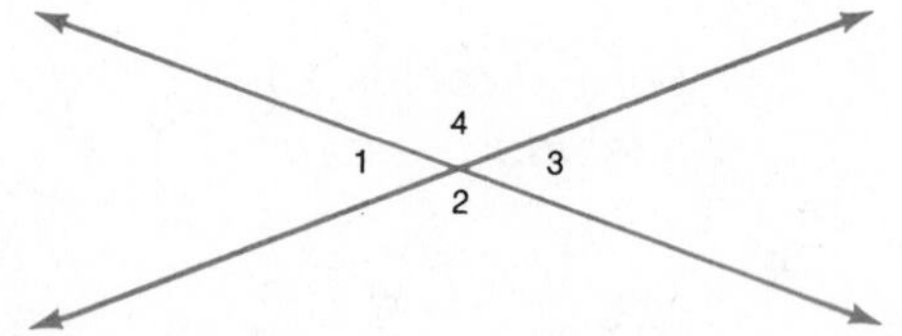

3. Compare $m\angle 1$ with $m\angle 3$, and $m\angle 2$ with $m\angle 4$.
4. Repeat Steps **1–3,** making $m\angle 1 = 80$.
5. Repeat Steps **1–3,** making $m\angle 1 = 110$.
6. Which angles in the figure are vertical angles?
7. What do your answers to Step **3** tell you about the measures of vertical angles?

2-5 Two-Column Proofs

You were introduced to the paragraph and two-column forms of proof in Chapter 1. Most proofs in geometry use two columns.

In general, each statement in a proof (except the Given) is a conclusion that is reached by using the statement or statements that preceded it. The statements that are used are indicated in the Reasons column as (1), (2), (3), and so on. In the proof that follows, note that Statements 3 and 6 are used to arrive at Statement 7.

Theorem 2-6: If two angles are supplements of the same angle, then they are congruent.

Given: $\angle A$ and $\angle C$ are supplementary angles.
$\angle B$ and $\angle C$ are supplementary angles.

Prove: $\angle A \cong \angle B$

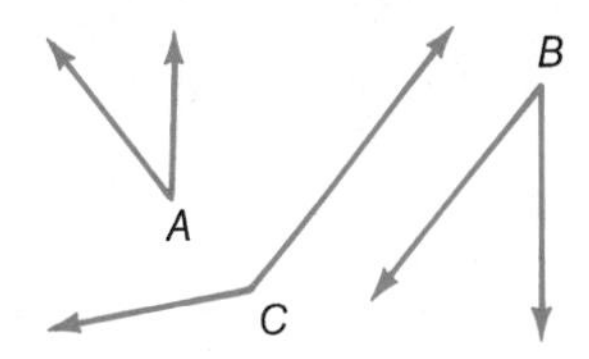

Statements	Reasons
1. $\angle A$ and $\angle C$ are supplementary.	1. Given
2. $m\angle A + m\angle C = 180$	2. (1). Supplementary angles are two angles whose measures have a sum of 180.
3. $m\angle A = 180 - m\angle C$	3. (2). Addition Postulate for Equations
4. $\angle B$ and $\angle C$ are supplementary.	4. Given
5. $m\angle B + m\angle C = 180$	5. (4). Definition of supplementary angles
6. $m\angle B = 180 - m\angle C$	6. (5). Addition Postulate for Equations
7. $m\angle A = m\angle B$	7. (3). (6). Substitution Principle
8. $\therefore \angle A \cong \angle B$	8. (7). Angles that have the same measure are congruent.

The $\therefore$ in Statement 8 means therefore.

The proof of the following theorem is similar to the proof of Theorem 2-6. Notice, however, that this proof combines steps. (See Steps 2 and 3.) Two steps can be combined into one if they have the same reason and confusion does not result.

Theorem 2-7: If two angles are complements of the same angle, then they are congruent.

Given: $\angle A$ and $\angle C$ are complementary angles.
$\angle B$ and $\angle C$ are complementary angles.

Prove: $\angle A \cong \angle B$

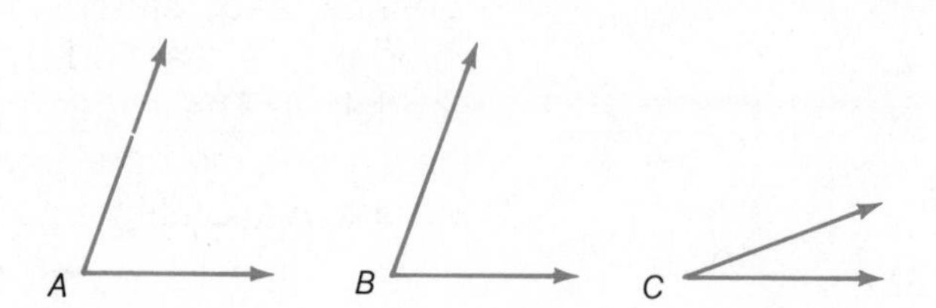

Statements	Reasons
1. $\angle A$ and $\angle C$ are complementary $\angle B$ and $\angle C$ are complementary	1. Given
2. $m\angle A + m\angle C = 90$ $m\angle B + m\angle C = 90$	2. (1). Complementary angles are two angles whose measures have a sum of 90.
3. $m\angle A = 90 - m\angle C$ $m\angle B = 90 - m\angle C$	3. (2). Addition Postulate for Equations
4. $m\angle A = m\angle B$	4. (3). Substitution Principle
5. $\therefore \angle A \cong \angle B$	5. (4). Angles that have the same measure are congruent.

Two theorems similar to Theorems 2-6 and 2-7 are given below. You are asked to prove them in the Exercises.

Theorem 2-8: If two angles are supplements of congruent angles, then they are congruent.

Theorem 2-9: If two angles are complements of congruent angles, then they are congruent.

If a theorem is not in the form of a conditional, rewrite it as a conditional. A brief plan of the proof can also help.

Theorem 2-10: Vertical angles are congruent.

This can be rewritten as a conditional: If two lines intersect, then the vertical angles formed are congruent.

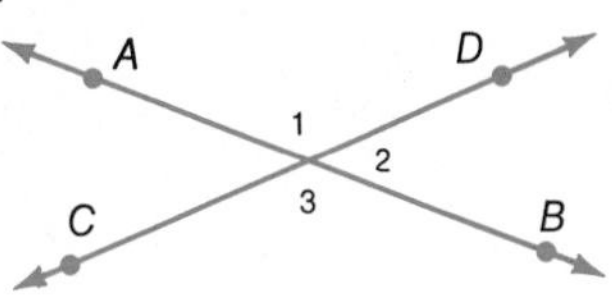

Given: $\overleftrightarrow{AB}$ and $\overleftrightarrow{CD}$ intersect.

Prove: $\angle 1 \cong \angle 3$

Plan: Prove that $\angle 1$ and $\angle 2$ are supplementary and that $\angle 3$ and $\angle 2$ are supplementary. Then use Theorem 2-6.

Statements	Reasons
1. $\overleftrightarrow{AB}$ and $\overleftrightarrow{CD}$ intersect.	1. Given
2. $\angle 1$ and $\angle 2$ are a linear pair. $\angle 3$ and $\angle 2$ are a linear pair.	2. (1). Definition of linear pair
3. $\angle 1$ and $\angle 2$ are supplementary. $\angle 3$ and $\angle 2$ are supplementary.	3. (2). If two angles form a linear pair, then they are supplementary.
4. $\therefore \angle 1 \cong \angle 3$	4. (3). If two angles are supplements of the same angle, then they are congruent.

Steps for Writing a Two-Column Proof

1. If the theorem is not in the form of a conditional, rewrite it as a conditional.
2. Draw a figure to represent the Given and the Prove.
3. Plan the proof, either mentally or on paper.
4. Write the statements and reasons in the proof.

Try These

*For Exercises **1–3**, refer to the figure at the right. Lines DE and GB intersect at A, $\overrightarrow{AC} \perp \overleftrightarrow{DE}$, and $\overrightarrow{AF} \perp \overleftrightarrow{GB}$.*

1. Why is $\angle 1$ congruent to $\angle 4$?
2. What four angles are right angles?
3. If $\angle 3$ and $\angle 5$ are both complementary to $\angle 4$, why is $\angle 3$ congruent to $\angle 5$?

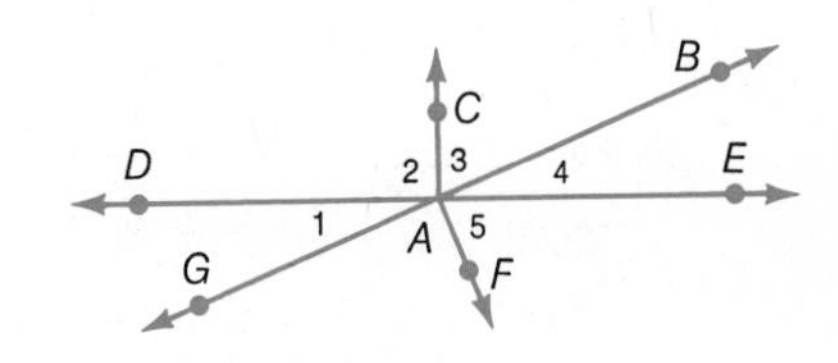

4. Supply the reasons in the following proof.

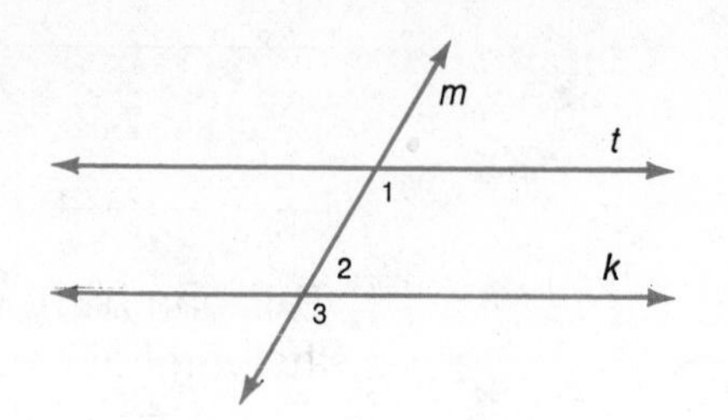

Given: Lines t and k intersect line m; $\angle 1$ and $\angle 2$ are supplementary.

Prove: $\angle 1 \cong \angle 3$

Plan: Prove that $\angle 1$ and $\angle 3$ are supplements of the same angle and then use Theorem 2-6.

Statements	Reasons
1. Lines k and m intersect.	1. ___?___
2. $\angle 3$ and $\angle 2$ form a linear pair.	2. (1). ___?___
3. $\angle 3$ and $\angle 2$ are supplementary.	3. (2). ___?___
4. $\angle 1$ and $\angle 2$ are supplementary.	4. ___?___
5. $\therefore \angle 1 \cong \angle 3$	5. (3). (4). ___?___

Exercises

a

1. Supply the reasons in the following proof.

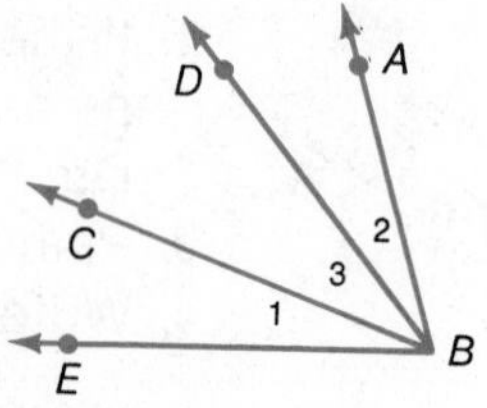

Given: $\angle ABC \cong \angle DBE$

Prove: $\angle 2 \cong \angle 1$

Statements	Reasons
1. $\angle ABC \cong \angle DBE$	1. ___?___
2. $m\angle ABC = m\angle DBE$	2. (1). ___?___
3. $m\angle 3 + m\angle 2 = m\angle ABC$ $m\angle 3 + m\angle 1 = m\angle DBE$	3. Angle Addition Property
4. $m\angle 3 + m\angle 2 = m\angle 3 + m\angle 1$	4. (2). (3). ___?___
5. $m\angle 2 = m\angle 1$	5. (4). ___?___
6. $\therefore \angle 2 \cong \angle 1$	6. (5). ___?___

2. Supply the missing reasons for the proof of Theorem 2-9.

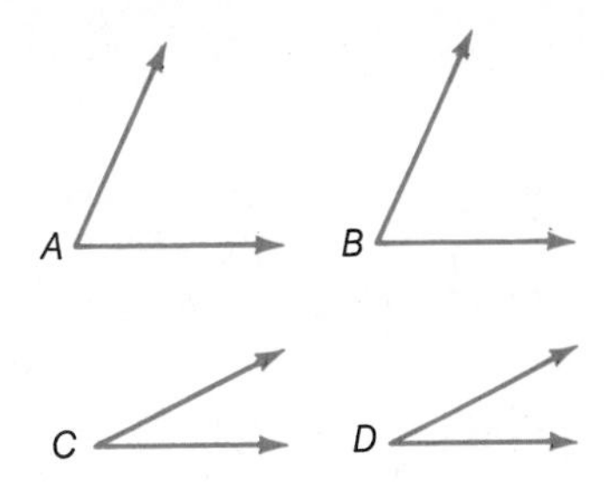

Given: $\angle A \cong \angle B$; $\angle A$ and $\angle C$ are complementary; $\angle B$ and $\angle D$ are complementary.

Prove: $\angle C \cong \angle D$

Statements	Reasons
1. $\angle A$ and $\angle C$ are complementary. $\angle B$ and $\angle D$ are complementary.	1. ?
2. $m\angle A + m\angle C = 90$; $m\angle B + m\angle D = 90$	2. ?
3. $m\angle A + m\angle C = m\angle B + m\angle D$	3. ?
4. $\angle A \cong \angle B$	4. ?
5. $m\angle A = m\angle B$	5. ?
6. $m\angle A + m\angle C - m\angle A = m\angle B + m\angle D - m\angle B$	6. ?
7. $m\angle C = m\angle D$	7. ?
8. $\angle C \cong \angle D$	8. ?

3. Prove Theorem 2-8. Use the proof in Exercise **2** as a guide.

*Write a two-column proof for each exercise. Use the figure at the right below for Exercises **4–11.***

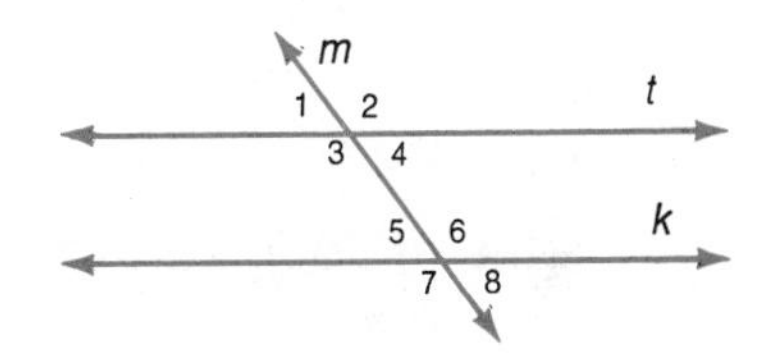

4. Given: $\angle 3$ and $\angle 5$ are supplementary.
Prove: $\angle 1 \cong \angle 5$

5. Given: $\angle 4$ and $\angle 6$ are supplementary.
Prove: $\angle 2 \cong \angle 6$

6. Given: $\angle 2 \cong \angle 7$
Prove: $\angle 2 \cong \angle 6$

7. Given: $\angle 1 \cong \angle 8$
Prove: $\angle 1 \cong \angle 5$

8. Given: $\angle 1$ and $\angle 7$ are supplementary.
Prove: $\angle 4$ and $\angle 6$ are supplementary.

9. Given: $\angle 2$ and $\angle 5$ are supplementary.
Prove: $\angle 3$ and $\angle 8$ are supplementary.

10. Given: $\angle 1 \cong \angle 8$
Prove: $\angle 2 \cong \angle 7$

11. Given: $\angle 3 \cong \angle 6$
Prove: $\angle 4 \cong \angle 5$

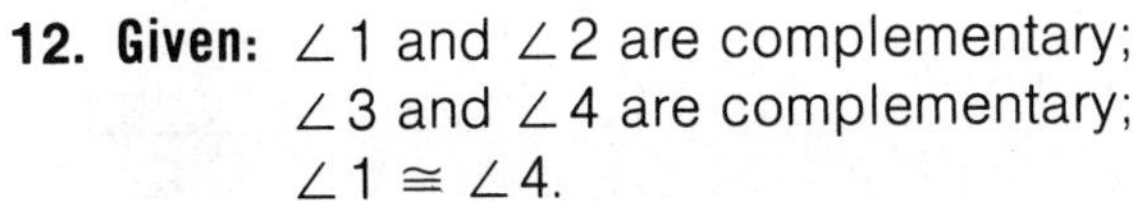

12. Given: $\angle 1$ and $\angle 2$ are complementary; $\angle 3$ and $\angle 4$ are complementary; $\angle 1 \cong \angle 4$.
Prove: $\angle 2 \cong \angle 3$ (See Exercise 2.)

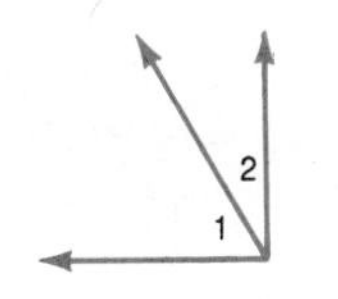

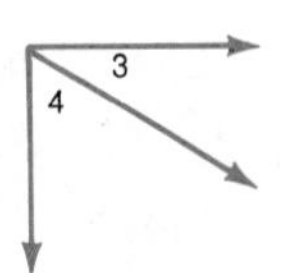

13. **Given:** $\overrightarrow{BA} \perp \overline{BC}$; $\overrightarrow{CD} \perp \overline{BC}$;
$\angle 2 \cong \angle 4$

Prove: $\angle 1 \cong \angle 3$

14. **Given:** B is between A and C;
C is between B and D; $AC = BD$

Prove: $AB = CD$

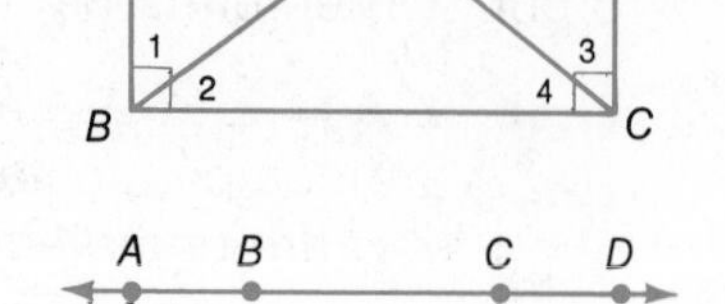

15. **Given:** In $\triangle ABC$, $\angle ABC$ is a right angle, $\angle 1 \cong \angle C$, and $\angle 2 \cong \angle A$.

Prove: $\angle A$ and $\angle C$ are complementary.

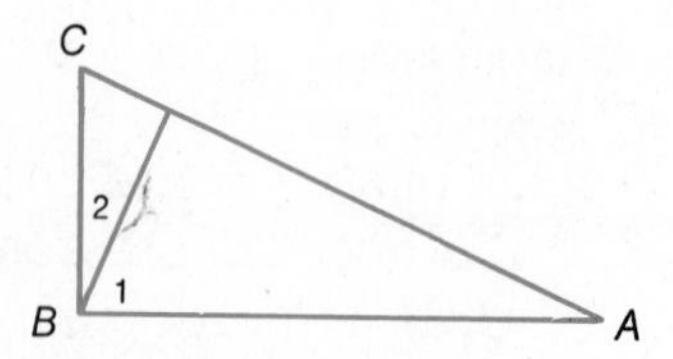

Use the figure below for Exercises **16–23.** *Give a reason for each conclusion stated. Use a definition, a postulate, or a proved theorem.*

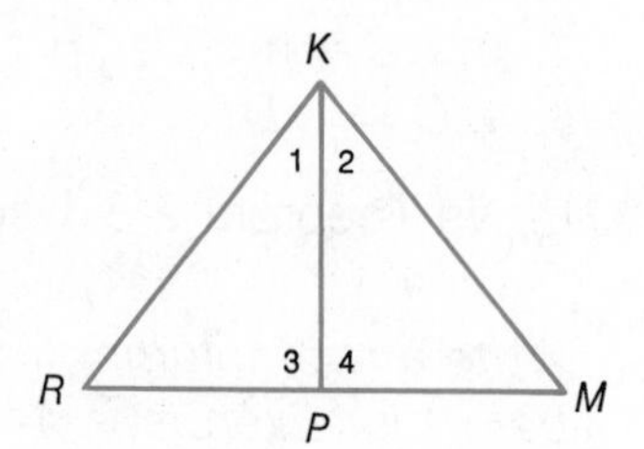

16. $\triangle KRM$ is isosceles with base RM.
$\therefore \overline{RK} \cong \overline{MK}$

17. $\overrightarrow{KP}$ is the bisector of $\angle RKM$.
$\therefore m\angle 1 = m\angle 2$

18. $m\angle 1 = m\angle 2$
$\therefore \overrightarrow{KP}$ is the bisector of $\angle RKM$

19. $\overline{KP}$ bisects $\overline{RM}$. $\therefore \overline{RP} \cong \overline{PM}$

20. P is between R and M.
$\therefore RP + PM = RM$

21. P is the midpoint of $\overline{RM}$.
$\therefore \overline{RM}$ has no other midpoint.

22. P is the midpoint of $\overline{RM}$.
$\therefore \overline{RP} \cong \overline{PM}$

23. $\angle 3$ is a right angle.
$\therefore \overline{RP} \perp \overline{PK}$

Write a two-column proof for each exercise.

24. **Given:** M is the midpoint of $\overline{RT}$.
Prove: $RM = \frac{1}{2}RT$

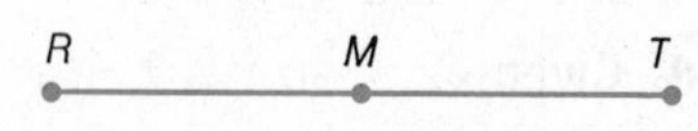

b

25. **Given:** $m\angle 1 = 2m\angle B$;
$m\angle B = m\angle D$

Prove: $m\angle 2 = 2m\angle D$

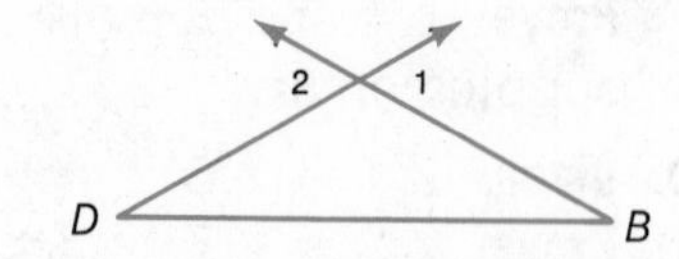

26. **Given:** $AB = BC$; D is the midpoint of $\overline{AB}$; $DE = \frac{1}{2}BC$

Prove: $\triangle ADE$ is isosceles.

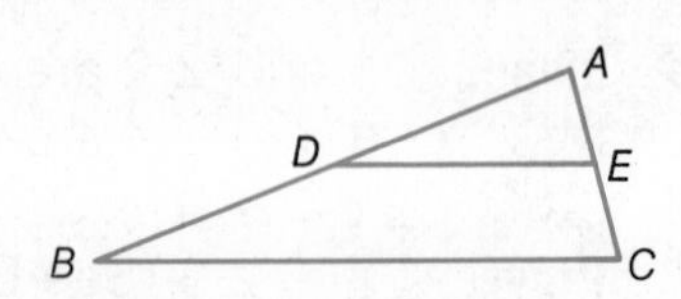

Remember

Classify each statement as True or False. If a statement is false, tell why it is false.

1. Two lines that form a right angle are perpendicular to each other.
2. Line k is perpendicular to line m is written $k \perp m$.
3. Adjacent angles are vertical angles.
4. Two angles that form a linear pair are complementary.
5. All right angles are congruent.

The answers are on page 92. If you need help, see pages 57 and 58.

2-6 Theorems About Perpendicular Lines

Remember to prepare a plan (or outline) of a proof before you begin to write the statements and reasons. The plan should include the major steps of the proof.

Theorem 2-11: If one angle of a linear pair is a right angle, then the other is also a right angle.

Given: $\angle 1$ and $\angle 2$ are a linear pair;
$\angle 1$ is a right angle.

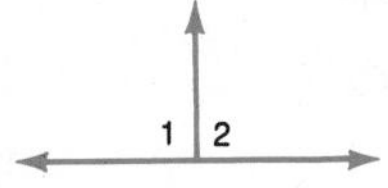

Prove: $\angle 2$ is a right angle.

Plan: Show that since $m\angle 1 + m\angle 2 = 180$ and $m\angle 1 = 90$, then $m\angle 2 = 90$.

The proof is asked for in the Exercises. This theorem is needed to prove Theorem 2-12.

Theorem 2-12: If two intersecting lines form one right angle, then they form four right angles.

Given: Lines k and m intersect, forming angles 1, 2, 3, and 4; $\angle 1$ is a right angle.

Prove: Angles 2, 3, and 4 are right angles.

Plan: Show that each of the following pairs of angles is a linear pair: $\angle 1$ and $\angle 2$, $\angle 1$ and $\angle 4$, $\angle 2$ and $\angle 3$.

Statements	Reasons
1. Lines k and m intersect, forming angles 1, 2, 3, and 4; $\angle 1$ is a right angle.	1. Given
2. $\angle 1$ and $\angle 2$ are a linear pair. $\angle 1$ and $\angle 4$ are a linear pair.	2. (1). Definition of linear pair
3. $\angle 2$ is a right angle, and $\angle 4$ is a right angle.	3. (1). (2). If one angle of a linear pair is a right angle, then the other is also a right angle.
4. $\angle 2$ and $\angle 3$ are a linear pair.	4. (1). Definition of linear pair
5. $\angle 3$ is a right angle.	5. (3). (4). Theorem 2-11

The following theorem is called a corollary. A **corollary** is a theorem that follows directly from a theorem or from accepted statements, such as definitions. Corollary 2-13 follows from Theorem 2-12.

Corollary 2-13: Perpendicular lines form four right angles.

Corollaries, like theorems, postulates and definitions, can be used as reasons in proofs.

Corollary 2-14 follows from the definitions of right angle and congruent angles.

Corollary 2-14: All right angles are congruent.

Notice that the "if" and "then" parts in Theorem 2-15 are reversed in Theorem 2-16.

Theorem 2-15: If congruent adjacent angles are formed by two intersecting lines, then the lines are perpendicular.

Theorem 2-16: If two lines are perpendicular, then they form congruent adjacent angles.

You can use the following proof of Theorem 2-15 to help you prove Theorem 2-16.

Given: Lines t and k intersect; angles 1 and 2 are adjacent; $\angle 1 \cong \angle 2$.

Prove: $t \perp k$

Plan: Show that either $\angle 1$ or $\angle 2$ is a right angle. Then $t \perp k$.

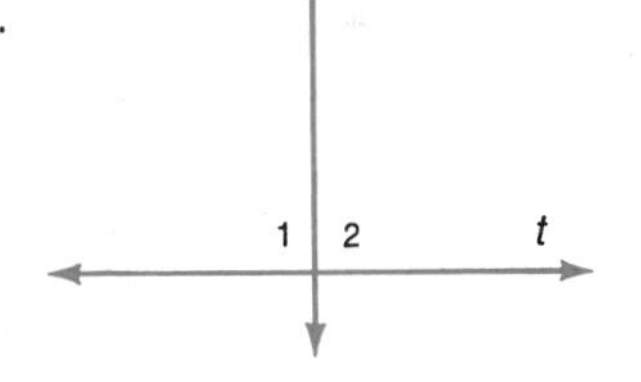

Statements	Reasons
1. Lines t and k intersect. Angles 1 and 2 are adjacent.	1. Given
2. Angles 1 and 2 are a linear pair.	2. (1). Definition of linear pair
3. Angles 1 and 2 are supplementary.	3. (2). If two angles form a linear pair, then they are supplementary.
4. $m\angle 1 + m\angle 2 = 180$	4. (3). Definition of supplementary angles
5. $\angle 1 \cong \angle 2$	5. Given
6. $m\angle 1 = m\angle 2$	6. (5). Definition of congruent angles
7. $m\angle 1 + m\angle 1 = 180$	7. (4). (6). Substitution Principle
8. $m\angle 1 = 90$	8. (7). Multiplication Postulate for Equations
9. $\angle 1$ is a right angle.	9. (8). Definition of right angle
10. $t \perp k$	10. (9). Definition of perpendicular lines

Theorem 2-16 is the converse of Theorem 2-15, and Theorem 2-15 is the converse of Theorem 2-16. When the "if" and "then" parts of a conditional are reversed, the **converse** is formed. If both a conditional and its converse are true, then the conditional and its converse can be written as a **biconditional.** A biconditional contains the phrase if and only if. This phrase means that you must prove both the conditional and its converse.

The biconditional for Theorems 2-15 and 2-16 could be written as follows.

> Two lines are perpendicular if and only if they form congruent adjacent angles.

or

> Congruent adjacent angles are formed by two intersecting lines if and only if the lines are perpendicular.

Try These

Classify each statement as True or False. If a statement is false, state why it is false.

1. If $\overleftrightarrow{PQ} \perp \overleftrightarrow{ST}$ at R, then $\angle PRT \cong \angle TRQ$.
2. If $\angle 1$ and $\angle 2$ are a linear pair and $m\angle 1 = 90$, then $m\angle 2 < 90$.
3. If $\overleftrightarrow{PQ} \perp \overleftrightarrow{ST}$ at R, then $\angle PRT$ and $\angle SRQ$ are adjacent angles.
4. If $m\angle TER = 90$ and $m\angle TES = 90$, then R, E, and S are noncollinear points.
5. If two angles are congruent and complementary, then each angle is a right angle.
6. Perpendicular lines form congruent adjacent angles.

Write the biconditional as two separate statements.

7. A triangle is equilateral if and only if it is equiangular.

Write the two conditional statements as a biconditional.

8. **a.** If a triangle has two congruent sides, then it is isosceles.
   b. If a triangle is isosceles, then it has two congruent sides.
9. **a.** If two angles are complementary, then the sum of their measures is 90.
   b. If the sum of the measures of two angles is 90, then they are complementary.
10. **a.** If an angle is a right angle, then its measure is 90.
    b. If the measure of an angle is 90, then it is a right angle.

Exercises

*In Exercises **1–6,** give a reason for each statement. Use a theorem or a corollary from this section. Refer to the figure at the right below for Exercises **1–3.***

1. If $\angle 1$ is a right angle, then $\angle 2$, $\angle 3$, and $\angle 4$ are right angles.

2. If lines k and t are perpendicular, then $\angle 1 \cong \angle 2$.

3. If $\angle 2 \cong \angle 3$, then lines k and t are perpendicular.

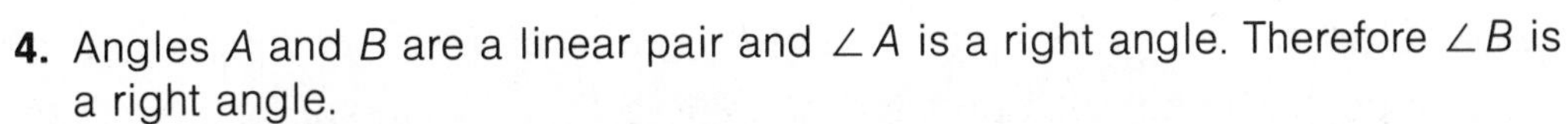

4. Angles A and B are a linear pair and $\angle A$ is a right angle. Therefore $\angle B$ is a right angle.

5. Lines AB and CD intersect at E. If adjacent angles CEB and CEA are congruent, then $\overleftrightarrow{AB} \perp \overleftrightarrow{CD}$.

6. If $\angle Q$ and $\angle R$ are right angles, then $\angle Q \cong \angle R$.

*For Exercises **7–10,** write one or more conclusions that must follow from the Given. Justify your answer with a definition, theorem, or corollary.*

7. Given: $\overline{AB} \perp \overline{CD}$
Conclusion: ?

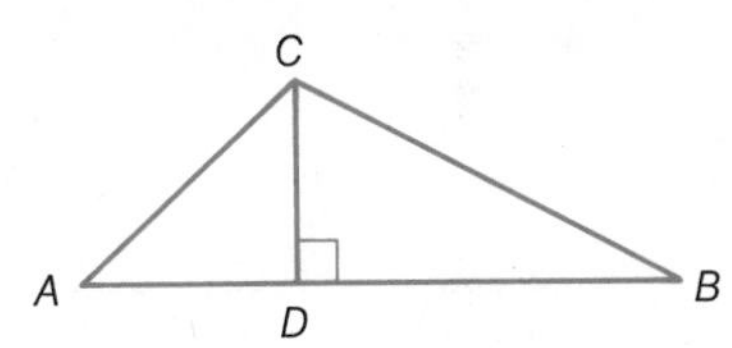

8. Given: $\angle 1 \cong \angle 2$
Conclusion: ?

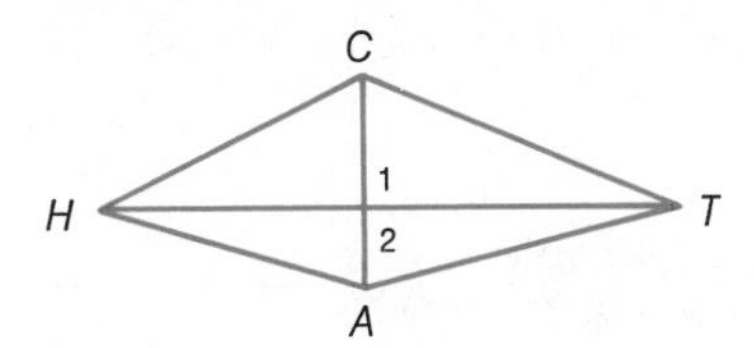

9. Given: $\angle KQH$ is a right angle.
Conclusion: ?

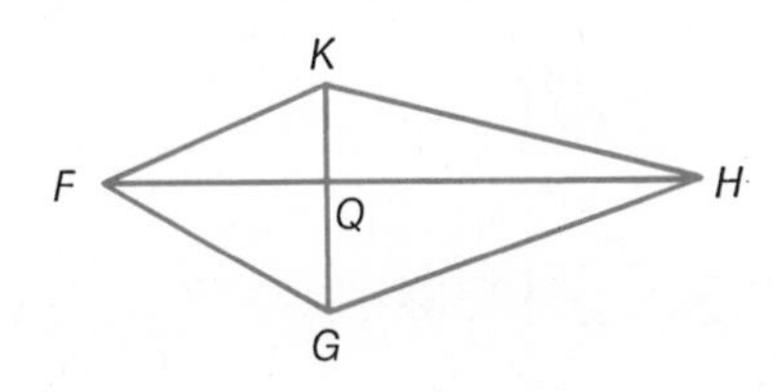

10. Given: $\overline{FH} \perp \overline{KQ}$
Conclusion: ?

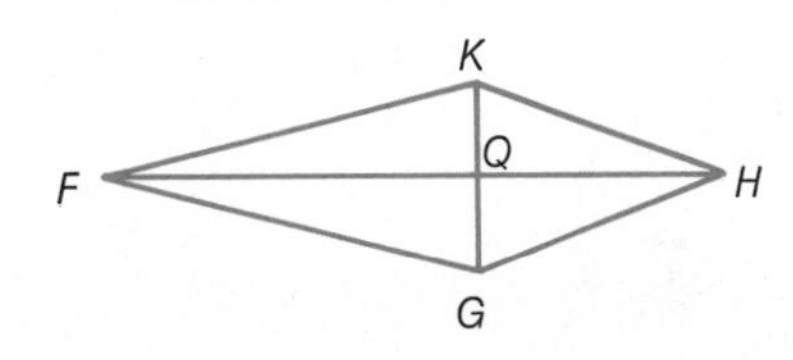

11. Prove Theorem 2-11. (HINT: Follow the plan on page 75.)
12. Prove Theorem 2-16. (HINT: Use the proof of Theorem 2-15 as a guide.)

*For Exercises **13–15**, rewrite each biconditional as two separate conditionals.*

13. An angle is a right angle if and only if the sides of the angle are perpendicular.
14. A triangle is scalene if and only if no two of the sides are congruent.
15. A triangle is isosceles if and only if it has two congruent sides.

Write the converse of each conditional.

16. If two angles form a linear pair, then they are supplementary.
17. If two angles are supplements of the same angle, then they are congruent.
18. If two angles are complements of congruent angles, then they are congruent.
19. If point E is between points D and F and $DE = EF$, then E is the midpoint of $\overline{DF}$.
20. If two angles are vertical angles, then they are congruent.
21. For Exercises **16–20**, classify the converse of each conditional as True or False.

Prove each statement.

b

22. If two angles are congruent and supplementary, then each is a right angle.
23. If two lines intersect, then four pairs of supplementary angles are formed.

PUZZLE

In the figure below, try to draw four straight lines that will pass through the ten dots. Lifting your pencil from the paper is not allowed.

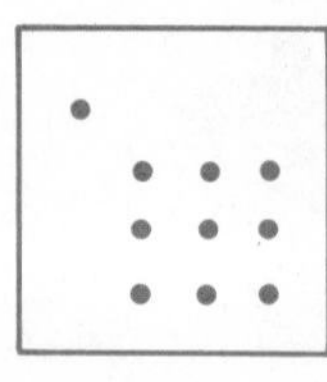

2-7 Polygons

A polygon is a closed plane figure with segments as sides. The table below shows five different polygons. Polygons may be classified by the number of sides.

Polygon	Model	Number of Sides
Triangle	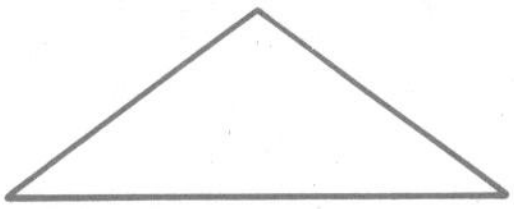	3
Quadrilateral	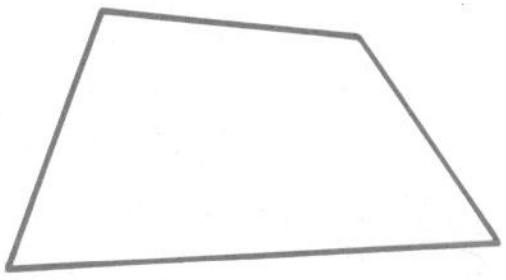	4
Pentagon	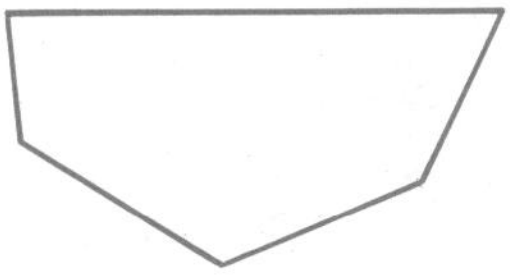	5
Hexagon		6
Octagon	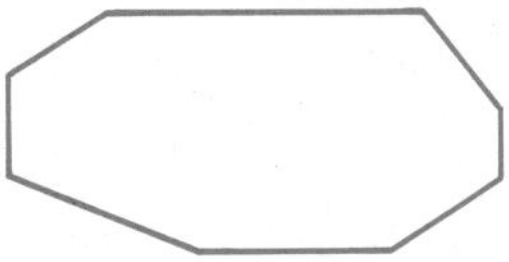	8

A **convex polygon** is a polygon such that no line containing a side of the polygon also contains a point in the interior of the polygon.

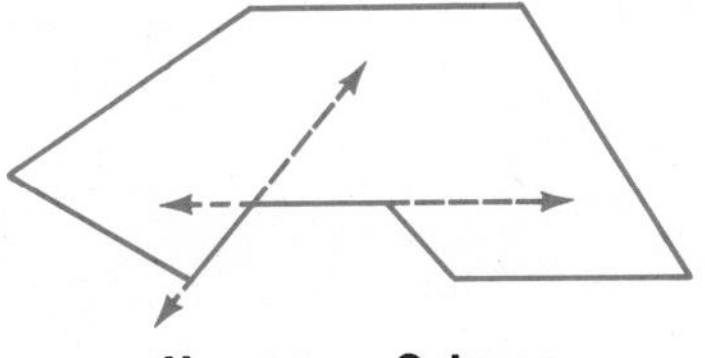

Nonconvex Octagon

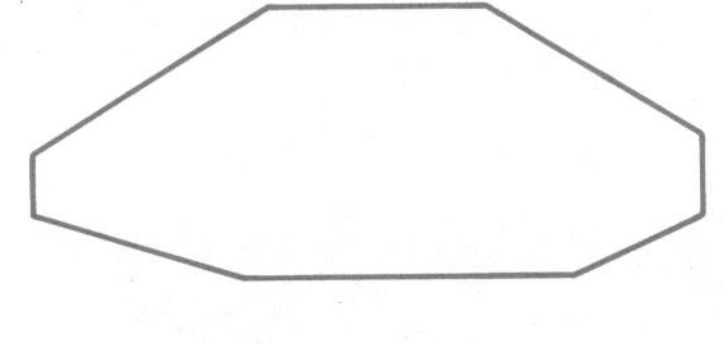

Convex Octagon

In this book, polygon always means convex polygon.

The polygon below is called hexagon *ABCDEF.* Any two sides with a common endpoint, such as $\overline{CD}$ and $\overline{DE}$ are **consecutive,** or **adjacent,** sides. Any two angles with a common side, such as $\angle E$ and $\angle F$, are **consecutive** angles. Segments such as $\overline{AE}$ or $\overline{AD}$, are diagonals of the polygon.

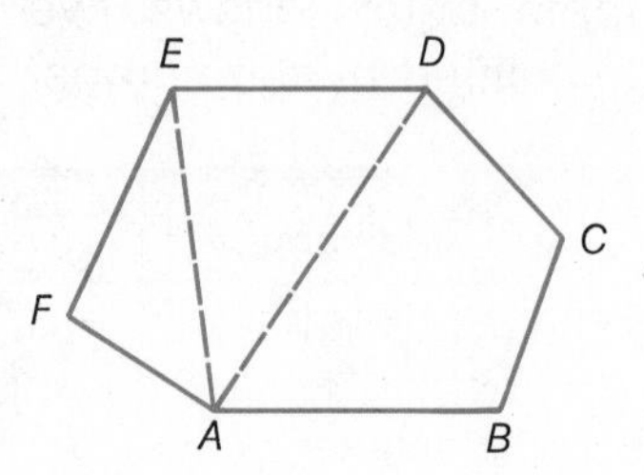

Definition: A **diagonal of a polygon** is a segment, other than a side, joining any two vertices.

A **triangle** is a polygon with three sides. A triangle has no diagonals because each of its sides is adjacent to the other two. However, certain other segments relate to triangles.

Segment	Model	Definition
Median *AD*		A **median** of a triangle is a segment from one vertex to the midpoint of the opposite side.
Altitude *BP*		An **altitude of a triangle** is a segment from one vertex perpendicular to the opposite side, or perpendicular to the line containing the opposite side.

The **perimeter** of a polygon is the sum of the lengths of its sides. Thus, for the triangle at the right,

$$P = a + b + c$$

The **interior of a triangle** is the intersection of the interiors of two of its angles.

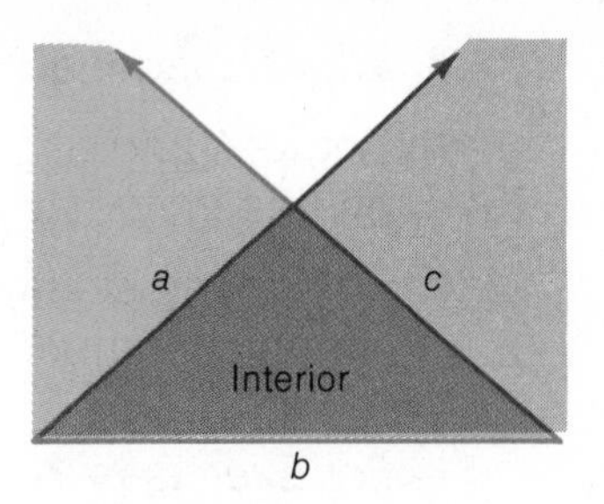

Try These

Write the letter of the response that answers each question. Refer to the figure at the right below.

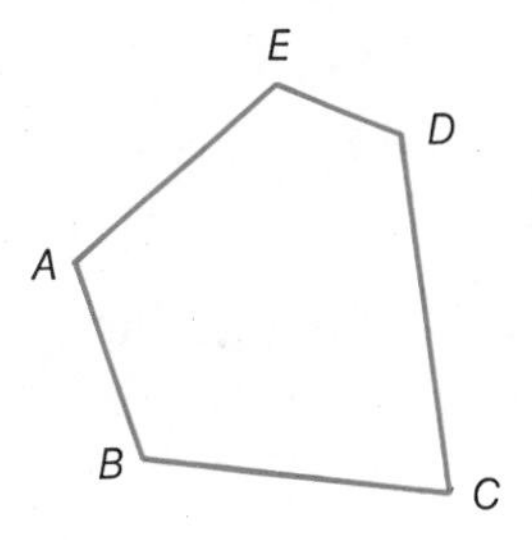

1. Polygon *ABCDE* is a _?_.
   a. quadrilateral **b.** pentagon **c.** hexagon
2. $\overline{AB}$ and _?_ are adjacent sides.
   a. $\overline{BC}$ **b.** $\overline{DE}$ **c.** $\overline{CD}$
3. $\angle C$ and _?_ are consecutive angles.
   a. $\angle D$ **b.** $\angle E$ **c.** $\angle A$
4. In polygon *ABCDE*, a diagonal with *A* as an endpoint is _?_.
   a. $\overline{AD}$ **b.** $\overline{AE}$ **c.** $\overline{AB}$
5. If $\overline{AD}$ is drawn, polygon *ABCD* is a _?_.
   a. quadrilateral **b.** pentagon **c.** hexagon
6. If *F* is the midpoint of $\overline{AD}$, then $\overline{EF}$ is a(n) _?_ of triangle *ADE*.
   a. altitude **b.** median **c.** angle bisector

Exercises

*For Exercises **1–6**, refer to the figure at the right.*

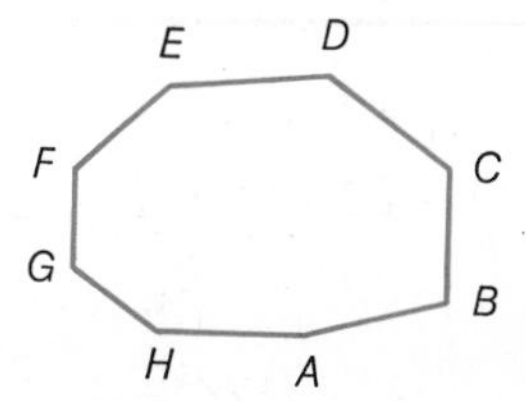

a

1. What two sides are adjacent to side *BC*?
2. What sides are adjacent to side $\overline{FG}$? to $\overline{DE}$?
3. Name all the diagonals that have *H* as one endpoint.

4. Which diagonals have E as one endpoint?
5. Angle A and angle B are consecutive angles. What other pair of consecutive angles includes A? What other pair includes B?
6. How many sides has polygon $ABCDEFGH$? What is the name of a polygon with this number of sides?

*For Exercises **7–14,** $\overline{FC} \perp \overline{AE}$. Classify each statement as True or False.*

7. $\overline{FC}$ is an altitude of $\triangle BFD$.
8. In $\triangle AFC$, $\overrightarrow{FB}$ is an angle bisector.
9. In $\triangle AFC$, $\overline{FB}$ is a median.
10. $\overline{FC}$ is a median of $\triangle AFD$.
11. $\overline{FC}$ is an altitude of $\triangle DEF$.
12. In $\triangle BFD$, $\overrightarrow{FC}$ is an angle bisector.
13. $\overline{FC}$ is an altitude of $\triangle ACF$.
14. In $\triangle CEF$, $\overline{FD}$ is a median.

*For Exercises **15–17,** tell whether $\overline{CD}$ is an altitude or a median of $\triangle ABC$. Use the square grid as a guide.*

15.

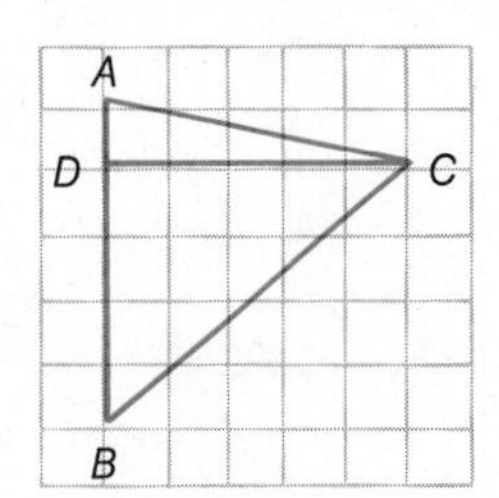

16.

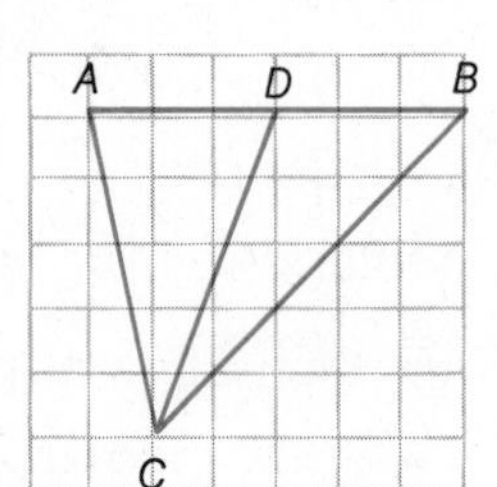

17.

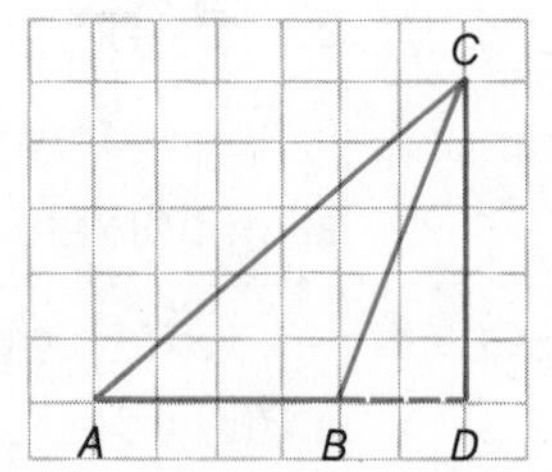

*In the figure at the right, $\overline{AC} \perp \overline{BD}$ at E. Use the information shown to identify any altitudes, medians, or angles bisectors for the triangles named in Exercises **18–23.***

18. $\triangle ADB$
19. $\triangle ADC$
20. $\triangle DCE$
21. $\triangle DCB$
22. $\triangle ABC$
23. $\triangle ABE$

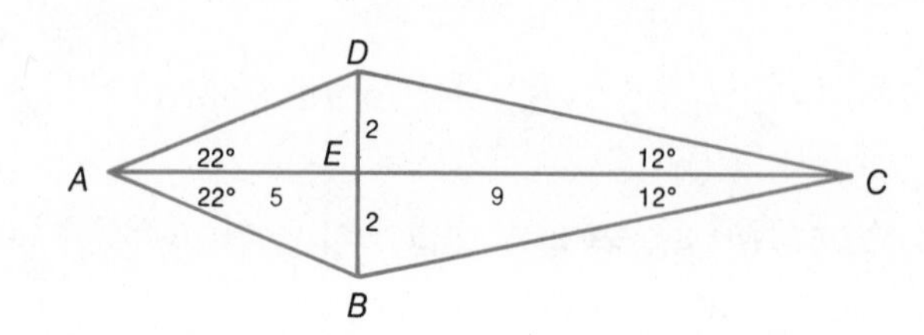

24. What is the perimeter of a triangle if each side measures 2.4?

25. Each side of a pentagon measures 8.6. What is the perimeter of the pentagon?

26. The perimeter of a quadrilateral is 47. If three consecutive sides measure 8, 10, and 15, what is the length of the fourth side?

27. In $\triangle RTS$ at the right, $ST = TR$, $\overline{RW}$ is a median, $WS = 3\frac{1}{2}$, and $RS = 8$. Find the perimeter of the triangle.

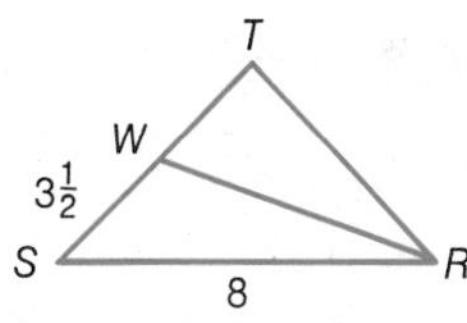

b

28. The perimeter of a pentagon is 37. Two sides of the pentagon are congruent and the other sides measure 8.5, 3.7, and 9.5. What is the length of each of the congruent sides?

29. The sides of a triangle have measures of $6y + 2$, $6y + 2$, and $4y - 1$. Express the perimeter in terms of y.

30. If the sides of a quadrilateral are represented by $2x$, $3x$, $2x$, and $3x$, and the perimeter is 170 units, what is the length of each side?

31. **Given:** $\overleftrightarrow{AB} \perp \overleftrightarrow{XY}$; $\angle 1 \cong \angle 4$

Prove: $\overrightarrow{XY}$ bisects $\angle WXZ$.

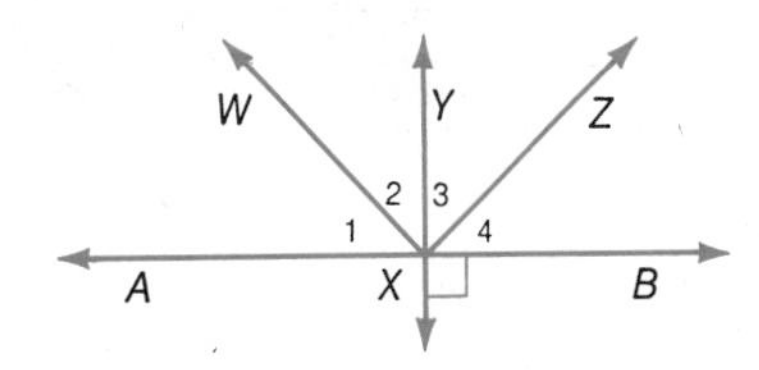

32. **Given:** $\overleftrightarrow{AB} \perp \overleftrightarrow{XY}$; $\overrightarrow{XY}$ bisects $\angle WXZ$; $\angle 1 \cong \angle 2$

Prove: $\angle 3 \cong \angle 4$

PUZZLE

Eight round discs lie in a row. You can jump any disc over exactly two others, either two single discs or a stack of two, onto the top of the next disc.

How can the discs be moved so that you end up with four stacked pairs?

1 2 3 4 5 6 7 8

Inductive Reasoning

You use deductive reasoning when you write a formal proof of a theorem. In deductive reasoning, you arrive at a conclusion that is true for all members of a set. For example, having proved Theorem 2-10, the Vertical Angle Theorem, on page 71, you do not have to measure the vertical angles that are formed when two lines intersect in order to verify that these angles are congruent.

Another kind of reasoning, called inductive, is illustrated below.

Problem: Determine whether there is a relationship between the length of the median to the hypotenuse and the length of the hypotenuse in a right triangle.

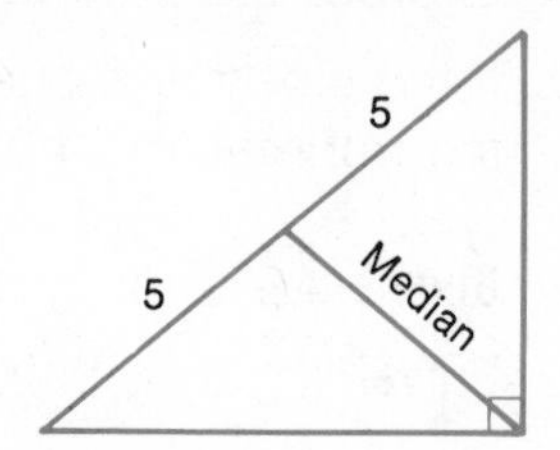

Method: Draw four right triangles, each of a different size.
In each triangle, draw the median to the hypotenuse.
In each triangle, measure the length of the median and the length of the hypotenuse.
In each triangle, compare the length of the median to the length of the hypotenuse.

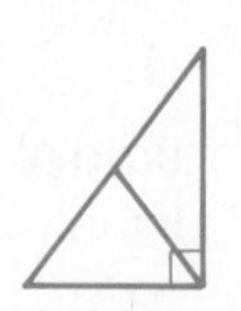

Median:	10 mm	9 mm	12.5 mm	15 mm
Hypotenuse:	20 mm	18 mm	25 mm	30 mm

Conclusion: In a right triangle, the length of the median to the hypotenuse is one half the length of the hypotenuse.

In **inductive reasoning,** you assign a property (conclusion) held by some members of a set to all members of that set. Here is an example.

Problem: For a quadrilateral whose vertices lie on a circle, determine whether there is a relationship with regard to the sum of the measures of the opposite angles.

Method: Draw three congruent circles.
Select any four points on each circle, and connect the points to form a quadrilateral.
Find the sum of the measures of each pair of opposite angles.

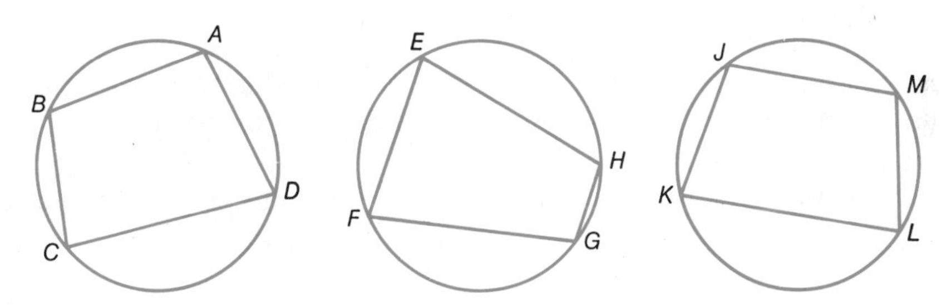

$m\angle A + m\angle C = 180$ $m\angle E + m\angle G = 180$ $m\angle J + m\angle L = 180$
$m\angle B + m\angle D = 180$ $m\angle F + m\angle H = 180$ $m\angle K + m\angle M = 180$

Conclusion: If the vertices of a quadrilateral lie on a circle, then the sum of the measures of each pair of opposite angles is 180.

Inductive reasoning is not a method of proof. However, the process of inductive reasoning can lead to statements that can be proved deductively.

Can You Solve These?

1. Draw four different triangles and measure each angle of each triangle. Add the measures of the angles in each triangle. State your conclusion.
2. Draw at least four pentagons and measure each angle. State a conclusion about the sum of the measures of the angles in a pentagon.

Chapter Objectives and Review

Objective: To recall, and give examples of, the important mathematical terms of the chapter.

1. Be sure that you know the meanings of these mathematical terms used in Chapter 2.

A between *B* and *C* (p. 41)
absolute value (p. 40)
acute angle (p. 49)
adjacent angles (p. 57)
adjacent sides (p. 82)
altitude (p. 82)
angle bisector (p. 51)
$\overrightarrow{AY}$ between $\overrightarrow{AX}$ and $\overrightarrow{AZ}$ (p. 50)
biconditional (p. 78)
bisect (p. 43)
bisector of an angle (p. 51)
complementary angles (p. 57)
congruent angles (p. 51)
congruent segments (p. 43)
consecutive angles (p. 82)
converse (p. 77)
convex polygon (p. 81)
corollary (p. 76)
diagonal (p. 82)
distance between points (p. 40)
edge of a half-plane (p. 48)
equivalence relation (p. 63)
exterior of an angle (p. 48)
hexagon (p. 81)
identity (p. 64)
interior of an angle (p. 48)
linear pair (p. 57)
line segment (p. 42)
measure of an angle (p. 49)
median (p. 82)
midpoint (p. 42)
obtuse angle (p. 49)
octagon (p. 81)
pentagon (p. 81)
perpendicular bisector (p. 60)
perpendicualr lines (p. 58)
polygon (p. 81)
quadrilateral (p. 81)
right angle (p. 49)
supplementary angles (p. 57)
triangle (p. 81)
vertical angles (p. 57)

Objective: To use absolute value to determine the distance between pairs of points on the number line. (Section 2-1)

Find the distance between the points with the given coordinates.

2. 7; 16 **3.** −3; 8 **4.** −15; −6 **5.** 0; −3

Objective: To use the definitions of betweenness for points and midpoint. (Section 2-1)

Complete each statement.

P Q T R
5 $12\frac{1}{2}$ 15 20

6. Point T is between Q and ___?___.

7. ___?___ is the midpoint of $\overline{PR}$.

8. $PR = 2$ ___?___

Objective: To use the Protractor Postulate to determine angle measure. Section 2-2)

Use the figure at the right to find the angle measures.

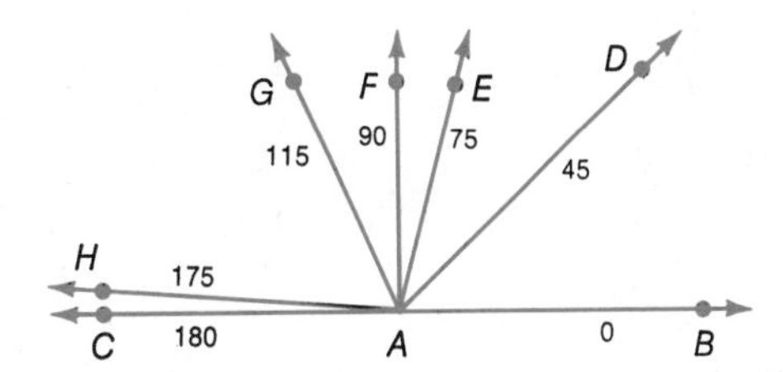

9. $\angle BAE$
10. $\angle DAG$
11. $\angle FAH$
12. $\angle HAC$
13. $\angle BAH$
14. $\angle FAC$
15. $\angle FAB$
16. $\angle DAE$

Objective: To use the definitions of betweenness for rays and angle bisector to determine angle measures. (Section 2-2)

17. If $m\angle RQP = 69$, $m\angle RQT$ is 31, and $\overrightarrow{QT}$ is between $\overrightarrow{QR}$ and $\overrightarrow{QP}$, find $m\angle TQP$.

18. If $\overrightarrow{QT}$ bisects $\angle PQR$ and $m\angle TQP = 21\frac{1}{2}$, find $m\angle PQR$.

Objective: To identify supplementary angles, complementary angles, linear pairs, and vertical angles. (Section 2-3)

Use the figure at the right to classify each pair of angles as supplementary, complementary, adjacent, linear pair, vertical, or none of these.

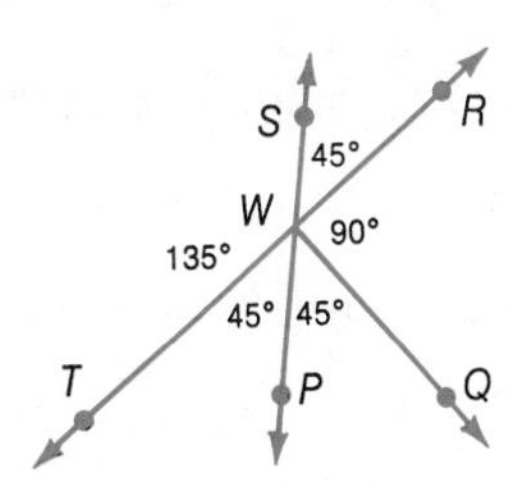

19. $\angle SWT$ and $\angle TWP$
20. $\angle SWR$ and $\angle TWP$
21. $\angle RWQ$ and $\angle QWP$
22. $\angle QWP$ and $\angle PWT$
23. $\angle SWT$ and $\angle QWP$
24. $\angle SWR$ and $\angle QWP$

Complete each statement.

25. If $\angle P$ is a complement of $\angle Q$, then $m\angle P + m\angle Q =$ ___?___.

26. If $\angle P$ and $\angle Q$ form a linear pair, then $m\angle P + m\angle Q =$ ___?___.

27. If $\angle P$ and $\angle Q$ form a linear pair, then $\angle P$ and $\angle Q$ are __?__ angles.

28. If $\angle P \cong \angle Q$, and $\angle P$ is supplementary to $\angle Q$, then $m\angle P =$ __?__ and $m\angle Q =$ __?__.

29. $\angle RST$ and $\angle TSQ$ form a linear pair and $\angle RST \cong \angle TSQ$. Then $\overline{TS}$ __?__ $\overline{QR}$.

30. $\angle RST$ and $\angle TSQ$ form a linear pair. $\angle RST \cong \angle TSQ$, and $\overline{QS} \cong \overline{SR}$. Then $\overleftrightarrow{TS}$ is the __?__ of $\overline{QR}$.

Objective: To identify an equivalence relation. (Section 2-4)

Determine whether each of the following is an equivalence relation.

31. Is congruent to for segments
32. Is complementary to for angles
33. Is perpendicular to for coplanar lines

Objective: To write a two-column proof. (Section 2-5)

Write a two-column proof for each exercise.

34. **Given:** $p \perp q$; $\angle 1$ is complementary to $\angle 3$.
Prove: $m\angle 2 = m\angle 3$

35. **Given:** Lines p, q, and r intersect at E; $\angle 1 \cong \angle 2$.
Prove: $\overrightarrow{EG}$ bisects $\angle PEN$

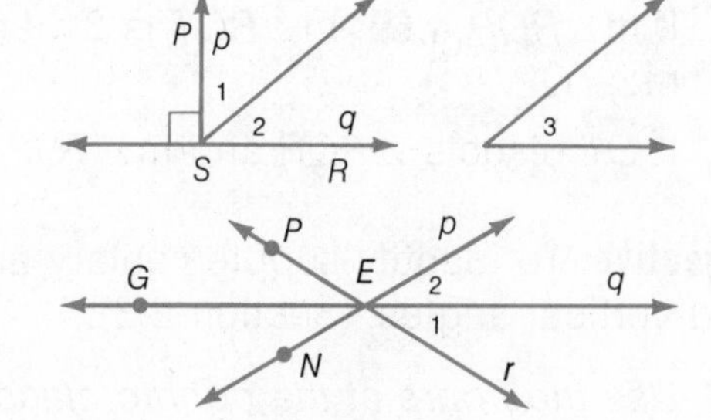

36. **Given:** $\angle 1 \cong \angle 2$; $\angle 1$ and $\angle 2$ are a linear pair.
Prove: $t \perp s$

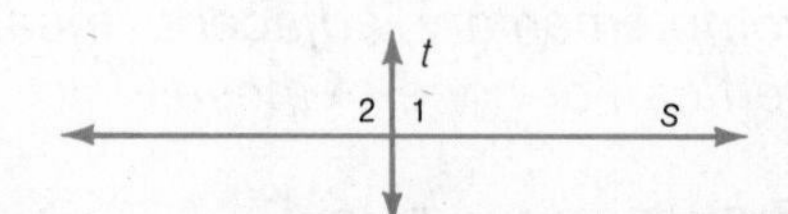

Objective: To use theorems about perpendicular lines in proofs. (Section 2-6)

Write a two-column proof for each exercise.

37. ABC is a right triangle with right angle at C; $\overline{CD} \perp \overline{AB}$. Prove that $\angle ACB \cong \angle ADC$.

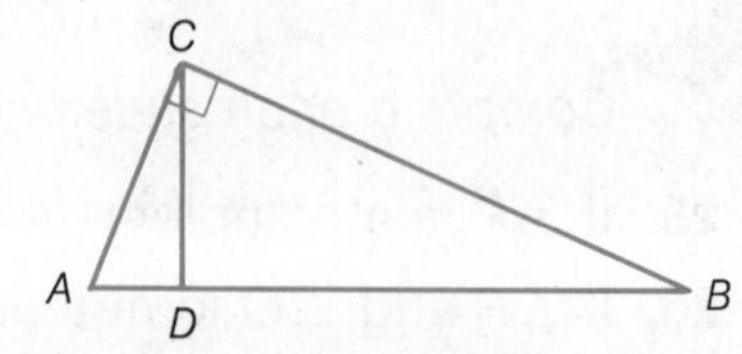

38. Ray DC is perpendicular to line AB and $\angle 2 \cong \angle 3$.

Prove that $\angle 1 \cong \angle 4$.

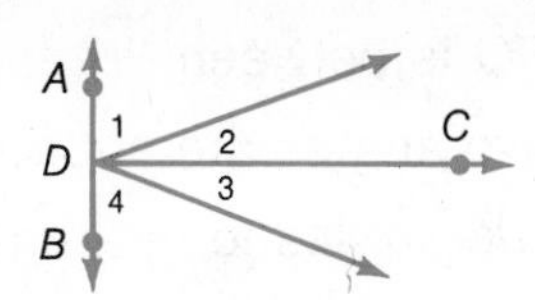

Objective: To identify polygons and some properties of polygons. (Section 2-7)

Complete each statement.

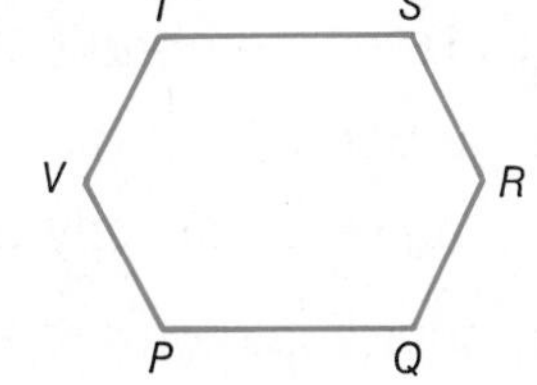

39. Polygon $PQRSTV$ is a __?__.

40. In polygon $PQRSTV$, $\overline{SR}$ and __?__ are consecutive sides.

41. In polygon $PQRSTV$, $\angle V$ and $\angle$ __?__ are consecutive angles.

42. In polygon $PQRSTV$, $\overline{SP}$ is a __?__ of the polygon.

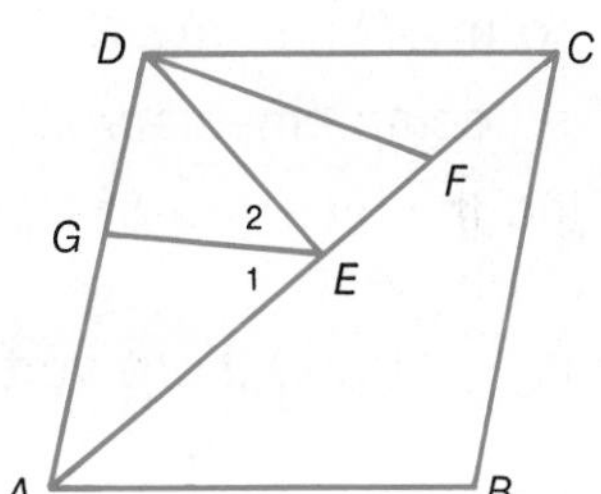

43. If $\overline{DE} \perp \overline{AC}$, then $\overline{DE}$ is an altitude of $\triangle$ __?__.

44. If $\overline{EF} \cong \overline{FC}$, then $\overline{DF}$ is a median of $\triangle$ __?__.

45. If $m\angle 1 = m\angle 2$, then $\overrightarrow{EG}$ is an angle bisector of $\triangle$ __?__.

46. If $\overline{DE}$ is a median of $\triangle DAC$, $EF = 7$ and $AC = 39$, $FC =$ __?__.

47. If $\overline{DE}$ is an altitude of $\triangle DAF$, and $\overrightarrow{EG}$ bisects $\angle DEA$, $m\angle 2 =$ __?__.

Chapter Test

*In Exercises **1–10,** classify each statement as True or False. If a statement is false, explain why it is false.*

1. Point Z is between points X and Y, $XY = 15$, and $XZ = ZY$. Then $XZ = 7\frac{1}{2}$.
2. If B is the midpoint of $\overline{CD}$, and $CB = 12$, then $CD = 6$.
3. If $\overrightarrow{PQ}$ bisects $\angle MPR$, and $m\angle MPQ = 33$, $m\angle MPR = 66$.

4. If $\overrightarrow{PQ}$ is between $\overrightarrow{PR}$ and $\overrightarrow{PM}$, then $\angle MPQ \cong \angle QPR$.
5. If two angles are supplementary, then they form a linear pair.
6. If two angles form a linear pair, then they are supplementary.
7. Vertical angles are the adjacent angles formed when two straight lines intersect.
8. If $\overline{AB}$ is the perpendicular bisector of $\overline{CD}$ and meets $\overline{CD}$ at E, then $\overline{CE} \cong \overline{ED}$.
9. If $\overline{AB}$ is the perpendicular bisector of $\overline{CD}$ and meets $\overline{CD}$ at E, then $\overline{CD}$ is the perpendicular bisector of $\overline{AB}$ at E.
10. A triangle has exactly one diagonal.
11. The coordinate of A is -11 and the coordinate of C is 7. Find AC.
12. If $m\angle R + m\angle S = 165$ and the $m\angle S$ is 30 less than three times $m\angle R$, find $m\angle R$ and $m\angle S$.
13. Two complementary angles are congruent. Find the measure of each angle.
14. Find the measure of an angle that is four times the measure of its supplement.
15. Angles 1 and 2 are vertical angles and $m\angle 1 = 43$. Find $m\angle 2$.

Write a two-column proof for each exercise.

16. **Given:** Lines AB, CD, and EF; $\angle 1 \cong \angle 3$
    Prove: $\angle 2 \cong \angle 1$

17. **Given:** $\angle BCA$ is a right angle; $\angle 1$ and $\angle 2$ are complementary.
    Prove: $\angle 3 \cong \angle 1$

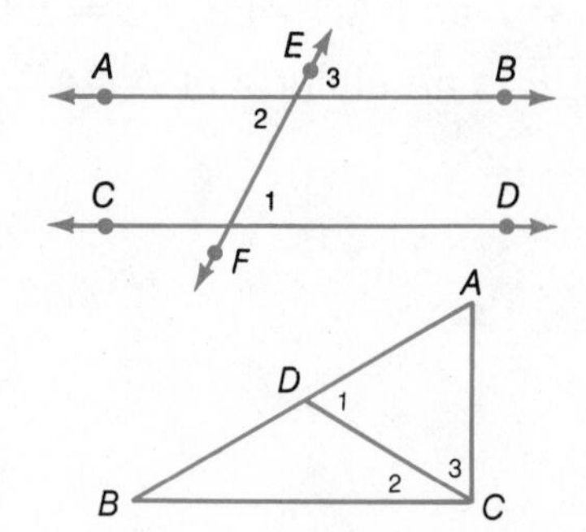

Answers to Remember

Page 56: **1.** P **2.** $\overrightarrow{PS}$; $\overrightarrow{PQ}$ **3.** PS **4.** PS **5.** SPR

Page 75: **1.** True **2.** True **3.** False **4.** False **5.** True

Chapter 3
Congruent Triangles

3-1 Congruence

Triangles that have the same size and shape are congruent. In triangles *ABC* and *DEF*,

$\angle A \cong \angle D$ $\overline{AB} \cong \overline{DE}$

$\angle B \cong \angle E$ $\overline{BC} \cong \overline{EF}$

$\angle C \cong \angle F$ $\overline{CA} \cong \overline{FD}$

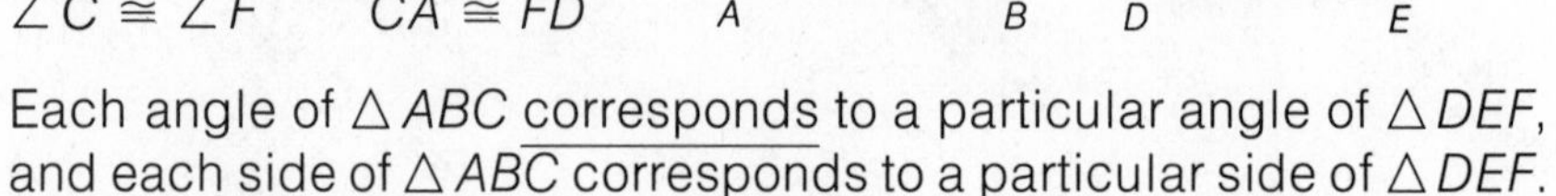

Each angle of $\triangle ABC$ corresponds to a particular angle of $\triangle DEF$, and each side of $\triangle ABC$ corresponds to a particular side of $\triangle DEF$.

$ABC \leftrightarrow DEF$ ⟵ Read: "*ABC* corresponds to *DEF*."

Definition: A correspondence between two triangles is a **congruence** if the corresponding angles and the corresponding sides are congruent.

In triangles *ABC* and *DEF*, the corresponding angles are congruent and the corresponding sides are congruent. Thus,

$\triangle ABC \cong \triangle DEF$ ⟵ Read: "$\triangle ABC$ is congruent to $\triangle DEF$."

Example 1

$\triangle THE \cong \triangle QNR$. Name the corresponding congruent parts.

Correspondence	Corresponding Parts
$THE \leftrightarrow QNR$	$\angle T \leftrightarrow \angle Q$; $\angle H \leftrightarrow \angle N$; $\angle E \leftrightarrow \angle R$ or $\angle T \cong \angle Q$; $\angle H \cong \angle N$; $\angle E \cong \angle R$
$THE \leftrightarrow QNR$	$\overline{TH} \leftrightarrow \overline{QN}$; $\overline{HE} \leftrightarrow \overline{NR}$; $\overline{TE} \leftrightarrow \overline{QR}$ or $\overline{TH} \cong \overline{QN}$; $\overline{HE} \cong \overline{NR}$; $\overline{TE} \cong \overline{QR}$

In Example 1, $THE \leftrightarrow QNR$ is a congruence, but $THE \leftrightarrow QRN$ is not a congruence. That is, the correspondence $THE \leftrightarrow QNR$ is not the same as $THE \leftrightarrow QRN$.

Example 2

$\triangle RST \cong \triangle XYZ$. Which of these correspondences is a congruence?

a. $RST \leftrightarrow XYZ$
b. $TSR \leftrightarrow ZXY$
c. $STR \leftrightarrow YZX$
d. $SRT \leftrightarrow YZX$

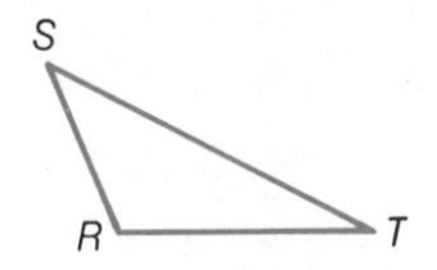

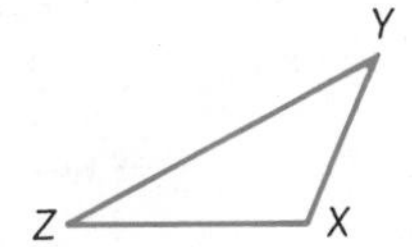

Since $\triangle RST \cong \triangle XYZ$, $\angle R \leftrightarrow \angle X$, $\angle S \leftrightarrow \angle Y$, and $\angle T \leftrightarrow \angle Z$.

a. $RST \leftrightarrow XYZ$ Yes

b. $TSR \leftrightarrow ZXY$ No

c. $STR \leftrightarrow YZX$ Yes

d. $SRT \leftrightarrow YZX$ No

The definition of congruent triangles can also be written:

> **Two triangles are congruent** if their corresponding parts are congruent.

A geometric figure is congruent to itself by the reflexive property of congruence. In a proof, you may refer to this property as Identity.

Try These

Complete each statement.

1. $\triangle ABC \cong \triangle DEF$. The corresponding congruent parts are _?_.
2. $\triangle RST \cong \triangle XYZ$. $\overline{ST} \leftrightarrow$ _?_
3. $\triangle QPV \cong \triangle GHJ$. $\angle V \leftrightarrow$ _?_
4. $\triangle FCZ \cong \triangle RPT$. $\overline{ZF} \cong$ _?_
5. $\triangle GFH \cong \triangle JKP$. $\angle F \cong \angle$ _?_

In the triangle at the right, $ACB \leftrightarrow ACD$ is a congruence. Name the correspondences below that are not congruences.

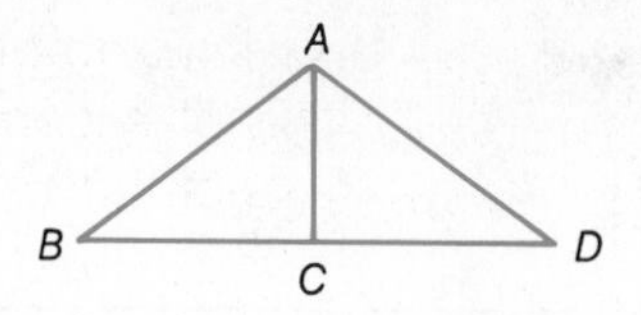

6. $BAC \leftrightarrow DAC$ **7.** $CBA \leftrightarrow CAD$ **8.** $DCA \leftrightarrow BAC$

$\triangle RST \cong \triangle HGK$. Complete each correspondence correctly.

9. RT __?__ $\leftrightarrow$ HK __?__

10. $STR \leftrightarrow$ __?__ K __?__

11. __?__ __?__ $R \leftrightarrow$ __?__ GH

12. $TRS \leftrightarrow$ __?__ __?__ __?__

Exercises

In the figure below, $\triangle ACB \cong \triangle DFE$. Complete each statement by supplying the missing symbols.

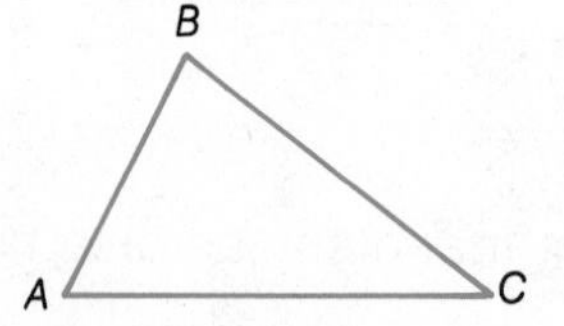

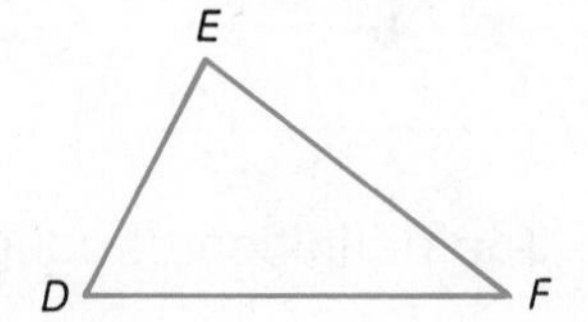

a

1. The correspondence A __?__ __?__ $\leftrightarrow$ __?__ $F\ E$ is a congruence.

2. The correspondence BA __?__ $\leftrightarrow$ __?__ __?__ __?__ is a congruence.

3. $\angle A \cong \angle$ __?__ **4.** $\angle C \cong \angle$ __?__ **5.** $\angle B \cong \angle$ __?__

6. $\overline{AC} \cong$ __?__ **7.** $\overline{CB} \cong$ __?__ **8.** $\overline{BA} \cong$ __?__

9. If the correspondence $GHR \leftrightarrow JKP$ is a congruence, name three pairs of congruent angles and three pairs of congruent sides in the following triangles.

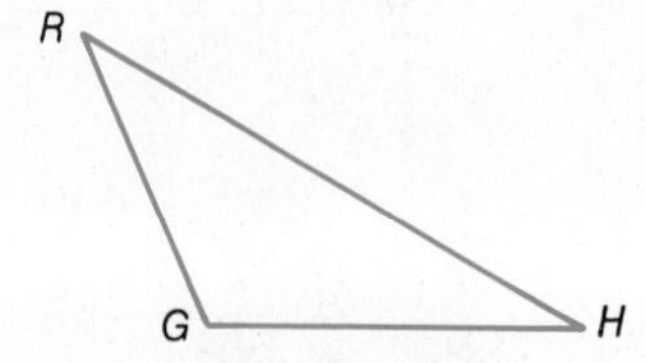

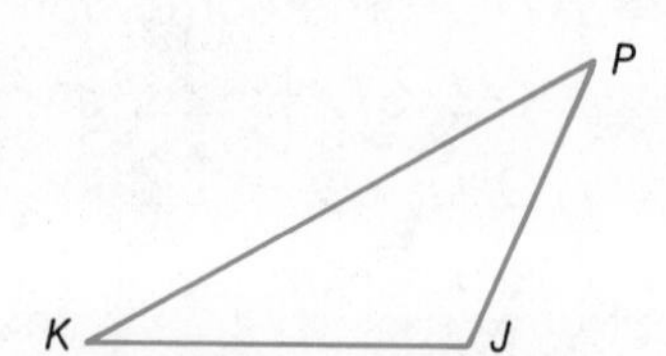

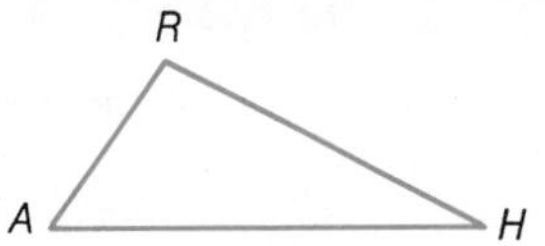

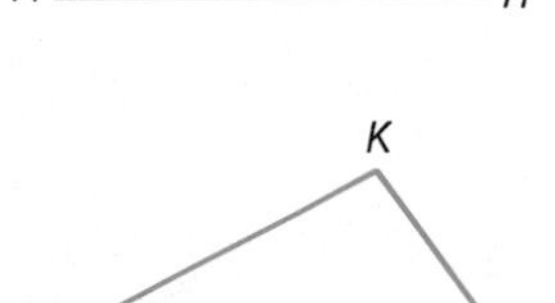

*Given that $\triangle AHR \cong \triangle MBK$, determine which correspondences in Exercises **10–17** are congruences.*

10. $ARH \leftrightarrow MKB$

11. $ARH \leftrightarrow MBK$

12. $RHA \leftrightarrow MBK$

13. $RHA \leftrightarrow KBM$

14. $HAR \leftrightarrow BKM$

15. $RAH \leftrightarrow KMB$

16. $HAR \leftrightarrow BMK$

17. $AHR \leftrightarrow MBK$

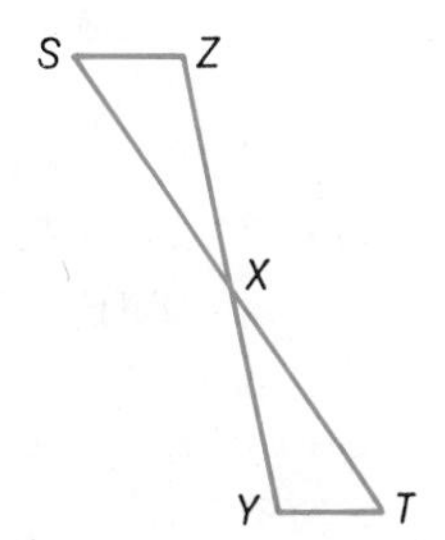

Given that $\triangle TXY \cong \triangle SXZ$, complete the correspondences so that they are congruences.

18. $YXT \leftrightarrow$ _?_ X _?_

19. $YTX \leftrightarrow$ _?_ _?_ X

20. $XTY \leftrightarrow$ _?_ _?_ _?_

21. $TXY \leftrightarrow$ _?_ _?_ _?_

22. $XYT \leftrightarrow$ _?_ Z _?_

23. $TYX \leftrightarrow$ _?_ _?_ _?_

*For Exercises **24–26,** refer to the figure for Exercises **18–23.***

24. What angle in $\triangle XZS$ corresponds to $\angle Y$ in $\triangle XYT$?

25. Which side of $\triangle XZS$ corresponds to $\overline{YT}$ in $\triangle XYT$?

26. Which side of $\triangle XZS$ corresponds to $\overline{YX}$ in $\triangle XYT$?

27. Is a line segment congruent to itself? Why?

28. Is an angle congruent to itself? Why?

29. Is a triangle congruent to itself? Why?

Use the given figure and information to name three pairs of congruent angles and three pairs of congruent sides.

30. $\triangle EHG \cong \triangle KFG$

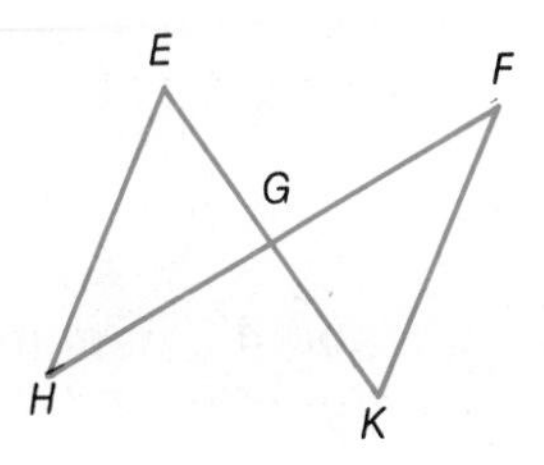

31. $\triangle ABC \cong \triangle CDA$

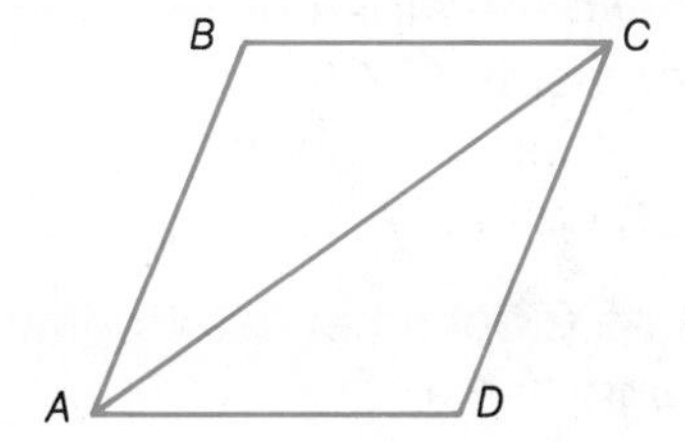

32. $\triangle ABC \cong \triangle BAD$
$\triangle ACE \cong \triangle BDE$

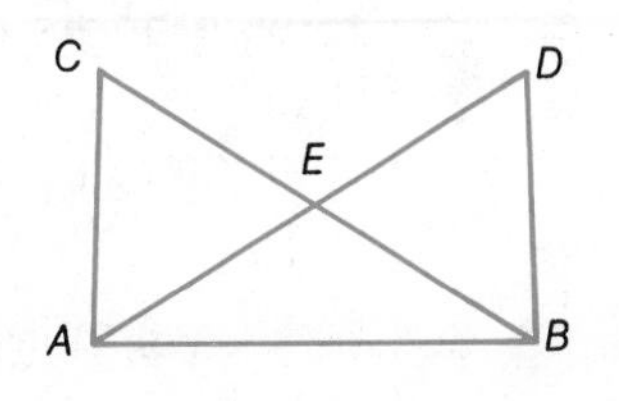

33. Name the triangles in the figure at the left below that appear to be congruent. Name the three pairs of corresponding sides.

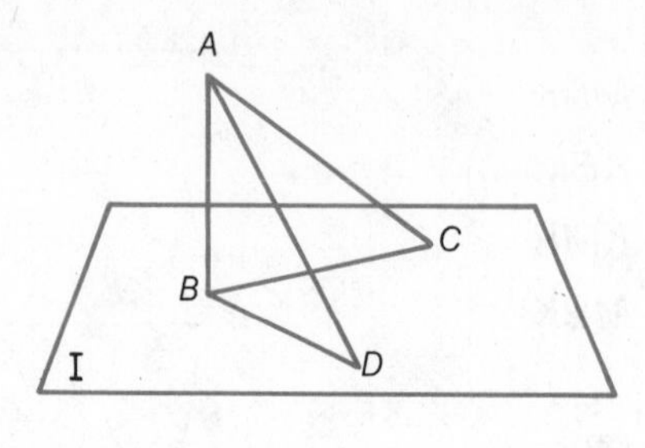

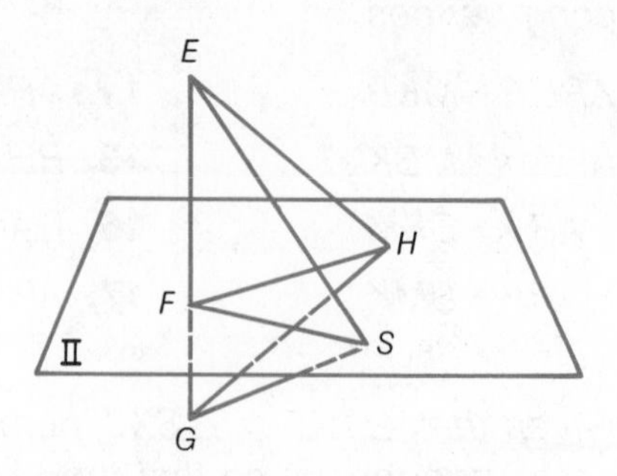

b

34. Use the figure at the right above to name two pairs of triangles that appear to be congruent.

Use the figure at the right above and Exercise 34 to complete each statement.

35. $\angle FES \cong \angle$ _?_ **36.** $\angle EHF \cong \angle$ _?_ **37.** $\overline{FS} \cong$ _?_

38. $\overline{GS} \cong$ _?_ **39.** $\overline{FE} \cong$ _?_ **40.** $\angle GSF \cong \angle$ _?_

think–draw–see

Can you copy $\triangle ABC$ using exactly 3 of the 6 parts? Try each experiment. You will need a protractor, a centimeter ruler, and some straws.

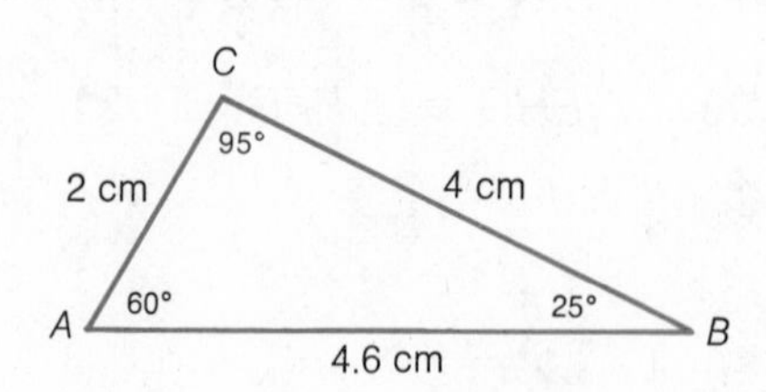

1. Draw a segment 4.6 centimeters long. At the ends of the segment, draw angles of 60° and 25°. Complete the triangle and compare with $\triangle ABC$.

2. Draw an angle of 60°. On the sides of the angle, mark off segments of 4.6 centimeters and 2 centimeters. Join the endpoints. Compare with $\triangle ABC$.

3. Cut straws that measure 2 centimeters, 4 centimeters, and 4.6 centimeters. Place them together end-to-end to form a triangle. Compare with $\triangle ABC$.

3-2 Congruent Triangles/S.A.S.

To show that two triangles are congruent, it is not necessary to know that all six corresponding parts are congruent. Look at the table below and on the following page to determine the <u>least</u> number of congruent corresponding parts needed.

Number of Congruent Parts	Models	Triangles Congruent?
One Part		
One side	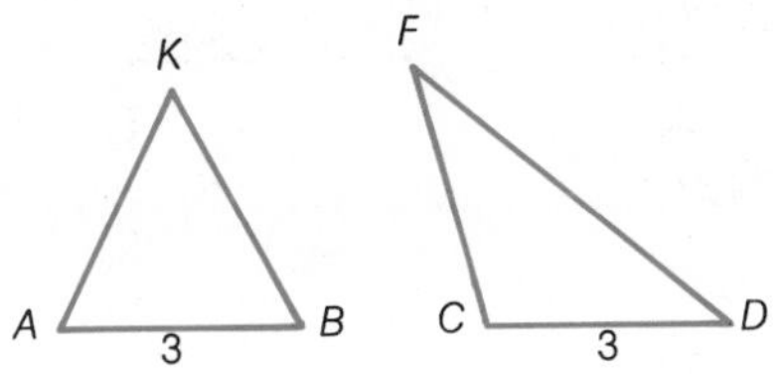	No
One angle	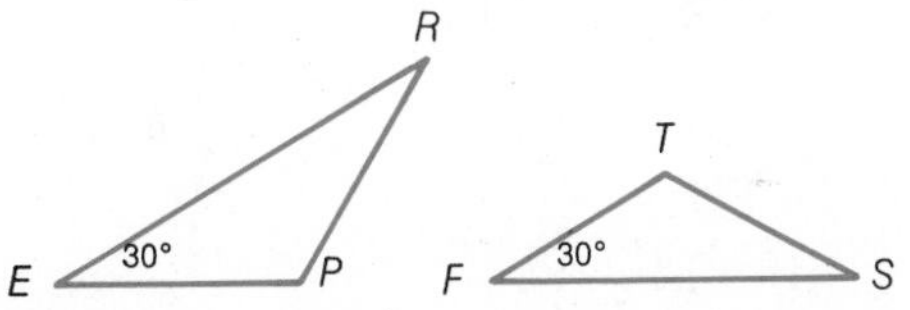	No
Two Parts		
Two sides	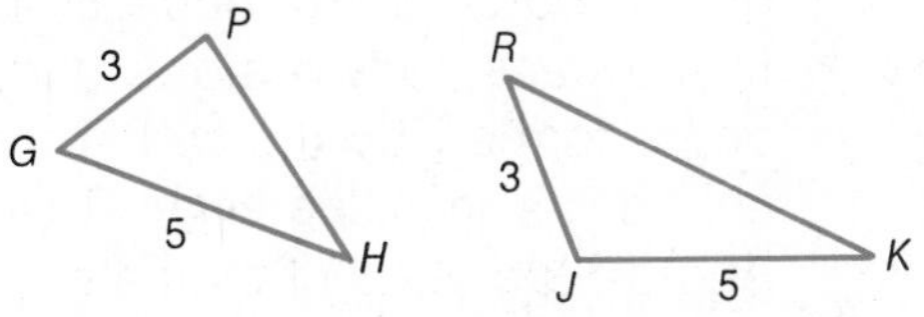	No
Two angles	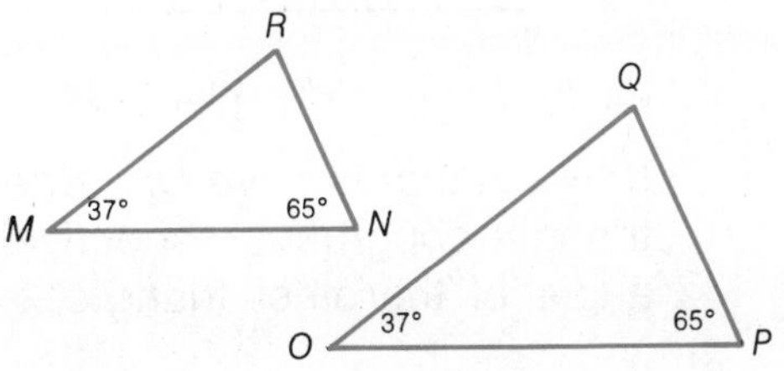	No

Number of Congruent Parts	Models	Triangles Congruent?
Two Parts (cont.)		
One side, one angle	P 40° 5 Q R; T 5 40° V W	No
Three Parts		
Two sides, one angle	Q 35° 7 S 4.5 R; T 35° 7 V 4.5 U	No
Two sides, included angle	A 35° 5 B 6 C; D 35° 5 E 6 F	Yes

The table shows that you need at least three corresponding congruent parts to conclude that two triangles are congruent. Also, in the case of two sides and one angle, the angle must be the angle formed by the two corresponding congruent sides. This is called the **included angle.** The congruence is stated in the Side-Angle-Side (S.A.S.) Postulate.

Postulate 11: S.A.S. Postulate

If two triangles have two sides and the included angle of one triangle congruent respectively to two sides and the included angle of the other triangle, then the triangles are congruent.

Note that the same mark on two corresponding parts indicates congruence. A common side is marked ⫴ to remind you that it is congruent by identity.

Example 1

Name the pairs of triangles that are congruent by the S.A.S. Postulate.

a.

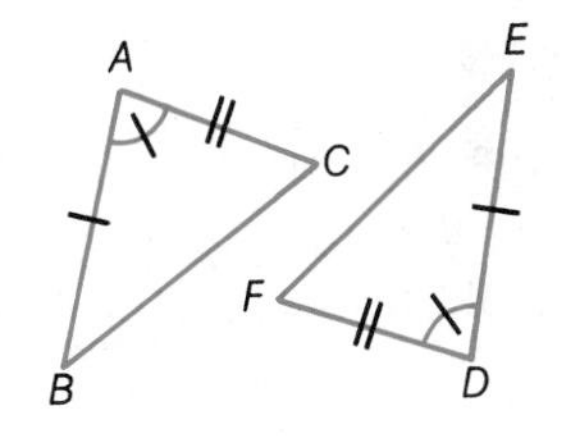

b.

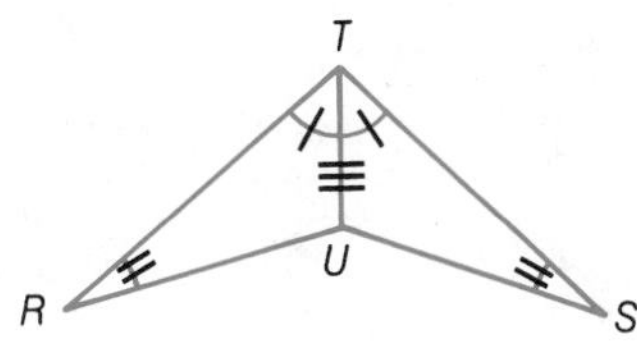

c.

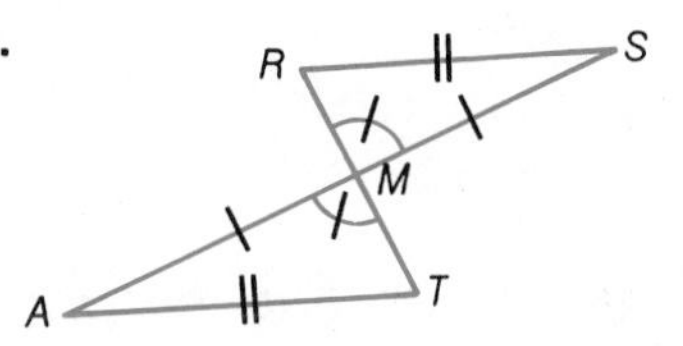

d.

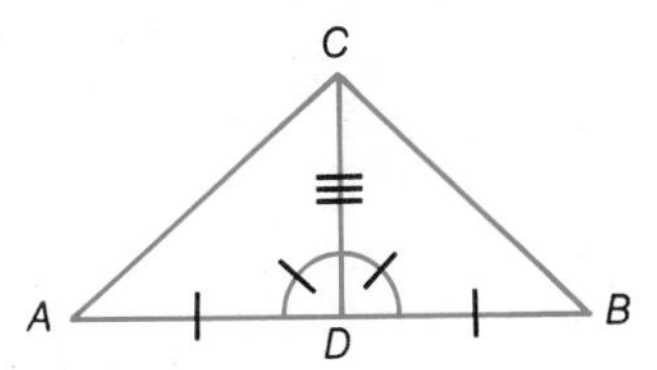

Answer: In **a,** $\triangle ABC \cong \triangle DEF$ by the S.A.S. Postulate.
In **d,** $\triangle ADC \cong \triangle BDC$ by the S.A.S. Postulate.

Unless otherwise indicated, you may assume the following from the appearance of the figure. You will need to make these assumptions in writing proofs.

---

1. Lines, segments, rays, and angles
2. Collinearity of points on a line
3. Betweenness with respect to points on a line
4. Betweenness with respect to coplanar rays with the same vertex
5. Intersection of lines, rays, or segments
6. Location of points with respect to half-planes
7. Adjacent angles and linear pairs

Example 2

Tell which statements can be assumed from the appearance of the figure at the left below.

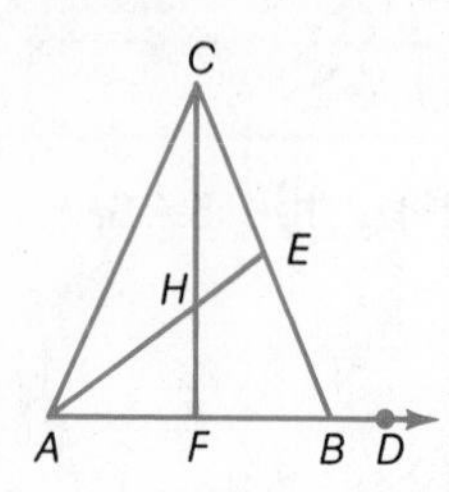

a. $\overrightarrow{AD}$ is a ray. **b.** A, H, and E are collinear points.

c. $\overline{CF} \perp \overline{AB}$. **d.** $\overline{CF}$ bisects $\angle ACB$.

e. Angles CAE and EAF are adjacent angles.

f. $\overline{CF}$ and $\overline{AE}$ intersect at H.

Answer: Statements **a, b, e,** and **f** can be assumed from the appearance of the figure. (See page 101.) The remaining two statements, **c** and **d,** cannot.

Try These

Name the pairs of triangles that are congruent by the S.A.S. Postulate.

1.

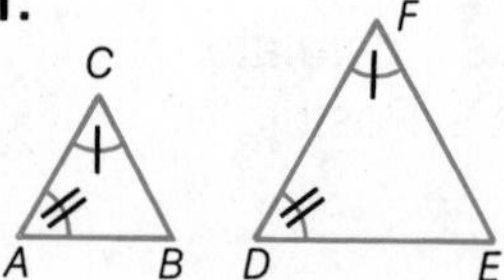

2.

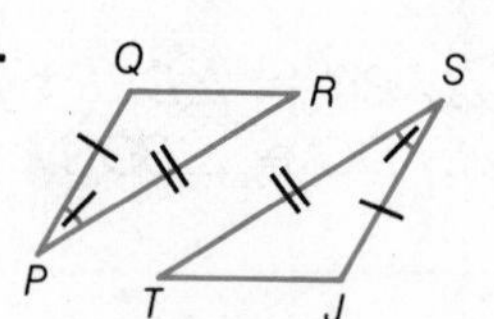

3.

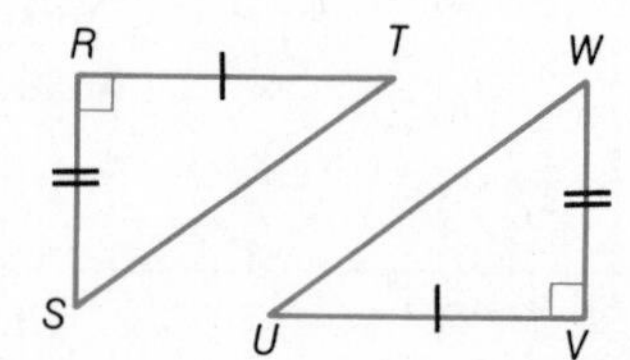

4.

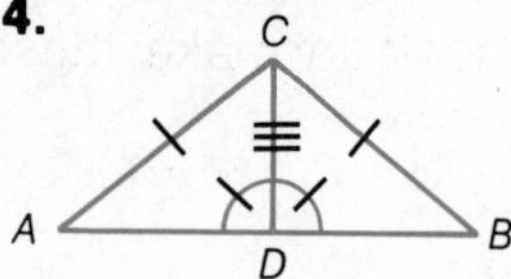

5.

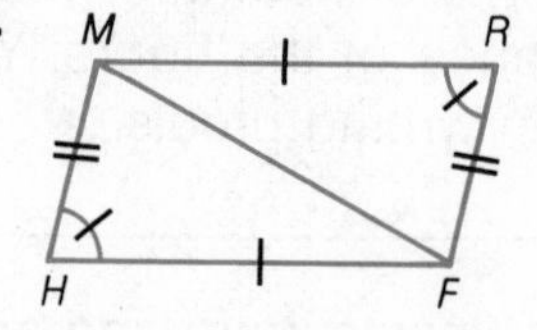

6.

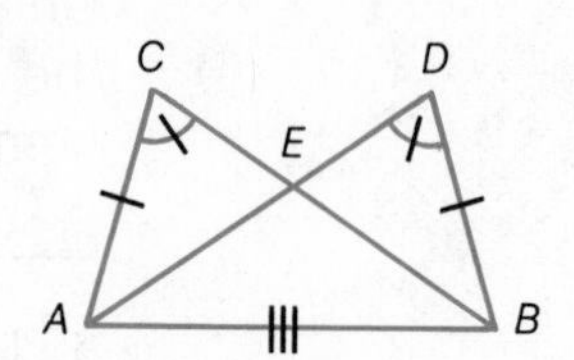

For Exercises **7–14,** *write* Yes *if the statement can be assumed from the appearance of the figure. Otherwise, write* No.

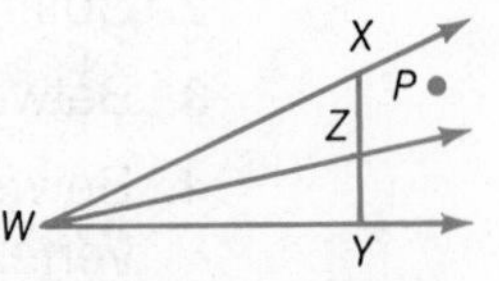

7. $\overrightarrow{WX}$, $\overrightarrow{WZ}$, and $\overrightarrow{WY}$ are rays.

8. W, Z, and P are collinear.

9. $\overline{XZ}$ and $\overline{WZ}$ are segments.

10. $\overrightarrow{WZ}$ and $\overline{XY}$ intersect at Z.

11. $m\angle WYX = 90$

12. $\overrightarrow{WZ}$ bisects $\angle XWY$.

13. $\overrightarrow{WY}$ determines a line.

14. Z is the midpoint of $\overline{XY}$.

Exercises

The S.A.S. *relationship can occur in three ways in a triangle. These ways are shown for $\triangle ABC$ below.*

In Exercises **1–3,** *make similar drawings to show how the* S.A.S. *relationship could occur in each triangle.*

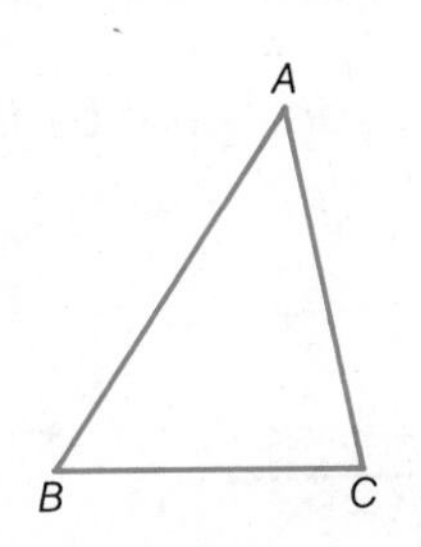

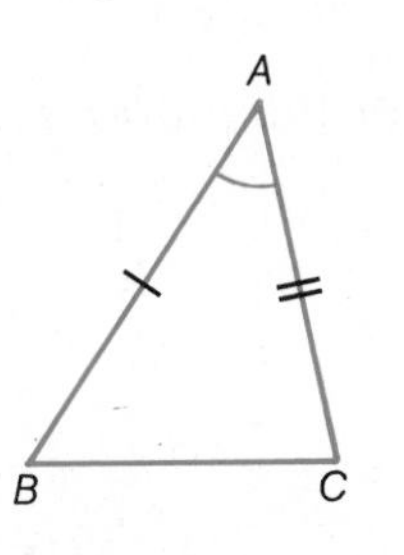

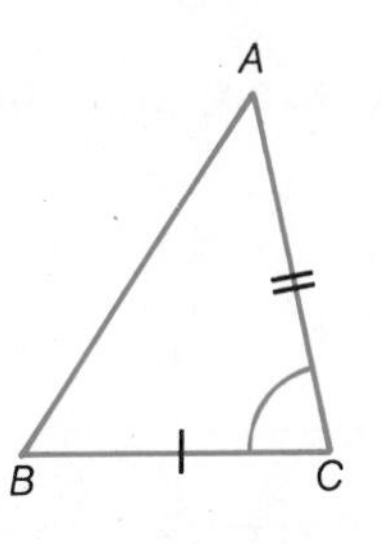

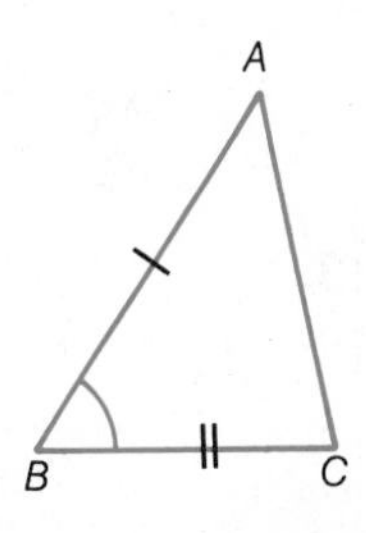

a

1.

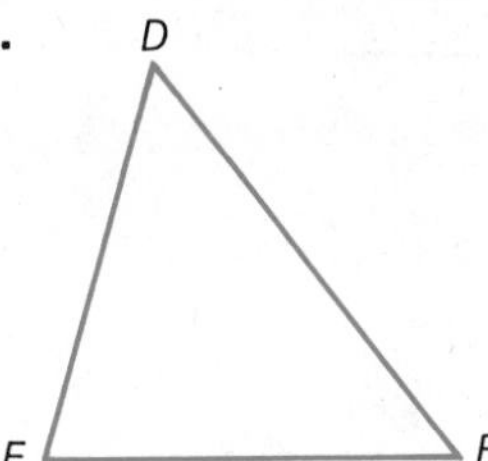

2.

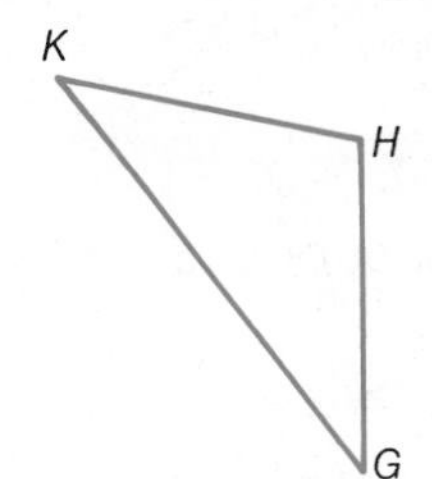

3.

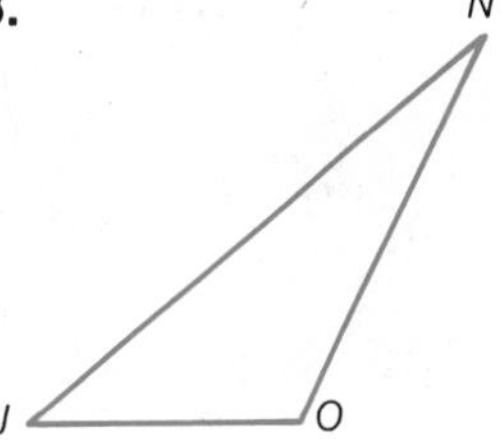

For Exercises **4–9,** *name the pairs of triangles that are congruent by the* S.A.S. *Postulate.*

4.

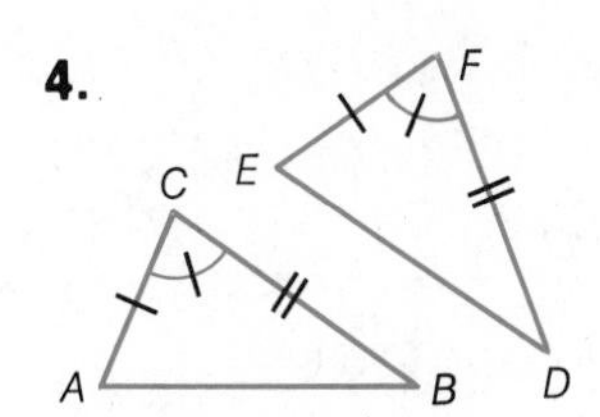

5.

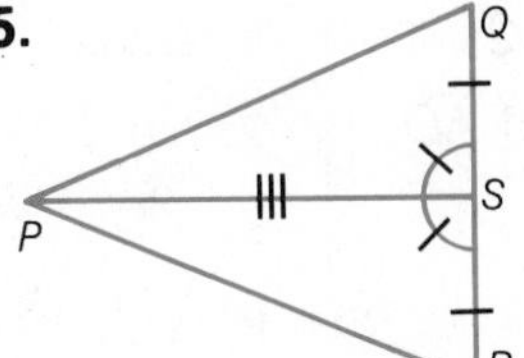

6.

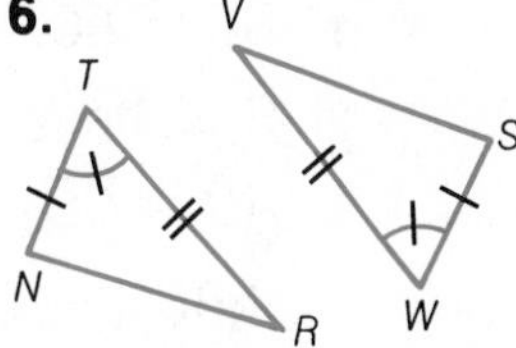

7.

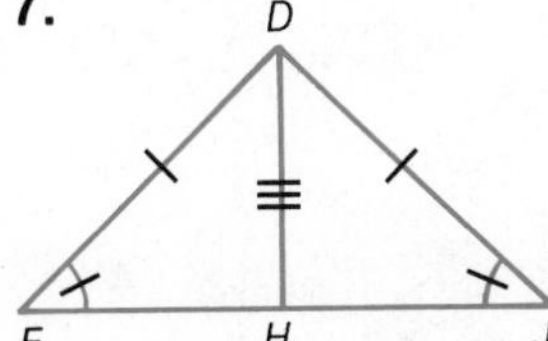

8.

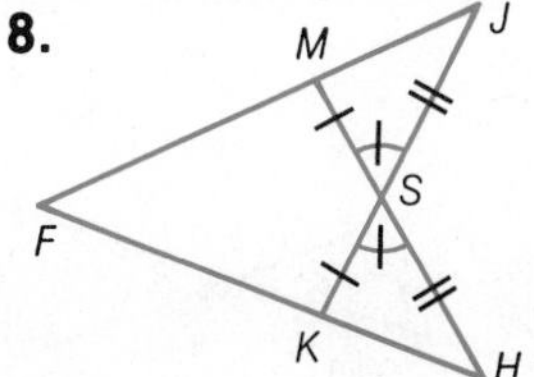

9.

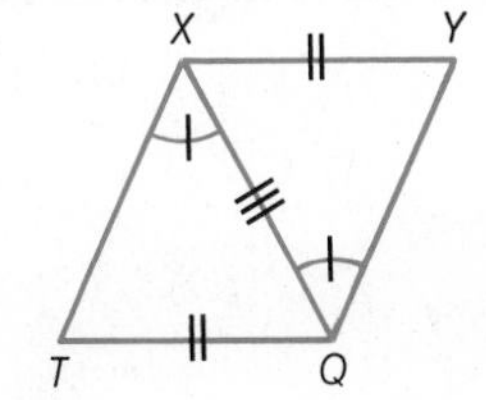

*For Exercises **10–12,** tell why the triangles are not congruent by the* S.A.S. *Postulate.*

10.

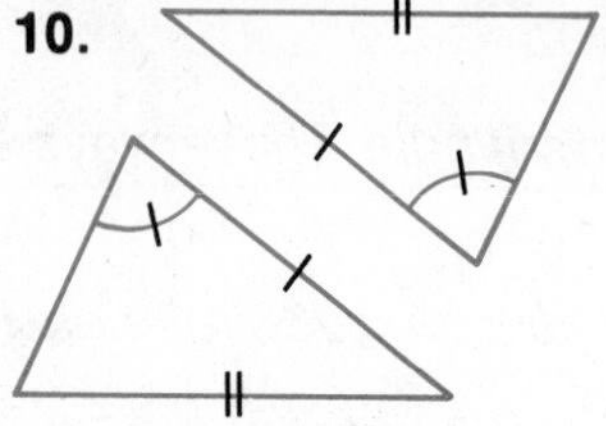

11.

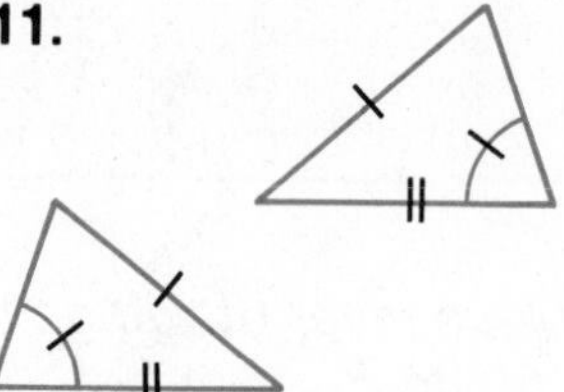

12.

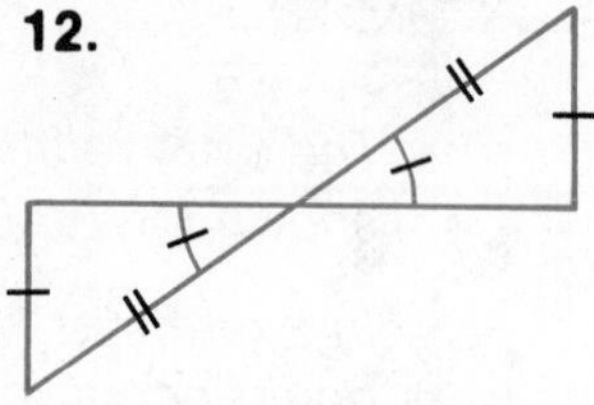

*For Exercises **13–14,** tell whether the triangles are congruent by the* S.A.S. *Postulate.*

13.

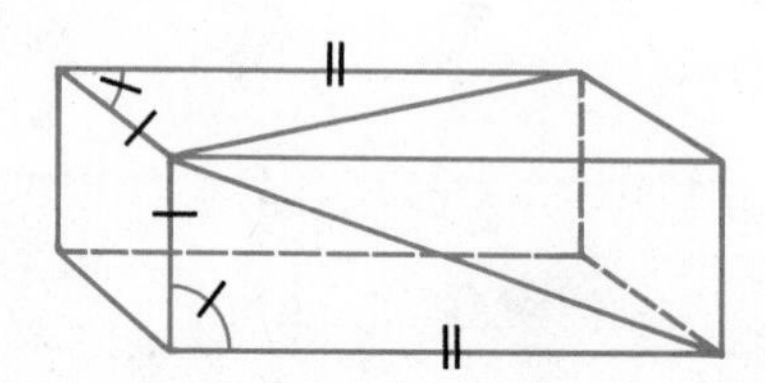

14.

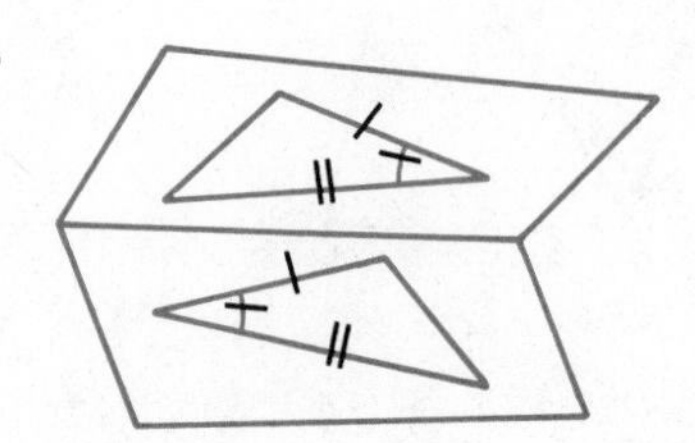

*For Exercises **15–16,** supply the missing statements and reasons.*

15. Given: $\overline{BC} \cong \overline{EC}$, $\angle 1 \cong \angle 2$;
C is the midpoint of $\overline{AD}$.

Prove: $\triangle ABC \cong \triangle DEC$

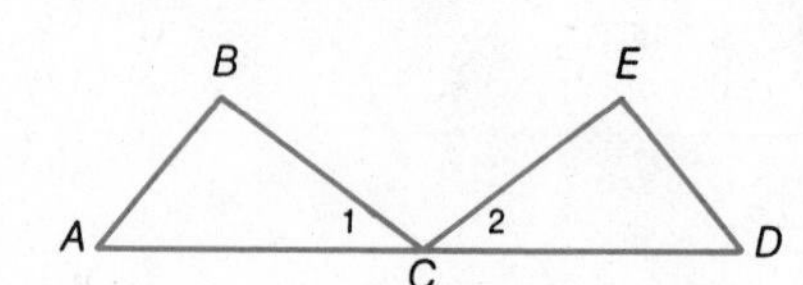

Statements	Reasons
1. $\overline{BC} \cong \overline{EC}$, $\angle 1 \cong \angle 2$	1. ?
2. C is the midpoint of $\overline{AD}$.	2. ?
3. $\overline{AC} \cong \overline{CD}$	3. (2). ?
4. $\triangle ABC \cong \triangle DEC$	4. (1). (3). ?

16. Given: $\overline{AB}$ and $\overline{CD}$ bisect each other at E.

Prove: $\angle D \cong \angle C$

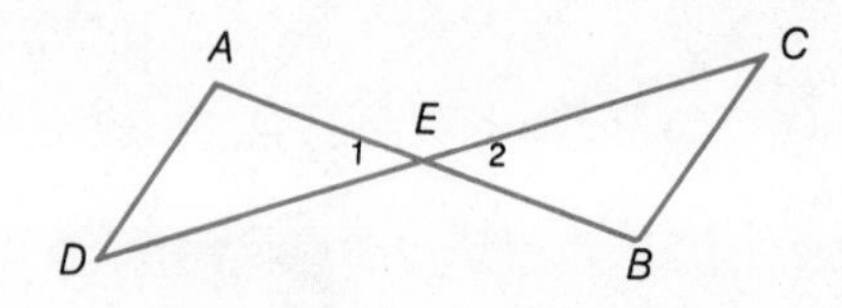

Statements	Reasons
1. $\overline{AB}$ and $\overline{CD}$ intersect.	1. ___?___
2. $\angle 1 \cong \angle 2$	2. (1). ___?___
3. $\overline{AB}$ bisects $\overline{CD}$. $\overline{CD}$ bisects $\overline{AB}$.	3. ___?___
4. $\overline{AE} \cong \overline{EB}$; $\overline{CE} \cong \overline{ED}$	4. (3). ___?___
5. $\triangle AED \cong \triangle$ ___?___	5. (2). (4). S.A.S. Postulate
6. $\angle$ ___?___ $\cong \angle$ ___?___	6. (5). Corresponding parts of congruent triangles are congruent.

17. Use the Given and figure of Exercise **15,** but change the Prove to: $\overline{BA} \cong \overline{ED}$. Write the complete proof.

18. Use the Given and figure of Exercise **16,** but change the Prove to: $\angle A \cong \angle B$. Write the complete proof.

Complete each proof by supplying the necessary statements and reasons. (HINT: *It may be necessary to add additional steps.*)

19. **Given:** $\overline{AB} \cong \overline{CD}$; $\angle ABD \cong \angle CDB$

Prove: $\overline{AD} \cong \overline{CB}$

Statements	Reasons
1. $\overline{AB} \cong \overline{CD}$; $\angle ABD \cong \angle CDB$	1. ___?___
2. $\overline{BD} \cong \overline{BD}$	2. ___?___

20. **Given:** $\overline{AR} \cong \overline{MS}$; C bisects $\overline{RS}$; $\angle S$ and $\angle 2$ are supplementary.

Prove: $\angle A \cong \angle M$

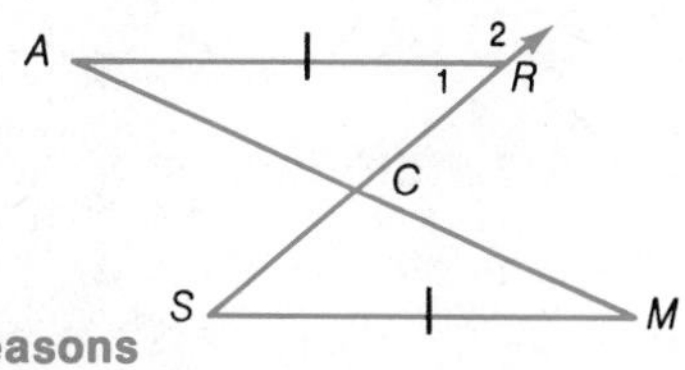

Statements	Reasons
1. $\overline{AR} \cong \overline{MS}$	1. ___?___
2. C bisects $\overline{RS}$.	2. ___?___
3. $\overline{RC} \cong \overline{SC}$	3. (2). ___?___
4. $\angle 1$ and $\angle 2$ form a linear pair.	4. Definition of linear pair.
5. $\angle 1$ and $\angle 2$ are supplementary.	5. ___?___

Definitions and If and Only If

Every definition must be reversible. This means that if a definition is written as a conditional, then the converse of the conditional must also be true. Thus, every definition is a biconditional.

Definition as a Conditional	Converse
If the corresponding parts of triangles are congruent, then the triangles are congruent.	If triangles are congruent, then their corresponding parts are congruent.
If the sum of the measures of two angles is 90, then the angles are complementary.	If two angles are complementary, then the sum of their measures is 90.

Thus, a definition can be written in "if and only if" form.

Triangles are congruent if and only if their corresponding parts are congruent.

Two angles are complementary if and only if the sum of their measures is 90.

Since every definition is a biconditional, it is not necessary to write a definition in "if and only if" form.

Can You Solve These?

Write each definition as a biconditional.

1. A geometric figure is an angle if it is the union of two distinct noncollinear rays with a common endpoint.
2. If all three angles of a triangle are congruent, the triangle is equiangular.
3. Supplementary angles are two angles whose measures have a sum of 180.
4. A right angle is an angle whose measure is 90.
5. An obtuse triangle is a triangle that has an obtuse angle.

3-3 Congruent Triangles/A.S.A. and S.S.S.

Other combinations of congruent angles and sides can be used to prove triangles congruent.

Number of Congruent Parts	Models	Triangles Congruent?
Three Parts		
Two angles, included side	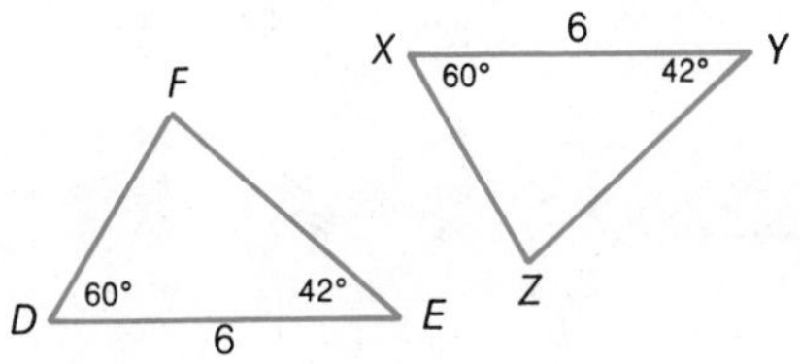	Yes
Three sides	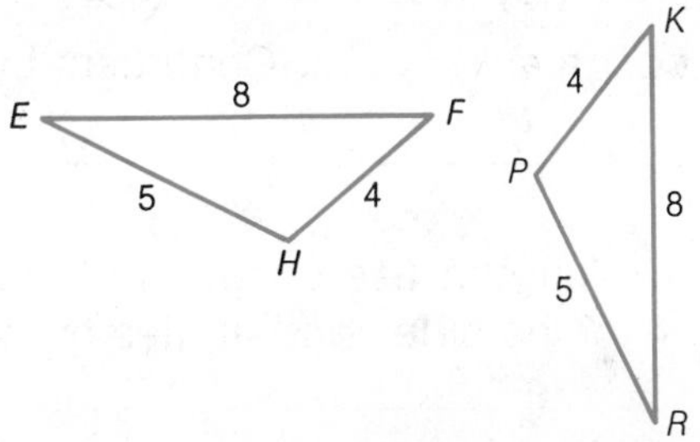	Yes

The first example in the table leads to the Angle-Side-Angle (A.S.A.) Postulate. Note that the congruent sides must be those **included** by the corresponding congruent angles.

Postulate 12: A.S.A. Postulate

If two triangles have two angles and the included side of one triangle congruent respectively to two angles and the included side of the other triangle, then the triangles are congruent.

The second example in the table leads to the Side-Side-Side (S.S.S.) Postulate.

Postulate 13: S.S.S. Postulate

If two triangles have three sides of one triangle congruent respectively to the three sides of the other triangle, then the triangles are congruent.

Example 1

For each pair of triangles, state whether they are congruent by A.S.A., S.S.S., or not congruent.

a.

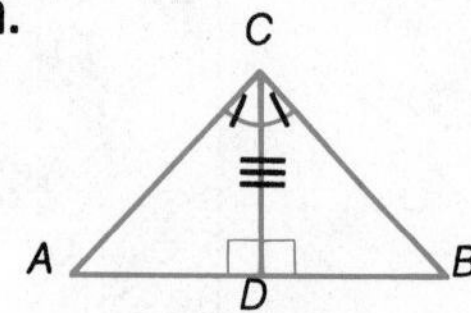

b.

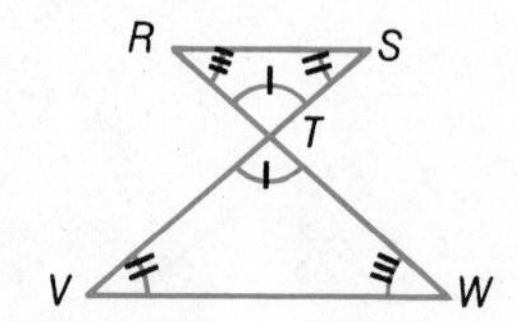

c.

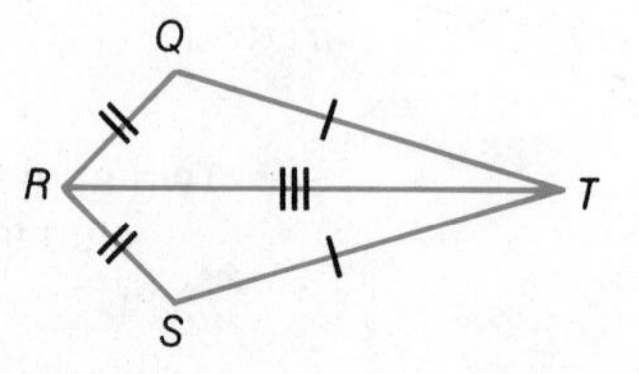

a. Congruent by A.S.A. ⟵ **Side *DC* is included between congruent angles.**

b. Not congruent **c.** Congruent by S.S.S.

You can use congruent triangles to find the unknown measures of the sides and angles of the triangles.

Example 2

Given: $\triangle QHT \cong \triangle PYT$

Find: HT and $m\angle Y$

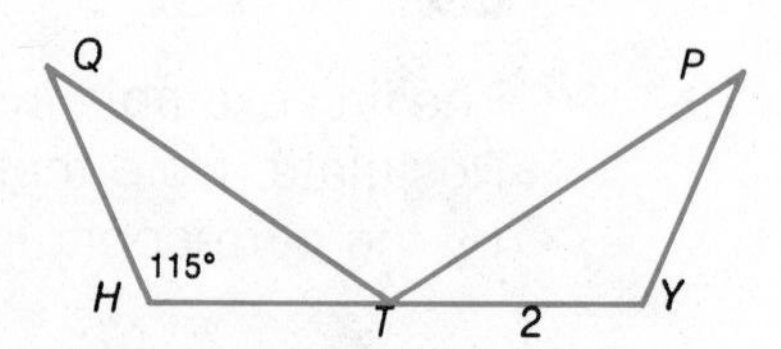

$\overline{HT} \cong \overline{YT}$ ⟵ Corresponding parts of congruent triangles are congruent. (C.P.C.T.C.)

$HT = 2$ cm ⟵ Corresponding parts have equal measures.

$\angle Y \cong \angle H$ ⟵ Corresponding congruent angles

$m\angle Y = 115$ ⟵ Corresponding parts have equal measures.

You can use congruent triangles in the proofs of constructions.

Example 3

Prove the construction on page 47: Bisecting a Segment.

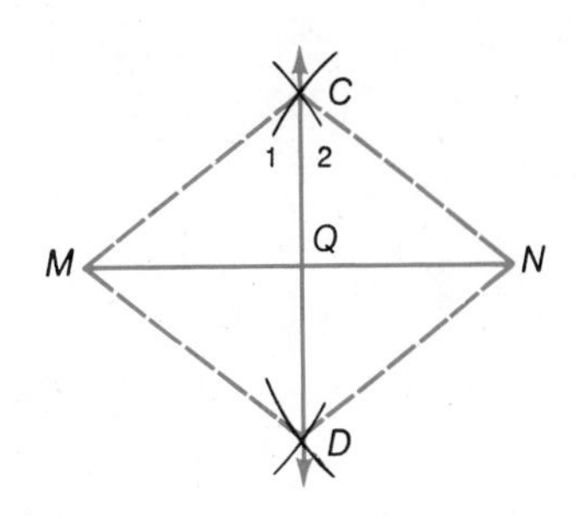

Statements	Reasons
1. Draw $\overline{CM}$, $\overline{CN}$, $\overline{ND}$, and $\overline{MD}$.	1. For any two distinct points, there is exactly one line containing them.
2. $\overline{MC} \cong \overline{NC}$ and $\overline{MD} \cong \overline{ND}$	2. Congruent circles have congruent radii.
3. $\overline{CD} \cong \overline{CD}$	3. Identity
4. $\triangle MCD \cong \triangle NCD$	4. (2). (3). S.S.S. Postulate
5. $\angle 1 \cong \angle 2$	5. (4). C.P.C.T.C.
6. $\overline{CQ} \cong \overline{CQ}$	6. Identity
7. $\triangle MCQ \cong \triangle NCQ$	7. (2). (5). (6). S.A.S. Postulate
8. $\overline{MQ} \cong \overline{NQ}$	8. (7). C.P.C.T.C.
9. Q is the midpoint of $\overline{MN}$.	9. (8). Definition of midpoint

Try These

For Exercises **1–2,** *find the missing measures.*

1. Given: $\triangle ABC \cong \triangle DBE$
Find: AB, BE, ED

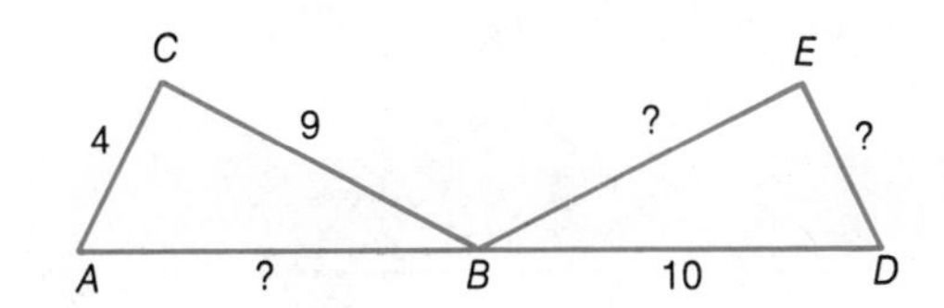

2. Given: $\triangle FJH \cong \triangle HGF$
Find: $m\angle HFG$, $m\angle FHG$

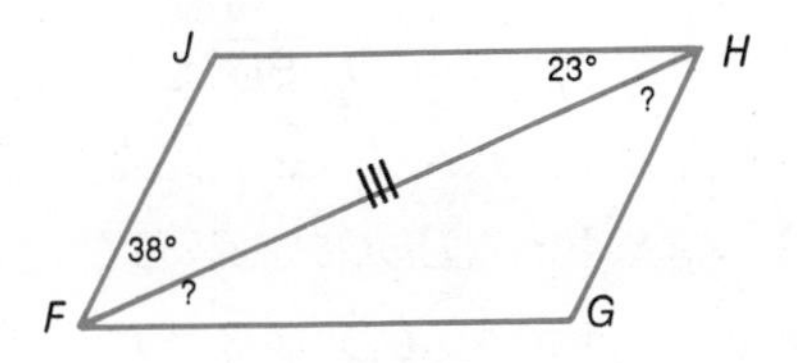

*In Exercises **3–5**, the corresponding congruent parts of a pair of triangles are marked. State whether the triangles are congruent by* S.A.S., S.S.S., *or* A.S.A.

3.

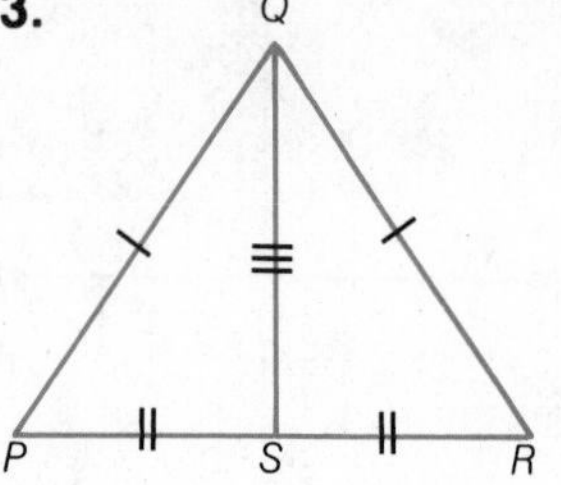

4.

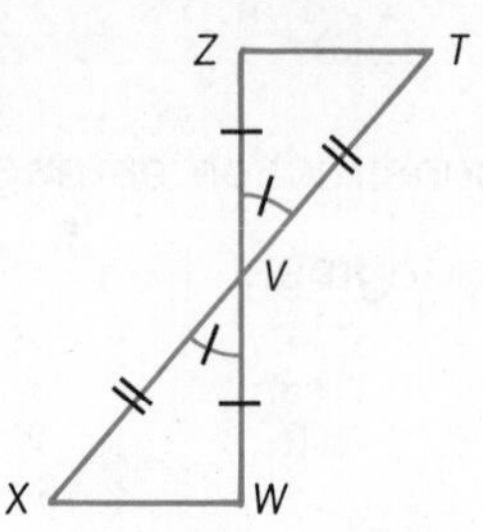

5.

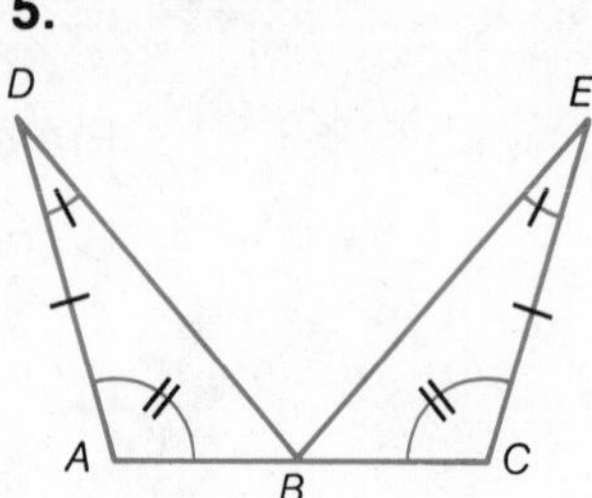

Exercises

The A.S.A. *relationship can occur in three ways. They are shown for* $\triangle ABC$ *below. In Exercises **1–3**, make similar drawings to show how the* A.S.A. *could occur in each triangle.*

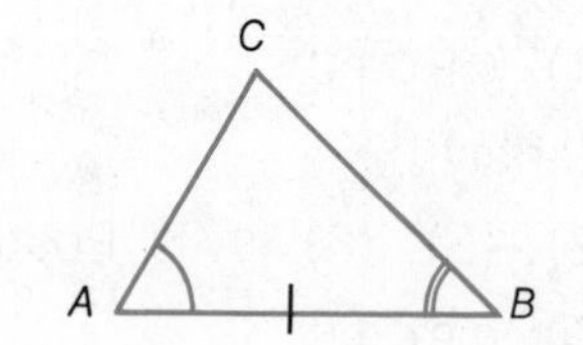

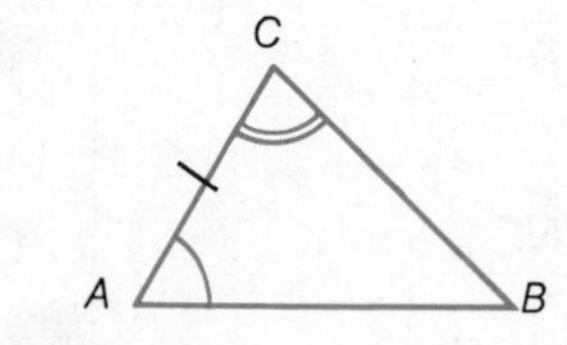

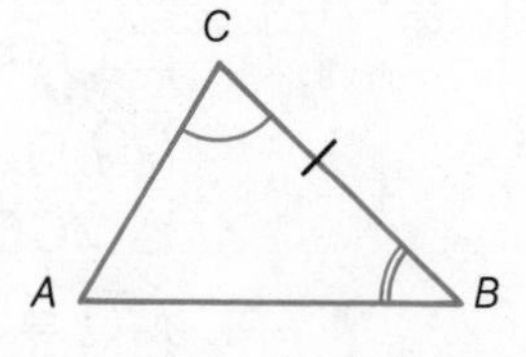

a

1.

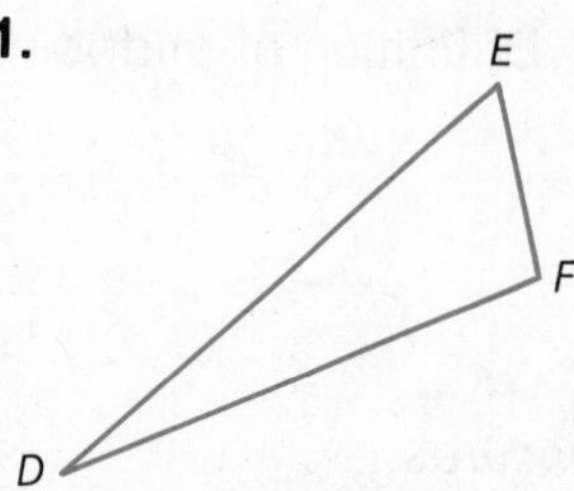

2.

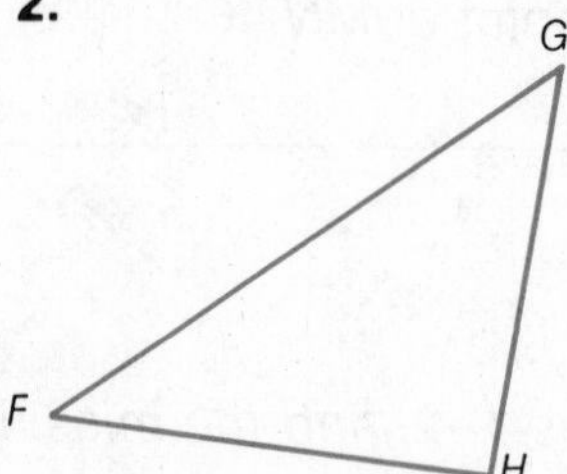

3.

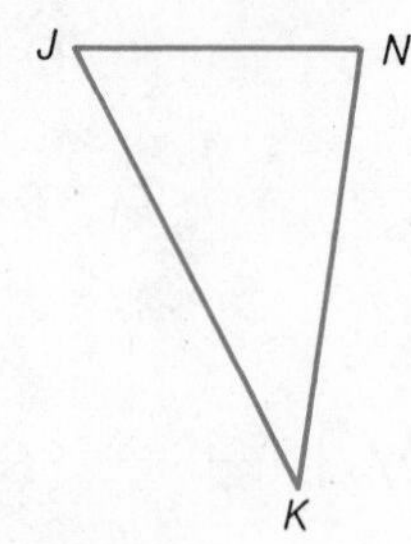

*For Exercises **4–21**, replace the __?__ with the required angle or side so that the indicated relationship is correct.*

4. S.A.S. for $\triangle ABD$: $\overline{BD}$; $\angle 3$; __?__

5. A.S.A. for $\triangle ABD$: $\angle A$; __?__; $\angle 1$

6. A.S.A. for $\triangle BDC$: $\angle 2$; $\overline{BC}$; __?__

7. S.S.S. for $\triangle ABD$: $\overline{AB}$; $\overline{BD}$; __?__

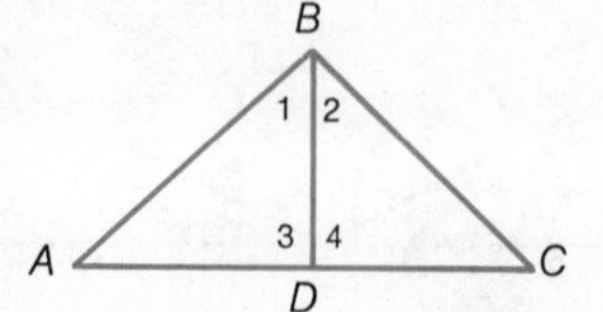

8. S.A.S. for $\triangle MTR$: $\overline{RT}$; ___?___; $\overline{MT}$

9. S.A.S. for $\triangle MTQ$: ___?___; $\angle 5$; ___?___

10. A.S.A. for $\triangle MTQ$: ___?___; $\overline{MT}$; ___?___

11. S.A.S. for $\triangle TOR$: $\overline{TR}$; ___?___; $\overline{RO}$

12. A.S.A. for $\triangle MOQ$: $\angle 3$; $\overline{MQ}$; ___?___

13. S.S.S. for $\triangle MOR$: $\overline{RO}$; ___?___; $\overline{MR}$

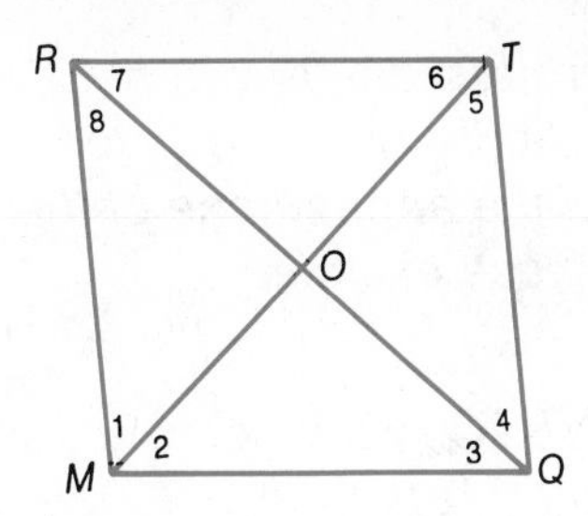

14. A.S.A. for $\triangle CEB$: ___?___; $\overline{CE}$; ___?___

15. S.A.S. for $\triangle CDB$: ___?___; $\angle 2$; ___?___

16. S.A.S. for $\triangle ACD$: ___?___; $\angle 5$; ___?___

17. S.S.S. for $\triangle ACE$: $\overline{CA}$; ___?___; $\overline{AE}$

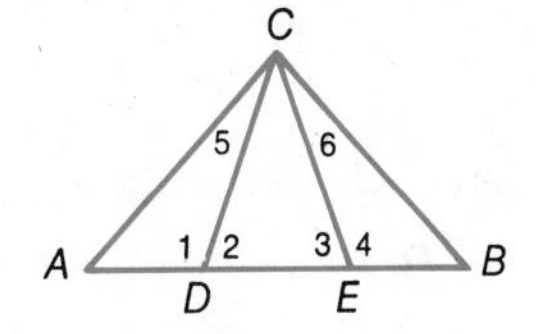

18. S.A.S. for $\triangle XYP$: ___?___; $\angle Y$; ___?___

19. A.S.A. for $\triangle XZW$: ___?___; $\overline{XZ}$; ___?___

20. A.S.A. for $\triangle XZY$: ___?___; $\overline{XZ}$; ___?___

21. S.S.S. for $\triangle WXZ$: ___?___; $\overline{WZ}$; $\overline{ZX}$

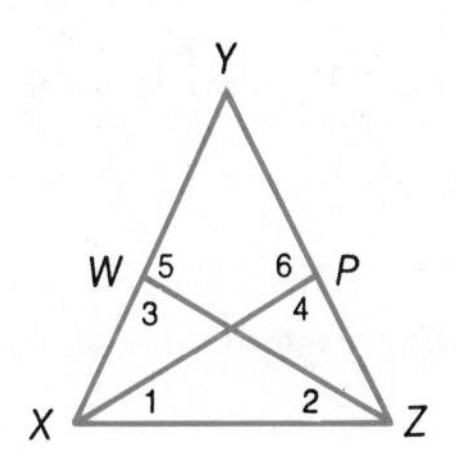

For Exercises **22–27,** *state whether each pair of triangles is congruent by the* S.A.S. *Postulate, the* A.S.A. *Postulate, or the* S.S.S. *Postulate. If none of these applies, write* *None.*

22.

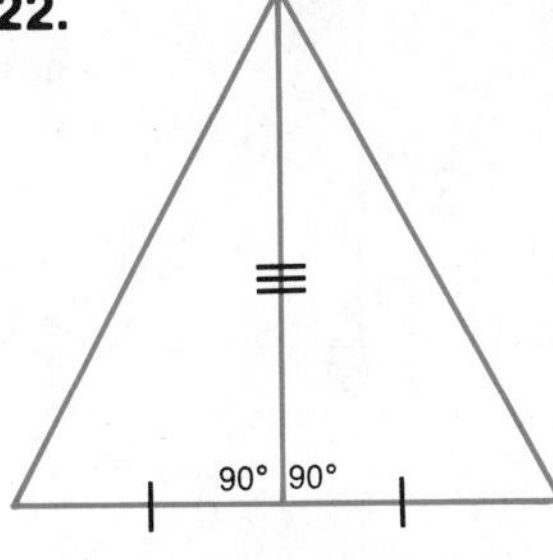

23.

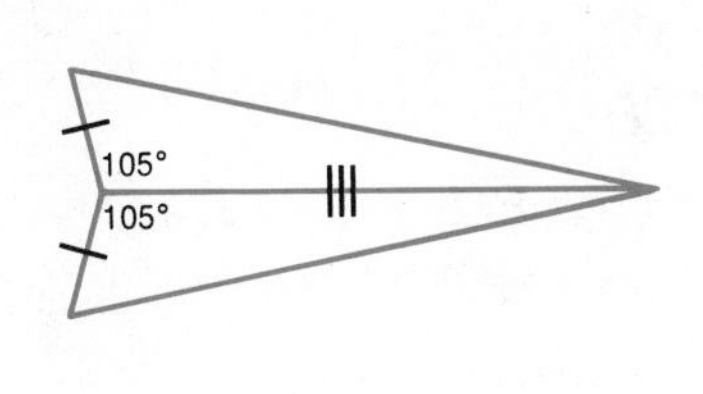

24.

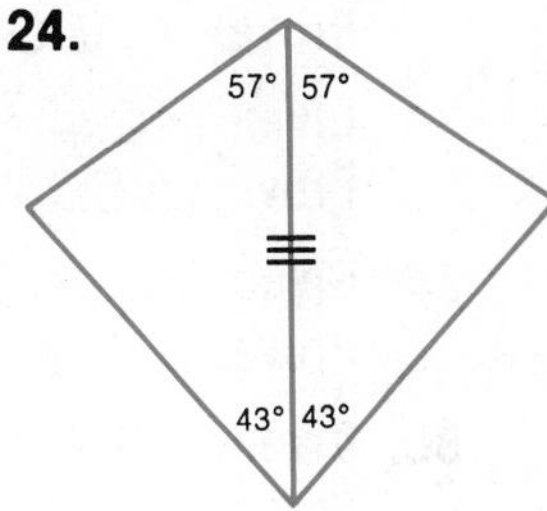

25.

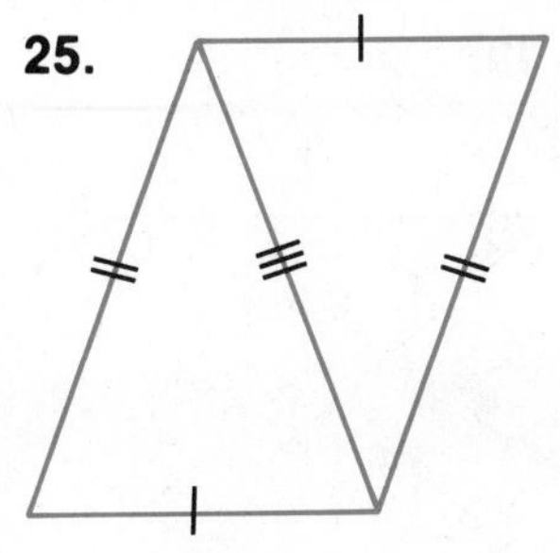

26.

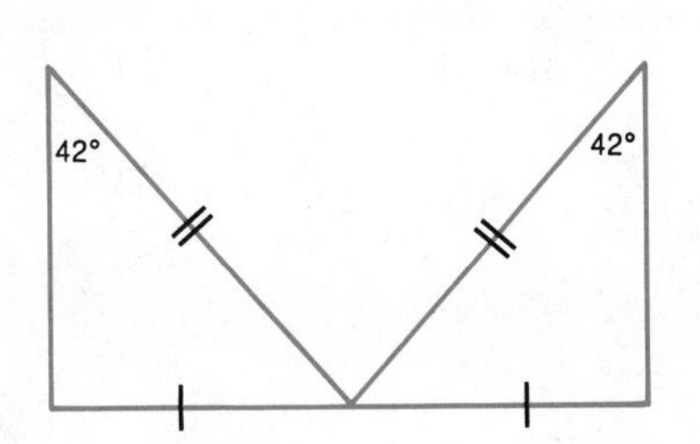

27.

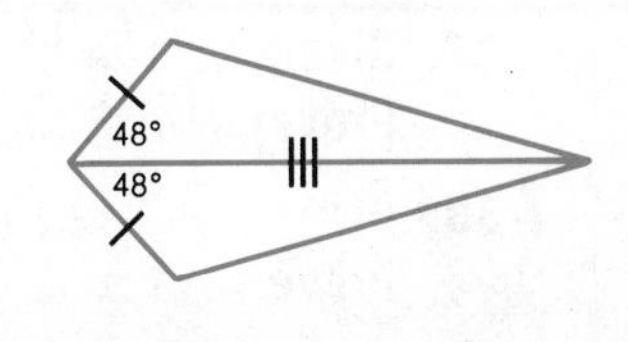

*Exercises **28–32** will help you learn to state conditions from the given conditions, and not from the appearance of the figure. Use $\triangle BAC$ for these exercises.*

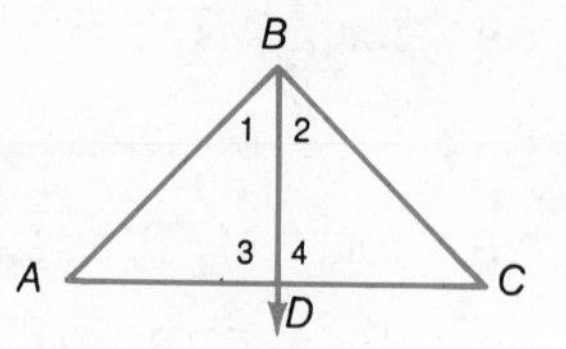

28. In $\triangle BAC$, $\overrightarrow{BD}$ bisects $\angle ABC$. Choose the only correct conclusion.

a. $\overline{BA} \cong \overline{BC}$ **b.** $\angle 1 \cong \angle 2$ **c.** $\angle 3 \cong \angle 4$ **d.** $\angle A \cong \angle C$

29. In $\triangle BAC$, $\overline{BD} \perp \overline{AC}$. Choose the only correct conclusion.

a. $\overline{BA} \cong \overline{BC}$ **b.** $\angle 1 \cong \angle 2$ **c.** $\angle 3 \cong \angle 4$ **d.** $\angle A \cong \angle C$

30. In $\triangle BAC$, $\overrightarrow{BD}$ bisects $\overline{AC}$. Choose the only correct conclusion.

a. $\overline{BA} \cong \overline{BC}$ **b.** $\angle 3 \cong \angle 4$ **c.** $\angle A \cong \angle C$ **d.** $\overline{AD} \cong \overline{DC}$

31. If the only thing you know about $\triangle BAC$ is that $\overline{BD} \perp \overline{AC}$, can you draw the figure so that $\overline{AB}$ is not congruent to $\overline{CB}$? If so, draw it. If not, state why not.

32. If the only thing you know about $\triangle BAC$ is that $\overline{BD}$ bisects $\overline{AC}$, can you draw the figure so that $\overline{AB}$ is not congruent to $\overline{CB}$? If so, draw it. If not, state why not.

*Write a proof for each of the following. Use $\triangle ABC$ at the right below for Exercises **33–36.***

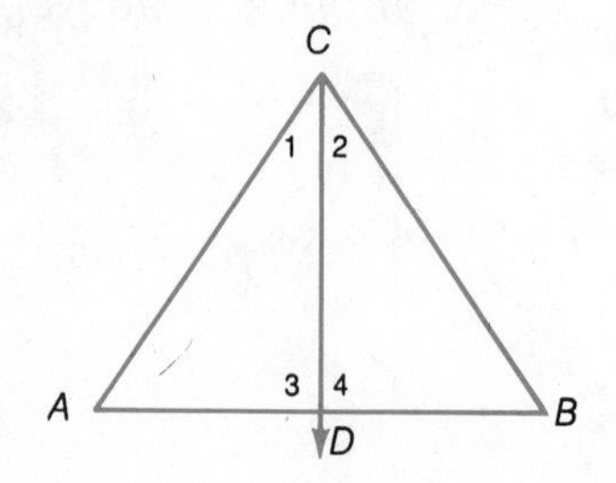

33. Given: $\angle 1 \cong \angle 2$; $\angle 3 \cong \angle 4$
Prove: $\triangle ADC \cong \triangle BDC$

34. Given: $\overline{AC} \cong \overline{BC}$; $\angle 1 \cong \angle 2$
Prove: $\triangle CDA \cong \triangle CDB$

35. Given: $\angle A \cong \angle B$; $\overline{AD} \cong \overline{BD}$, $\angle 3 \cong \angle 4$
Prove: $\angle 1 \cong \angle 2$

36. Given: $\overrightarrow{CD}$ bisects $\angle ACB$; $\angle 3 \cong \angle 4$
Prove: $\angle A \cong \angle B$

*Use the figure at the right below for Exercises **37–39.***

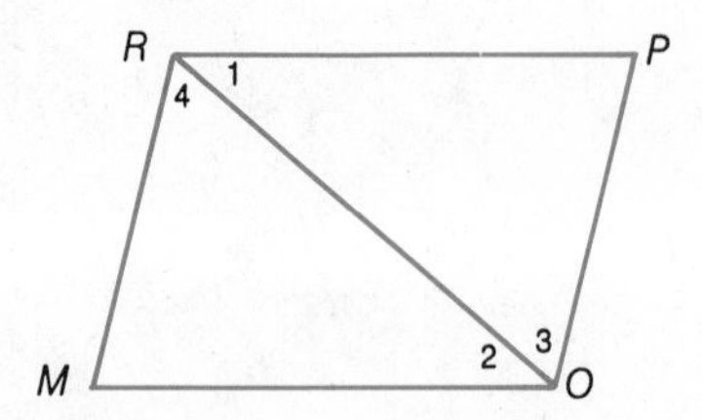

37. Given: $\angle 1 \cong \angle 2$; $\angle 3 \cong \angle 4$
Prove: $\overline{PR} \cong \overline{MO}$

38. Given: $\overline{MO} \cong \overline{PR}$; $\overline{RM} \cong \overline{OP}$
Prove: $\angle 1 \cong \angle 2$

39. Given: $\overline{RM} \cong \overline{OP}$; $\angle 3 \cong \angle 4$
Prove: $\angle 1 \cong \angle 2$

b

40. Prove the construction on page 54:

Constructing an Angle Congruent to a Given Angle.

Plan of Proof: Draw $\overline{HK}$ and $\overline{MJ}$. Prove $\triangle FHK \cong \triangle XMJ$ by the S.S.S. Postulate.

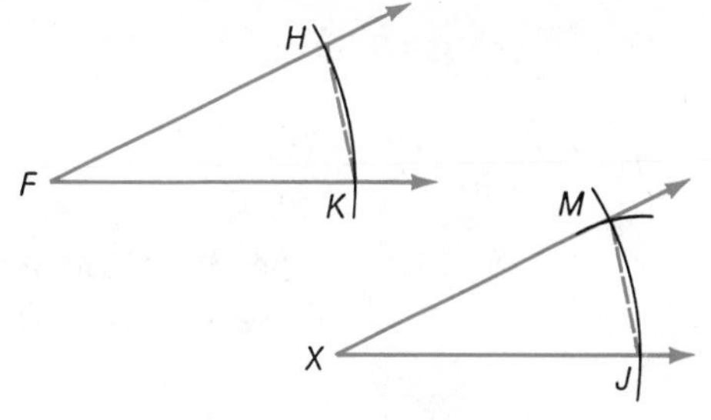

41. Prove the construction on page 55:

Bisecting an Angle.

Plan of Proof: Draw $\overline{DF}$ and $\overline{EF}$. Prove $\triangle BDF \cong \triangle BEF$ by the S.S.S. Postulate. Then $\angle DBF \cong \angle FBE$ by C.P.C.T.C. and $\overrightarrow{BF}$ is an angle bisector by definition.

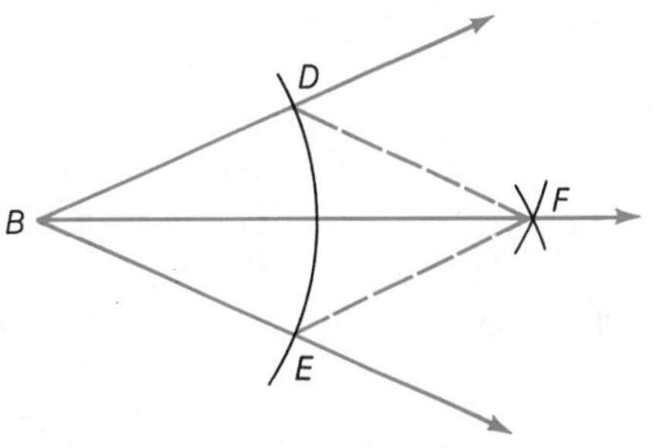

42. Construct the perpendicular bisector of a line segment. (HINT: Follow the procedure for bisecting a line segment on page 47.) Prove your construction.

43. Given: $\angle 1$ and $\angle B$ are supplementary; $\overline{BC} \cong \overline{EG}$; $\overline{DB} \cong \overline{HE}$

Prove: $\angle D \cong \angle H$

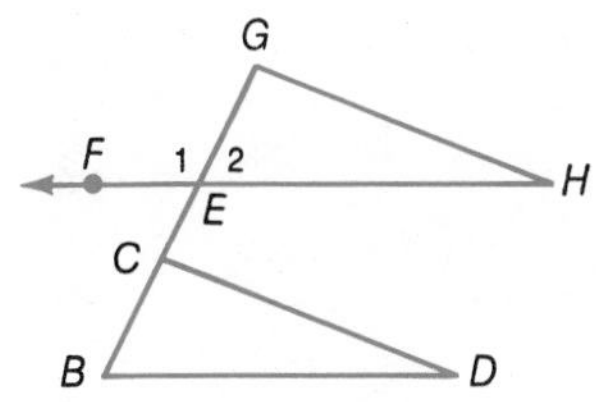

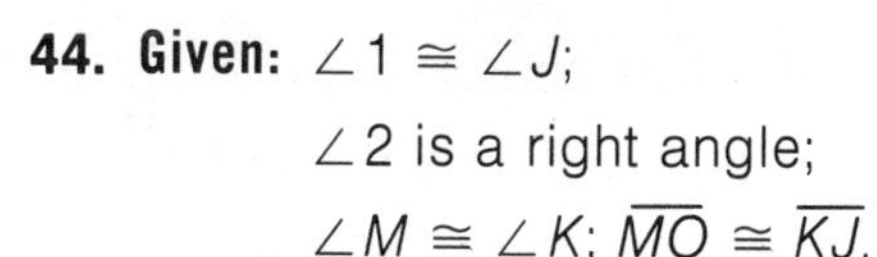

44. Given: $\angle 1 \cong \angle J$; $\angle 2$ is a right angle; $\angle M \cong \angle K$; $\overline{MO} \cong \overline{KJ}$.

Prove: $\angle Q \cong \angle 3$

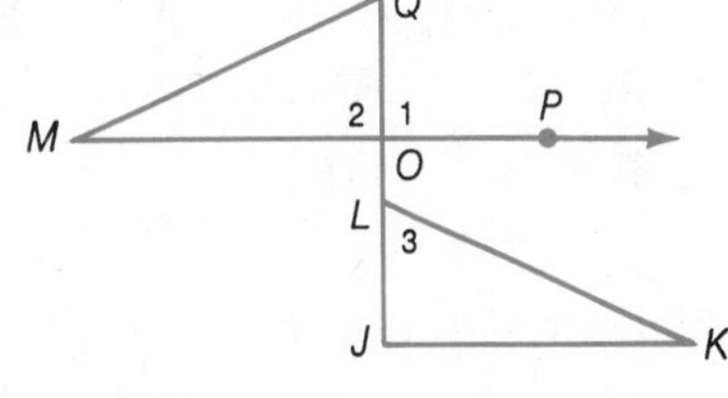

45. Given: $\angle YWX \cong \angle ZWX$; $\angle YXW \cong \angle ZXW$

Prove: $\triangle WXY \cong \triangle WXZ$; $\overline{WY} \cong \overline{WZ}$

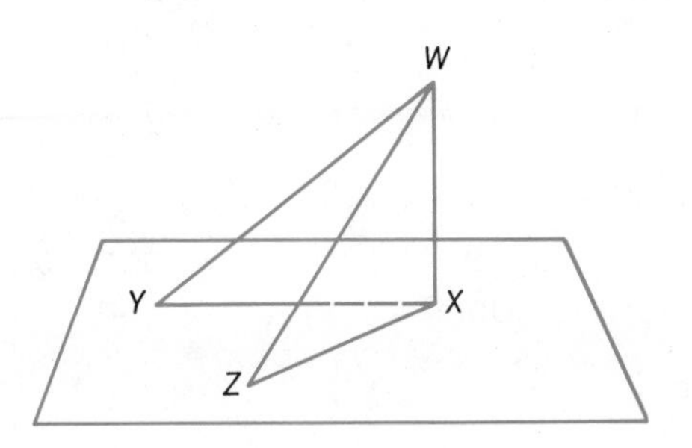

46. Given: $\overline{AB} \cong \overline{CD}$; $\angle ABC \cong \angle CDB$; $\overline{BC} \cong \overline{DB}$

Prove: $\triangle CBA \cong \triangle BDC$

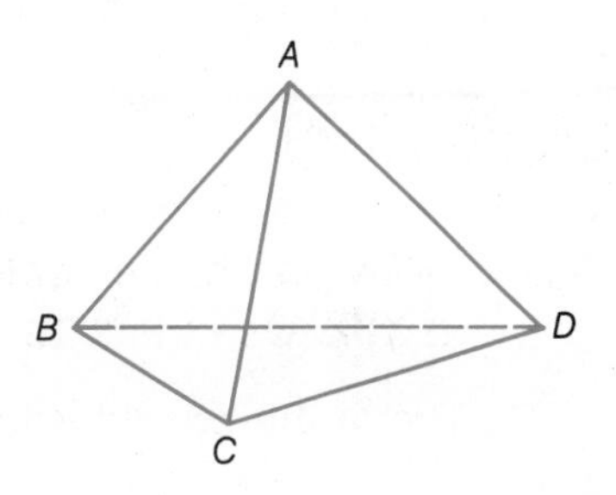

Construction

Constructing a Triangle Congruent to a Given Triangle

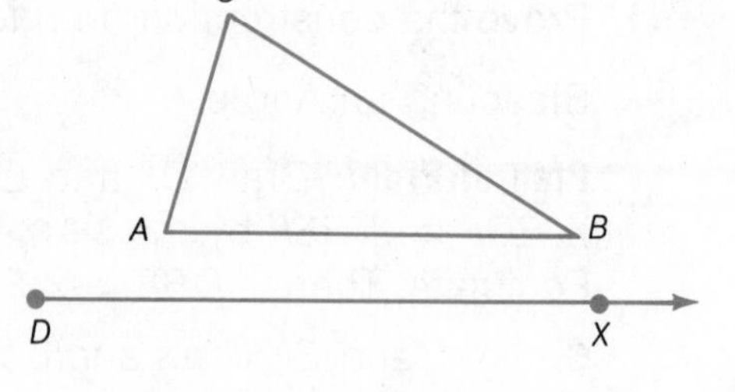

Given: $\triangle ABC$

Required: To construct a triangle congruent to triangle ABC

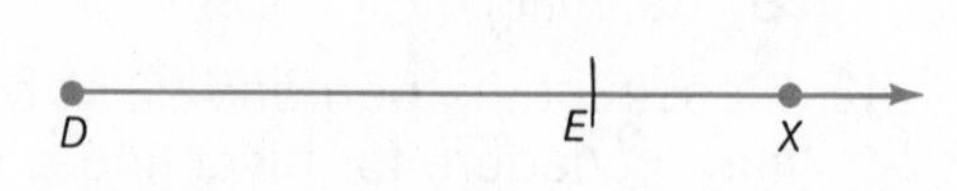

1. Draw any ray DX longer than $\overline{AB}$.

2. With D as center and the length of $\overline{AB}$ as radius, construct segment DE congruent to $\overline{AB}$.

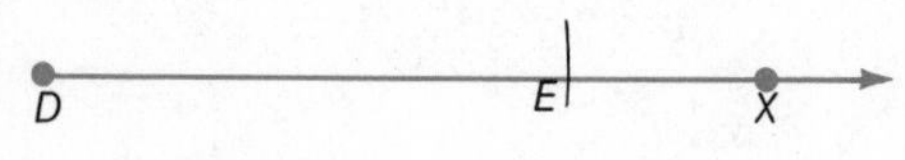

3. With D as center and the length of $\overline{AC}$ as radius, make an arc above $\overrightarrow{DX}$. With E as center and the length of $\overline{BC}$ as radius, make an arc intersecting the first arc. Label the point of intersection F.

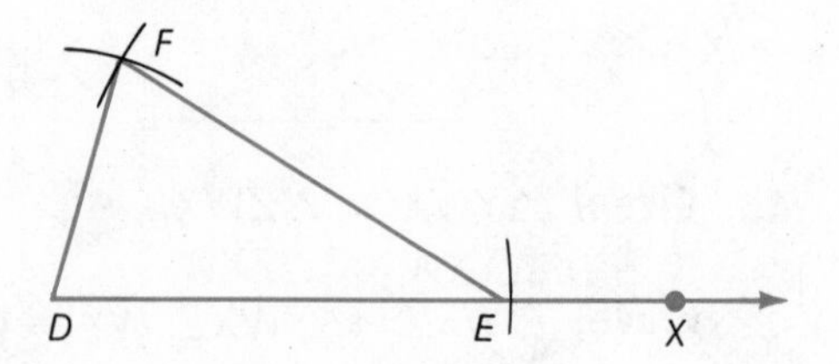

4. Draw $\overline{DF}$ and $\overline{EF}$.

Then $\triangle DEF \cong \triangle ABC$ by the S.S.S. Postulate and $\triangle DEF$ is the required triangle.

Exercises

1. Draw an obtuse scalene triangle XYZ. Construct a triangle congruent to $\triangle XYZ$. Use the S.S.S. Postulate to do this construction.

2. Prove the construction of Exercise 1.

3. Draw an acute scalene triangle *NPR*. Construct a triangle congruent to $\triangle NPR$. Use the S.A.S. Postulate to do this construction.

4. Draw an acute scalene triangle *MVS*. Construct a triangle congruent to $\triangle MVS$. Use the A.S.A. Postulate to do this construction.

Draw an isosceles triangle DPR having $\overline{DP}$ as its base.

5. Construct $\triangle GEF$ congruent to $\triangle DPR$. Use the S.S.S. Postulate to do the construction.

6. Construct $\triangle SQV$ congruent to $\triangle DPR$. Use the A.S.A. Postulate to do the construction.

7. Construct $\triangle WYZ$ congruent to $\triangle DPR$. Use the S.A.S. Postulate to do the construction.

PUZZLE

Each figure below can be formed by fitting together two pieces of a rectangle that measures 4 by 6 centimeters.

For each figure, draw a rectangle of the dimensions given above. Then cut the rectangle into two pieces such that, when they are refitted together, the new figure is formed. Flipping a piece over is allowed.

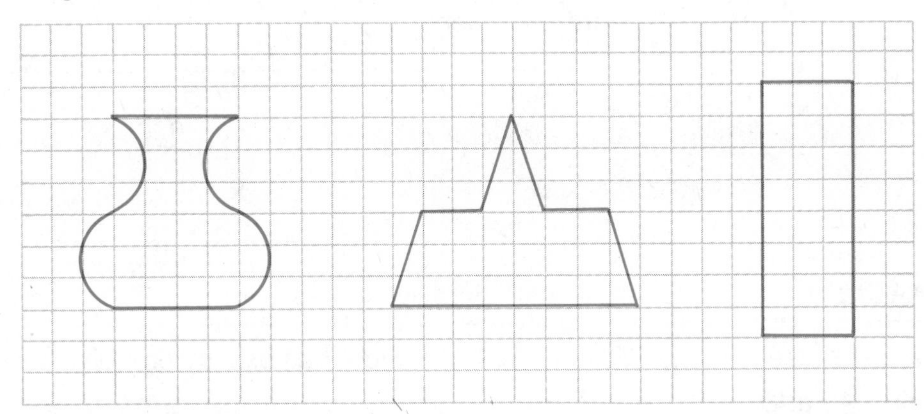

Remember

1. Write the converse of this conditional statement: If two lines are perpendicular, then they form four pairs of congruent adjacent angles.

2. Write the conditional and its converse as a biconditional.

The answers are on page 152. If you need help, see page 78.

3-4 Isosceles Triangle Theorems

Each triangle below is isosceles. Use a protractor to measure the base angles of each triangle.

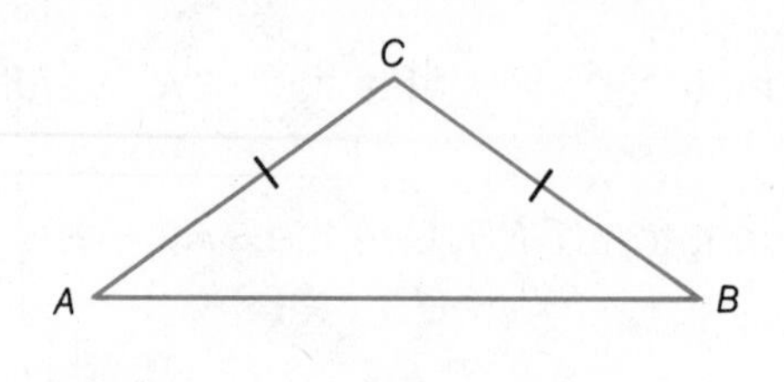

$m\angle A = m\angle B = 35$

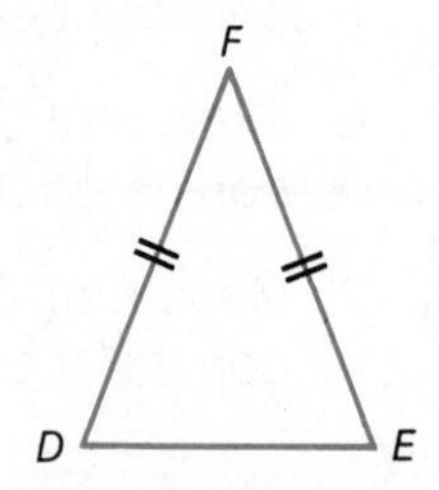

$m\angle D = m\angle E = 68$

These results suggest the Isosceles Triangle Theorem.

Theorem 3-1: Isosceles Triangle Theorem

If two sides of a triangle are congruent, then the angles opposite these sides are congruent.

Given: $\triangle ABC$ with $\overline{AC} \cong \overline{BC}$

Prove: $\angle A \cong \angle B$

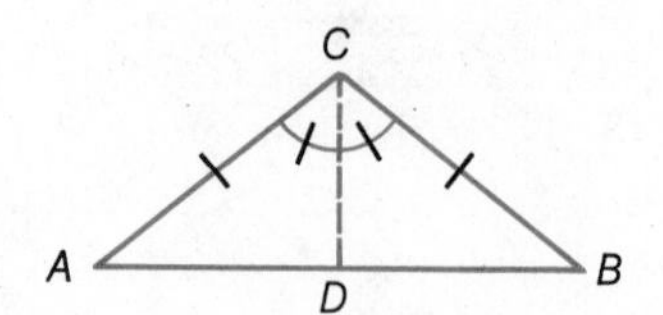

Statements	Reasons
1. Draw a ray bisecting $\angle ACB$ and meeting $\overline{AB}$ at D.	1. An angle has exactly one bisector.
2. $m\angle ACD = m\angle BCD$	2. (1). Definition of angle bisector
3. $\angle ACD \cong \angle BCD$	3. (2). Angles that have the same measure are congruent.
4. $\overline{AC} \cong \overline{BC}$	4. Given
5. $\overline{CD} \cong \overline{CD}$	5. Identity
6. $\therefore \triangle ACD \cong \triangle BCD$	6. (3). (4). (5). S.A.S. Postulate
7. $\therefore \angle A \cong \angle B$	7. (6). C.P.C.T.C.

The Isosceles Triangle Theorem can be extended to equilateral triangles.

Corollary	Model	Outline of Proof
3-2: If the three sides of a triangle are congruent, then the three angles are also congruent.	C, A, B	$\overline{AC} \cong \overline{BC}$ $\therefore \angle A \cong \angle B$ $\overline{AB} \cong \overline{BC}$ $\therefore \angle A \cong \angle C$ $\therefore \angle A \cong \angle B \cong \angle C$

A triangle with three congruent angles is **equiangular.**

The converse of Theorem 3-1 is Theorem 3-3. You are asked to prove the converse in the Exercises.

Theorem 3-3: If two angles of a triangle are congruent, then the sides opposite these angles are congruent.

The converse of Corollary 3-2 is also a Corollary.

Corollary	Model	Outline of Proof
3-4: If the three angles of a triangle are congruent, then the three sides are congruent.	C, A, B	$\angle A \cong \angle B$ $\therefore \overline{AC} \cong \overline{BC}$ $\angle A \cong \angle C$ $\therefore \overline{AB} \cong \overline{BC}$ $\therefore \overline{AC} \cong \overline{BC} \cong \overline{AB}$

Try These

*In Exercises **1–3,** name the theorem or corollary restated by each sentence.*

1. Every equilateral triangle is an equiangular triangle.
2. The base angles of an isosceles triangle are congruent.
3. Every equiangular triangle is an equilateral triangle.
4. Restate Theorems 3-1 and 3-3 as a biconditional.
5. Restate Corollaries 3-2 and 3-4 as a biconditional.

*For Exercises **6–8** use the information indicated on each figure to state whatever conclusions you can about the unmarked sides and angles in the figure.*

6.

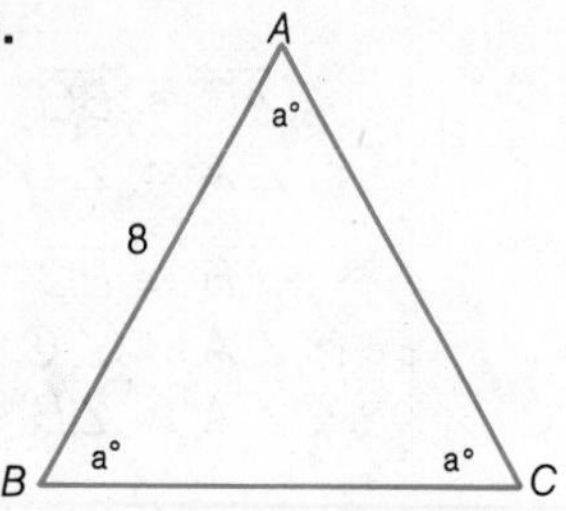

7.

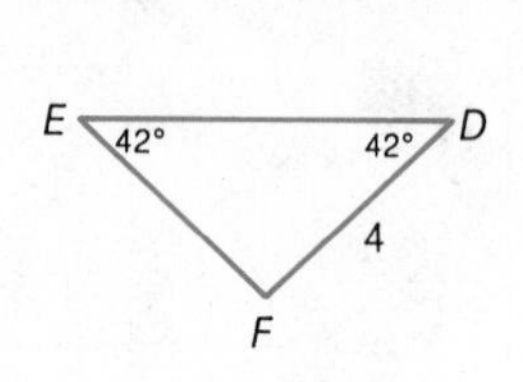

8.

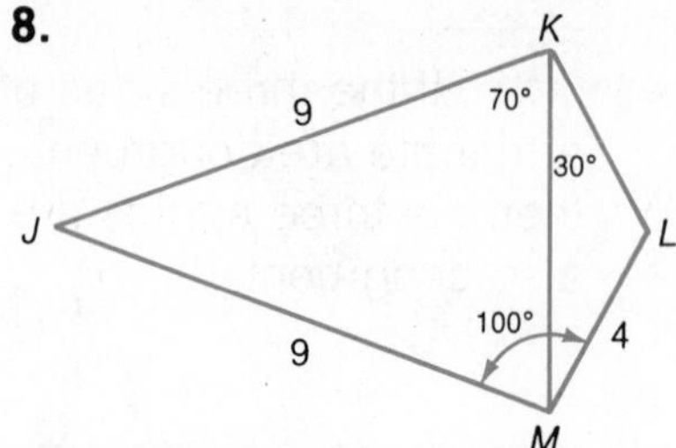

Exercises

a

1. In the figure at the right, $\overline{CA} \cong \overline{CB}$. Explain how to prove that $\angle 3 \cong \angle 4$.

2. In the figure at the right, $\angle 3 \cong \angle 4$. Explain how to prove that $\triangle ABC$ is isosceles.

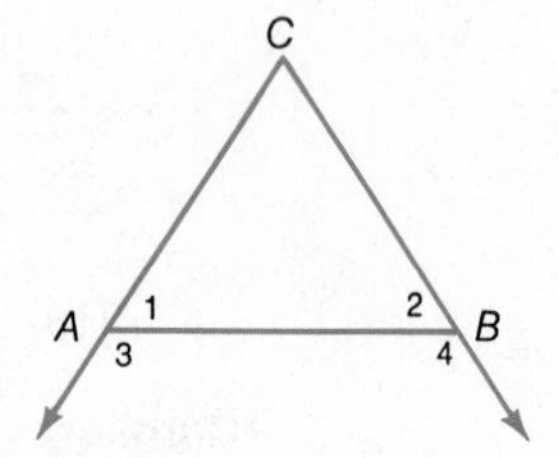

*In Exercises **3–11,** prove each statement.*

3. If $\overline{BE} \cong \overline{CE}$, and $\angle ABC \cong \angle DCB$, then $\angle 1 \cong \angle 3$.

4. If $\angle 2 \cong \angle 4$, then $\triangle BEC$ is isosceles.

5. If $\overline{BE} \cong \overline{CE}$, $\overrightarrow{BA} \perp \overline{BC}$, and $\overrightarrow{CD} \perp \overline{BC}$, then $\angle 1 \cong \angle 3$.

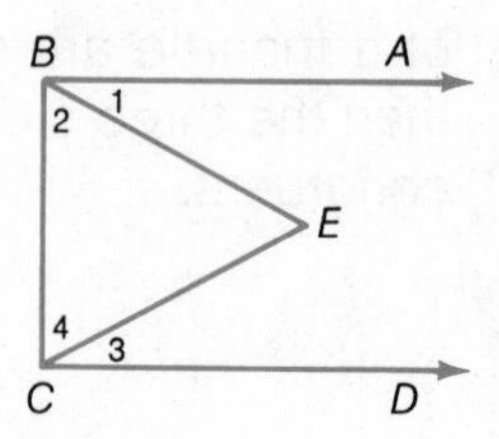

*Use $\triangle PQR$ at the right below for Exercises **6–11.***

6. If $\overline{PQ} \cong \overline{PR}$ and $\overline{SQ} \cong \overline{TR}$, then $\angle 1 \cong \angle 2$.

7. If $\angle Q \cong \angle R$ and $\angle 1 \cong \angle 2$, then $\overline{SQ} \cong \overline{TR}$.

8. If $\overline{PS} \cong \overline{PT}$ and $\overline{SQ} \cong \overline{TR}$, then $\angle Q \cong \angle R$.

9. If $\angle 1 \cong \angle 2$ and $\overline{SQ} \cong \overline{TR}$, then $\angle Q \cong \angle R$.

10. If $\overline{PS} \cong \overline{PT}$, $\angle Q \cong \angle 1$, and $\angle R \cong \angle 2$, then $\triangle RQP$ is isosceles.

11. If $\overline{PS} \cong \overline{SQ}$, $\overline{PT} \cong \overline{TR}$, and $\overline{PQ} \cong \overline{PR}$, then $\angle 1 \cong \angle 2$.

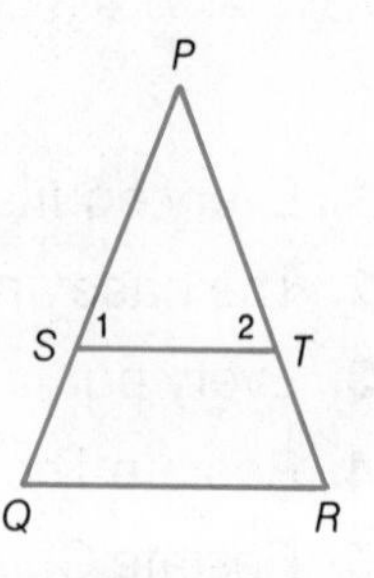

Use the theorems and corollaries of this section to draw any conclusions you can from each statement in Exercises **12–15.** *Give a reason for each conclusion stated.*

12. No two angles of $\triangle ABC$ are congruent.

13. No two sides of $\triangle XYZ$ are congruent.

14. A triangle is not equiangular.

15. A triangle is not equilateral.

In the figure, $\triangle VQW$ is in plane I and $\triangle TQW \cong \triangle TQV$.

16. Prove that $\triangle QVW$ is isosceles.

17. Prove that $\angle QVW \cong \angle QWV$.

18. Prove that $\triangle TVW$ is isosceles.

19. Prove that $\angle TVW \cong \angle TWV$.

20. Prove Corollary 3–2. (HINT: Follow the outline on page 117.)

21. Prove Corollary 3–4. (HINT: Follow the outline on page 117.)

b

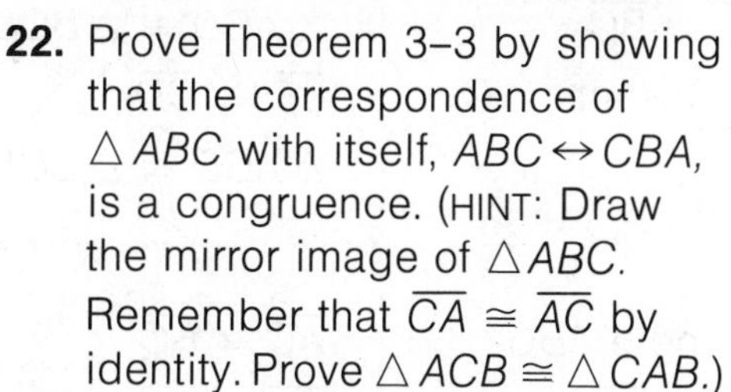

22. Prove Theorem 3–3 by showing that the correspondence of $\triangle ABC$ with itself, $ABC \leftrightarrow CBA$, is a congruence. (HINT: Draw the mirror image of $\triangle ABC$. Remember that $\overline{CA} \cong \overline{AC}$ by identity. Prove $\triangle ACB \cong \triangle CAB$.)

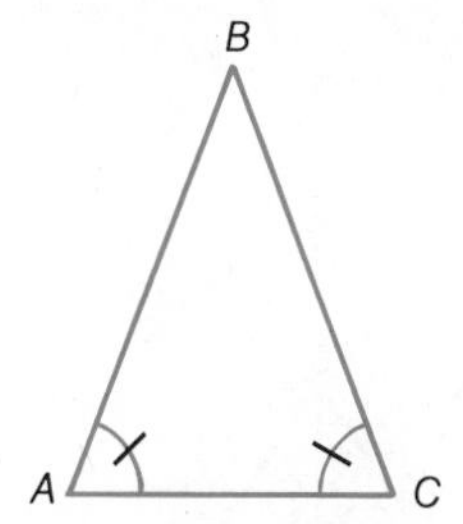

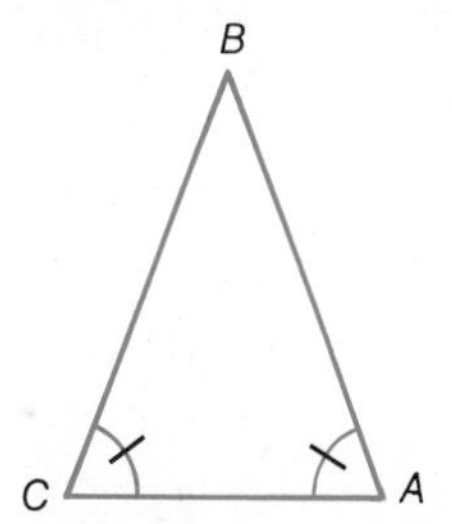

Remember

1. Complete this statement: A biconditional always contains the phrase ___?___.

Write each biconditional as a conditional and its converse.

2. An angle is a right angle if and only if its measure is 90.

3. A triangle is an acute triangle if and only if all its angles are acute angles.

The answers are on page 152. If you need help, see page 78.

3-5 More Isosceles Triangle Theorems

By definition, the bisector of an angle is a ray. However, for convenience, we shall refer to any segment that lies on the bisector of an angle as the bisector of the angle.

Two congruent triangles are formed when the bisector of the vertex angle of an isosceles triangle is drawn and when the median to the base of an isosceles triangle is drawn.

Model	Given	Outline of Proof
C, A, D, B	Triangle *ABC*; $\overline{AC} \cong \overline{BC}$; $\overline{CD}$ bisects $\angle C$.	$\overline{AC} \cong \overline{BC}$ $\angle ACD \cong \angle BCD$ $\overline{CD} \cong \overline{CD}$ $\triangle ACD \cong \triangle BCD$
C, A, D, B	Triangle *ABC*; $\overline{AC} \cong \overline{BC}$; $\overline{CD}$ is the median to $\overline{AB}$.	$\overline{AC} \cong \overline{BC}$ $\overline{AD} \cong \overline{BD}$ $\overline{CD} \cong \overline{CD}$ $\triangle ACD \cong \triangle BCD$

For both triangles above, you can also prove that the angles at *D* are right angles, and that $\overline{CD} \perp \overline{AB}$. Thus, $\overline{CD}$ is the perpendicular bisector of $\overline{AB}$.

Theorem 3-5: The bisector of the vertex angle of an isosceles triangle is the perpendicular bisector of the base.

Theorem 3-6: The median from the vertex angle of an isosceles triangle is perpendicular to the base and bisects the vertex angle.

You are asked to prove Theorems 3-5 and 3-6 in the Exercises.

In the figure at the right, point P is equidistant from points A and B because $PA = PB = 3$ centimeters. Similarly, point Q is equidistant from points A and B because $QA = QB = 2$ centimeters.

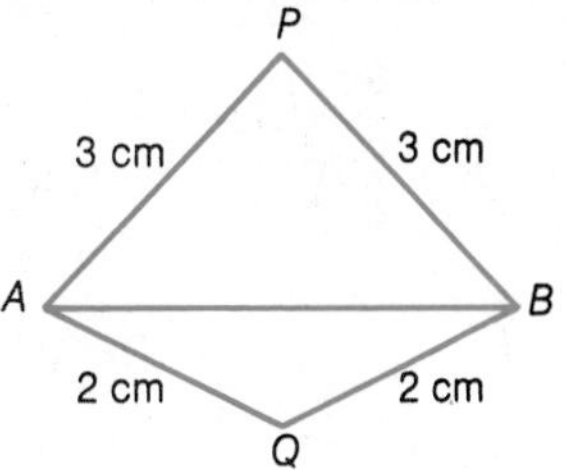

Definition: A point P is **equidistant** from two other points A and B if $PA = PB$.

Example

In the figure, $\overleftrightarrow{CD}$ is the perpendicular bisector of $\overline{AB}$. Explain why point C is equidistant from points A and B.

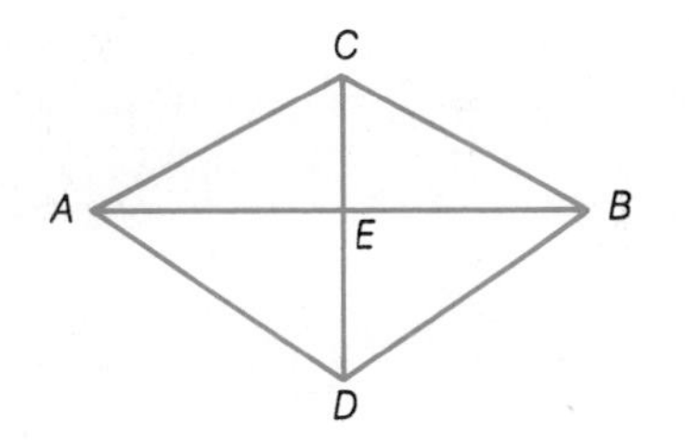

Statement		Reason
$\overline{CE} \cong \overline{CE}$	←	Identity
$\overline{AE} \cong \overline{BE}$	←	The bisector of a segment forms two congruent segments.
$\angle AEC \cong \angle BEC$	←	Perpendicular lines form right angles and all right angles are congruent.
$\triangle ACE \cong \triangle BCE$	←	S.A.S. Postulate
$\overline{AC} \cong \overline{BC}$	←	C.P.C.T.C.
$AC = BC$	←	Congruent segments have equal measures.
C is equidistant from A and B.	←	Definition of equidistant

You can use the same procedure to show that triangles ADE and BDE are congruent, and that point D is also equidistant from points A and B. This suggests the following theorem.

Theorem 3-7: Any point on the perpendicular bisector of a segment is equidistant from the endpoints of the segment.

In the figure at the right, triangles ABC and ADB are isosceles. This means that points C and D are both equidistant from points A and B. It can then be shown that $\overleftrightarrow{CD}$ is the perpendicular bisector of $\overline{AB}$.

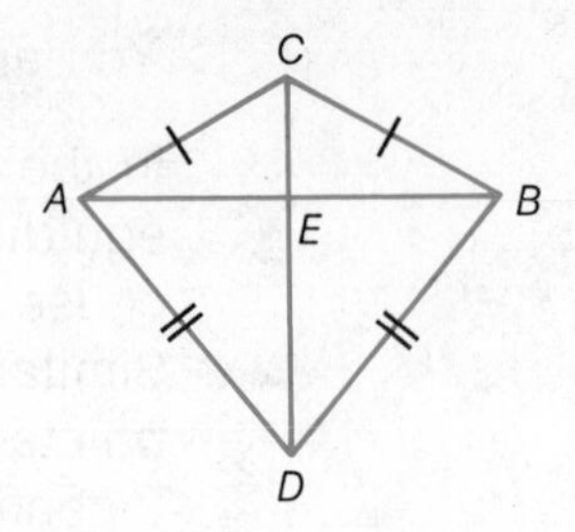

To show that $\overleftrightarrow{CD}$ is the perpendicular bisector of $\overline{AB}$, you must show two things.

1. $\overleftrightarrow{CD} \perp \overline{AB}$ and **2.** $\overleftrightarrow{CD}$ bisects $\overline{AB}$.

Theorem 3-8: In a plane, a line is the perpendicular bisector of a given segment if and only if it is determined by two points equidistant from the endpoints of the segment.

Theorem 3-8 is a biconditional; that is, it can be restated as a conditional and its converse. To prove Theorem 3-8, you must prove both the conditional and its converse. You are asked to do this in the Exercises.

Try These

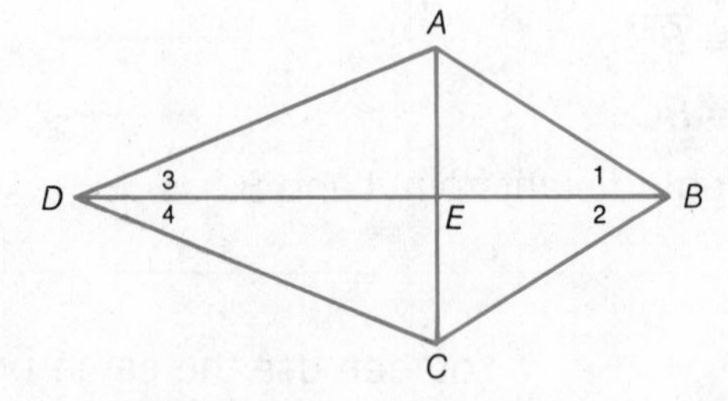

1. In $\triangle ABC$, $\angle 1 \cong \angle 2$. Is $\overline{BE} \perp \overline{AC}$?

2. In $\triangle ABC$, $\overline{AB} \cong \overline{BC}$ and $\angle 1 \cong \angle 2$. Is $\overline{BE} \perp \overline{AC}$?

3. In $\triangle ABC$, $\overline{AB} \cong \overline{BC}$ and $\angle 1 \cong \angle 2$. Is $\overline{AE} \cong \overline{EC}$?

4. In $\triangle ABC$, $\overline{AB} \cong \overline{BC}$ and $\angle 1 \cong \angle 2$. Is $\overline{BE}$ the perpendicular bisector of $\overline{AC}$?

5. In $\triangle ADC$, $\overline{DE}$ is the median to $\overline{AC}$. Is $\overline{DE} \perp \overline{AC}$?

6. In $\triangle ADC$, $\overline{DE}$ is the median to $\overline{AC}$. Is $\angle 3 \cong \angle 4$?

7. In $\triangle ADC$, $\overline{AD} \cong \overline{CD}$ and $\overline{DE}$ is the median to $\overline{AC}$. Is $\overline{DE} \perp \overline{AC}$?

8. In $\triangle ADC$, $\overline{AD} \cong \overline{CD}$ and $\overline{DE}$ is the median to $\overline{AC}$. Is $\angle 3 \cong \angle 4$?

9. In $\triangle ADC$, $\overline{AC} \cong \overline{CD}$. Is point D equidistant from points A and C?

10. E is a point on $\overline{AC}$ and E is on the perpendicular bisector of $\overline{AC}$. Is $\overline{AE} \cong \overline{CE}$?

11. Point D is equidistant from points A and C and point B is equidistant from points A and C. Is $\overleftrightarrow{DB}$ the perpendicular bisector of $\overline{AC}$?

12. $\overline{AB} \cong \overline{BC}$ and $\overline{AD} \cong \overline{DC}$. Is $\overleftrightarrow{AC}$ the perpendicular bisector of $\overline{DB}$?

Exercises

In the figure at the right, triangle DFG is equilateral, $GF = 8$, $m\angle F = 60$, and $\overline{GE}$ bisects $\angle DGF$.

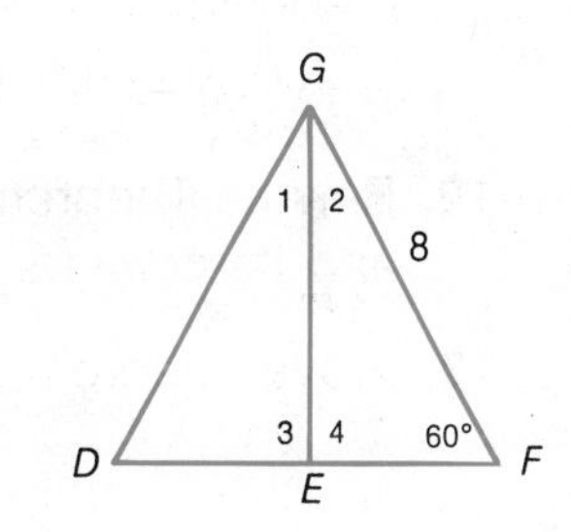

a

1. Find DG, DF, DE, and EF.

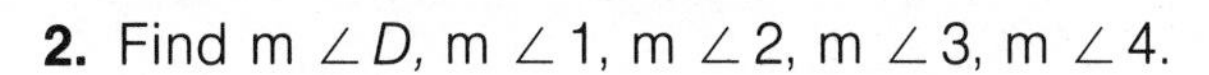

2. Find $m\angle D$, $m\angle 1$, $m\angle 2$, $m\angle 3$, $m\angle 4$.

In the figure at the right, $\overline{HQ} \cong \overline{HJ}$, $\overline{QK} \cong \overline{JK}$, $m\angle 2 = 72$, $m\angle 3 = 24$, and $QJ = 18$.

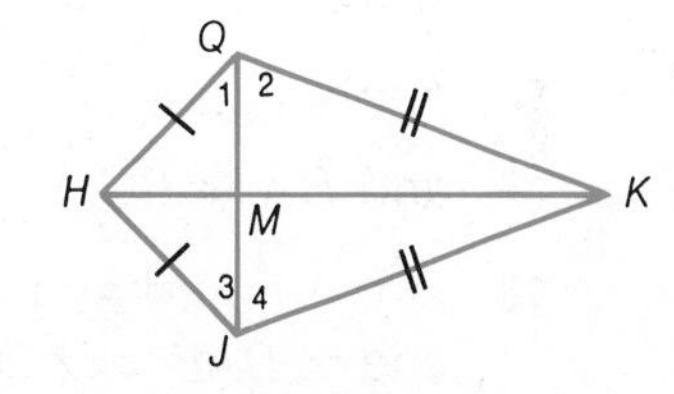

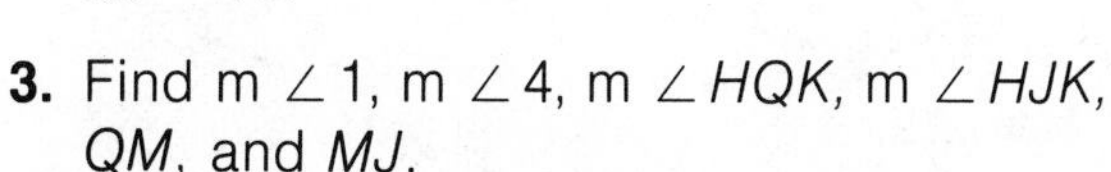

3. Find $m\angle 1$, $m\angle 4$, $m\angle HQK$, $m\angle HJK$, QM, and MJ.

In the figure at the right, $\overline{PQ} \cong \overline{QR} \cong \overline{RS} \cong \overline{SP}$.

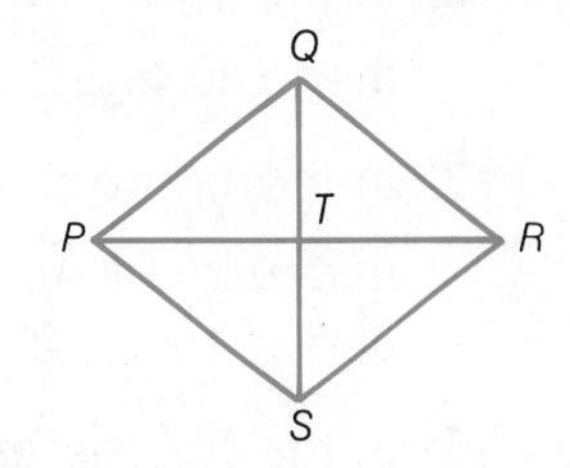

4. Name four right triangles.

5. Name four isosceles triangles.

Use $\triangle ABC$ to explain why each statement is true.

6. In an isosceles triangle, the perpendicular bisector of the base bisects the vertex angle.

7. If the perpendicular bisector of one side of a triangle passes through the opposite vertex, the triangle is isosceles.

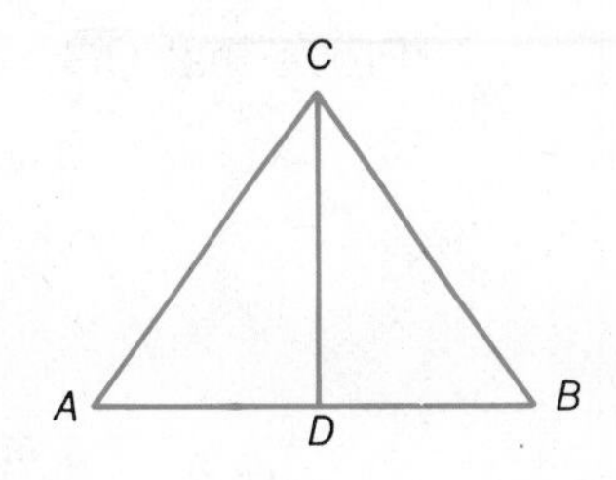

8. If line segment XY is the base for isosceles triangles XCY, XDY, XEY, XFY, and XGY, prove that points C, D, E, F, and G are collinear.

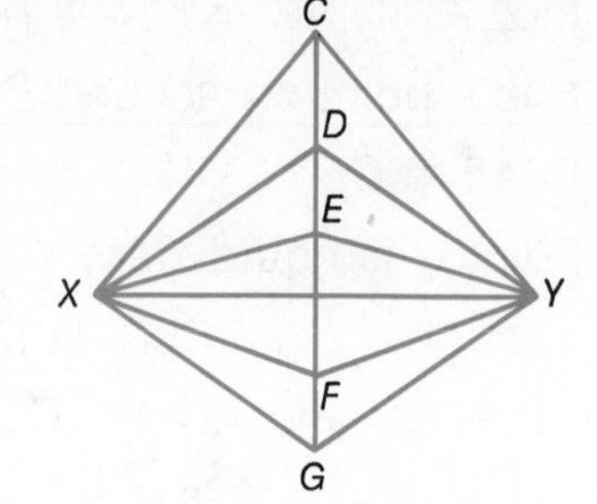

9. Prove Theorem 3-5. (HINT: Follow the outline on page 120.)

10. Prove Theorem 3-6. (HINT: Follow the outline on page 120.)

11. **Given:** Triangles SQZ and SEZ with base $\overline{SZ}$ are isosceles.

Prove: $\overleftrightarrow{QE}$ is the perpendicular bisector of $\overline{SZ}$.

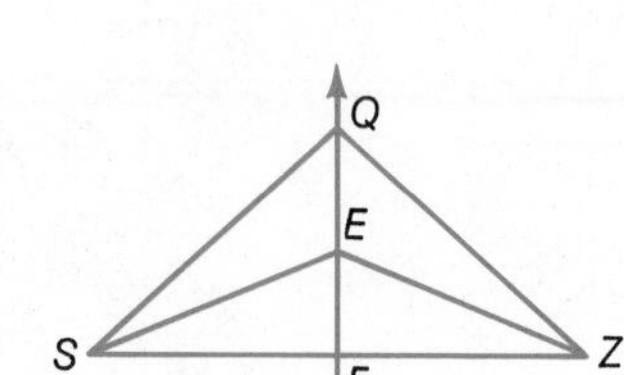

12. Rewrite Theorem 3-7 as a conditional and its converse.

13. Prove Theorem 3-7. (HINT: Follow the method of the Example on page 121.)

Write a proof for each statement.

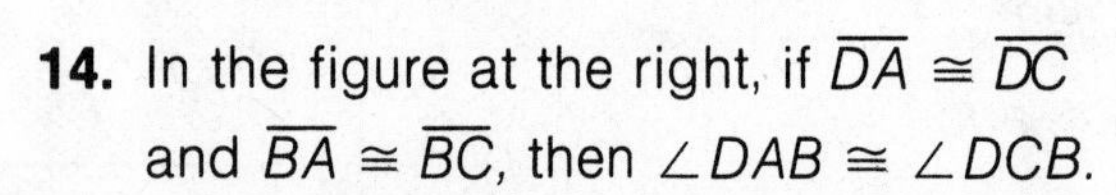

14. In the figure at the right, if $\overline{DA} \cong \overline{DC}$ and $\overline{BA} \cong \overline{BC}$, then $\angle DAB \cong \angle DCB$.

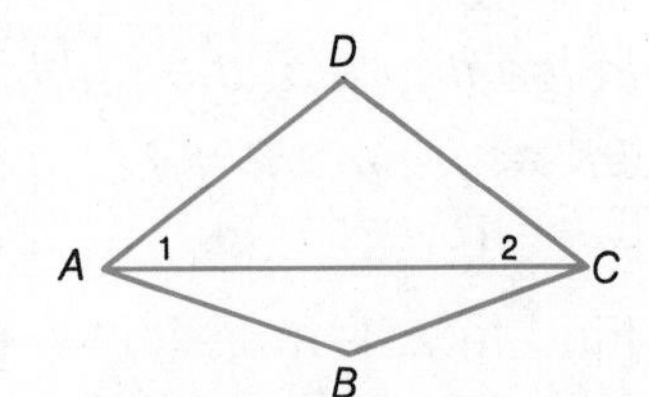

15. In the figure at the right, if $\overline{BA} \cong \overline{BC}$ and $\angle DAB \cong \angle DCB$, then $\angle 1 \cong \angle 2$.

16. In the figure at the right, if $\angle ADE \cong \angle BED$, then $\overline{DC} \cong \overline{EC}$.

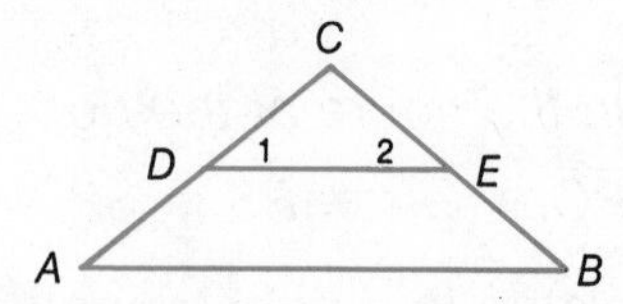

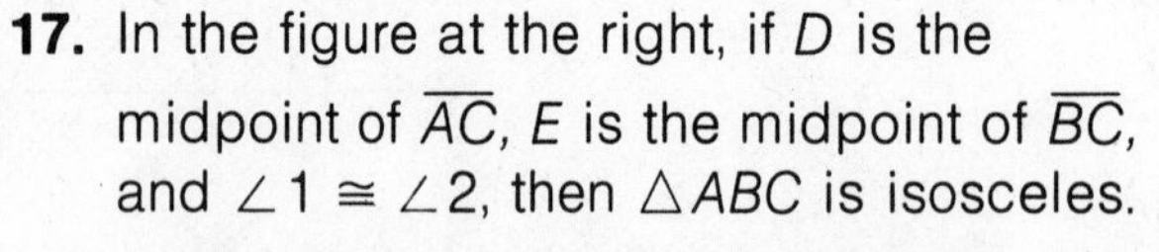

17. In the figure at the right, if D is the midpoint of $\overline{AC}$, E is the midpoint of $\overline{BC}$, and $\angle 1 \cong \angle 2$, then $\triangle ABC$ is isosceles.

18. In the figures below, $\overline{AB} \cong \overline{DE}$, $\overline{BC} \cong \overline{EF}$, $\overline{AC} \cong \overline{DF}$, and $\angle 1 \cong \angle 2$. Prove that $\overline{CG} \cong \overline{FH}$.

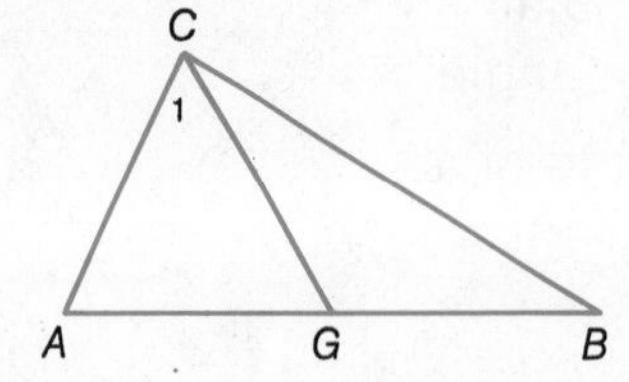

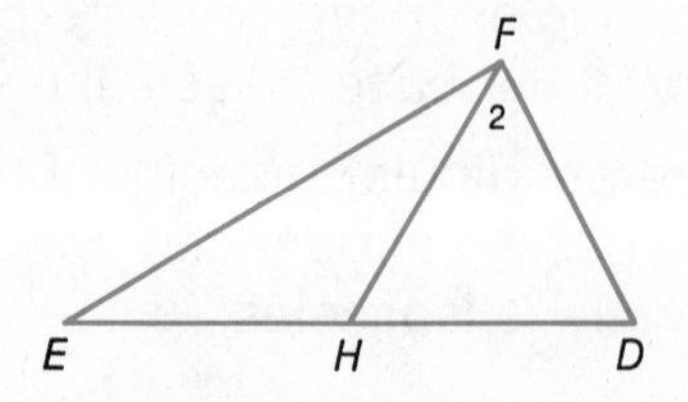

19. Use the figures for Exercise 18 to prove that if $\overline{AB} \cong \overline{DE}$, $\overline{BC} \cong \overline{EF}$, $\overline{AC} \cong \overline{DF}$, and G and H are the midpoints of $\overline{AB}$ and $\overline{DE}$ respectively, then $\overline{CG} \cong \overline{FH}$.

20. In the figure at the right, prove that if $\overline{MS} \cong \overline{RS}$ and $\overline{MT} \cong \overline{RT}$, then $\overline{MO} \cong \overline{RO}$.

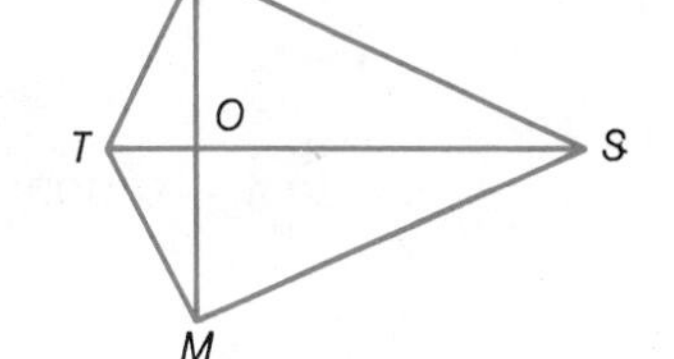

21. In the figure at the right, prove that if $\overline{MS} \cong \overline{RS}$ and $\overline{MO} \cong \overline{RO}$, then $\overline{MT} \cong \overline{RT}$.

22. Prove Theorem 3-8.

Part I **Given:** Points C and D are each equidistant from points A and B.

Prove: $\overleftrightarrow{CD}$ is the perpendicular bisector of $\overline{AB}$.

Plan: Prove $\triangle CAD \cong \triangle CBD$ and $\triangle ACE \cong \triangle BCE$.

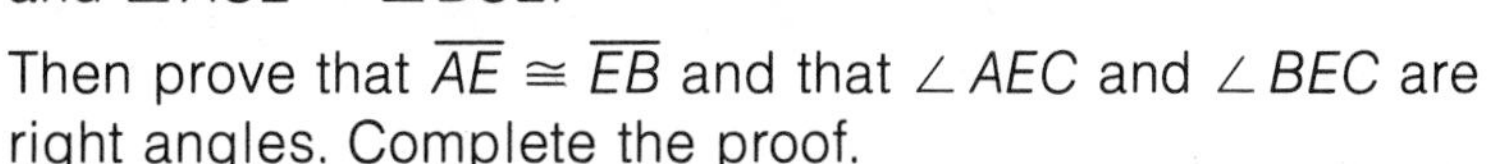

Then prove that $\overline{AE} \cong \overline{EB}$ and that $\angle AEC$ and $\angle BEC$ are right angles. Complete the proof.

Part II **Given:** $\overleftrightarrow{CD}$ is the perpendicular bisector of $\overline{AB}$.

Prove: Points C and D are each equidistant from points A and B.

Plan: Since $\overleftrightarrow{CD}$ bisects $\overline{AB}$, $\overline{AE} \cong \overline{EB}$. Since $\overleftrightarrow{CD} \perp \overline{AB}$, $\angle CEA \cong \angle CEB$ and $\angle AED \cong \angle BED$.
Prove $\triangle AEC \cong \triangle BEC$ and $\triangle AED \cong \triangle BED$.
Then $\overline{AC} \cong \overline{BC}$ and $\overline{DA} \cong \overline{DB}$. Complete the proof.

Given: *$\overline{AC}$ is contained in plane* I *and $\overline{BD}$ intersects plane* I *at A.*
$\overline{AC}$ is the perpendicular bisector of $\overline{BD}$.

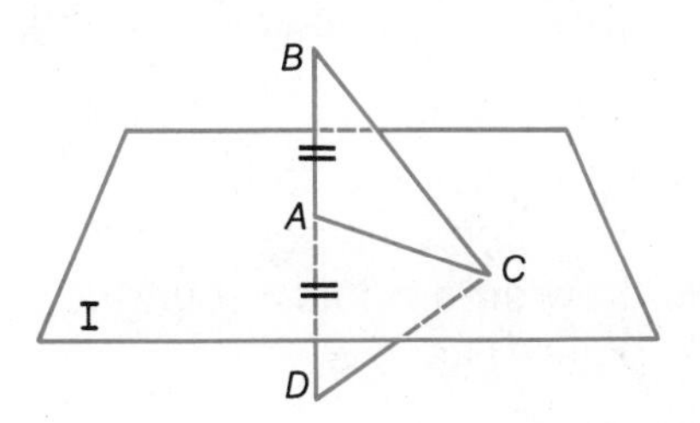

23. Prove: $\triangle BAC \cong \triangle DAC$

24. Prove: $\angle B \cong \angle D$.

25. Prove: $\triangle BCD$ is isosceles.

Constructions

Constructing a Line Perpendicular to a Given Line at a Given Point on the Line

Given: Line q and point C on line q

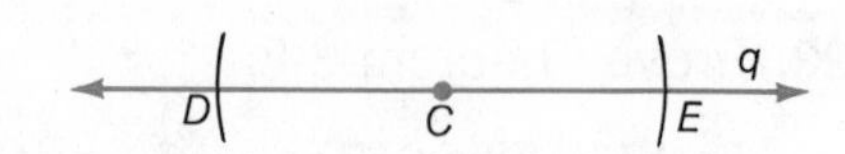

Required: To construct $\overleftrightarrow{CF}$ perpendicular to line q

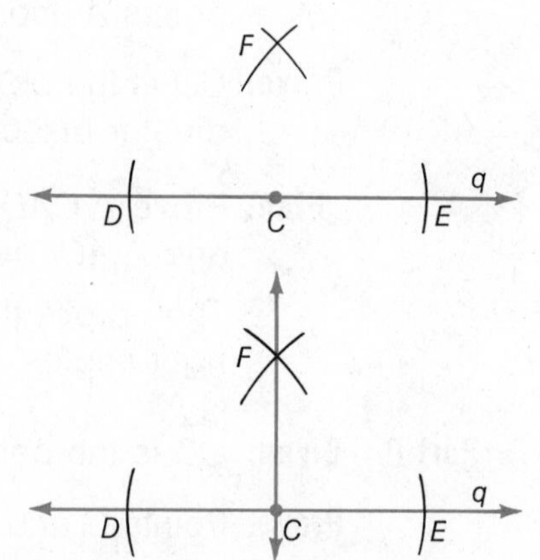

1. With C as center and using the same radius, construct arcs that intersect line q at D and E.
2. With D as center and a radius greater than DC, construct an arc on one side of line q. Use the same radius and E as center to construct a second arc that intersects the first arc at F.
3. Draw $\overleftrightarrow{FC}$.

   Then line FC is perpendicular to line q. You are asked to prove this construction in the Exercises.

Constructing a Line Perpendicular to a Given Line Through a Given Point Not on the Line

Given: Line k and a point C not on line k

Required: To construct $\overleftrightarrow{CF}$ perpendicular to line k

1. With C as center and radius greater than the distance from C to line k, draw an arc intersecting k in two points D and E.

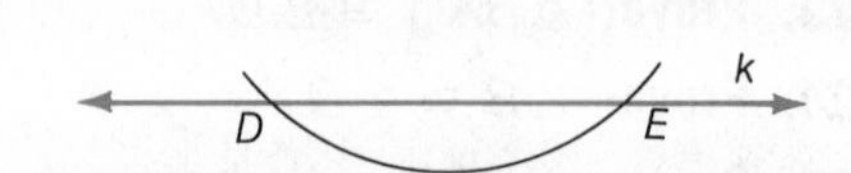

2. With D as center and radius more than $\frac{1}{2}$ DE, draw an arc below line k. Using the same radius and E as center, draw another arc intersecting the first at F.

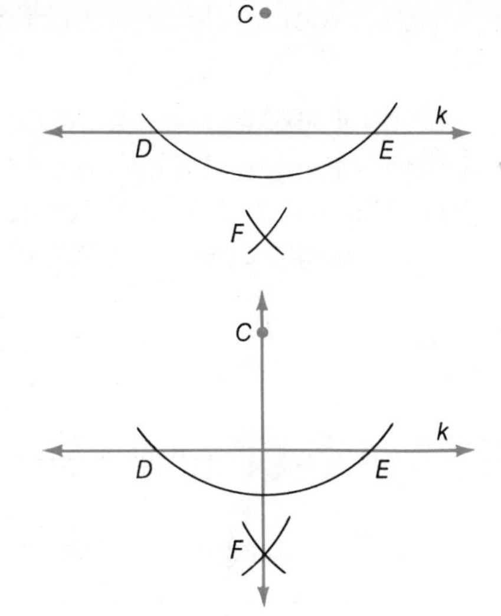

3. Draw $\overleftrightarrow{CF}$.

Then line CF is perpendicular to line k. You are asked to prove this construction in the Exercises.

Exercises

1. Draw a line segment AB. Construct lines perpendicular to $\overline{AB}$ at A and B.
2. Draw an acute scalene triangle ABC. Construct a segment from C perpendicular to $\overline{AB}$.
3. Draw an acute scalene triangle ABC. Construct the perpendicular bisectors of $\overline{AB}$, $\overline{BC}$, and $\overline{CA}$. (HINT: Follow the procedure on page 47.)
4. Draw an obtuse scalene triangle ABC with the obtuse angle at B. Construct a segment from B perpendicular to $\overline{AC}$.
5. Draw a right triangle CAB with the right angle at A. From A, construct a segment perpendicular to $\overline{BC}$.
6. Draw two adjacent angles, $\angle CBD$ and $\angle DBA$. Choose any point E on $\overrightarrow{BD}$. From E, construct a segment perpendicular to $\overrightarrow{BA}$ and a segment perpendicular to $\overrightarrow{BC}$.
7. Write a proof for the construction: Constructing a Line Perpendicular to a Given Line at a Given Point on the Line. (HINT: Draw $\overline{FD}$ and $\overline{FE}$. Then prove $\triangle FCD \cong \triangle FCE$.)

8. Write a proof for the construction: Constructing a Line Perpendicular to a Given Line Through a Given Point not on the Line.

9. Construct angles having the following measures: 90; 45; 135.

10. Construct angles having the following measures: 60; 30; 15; 120; 150; 105; 165. (HINT: Begin by constructing an equilateral triangle. The measure of each angle of an equilateral triangle is 60.)

PUZZLE

Sixteen discs are arranged in a square as shown in Figure 1. Two players alternately remove one to four discs. In a single play, the discs removed must come from a single column or from a single horizontal row. The discs must also be adjacent with no gaps in between. The player that takes the last disc loses the game.

Two games in progress are shown in Figures 2 and 3. On each square, find the next move that guarantees that you will win.

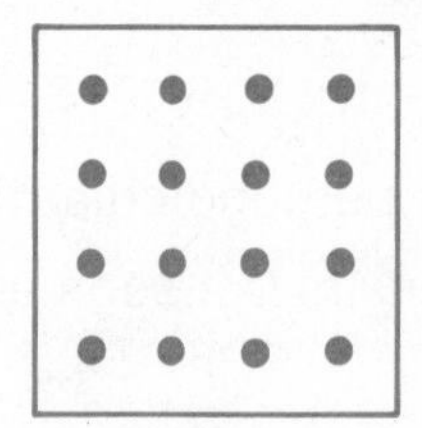

Figure 1

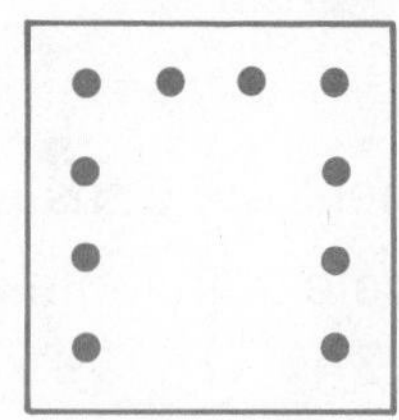

Figure 2

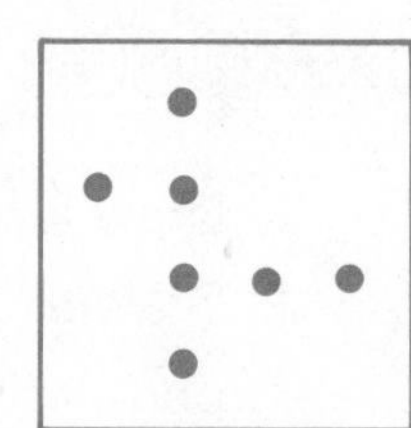

Figure 3

Remember

Classify each statement as True or False.

1. The bisector of an angle forms two angles of equal measure.
2. The bisector of an angle of a triangle is also a median of the triangle.
3. Three points determine exactly one line.

The answers are on page 152. If you need help, see pages 51, 82, and 120.

Mathematics and Electronics

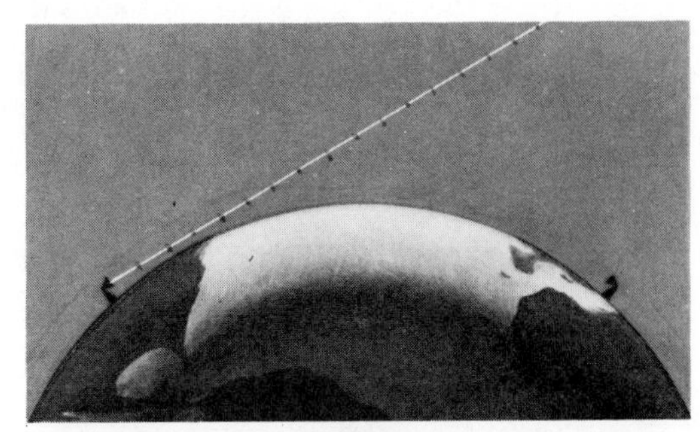

FIGURE 1

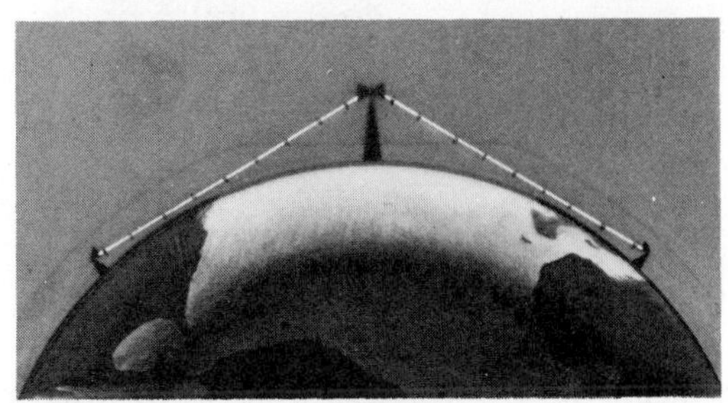

FIGURE 2

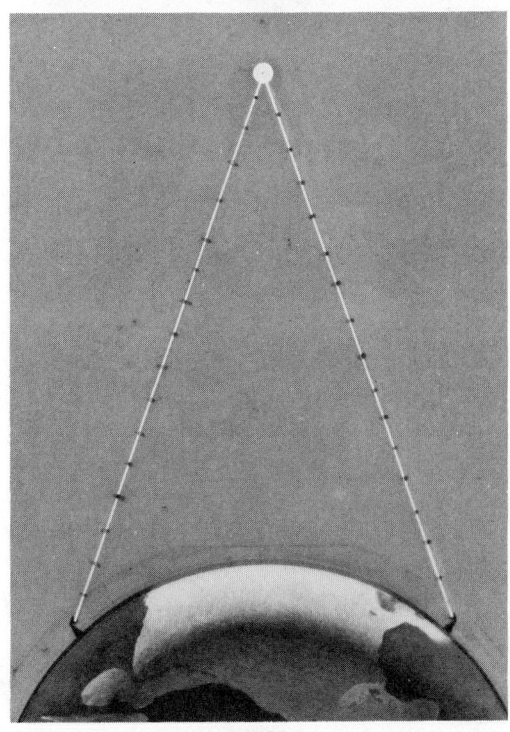

FIGURE 3

Electrical and **electronics engineers** comprise the largest group of engineers in the electronics industry. Entry into these careers requires a minimum of a bachelor's degree in electrical or electronics engineering, although a degree in mathematics may qualify a person for a beginning job.

One of the major problems in communications, such as in the telephone industry, is caused by the earth's curvature.

Microwave signals are used to transmit sound. Since microwave signals travel in a straight line, they cannot follow the curvature of the earth. (*Figure 1*)

In order to send the microwave signal to another part of the earth, the signal must be reflected in space back to the earth. To reflect a microwave signal that is sent over the ocean would require that a tower with a height of approximately 790 kilometers be built in the middle of the ocean. (*Figure 2*)

The solution to this problem involves the use of a satellite, rather than a tower, as a reflector. (*Figure 3*)

3-6 Overlapping Triangles

Sometimes you can use the Segment Addition Property (page 41) to show that two segments are congruent.

Example 1

In the figure below, $\overline{AB} \cong \overline{CD}$. Explain why $\overline{AC} \cong \overline{BD}$.

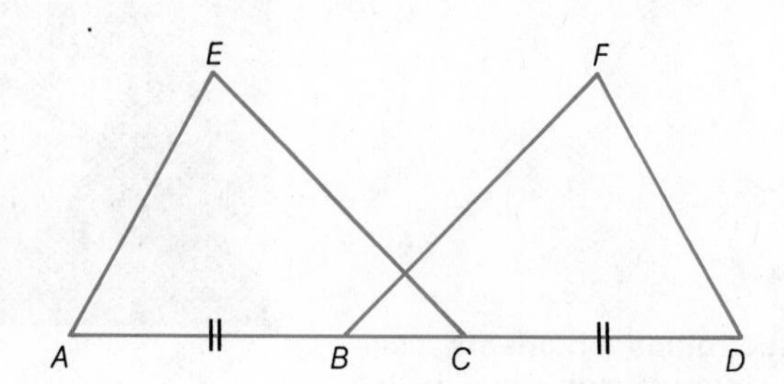

$AB = CD$ ← Congruent segments have the same measure.

$AB + BC = CD + BC$ ← Addition Property of Equations

$AB + BC = AC$ and $BC + CD = BD$ ← Segment Addition Property

$AC = BD$ ← Substitution Principle

$\overline{AC} \cong \overline{BD}$ ← Congruent segments have the same measure.

Overlapping triangles share overlapping sides or overlapping angles.

Example 2

Given: $\angle GKR \cong \angle JKH$

$\overline{GK} \cong \overline{JK}$

Prove: $\triangle GKH \cong \triangle JKR$

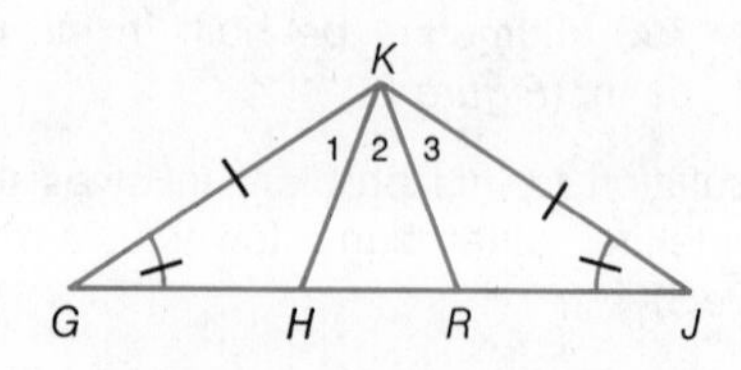

Statements	Reasons
1. $\angle GKR \cong \angle JKH$; $\overline{GK} \cong \overline{JK}$	1. Given
2. $\angle G \cong \angle J$	2. (1). Isosceles Triangle Theorem
3. $m\angle GKR = m\angle JKH$	3. (1). Congruent angles have equal measures.
4. $m\angle GKR = m\angle 1 + m\angle 2$ $m\angle JKH = m\angle 2 + m\angle 3$	4. Angle Addition Property
5. $m\angle 1 + m\angle 2 = m\angle 3 + m\angle 2$	5. (3). (4). Substitution Principle
6. $\therefore m\angle 1 = m\angle 3$	6. (5). Addition Property of Equations
7. $\therefore \angle 1 \cong \angle 3$	7. (6). Congruent angles have equal measures.
8. $\therefore \triangle GKH \cong \triangle JKR$	8. (1). (2). (7). A.S.A. Postulate

Sometimes you need to draw additional segments in order to do a proof.

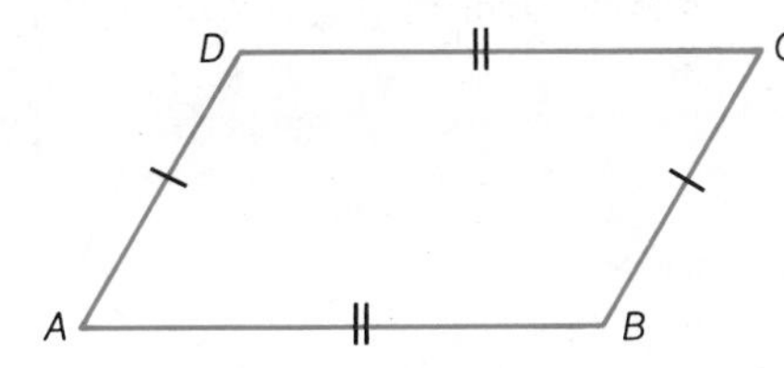

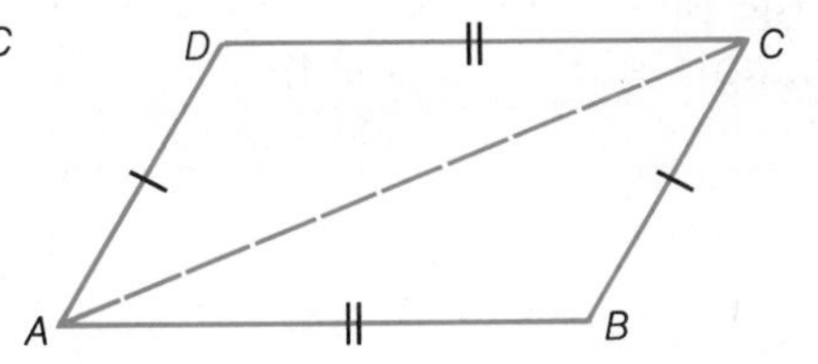

If you draw $\overline{AC}$, $\triangle ADC \cong \triangle CBA$ by S.S.S. Postulate.

Example 3

Given: $\overline{AB} \cong \overline{CD}$; $\overline{AD} \cong \overline{CB}$

Prove: $\angle D \cong \angle B$

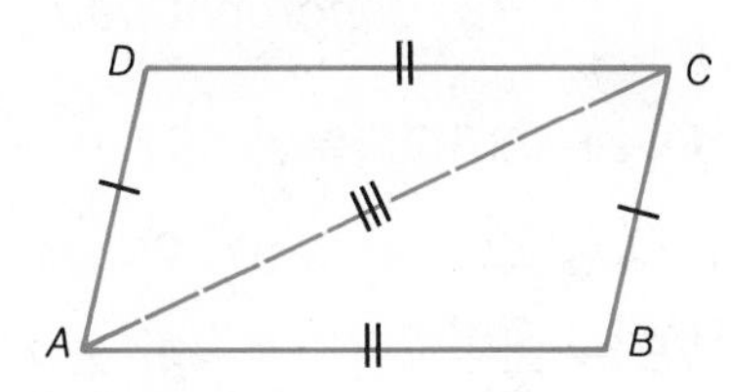

Statements	Reasons
1. Draw $\overline{AC}$	1. Two points determine a line.
2. $\overline{AB} \cong \overline{CD}$; $\overline{AD} \cong \overline{CB}$	2. Given
3. $\overline{AC} \cong \overline{AC}$	3. Identity
4. $\therefore \triangle ACD \cong \triangle CAB$	4. (2). (3). S.S.S. Postulate
5. $\therefore \angle D \cong \angle B$	5. (4). C.P.C.T.C.

When you draw additional line segments, you must be sure that you do not impose impossible conditions.

Example 4

State whether you can draw each line segment. Explain.

a. Draw $\overline{FG}$, the median from F to $\overline{DE}$.

b. Draw $\overline{FG}$, the bisector of $\angle F$, where G is a point on $\overline{DE}$.

c. Draw $\overline{FG}$, the bisector of $\angle F$ where G is the midpoint of $\overline{DE}$.

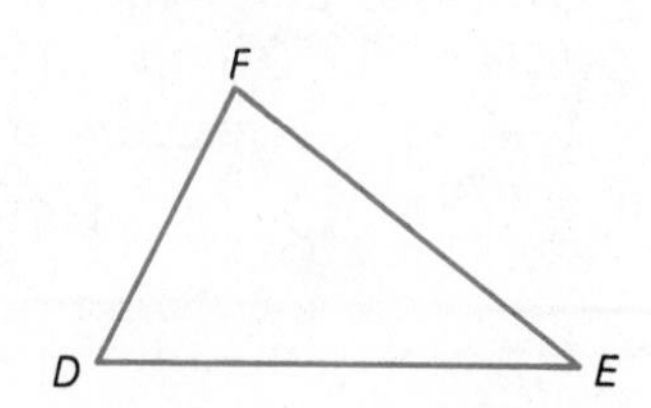

a. Yes. Every line segment has one midpoint, and two points (F and G) determine a line.

b. Yes. Every angle has a bisector. It will intersect the opposite side of the triangle at some point.

c. No. Every angle has a bisector, but it will not always intersect the opposite side of the triangle at its midpoint.

Try These

For every pair of congruent triangles, state the corresponding congruent parts.

Given: $\triangle RQV \cong \triangle SPT$

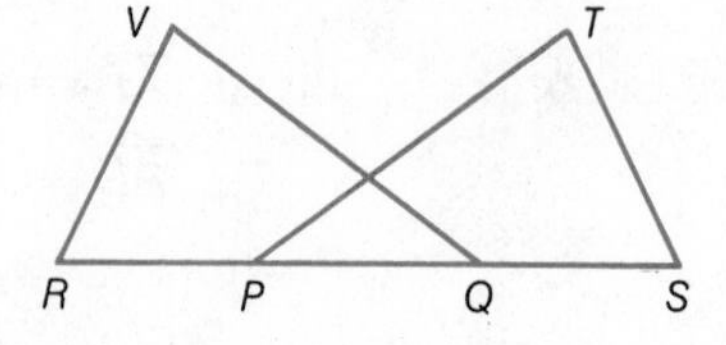

1. $\overline{RQ} \cong$ ___?___

2. $\angle R \cong \angle$ ___?___

3. $\overline{VR} \cong$ ___?___

4. $\angle VQR \cong \angle$ ___?___

Given: $\triangle CDB \cong \triangle CEA$

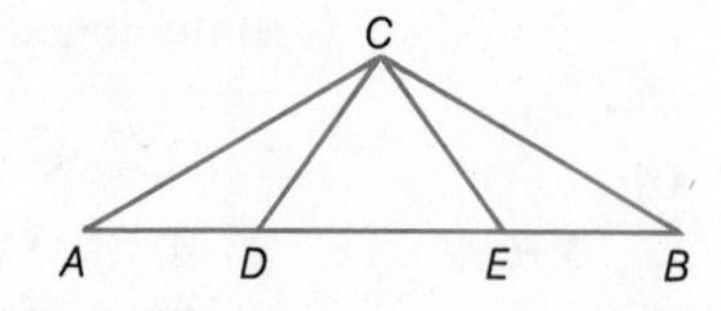

5. $\angle ACE \cong \angle$ ___?___

6. $\overline{CD} \cong$ ___?___

7. $\angle CEA \cong \angle$ ___?___

8. $\overline{BD} \cong$ ___?___

Given: $\triangle GHF \cong \triangle HGK$

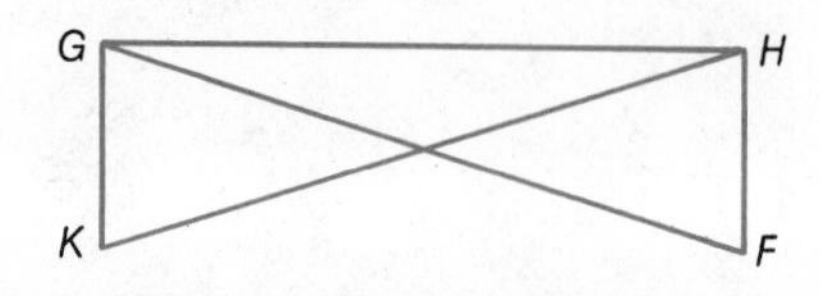

9. $\overline{GH} \cong$ ___?___

10. $\angle KGH \cong \angle$ ___?___

11. $\angle K \cong \angle$ ___?___

12. $\angle HGF \cong \angle$ ___?___

Exercises

a

1. In figure *HQGF* below, name three pairs of triangles that appear to be congruent. Do the same for $\triangle KRM$.

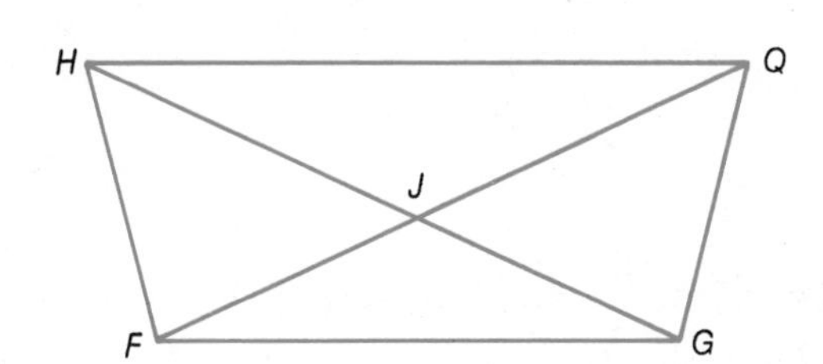

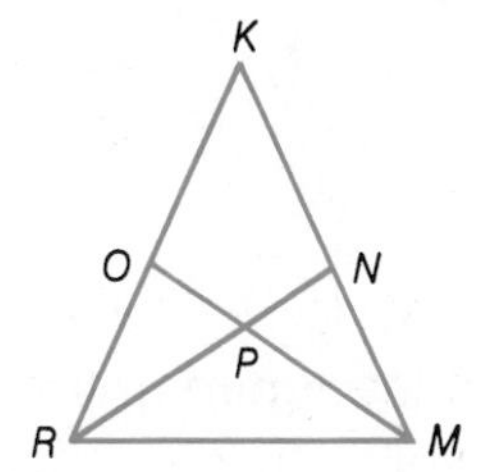

In Exercises **2–5,** *use figure HQGF and figure KRM to list the corresponding parts needed to complete each congruence correspondence.*

	S.A.S.	A.S.A.	S.S.S.
2.	$\triangle FGQ$: _?_; $\angle QFG$; $\overline{FG}$	$\angle GQF$; $\overline{QF}$; _?_	$\overline{FG}$; $\overline{GQ}$; _?_
	$\triangle GFH$: $\overline{HG}$; _?_; $\overline{GF}$	$\angle FHG$; _?_; $\angle HGF$	$\overline{GF}$; _?_; $\overline{HG}$
3.	$\triangle KNR$: $\overline{RK}$; _?_; $\overline{KN}$	$\angle KRN$; $\overline{RN}$; _?_	$\overline{RK}$; $\overline{KN}$; _?_
	$\triangle KOM$: $\overline{MK}$; _?_; $\overline{KO}$	_?_; $\overline{MO}$; _?_	_?_; $\overline{KO}$; $\overline{OM}$
4.	$\triangle HJF$: _?_; $\angle HFJ$; _?_	_?_; $\overline{HJ}$; _?_	$\overline{HJ}$; _?_; _?_
	$\triangle QJG$: _?_; $\angle QGJ$; _?_	_?_; $\overline{QJ}$; _?_	$\overline{QJ}$; _?_; _?_
5.	$\triangle RMN$: _?_; $\angle MNR$; _?_	_?_; $\overline{NR}$; _?_	_?_; $\overline{RM}$; _?_
	$\triangle MRO$: _?_; $\angle ROM$; _?_	_?_; $\overline{OM}$; _?_	_?_; $\overline{MR}$; _?_

6. In the figure below, $\overline{BC} \cong \overline{DC}$ and $\overline{AB} \cong \overline{ED}$. Prove that $\angle A \cong \angle E$. What triangle appears to be congruent to $\triangle ACD$? Prove that the two triangles are congruent.

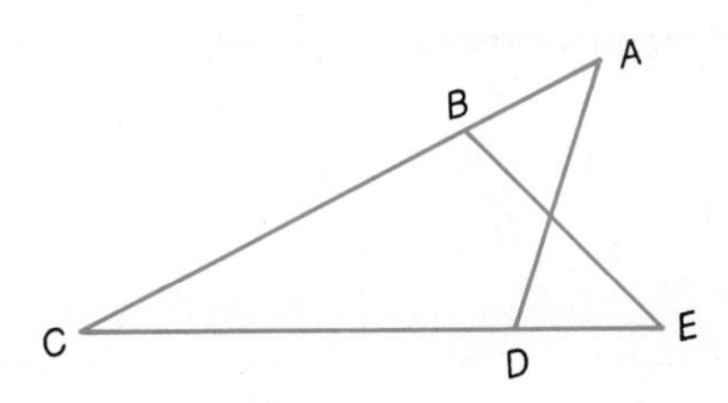

7. In the figure at the left below, $\overline{XW} \cong \overline{YU}$ and $\angle ZXY \cong \angle ZYX$. Prove that $\overline{XU} \cong \overline{YW}$. (HINT: Prove $\triangle XWY \cong \triangle YUX$.)

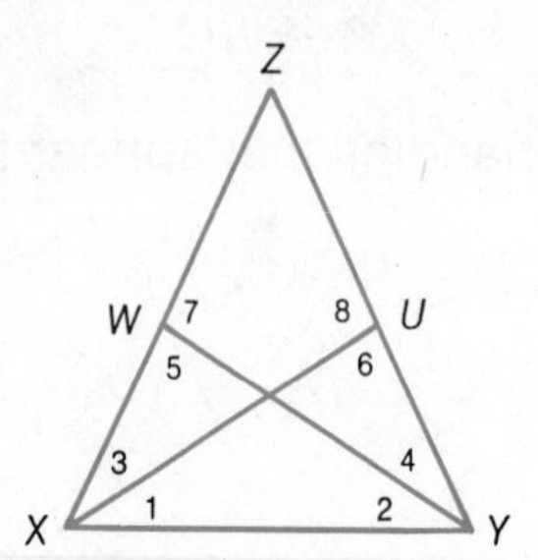

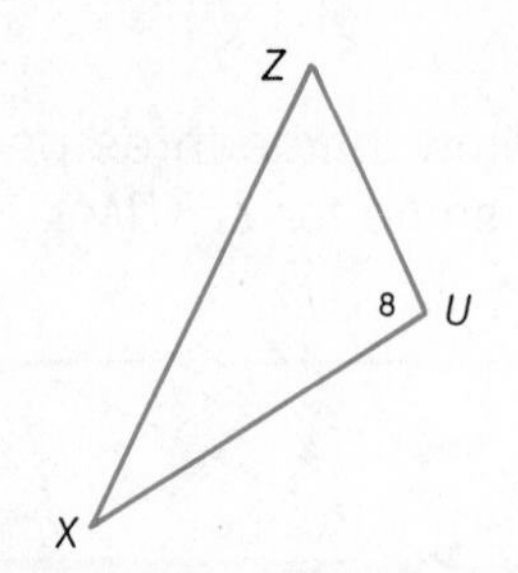

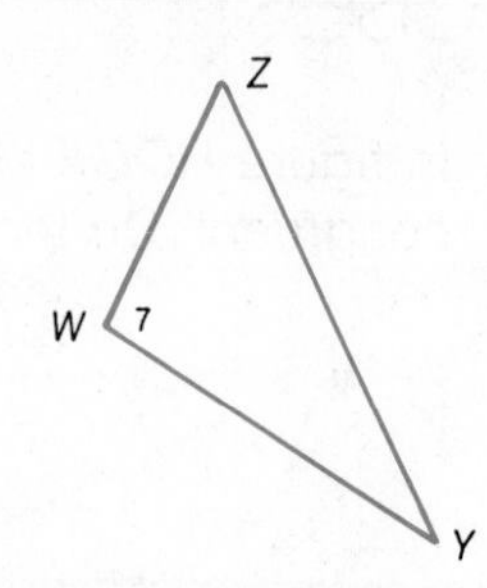

8. In the figure at the left above, $\overline{XZ} \cong \overline{YZ}$ and $\overline{XW} \cong \overline{YU}$. Prove $\angle 7 \cong \angle 8$. (HINT: Draw $\triangle XUZ$ and $\triangle YWZ$ separately as in the figure at the right above. Remember that $\angle Z \cong \angle Z$ by identity.)

9. Given that $\overline{XW} \cong \overline{YU}$ and $\overline{XU} \cong \overline{YW}$. Prove $\angle 7 \cong \angle 8$.

*For Exercises **10–13**, state whether it is always possible to draw each line or segment. Give reasons for each answer.*

Given: Segment RS and Q, a point not on $\overline{RS}$.

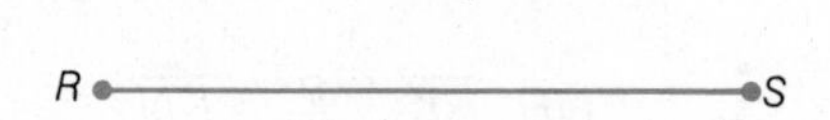

10. Let M be the midpoint of $\overline{RS}$. Draw $\overline{QM}$.

11. Let M be the midpoint of $\overline{RS}$. Draw line QM perpendicular to $\overline{RS}$ at M.

12. Let M be the midpoint of $\overline{RS}$. Through M, draw a line that is perpendicular to $\overline{RS}$ and that contains point Q.

13. From Q, draw a line perpendicular to $\overleftrightarrow{RS}$.

14. Given: $\overline{TR} \cong \overline{TW}$; $\overline{VR} \cong \overline{VW}$
Prove: $\angle W \cong \angle R$

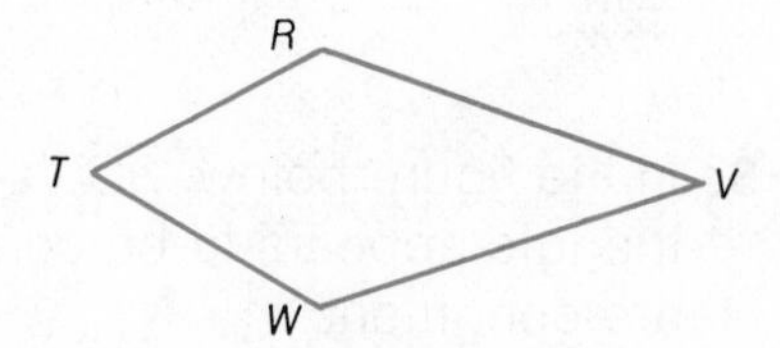

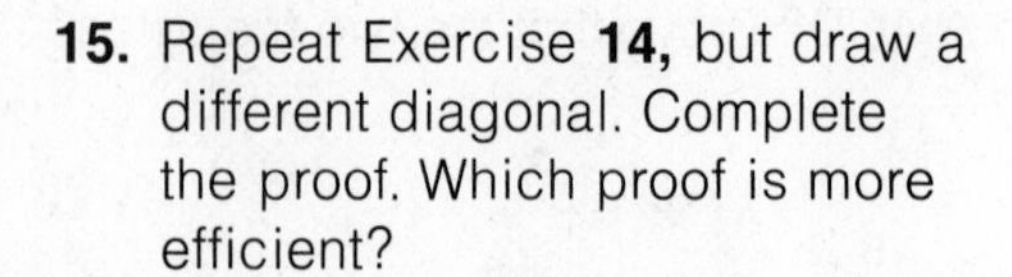

15. Repeat Exercise **14,** but draw a different diagonal. Complete the proof. Which proof is more efficient?

16. Given: $\overline{XY} \cong \overline{XZ}$
$\overline{AY} \cong \overline{AZ}$
Prove: $\angle Y \cong \angle Z$

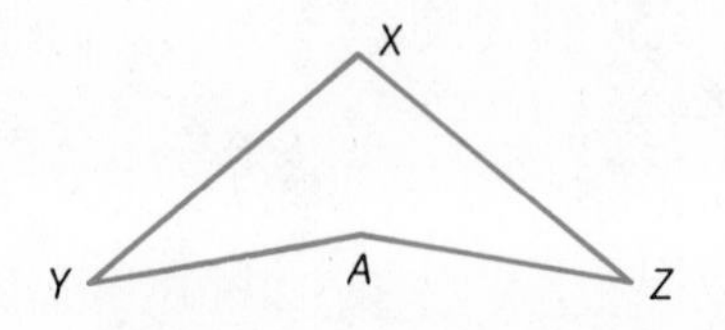

3-7 Indirect Proof

Mathematical statements are either true or false.

All right angles are congruent. ⟵ True

A triangle can have more than one obtuse angle. ⟵ False

No mathematical statement is both true and false at the same time. Such a statement would be a **contradiction.**

$5 < 7$ and $5 \nless 7$ ⟵ Contradiction

The **negation** of a statement says the opposite of the original statement. The negation is false if the original statement is true; it is true if the original statement is false.

Statement	True or False?	Negation	True or False?
$5 + 1 = 6$	T	$5 + 1 \neq 6$	F
All right angles are congruent.	T	Not all right angles are congruent.	F
A 45°-angle is not an acute angle.	F	A 45°-angle is an acute angle.	T

The **indirect method of proof** uses negation. You begin by writing the negation of the conclusion. Then you reason from this until you reach a contradiction.

Example 1

Write the first step you would use in an indirect proof of each of the following conditionals.

a. If $\angle 1 \cong \angle 2$, then $m\angle 1 = m\angle 2$.
b. If $m\angle 1 + m\angle 2 \neq 90$, then $\angle 1$ and $\angle 2$ are not complementary.

Answer: **a.** Assume that $m\angle 1 \neq m\angle 2$.
b. Assume that $\angle 1$ and $\angle 2$ are complementary.

Example 2

Given: $\angle A$ is not congruent to $\angle B$.
Prove: $\angle A$ and $\angle B$ are not both right angles.

Statement	Reason
Assume $\angle A$ and $\angle B$ are right angles.	Assume the negation of the statement to be proved.
$\therefore \angle A \cong \angle B$	All right angles are congruent.
But $\angle A$ is not congruent to $\angle B$.	Given. Statements 2 and 3 contradict each other.
Therefore, $\angle A$ and $\angle B$ are not both right angles.	The assumption leads to a contradiction so it must be false and the original statement must be true.

An indirect proof is usually written in paragraph form. To write an indirect proof, follow these steps.

1. Assume the negation of what you want to prove.

2. Reason directly until you reach a contradiction.

3. State that your assumption in Step 1 must have been false, so the original conclusion must be true.

Example 3

Prove by the indirect method:

If $\angle A$ is not congruent to $\angle B$, then $\overline{BC}$ is not congruent to $\overline{AC}$.

C
A B

Given: $\angle A$ is not congruent to $\angle B$.
Prove: $\overline{BC}$ is not congruent to $\overline{AC}$.

Assume that $\overline{BC} \cong \overline{AC}$.
Then $\triangle ABC$ is isosceles and $\angle A \cong \angle B$ by the Isosceles Triangle Theorem.
But, by hypothesis, $\angle A$ is not congruent to $\angle B$.
Therefore, the assumption that $\overline{BC} \cong \overline{AC}$ is false, and $\overline{BC}$ is not congruent to $\overline{AC}$.

Try These

Write the negation of each statement.

1. $\angle 1 \cong \angle 2$

2. $\overline{AB} \perp \overline{CD}$

3. $m\angle C \neq m\angle D$

4. Angles 3 and 4 are not complementary.

5. Angles A and B are supplementary.

6. Segments AB and CD are not congruent.

Exercises

Use the indirect method of proof for each exercise. The symbol $\ncong$ means "is not congruent to."

a

1. Given: $\angle 1 \ncong \angle 2$

Prove: $\angle 1 \ncong \angle 3$

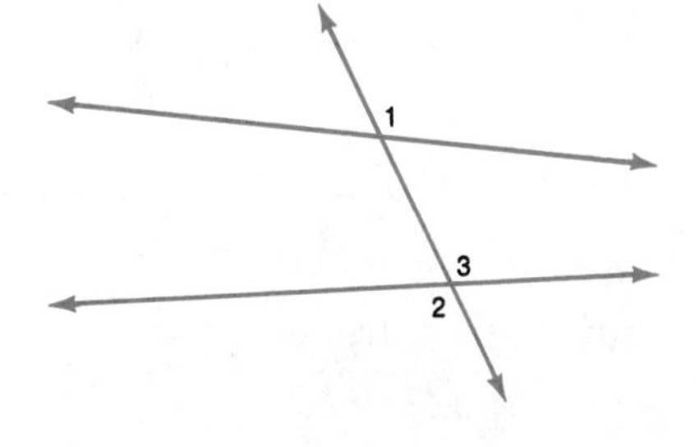

2. Given: $\angle 1 \ncong \angle 3$

Prove: $\angle 1$ and $\angle 2$ are not supplementary.

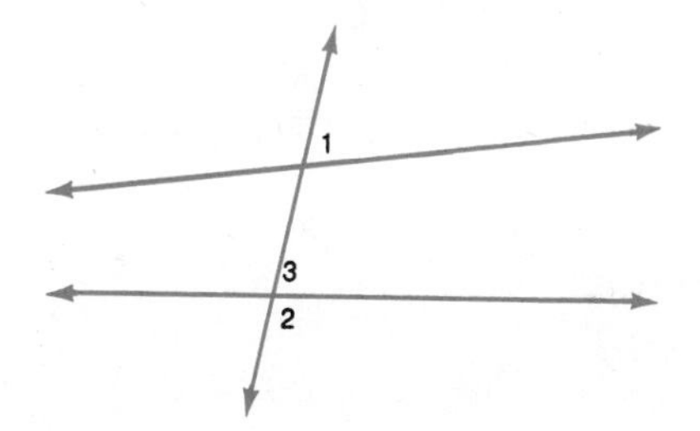

3. Prove: If $\angle A \ncong \angle B$, then $\angle A$ and $\angle B$ are not vertical angles.

4. Given: $\angle 1 \ncong \angle 3$

Prove: $\angle 2 \ncong \angle 4$

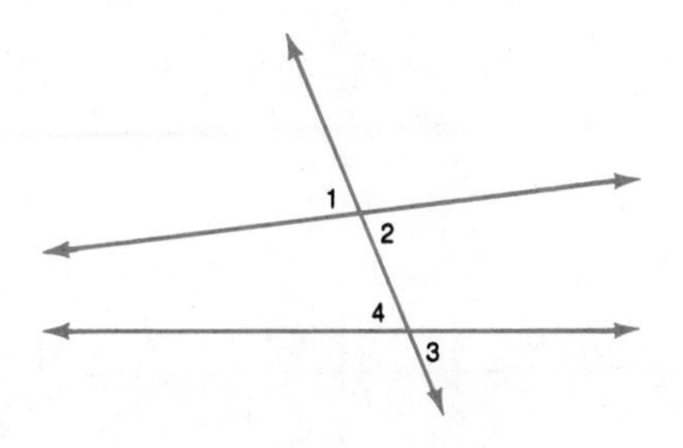

5. Given: $\angle 5$ and $\angle 7$ are not supplementary.

Prove: $\angle 6$ and $\angle 8$ are not supplementary.

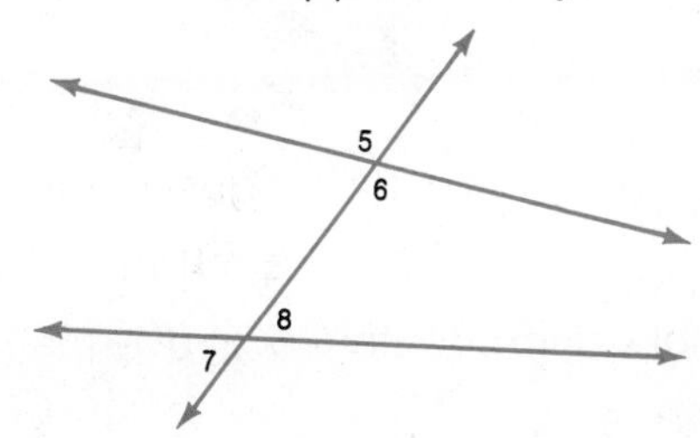

6. Given: $\overline{MT}$ bisects $\angle HMS$;
$\overline{MT}$ is not a median.

Prove: $\overline{MS} \not\cong \overline{MH}$

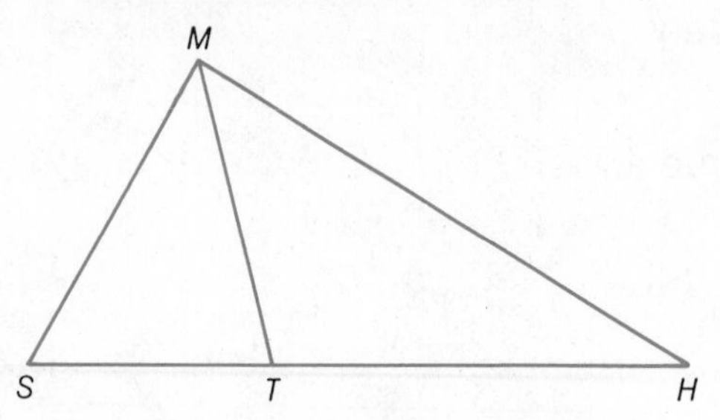

7. Given: $\overline{RN} \cong \overline{RA}$;
$\angle 1 \not\cong \angle 2$

Prove: $\overline{RK}$ is not a median.

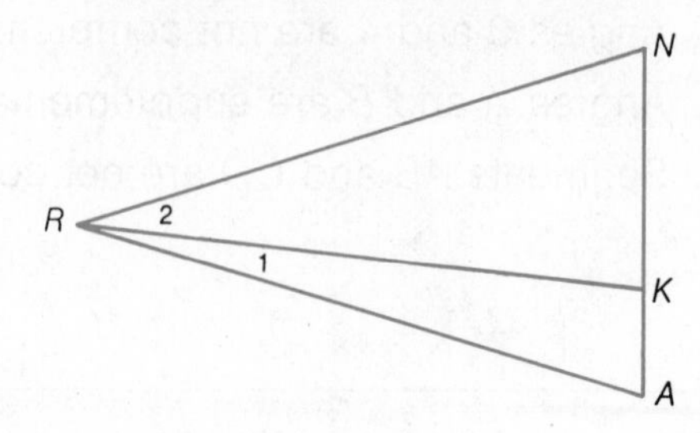

8. Given: $\overline{GZ}$ is a median;
$\angle 1 \not\cong \angle 2$

Prove: $\overline{ZQ} \not\cong \overline{ZP}$

9. Given: $\angle 1 \not\cong \angle 2$

Prove: $m\angle 1 \neq 90$

10. Given: $\overline{BK} \perp \overline{KH}$; $\overline{RH} \perp \overline{KH}$;
$\angle B \not\cong \angle R$

Prove: $\overline{RH} \not\cong \overline{BK}$

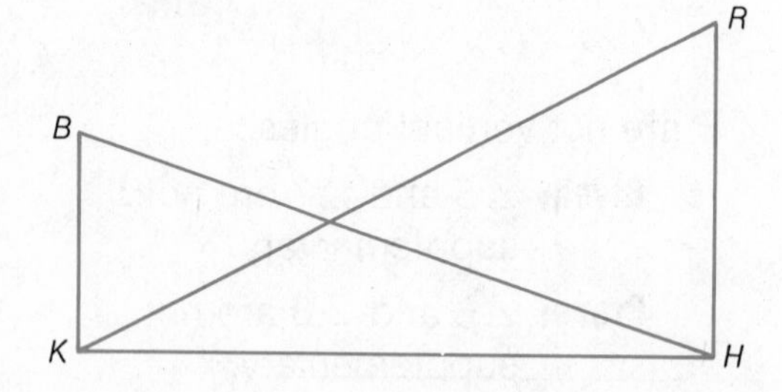

11. Given: $\triangle MRT$ is scalene;
$\overline{RS}$ bisects $\angle R$.

Prove: $\overline{RS}$ is not perpendicular to $\overline{MT}$.

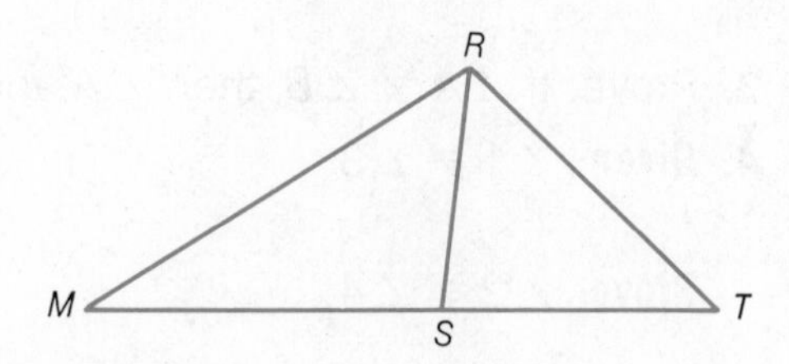

12. In the figure at the right, $\overleftrightarrow{PQ} \perp \overleftrightarrow{AB}$, R is a point on $\overleftrightarrow{QP}$ such that $\overline{RA}$ is not congruent to $\overline{RB}$. Prove that $\overline{AP}$ is not congruent to $\overline{BP}$.

Use the figure at the right for Exercises ***13–14.***

13. Given: $\overline{TA} \cong \overline{TB}$;
$m\angle 1 \neq m\angle 2$

Prove: $AX \neq BW$

14. Given: $\overline{TW} \ncong \overline{TX}$;
$\overline{TA} \cong \overline{TB}$

Prove: $BX \neq AW$

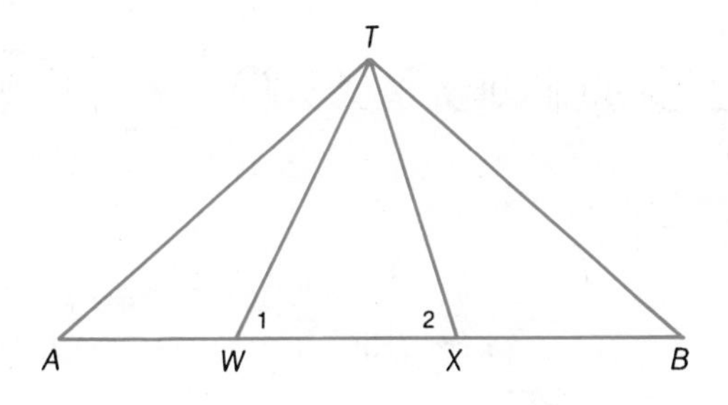

Remember

Use the figure and the information in each exercise to see whether you can prove triangles congruent. If so, name the triangles and give a reason.

1. $\angle 5 \cong \angle 6$, $\overline{AC} \cong \overline{BC}$
2. $\angle 1 \cong \angle 2$, $\angle 3 \cong \angle 4$
3. $\overline{AC} \cong \overline{BC}$, $\angle ADC \cong \angle BDC$
4. $\overline{AE} \cong \overline{BE}$, $\overline{AD} \cong \overline{BD}$

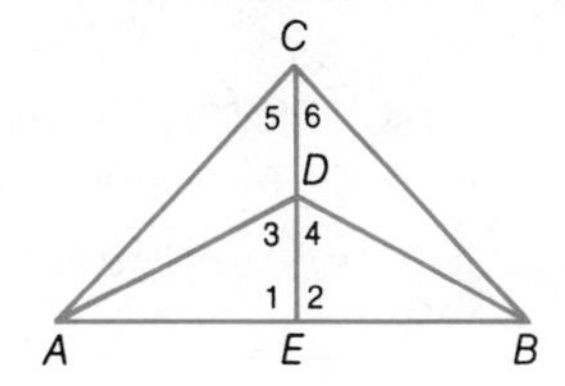

The answers are on page 152. If you need help, see pages 100, 107, and 108.

think–draw–see

1. Draw any right triangle ABC with right angle at A.
2. Draw any ray $\overrightarrow{EY}$. At point E on $\overrightarrow{EY}$, copy $\angle B$ such that $\angle E \cong \angle B$. Mark off $\overline{EF}$ so that $\overline{EF} \cong \overline{BC}$.
3. From point F construct $\overline{FD}$ such that $\overline{FD} \perp \overrightarrow{EY}$.
4. Compare the measures of $\overline{AB}$ and $\overline{DE}$, of $\overline{AC}$ and $\overline{DF}$, of $\angle C$ and $\angle F$. Are triangles ABC and DEF congruent? Do you think that two right triangles will be congruent if an acute angle and the hypotenuse of one are congruent, respectively, to an acute angle and the hypotenuse of the second?

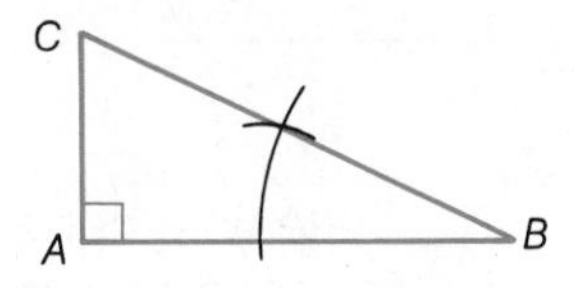

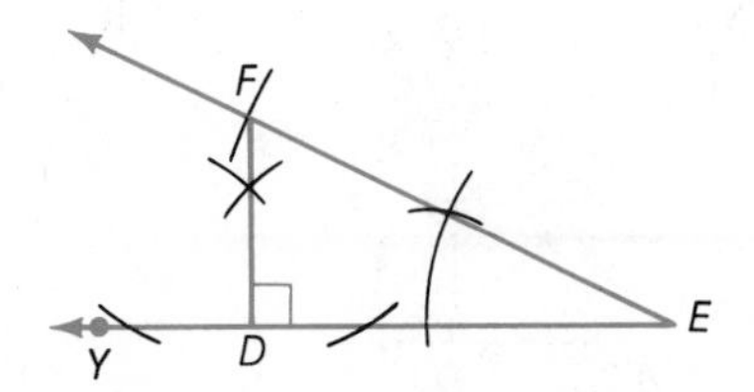

3-8 Congruence in Right Triangles

The Hypotenuse-Acute Angle (H.A.) Postulate can be used to prove right triangles congruent.

Postulate 14: Hypotenuse—Acute Angle Postulate

If two right triangles have the hypotenuse and an acute angle of one triangle congruent respectively to the hypotenuse and an acute angle of the other, then the triangles are congruent.

The Hypotenuse-Leg (H.L.) Theorem provides another way to prove right triangles congruent. A proof of this theorem is asked for in the Exercises.

Theorem 3-9: Hypotenuse-Leg Theorem

If two right triangles have the hypotenuse and one leg of one triangle congruent respectively to the hypotenuse and one leg of the other, then the triangles are congruent.

Example

State whether each pair of triangles is congruent. Give a reason for each answer.

a.

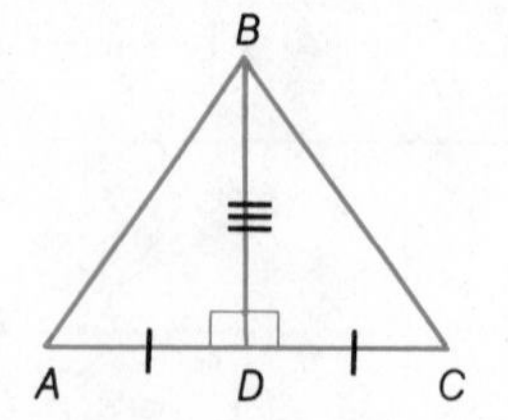

b.

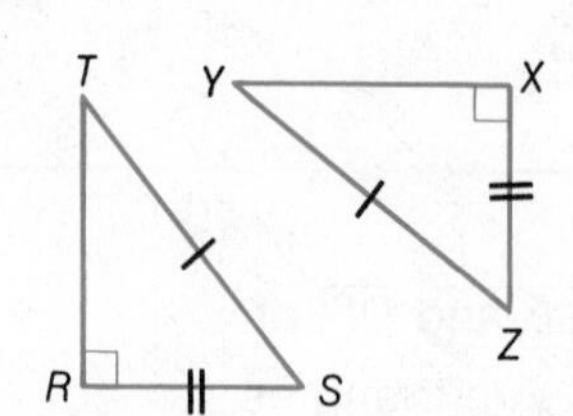

c.

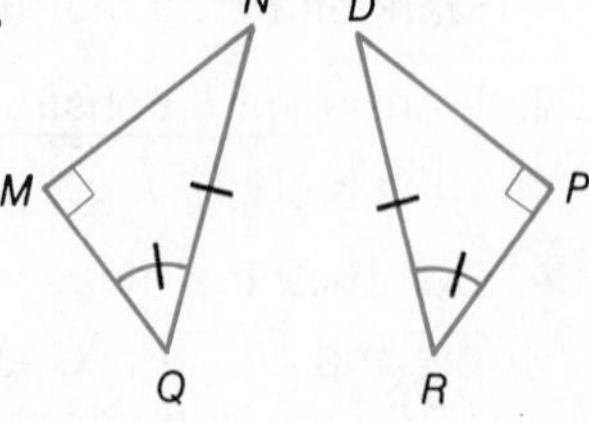

a. Yes, by S.A.S. **b.** Yes, by H.L. **c.** Yes, by H.A.

Corollary 3-10 follows directly from Theorem 3-9. You are asked to prove this corollary in the Exercises.

Corollary 3-10: In an isosceles triangle, the altitude to the base bisects the base and bisects the vertex angle.

The distance from a point to a line is the length of the segment perpendicular to the line from the point. Theorem 3-11 says that there is only one such line.

Theorem 3-11: Through a point not on a line, there is exactly one line perpendicular to a given line.

Point C at the right is 1.1 units from each side of $\angle X$. It is <u>equidistant</u> from the sides of the angle.

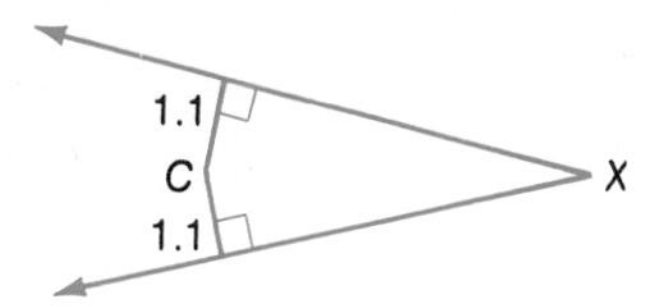

Two theorems concerning angle bisectors follow.

Theorem 3-12: If a point is on the bisector of an angle, it is equidistant from the sides of the angle.

Given: $\overrightarrow{BD}$ bisects $\angle ABC$; G is any point on $\overrightarrow{BD}$; $\overline{GF} \perp \overrightarrow{BC}$; $\overline{GE} \perp \overrightarrow{BA}$

Prove: $GF = GE$

Plan: Prove $\triangle BGF \cong \triangle BGE$. Then $\overline{GF} \cong \overline{GE}$ and $GF = GE$.

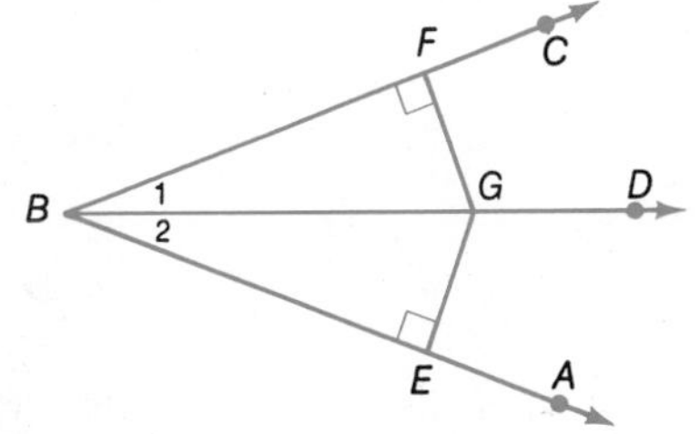

The converse of Theorem 3-12 is also a theorem.

Theorem 3-13: If a point in the interior of an angle is equidistant from the sides of the angle, then it is on the bisector of the angle.

Given: $QR = QS$; $\overline{QR} \perp \overrightarrow{TR}$ and $\overline{QS} \perp \overrightarrow{TS}$

Prove: $\overrightarrow{TQ}$ bisects $\angle RTS$.

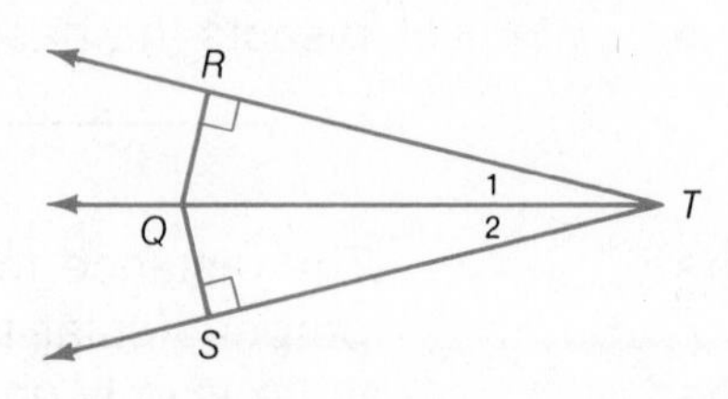

Plan: Use T and Q to determine $\overrightarrow{TQ}$. Prove $\triangle TRQ \cong \triangle TSQ$. Then prove $\angle 1 \cong \angle 2$.

Theorems 3-12 and 3-13 can be restated as a biconditional. You are asked to state the biconditional and to write a formal proof of each theorem in the Exercises.

Try These

*For Exercises **1–3,** state whether each pair of triangles is congruent. Give a reason for each answer.*

1.

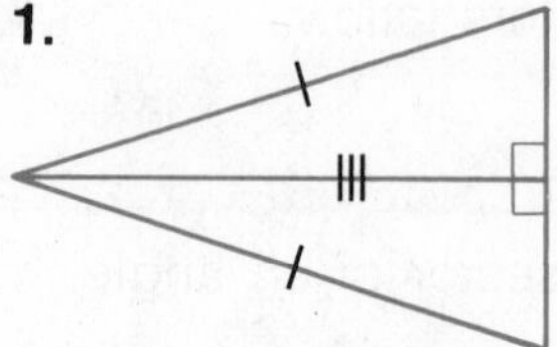

2.

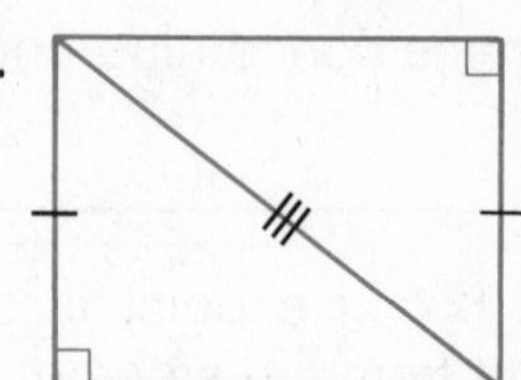

3.

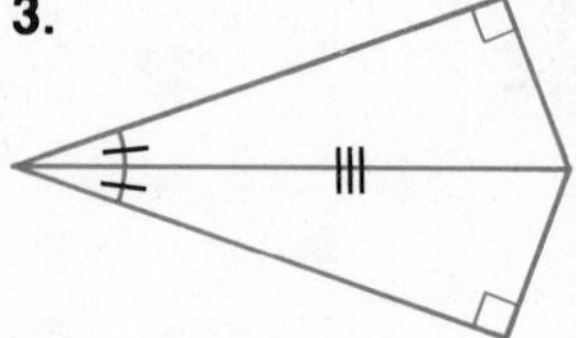

4. Restate Theorems 3-12 and 3-13 as a biconditional.

Exercises

1. In the figure at the right, angles P and R are right angles and $\angle 1 \cong \angle 2$. Prove that $\overline{PS} \cong \overline{RQ}$.

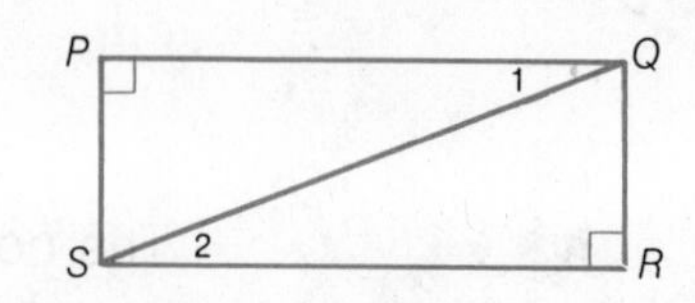

2. In the figure at the left below, $\overline{AD}$ is the altitude in isosceles triangle ABC with base BC. Prove that $\angle 1 \cong \angle 2$.

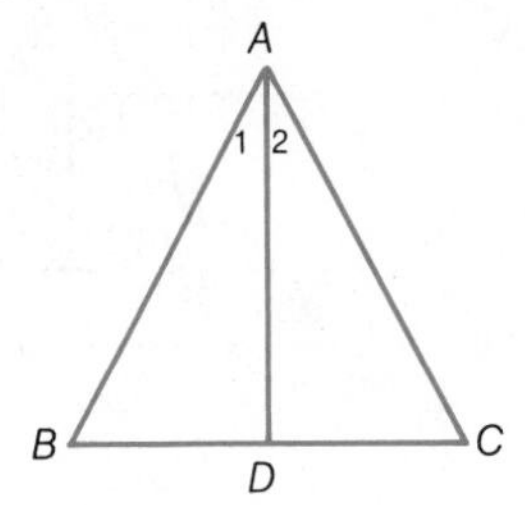

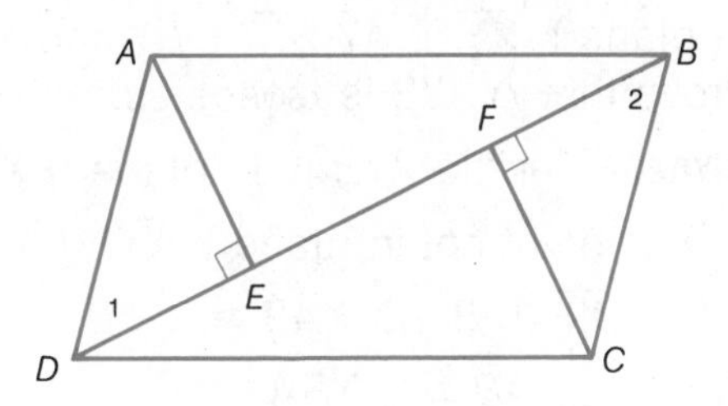

3. In the figure at the right above, $\overline{AB} \cong \overline{CD}$, $\overline{BE} \cong \overline{DF}$, $\overline{AE} \perp \overline{BD}$, and $\overline{CF} \perp \overline{BD}$. Prove that $\angle 1 \cong \angle 2$.

Use the figure at the right for Exercises **4–5.**

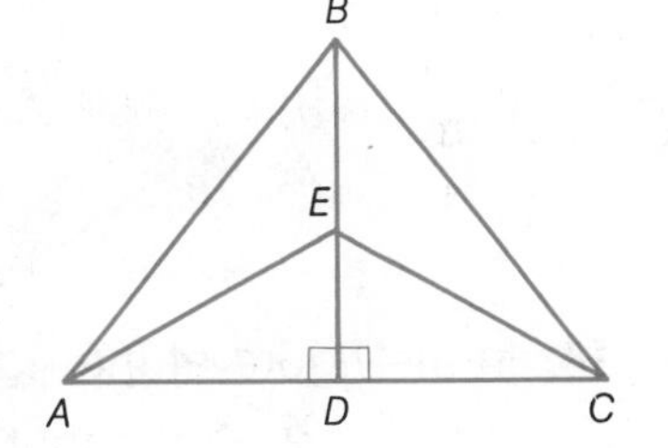

4. Triangle ABC is isosceles, with $\overline{AB} \cong \overline{CB}$. $\overline{BD}$ is the altitude to $\overline{AC}$ and E is any point between B and D. Prove that $\triangle EAD \cong \triangle ECD$.

5. Use the Given for Exercise 4 to prove that $\triangle BAE \cong \triangle BCE$.

6. In the figure at the left below, $\overline{PA} \cong \overline{PD}$, $\overline{AT} \cong \overline{DO}$, and $\overline{UP} \perp \overline{AD}$. Prove that $\triangle PUT \cong \triangle PUO$.

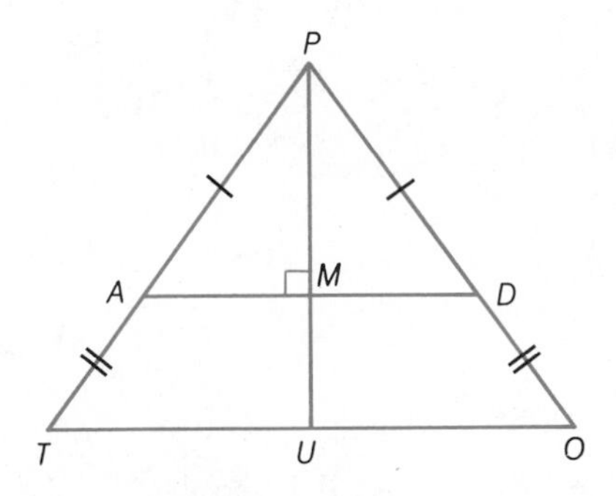

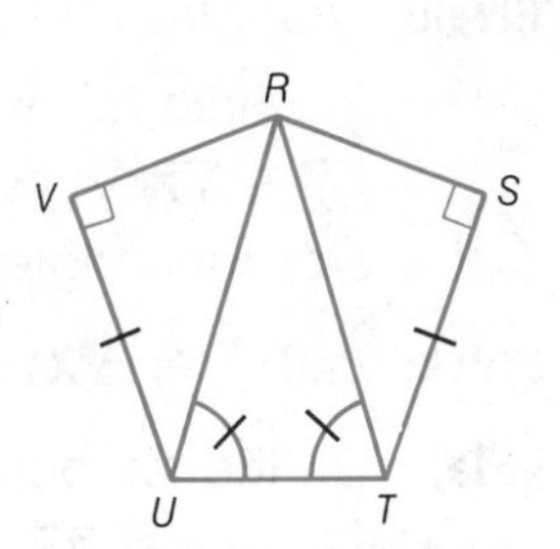

7. In pentagon $RSTUV$, angles S and V are right angles. $\overline{ST} \cong \overline{VU}$, and $\angle RTU \cong \angle RUT$. Prove that $\overline{VR} \cong \overline{SR}$.

8. Prove Corollary 3-10. (HINT: Use the H.L. theorem.)

9. Prove Theorem 3-12. (Follow the plan on page 141.)

10. Prove Theorem 3-13. (Follow the plan on page 142.)

*Use the figure at the right below for Exercises **11–12.***

11. Triangle AYB is in plane I, X is a point not in plane I, $\overline{XY} \perp \overline{AY}$, $\overline{XY} \perp \overline{BY}$ and $\overline{XA} \cong \overline{XB}$. Prove that $\triangle AYB$ is isosceles.

12. Given: Triangle AYB is in plane I; X is a point not in plane I; $\overline{XY} \perp \overline{AY}$; $\overline{XY} \perp \overline{BY}$; $\angle XAB \cong \angle XBA$

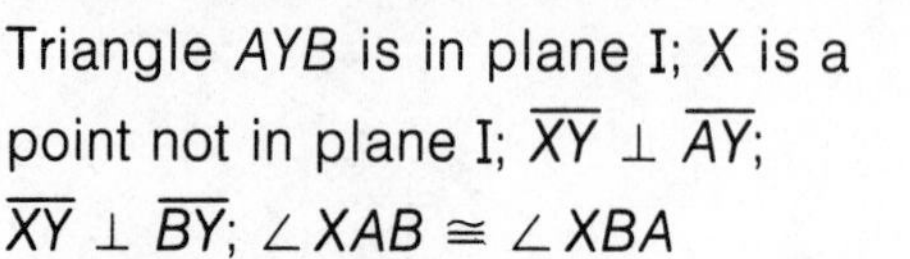

Prove: $\angle YAB \cong \angle YBA$

b

13. In $\triangle AKS$ below, $\overline{KQ} \perp \overline{AS}$, $\overline{SP} \perp \overline{AK}$, and $\overline{KQ} \cong \overline{SP}$. Prove that there are three pairs of congruent triangles.

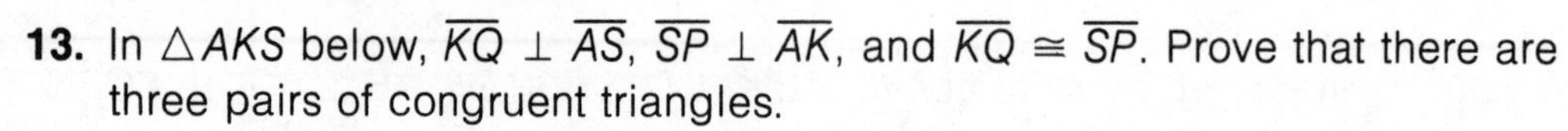

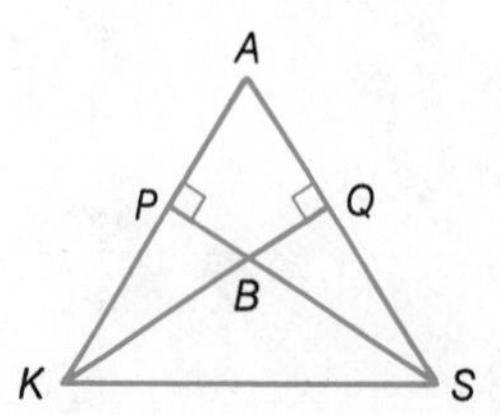

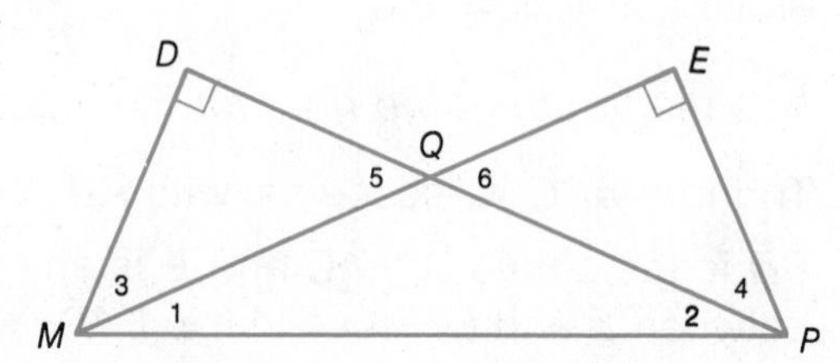

14. In the figure at the right above, angles D and E are right angles, and $\angle 1 \cong \angle 2$. Prove that $\overline{DQ} \cong \overline{EQ}$.

15. In the figure for Exercise **13,** $\triangle AKS$ is isosceles with base $\overline{KS}$, and $\overline{SP}$ and $\overline{KQ}$ are altitudes from S and K respectively. Prove that $\angle BKS \cong \angle BSK$.

c

16. Write a proof of the Hypotenuse-Leg Theorem.

Given: Triangles RST and XYZ in which $\overline{RS} \cong \overline{XY}$; $\overline{RT} \cong \overline{XZ}$; $\angle T$ and $\angle Z$ are right angles.

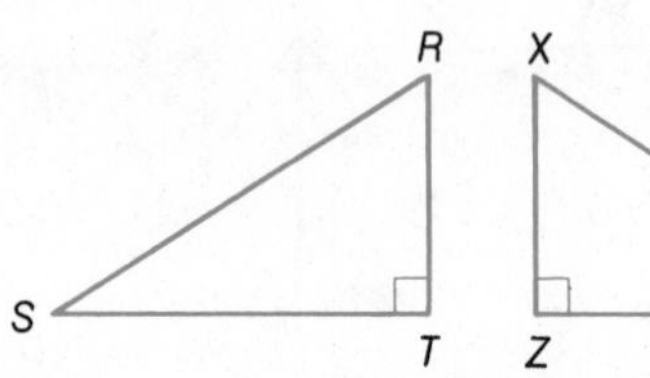

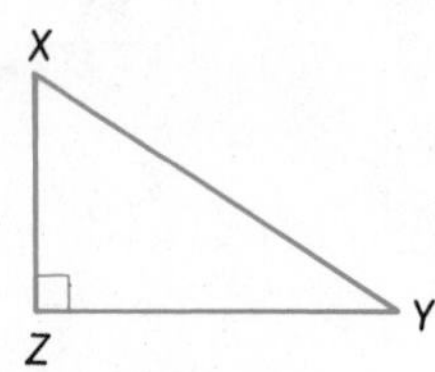

Prove: $\triangle RST \cong \triangle XYZ$

Plan: On the ray opposite $\overrightarrow{ZY}$ choose point A such that $\overline{ZA} \cong \overline{TS}$. Draw $\overline{AX}$. Angles 1 and 2 are a linear pair, so $\angle 1$ is a right angle and $\angle 1 \cong \angle T$. Therefore $\triangle RST \cong \triangle XAZ$. Since $\overline{RS} \cong \overline{XA}$, then $\overline{XA} \cong \overline{XY}$. In $\triangle XAY$, $\angle A \cong \angle Y$. Since $\angle S \cong \angle A$, $\angle S \cong \angle Y$. In right triangles RST and XYZ, $\overline{RS} \cong \overline{XY}$ and $\angle S \cong \angle Y$. Complete the proof.

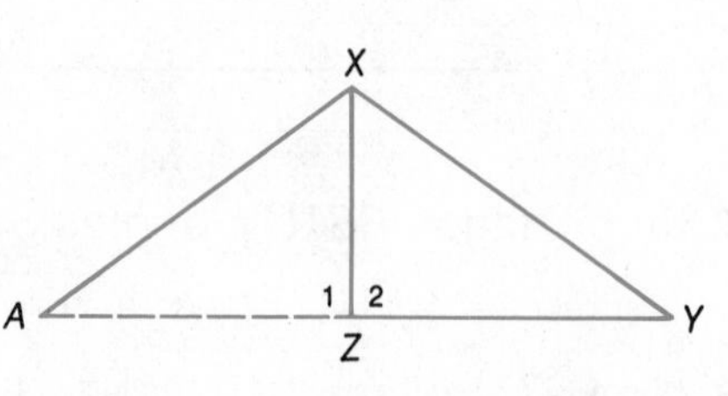

Contrapositive and Indirect Proof

When both parts of a conditional are negated, the **inverse** is formed. If a conditional is true, its inverse is not necessarily true.

Conditional	**Inverse**
If triangles are congruent, then corresponding sides are congruent.	If triangles are not congruent, then corresponding sides are not congruent.

When the "if" and "then" parts of an inverse are interchanged, the **contrapositive** of the original conditional statement is formed. Compare the conditional above with its contrapositive below.

Contrapositive

If the corresponding sides of triangles are not congruent, then the triangles are not congruent.

In an indirect proof, you prove a conditional by proving its contrapositive. If a conditional is true, then its contrapositive is also true.

To write the contrapositive of a conditional, it is generally easier if you first write the inverse. Then interchange the "if" and "then" parts of the inverse.

Can You Solve These?

Write the inverse and then the contrapositive of each conditional.

1. If two angles are right angles, then they are congruent.
2. If corresponding sides of triangles are congruent, then the triangles are congruent.
3. If a triangle is equilateral, then it is equiangular.

Mathematics and Civil Engineering

Civil engineers design and supervise the construction of roads, harbors, airfields, tunnels, buildings, and bridges.

A major concern of a civil engineer in designing a bridge is to determine what effect, if any, the earth's curvature may have on the structure.

In designing this bridge, the engineer could view the earth as a plane (having only two dimensions). The supporting towers are parallel to each other and are perpendicular to the earth's surface.

A bachelor's degree in an engineering specialty (aerospace, chemical, agricultural, civil, and so on) is generally the minimum requirement for beginning engineering jobs. A minimum of three years of high school mathematics is needed to enter an engineering college. The first two years of the college curriculum with emphasis on mathematics, physics, and chemistry courses are basically the same for all engineering candidates. The last two years are devoted to the specialty, such as civil engineering.

In designing the Verrazano-Narrows Bridge in New York City, the engineer viewed the earth as three-dimensional. The two towers are perpendicular to the earth but are not *parallel to each other. They are about four cm farther apart at the top than at their bases.*

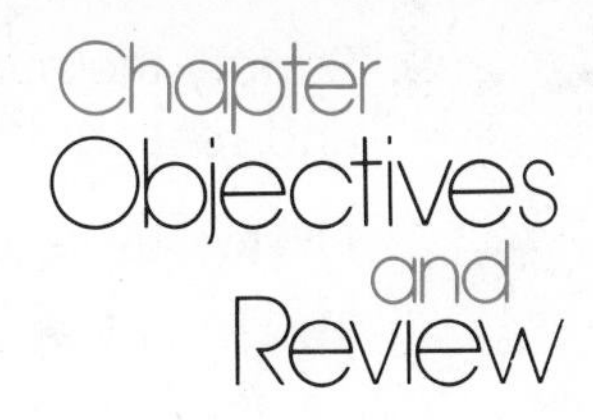

Objective: To recall, and give examples of, the important mathematical terms of the chapter.

1. Be sure that you know the meanings of these mathematical terms used in Chapter 3.

congruent triangles (p. 95)
contradiction (p. 135)
equiangular triangle (p. 117)
equidistant
  point from two points (p. 121)
identity congruence (p. 95)
included angle (p. 100)
indirect proof (p. 135)
negation (p. 135)
perpendicular bisector (p. 120)

Objective: To identify corresponding congruent parts of two congruent triangles. (Section 3-1)

In the figure at the right, $\triangle GRD \cong \triangle HTC$. Complete each statement by supplying the missing symbols.

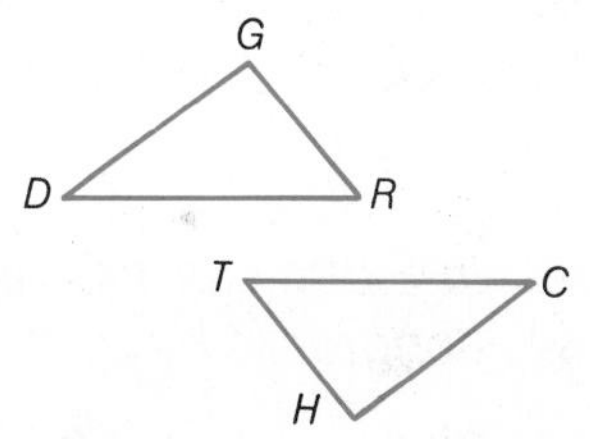

2. $\underline{\ ?\ }\ \underline{\ ?\ }\ \underline{\ ?\ } \leftrightarrow \underline{\ ?\ }\,CT$
3. $\angle R \cong \angle \underline{\ ?\ }$
4. $\overline{GD} \cong \underline{\ ?\ }$
5. $\overline{RD} \cong \underline{\ ?\ }$

Objective: To use the S.A.S. Postulate to determine whether two triangles are congruent. (Section 3-2)

*For Exercises **6–8,** tell whether each pair of triangles is congruent by the* S.A.S. *Postulate.*

6. 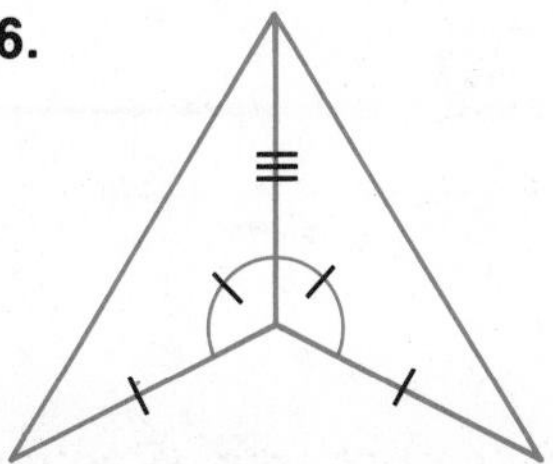

7. 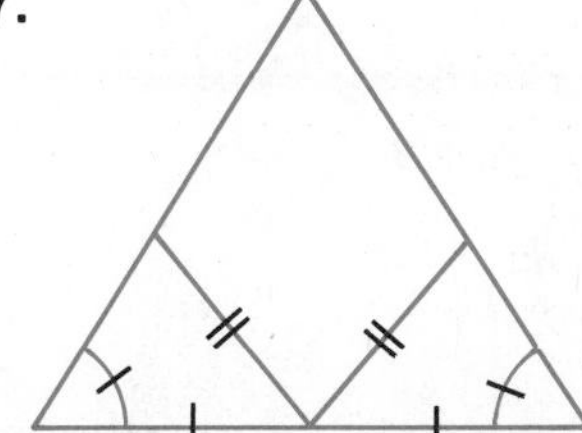

8. 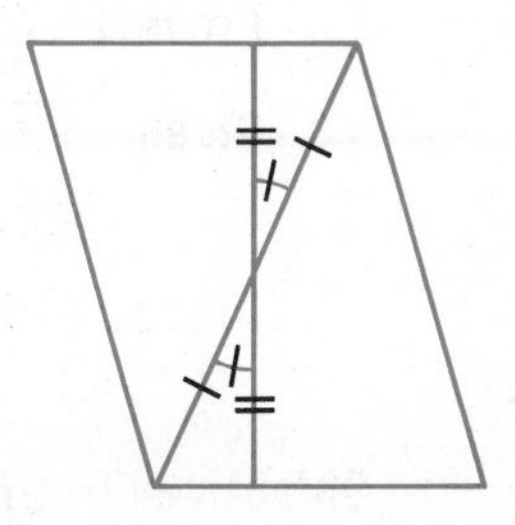

9. Supply the missing statements and reasons.

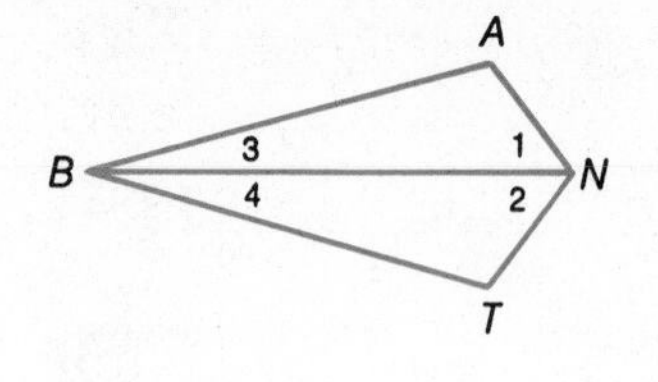

Given: $\overline{AN} \cong \overline{TN}$; $\angle 1 \cong \angle 2$

Prove: $\angle 3 \cong \angle 4$

Statements	Reasons
1. $\overline{AN} \cong \overline{TN}$; $\angle 1 \cong \angle 2$	1. ___?___
2. ___?___	2. Identity
3. $\triangle ANB \cong \triangle TNB$	3. (1). (2). ___?___
4. ___?___	4. (3). C.P.C.T.C.

Objective: To use the A.S.A. and S.S.S. Postulates to determine whether two triangles are congruent. (Section 3-3)

Replace the ___?___ *with the required angle or side so that the indicated relationship is correct.*

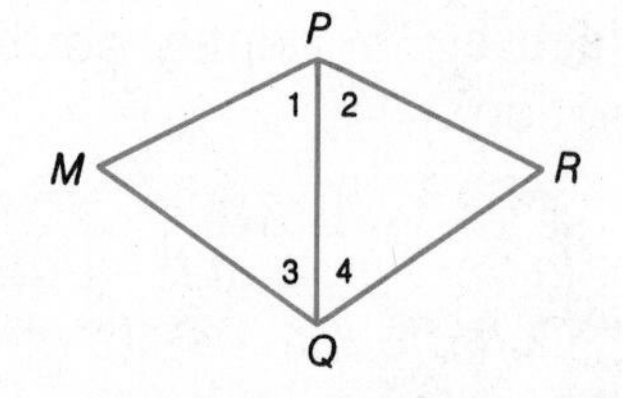

10. S.S.S. for $\triangle PMQ$: $\overline{PQ}$; $\overline{MQ}$; ___?___

11. A.S.A. for $\triangle PMQ$: $\angle 1$; $\overline{PQ}$; ___?___

12. S.S.S. for $\triangle PRQ$: ___?___; $\overline{PQ}$; $\overline{RQ}$

13. A.S.A. for $\triangle PRQ$: $\angle 2$; $\overline{PQ}$; ___?___

In Exercises ***14–16,*** *state whether each pair of triangles can be proved congruent by* S.A.S., A.S.A., *or* S.S.S. *If two ways are possible, state both.*

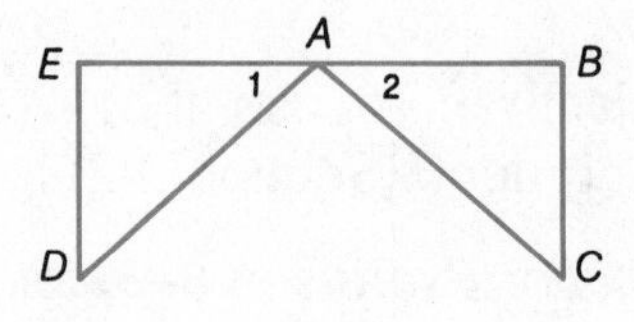

14. Given: $\angle 1 \cong \angle 2$; $\overline{DA} \cong \overline{CA}$; $\angle D \cong \angle C$

Prove: $\triangle EAD \cong \triangle BAC$

15. Given: A is the midpoint of $\overline{EB}$; $\overline{DE} \cong \overline{CB}$; $\overline{DA} \cong \overline{CA}$

Prove: $\triangle EAD \cong \triangle BAC$

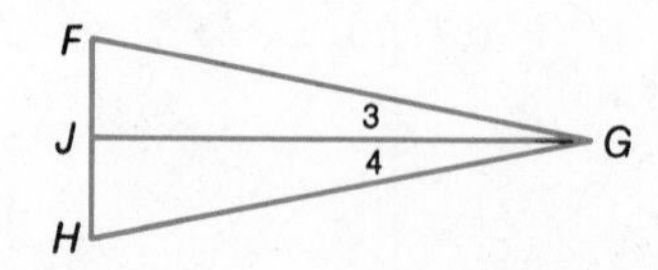

16. Given: $\overline{GJ}$ bisects $\angle FGH$; $\overline{FG} \cong \overline{HG}$; $\angle F \cong \angle H$

Prove: $\triangle GJF \cong \triangle GJH$

Objective: To apply the Isosceles Triangle theorem and its converse. (Section 3-4)

*For Exercises **17–19,** use the indicated information to state whatever conclusion you can about the unmarked sides and angles in each figure.*

17.

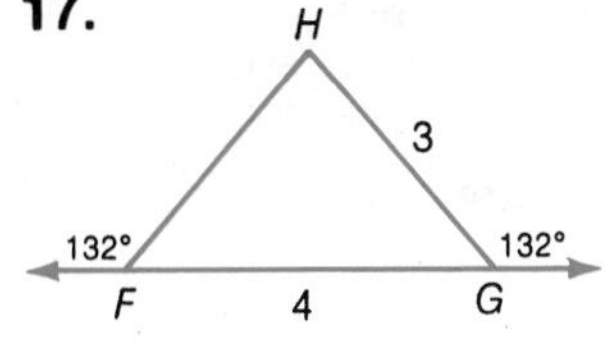

18.

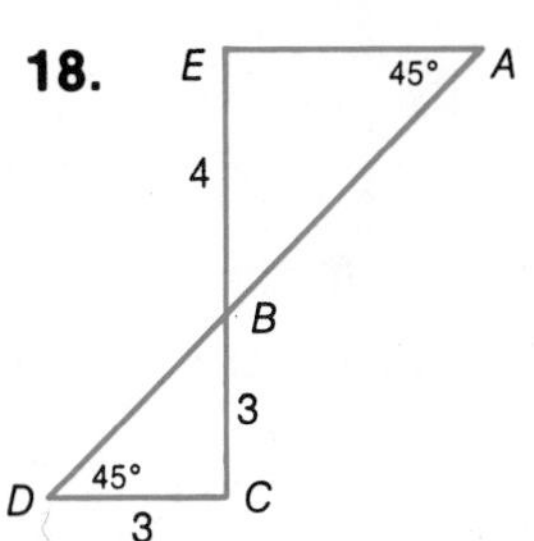

19.

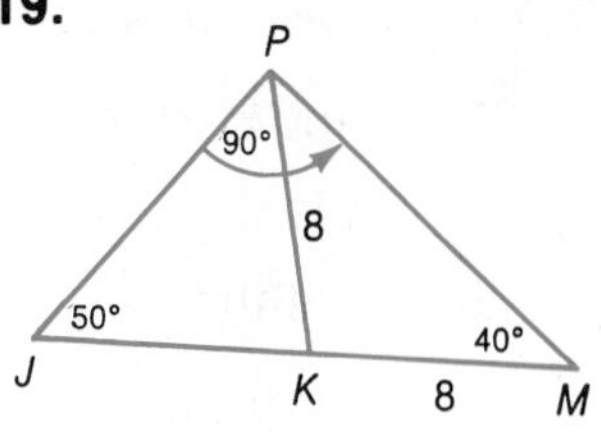

*Use the figures below to prove the statements in Exercises **20–22.***

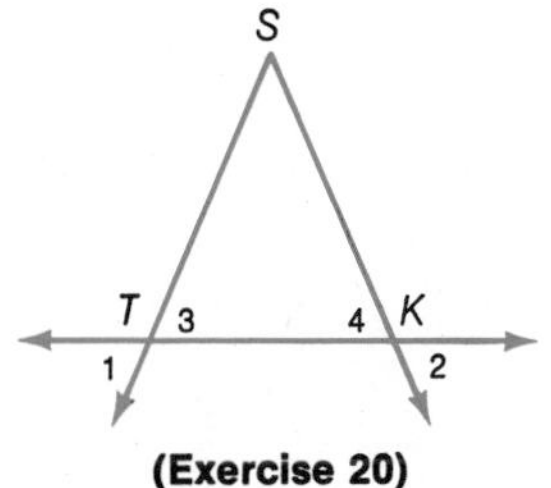

(Exercise 20)

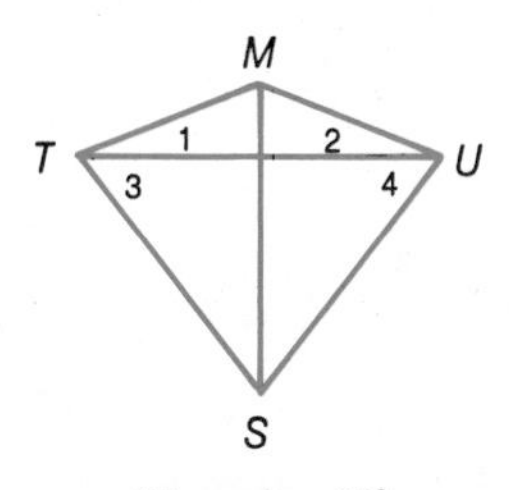

(Exercise 21)

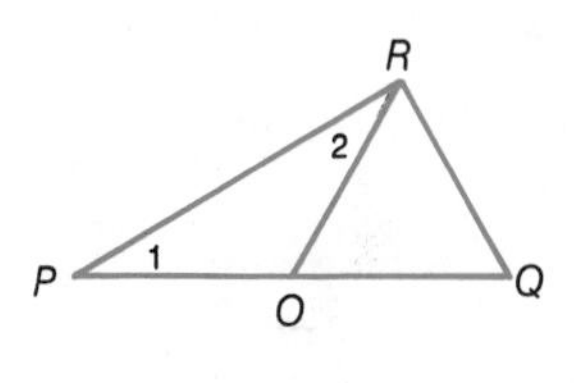

(Exercise 22)

20. If $\angle 1 \cong \angle 2$, then $\triangle TKS$ is isosceles.

21. If $\angle 1 \cong \angle 2$ and $\angle 3 \cong \angle 4$, then $\triangle STM \cong \triangle SUM$.

22. If O is the midpoint of $\overline{PQ}$ and $\overline{OQ} \cong \overline{OR}$, then $\angle 1 \cong \angle 2$.

Objective: To apply other theorems associated with an isosceles triangle. (Section 3-5)

*In Exercises **23–24,** complete the conclusion. Then state the theorem that gives the reason for the conclusion.*

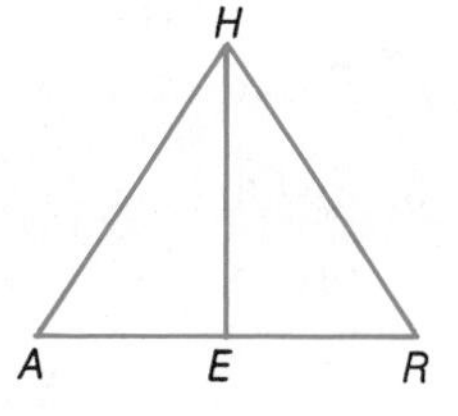

23. Given: $\triangle HAR$ is isosceles with vertex angle AHR. $\overline{HE}$ bisects $\angle AHR$.
Conclusion: _?_ $\perp$ _?_ and _?_ bisects _?_.

24. Given: $\triangle HAR$ is isosceles with $\overline{HA} \cong \overline{HR}$. $\overline{HE}$ is a median.
Conclusion: _?_ $\perp$ _?_ and _?_ bisects _?_.

Objective: To identify the perpendicular bisector of a segment. (Section 3-5)

Classify each statement as True or False.

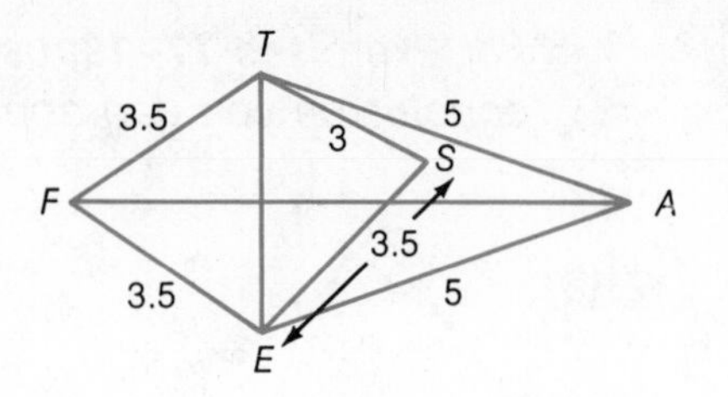

25. Point A is equidistant from T and E.

26. Point S is equidistant from T and E.

27. Point E is equidistant from F and A.

28. $\overline{FA}$ is the perpendicular bisector of $\overline{TE}$.

29. $\overline{TE}$ is the perpendicular bisector of $\overline{FA}$.

Objective: To identify corresponding congruent parts of overlapping triangles. (Section 3-6)

Supply the missing statements and reasons.

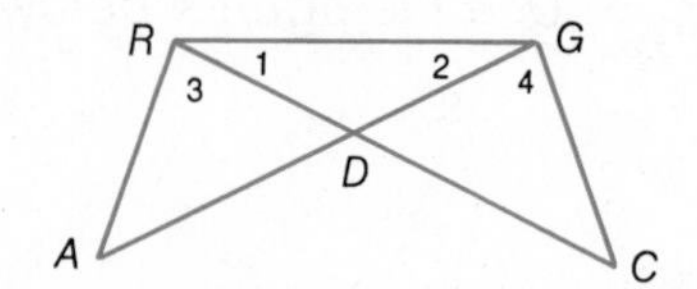

30. Given: $\angle ARG \cong \angle CGR$, $\overline{DG} \cong \overline{DR}$

Prove: $m\angle 3 = m\angle 4$

Statements	Reasons
1. $\angle ARG \cong \angle CGR$, $\overline{DG} \cong \overline{DR}$	1. ?
2. In $\triangle RDG$, $\angle 1 \cong \angle 2$	2. (1). ?
3. $m\angle ARG = m\angle CGR$, $m\angle 1 = m\angle 2$	3. (1). (2). ?
4. $m\angle ARG = m\angle 1 + m\angle 3$ $m\angle CGR =$? + ?	4. Angle Addition Property
5. $m\angle 1 + m\angle 3 = m\angle 2 + m\angle 4$	5. (3). (4). ?
6. $\therefore$?	6. (3). (5). Addition Property of Equations

Objective: To use the indirect method of proof. (Section 3-7)

Write the negation of each statement.

31. $\triangle RST$ is an isosceles triangle.

32. $m\angle 1 + m\angle 2 \neq m\angle A$

Prove by the indirect method.

33. Given: $\overline{BC} \ncong \overline{BA}$; $\overline{BD} \perp \overline{CA}$

Prove: $\overline{DC} \ncong \overline{DA}$

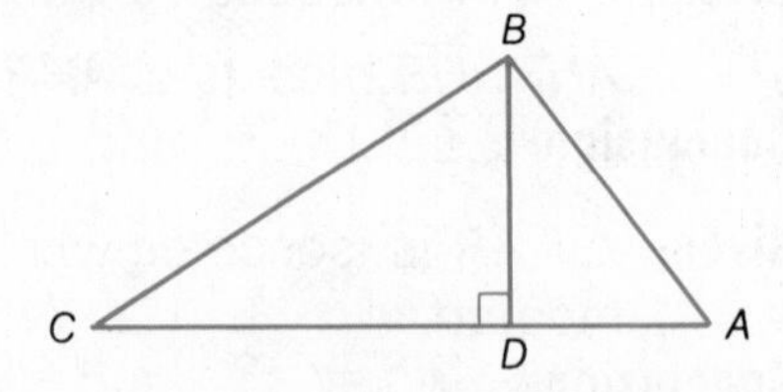

Objective: To use the H.A. Postulate and the H.L. Theorem to prove two right triangles are congruent. (Section 3-8)

State whether each pair of triangles is congruent. Explain.

34.

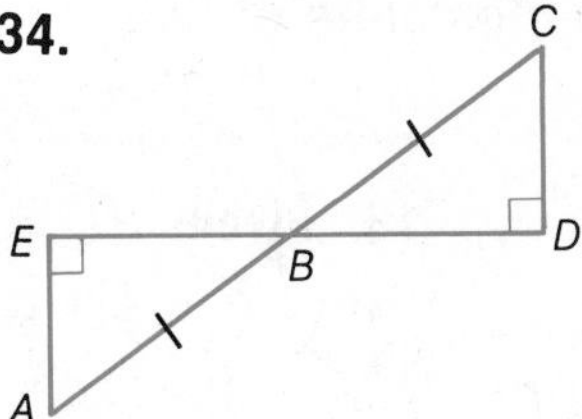

35.

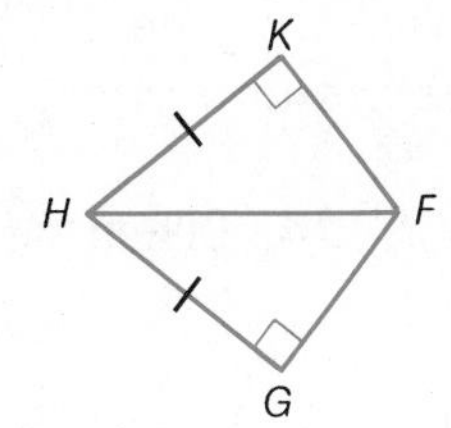

36.

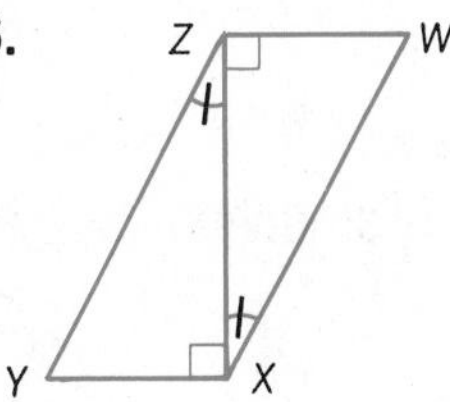

Chapter Test

In the figure, $\triangle DRT \cong \triangle SNT$. Complete each statement.

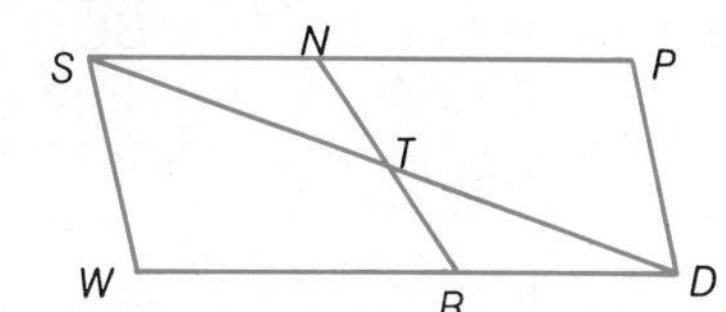

1. $\overline{TR} \cong$ __?__
2. $\angle TDR \cong$ __?__
3. $\angle DTR \cong$ __?__
4. $\overline{DT} \cong$ __?__

State whether each pair of triangles can be proved congruent by S.A.S., A.S.A., *or* S.S.S. *If two ways are possible, state both.*

5.

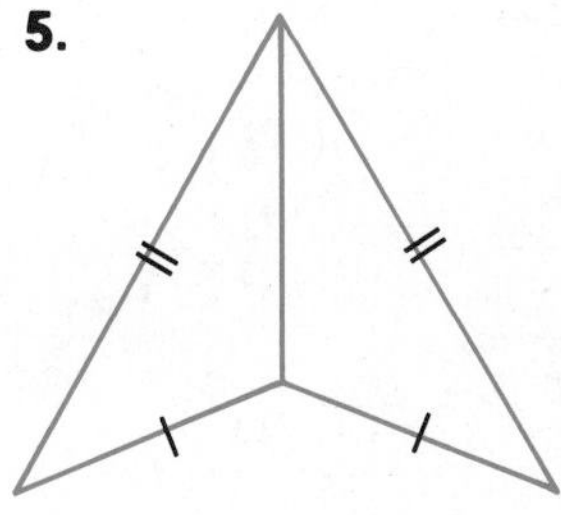

6.

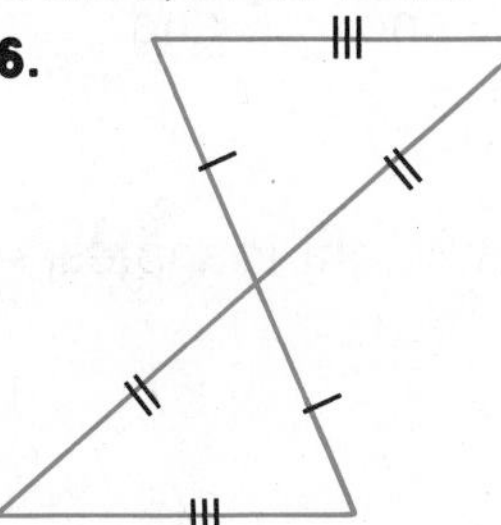

7.

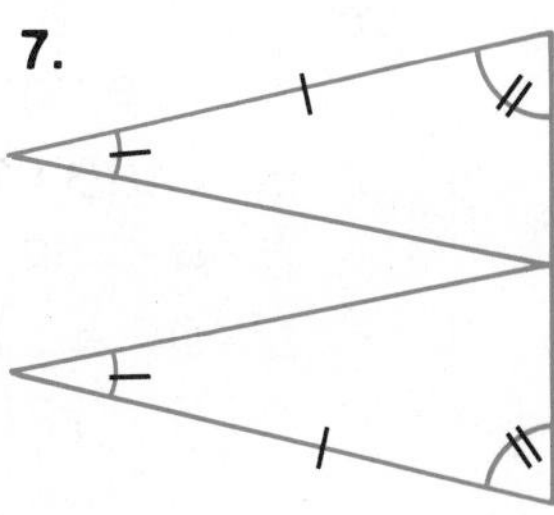

Classify each statement as True *or* False.

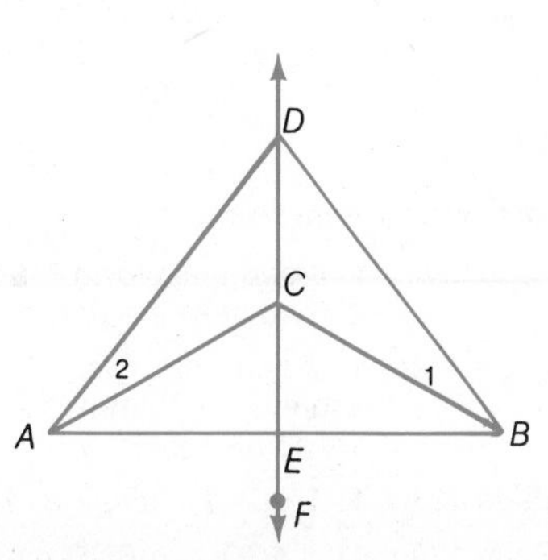

8. If $\angle 1 \cong \angle 2$, then $\overline{DA} \cong \overline{DB}$.
9. If $\angle DBA \cong \angle DAB$, then $\overline{DA} \cong \overline{DB}$.
10. If $DA = DB$, then $\overleftrightarrow{DC}$ is the perpendicular bisector of $\overline{AB}$.

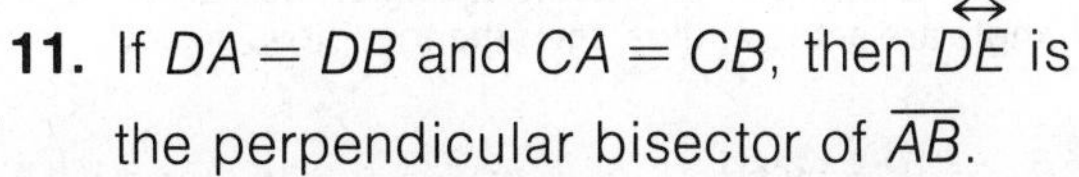

11. If $DA = DB$ and $CA = CB$, then $\overleftrightarrow{DE}$ is the perpendicular bisector of $\overline{AB}$.

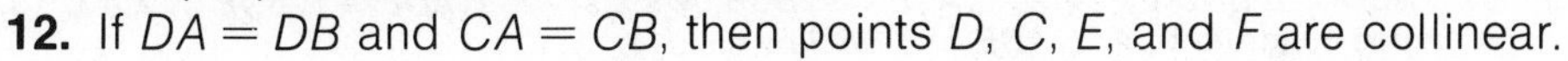

12. If $DA = DB$ and $CA = CB$, then points D, C, E, and F are collinear.

*For Exercises **13–15,** use the given information to state which pair of triangles can be proved congruent. Then state the postulate or theorem that tells why the triangles are congruent.*

13. Given: $m\angle PSR = 90$;
$m\angle QRS = 90$;
$\overline{PR} \cong \overline{QS}$

14. Given: $\overline{AB} \cong \overline{CD}$;
$\overline{CF} \cong \overline{BE}$;
$\angle ACF \cong \angle DBE$

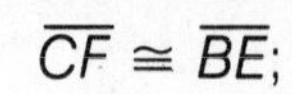
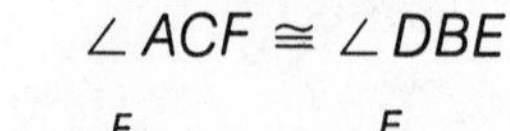
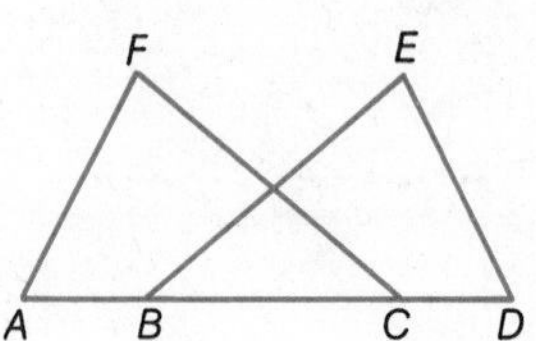

15. Given: $\overline{BE} \cong \overline{CE}$;
$\angle 3 \cong \angle 4$

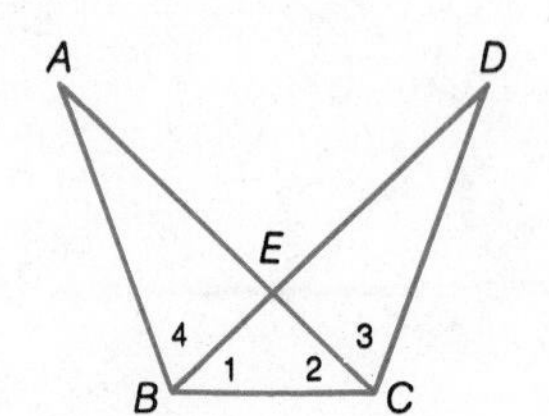

16. Supply the missing reasons.

Given: $\angle 1 \cong \angle 2$; $\overline{AE} \cong \overline{BC}$;
$\angle E$ and $\angle C$ are right angles.

Prove: $\overline{ED} \cong \overline{CD}$

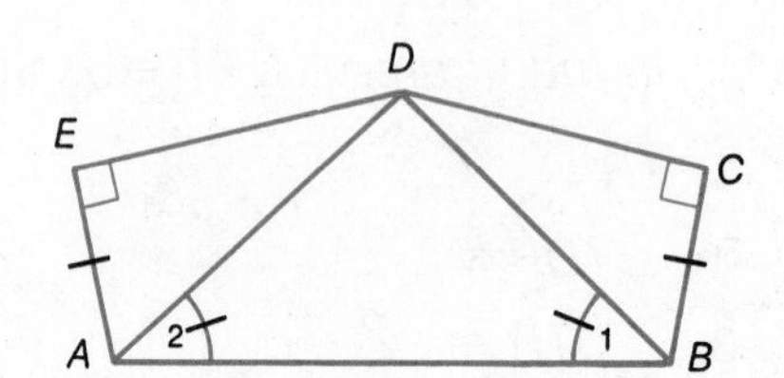

Statements	Reasons
1. $\angle 1 \cong \angle 2$, $\overline{AE} \cong \overline{BC}$, and $\angle E$ and $\angle C$ are right angles.	1. ?
2. In $\triangle ABD$, $\overline{AD} \cong \overline{BD}$.	2. ?
3. $\triangle ADE$ and $\triangle BDC$ are right triangles.	3. ?
4. $\triangle ADE \cong \triangle BDC$	4. ?
5. $\therefore \overline{ED} \cong \overline{CD}$	5. ?

Answers to Remember

Page 115: **1.** If two lines form four pairs of congruent adjacent angles, then they are perpendicular. **2.** Two lines are perpendicular if and only if they form four pairs of congruent adjacent angles.

Page 119: **1.** If and only if **2.** If an angle is a right angle, then its measure is 90. If the measure of an angle is 90, then it is a right angle. **3.** If a triangle is an acute triangle, then all of its angles are acute angles. If all angles of a triangle are acute angles, then the triangle is an acute triangle.

Page 128: **1.** True **2.** False **3.** False

Page 139: **1.** $\triangle ACD \cong \triangle BCD$ by S.A.S.; $\triangle ACE \cong \triangle BCE$ by S.A.S. **2.** $\triangle ADE \cong \triangle BDE$ by A.S.A. **3.** No triangles congruent **4.** $\triangle ADE \cong \triangle BED$ by S.S.S.

Chapter 4
Parallel Lines

4-1 Interior and Exterior Angles

In $\triangle ABC$, $\angle 1$ is an **exterior angle of the triangle** because it forms a linear pair with an angle of the triangle. To form an exterior angle of a triangle, extend one side of the triangle.

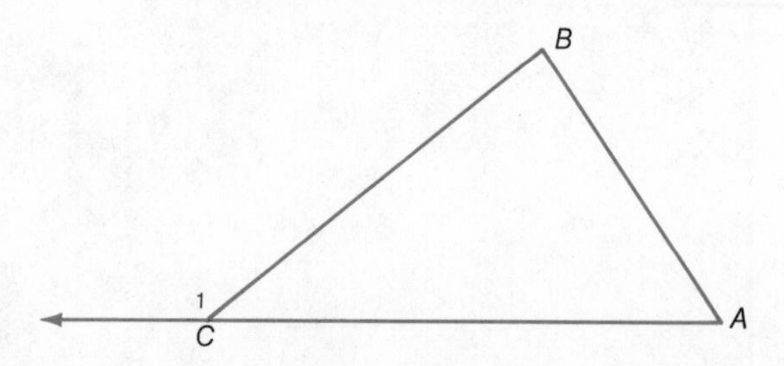

Angles A and B are the **remote interior angles** of $\angle 1$. They are the angles of the triangle not adjacent to $\angle 1$.

Example 1

In $\triangle DEF$, name the exterior angles shown. Name the remote interior angles for each exterior angle.

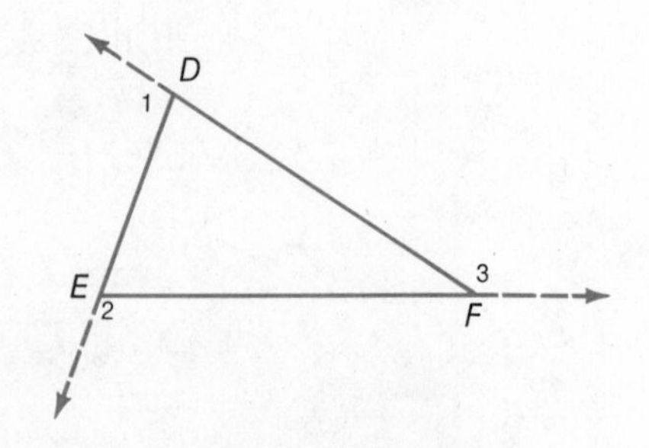

Exterior Angle	Remote Interior Angles
$\angle 1$	$\angle DEF$ and $\angle DFE$
$\angle 2$	$\angle EDF$ and $\angle DFE$
$\angle 3$	$\angle FDE$ and $\angle DEF$

Example 2

In $\triangle GHK$, compare the measure of each exterior angle shown with the measures of its remote interior angles.

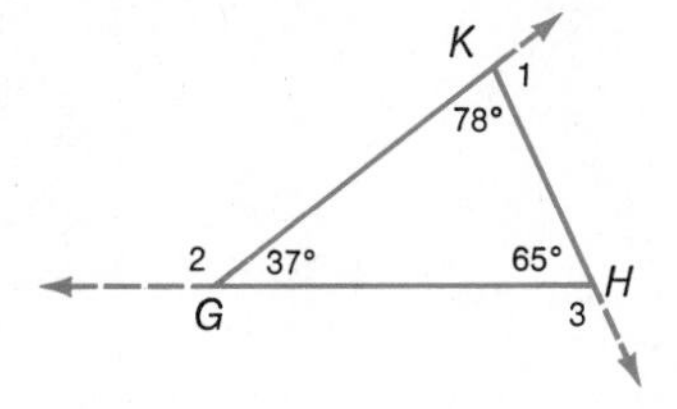

$m\angle 1 = 180 - 78 = 102$

$m\angle 2 = 180 - 37 = 143$

$m\angle 3 = 180 - 65 = 115$

Exterior Angle	**Remote Interior Angles**	**Comparison**
$m\angle 1 = 102$	$m\angle G = 37$ $m\angle H = 65$	$m\angle 1 > m\angle G$ $m\angle 1 > m\angle H$
$m\angle 2 = 143$	$m\angle K = 78$ $m\angle H = 65$	$m\angle 2 > m\angle K$ $m\angle 2 > m\angle H$
$m\angle 3 = 115$	$m\angle G = 37$ $m\angle K = 78$	$m\angle 3 > m\angle G$ $m\angle 3 > m\angle K$

Example 2 suggests Theorem 4-1.

Theorem 4-1: Exterior Angle Inequality Theorem

The measure of an exterior angle of a triangle is greater than the measure of either of its remote interior angles.

Given: $\angle BCD$ is an exterior angle of $\triangle ABC$.

Prove: $m\angle BCD > m\angle B$; $m\angle BCD > m\angle BAC$

Plan: Draw $\overrightarrow{AE}$ through M, the midpoint of $\overline{BC}$. Choose E so that $ME = AM$. Draw $\overline{CE}$. Show that $\triangle BMA \cong \triangle CME$ by S.A.S. and that $m\angle B = m\angle 1$. Thus, $m\angle BCD = m\angle B + m\angle 2$, and $m\angle BCD > m\angle B$. Prove that $m\angle BCD > m\angle A$ in a similar manner.

A **transversal** is a line that intersects (or cuts) two other lines in two different points. In the figures below, transversal *t* intersects lines *y* and *s* to form **interior** and **exterior angles.**

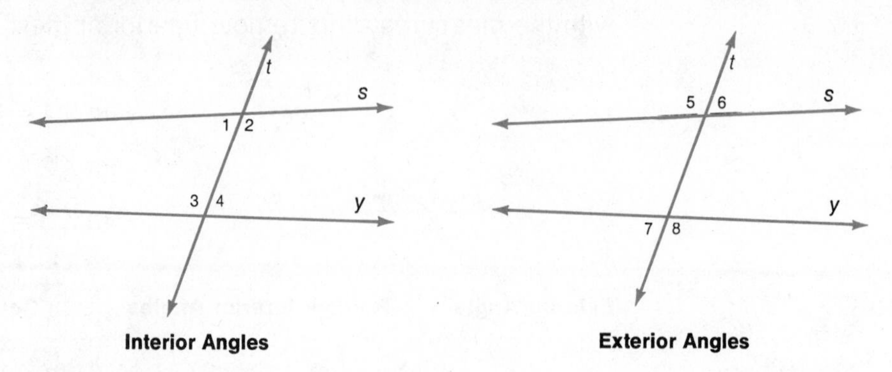

Alternate angles are nonadjacent angles on opposite sides of a transversal.

Alternate Interior Angles	Alternate Exterior Angles
$\angle 1$ and $\angle 4$	$\angle 6$ and $\angle 7$
$\angle 2$ and $\angle 3$	$\angle 5$ and $\angle 8$

Example 3

Refer to the figure at the right to name each of the following.

a. Interior angles
b. Exterior angles
c. Alternate interior angles
d. Alternate exterior angles

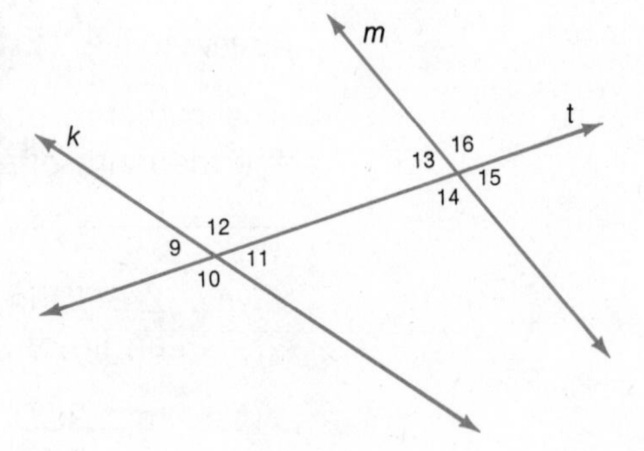

a. Interior: $\angle 11$, $\angle 12$, $\angle 13$, $\angle 14$
b. Exterior: $\angle 9$, $\angle 10$, $\angle 15$, $\angle 16$
c. Alternate interior: $\angle 11$ and $\angle 13$, $\angle 12$ and $\angle 14$
d. Alternate exterior: $\angle 9$ and $\angle 15$, $\angle 10$ and $\angle 16$

Try These

Refer to $\triangle ABC$ to complete each sentence.

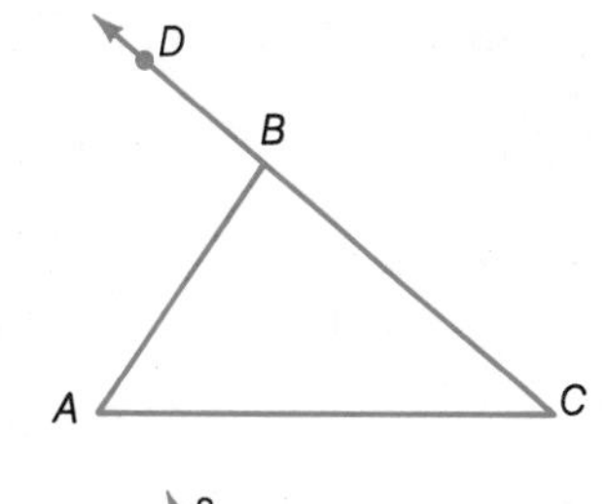

1. Angle __?__ is an exterior angle of $\triangle ABC$.
2. Angle __?__ and angle __?__ are the remote interior angles of $\angle ABD$.
3. $m\angle ABD$ __?__ $m\angle A$ ($>$, $<$, or $=$)
4. $m\angle ABD$ __?__ $m\angle C$ ($>$, $<$, or $=$)

*Refer to the figure at the right for Exercises **5–9.** Match the pairs of angles in Exercises **5–9** with a correct name in **a–e.***

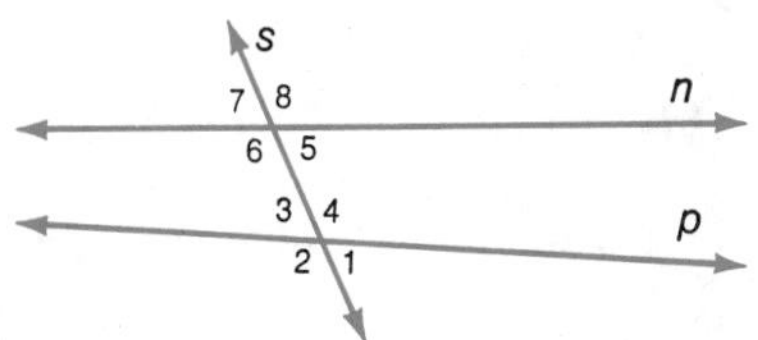

5. $\angle 6$ and $\angle 4$, $\angle 5$ and $\angle 3$
6. $\angle 7$ and $\angle 1$, $\angle 8$ and $\angle 2$
7. $\angle 5$ and $\angle 4$, $\angle 6$ and $\angle 3$
8. $\angle 7$ and $\angle 8$, $\angle 1$ and $\angle 2$
9. $\angle 5$ and $\angle 6$, $\angle 3$ and $\angle 4$

a. Interior angles
b. Interior angles on the same side of the transversal
c. Alternate interior angles
d. Exterior angles
e. Alternate exterior angles

Exercises

*Refer to the figure below for Exercises **1–4.** Classify each statement as* <u>True</u> *or* <u>False</u>.

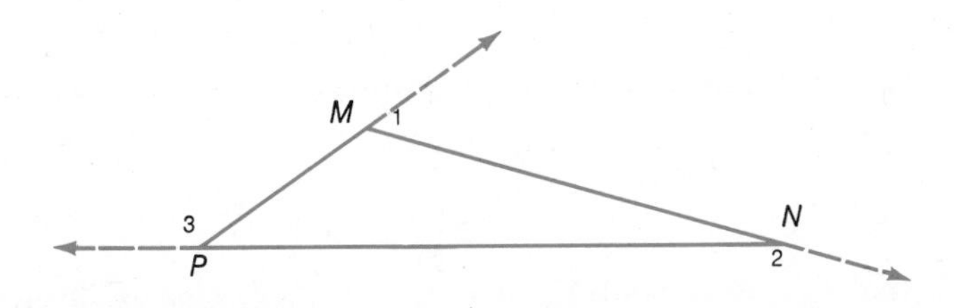

a

1. $\angle 3 > \angle MNP$
2. $\angle MPN < \angle 1$
3. $\angle 2 < \angle PMN$
4. $\angle MNP > \angle 1$

In the figure at the right, H is a point on $\overline{GF}$. Use the figure to complete each statement in Exercises **5–12.**

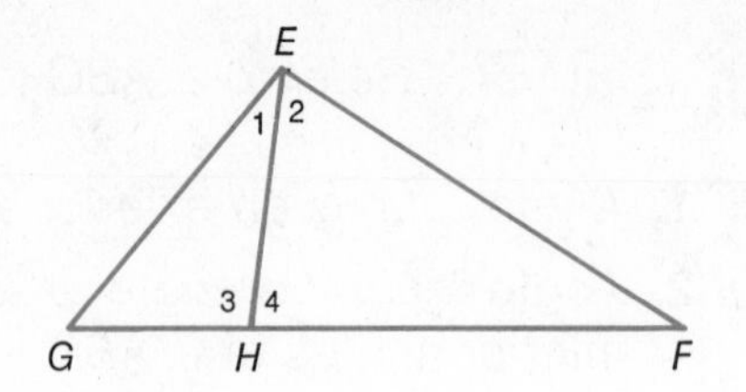

5. $\angle 3$ is an exterior angle for $\triangle$ _?_.

6. $\angle 4$ is an exterior angle for $\triangle$ _?_.

7. $\angle$ _?_ and $\angle$ _?_ are remote interior angles for $\angle 3$.

8. $\angle$ _?_ and $\angle$ _?_ are remote interior angles for $\angle 4$.

9. $m\angle 3$ _?_ $m\angle F$ ($>$, $<$, or $=$)

10. $m\angle 1$ _?_ $m\angle 4$ ($>$, $<$, or $=$)

11. $m\angle G$ _?_ $m\angle 4$ ($>$, $<$, or $=$)

12. $m\angle 2$ _?_ $m\angle 3$ ($>$, $<$, or $=$)

For each given pair of lines and transversal, name the interior angles, exterior angles, alternate interior angles, and alternate exterior angles.

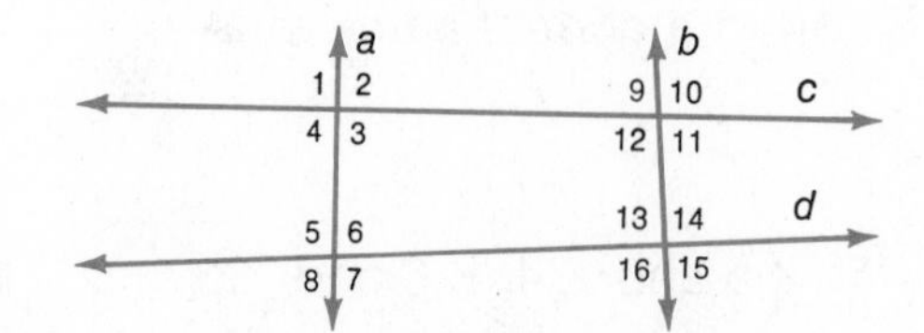

13. Lines *c* and *d*, transversal *a*

14. Lines *c* and *d*, transversal *b*

15. Lines *a* and *b*, transversal *c*

16. Lines *a* and *b*, transversal *d*

17. Prove Theorem 4-1. (HINT: Follow the plan on page 155. To prove $m\angle BCD > m\angle A$, extend $\overrightarrow{BC}$ to a point *P* and show that $m\angle BCD = m\angle ACP$.)

b

18. Use the figure at the right to prove that $m\angle 1 > m\angle 3$.

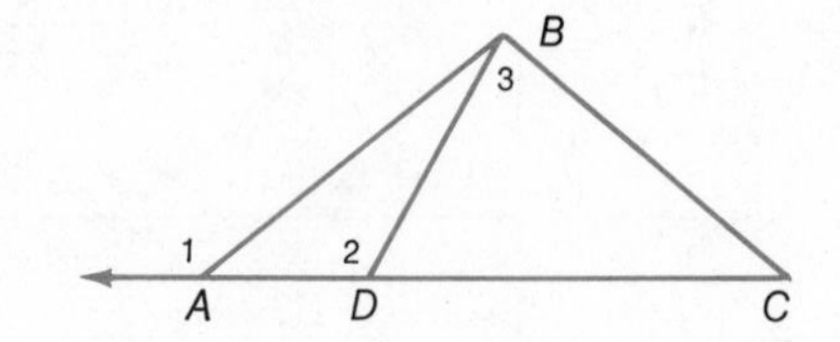

Remember

Classify each statement as True *or* False*. If a statement is false, tell why it is false.*

1. A mathematical statement can be both true and false at the same time.

2. The negation of a statement is its converse.

3. A contradiction is a statement such as $\angle A \cong \angle B$ and $\angle A \ncong \angle B$.

4. The first step in an indirect proof is to assume the negation of what you want to prove.

The answers are on page 197. If you need help, see pages 135 and 136.

4-2 Parallel Lines and Angles

Recall that **parallel lines** are lines in the same plane that do not intersect. Lines *r* and *s* below are parallel.

$r \parallel s$ ⟵ Read: "Line *r* is parallel to line *s*."

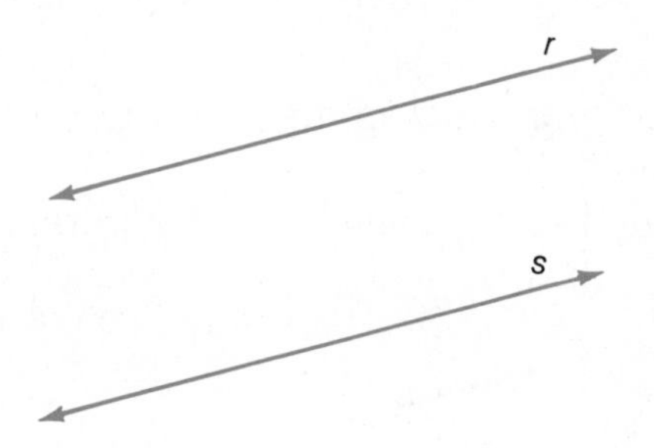

Suppose that a point and a line, such as point *P* and line *k* are given. Postulate 15 states that there is exactly one line through *P* parallel to line *k*.

Postulate 15: Through a point not on a given line, there is exactly one line parallel to the given line.

There are two theorems that show a relationship between two lines cut by a transversal and the alternate interior angles that are formed.

Theorem 4-2: If two lines are cut by a transversal so that alternate interior angles are congruent, then the lines are parallel.

Given: Lines k and m are cut by transversal t; $\angle 1 \cong \angle 2$

Prove: $k \parallel m$

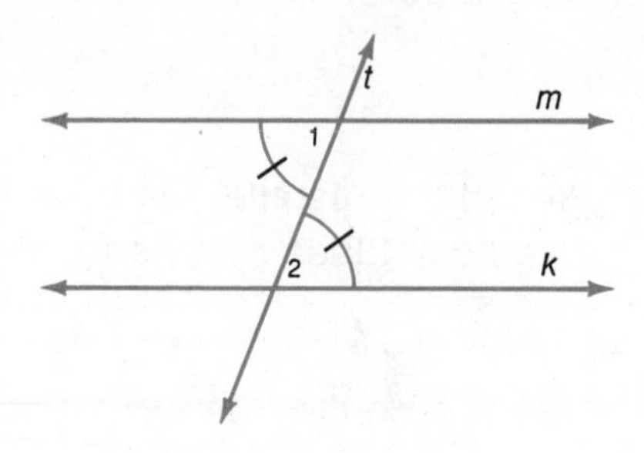

The indirect method is used.

Proof: Assume k is <u>not</u> parallel to m (see the figure below).

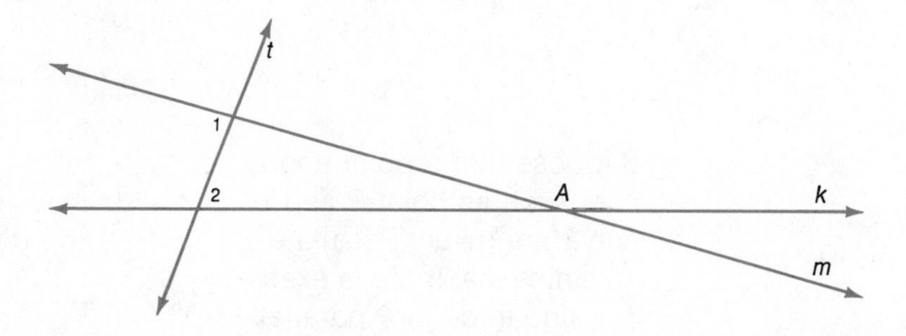

If k and m are not parallel, then they intersect in some point A.

$\angle 1$ is an exterior angle of the triangle formed by lines k, m, and t.

Then $m\angle 1 > m\angle 2$ by the Exterior Angle Inequality Theorem.

Thus, $m\angle 1 = m\angle 2$ and $m\angle 1 > m\angle 2$. This is a contradiction.

The assumption that k is not parallel to m must be false. Therefore, $k \parallel m$.

Theorem 4-3 is the converse of Theorem 4-2. Thus, the two theorems can be restated as a biconditional.

Theorem 4-3: If two parallel lines are cut by a transversal, then alternate interior angles are congruent.

Given: Line t is a transversal; $k \parallel m$

Prove: $\angle 1 \cong \angle 2$

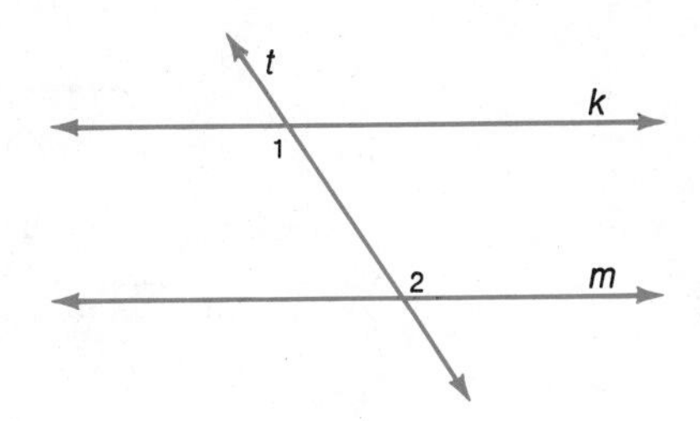

The indirect method is used.

Proof: Assume $\angle 1 \ncong \angle 2$ (see the figure below).

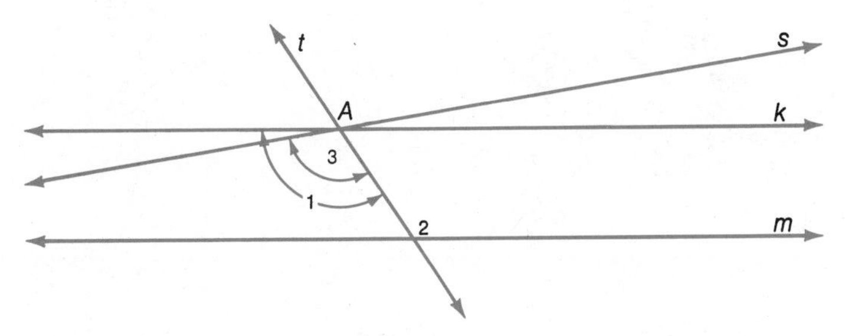

By Postulate 9 there is an angle, $\angle 3$, formed by line t and a line s through a point A such that $\angle 3 \cong \angle 2$.

Thus, $s \parallel m$ by Theorem 4-2.

Two lines, s and k, are parallel to m and pass through point A. This contradicts Postulate 15.

The assumption that $\angle 1$ is not congruent to $\angle 2$ must be false. Then $\angle 1 \cong \angle 2$.

Remember that segments of parallel lines are parallel and that lines and rays determined by parallel segments are parallel.

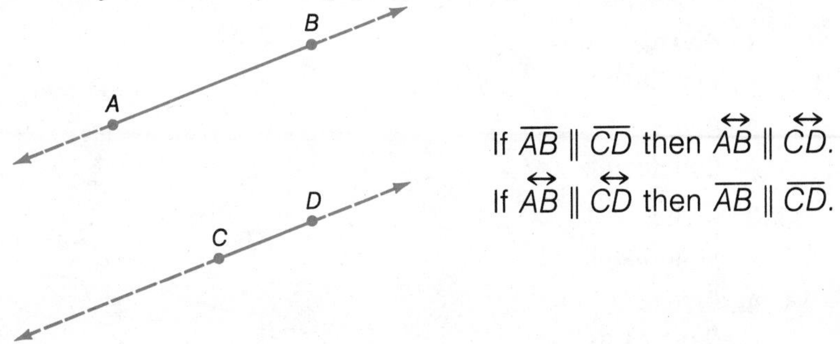

If $\overline{AB} \parallel \overline{CD}$ then $\overleftrightarrow{AB} \parallel \overleftrightarrow{CD}$.
If $\overleftrightarrow{AB} \parallel \overleftrightarrow{CD}$ then $\overline{AB} \parallel \overline{CD}$.

Try These

For each figure below, $\angle 1 \cong \angle 2$. Name the lines or segments that are parallel.

1.

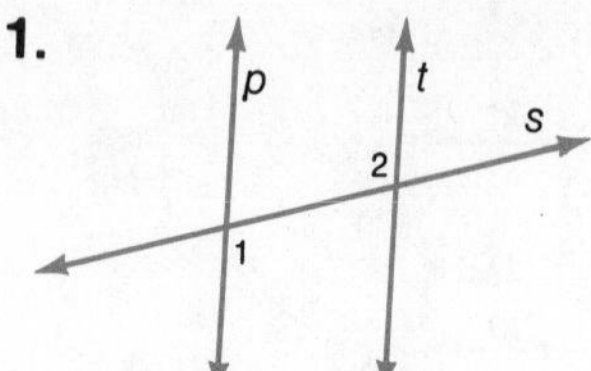

2.

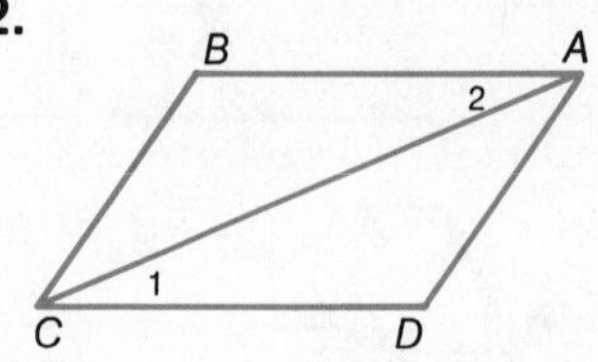

3.

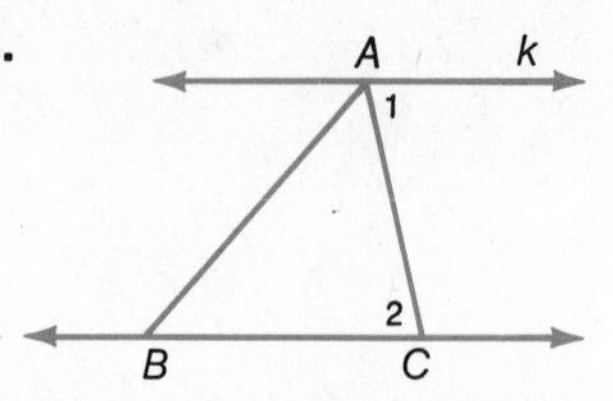

For each figure below, line a is parallel to line b. Name only the pairs of congruent alternate interior angles that are numbered.

4.

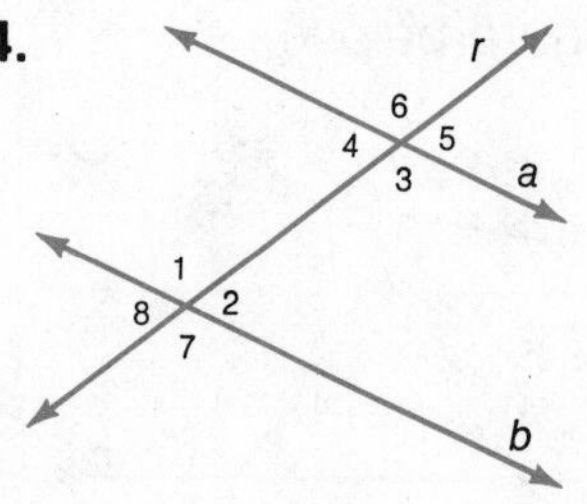

5.

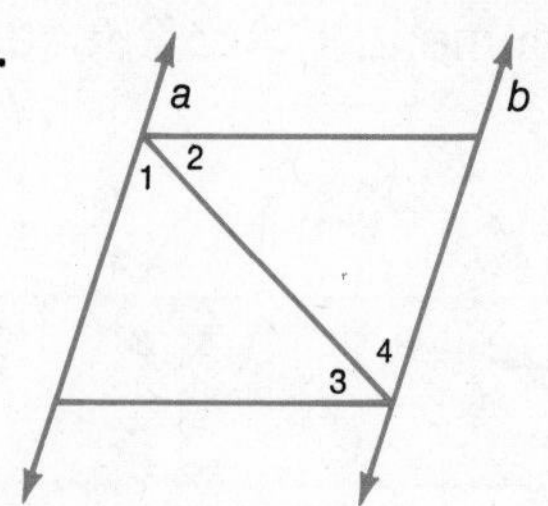

6.

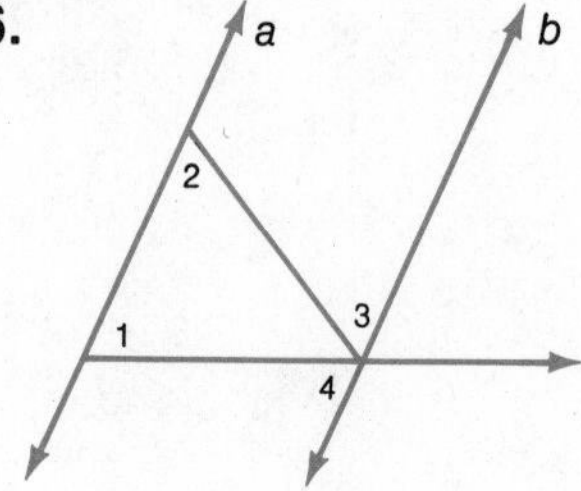

7. Restate Theorems 4-2 and 4-3 as a biconditional.

Exercises

*For Exercises **1–4,** use the given information and the figure below to complete each conclusion.*

a

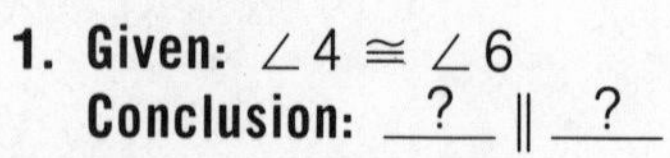

1. Given: $\angle 4 \cong \angle 6$
Conclusion: ? $\parallel$?

2. Given: $\angle 5 \cong \angle 9$
Conclusion: ? $\parallel$?

3. Given: $\angle 13 \cong \angle 11$
Conclusion: ? $\parallel$?

4. Given: $\angle 4 \cong \angle 16$
Conclusion: ? $\parallel$?

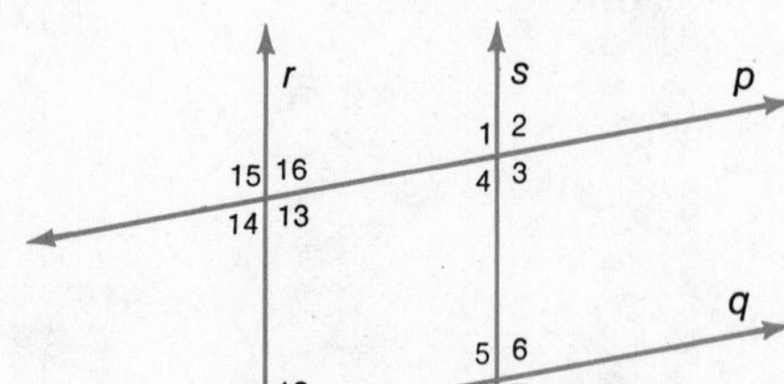

*For Exercises **5–6,** use the figure for Exercises **1–4.***

5. If $p \parallel q$, name 4 pairs of congruent alternate interior angles.

6. If $r \parallel s$, name 4 pairs of congruent alternate interior angles.

*For Exercises **7–12,** use the given information and figure to complete each conclusion.*

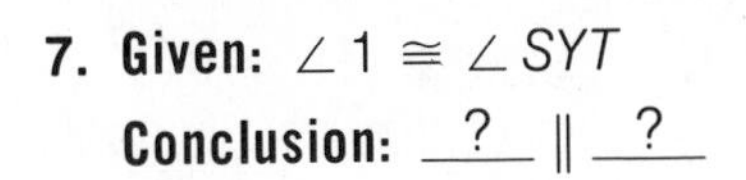

7. Given: $\angle 1 \cong \angle SYT$

Conclusion: $\underline{\ ?\ } \parallel \underline{\ ?\ }$

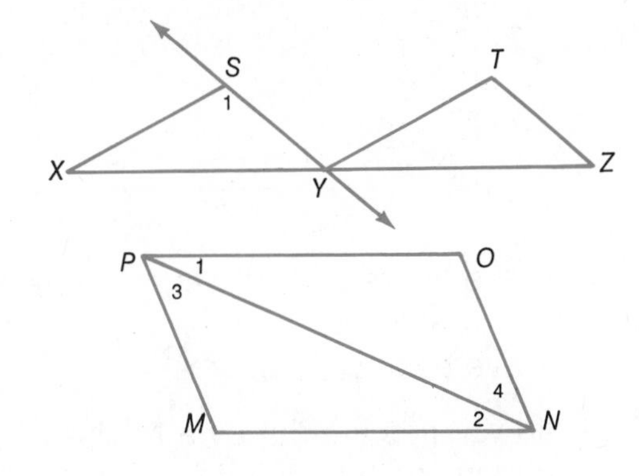

8. Given: $\angle T \cong \angle TYS$

Conclusion: $\underline{\ ?\ } \parallel \underline{\ ?\ }$

9. Given: $\overline{MN} \parallel \overline{PO}$

Conclusion: $\angle \underline{\ ?\ } \cong \angle \underline{\ ?\ }$

10. Given: $\overline{MP} \parallel \overline{NO}$

Conclusion: $\angle \underline{\ ?\ } \cong \angle \underline{\ ?\ }$

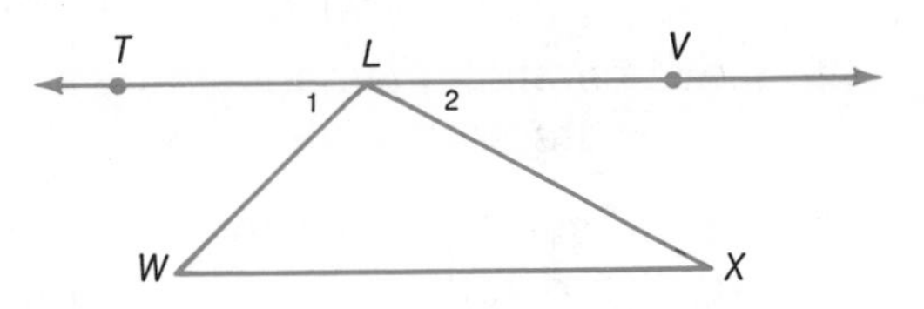

11. Given: $\angle 1 \cong \angle W$

Conclusion: $\underline{\ ?\ }$

12. Given: $\angle 2 \cong \angle X$

Conclusion: $\underline{\ ?\ }$

*Use the figure at the right for Exercises **13–14.***

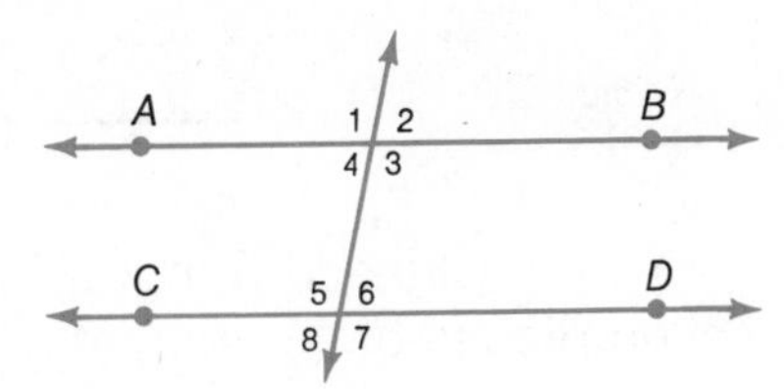

13. Given: $\overleftrightarrow{AB} \parallel \overleftrightarrow{CD}$; $m\angle 3 = 100$

Find: $m\angle 5$; $m\angle 6$; $m\angle 7$

14. Given: $\overleftrightarrow{AB} \parallel \overleftrightarrow{CD}$; $m\angle 6 = 38$

Find: $m\angle 4$; $m\angle 2$

*Use the figure at the right for Exercises **15–16.***

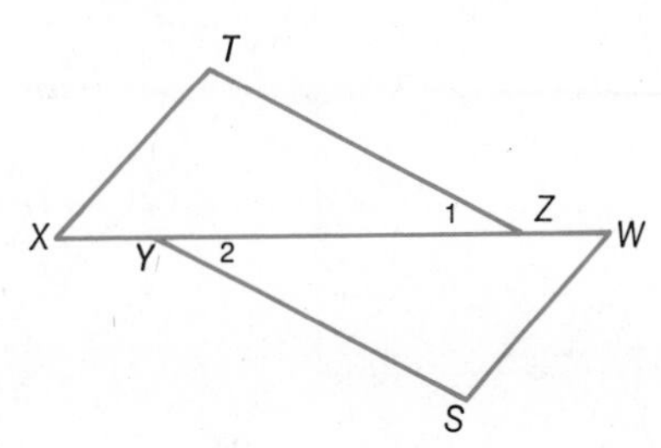

15. Given: $\overline{XY} \cong \overline{ZW}$; $\overline{TZ} \cong \overline{SY}$;
$\angle 1 \cong \angle 2$

Prove: $\overline{XT} \parallel \overline{WS}$

16. Given: $\overline{XT} \cong \overline{WS}$; $\overline{XY} \cong \overline{ZW}$;
$\overline{TZ} \cong \overline{SY}$

Prove: $\overline{TZ} \parallel \overline{SY}$

b

17. In the figure at the left below, $\overrightarrow{FK}$ bisects $\angle GFH$, $\overrightarrow{HJ}$ bisects $\angle PHF$, and $\angle 1 \cong \angle 2$. Prove that $\overrightarrow{FG} \parallel \overrightarrow{HP}$.

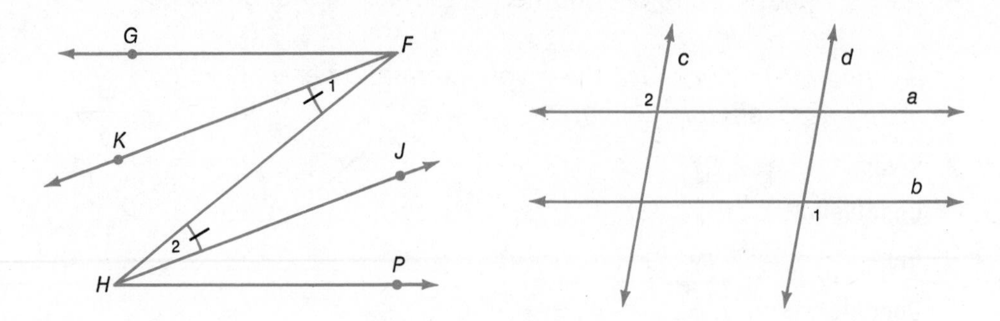

18. In the figure at the right above, $a \parallel b$ and $c \parallel d$. Prove that $\angle 1 \cong \angle 2$.

Prove each statement.

19. If two lines are cut by a transversal so that alternate exterior angles are congruent, then the lines are parallel.

20. If two parallel lines are cut by a transversal, then the alternate exterior angles are congruent.

21. If both pairs of opposite sides of a quadrilateral are congruent, then they are also parallel.

PUZZLE

This is a Chinese Tangram puzzle. How can you arrange the seven pieces of the square at the left to make the figure of a cat?

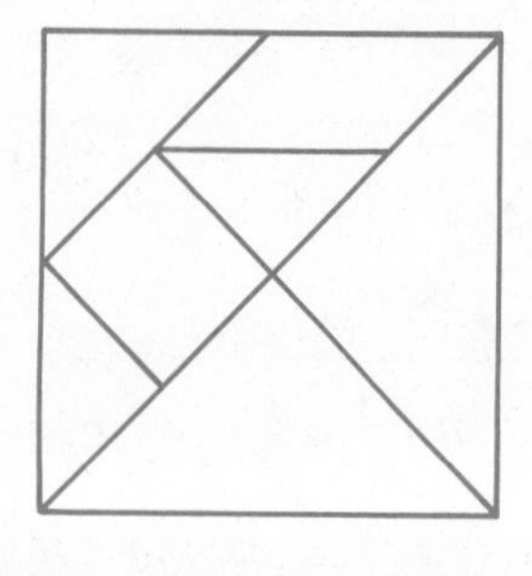

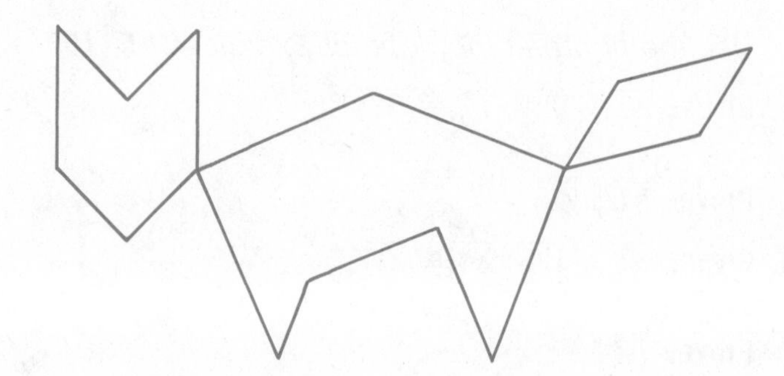

4-3 More Angle Relationships

You can use supplementary interior angles on the same side of a transversal to explain why two lines are parallel.

Example 1

In the figure at the right, $m\angle 2 = 60$ and $m\angle 3 = 120$. Explain why lines r and s are parallel.

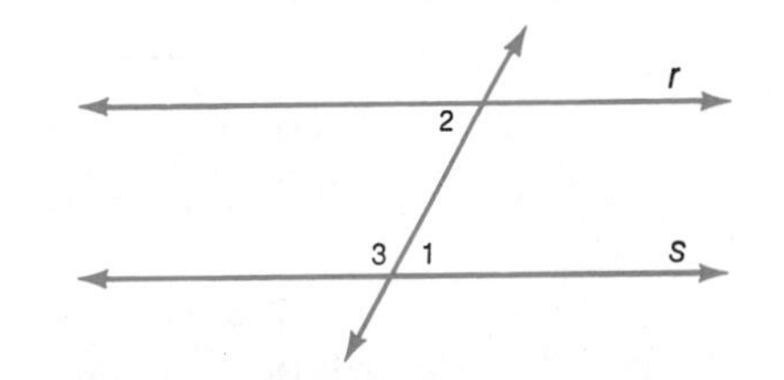

Angles 1 and 3 form a linear pair.	←	Definition of linear pair
$m\angle 1 + m\angle 3 = 180$	←	If two angles form a linear pair, then they are supplementary.
$m\angle 2 + m\angle 3 = 180$	←	Addition Postulate for Equations
$\angle 1 \cong \angle 2$	←	Supplements of the same angle are congruent.
$\therefore r \parallel s$	←	If two lines are cut by a transversal so that alternate interior angles are congruent, then the lines are parallel.

Example 1 suggests Theorem 4-4. You are asked to prove this theorem in the Exercises.

Theorem 4-4: If two lines are cut by a transversal so that interior angles on the same side of the transversal are supplementary, then the lines are parallel.

If you know that two lines are parallel, you can prove that interior angles on the same side of the transversal are supplementary.

Theorem 4-5: If two parallel lines are cut by a transversal, then interior angles on the same side of the transversal are supplementary.

You are asked to prove Theorem 4-5 in the Exercises. Note that Theorems 4-4 and 4-5 are converses of each other and that they can be restated as a biconditional.

Parallel lines can be used to determine a plane.

Theorem 4-6: Two parallel lines determine exactly one plane.

Several theorems relate parallel and perpendicular lines in a plane.

Example 2

In the figure at the right, $k \perp t$ and $m \perp t$. Explain why $k \parallel m$.

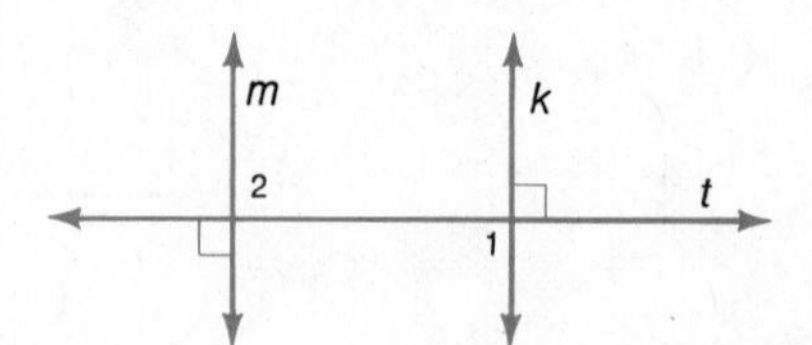

Angles 1 and 2 are right angles.	⟵	**Perpendicular lines form four right angles.**
$\angle 1 \cong \angle 2$	⟵	**All right angles are congruent.**
$\therefore k \parallel m$	⟵	**Since alternate interior angles are congruent, the lines are parallel.**

Example 2 suggests Theorem 4-7. You are asked to prove this theorem in the Exercises.

Theorem 4-7: In a plane, if two lines are both perpendicular to a third line, then the two lines are parallel.

Example 3

In the figure at the right, $n \parallel p$ and $n \perp q$. Explain why $q \perp p$.

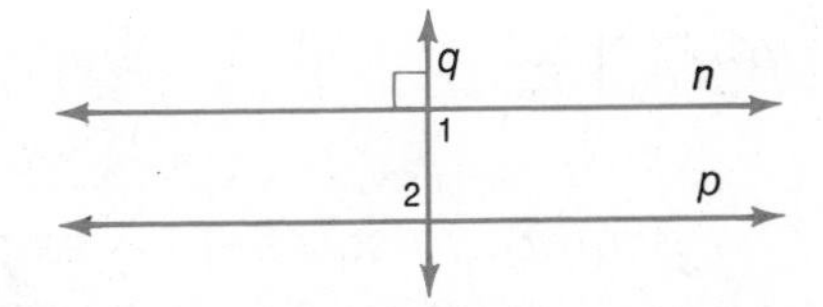

$\angle 1 \cong \angle 2$	⟵	If two parallel lines are cut by a transversal, then alternate interior angles are congruent.
$m\angle 1 = m\angle 2$	⟵	Congruent angles have equal measures.
$m\angle 1 = 90$	⟵	Perpendicular lines form four right angles.
$m\angle 2 = 90$	⟵	Substitution Principle
$q \perp p$	⟵	Definition of perpendicular lines

Example 3 suggests this theorem. You are asked to prove Theorem 4-8 in the Exercises.

Theorem 4-8: In a plane, if a line is perpendicular to one of two parallel lines, then it is perpendicular to the other line also.

Try These

*For Exercises **1–4,** $s \parallel t$.*

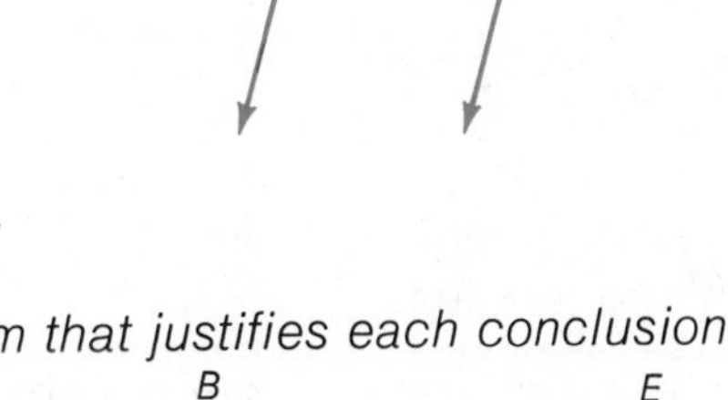

1. If $m\angle 2 = 63$, find $m\angle 3$.
2. If $m\angle 4 = 87$, find $m\angle 6$.
3. If $m\angle 6 = 3m\angle 7$, find $m\angle 6$ and $m\angle 7$.
4. In $m\angle 6 = x$, find $m\angle 7$ in terms of x.

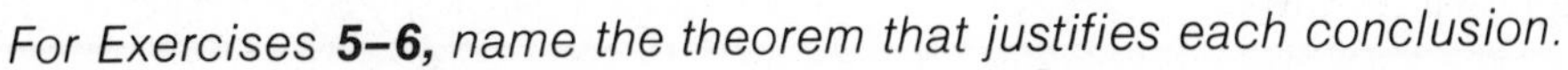
*For Exercises **5–6,** name the theorem that justifies each conclusion.*

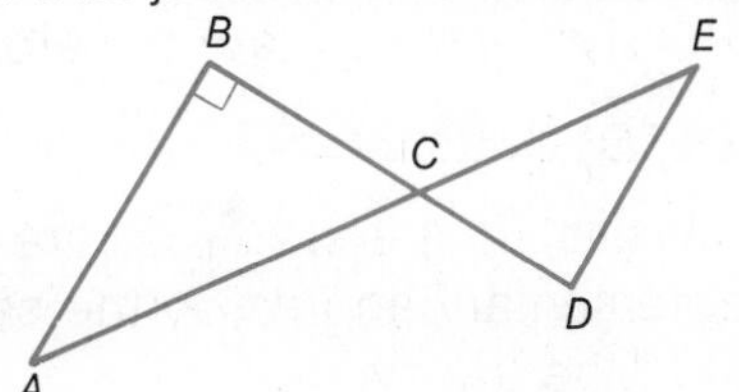

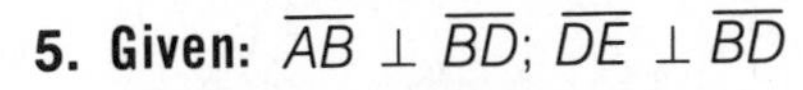
5. **Given:** $\overline{AB} \perp \overline{BD}$; $\overline{DE} \perp \overline{BD}$

   Conclusion: $\overline{AB} \parallel \overline{DE}$

6. **Given:** $\overline{AB} \parallel \overline{DE}$; $\overline{BD} \perp \overline{AB}$

   Conclusion: $\overline{BD} \perp \overline{DE}$

Exercises

*For Exercises **1–11,** use the given information to complete the conclusion. State the definition, postulate, or theorem that justifies each conclusion.*

a

1. **Given:** $m\angle 3 = 125$; $m\angle 6 = 55$

   Conclusion: __?__ $\parallel$ __?__

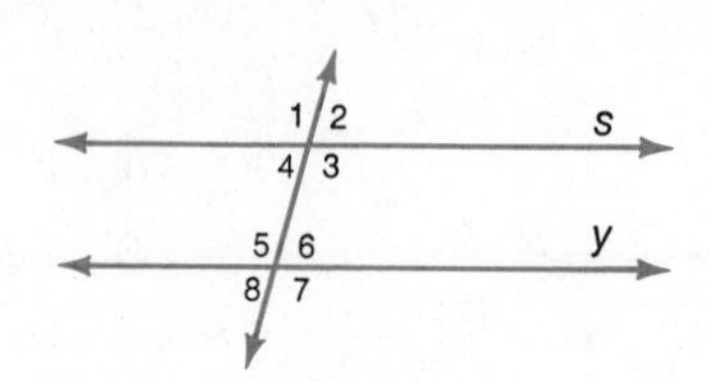

2. **Given:** $s \parallel y$; $m\angle 4 = 70$

   Conclusion: $m\angle 5 =$ __?__

3. **Given:** $\angle DCB$ and $\angle B$ are supplementary.

   Conclusion: __?__ $\parallel$ __?__

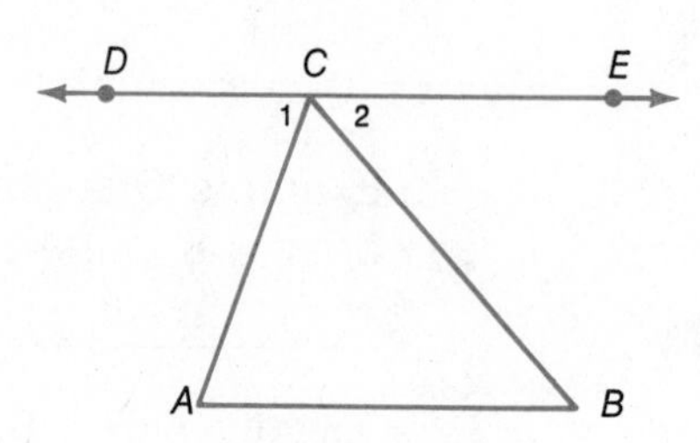

4. **Given:** $\angle ECA$ and $\angle A$ are supplementary.

   Conclusion: __?__ $\parallel$ __?__

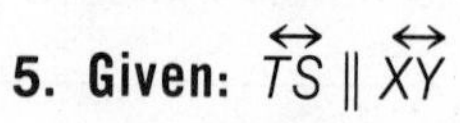

5. **Given:** $\overleftrightarrow{TS} \parallel \overleftrightarrow{XY}$

   Conclusions: a. $\angle XYZ$ and $\angle$ __?__ are alternate interior angles.

   b. $\angle$ __?__ and $\angle XYZ$ are interior angles on the same side of the transversal.

   c. $\angle$ __?__ and $\angle TZX$ are supplementary.

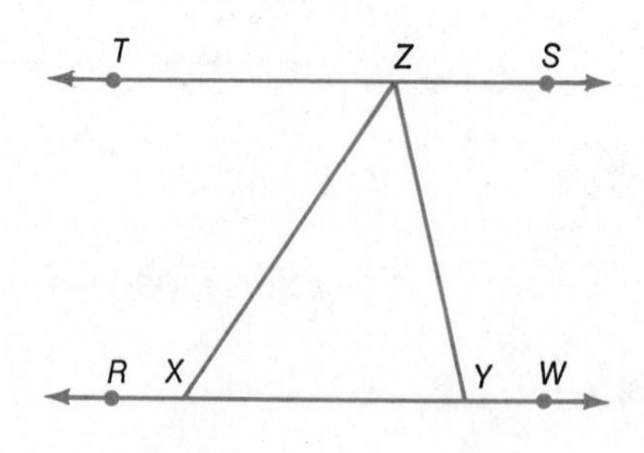

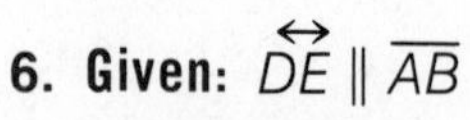

6. **Given:** $\overleftrightarrow{DE} \parallel \overline{AB}$

   Conclusion: $\angle$ __?__ and $\angle$ __?__ are congruent alternate interior angles.

   (NOTE: Two answers are possible.)

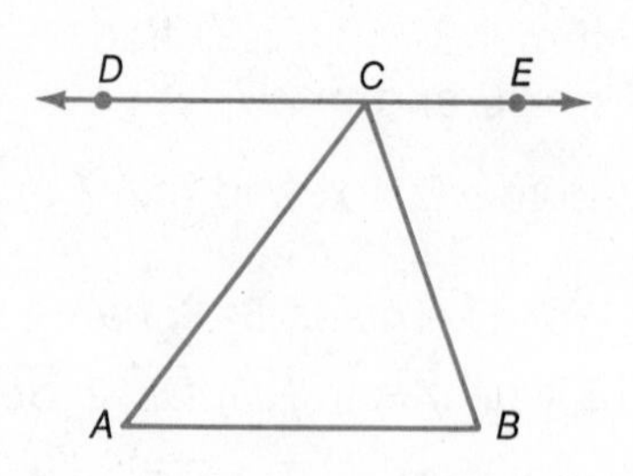

7. **Given:** $\overleftrightarrow{DE} \parallel \overline{AB}$

   Conclusion: $\angle A$ and $\angle$ __?__ are supplementary angles on the same side of the transversal.

8. **Given:** $\angle G$ and $\angle GMK$ are supplementary; $m\angle 1 = 58$; $m\angle 2 = 48$

Conclusions: $m\angle KMH = \underline{\ ?\ }$

$m\angle H = \underline{\ ?\ }$

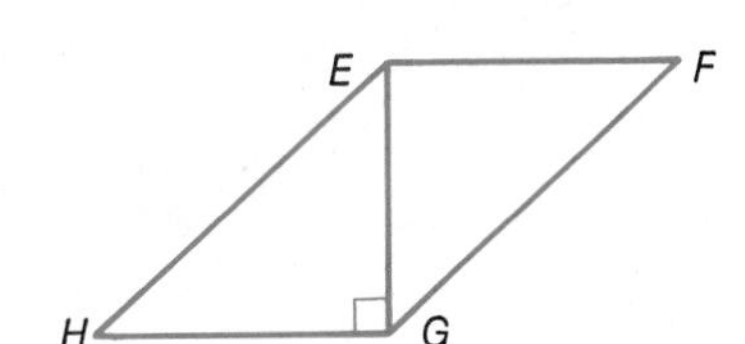

9. **Given:** $\angle G$ and $\angle GMK$ are supplementary; $m\angle 1 = 58$; $m\angle 2 = 48$

Conclusions: $m\angle KMG = \underline{\ ?\ }$

$m\angle G = \underline{\ ?\ }$

10. **Given:** $\overline{EF} \parallel \overline{HG}$; $\overline{EG} \perp \overline{HG}$

Conclusion: $\overline{EG}$ $\underline{\ ?\ }$ $\overline{EF}$

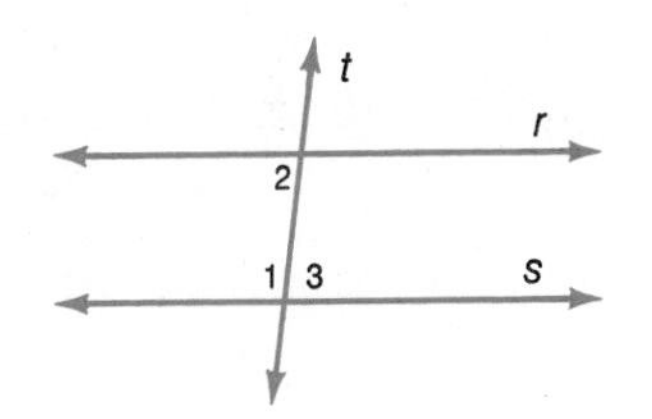

11. **Given:** $\overline{EF} \perp \overline{EG}$; $\overline{HG} \perp \overline{EG}$

Conclusion: $\overline{EF}$ $\underline{\ ?\ }$ $\overline{HG}$

12. Complete the proof of Theorem 4-4.

Given: Lines r and s are cut by transversal t, forming supplementary angles 1 and 2

Prove: $r \parallel s$

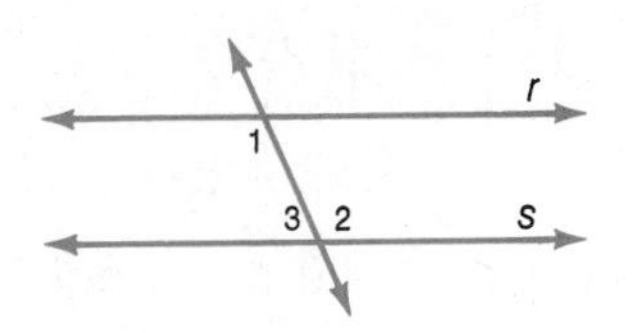

Statements	Reasons
1. $\angle 1$ and $\angle 2$ are supplementary.	1. Given
2. $\angle 1$ and $\angle 3$ are a linear pair.	2. Definition of linear pair

13. Complete the proof of Theorem 4-5.

Given: $r \parallel s$

Prove: $\angle 1$ and $\angle 3$ are supplementary.

Statements	Reasons
1. $r \parallel s$	1. $\underline{\ ?\ }$
2. $\angle 1 \cong \angle 2$	2. (1). $\underline{\ ?\ }$
3. $\angle 2$ and $\angle 3$ form a linear pair.	3. $\underline{\ ?\ }$
4. $m\angle 2 + m\angle 3 = 180$	4. (3). $\underline{\ ?\ }$
5. $m\angle 1 = m\angle 2$	5. (2). $\underline{\ ?\ }$
6. $m\angle 1 + m\angle 3 = 180$	6. (4). (5). $\underline{\ ?\ }$
7. $\angle 1$ and $\angle 3$ are supplementary.	7. (6). $\underline{\ ?\ }$

14. State Theorems 4-4 and 4-5 as a biconditional.

15. Prove Theorem 4-7. (HINT: Follow the method of Example 2.)

16. Prove Theorem 4-8. (HINT: Follow the method of Example 3.)

17. In $\triangle ABC$ below, $\overline{DE} \perp \overline{BC}$ and $m\angle B = 90$. Prove that $\overline{AB} \parallel \overline{DE}$.

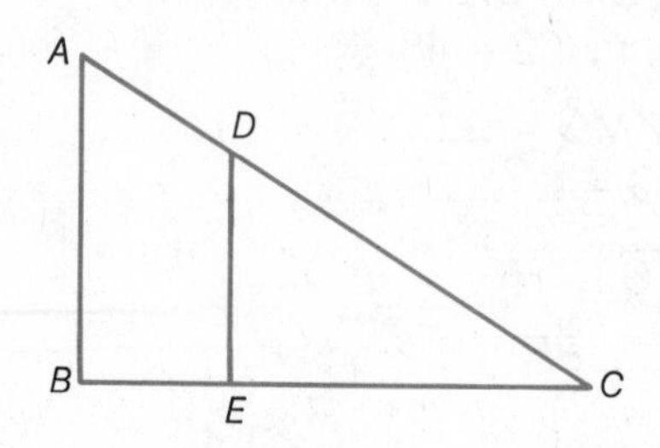

18. In the figure for Exercise **17**, $\triangle ABC$ is a right triangle with the right angle at B and $\overline{AB} \parallel \overline{DE}$. Prove that $\triangle DEC$ is a right triangle.

b

19. In the figure at the right, $m\angle 1 = 3x + 16$, $m\angle 2 = 2x - 11$, and line k is parallel to line n. Find x.

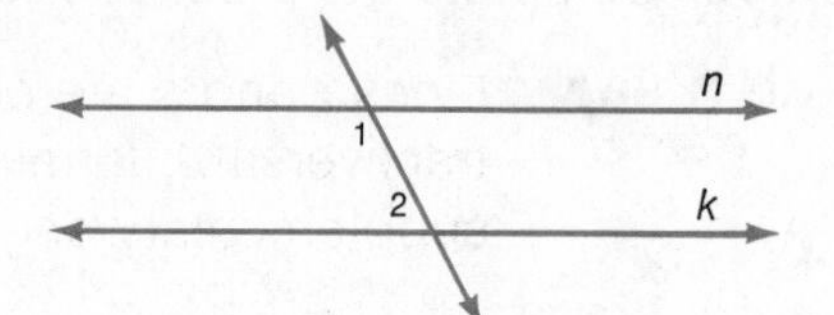

20. Prove Theorem 4-6.

Plan: By definition, parallel lines are coplanar. You must prove that they lie in exactly one plane. In the figure, line k is parallel to line m. Line m contains at least two points, A and B. Then line k and point A determine exactly one plane.

Complete the proof.

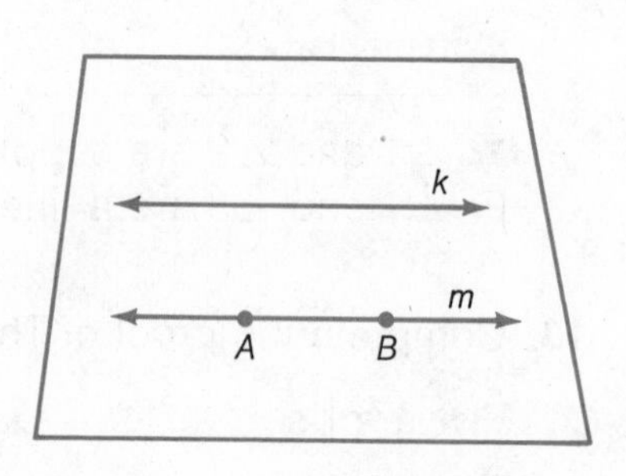

Write a proof for each statement in Exercises ***21–23.***

C

21. If two parallel lines are cut by a transversal, then the bisectors of two alternate interior angles are parallel.

22. Given that two lines are cut by a transversal, two alternate exterior angles are not congruent if and only if the two lines are not parallel.

23. If two parallel lines are cut by a transversal, the bisectors of two interior angles on the same side of the transversal are perpendicular.

Remember

*In Exercises **1–6,** describe each pair of angles as alternate interior, alternate exterior, or interior angles on the same side of a transversal.*

1. $\angle 1$ and $\angle 4$
2. $\angle 3$ and $\angle 8$
3. $\angle 6$ and $\angle 7$
4. $\angle 4$ and $\angle 9$
5. $\angle 1$ and $\angle 8$
6. $\angle 2$ and $\angle 5$

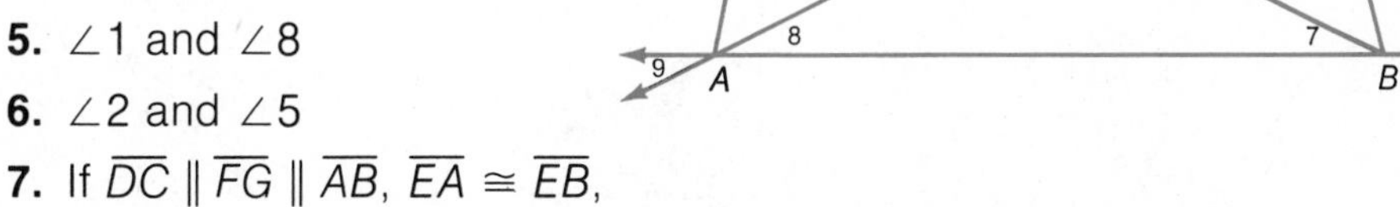

7. If $\overline{DC} \parallel \overline{FG} \parallel \overline{AB}$, $\overline{EA} \cong \overline{EB}$, and $m\angle 1 = 28$, find the measures of all the numbered angles.

The answers are on page 197. If you need help, see page 156.

think–draw–see

1. Draw a line *m* and a point *Q* not on line *m*.

2. Draw any line through *Q* so that it intersects *m*. Call the angle $\angle 1$.

3. Copy $\angle 1$ at *Q*. (Use a protractor or construct $\angle Q \cong \angle 1$.)

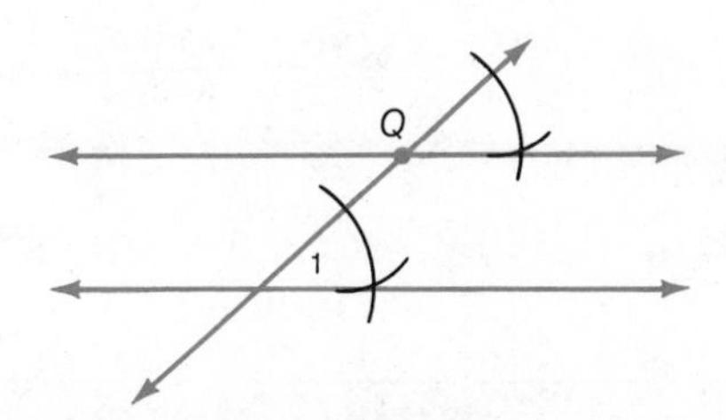

4. What seems to be true about line *m* and the new line *r*?

4-4 Corresponding Angles of Parallel Lines

In each figure below, ∠1 and ∠2 are **corresponding angles.**

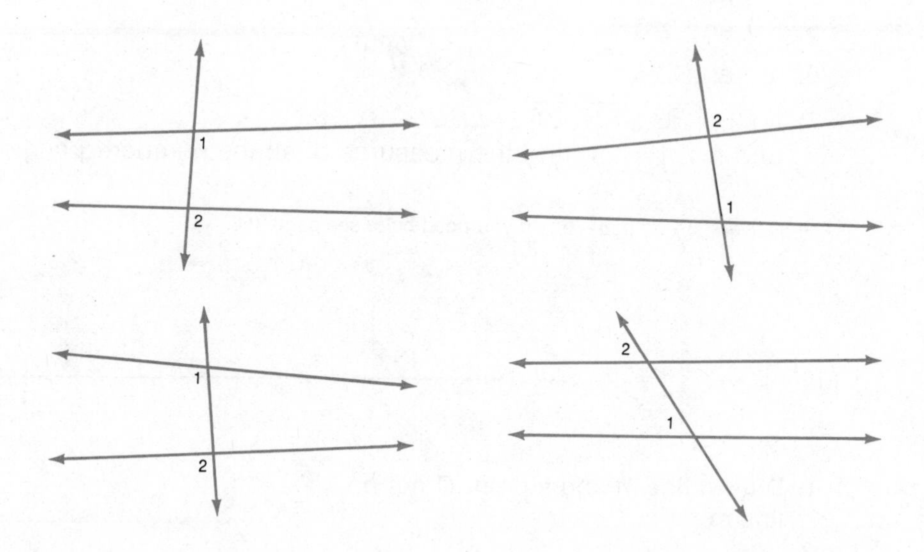

Example 1

Use the figure to name the corresponding angle for each angle in the table.

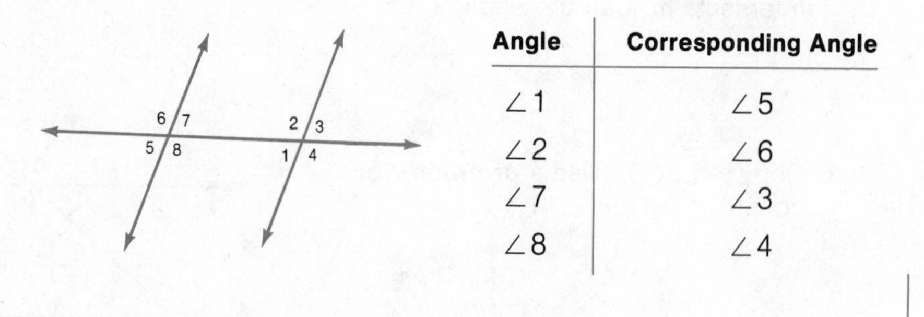

Angle	Corresponding Angle
∠1	∠5
∠2	∠6
∠7	∠3
∠8	∠4

Corresponding angles can be used to show that lines are parallel.

Example 2

In the figure at the right, $m\angle 1 = m\angle 2 = 60$. Explain why lines r and s are parallel.

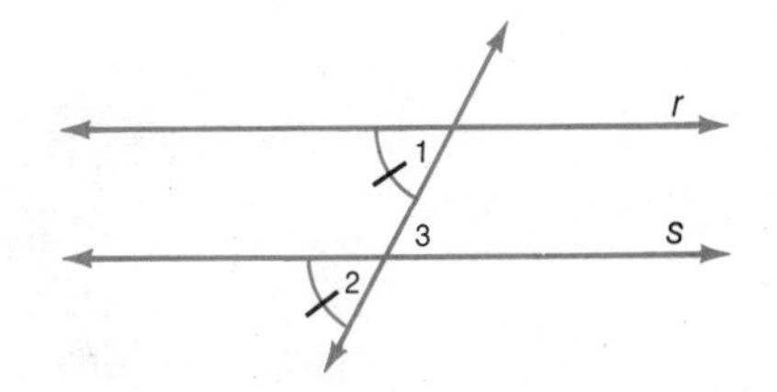

$\angle 1 \cong \angle 2$ ⟵ Angles that have the same measure are congruent.

$\angle 2 \cong \angle 3$ ⟵ Vertical angles are congruent.

$\angle 1 \cong \angle 3$ ⟵ Transitive Property of Congruence

$r \parallel s$ ⟵ If two lines are cut by a transversal so that alternate interior angles are congruent, then the lines are parallel.

Example 2 suggests this theorem.

Theorem 4-9: If two lines are cut by a transversal so that corresponding angles are congruent, then the lines are parallel.

The converse of Theorem 4-9 is also a theorem.

Theorem 4-10: If two parallel lines are cut by a transversal, then corresponding angles are congruent.

Theorems 4-9 and 4-10 can be restated as a biconditional. You are asked to prove these theorems in the Exercises.

The proof outlined on page 174 for Theorem 4-11 is for coplanar lines. However, Theorem 4-11 can be proved for three or more lines that are not all coplanar.

Theorem 4-11: Two distinct lines parallel to the same line are parallel to each other.

Given: $a \parallel c$; $b \parallel c$

Prove: $a \parallel b$

Plan: If lines a, b, and c are coplanar, draw transversal t. Prove that $\angle 1 \cong \angle 2$. Then use Theorem 4-9.

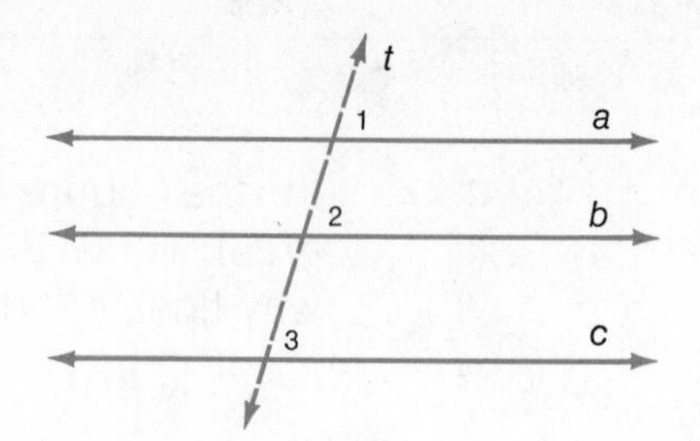

Try These

*Use the figure at the right for Exercises **1–4.***

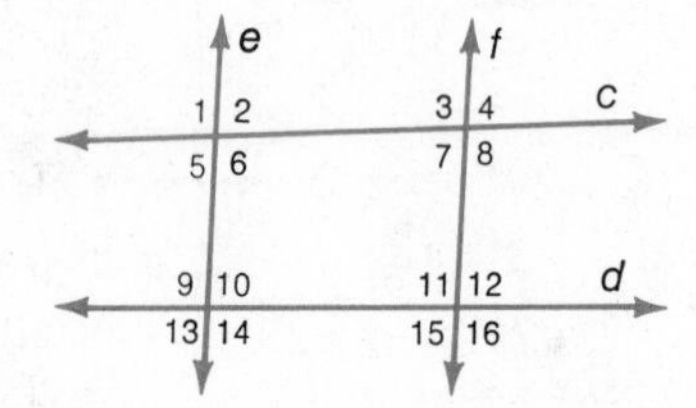

	Lines	Transversal	Alternate Interior Angles	Corresponding Angles
1.	c,d	e	?	?
2.	c,d	f	?	?
3.	e,f	c	?	?
4.	e,f	d	?	?

Exercises

a

1. Name five pairs of corresponding angles in Figure 1.

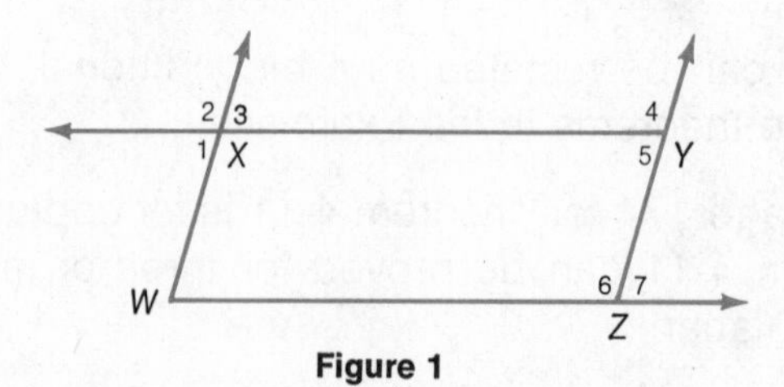

Figure 1

Figure 2

*Use Figure 2 to answer Exercises **2–3.***

2. For $\overline{AC}$, $\overrightarrow{BE}$ and transversal $\overrightarrow{AD}$, name the corresponding angles.

3. For $\overline{AC}$, $\overrightarrow{BE}$ and transversal $\overline{CB}$, name the alternate interior angles.

*Use the given information to complete the conclusion. Name the theorem or postulate that justifies your answer. Use Figure 1 on page 174 for Exercises **4–5** and Figure 2 on page 174 for Exercises **6–8.***

4. Given: $\angle W \cong \angle 3$
Conclusion: $\underline{\ ?\ } \parallel \underline{\ ?\ }$

5. Given: $\angle 1 \cong \angle 5$
Conclusion: $\underline{\ ?\ } \parallel \underline{\ ?\ }$

6. Given: $\angle A \cong \angle 2$
Conclusion: $\underline{\ ?\ } \parallel \underline{\ ?\ }$

7. Given: $\angle 1 \cong \angle C$
Conclusion: $\underline{\ ?\ } \parallel \underline{\ ?\ }$

8. Given: $\overline{AC} \parallel \overrightarrow{BE}$, transversal $\overleftrightarrow{AD}$
Conclusion: $\angle \underline{\ ?\ } \cong \angle \underline{\ ?\ }$

9. Given: $\overline{VP} \parallel \overline{RM}$
Conclusions: $\angle VPM \cong \angle \underline{\ ?\ }$
$\angle 5 \cong \angle \underline{\ ?\ }$
$\angle 1 \cong \angle \underline{\ ?\ }$

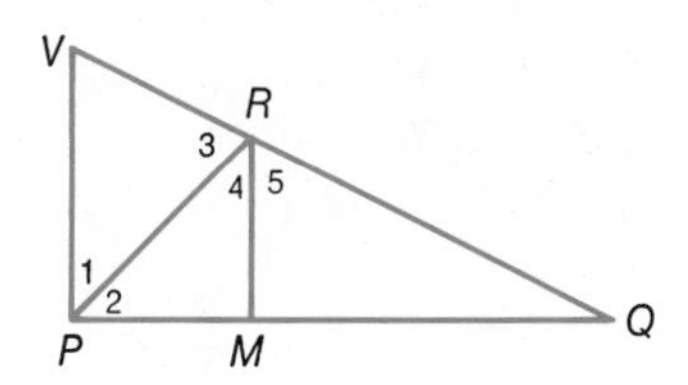

10. Given: $\overline{FD} \parallel \overline{AC}$; $\overline{EF} \parallel \overline{CB}$;
$m\angle BDF = 110$; $m\angle A = 40$
Conclusions: $m\angle C = \underline{\ ?\ }$
$m\angle AEF = \underline{\ ?\ }$
$m\angle 7 = \underline{\ ?\ }$
$m\angle 8 = \underline{\ ?\ }$
$m\angle B = \underline{\ ?\ }$

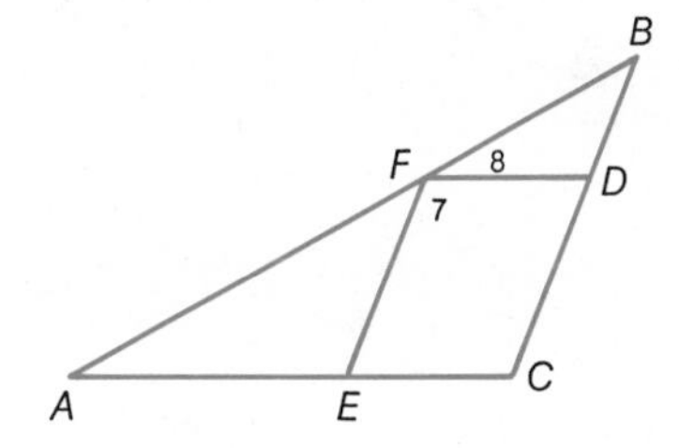

11. Given: $\overline{AB} \parallel \overline{XY}$; $\overline{CD} \parallel \overline{XY}$
Conclusion: $\underline{\ ?\ } \parallel \underline{\ ?\ }$

12. Given: $\overline{LM} \parallel \overline{KJ}$; $\overline{LM} \parallel \overline{GH}$
Conclusion: $\underline{\ ?\ } \parallel \underline{\ ?\ }$

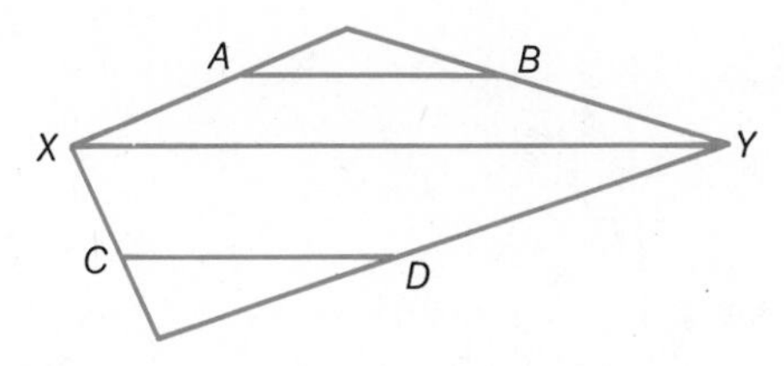

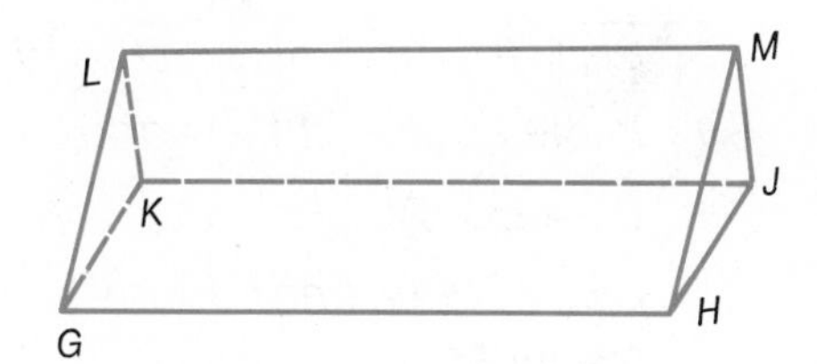

13. Restate Theorems 4-9 and 4-10 as a biconditional.

14. Prove Theorem 4-9. (HINT: Follow the procedure of Example 2.)

15. Prove Theorem 4-10.

16. Prove Theorem 4-11 for three coplanar lines. (HINT: Follow the plan on page 174.)

17. In $\triangle ABC$ at the right, $\angle A \cong \angle 1$. Prove that $\angle B \cong \angle 2$. (HINT: First use Theorem 4-9. Then use Theorem 4-10.)

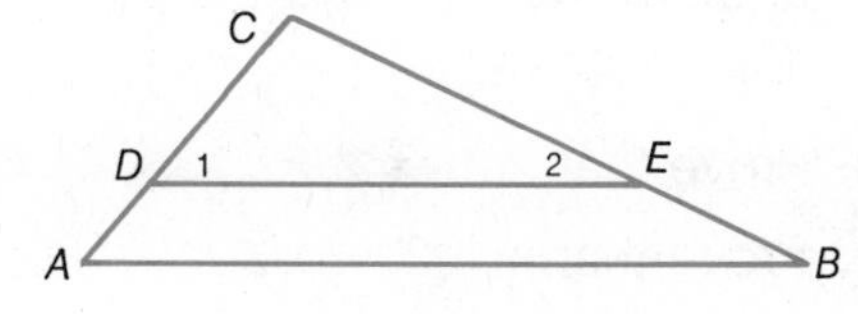

18. Complete the proof.

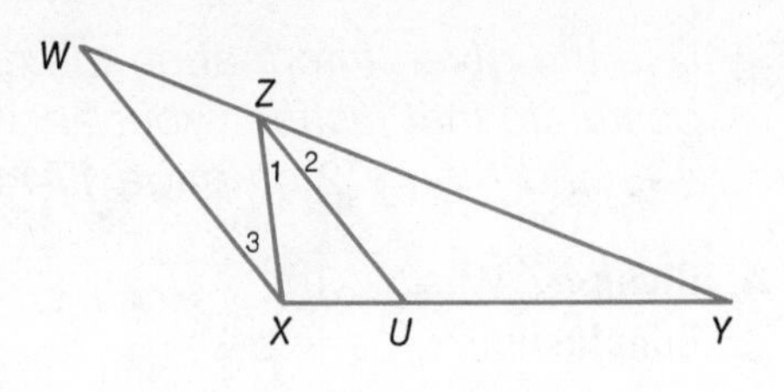

Given: $\overline{ZU} \parallel \overline{WX}$; $\angle 1 \cong \angle 2$

Prove: $\overline{ZW} \cong \overline{ZX}$

Statements	Reasons
1. $\angle 1 \cong \angle 2$; $\overline{ZU} \parallel \overline{WX}$	1. Given
2. $\angle 1 \cong \angle 3$	2. (1). ___?___
3. ___?___	3. (1). (2). Transitive property of $\cong$
4. $\angle 2 \cong \angle W$	4. ___?___
5. $\angle 3 \cong \angle W$	5. ___?___
6. ___?___	6. ___?___

19. In the figure at the left below, $\overline{FD} \parallel \overline{AC}$ and $\overline{EF} \parallel \overline{CB}$. Prove that $\angle C \cong \angle EFD$ and that $\angle CEF \cong \angle FDC$.

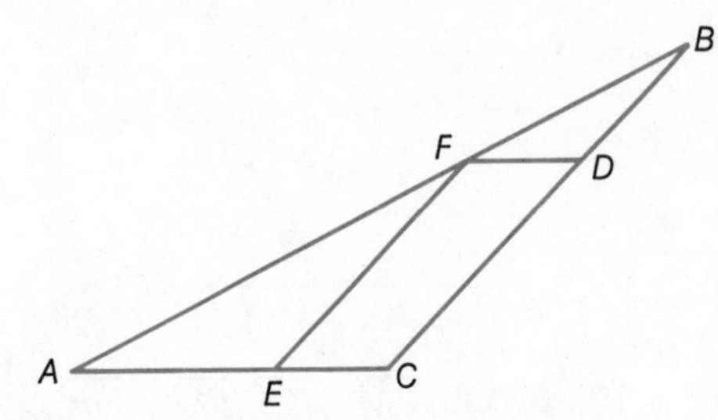

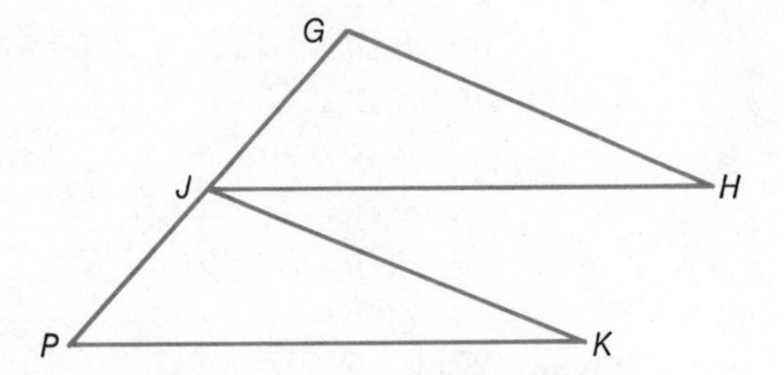

20. In the figure at the right above, J is the midpoint of $\overline{GP}$, $\overline{GH} \parallel \overline{JK}$ and $\overline{PK} \parallel \overline{JH}$. Prove that $\overline{JH} \cong \overline{PK}$.

In the figures at the right, $\overleftrightarrow{BD} \parallel \overrightarrow{EG}$, $\overrightarrow{AC} \parallel \overrightarrow{EF}$, *and* $\overleftrightarrow{BD}$, $\overrightarrow{AC}$, $\overrightarrow{EG}$, *and* $\overrightarrow{EF}$ *are coplanar.*

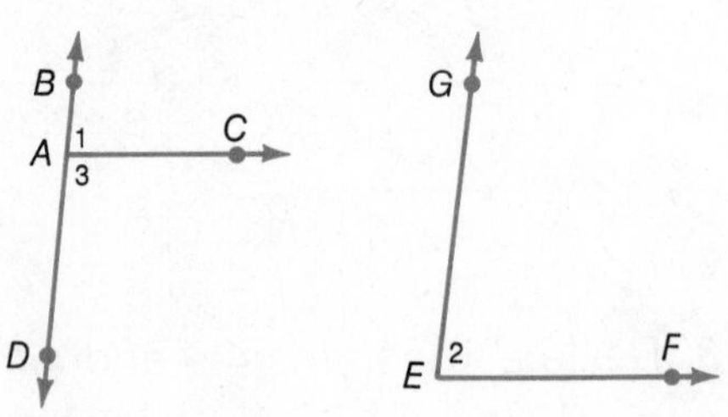

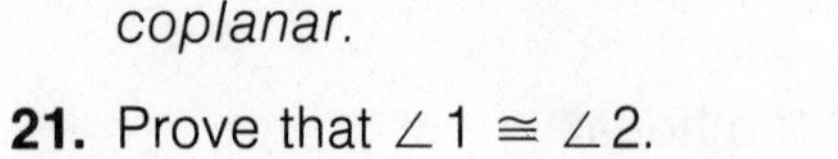

21. Prove that $\angle 1 \cong \angle 2$.

22. Prove that $m\angle 2 + m\angle 3 = 180$.

In the figures at the right, $\overleftrightarrow{BD} \perp \overrightarrow{EG}$, $\overrightarrow{AC} \perp \overrightarrow{EF}$, $\overleftrightarrow{BD} \parallel \overrightarrow{EF}$, *and* $\overleftrightarrow{BD}$, $\overrightarrow{AC}$, $\overrightarrow{EF}$, *and* $\overrightarrow{EG}$ *are coplanar.*

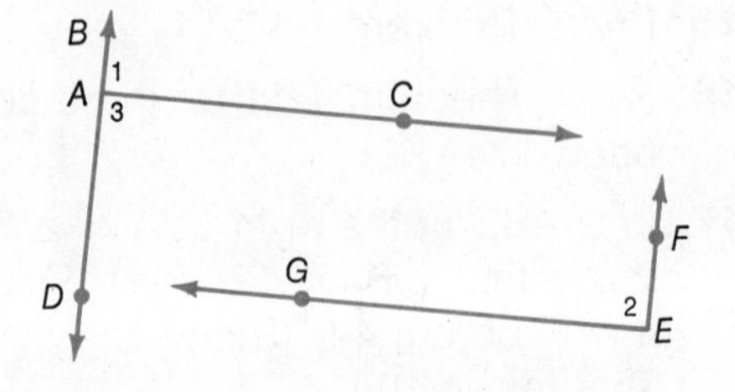

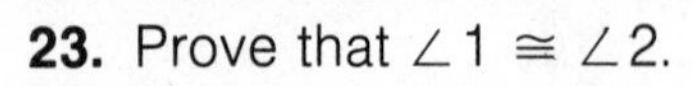

23. Prove that $\angle 1 \cong \angle 2$.

24. Prove that $m\angle 2 + m\angle 3 = 180$.

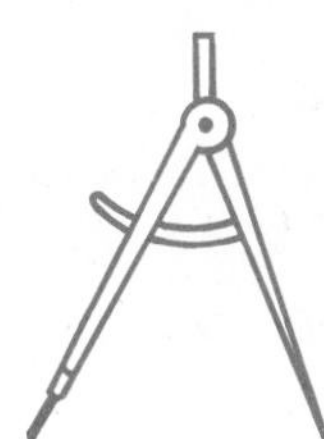

Construction

Constructing a Line Parallel to a Given Line

Given: Line q and point P not on line q

Required: To construct a line, $\overleftrightarrow{PT}$, that contains point P and is parallel to line q

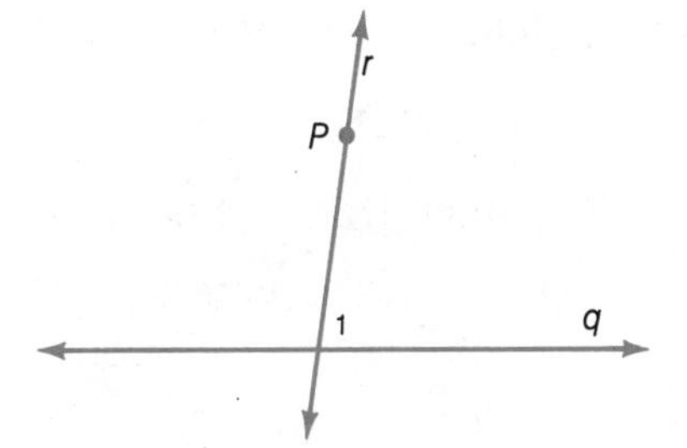

1. Draw a line, r, that contains P and intersects line q. Label the angle formed by the intersecting lines $\angle 1$.

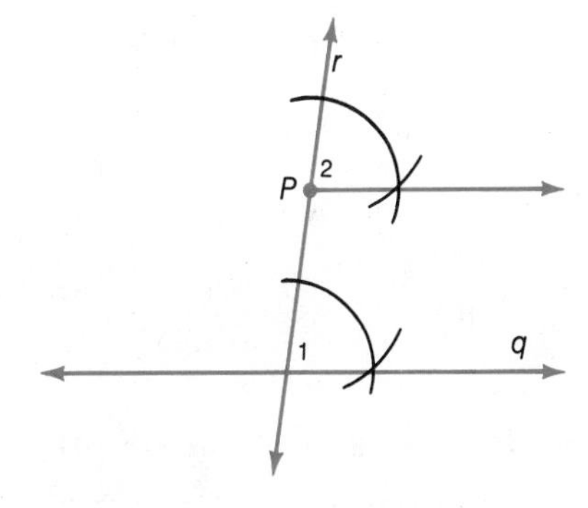

2. At point P construct $\angle 2$, such that $\angle 1$ and $\angle 2$ are corresponding congruent angles.

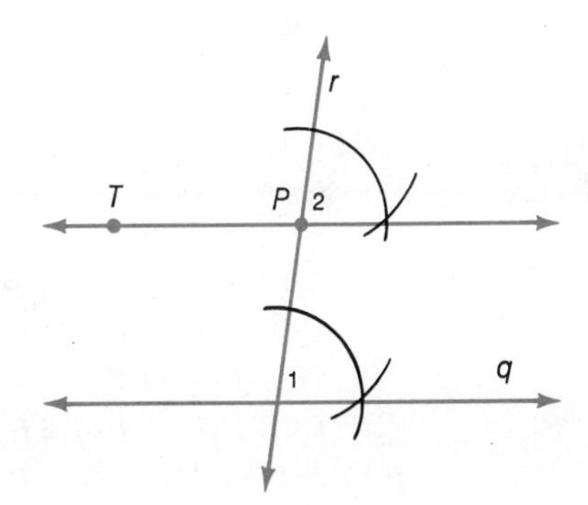

3. Draw $\overleftrightarrow{PT}$.

Then, since $\angle 1 \cong \angle 2$, $\overleftrightarrow{PT} \parallel$ line q by Theorem 4-9.

Exercises

1. Through a point A not on line r, construct line XA parallel to line r.
2. Draw an acute scalene triangle and label it ABC. Through C, construct a line parallel to $\overline{AB}$.
3. Use a protractor to draw angle XYZ with a measure of 120°. Through point Z, construct line ZQ parallel to $\overrightarrow{YX}$, and through point X construct line XT parallel to $\overrightarrow{YZ}$.
4. At point T on a line TR construct a right angle RTN. At point R on line TR construct line RV parallel to $\overleftrightarrow{TN}$.
5. **Given:** $\overleftrightarrow{AB}$

   Required: To construct a line EF parallel to $\overleftrightarrow{AB}$ at a distance of 2 centimeters from $\overleftrightarrow{AB}$. (HINT: Begin with $\overleftrightarrow{AB}$ and a segment whose length is 2 centimeters.)

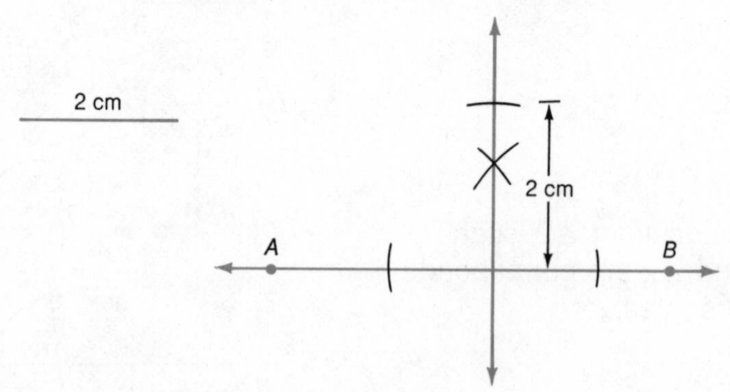

6. Draw an acute scalene triangle ABC and construct altitude BD. Then construct a line that intersects $\overline{AB}$, is parallel to $\overline{AC}$, and whose distance from $\overline{AC}$ is $\frac{1}{2}BD$.

PUZZLE

One fourth of a square has been cut away. How can you cut the remaining three quarters into four congruent parts? (HINT: No part is a square or a triangle.)

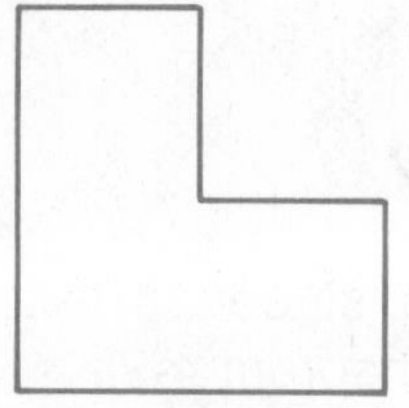

4-5 The Angles of a Triangle

You have often used the Triangle–Sum Theorem when finding the measures of the angles of a triangle. Now you can prove the theorem.

Theorem 4-12: Triangle–Sum Theorem

The sum of the measures of the angles of a triangle is 180.

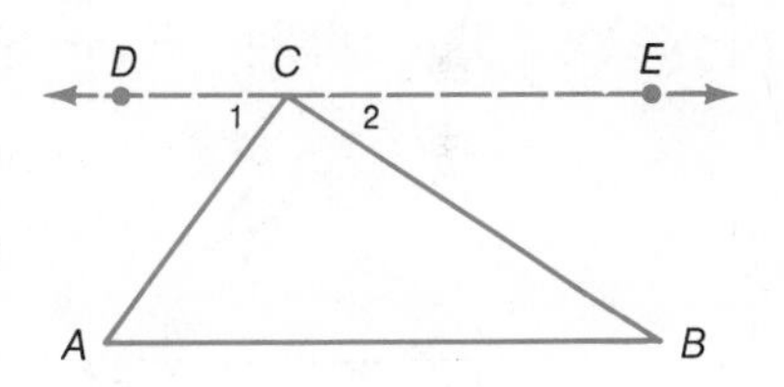

Given: Triangle ABC

Prove: $m\angle A + m\angle B + m\angle ACB = 180$

Statements	Reasons
1. Through point C, draw $\overleftrightarrow{DE}$ parallel to $\overline{AB}$.	1. Postulate 15, page 159
2. $\angle 1$ and $\angle ACE$ are a linear pair.	2. Definition of a linear pair
3. $m\angle 1 + m\angle ACE = 180$	3. (2). If two angles form a linear pair, then they are supplementary.
4. $m\angle 2 + m\angle ACB = m\angle ACE$	4. Angle Addition Property
5. $m\angle 1 + m\angle 2 + m\angle ACB = 180$	5. (3). (4). Substitution Principle
6. $\angle A \cong \angle 1$, $\angle B \cong \angle 2$	6. (1). If parallel lines are cut by a transversal, alternate interior angles are congruent.
7. $m\angle A = m\angle 1$, $m\angle B = m\angle 2$	7. (6). Congruent angles have equal measures.
8. $m\angle A + m\angle B + m\angle ACB = 180$	8. (5). (7). Substitution Principle

You can use the Triangle–Sum Theorem to find the measures of angles in a triangle.

Example 1

Find the measure of angle A.

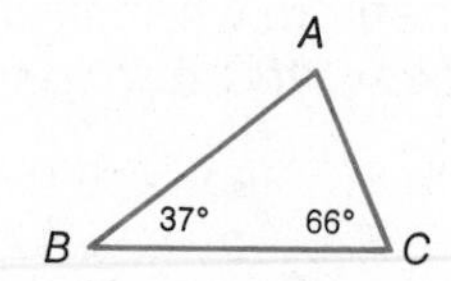

$37 + 66 + m\angle A = 180$ ⟵ Triangle–Sum Theorem
$103 + m\angle A = 180$ ⟵ Solve for $m\angle A$.
$m\angle A = 180 - 103$
$m\angle A = 77$

Example 2

Find the measure of angle R.

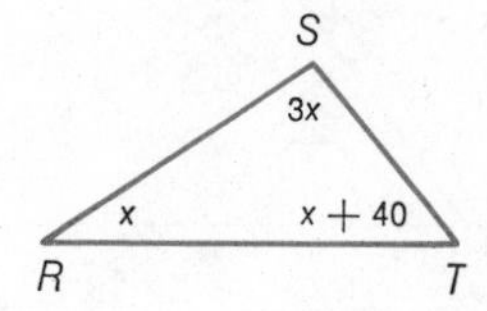

$x + 3x + x + 40 = 180$ ⟵ Triangle–Sum Theorem
$5x + 40 = 180$ ⟵ Solve for x.
$5x = 140$
$x = 28$ ⟵ $m\angle R$

You can also use the Triangle–Sum Theorem to show that angles are congruent.

Example 3

Show that $\angle 1 \cong \angle 2$.

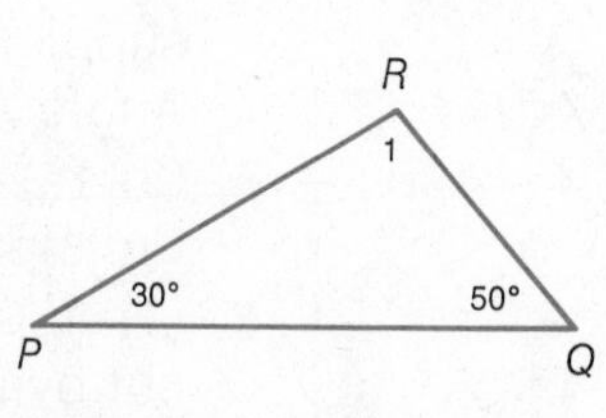

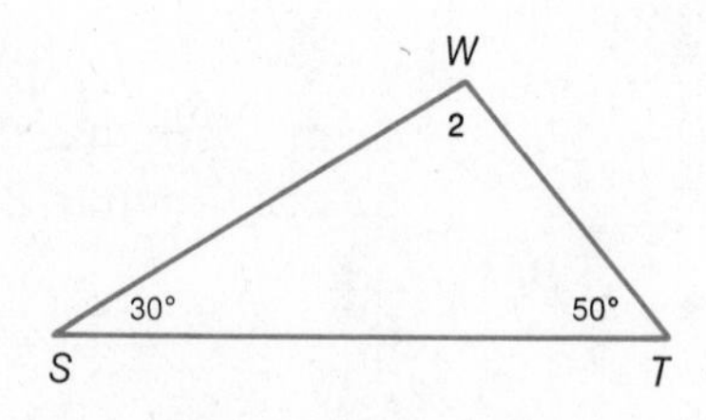

$30 + 50 + m\angle 1 = 180$ | $30 + 50 + m\angle 2 = 180$
$80 + m\angle 1 = 180$ | $80 + m\angle 2 = 180$
$m\angle 1 = 100$ ⟵ Equal measures ⟶ $m\angle 2 = 100$

$\therefore \angle 1 \cong \angle 2$

Example 3 suggests Corollary 4-13.

Corollary 4-13: If two angles of one triangle are congruent to two angles of another triangle, then the third angles are congruent.

Another corollary of the Triangle–Sum Theorem follows. You are asked to prove the corollary in the Exercises.

Corollary 4-14: A triangle can have no more than one right angle or one obtuse angle.

Try These

*For each set of conditions in Exercises **1–6,** choose the correct conclusion in Column A.*

	Column A
1. In $\triangle ABC$, $m\angle A = 60$, $m\angle B = 70$.	**a.** $m\angle C = 60$
2. In $\triangle ABC$, $m\angle A = 120$, $m\angle B = 34$.	**b.** $m\angle C = 80$
3. $\triangle ABC$ is equilateral.	**c.** $m\angle C = 65$
4. In $\triangle ABC$, $m\angle B = 90$, $m\angle A = 25$.	**d.** $m\angle C = 26$
5. In $\triangle ABC$, $m\angle A = x$, $m\angle B = 2x$,	**e.** $m\angle C = 30$
$m\angle C = 3x$.	**f.** $m\angle C = 50$
6. In $\triangle ABC$, $\overline{AB} \cong \overline{AC}$, $m\angle A = 50$.	**g.** $m\angle C = 90$

*For Exercises **7** and **8,** name the corollary that justifies the conclusion that $\angle 1 \cong \angle 2$.*

7.

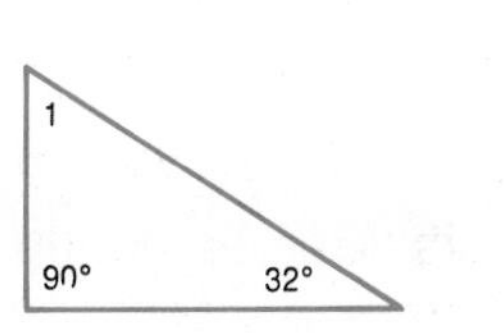

8.

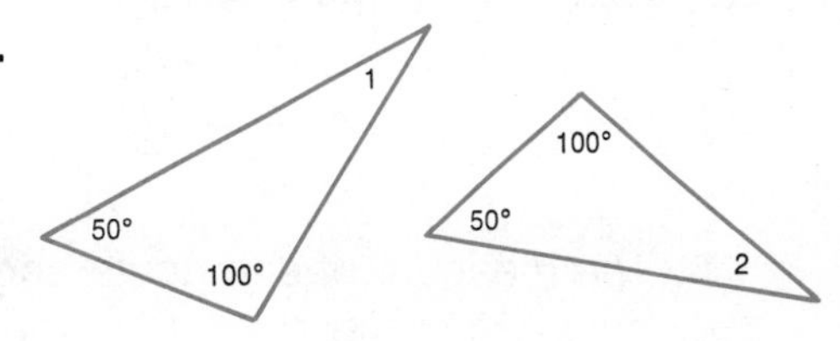

Exercises

*For Exercises **1–7**, use the given information to complete the conclusion.*

a

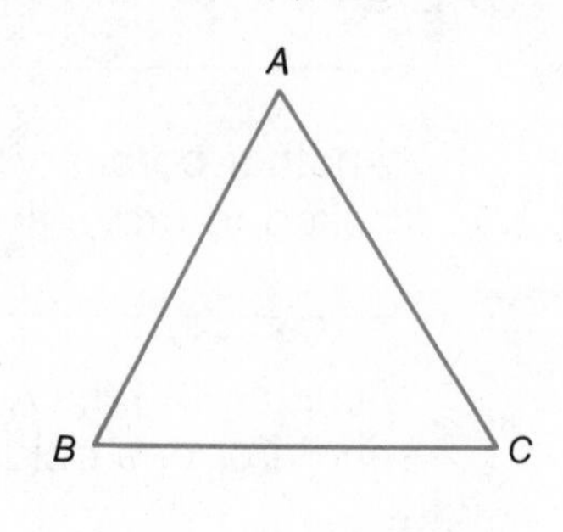

1. **Given:** $AC = BC$; $m\angle A = 50$
   Conclusion: $m\angle C =$ ___?___
2. **Given:** $AC = BC$; $m\angle C = 40$
   Conclusions: $m\angle A =$ ___?___
   $m\angle B =$ ___?___
3. **Given:** $AB = BC$; $m\angle A = 60$
   Conclusions: $m\angle C =$ ___?___
   $m\angle B =$ ___?___
4. **Given:** $\overline{PS}$ bisects $\angle QPR$;
   $m\angle Q = 25$; $m\angle R = 45$
   Conclusions: $m\angle 1 =$ ___?___
   $m\angle 3 =$ ___?___
   $m\angle 4 =$ ___?___

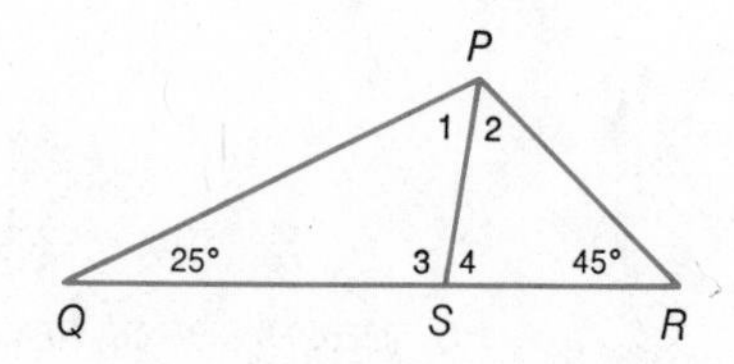

5. **Given:** $\overleftrightarrow{XY} \parallel \overleftrightarrow{ZW}$; $m\angle 2 = 80$;
   $m\angle 4 = 140$
   Conclusions: $m\angle 1 =$ ___?___
   $m\angle 3 =$ ___?___ $m\angle 5 =$ ___?___
   $m\angle 6 =$ ___?___ $m\angle 7 =$ ___?___

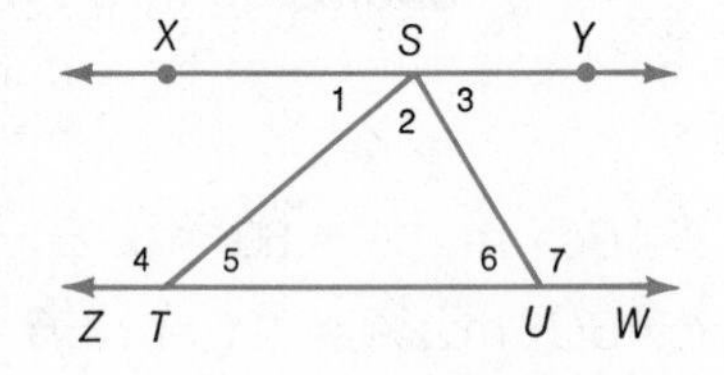

6. **Given:** $\overleftrightarrow{XY} \parallel \overleftrightarrow{ZW}$; $m\angle 2 = 70$;
   $m\angle 5 = 30$
   Conclusions: $m\angle 1 =$ ___?___
   $m\angle 3 =$ ___?___ $m\angle 4 =$ ___?___
   $m\angle 6 =$ ___?___ $m\angle 7 =$ ___?___
7. **Given:** $\angle ABC$ is a right angle;
   $\overline{BD} \perp \overline{AC}$; $m\angle 1 = 30$
   Conclusions: $m\angle 2 =$ ___?___
   $m\angle 3 =$ ___?___
   $m\angle 4 =$ ___?___
   $m\angle A =$ ___?___
   $m\angle C =$ ___?___

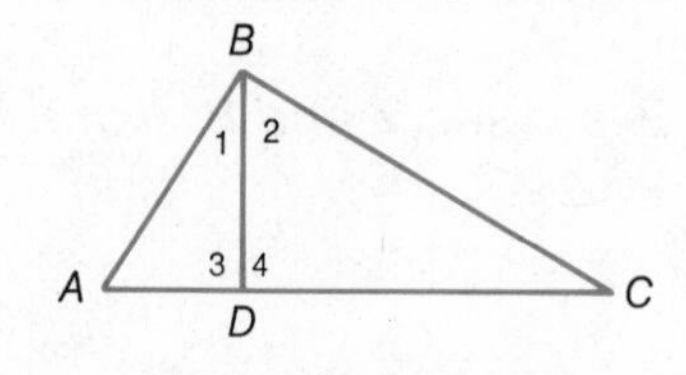

8. The measure of one acute angle of a right triangle is three times the measure of the other. Find the measure of each acute angle.

9. Find the measure of each angle of $\triangle ABC$ if $m\angle A = x$, $m\angle B = 3x + 12$, and $m\angle C = 2x + 40$.

10. Find the measure of each angle of $\triangle ABC$ if $m\angle A = 3x$, $m\angle B = 5x - 70$, and $m\angle C = 4x + 10$.

11. Use Theorem 4-12 to find the sum of the measures of the angles of any quadrilateral. (HINT: Draw a diagonal.)

12. Prove Corollary 4-13. (HINT: Follow the method of Example 3.)

13. Prove Corollary 4-14. (HINT: Assume that a triangle has more than one right angle. Show that this is not possible. Do the same for a triangle with two obtuse angles.)

14. In triangles *ABC* and *AED* below, $\angle 1 \cong \angle 2$. Prove that $\angle B \cong \angle E$. (HINT: $\angle A$ is an angle of both triangles. Use this fact and Corollary 4-13.)

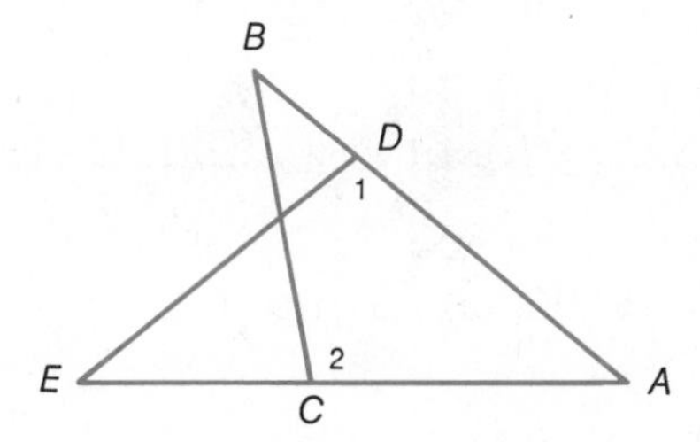

15. In $\triangle EFJ$ below, triangles *FEJ* and *GHJ* have right angles at *E* and *H*. Prove that corresponding angles of the triangles are congruent.

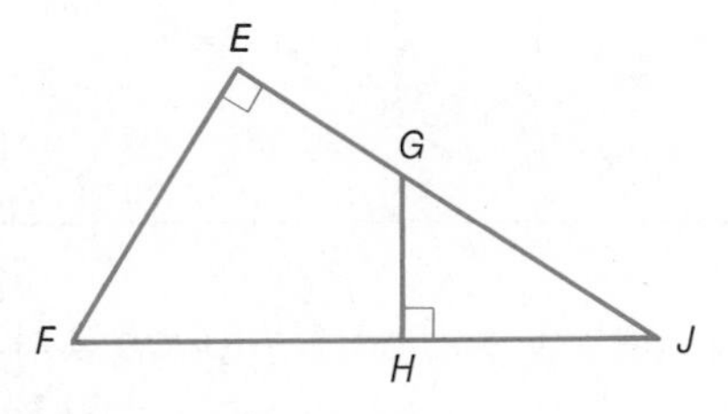

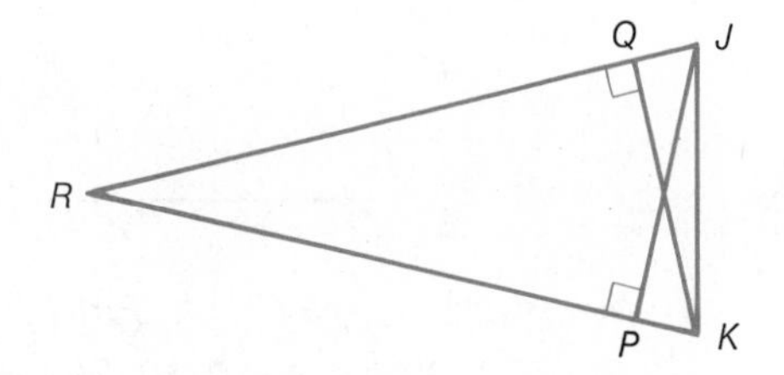

16. In $\triangle JKR$ above, $\overline{JP}$ is the altitude from *J*, and $\overline{KQ}$ is the altitude from *K*. Prove that the corresponding angles of triangles *RPJ* and *RQK* are congruent.

In $\triangle BAC$, $\angle ABC$ is a right angle, and $\overline{BD} \perp \overline{AC}$.

17. Prove that $\angle 1 \cong \angle C$.

18. Prove that $\angle 2 \cong \angle A$.

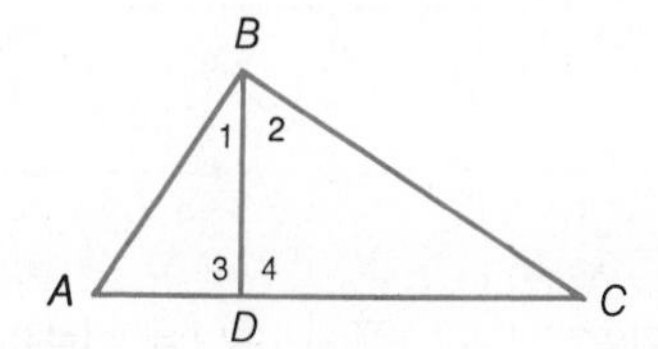

19. In $\triangle ABC$, side AB is extended through D, and $\overrightarrow{BE} \parallel \overline{AC}$. Use the given information to explain another proof of the Triangle–Sum Theorem.

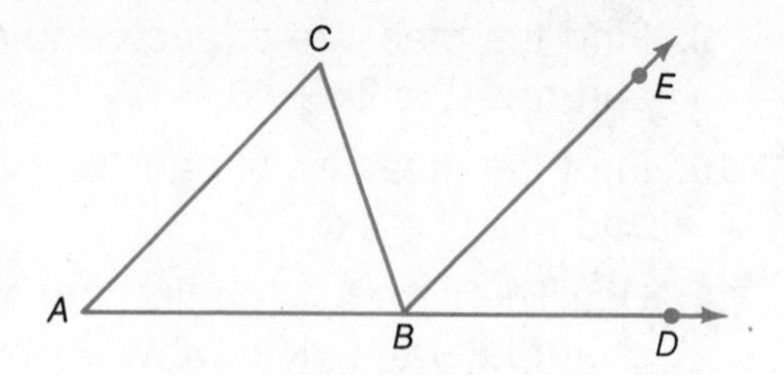

20. In $\triangle ABC$ below, $m\angle A = 60$ and $m\angle C = 80$. Find x, the measure of the acute angle that is determined by the bisectors of the exterior angles at B and at C as shown.

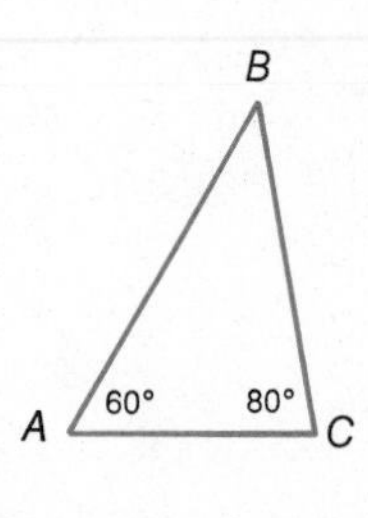

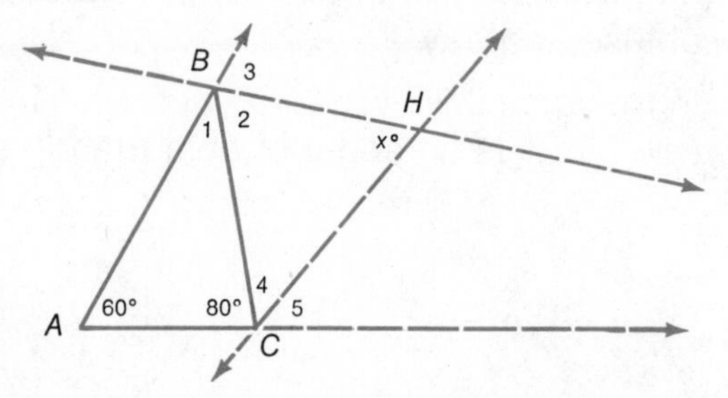

C **21.** Use the figure for Exercise 20 and $m\angle A = y$ to find an expression for x in terms of y.

22. In Exercise **21,** prove that $\angle BHC$ must be acute.

Remember

In the figure below, $h \parallel k$. Find the measures of angles 1 through 6 in order. Give a reason for each answer.

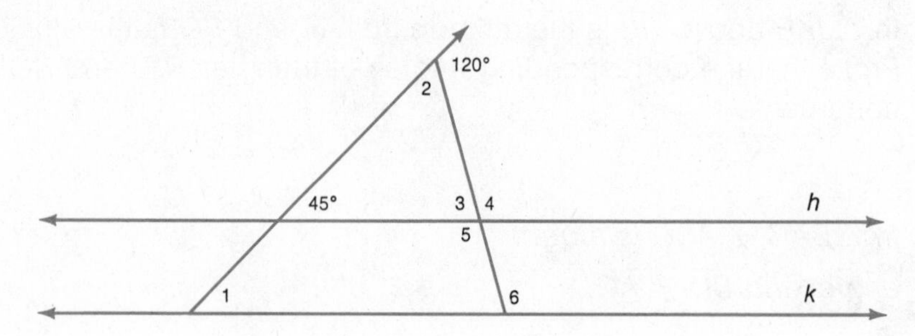

The answers are on page 197. If you need help, see pages 58, 71, 173 and 179.

4-6 Other Corollaries

Several other corollaries follow from the Triangle–Sum Theorem.

Corollary 4-15: The acute angles of a right triangle are complementary.

Corollary 4-16: The measure of each angle of an equilateral triangle is 60.

Corollary 4-17: **S.A.A. Corollary**

If two triangles have a side and two angles of one congruent respectively to a side and two angles of the other, then the triangles are congruent.

You can use the Triangle–Sum Theorem to relate an exterior angle of the triangle to its remote interior angles.

Example

Angle 1 is an exterior angle of $\triangle PRQ$. Explain why $m\angle 1 = m\angle P + m\angle R$.

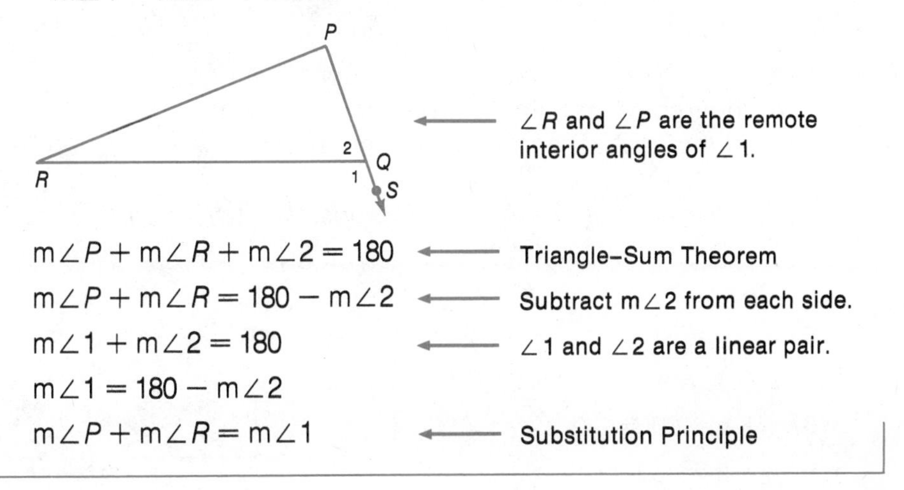
P
R
Q
S
1
2
∠R and ∠P are the remote interior angles of ∠1.

$m\angle P + m\angle R + m\angle 2 = 180$ ← Triangle–Sum Theorem

$m\angle P + m\angle R = 180 - m\angle 2$ ← Subtract $m\angle 2$ from each side.

$m\angle 1 + m\angle 2 = 180$ ← $\angle 1$ and $\angle 2$ are a linear pair.

$m\angle 1 = 180 - m\angle 2$

$m\angle P + m\angle R = m\angle 1$ ← Substitution Principle

The Example suggests the following corollary.

Corollary 4-18: Exterior Angle-Sum Corollary for Triangles

The measure of one exterior angle of a triangle equals the sum of the measures of its remote interior angles.

Try These

Write the letter of the response that completes each statement.

1. The acute angles of a right triangle are

a. supplementary. **b.** complementary. **c.** a linear pair.

2. The measure of an exterior angle of an equilateral triangle is

a. 60. **b.** 90. **c.** 120.

3. The measure of an exterior angle of one of the acute angles of a right triangle is always

a. 90. **b.** greater than 90. **c.** less than 90.

4. If two right triangles have the hypotenuse and an acute angle of one congruent respectively to the hypotenuse and an acute angle of the other, then the triangles

a. are always congruent.
b. are sometimes congruent.
c. are never congruent.

5. If triangles *ABC* and *DEF* are equilateral triangles, then

a. their corresponding sides are congruent.
b. their corresponding angles are congruent.
c. triangles *ABC* and *DEF* are congruent.

For right triangle BCA, state the postulate, theorem, or corollary that justifies each statement.

6. $x + y = 90$

7. $x + 90 = z$

8. $x + y + 90 = 180$

9. $y + z = 180$

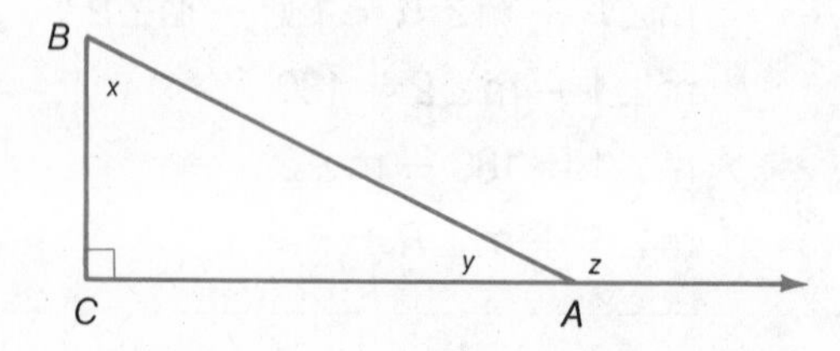

Exercises

*In Exercises **1–2,** name the pairs of complementary angles in the right triangles given.*

a

1. $\triangle ACD$; $\triangle ABE$

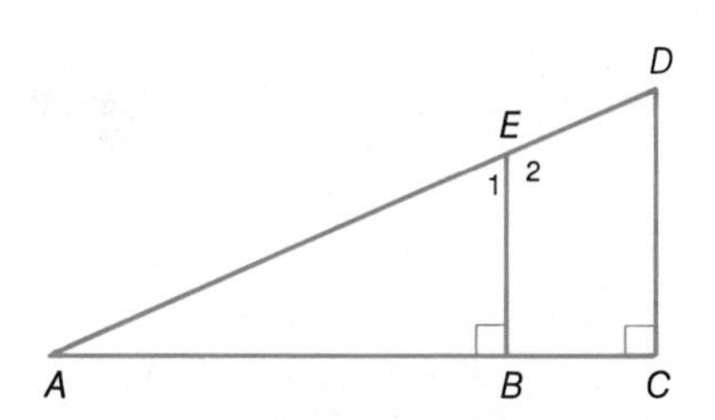

2. $\triangle FGJ$; $\triangle JGH$; $\triangle FJH$

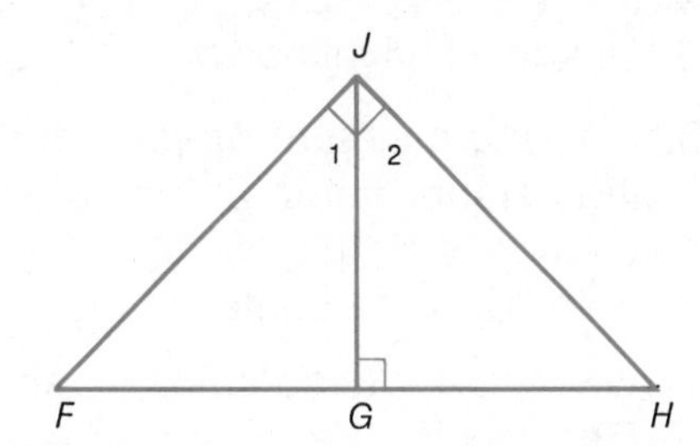

Use the information given to find the measures of the numbered angles.

3. $\overline{YZ} \parallel \overline{WX}$

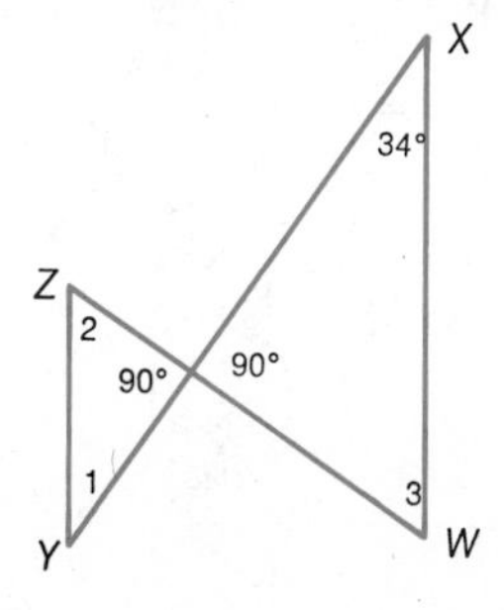

4. $\overline{BC} \parallel \overline{DE}$; $\overline{FD} \perp \overline{DE}$

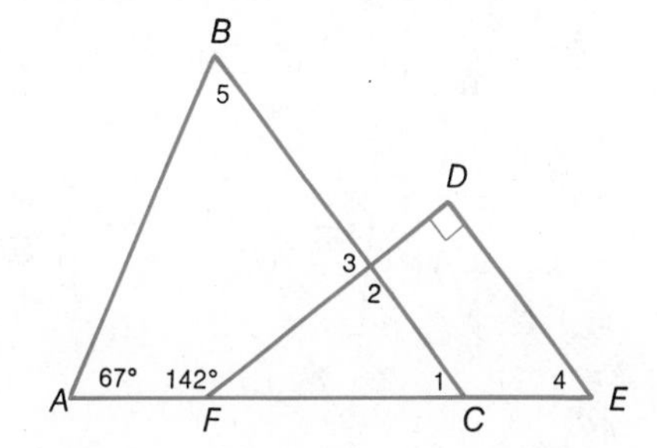

Triangles ABC and DEF are equilateral. Classify each of the following statements as Sometimes True, Always True, or Never True.

5. $\angle A \cong \angle B$

6. $\angle C \cong \angle F$

7. $\triangle ABC \cong \triangle DEF$

8. In the figure at the right, $\overline{MS} \cong \overline{PR}$ and $\angle M \cong \angle P$. Prove that $\overline{SQ} \cong \overline{RQ}$. (HINT: Find another pair of congruent angles. Then prove $\triangle RQP \cong \triangle SQM$ by S.A.A.)

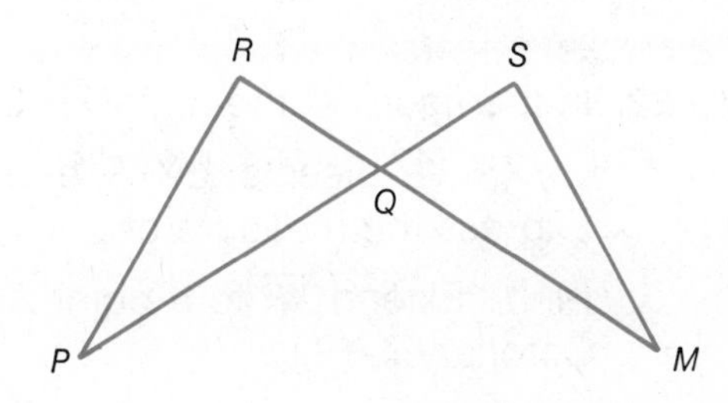

Copy and complete this chart. Use $\triangle PQR$.

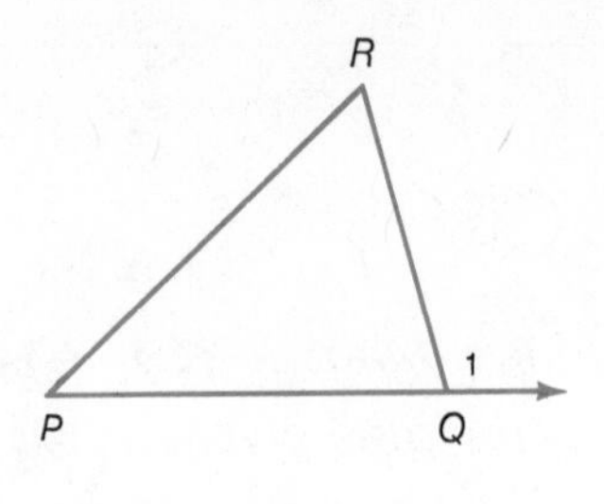

	$m\angle P$	$m\angle R$	$m\angle P + m\angle R$	$m\angle 1$
9.	70	75	?	?
10.	73	82	?	?
11.	Unknown	Unknown	112	?
12.	63	?	?	138
13.	?	87	161	?
14.	x	?	?	159
15.	Unknown	Unknown	?	143

16. Find the measure of each angle in an isosceles triangle if the measure of the exterior angle at the vertex is 124.

17. Point O is the center of the circle at the right, $\overline{OB} \cong \overline{OA}$, $\overline{BC}$ contains O, and $m\angle B = 35$. Find $m\angle COA$.

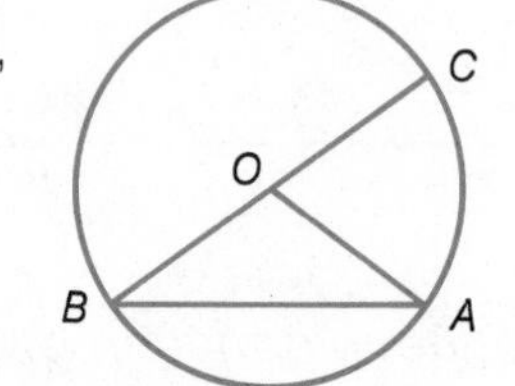

18. In circle O, $\overline{OB} \cong \overline{OA}$, $\overline{BC}$ contains O, and $m\angle COA = 100$. Find $m\angle B$.

19. In the figure at the left below, $\triangle ABC$ is isosceles with base AB. $\overline{BX}$ bisects $\angle ABC$ and $m\angle C = 30$. Find $m\angle 1$ and $m\angle 2$.

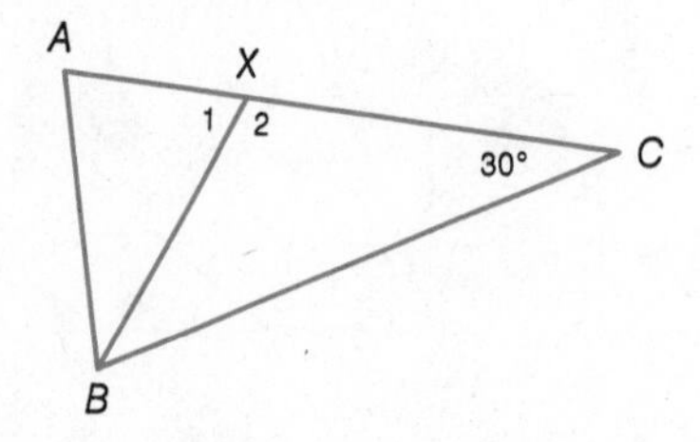

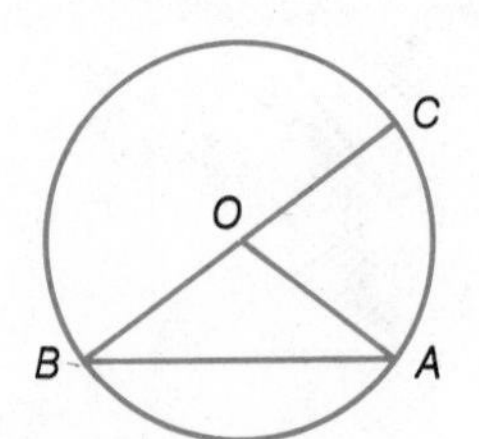

Use the circle at the right above for Exercises **20–21.** *In the circle, $\overline{OA} \cong \overline{OB}$.*

20. If $m\angle B = a$, find $m\angle COA$.

21. If $m\angle COA = a$, find $m\angle B$.

b

22. In the figure at the right, $\overline{XR}$ bisects $\angle YXS$, $\overline{YR}$ bisects $\angle XYS$, and $m\angle S = a$. Express the measure of $\angle R$ in terms of a.

(HINT: Extend $\overline{XR}$ to a point Z on $\overline{YS}$. Use Corollary 4-18.)

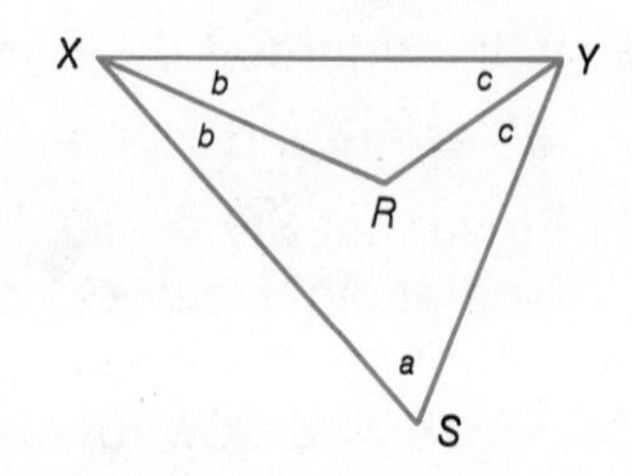

The two rays shown below are parallel.

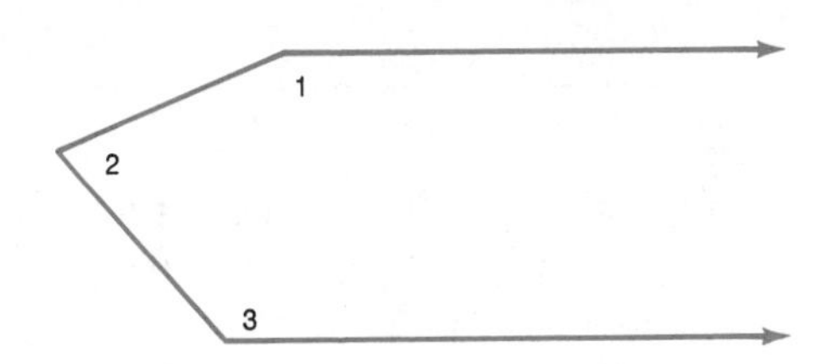

Can you find $m\angle 1 + m\angle 2 + m\angle 3$?

think–draw–see

1. Use a ruler to draw a polygon with the number of sides given.
   a. Four b. Five c. Six d. Seven
2. Use a protractor to measure each angle in the figures that you drew.
3. Copy and complete the table.

Number of sides	Sum of the Angle Measures
3	180
4	?
5	?
6	?
7	?

4. Use the completed table to predict the sum of the measures of the angles of a polygon of 8 sides.
5. Complete this statement: The sum of the measures of the angles of a polygon of n sides is ___?___.

4-7 The Angles of a Polygon

To find the sum of the measures of the angles of polygons of four or more sides, first draw all possible diagonals from one vertex of the polygon. Then use the Triangle Sum Theorem.

Polygon	Number of Sides	Number of Triangles	Sum of the Angle Measures
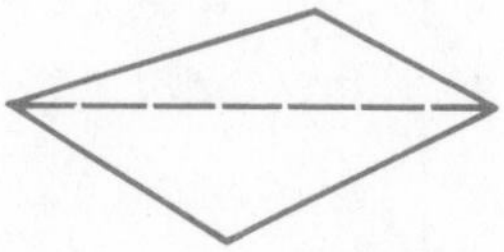	4	2	$2 \times 180 = 360$
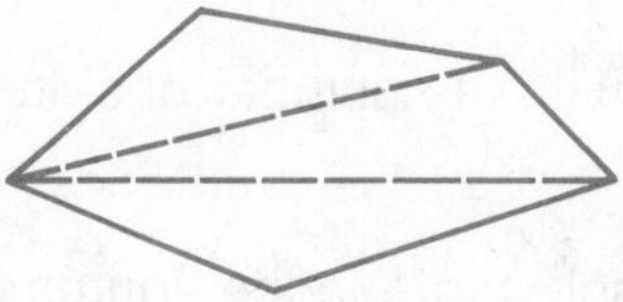	5	3	$3 \times 180 = 540$
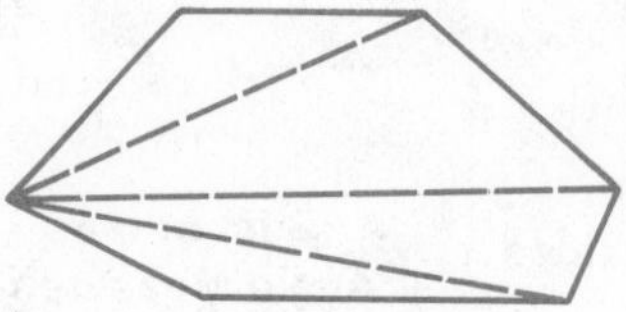	6	4	$4 \times 180 = 720$
	⋮	⋮	⋮
	n	$(n - 2)$	$(n - 2)180$

The pattern in the table suggests Theorem 4-19.

Theorem 4-19: Angle–Sum Theorem for Polygons

The formula for the sum, S, of the measures of the angles of a polygon of n sides is $S = (n - 2)180$.

Example 1

Find the sum of the measures of the angles of a polygon of 30 sides.

$S = (n - 2)180$ ⟵ **Angle-Sum Theorem for Polygons**

↓

$S = (30 - 2)180$

$S = 28 \cdot 180$

$S = 5040$

If you know that all the angles of a polygon are congruent, then you can find the measure of each angle of the polygon.

Example 2

All the angles of a polygon of 30 sides are congruent. Find the measure of each angle.

Let a = measure of each angle.

$30a = 5040$ ⟵ **The sum of the measures of the angles is 5040. (From Example 1)**

$a = 168$ ⟵ **Measure of each angle**

Example 2 suggests the next corollary.

Corollary 4-20: If a polygon has n sides and if all of its angles are congruent, then the formula for the measure, a, of one of its angles is

$$a = \frac{(n - 2)180}{n}.$$

Corollary 4-20 can also be used to find n, the number of sides of a polygon.

Example 3

The measure of each angle of a polygon is 165. Find the number of sides of the polygon.

$$a = \frac{(n-2)180}{n}$$

$\downarrow$

$$165 = \frac{(n-2)180}{n} \quad \longleftarrow \text{Multiply both sides by } n.$$

$$165n = (n-2)180 \quad \longleftarrow \text{Solve for } n.$$

$$165n = 180n - 360$$

$$-15n = -360$$

$$n = 24 \quad \longleftarrow \text{Number of sides}$$

If a polygon has all of its angles congruent, it is **equiangular.** If it has all of its sides congruent, it is **equilateral.** If a polygon is both equiangular and equilateral, it is a **regular polygon.**

	Equiangular	Equilateral	Regular
Polygons	Rectangle with sides 9, 7, 9, 7 and four right angles	Rhombus with sides 5, 5, 5, 5 and angles 125°, 55°, 125°, 55°	Square with sides 5, 5, 5, 5 and four right angles

Try These

Classify each sentence as <u>True</u> or <u>False</u>.

1. An isosceles triangle is a regular polygon.
2. An equilateral triangle is a regular polygon.
3. The sum of the measures of the interior angles of a polygon with 9 sides is 1260.
4. The measure of an interior angle of a regular polygon of 18 sides is 140.
5. If the measure of an interior angle of a regular polygon is 174, then the polygon has 60 sides.

Exercises

In Exercises **1–5,** *find the sum of the measures of the interior angles of a polygon with the given number of sides.*

1. 4 **2.** 8 **3.** 10 **4.** 5 **5.** 12

6. Would your answers to Exercises 1–5 change if the polygons were regular polygons? Explain.

7. Find the measure of one angle of a regular pentagon.

8. Find the measure of one angle of a regular hexagon.

In Exercises **9–13,** *find the measure of one angle of a regular polygon having the given number of sides.*

9. 8 **10.** 10 **11.** 15 **12.** 9 **13.** 14

In Exercises ***14–16,*** find the number of sides of a regular polygon if each angle has the following measure.

14. 156 **15.** 162 **16.** 168

17. Show that the sum of the measures of the angles of a polygon cannot be 1350.

18. Show that the sum of the measures of the angles of a polygon cannot be 1700.

19. Show that one angle of a regular polygon cannot have a measure of 152.

20. Show that one angle of a regular polygon cannot have a measure of 148.

Remember

In the figure, $\overrightarrow{EA}$ *and* $\overrightarrow{EC}$ *are opposite rays.*

1. Name two linear pairs.

2. $m\angle CED + m\angle$ ___?___ $= 180$

3. If $m\angle BEC = 32$, then $m\angle$ ___?___ $= 148$

The answers are on page 197. If you need help, see pages 57 and 58.

think–draw–see

1. Draw a polygon having more than three sides. Extend each side in succession so that there is one exterior angle at each vertex.

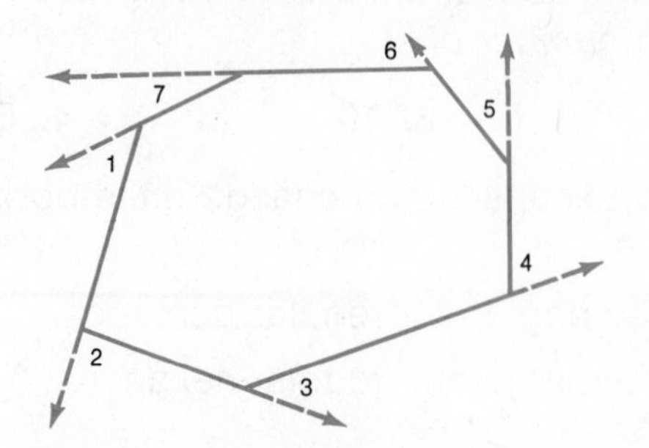

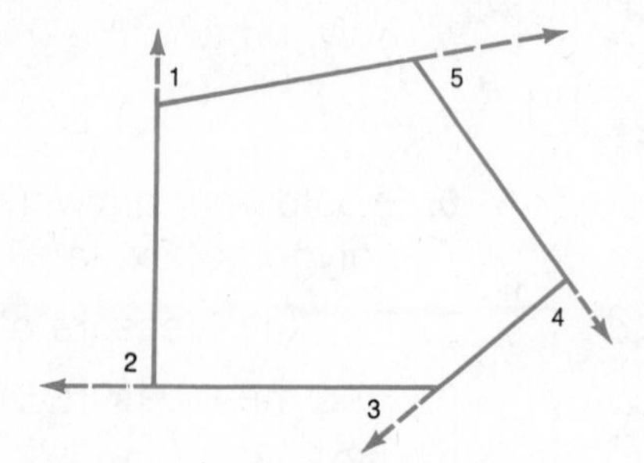

2. Use your protractor to find the measure of each exterior angle. Then find the sum of these exterior angles.
3. Repeat Steps 1 and 2 for three other polygons with a different number of sides.
4. Complete: The sum of the measures of the exterior angles of a polygon is __?__.

4-8 The Exterior Angles of a Polygon

The **exterior angles of a polygon** are formed by extending each side in succession. Note that the interior and exterior angle at each vertex form a linear pair.

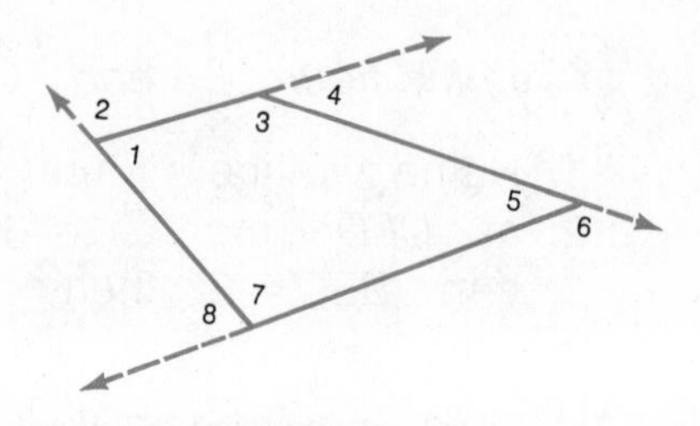

A polygon always has as many sides as vertices.

Polygon	(Number of sides)180	−	Sum of Interior Angles	=	Sum of Exterior Angles
Quadrilateral	$4 \cdot 180$	−	$(4-2)180$	=	$720-360$, or 360
Pentagon	$5 \cdot 180$	−	$(5-2)180$	=	$900-540$, or 360
Hexagon	$6 \cdot 180$	−	$(6-2)180$	=	$1080-720$, or 360
⋮	⋮		⋮		⋮
***n* sides**	$n \cdot 180$	−	$(n-2)180$	=	$180n-180n+360$, or 360

The sum of the measures of the exterior angles of a polygon does not depend on the number of sides. The sum is always 360.

Corollary 4-21: Exterior Angle–Sum Corollary for Polygons

The sum E of the measures of the exterior angles of a polygon made by extending each of its sides in succession is 360.

Example 1

Find the measure of one exterior angle of a regular polygon of twelve sides.

Let e = the measure of one exterior angle.

$12e = 360$ ⟵ There are 12 congruent angles.

$e = 30$ ⟵ Measure of each exterior angle

The measure of an exterior angle of an equiangular polygon can be written as a formula.

Corollary 4-22: If a polygon of n sides is equiangular, then the measure, e, of one of its exterior angles, is

$$e = \frac{360}{n}.$$

The formula, $e = \frac{360}{n}$, can be used to find the number of sides in an equiangular polygon if you know the measure of an interior angle.

Example 2

The measure of an interior angle of a regular polygon is 162. Find the number of sides. A portion of the polygon is shown below.

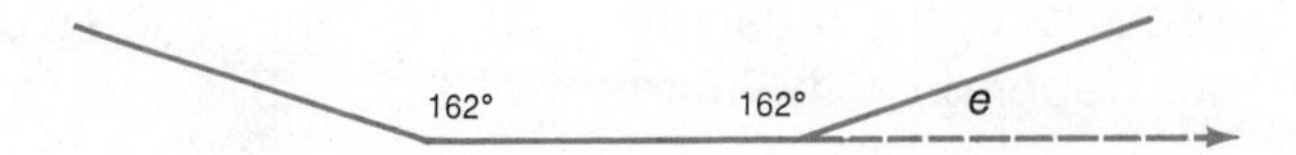

Let e = the measure of one exterior angle.

$162 + e = 180$ ← There is a linear pair at each vertex.

$e = 18$

$e = \frac{360}{n}$ ← Corollary 4-22

$18 = \frac{360}{n}$

$18n = 360$

$n = 20$ ← Number of sides

Try These

Find each of the following.

1. The sum of the measures of an interior angle and the adjacent exterior angle of a polygon
2. The sum of the measures of the exterior angles of a polygon of seven sides
3. The sum of the measures of the exterior angles of a hexagon
4. The measure of one exterior angle of a regular pentagon
5. The measure of one exterior angle of a regular polygon of nine sides

Exercises

a

1. The measure of each interior angle of a regular polygon is 160. Find the measure of each exterior angle and the number of sides.

*In Exercises **2–4,** find the sum of the measures of the exterior angles of a polygon with the given number of sides.*

2. 3 **3.** 4 **4.** n

*In Exercises **5–10,** find the measure of each exterior angle of a regular polygon with the given number of sides.*

5. 12 **6.** 24 **7.** 8 **8.** 10 **9.** 18 **10.** 15

*In Exercises **11–16,** find the number of sides of a regular polygon if each exterior angle has the given measure.*

11. 30 **12.** $22\frac{1}{2}$ **13.** $13\frac{1}{3}$ **14.** 8 **15.** $14\frac{2}{5}$ **16.** $32\frac{8}{11}$

b

17. The sum of the measures of the interior angles of a regular polygon is ten times as great as the sum of the measures of its exterior angles. Find the number of sides.
18. The measure of each exterior angle of a regular polygon is $\frac{2}{13}$ the measure of each interior angle. Find the number of sides.
19. In pentagon $ABCDE$, diagonals BE and BD are congruent, and triangles ABE and CBD are isosceles right triangles with $m\angle EAB = m\angle DCB = 90$. The measure of $\angle ABC$ is 15 more than the measure of $\angle CDE$. Find $m\angle ABC$.
20. The sum of the measures of the interior angles of a regular polygon is 60 more than 30 times that of one of the exterior angles. Find the number of sides.

Answers to Remember

Page 158: **1.** False, contradiction **2.** False, definition of converse **3.** True **4.** True

Page 171: **1.** Alternate interior **2.** Alternate interior **3.** Interior on the same side of a transversal **4.** Alternate exterior **5.** Alternate interior **6.** Alternate interior **7.** $m\angle 2 = 28$, $m\angle 3 = 28$, $m\angle 4 = 28$, $m\angle 5 = 28$, $m\angle 6 = 152$, $m\angle 7 = 28$, $m\angle 8 = 28$, $m\angle 9 = 28$.

Page 184: $m\angle 1 = 45$, Theorem 4-10 $m\angle 2 = 60$, Postulate 10 $m\angle 3 = 75$, Theorem 4-12 $m\angle 4 = 105$, Postulate 10 $m\angle 5 = 105$, Postulate 10 or Theorem 2-10 $m\angle 6 = 105$, Theorem 4-10 or Theorem 4-3.

Page 193: **1.** $\angle AEB$ and $\angle BEC$; $\angle AED$ and $\angle DEC$ **2.** DEA **3.** BEA

Drawing Three-Dimensional Figures

When three-dimensional figures are represented on paper, they are drawn in **perspective.** In Figure 1 at the right, the hands are holding a square piece of paper that represents plane I. Since the paper is tilted from the horizontal, it does not look like a square. The sides of the paper are extended to show that they appear to meet at a distant point V called the **vanishing point.**

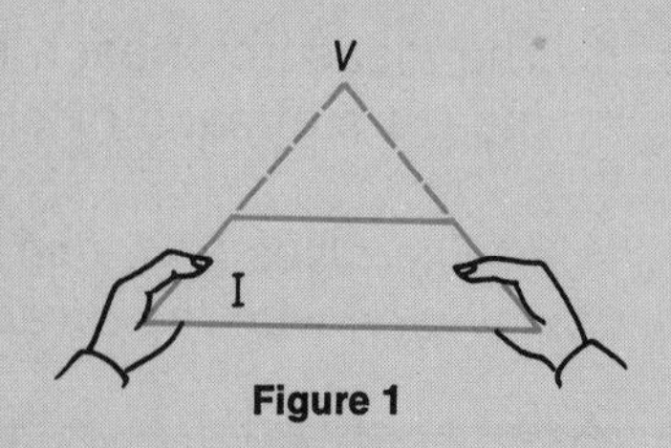

Figure 1

Drawing Intersecting Planes (Figure 2)

Draw $\overline{AB}$ and $\overline{CD}$ to represent the front edge of each plane (Figure 3). To draw this side view, a point V is placed above and to the right of $\overline{AB}$. Draw dashed segments AV, BV, CV, and DV. Place G on $\overline{AV}$ and H on $\overline{BV}$ such that $\overline{GH}$ is parallel to $\overline{AB}$. Draw dashed segment GH. Place E on $\overline{CV}$ and F on $\overline{DV}$ such that $\overline{EF}$ is parallel to $\overline{CD}$ (Figure 4). Complete the drawing (Figure 5).

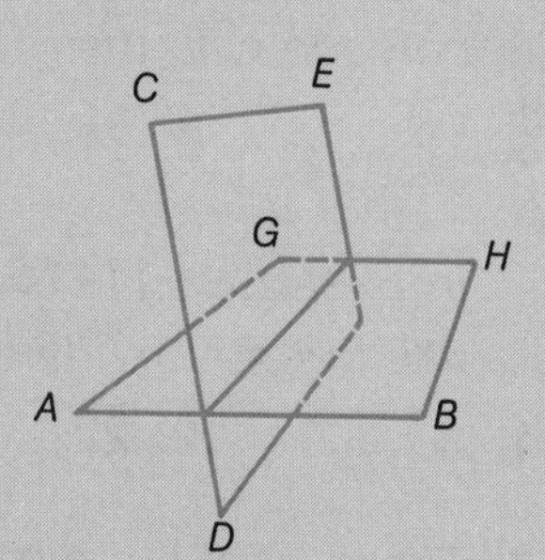

Figure 2

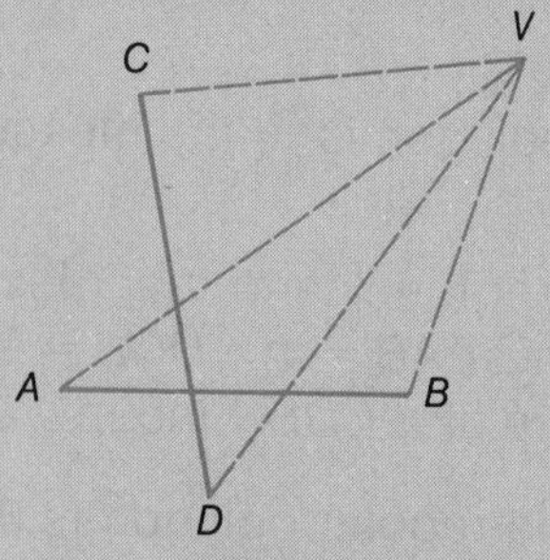

Figure 3

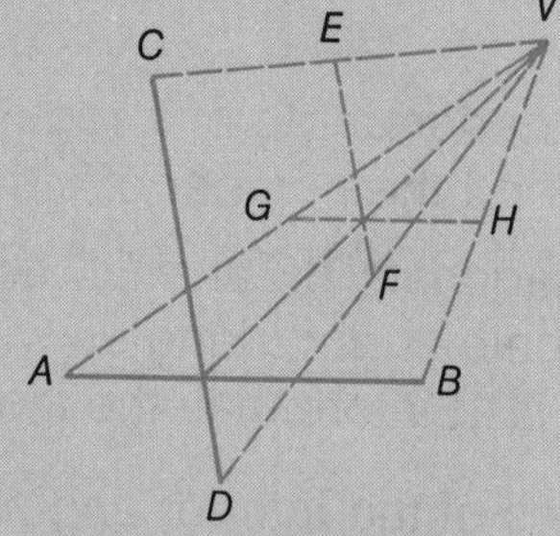

Figure 4

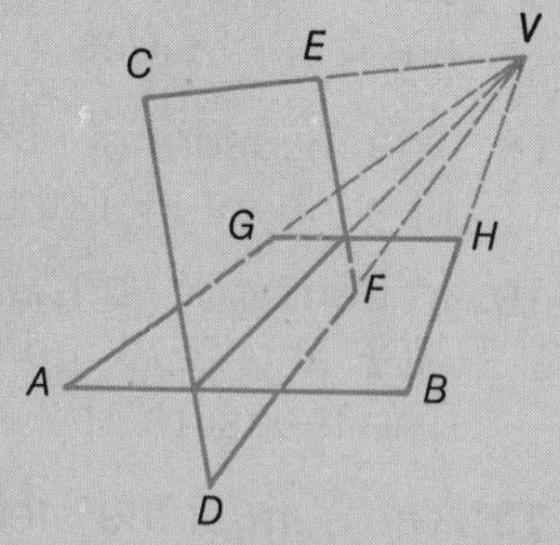

Figure 5

NOTE: Dashed lines show parts of one plane hidden by another.

Can You Solve These?

1. Copy $\overline{AB}$ and $\overline{CD}$ above. Place V above and to the left of $\overline{AB}$. Draw this view of the intersecting planes.
2. Draw $\overline{AB}$ perpendicular to the midpoint of $\overline{CD}$. Place V above and to the right of $\overline{AB}$. Draw this view of the intersecting planes.

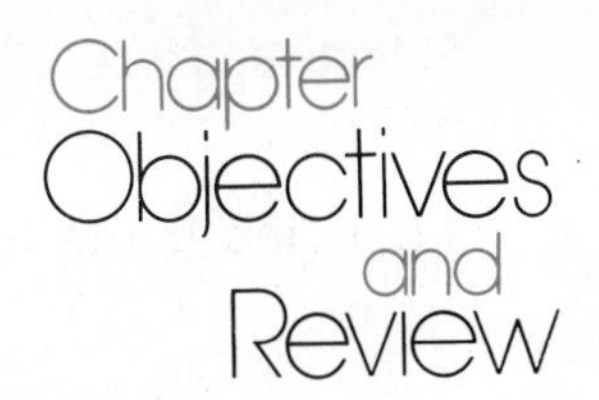

Chapter Objectives and Review

Objective: To recall, and give examples of, the important mathematical terms of this chapter.

1. Be sure that you know the meaning of these mathematical terms used in Chapter 4.

alternate angles (p. 156)
alternate exterior angles (p. 156)
alternate interior angles (p. 156)
corresponding angles (p. 172)
equiangular polygon (p. 192)
equilateral polygon (p. 192)
exterior angle
  of a polygon (p. 194)
  of a triangle (p. 154)
interior angle (p. 156)
parallel lines (p. 159)
regular polygon (p. 192)
remote interior angles (p. 154)
transversal (p. 156)

Objective: To apply the Exterior Angle Inequality Theorem. (Section 4-1)

Refer to $\triangle ABC$ to complete each sentence.

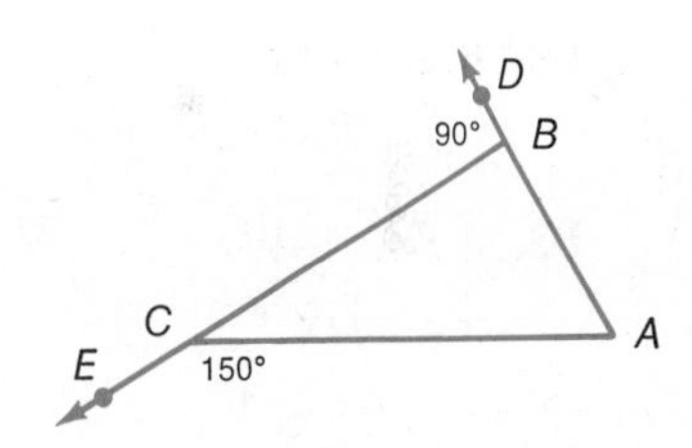

2. The two exterior angles shown in the figure are $\angle DBC$ and $\angle$ _?_.
3. For exterior angle DBC, the remote interior angles are $\angle$ _?_ and $\angle$ _?_.
4. $m\angle$ _?_ and $m\angle$ _?_ are each less than 150.
5. $m\angle$ _?_ and $m\angle$ _?_ are each less than 90.

Objective: To identify the angles formed when two lines are cut by a transversal. (Sections 4-1 and 4-4)

*For Exercises **6–10,** use the figure to name the following angles.*

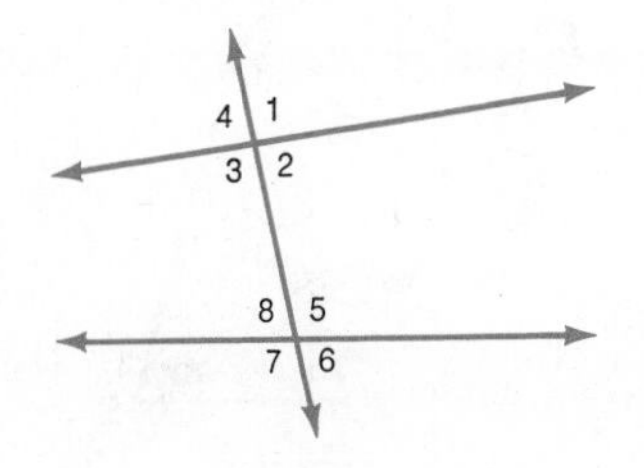

6. The interior angles
7. The exterior angles
8. Two pairs of alternate interior angles
9. Two pairs of alternate exterior angles
10. Four pairs of corresponding angles

Objective: To recognize the angle relationships that occur when two parallel lines are cut by a transversal. (Sections 4-2, 4-3, 4-4)

11. In the figure at the left below, $\overline{XW} \parallel \overline{YZ}$. Name one pair of congruent angles.

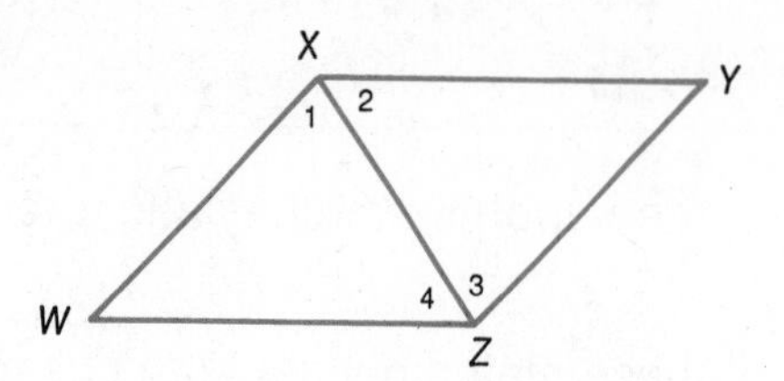

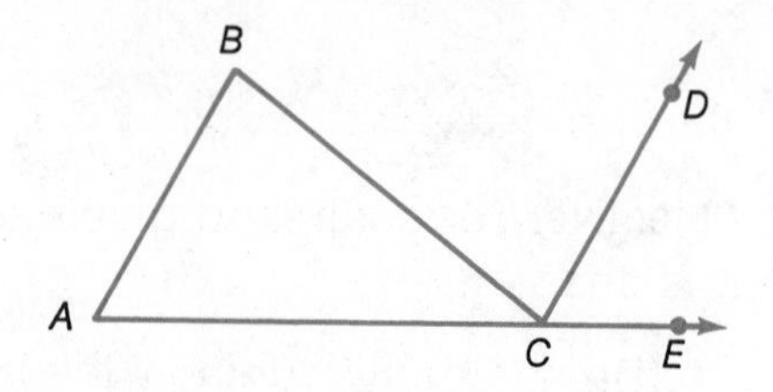

12. In the figure at the right above, $\overline{AB} \parallel \overrightarrow{CD}$, $m\angle A = 60$, and $m\angle B = 80$. Find $m\angle BCD$.

Objective: To recognize the conditions under which lines may be proved parallel. (Sections 4-2, 4-3, and 4-4)

Use the figure at the right and the given information to state which segments are parallel.

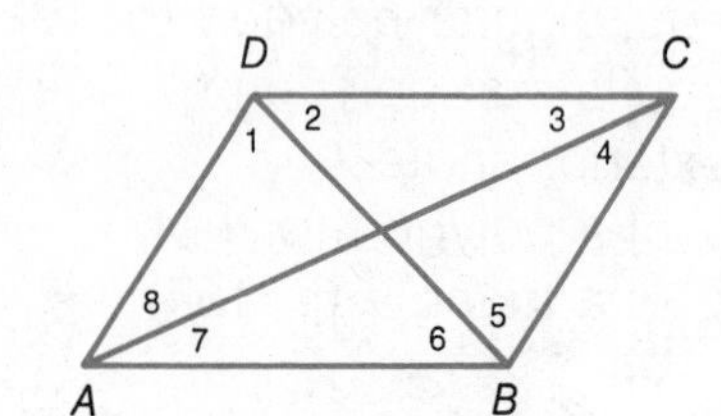

13. $\angle 1 \cong \angle 5$

14. $\angle 7 \cong \angle 3$

Complete each statement.

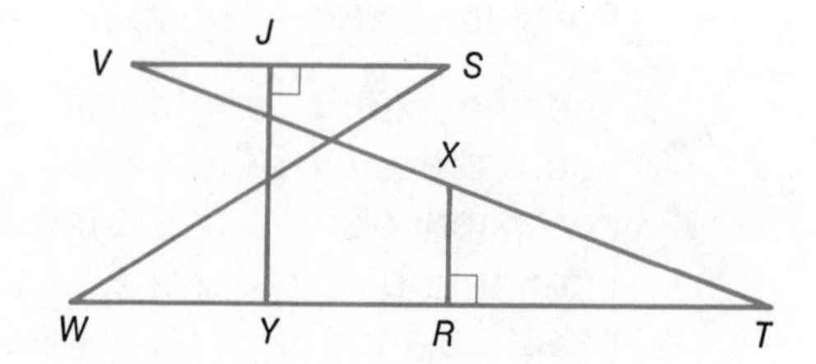

15. If $\overline{VS} \parallel \overline{WT}$ and $\overline{JY} \perp \overline{VS}$, then $\overline{JY}$ __?__ $\overline{WT}$.

16. If $\overline{RX} \perp \overline{WT}$ and $\overline{JY} \perp \overline{WT}$, then $\overline{RX}$ __?__ $\overline{JY}$.

Objective: To use the Triangle–Sum Theorem. (Section 4-5)

In the figures below, similar markings indicate congruent segments. Find the measures of the numbered angles.

17.

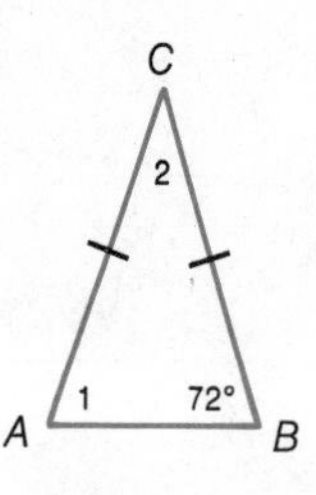

18.

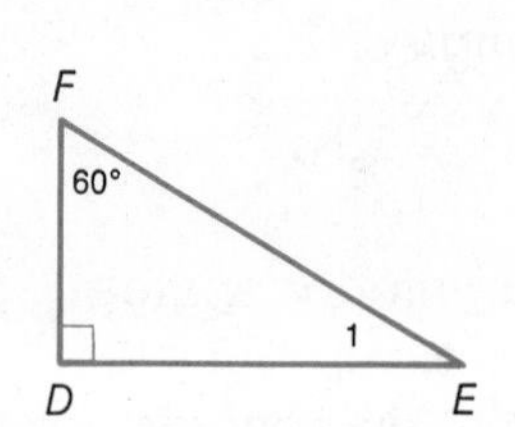

19.

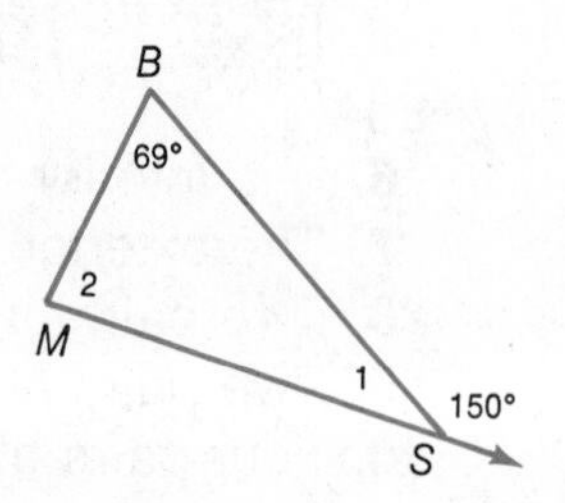

20. The measure of the vertex angle of an isosceles triangle is 82. Find the measure of each base angle.

21. In $\triangle ABC$, $m\angle A = 3x$, $m\angle B = 4x$, and $m\angle C = 3x - 20$. Find $m\angle A$, $m\angle B$, and $m\angle C$.

Objective: To use the corollaries of the Triangle–Sum Theorem. (Sections 4-5 and 4-6).

Classify each statement as True or False.

22. A right triangle can have an exterior angle with a measure of 150.

23. A right triangle can have acute angles with measures of 12 and 78.

24. An exterior angle at the base of an isosceles triangle can have a measure of 50.

25. For triangles ABC and DEF, $\angle A \cong \angle D$, $\angle B \cong \angle E$, and $m\angle C = 39$. Then $m\angle F = 39$.

26. It is possible for each angle of a triangle to have a measure of 70.

27. In equilateral triangle ABC, if the bisectors of $\angle A$ and $\angle B$ meet at D, then $m\angle ADB = 60$.

Objective: To use the Angle–Sum Theorem for Polygons. (Section 4-7)

28. Find the sum of the measures of the interior angles of a hexagon.

29. Find the measure of each interior angle of a regular polygon of 20 sides.

Objective: To use the Exterior Angle–Sum Corollary for Polygons. (Section 4-8)

30. The sum of the measures of the exterior angles of any polygon is ___?___.

31. The measure of an exterior angle of a regular decagon (10 sides) is ___?___.

32. If the measure of each exterior angle of a regular polygon is 20, then the polygon has ___?___ sides.

Chapter Test

*For Exercises **1–3,** state which segments and rays are parallel.*

1.

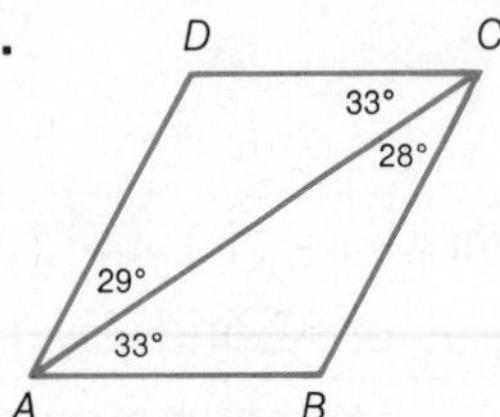

2.

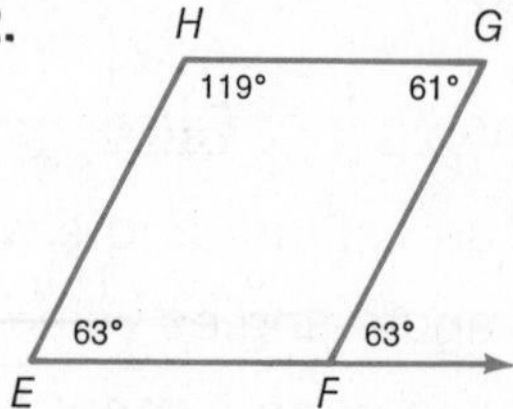

3.

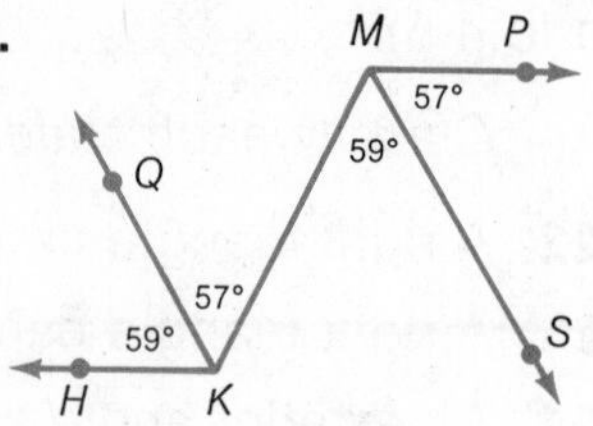

*For Exercises **4–6,** find $m\angle 1$ and $m\angle 2$.*

4. Given: $\overrightarrow{RS} \parallel \overline{PQ}$

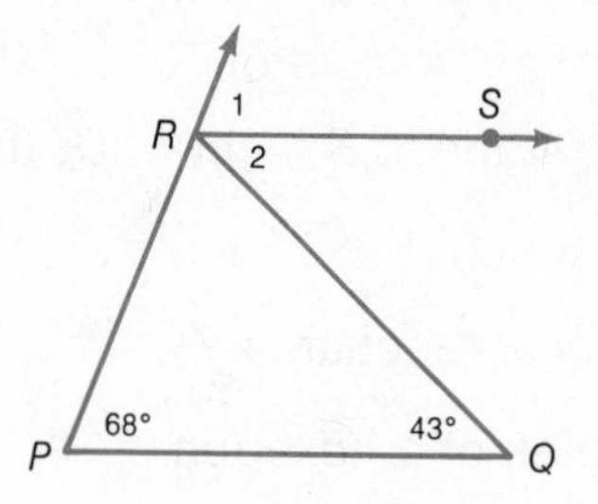

5. Given: $\overleftrightarrow{YN} \parallel \overline{MA}$

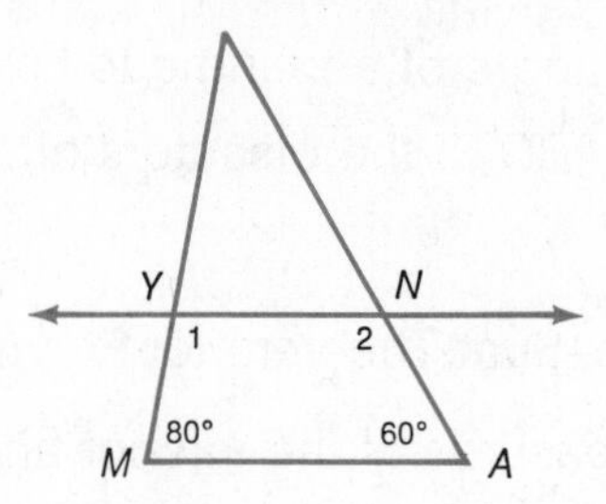

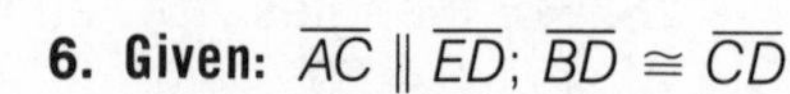

6. Given: $\overline{AC} \parallel \overline{ED}$; $\overline{BD} \cong \overline{CD}$

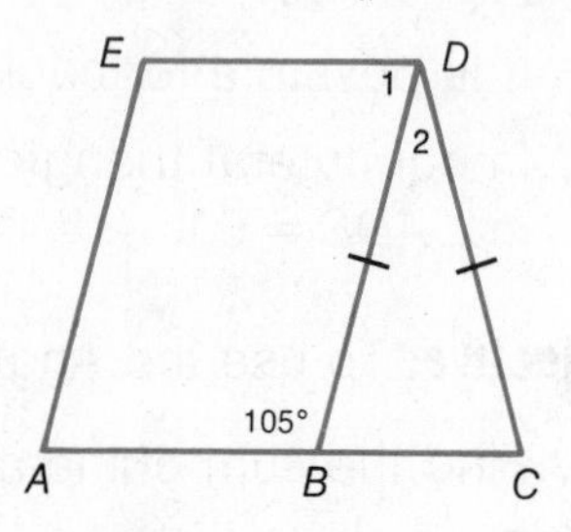

In the figure, $\overrightarrow{BA} \parallel \overrightarrow{CD}$ and $\overline{BE} \perp \overline{CD}$.

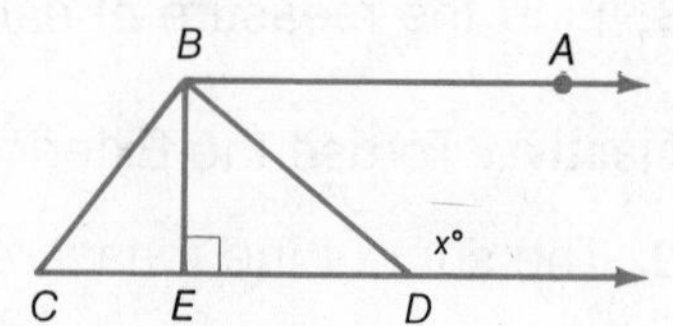

7. Find $m\angle ABC + m\angle C$.

8. Name complementary angles in $\triangle BEC$.

9. If $m\angle EBD = 50$, find x.

10. Given: Quadrilateral $ABCD$;
$\overline{CD} \perp \overline{BC}$; $\overline{BA} \perp \overline{BC}$

Prove: $\angle EDA \cong \angle A$

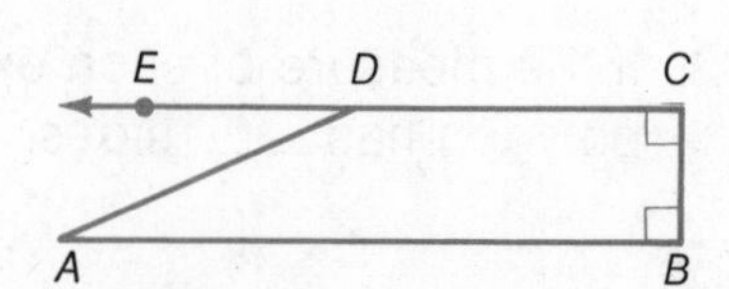

11. In an isosceles triangle, the vertex angle has a measure of 58. Find the measure of each base angle.

12. In $\triangle ABC$, $m\angle A = 2x$, $m\angle B = 2x + 15$, and $m\angle C = 3x - 10$. Find the measure of each angle.

13. Find the sum of the measures of the interior angles of a hexagon.

14. Find the measure of each interior angle of a regular pentagon.

15. Each exterior angle of a regular polygon has a measure of 15. Find the number of sides of the polygon.

Cumulative Review

Write the letter of the response that best answers each question.

1. Name the angle that has point B as its vertex.

a. $\angle BAC$ **b.** $\angle CBA$ **c.** $\angle FGB$ **d.** $\angle BCA$

2. Name the intersection of the two distinct lines $\overleftrightarrow{WX}$ and $\overleftrightarrow{XY}$.

a. $\overline{WY}$ **b.** Point Y **c.** Point W **d.** Point X

3. Tell which statement means the same as $\overline{AB} \cong \overline{CD}$.

a. $\overline{AB} = \overline{CD}$ **b.** $AB \cong CD$ **c.** $AB = CD$ **d.** $AC = BD$

4. Tell which term is undefined in geometry.

a. Segment **b.** Point **c.** Ray **d.** Angle

5. The midpoint of $\overline{PQ}$ is M. Tell which conclusion is correct.

a. $MP = PQ$ **b.** $QM = QP$ **c.** $PM = QP$ **d.** $PM = MQ$

Use the figure at the right for Exercises ***6–9.***

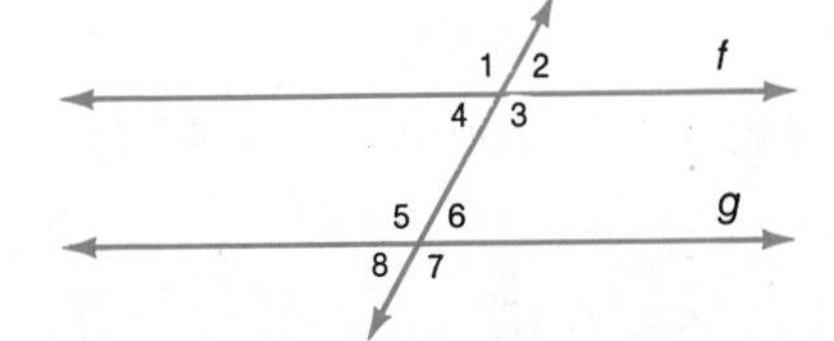

6. Name a pair of alternate interior angles.

a. 1 and 3 **b.** 3 and 5
c. 1 and 5 **d.** 1 and 7

7. Name a pair of corresponding angles.

a. 5 and 2 **b.** 4 and 8 **c.** 3 and 6 **d.** 4 and 6

8. Given that $f \parallel g$, name a pair of supplementary angles.

a. 4 and 8 **b.** 3 and 5 **c.** 7 and 5 **d.** 4 and 5

9. Given that $f \parallel g$, name the angle <u>not</u> congruent to $\angle 1$.

a. $\angle 3$ **b.** $\angle 5$ **c.** $\angle 8$ **d.** $\angle 7$

For Exercises ***10–17,*** *classify each statement as one of the following.*

a. Always true **b.** Sometimes true **c.** Never true

10. If three rays have the same endpoint, then one is between the other two.

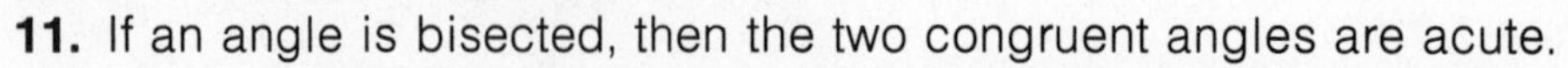

11. If an angle is bisected, then the two congruent angles are acute.
12. If two angles are complementary, then one of them can be obtuse.
13. If two angles are supplementary, then they form a linear pair.
14. If $m\angle ABC = 90$, then $\overrightarrow{BA} \perp \overrightarrow{BC}$.
15. Congruence for angles is reflexive, symmetric, and transitive.
16. The vertices of a triangle are coplanar.
17. Let n, p, and q be lines. If $n \perp p$ and $p \perp q$, then $n \perp q$.

*For each exercise in Exercises **18–20,** choose the postulate or theorem abbreviated below that can be used to prove $\triangle ABC \cong \triangle DEF$.*

a. S.A.S. **b.** A.S.A.
c. S.S.S. **d.** H.L.

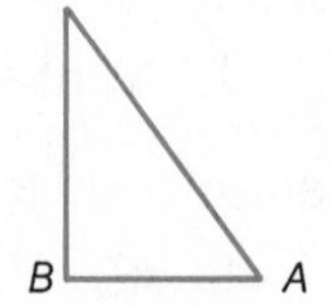

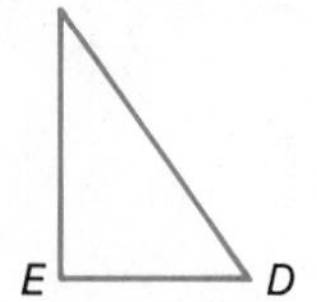

18. $\overline{AC} \cong \overline{DF}$; $\angle A \cong \angle D$; $\angle C \cong \angle F$

19. $AB = DE$; $AC = DF$; $BC = EF$

20. $m\angle B = m\angle E = 90$; $AB = BC = DE = EF$

21. State the number of diagonals that can be drawn from one vertex of an octagon.
a. 5 **b.** 7 **c.** 8 **d.** 9

22. Triangle PRM is isosceles and $PR = PM$. Name the base angles.
a. $\angle P$, $\angle A$ **b.** $\angle R$, $\angle M$ **c.** $\angle P$, $\angle M$ **d.** $\angle P$ only

23. Given that $\triangle ABC \cong \triangle NPQ$, choose the false conclusion.
a. $AC = NQ$ **b.** $\angle B \cong \angle P$ **c.** $\overline{PN} \cong \overline{BA}$ **d.** $\angle Q \cong \angle A$

24. Given that $\overrightarrow{CA} \perp \overrightarrow{CB}$ and $m\angle CAB = 35$, find $m\angle CBA$.
a. 55 **b.** 35 **c.** 90 **d.** 65

25. In an isosceles right triangle, find the measure of an obtuse exterior angle.
a. 45 **b.** 90 **c.** 120 **d.** 135

26. Name the triangle that cannot possibly exist.
a. Right scalene triangle **b.** Obtuse isosceles triangle
c. Obtuse right triangle **d.** Acute equilateral triangle

27. Find the sum of the measures of the angles of a hexagon.
a. 360 **b.** 540 **c.** 720 **d.** 1080

28. Find the measure of each exterior angle of a regular pentagon.
a. 120 **b.** 72 **c.** 108 **d.** 60

Chapter 5
Quadrilaterals

5-1 Parallelograms and their Properties

In the table below, the trapezoid is the only quadrilateral that is not a parallelogram.

Quadrilateral	Model	Definition
Trapezoid	base, D, C, A, B, base	A quadrilateral with exactly one pair of parallel sides. The parallel sides are the **bases** of the trapezoid. In an **isosceles trapezoid,** the nonparallel sides are congruent.
Parallelogram	N, P, T, V	A quadrilateral with both pairs of opposite sides parallel.
Rectangle	Y, S, D, R	A parallelogram with four right angles.
Rhombus	T, Z, X, Y	A parallelogram with all four sides congruent.
Square	M, Q, N, P	A rectangle with all four sides congruent.

Theorem 5-1 is used to prove other properties of parallelograms.

Theorem 5-1: A diagonal of a parallelogram forms two congruent triangles.

Example 1

Given: $ABCD$ is a parallelogram with diagonal $\overline{BD}$.

Prove: $\triangle ABD \cong \triangle CDB$

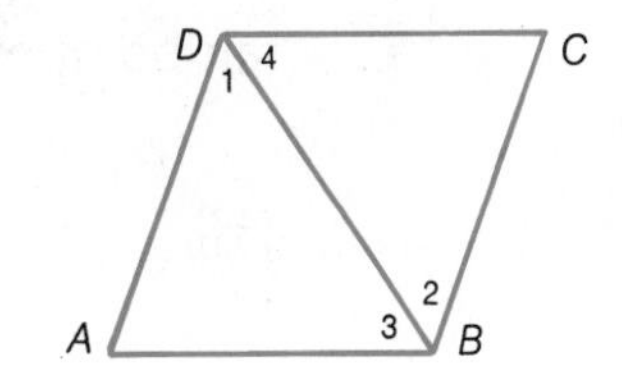

Statements	Reasons
1. $ABCD$ is a parallelogram.	1. Given
2. $\overline{AB} \parallel \overline{CD}$; $\overline{AD} \parallel \overline{CD}$	2. (1). The opposite sides of a parallelogram are parallel.
3. $\angle 1 \cong \angle 2$; $\angle 3 \cong \angle 4$	3. (1). (2). If parallel lines are cut by a transversal, alternate interior angles are congruent.
4. $\overline{BD} \cong \overline{DB}$	4. Identity
5. $\therefore \triangle ABD \cong \triangle CDB$	5. (3). (4). A.S.A.

Two corollaries can now be stated. You are asked to prove them in the Exercises.

Corollary 5-2: The opposite sides of a parallelogram are congruent.

Corollary 5-3: The opposite angles of a parallelogram are congruent.

You can use properties of parallelograms to show that parallel lines are always the same distance apart. The symbol for parallelogram is ▱.

Corollary 5-4: If two lines are parallel, then any two points on one of the lines are equidistant from the other line.

Example 2

In ▱$EFGH$, diagonals GE and HF meet at J. Explain why J is the midpoint of $\overline{GE}$ and $\overline{HF}$.

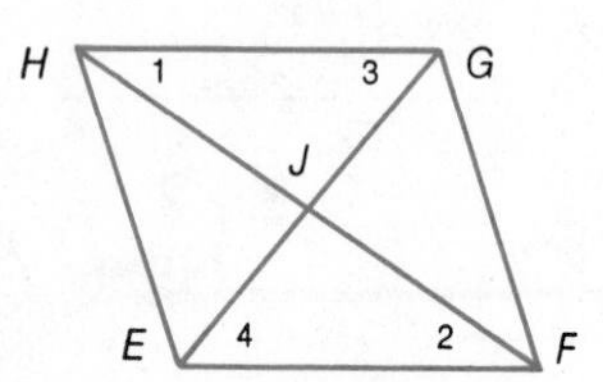

$\overline{HG} \cong \overline{EF}$	⟵	**Opposite sides of a ▱ are congruent.**
$\angle 1 \cong \angle 2$; $\angle 3 \cong \angle 4$	⟵	**Parallel lines cut by a transversal form congruent alternate interior angles.**
$\triangle HGJ \cong \triangle FEJ$	⟵	**A.S.A.**
$\overline{HJ} \cong \overline{FJ}$; $\overline{GJ} \cong \overline{EJ}$	⟵	**C.P.C.T.C.**
J is the midpoint of $\overline{GE}$ and of $\overline{HF}$.	⟵	**Definition of midpoint**

Example 2 suggests this theorem.

Theorem 5-5: The diagonals of a parallelogram bisect each other.

By extending the sides of a parallelogram, you can show that any two consecutive angles are supplementary.

$$m\angle 1 + m\angle 2 = 180$$

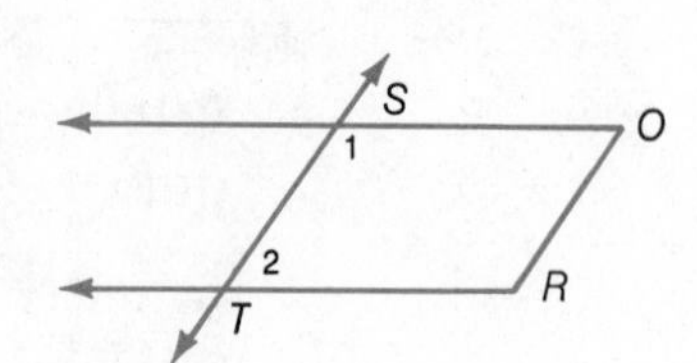

Theorem 5-6: Any two consecutive angles of a parallelogram are supplementary.

Try These

*Exercises **1–10** refer to ▱ABCD. Complete each statement.*

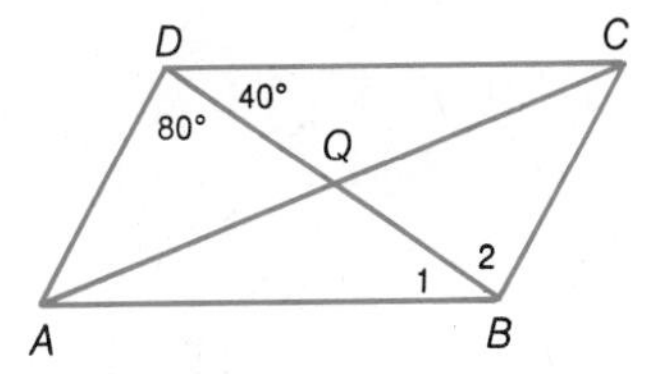

1. $\overline{DA} \parallel$ ___?___
2. $\overline{DC} \cong$ ___?___
3. $\angle ADC \cong$ ___?___
4. $\triangle ABC \cong \triangle$ ___?___
5. $\overline{QC} \cong$ ___?___
6. $\triangle ADQ \cong \triangle$ ___?___
7. $m\angle 1 =$ ___?___
8. $m\angle DAB =$ ___?___
9. $DB = 2($___?___$)$
10. $AQ = \frac{1}{2}($___?___$)$

Exercises

*For Exercises **1–9**, classify each statement as True or False. The statements refer to ▱ABCD.*

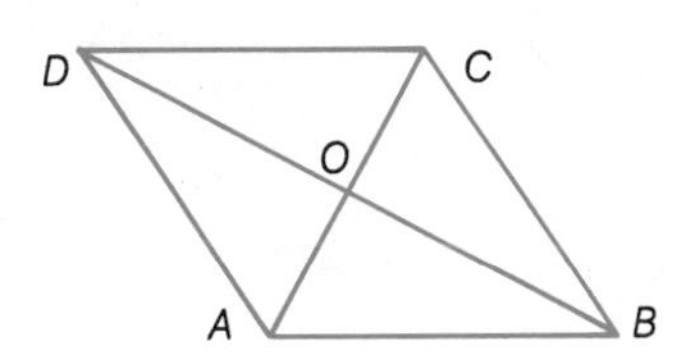

a

1. $\overline{AB} \cong \overline{CD}$ by definition of a parallelogram.
2. $\angle DAB$ and $\angle DCB$ are both supplementary to $\angle ABC$.
3. If $m\angle ABC = 86$, then $m\angle ADC$ cannot be 84.
4. If $AD = 6$ cm, then $BC = 6$ cm.
5. $AO = OC = DO = OB$
6. If $AO = 3$ dm, then $CO = 3$ dm.
7. $\triangle ABC \cong \triangle ABD$
8. $\triangle DOA \cong \triangle BOC$
9. $\triangle ABD \cong \triangle CDB$
10. Explain why all points of a parallelogram lie in the same plane.
11. In ▱XYZW, $m\angle X = 2m\angle Y$. Find the measure of each angle of the parallelogram.
12. The perimeter of a parallelogram is 50 centimeters and one side is 15 centimeters long. Find the length of each of the other sides.
13. The measure of one angle of a parallelogram is three times the measure of another angle, and the angles are consecutive. Find the measure of each angle of the parallelogram.
14. The perimeter of a parallelogram is 140. Two adjacent sides have lengths of $3x$ and $3x + 10$. Find the length of each side of the parallelogram.
15. Prove Corollary 5-2.
16. Prove Corollary 5-3.
17. Prove Corollary 5-4.
18. Prove Theorem 5-6.

5-2 Conditions Determining a Parallelogram

Examine the table to determine how much it is necessary to know about the sides of a quadrilateral before you can say it is a parallelogram.

Conditions	Model	Is it a ▱?	Explanation
Exactly one pair of parallel sides	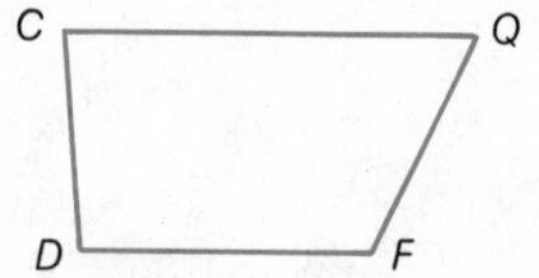 C Q D F	No	It is a trapezoid.
Two pairs of parallel sides	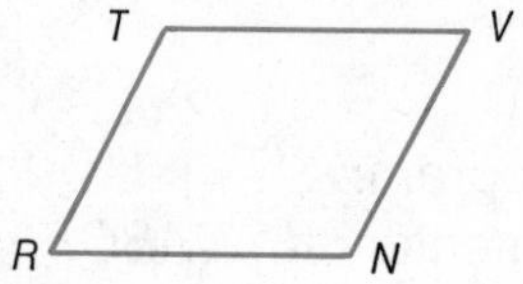 T V R N	Yes	Definition of parallelogram
Two pairs of congruent sides	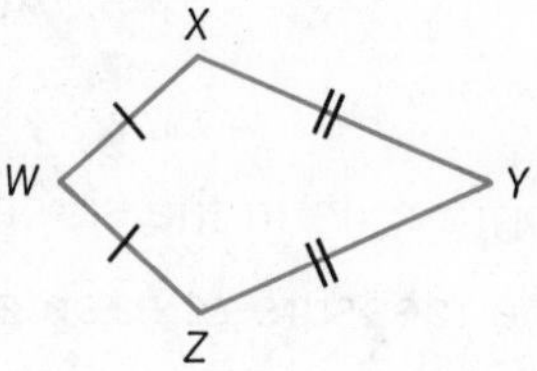 X W Y Z	Not necessarily	The quadrilateral can have two pairs of congruent sides, but the opposite sides need not be congruent.
Both pairs of opposite sides congruent.	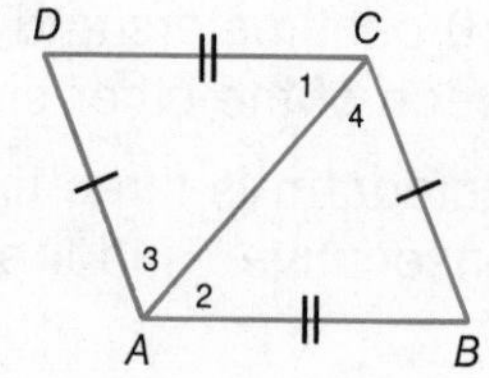 D C 1 4 3 2 A B	Yes	Draw diagonal AC. $\triangle ABC \cong \triangle CDA$ by s.s.s., and $\angle 1 \cong \angle 2$. $\therefore$ $\overline{DC} \parallel \overline{AB}$. Also $\angle 3 \cong \angle 4$, so $\overline{DA} \parallel \overline{BC}$.
One pair of sides both congruent and parallel.	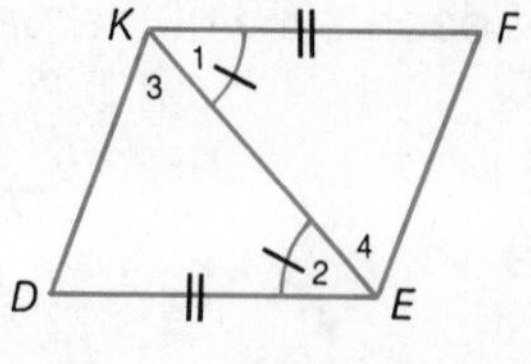 K F 1 3 4 2 D E	Yes	Draw diagonal KE. $\triangle FEK \cong \triangle DKE$ by S.A.S. So $\angle 4 \cong \angle 3$ and $\overline{KD} \parallel \overline{EF}$.

The information in the table suggests these theorems. The proofs of the theorems are asked for in the Exercises.

Theorem 5-7: If both pairs of opposite sides of a quadrilateral are congruent, then the quadrilateral is a parallelogram.

Theorem 5-8: If two sides of a quadrilateral are parallel and congruent, then the quadrilateral is a parallelogram.

Try These

State whether each quadrilateral is a parallelogram. Give a reason for each answer.

1.

2.

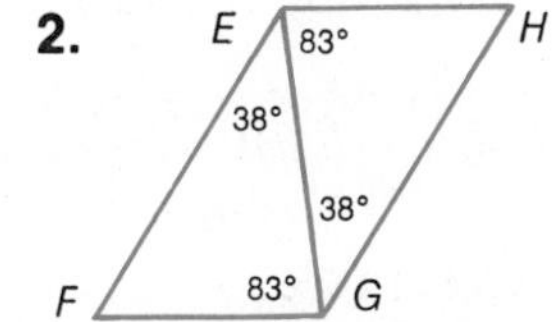

3.

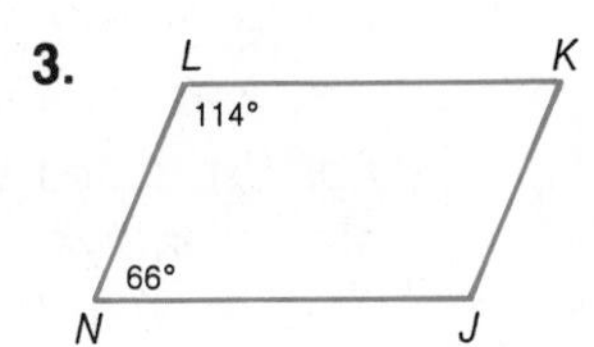

4.

5.

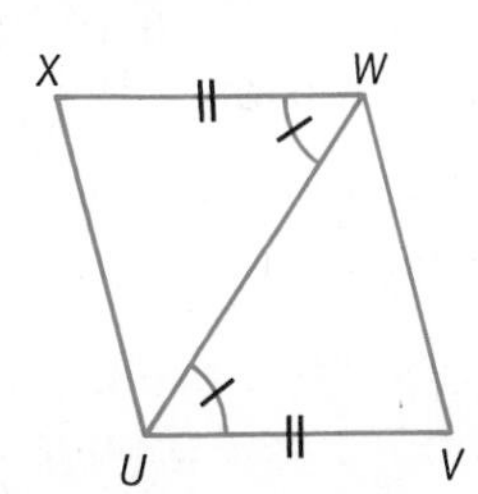

6.

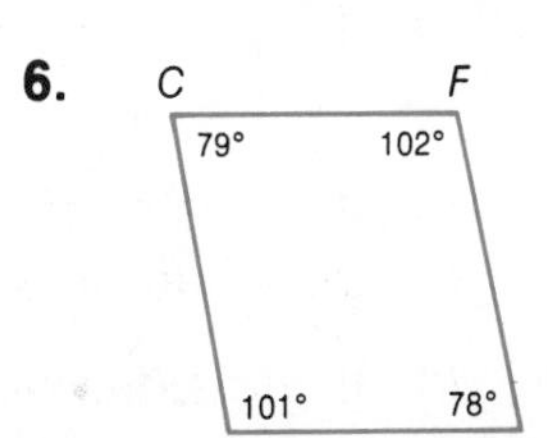

Exercises

Identify each statement in Exercises **1–5** *as* True *or* False. *Give a reason for each answer.*

a

1. If $ABCD$ is a parallelogram and $\overline{MN} \parallel \overline{AB}$, then $MNCD$ is also a parallelogram.

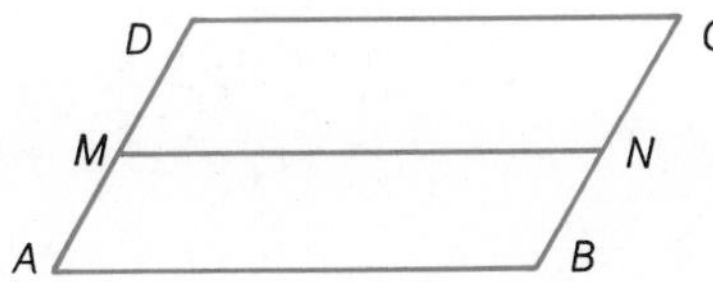

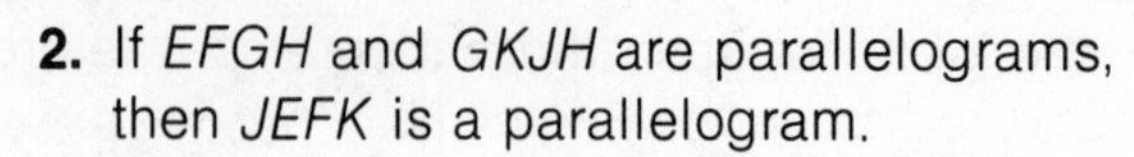

2. If $EFGH$ and $GKJH$ are parallelograms, then $JEFK$ is a parallelogram.

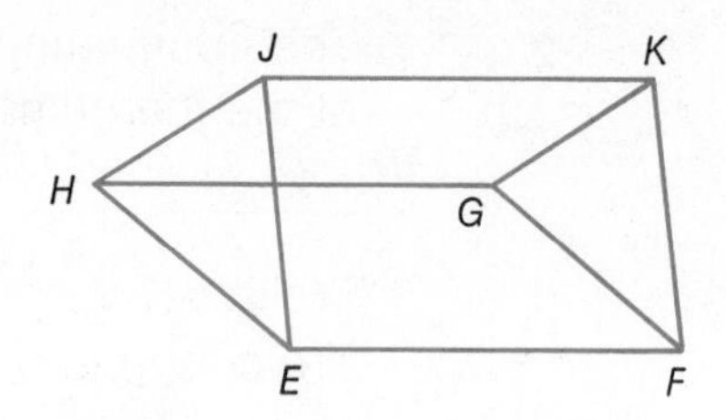

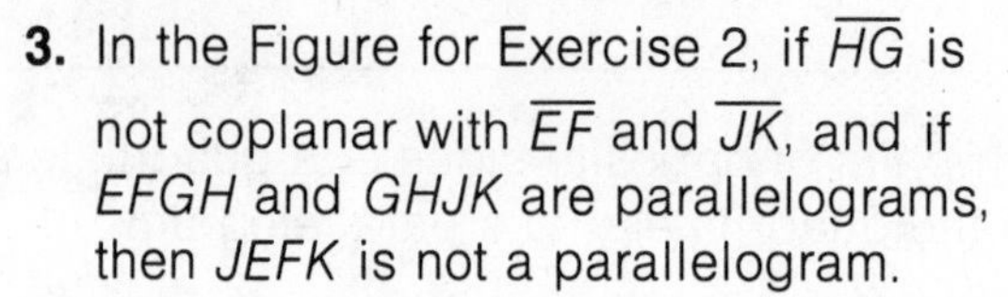

3. In the Figure for Exercise 2, if $\overline{HG}$ is not coplanar with $\overline{EF}$ and $\overline{JK}$, and if $EFGH$ and $GHJK$ are parallelograms, then $JEFK$ is not a parallelogram.
4. If a diagonal of a quadrilateral is drawn and two congruent triangles are formed, then the quadrilateral is a parallelogram.
5. If the diagonals of a quadrilateral bisect each other, then the quadrilateral is a parallelogram.
6. Prove Theorem 5-7. (HINT: Refer to the table on page 210.)
7. Prove Theorem 5-8. (HINT: Refer to the table on page 210.)
8. Prove Corollary 5-3 without using Theorem 5-1.

For Exercises ***9–12,*** *prove or disprove each statement. To disprove a statement, you have only to find one instance when the statement is false. This is called a* ***counterexample.***

9. If two sides of a quadrilateral are congruent and the other two sides are parallel, then the figure is a parallelogram.

b

10. If all pairs of consecutive angles of a quadrilateral are supplementary, then the figure is a parallelogram.
11. If two sides of a quadrilateral are parallel and two opposite angles are congruent, then the figure is a parallelogram.
12. Any segment containing the midpoint M of a diagonal of a parallelogram and having endpoints on opposite sides of the parallelogram is bisected at M.

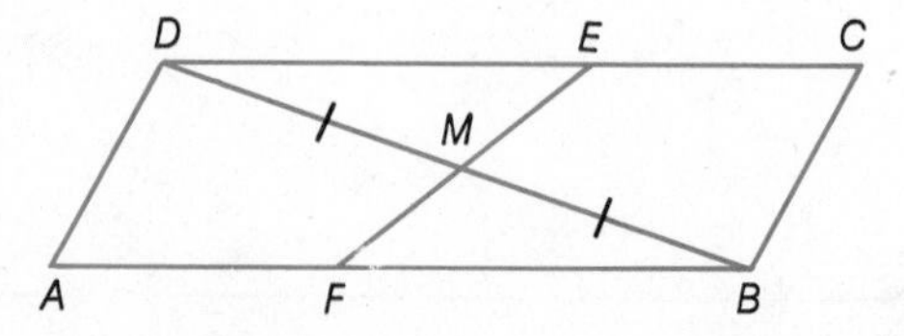

13. In the figure at the right, D is the midpoint of $\overline{AC}$ and E is the midpoint of $\overline{BC}$ and $\overline{DF}$. Prove that $\overline{DE} \parallel \overline{AB}$ and $DE = \frac{1}{2}AB$.

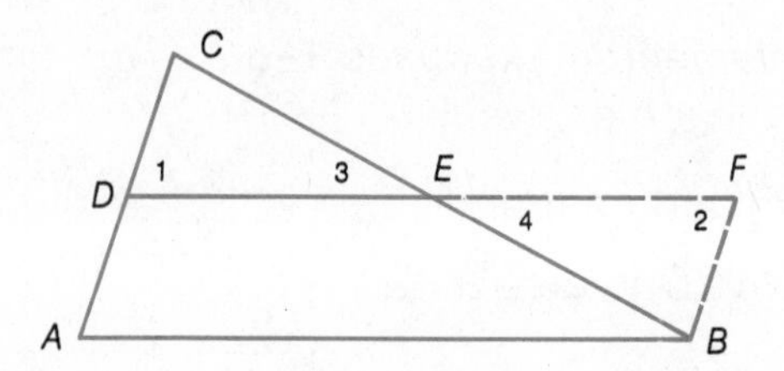

C 14. Prove: If the opposite angles of a quadrilateral are congruent, then the quadrilateral is a parallelogram.

PUZZLE

How can you place 12 coins on the squares of a checkerboard that has 64 squares if you must follow these directions.

1. Never place more than one coin on a square.
2. Never place more than two coins in a line (horizontal, vertical, or diagonal).

(HINT: Start by placing two coins as shown.)

Remember

Match each description on the left with the name of the figure it describes on the right.

1. A parallelogram with four right angles
2. A parallelogram with consecutive sides congruent
3. A rectangle with consecutive sides congruent
4. A quadrilateral with both pairs of opposite sides parallel

a. Parallelogram
b. Rectangle
c. Rhombus
d. Square
e. Trapezoid

The answers are on page 248. If you need help, see page 206.

5-3 Rectangle, Rhombus, and Square

Since rectangles, rhombuses, and squares are parallelograms, the properties of a parallelogram are the properties of a rectangle, a rhombus, and a square.

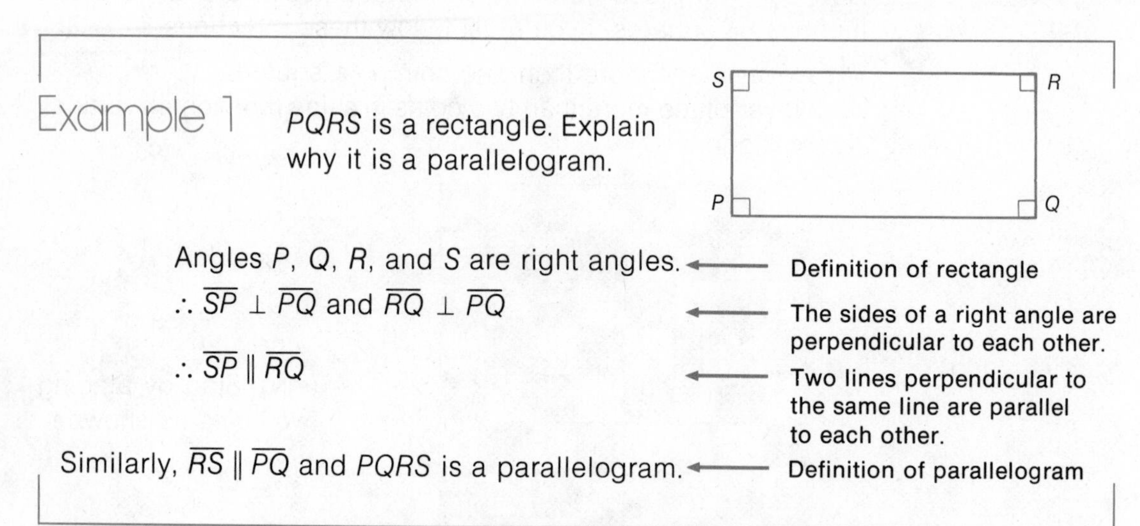

Example 1

PQRS is a rectangle. Explain why it is a parallelogram.

Angles *P*, *Q*, *R*, and *S* are right angles. ←	Definition of rectangle
$\therefore \overline{SP} \perp \overline{PQ}$ and $\overline{RQ} \perp \overline{PQ}$ ←	The sides of a right angle are perpendicular to each other.
$\therefore \overline{SP} \parallel \overline{RQ}$ ←	Two lines perpendicular to the same line are parallel to each other.
Similarly, $\overline{RS} \parallel \overline{PQ}$ and *PQRS* is a parallelogram. ←	Definition of parallelogram

Each quadrilateral also has its own special properties.

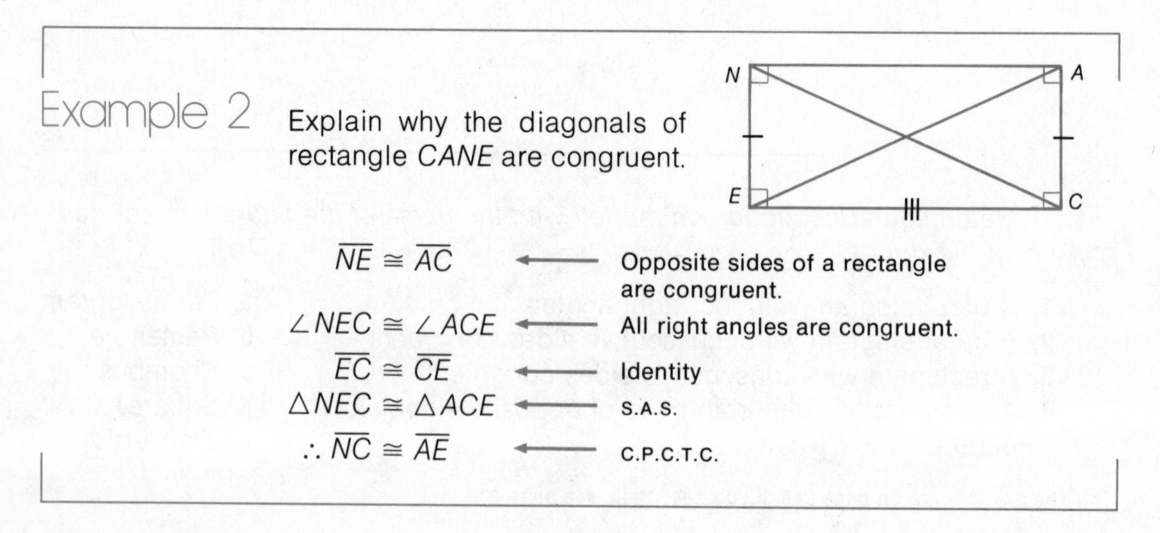

Example 2

Explain why the diagonals of rectangle *CANE* are congruent.

$\overline{NE} \cong \overline{AC}$ ←	Opposite sides of a rectangle are congruent.
$\angle NEC \cong \angle ACE$ ←	All right angles are congruent.
$\overline{EC} \cong \overline{CE}$ ←	Identity
$\triangle NEC \cong \triangle ACE$ ←	S.A.S.
$\therefore \overline{NC} \cong \overline{AE}$ ←	C.P.C.T.C.

Example 2 suggests Theorem 5-9.

Theorem 5-9: The diagonals of a rectangle are congruent.

The diagonals of a rhombus also have special properties.

Example 3

In rhombus *DRKF*, explain why $\overline{FR} \perp \overline{DK}$, $\angle 1 \cong \angle 2$, $\angle 3 \cong \angle 4$, $\angle 5 \cong \angle 6$, and $\angle 7 \cong \angle 8$.

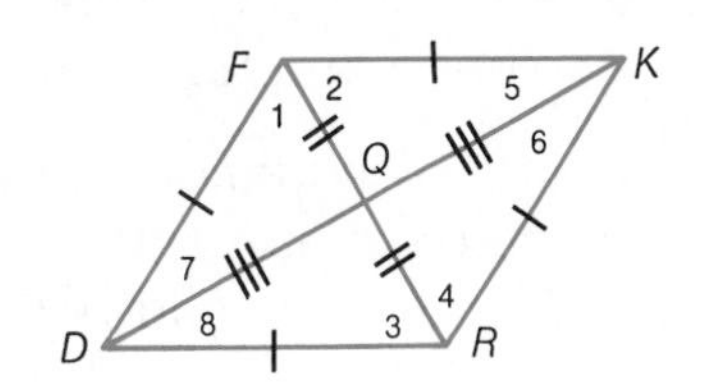

$\triangle DQF \cong \triangle KQF$ ← s.s.s.

$\angle DQF \cong \angle KQF$ ← c.p.c.t.c.

$\overline{FR} \perp \overline{DK}$ ← If congruent adjacent angles are formed by intersecting lines, then the lines are perpendicular.

$\triangle DQF \cong \triangle KQF \cong \triangle KQR \cong \triangle DQR$ ← s.s.s.

$\angle 1 \cong \angle 2, \angle 3 \cong \angle 4, \angle 5 \cong \angle 6, \angle 7 \cong \angle 8$ ← c.p.c.t.c.

Example 3 suggests these theorems. You are asked to prove them in the Exercises.

Theorem 5-10: The diagonals of a rhombus are perpendicular to each other.

Theorem 5-11: The diagonals of a rhombus bisect the angles of the rhombus.

Since a square is a rectangle, it follows that the diagonals of a square are congruent. Since a square is a rhombus, it also follows that the diagonals of a square are perpendicular to each other and that they bisect the angles of the square.

Try These

Complete each statement. Use the words parallelogram, rectangle, rhombus, or square.

1. Every rectangle is also a _?_.
2. Every rhombus is also a _?_.
3. Every square is also a _?_, a _?_, and a _?_.
4. A parallelogram with congruent diagonals is a _?_ or a _?_.
5. A parallelogram with perpendicular diagonals is a _?_ or a _?_.
6. A parallelogram whose diagonals are the perpendicular bisectors of each other is a _?_ or a _?_.
7. In rectangle $DASH$, diagonals DS and AH intersect at P and $DP = 2.8$ centimeters. Find DS, AP, PH, and AH.

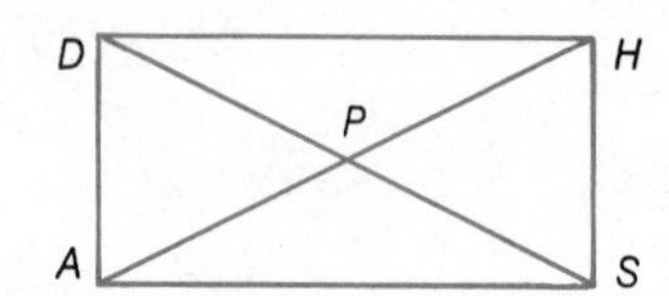

Exercises

*For Exercises **1–6**, refer to rectangle ADCB.*

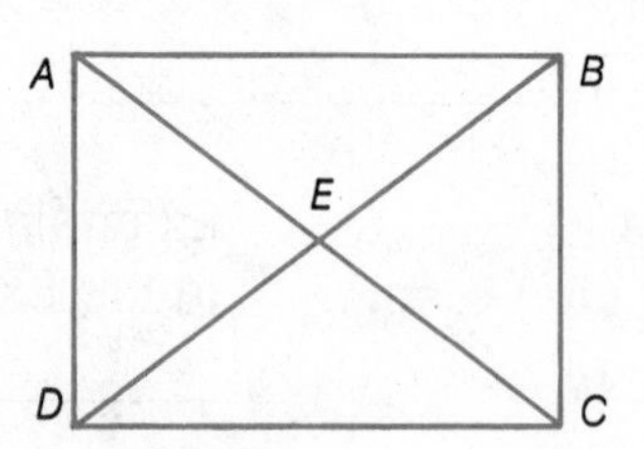

a

1. If $AE = 3$ meters, find AC, BE, BD, and DE.
2. Name the angles congruent to $\angle ABE$.
3. If $m\angle BAE = 30$, find $m\angle ABE$, $m\angle AEB$, $m\angle BEC$, $m\angle EBC$, $m\angle BCE$, $m\angle CDE$, and $m\angle EDA$.
4. Name four isosceles triangles in the figure.
5. Are the diagonals of the rectangle congruent?
6. Are the diagonals of the rectangle perpendicular to each other?

*For Exercises **7–12**, refer to square FPHG.*

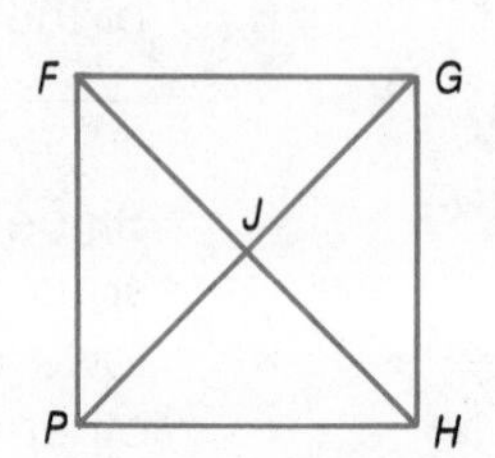

7. Give the measure of each acute angle.
8. Name eight triangles in the figure. State which of these are right triangles, and which are isosceles triangles.

9. If $HJ = 14$ cm, find FH and GP.
10. The perimeter of $FPHG$ is 18 units. Find HG.
11. Are the diagonals of the square congruent?
12. Are the diagonals of the square perpendicular to each other?

*For Exercises **13–18**, refer to rhombus KOMS.*

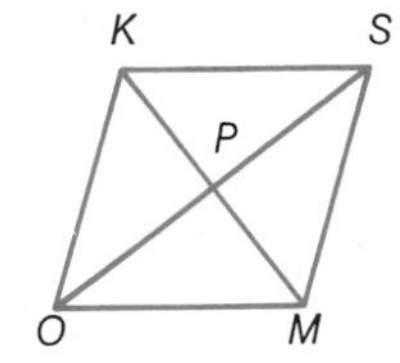

13. If $m\angle KOS = 25$, find $m\angle KOM$.
14. Name 4 isosceles triangles in the figure.
15. State three properties of diagonals KM and OS.
16. If $m\angle SKP = 50$, find the measures of the remaining seven acute angles.
17. Are the diagonals of the rhombus congruent?
18. Are the diagonals of the rhombus perpendicular to each other?
19. Name the properties that a rhombus and a rectangle have in common.
20. Name properties of a rhombus that are not properties of every parallelogram.
21. Name properties of a square that are not properties of every rectangle.
22. Name properties of a square that are not properties of every rhombus.
23. Name two kinds of parallelograms that are equilateral and two that are equiangular.
24. Prove that the diagonals of a square are congruent.
25. Prove Theorem 5-10. (HINT: Follow the method of Example 3.)
26. Prove Theorem 5-11. (HINT: Follow the method of Example 3.)

*Prove each statement in Exercises **27–30.***

27. If a quadrilateral is a square, then it is a parallelogram.
28. If a quadrilateral is a square, then it is a rhombus.
29. If a parallelogram has one right angle, then it has four right angles.
30. If a parallelogram has congruent diagonals, then it is a rectangle.

31. A quadrilateral has four congruent sides. Must it be a rhombus? Prove your answer.

32. A parallelogram has its diagonals perpendicular to each other. Must it be a rhombus? Prove your answer.

33. Prove that the base angles of an isosceles trapezoid are congruent. (HINT: Draw segments from T and R perpendicular to $\overline{PA}$).

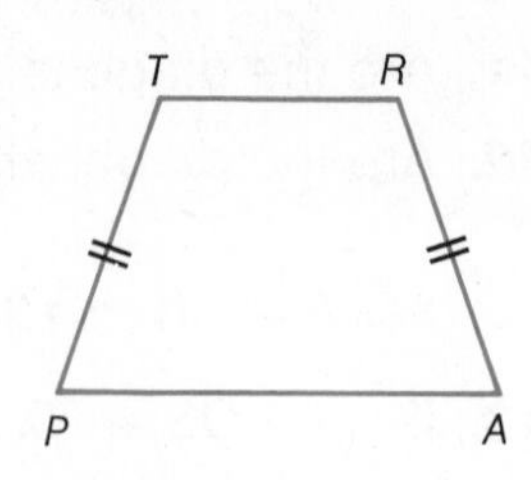

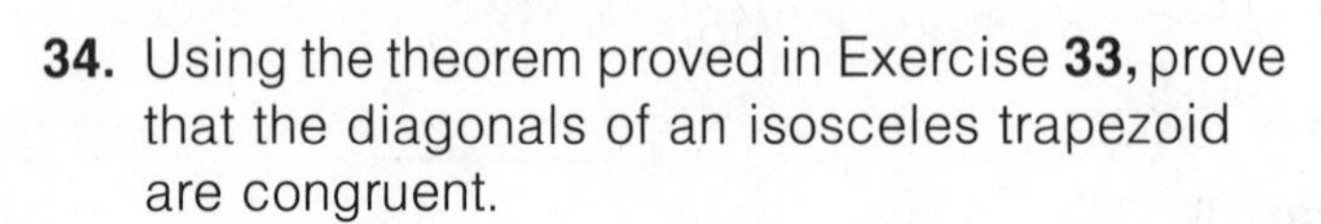

34. Using the theorem proved in Exercise **33,** prove that the diagonals of an isosceles trapezoid are congruent.

*For Exercises **35–37,** KETQ is a quadrilateral with* $\overline{KQ} \cong \overline{KE}$ *and* $\overline{QT} \cong \overline{ET}$.

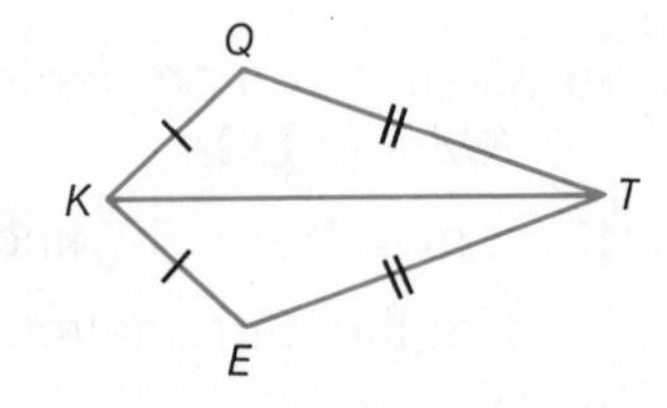

35. Prove that diagonal KT bisects $\angle QKE$ and $\angle QTE$.

36. Prove that $\angle Q \cong \angle E$.

37. In quadrilateral $KETQ$, draw $\overline{QE}$ intersecting $\overline{KT}$ at M. Prove that $\overline{KT}$ is the perpendicular bisector of $\overline{QE}$.

think–draw–see

1. Draw a large triangle ABC.
2. Find D, the midpoint of $\overline{AB}$, and E, the midpoint of $\overline{AC}$.
3. Draw $\overline{DE}$. Measure $\overline{DE}$ and $\overline{BC}$. Compare the measures.
4. Measure $\angle ADE$ and $\angle B$. Is $\overline{DE} \parallel \overline{BC}$?
5. Repeat Steps 1–4 for $\overline{AC}$ and$\overline{BC}$.
6. Repeat Steps 1–4 for $\overline{AB}$ and $\overline{BC}$.
7. What can you conclude about the length of the line segment that joins the midpoints of two sides of a triangle?

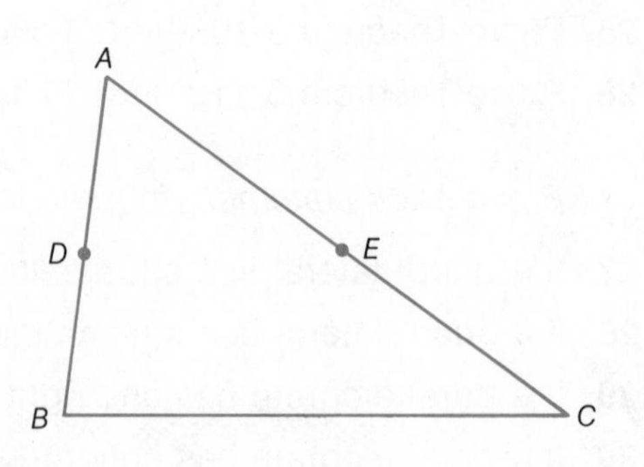

5-4 Midpoints and Parallel Lines

The properties of parallelograms are important in developing new theorems.

NOTE: The proof in the Example is written as a paragraph proof.

Example

Given: *THEM* is a parallelogram in which Q is the midpoint of $\overline{ME}$. $\overrightarrow{TM}$ and $\overrightarrow{HQ}$ are extended to Y.

Prove: M is the midpoint of $\overline{TY}$ and Q is the midpoint of $\overline{HY}$.

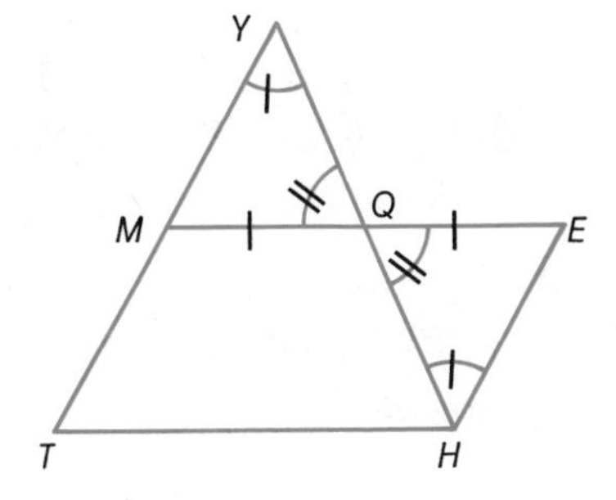

Proof: $\overline{MQ} \cong \overline{QE}$ by the definition of midpoint, $\angle MQY \cong \angle EQH$ by the Vertical Angle theorem, and $\angle MYQ \cong \angle EHQ$ because alternate interior angles formed by parallel lines are congruent. Thus, $\triangle QMY \cong \triangle QEH$ by S.A.A.

Then $\overline{YQ} \cong \overline{HQ}$ because they are corresponding parts of congruent triangles, and Q is the midpoint of $\overline{HY}$.

Also, $\overline{YM} \cong \overline{EH}$ by C.P.C.T.C. and $\overline{EH} \cong \overline{MT}$ because opposite sides of a parallelogram are congruent.

Therefore, $\overline{YM} \cong \overline{MT}$ by transitivity and M is the midpoint of $\overline{TY}$.

Theorem 5-12 is related to the Example. You are asked to prove this theorem in the Exercises.

Theorem 5-12: If a segment joins the midpoints of two sides of a triangle, then it is parallel to the third side and its length is one half the length of the third side.

Try These

Draw $\triangle ABC$ so that the lengths of its sides are 8, 6, and 5. Join the midpoints of the sides of $\triangle ABC$.

1. Give the lengths of the sides of each triangle formed.
2. Are the 4 triangles congruent?

In quadrilateral ADCB, E, F, H, and G are midpoints of the sides. Compare these measures.

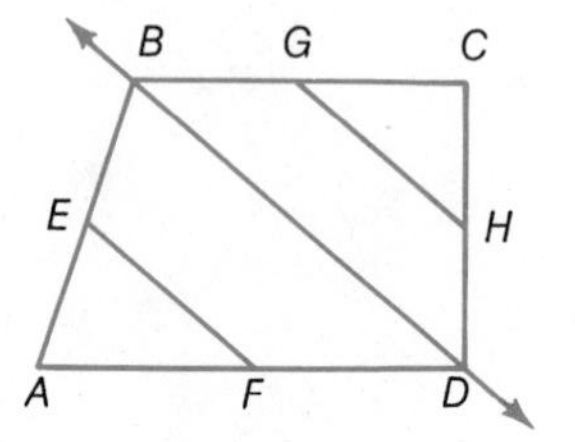

3. EF and BD **4.** GH and BD **5.** EF and GH
6. Is $\overline{EF} \parallel \overline{GH}$? Give a reason for your answer.

Exercises

a

1. In $\triangle ABC$ below, D and E are the midpoints of the sides, $m\angle A = 43$, and $m\angle B = 67$. Find $m\angle 1$, $m\angle 2$, $m\angle 3$, $m\angle 4$, and $m\angle C$.

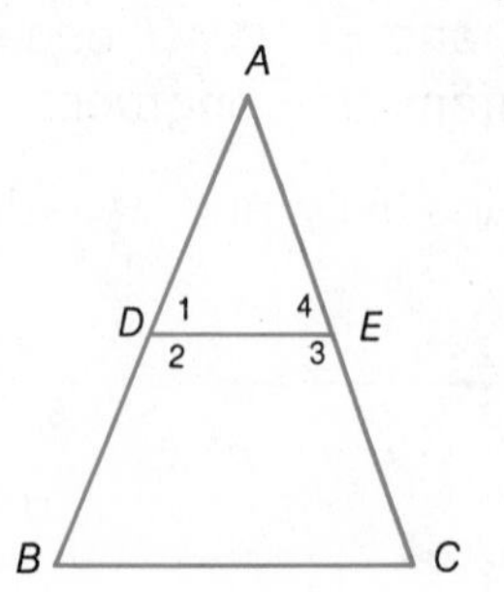

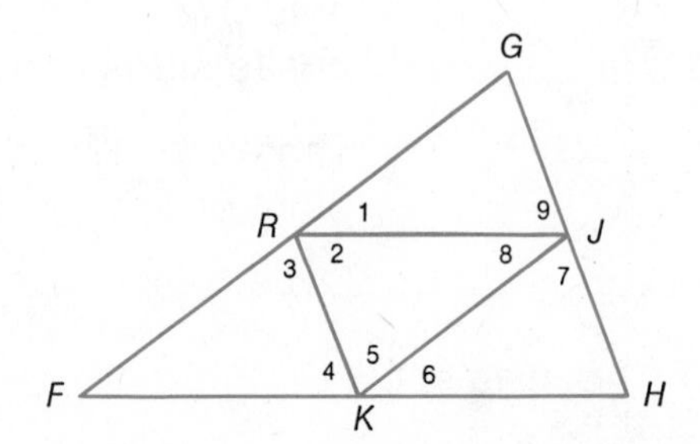

2. In $\triangle FHG$ above, R, J, and K are the midpoints of the sides, $m\angle F = 37$, and $m\angle G = 73$. Find $m\angle H$ and the measure of each numbered angle.

3. In the figure for Exercise **1,** if $\overline{BC}$ is 3 units long, find DE.

4. In the figure for Exercise **2,** if the perimeter of $\triangle FGH$ is 18 centimeters, what is the perimeter of $\triangle RJK$?

5. Each side of an equilateral triangle is 12 meters long. Segments join the midpoints of the sides. What is the perimeter of each triangle formed?

6. Each side of an equilateral triangle is x meters long. Segments join the midpoints of the sides. Express the perimeter of each triangle formed in terms of x.

*In Exercises **7–9,** exactly one of the lengths marked x, y, or z, can be found from the given information. Find that length.*

7.

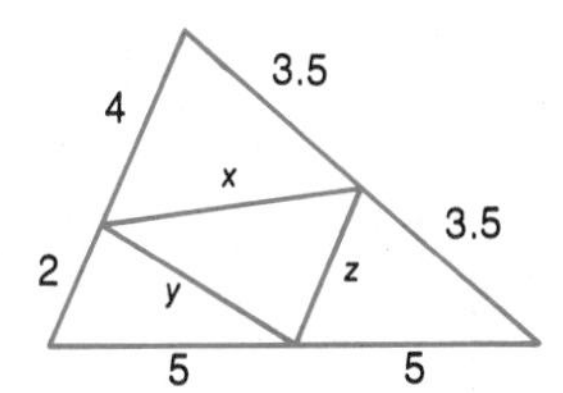

8.

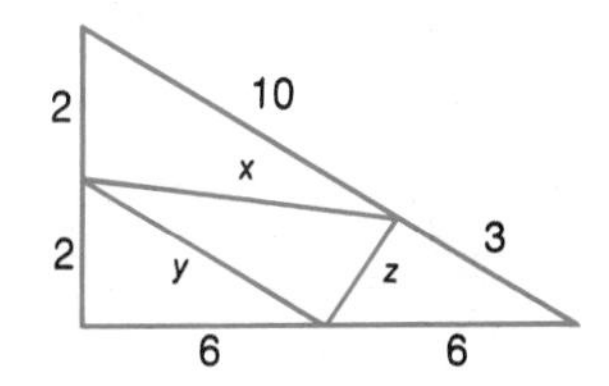

9.

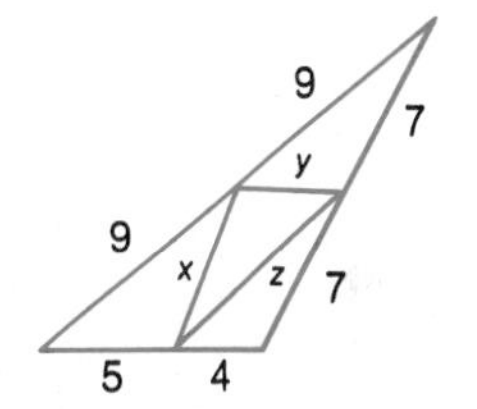

10. Supply the missing reasons for this proof of Theorem 5-12. (NOTE: The proof is continued on the following page.)

Given: In $\triangle ABC$, D and E are the midpoints of $\overline{AC}$ and $\overline{BC}$ respectively.

Prove: $\overline{DE} \parallel \overline{AB}$ and $DE = \frac{1}{2}AB$.

Plan: Extend $\overline{DE}$ its own length to F. Draw $\overline{BF}$. Now prove that $ABFD$ is a parallelogram.

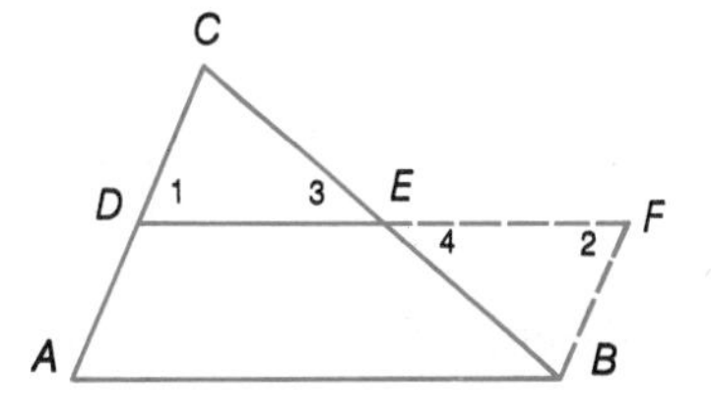

Statements	Reasons
1. Extend $\overline{DE}$ to F so that $\overline{EF} \cong \overline{DE}$.	1. Postulate 8a
2. Let $\overline{BF}$ join B and F.	2. Postulate 4
3. $\overline{BE} \cong \overline{EC}$	3. Definition of midpoint
4. $\angle 3 \cong \angle 4$	4. (1). __?__
5. $\triangle DEC \cong \triangle FEB$	5. (1), (3), (4). __?__
6. $\angle 1 \cong \angle 2$	6. (5). __?__

Statements (cont.)	Reasons (cont.)
7. $\overline{AD} \parallel \overline{BF}$	7. (6). Theorem 4-2
8. $\overline{DC} \cong \overline{BF}$	8. (5). ___?___
9. $\overline{AD} \cong \overline{DC}$	9. Definition of midpoint
10. $\overline{AD} \cong \overline{BF}$	10. (8), (9). ___?___
11. $ABFD$ is a ▱.	11. (7), (10). ___?___
12. $\overline{DE} \parallel \overline{AB}$	12. (11). ___?___
13. $\overline{DF} \cong \overline{AB}$	13. (11). ___?___

Complete the proof by showing that $DE = \frac{1}{2}DF$ *and (from Step 13) that* $DE = \frac{1}{2}AB$.

11. The diagonals of quadrilateral $ABCD$ measure 6 and 10. The midpoints of $\overline{AB}$, $\overline{BC}$, $\overline{CD}$, and $\overline{DA}$ are connected in that order. How long is each side of the new quadrilateral? Is the new quadrilateral a parallelogram?

12. In Exercise **11,** would you get a parallelogram regardless of the quadrilateral you used? Explain your answer.

13. $ABCD$ is a rectangle. E, F, G, and H are the midpoints of $\overline{AB}$, $\overline{BC}$, $\overline{CD}$, and $\overline{DA}$ respectively. Is $EFGH$ a rhombus? Prove your answer.

PUZZLE

This rectangle is divided into squares. The three smallest are 8, 15, and 17 units on a side. The two largest are 69 and 72 units on a side. How long is each side of each square?

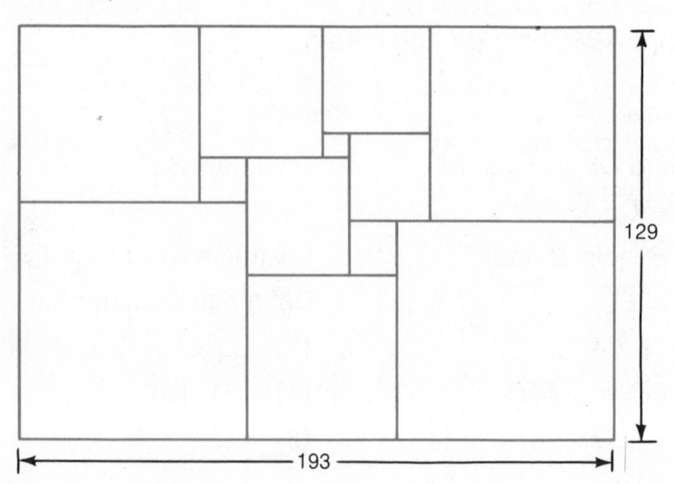

5-5 Parallel Lines and Congruent Segments

In the figure at the right, $\overline{AB}$ is the median of trapezoid $WXYZ$. This means that A is the midpoint of $\overline{WX}$ and B is the midpoint of $\overline{YZ}$.

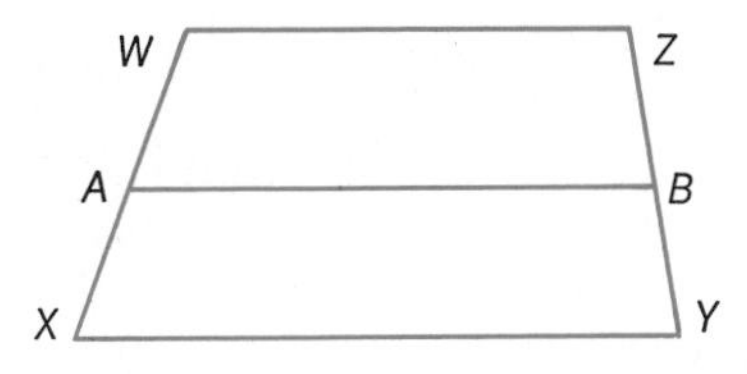

Definition: The **median of a trapezoid** is the segment joining the midpoints of the nonparallel sides.

Theorem 5-13 concerns the length of the median of a trapezoid. You are asked to prove this theorem in the Exercises.

Theorem 5-13: The median of a trapezoid is parallel to the bases and its length is one half the sum of the lengths of the bases.

Example 1

In trapezoid $WXYZ$, $\overline{AB}$ is the median, $WZ = 14.6$ centimeters, and $XY = 23.2$ centimeters. Find AB

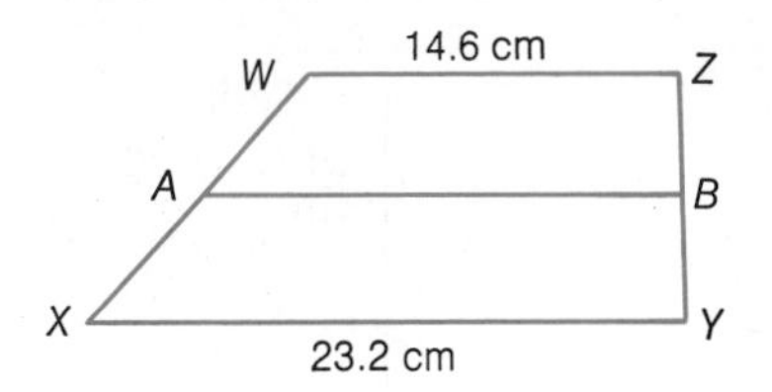

$AB = \frac{1}{2}(WZ + XY)$ ⟵ **From Theorem 5-13**

$= \frac{1}{2}(14.6 + 23.2)$

$= \frac{1}{2}(37.8)$

$= 18.9$ cm

The next theorem concerns three or more parallel lines and congruent segments on two or more transversals.

Theorem 5-14: If three or more parallel lines cut off congruent segments on one transversal, then they cut off congruent segments on any transversal.

Example 2

Parallel lines p, q, and r are cut by transversals k and n, and $\overline{AB} \cong \overline{BC}$. Classify each statement as True or False. Give a reason for each answer.

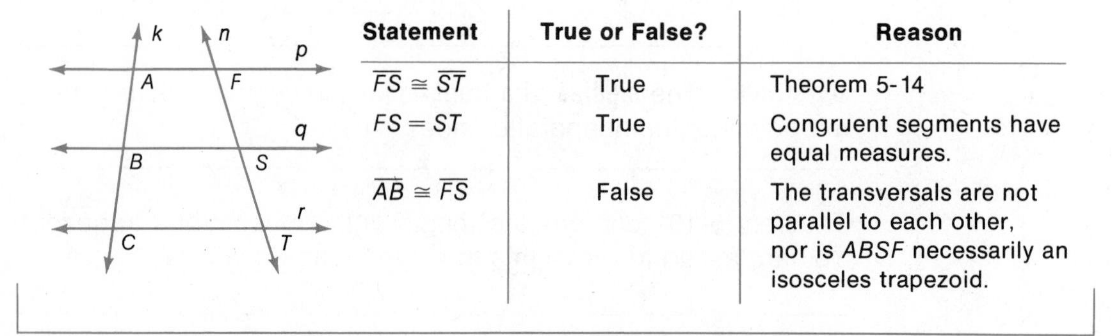

Statement	True or False?	Reason
$\overline{FS} \cong \overline{ST}$	True	Theorem 5-14
$FS = ST$	True	Congruent segments have equal measures.
$\overline{AB} \cong \overline{FS}$	False	The transversals are not parallel to each other, nor is $ABSF$ necessarily an isosceles trapezoid.

These corollaries follow from Theorem 5-14.

Corollary 5-15: If a line is parallel to one side of a triangle and bisects a second side, then it bisects the third side also.

Corollary 5-16: If a line is parallel to the bases of a trapezoid and bisects one of the nonparallel sides, then it bisects the other side also.

Try These

1. The bases of a trapezoid are 6 and 9 units long. Find the length of the median.

2. In the figure at the right, $AD = DB = 6$, $AC = 18$, and $DE \parallel BC$. Find AE and EC.

3. In the figure for Exercise **2,** $\angle AED \cong \angle C$, $AE = EC = 15$ and $AD = 10$. Find DB and AB.

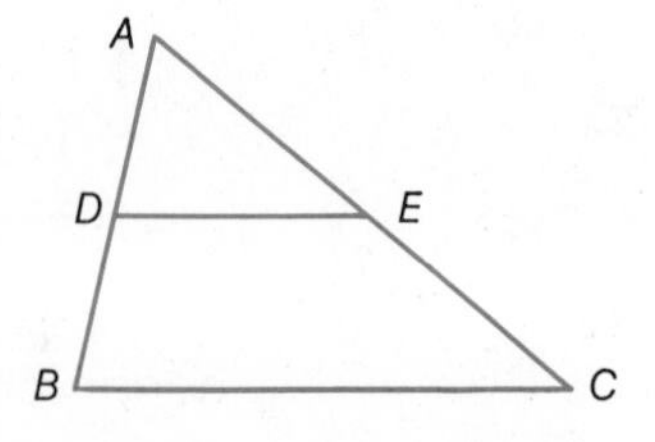

4. In the figure at the right, $\overline{SO} \parallel \overline{DQ} \parallel \overline{EV}$, $OQ = QV = 7$, and $SD = 4$. Find ED.

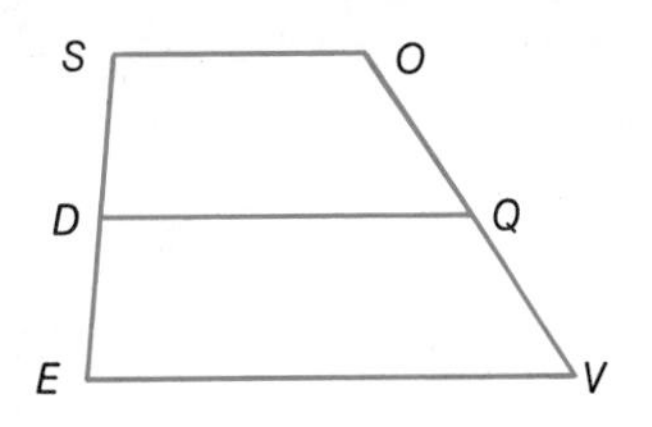

5. In the figure for Exercise **4,** $\angle OQD \cong \angle V$, $\angle EDQ \cong \angle S$, $QV = 8$, and D is the midpoint of $\overline{ES}$. Find QO and VO.

6. One base of a trapezoid measures 23 and its median measures 20. Find the length of the other base.

Exercises

*In Exercises **1–10,** find the missing lengths of a base or median of a trapezoid.*

a

	One Base	Other Base	Median
1.	15	25	?
2.	17	8	?
3.	9	$4\frac{1}{2}$	?
4.	$(12 + 3x)$	$(16 - 3x)$	?
5.	$(3b + 8)$	$(5b - 6)$	?
6.	r	s	?
7.	54	?	36
8.	23	?	15
9.	?	$12\frac{1}{2}$	20
10.	?	a	m

11. Segments AB, CD, and EF are drawn on ruled paper as shown in the figure. If $AB = 2\frac{1}{4}$, $CD = 2\frac{7}{8}$, and $EF = 3\frac{3}{8}$ how long is each smaller segment of $\overline{AB}$, of $\overline{CD}$, and of $\overline{EF}$?

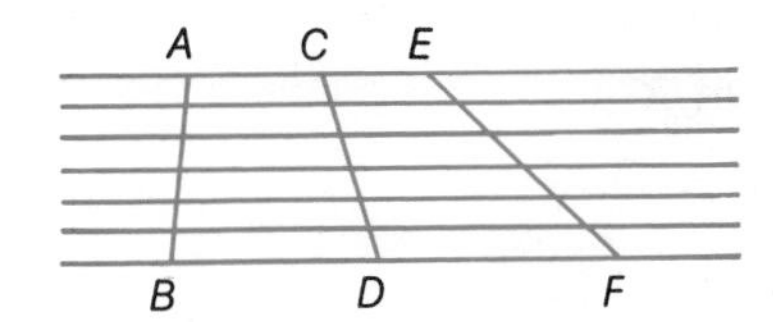

12. The median of a trapezoid is 9 centimeters in length and one of the bases is 13 centimeters. Find the length of the other base.

13. Supply the missing reasons for this proof of Theorem 5-13.

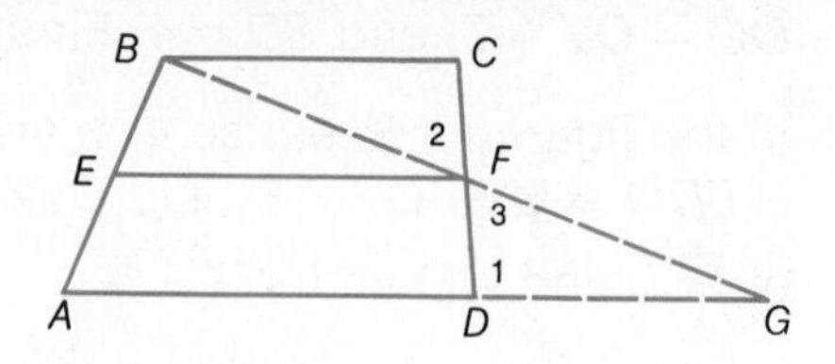

Given: Trapezoid $ABCD$ has median EF.

Prove: $\overline{EF} \parallel \overline{AD} \parallel \overline{BC}$
$EF = \frac{1}{2}(AD + BC)$

Statements	Reasons
1. Join B and F and extend $\overline{BF}$ to intersect $\overline{AD}$ extended to G.	1. Postulate 4
2. In triangles BCF and GDF, $\overline{CF} \cong \overline{FD}$	2. The median of a trapezoid is a segment joining the midpoints of the nonparallel sides.
3. $\overline{BC} \parallel \overline{AG}$	3. A trapezoid is a quadrilateral with exactly two sides parallel.
4. $\angle C \cong \angle 1$	4. (3). __?__
5. $\angle 2 \cong \angle 3$	5. (1). __?__
6. $\triangle BCF \cong \triangle GDF$	6. (2). (4). (5). __?__
7. In $\triangle ABG$, $\overline{BF} \cong \overline{FG}$.	7. (6). __?__
8. $\overline{BE} \cong \overline{EA}$	8. __?__
9. $\overline{EF} \parallel \overline{AD}$, $EF = \frac{1}{2}(AD + DG)$	9. (7). (8). Theorem 5-12
10. $\overline{BC} \cong \overline{DG}$	10. (6). __?__
11. $BC = DG$	11. (10). __?__
12. $EF = \frac{1}{2}(AD + BC)$	12. (9). (11). __?__
13. $\overline{EF} \parallel \overline{AD} \parallel \overline{BC}$	13. (3). (9). __?__

b **14.** Write the formula for the length of the median m of a trapezoid whose bases have lengths of b_1 and b_2. Solve this formula for b_1.

c **15.** Prove Theorem 5-14.

Given: Lines AB, CD, EF, and GH are parallel and cut transversal JK so that $\overline{LM} \cong \overline{MN} \cong \overline{NP}$. $\overleftrightarrow{QR}$ is any other transversal.

Prove: $\overline{ST} \cong \overline{TV} \cong \overline{VW}$

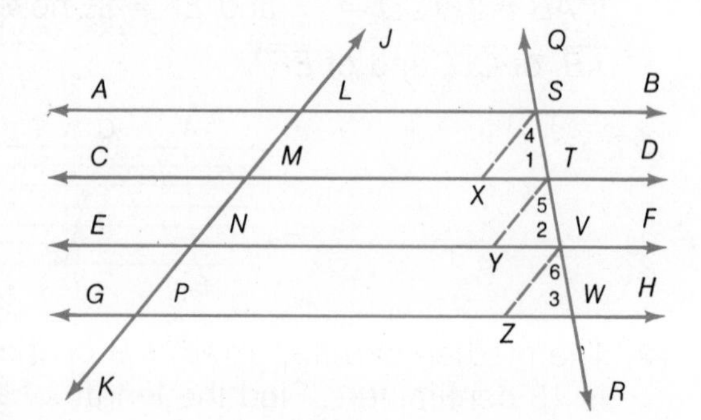

Constructions

Constructing a Parallelogram

Given: $\overline{BC}$; $\overline{BA}$; $\angle B$;

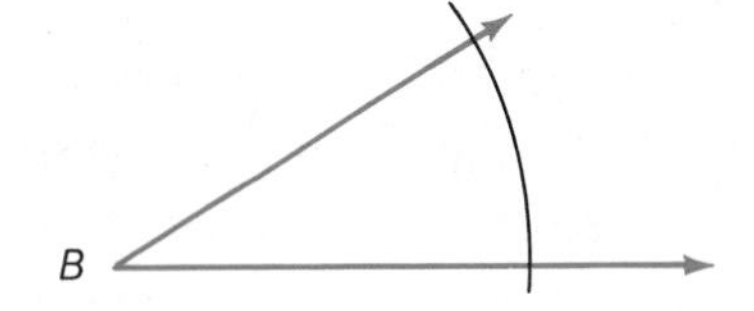

Required: To construct a parallelogram given two sides and the included angle.

1. Draw any ray. At the endpoint of the ray, construct an angle congruent to $\angle B$. Label it $\angle ZBY$.

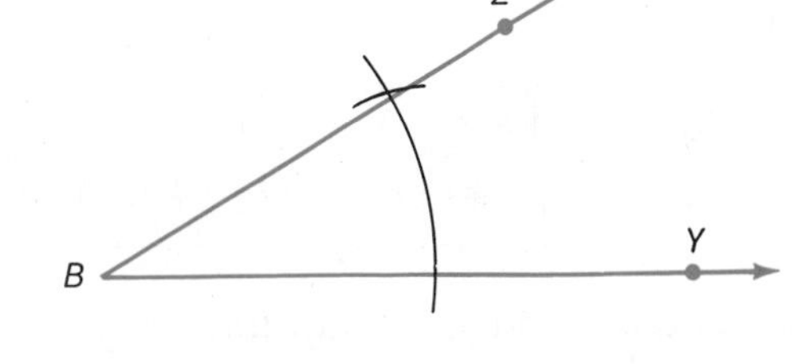

2. On $\overrightarrow{BY}$, mark off a segment congruent to $\overline{BA}$. On $\overrightarrow{BZ}$, mark off a segment congruent to $\overline{BC}$.

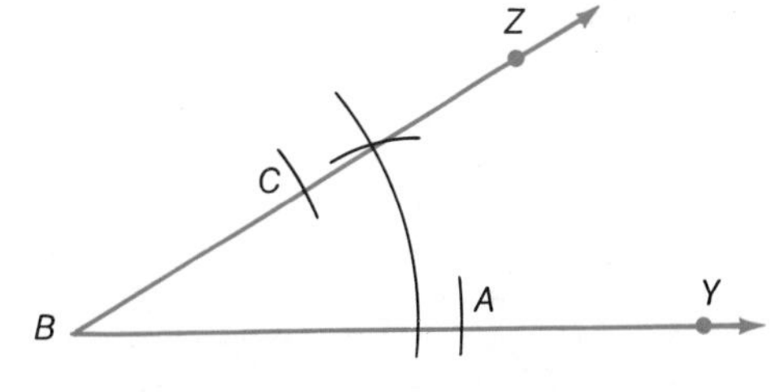

3. With A as center, and with the length of $\overline{BC}$ as radius, make an arc. Make a second arc using C as center and BA as radius. Name the intersection of the arcs, point D.

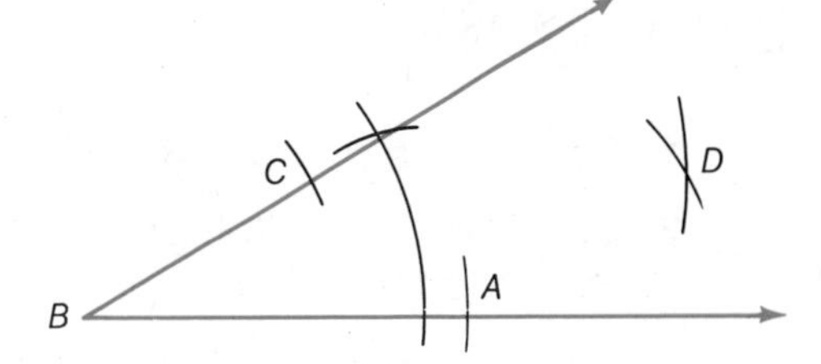

4. Draw $\overline{AD}$ and $\overline{CD}$.
$ABCD$ is a parallelogram.

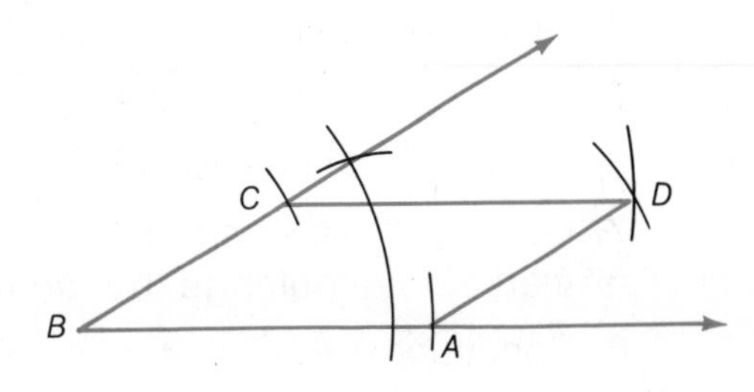

Dividing a Segment into Congruent Parts

Given: $\overline{AB}$

Required: To divide $\overline{AB}$ into three congruent parts.

1. Draw $\overrightarrow{AK}$ so that it makes any convenient angle with $\overline{AB}$. Start at A and, using any convenient radius, mark off three congruent segments in succession on $\overrightarrow{AK}$.

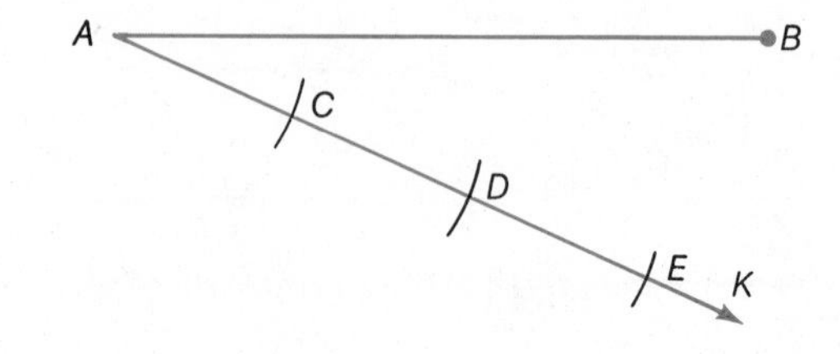

2. Draw $\overline{BE}$. At points D and C, construct an angle congruent to $\angle E$. Then $\overline{BE} \parallel \overline{JD} \parallel \overline{HC}$.

   Since parallel segments BE, JD, and HC cut off congruent segments on $\overrightarrow{AK}$, they cut off congruent segments on $\overline{AB}$.

   Thus, $\overline{AH} \cong \overline{HJ} \cong \overline{JB}$.

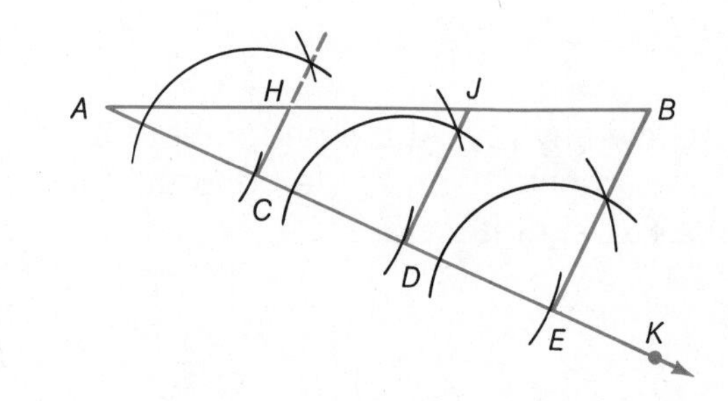

Exercises

1. Construct a parallelogram given two sides and an included angle of 60°.
2. Construct a parallelogram so that a side and two diagonals are equal in length to three given line segments.
3. Construct a quadrilateral, given the sides and one diagonal.
4. Divide a given segment into five congruent parts.
5. Divide a segment into seven congruent parts.
6. By construction, subtract $\frac{1}{3}$ of a given segment from $\frac{1}{2}$ of it.
7. Construct $\triangle ABC$ so that $m\angle A = 60$, $AB = 4$ cm, and $AC = 3$ cm. Use a marked straightedge, but do not use a protractor.
8. Construct $\triangle ABC$ so that $m\angle A = 30$, $m\angle B = 45$, and $AB = 3.5$ cm.

9. Construct $\triangle ABC$ so that $m\angle A = 60$, $m\angle C = 45$, and $AB = 2.7$ cm.
10. Construct $\square ABCD$ so that $AB = 3$ cm, $m\angle A = 60$, and $AD = 2$ cm.
11. Why can you not construct $\square ABCD$ with $m\angle A = 60$, $AB = 4$ cm, and $m\angle B = 100$?
12. Construct a quadrilateral, given four sides and one angle.
13. Through a given point outside a line, construct a line that will make a given angle with the given line.
14. Construct a rhombus, given its perimeter and one angle.
15. Construct a trapezoid, given the lengths of the two bases and the lengths of the nonparallel sides. When will this construction be impossible?
16. Construct a rhombus with one angle measuring 30.
17. Given the positions of the midpoints of the three sides of a triangle, construct the triangle.
18. Construct a parallelogram, given its diagonals.

PUZZLE

Find the sum of the angle measures at the five points of this star.

Remember

Restate each biconditional as a conditional and its converse.

1. A quadrilateral is a rhombus if and only if all its sides are congruent.
2. A quadrilateral is a parallelogram if and only if it has one pair of sides both parallel and congruent.

The answers are on page 248. If you need help, see page 78.

5-6 Inequalities in Triangles

In the triangle at the right, side AC is opposite $\angle B$, side BC is opposite $\angle A$, and $\angle C$ is the angle opposite side AB. Further, $AB > BC > AC$, and $m\angle C > m\angle A > m\angle B$. This leads to Theorems 5-17 and 5-18.

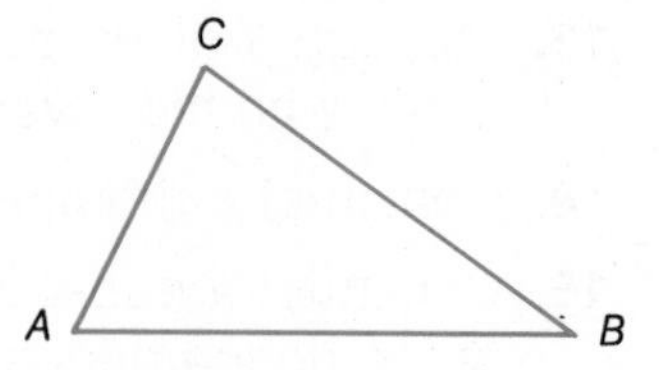

Theorem 5-17: If two sides of a triangle are not congruent, then the angles opposite these sides are not congruent, and the smaller angle is opposite the smaller side.

Theorem 5-18: If two angles of a triangle are not congruent, then the sides opposite these angles are not congruent, and the smaller side is opposite the smaller angle.

You are asked to prove these theorems in the Exercises.

Example 1

Use $\triangle EFG$, Theorems 5-17 and 5-18, and the given information to tell whether each conclusion is True or False.

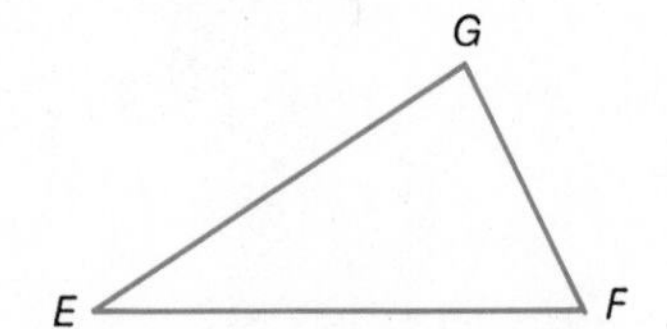

Given	Conclusion	True or False?
$\angle F \not\cong \angle G$	$\overline{GE} \not\cong \overline{EF}$	True
$GF < EF$	$m\angle E > m\angle G$	False
$m\angle G > m\angle F$	$EF > EG$	True
$EF > EG > GF$	$m\angle G > m\angle F > m\angle E$	True

Example 2

In the figure at the right, $\overline{PA} \perp$ line m and $\overline{PB}$ is not perpendicular to line m. Compare PA and PB.

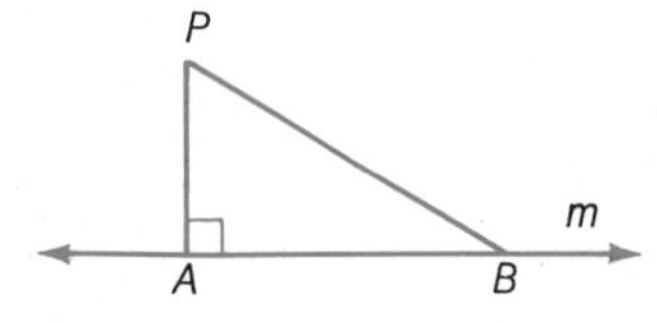

$m\angle PAB > m\angle PBA$ ⟵ In a right triangle, the measure of the right angle is greater than the measure of either acute angle.

$PA < PB$ ⟵ Theorem 5-18

Example 2 suggests this theorem. You are asked to prove the theorem in the Exercises.

Theorem 5-19: The perpendicular segment from a point to a line is the shortest distance from the point to the line.

Try These

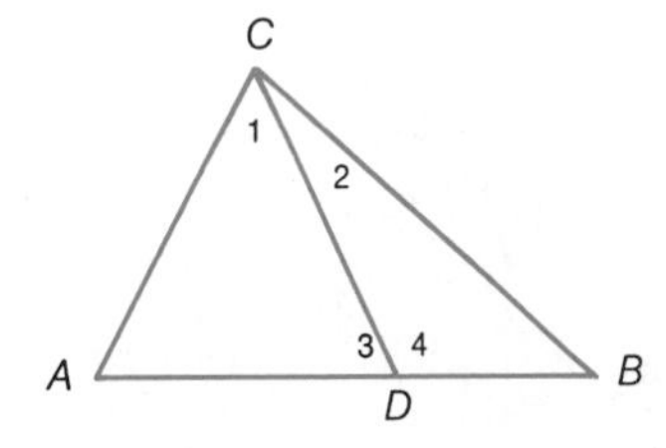

1. Name an exterior angle of $\triangle ADC$.
2. Compare $m\angle 4$ and $m\angle 1$.
3. Compare $m\angle 4$ and $m\angle A$.
4. Compare $m\angle 3$ and $m\angle 2$.

For Exercises **5–8,** $\overline{CA} \cong \overline{CD}$.

5. Compare $m\angle A$ and $m\angle 3$.
6. Compare $m\angle 3$ and $m\angle B$.
7. Compare $m\angle A$ and $m\angle B$.
8. Compare BC and AC.

Exercises

a

1. In $\triangle ABC$, $AB < BC < AC$. Compare the measures of the angles of the triangle in a similar way.
2. In $\triangle RST$, $m\angle S < m\angle T < m\angle R$. Compare the measures of the sides of the triangle in a similar way.

3. In the figure at the left below, $\overline{CD}$ bisects $\angle C$. Prove that $m\angle 3 > m\angle 1$.

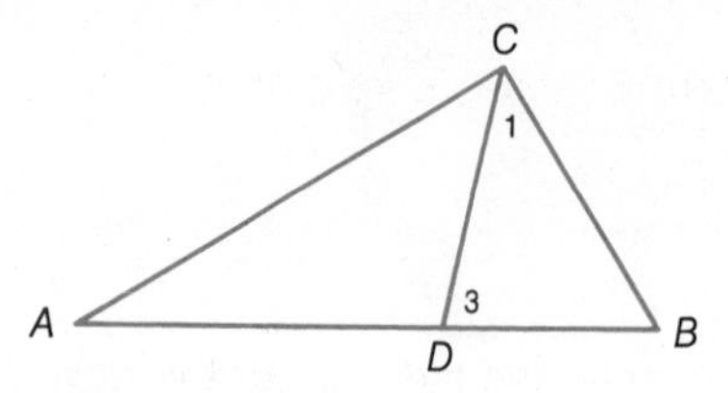

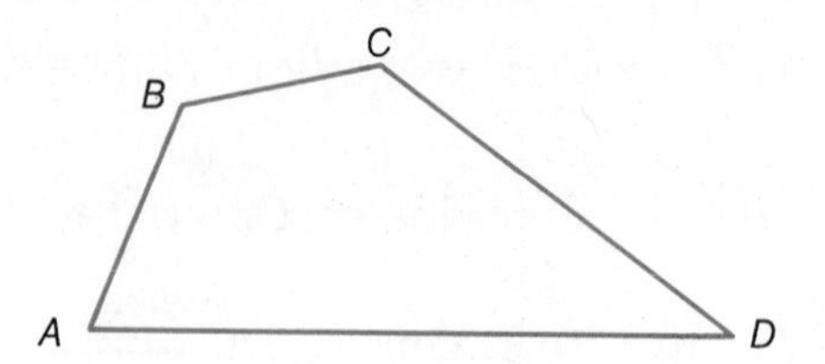

4. In quadrilateral *ADCB* at the right above, $AB > BC$ and $AD > DC$. Prove that $m\angle C > m\angle A$.

5. Explain why the hypotenuse of a right triangle is the longest side.

6. In quadrilateral *ABCD* below, $AB = BC$, $AD = DC$, and $AD > AB$. Prove that $m\angle B > m\angle D$.

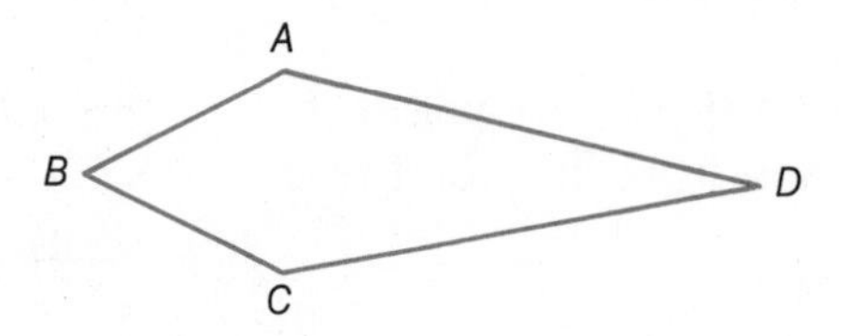

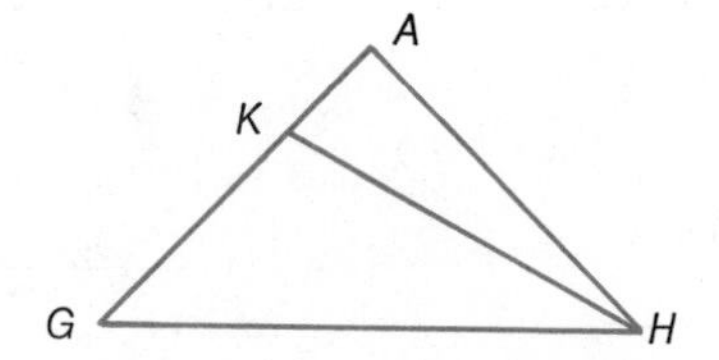

7. In $\triangle AGH$ at the right above, $\triangle AGH$ is isosceles with base *GH*. Prove that $KG < KH$.

8. In the figure at the left below, $\overline{LM}$ is the base of isosceles $\triangle KLM$. If $m\angle X > m\angle 4$, prove that $KM > XL$.

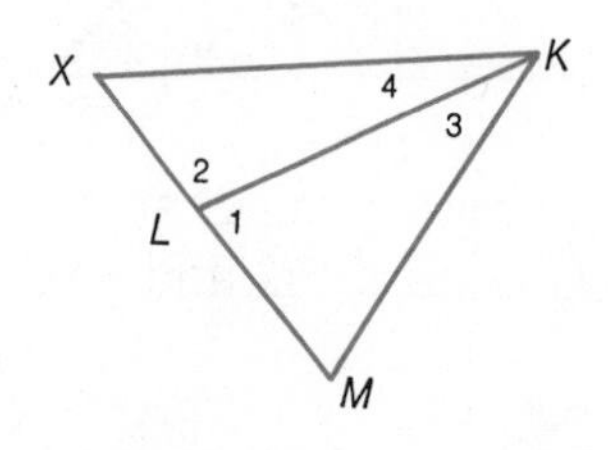

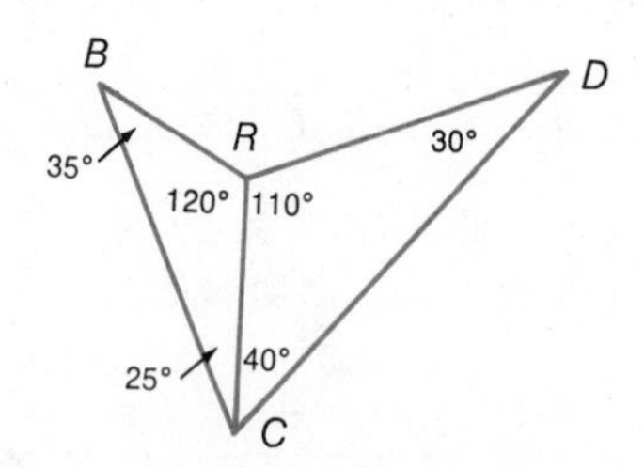

9. In quadrilateral *BCDR* above with angle measures as shown, which segment is the shortest?

10. In the figure for Exercise **8,** $\triangle XKM$ with base *KX* and $\triangle KLM$ with base *LM* are isosceles triangles. If $m\angle X < m\angle 2$, prove that $KX > XM$.

11. In $\triangle QRS$, the bisectors of angles *R* and *S* intersect each other at *T*. Let $m\angle R = 2x$, $m\angle S = 2y$, $m\angle Q = 2z$, and $m\angle T = w$. Show algebraically that $m\angle T > 90$.

12. In isosceles triangle XYZ with base XZ, P is a point between Y and Z. If $PY < XY$, prove $m\angle YXZ < m\angle YPX$.

13. $\overline{AD}$ bisects angle A of $\triangle ABC$. If D is a point between B and C, prove that $AC > CD$.

14. In $\triangle RST$, RX is a median and $RT > RS$. Prove that $m\angle TXR > m\angle T$.

15. Prove Theorem 5-19. (HINT: See Example 2.)

16. Prove Theorem 5-17.

Given: $BC > AC$

Prove: $m\angle A > m\angle B$

Plan: Select D on BC so that $CD = CA$. Show that since $m\angle A > m\angle 2$, and since $m\angle 2 = m\angle 1$, then $m\angle A > m\angle 1$. Since $m\angle 1 > m\angle B$ by Theorem 4-1, $m\angle A > m\angle B$.

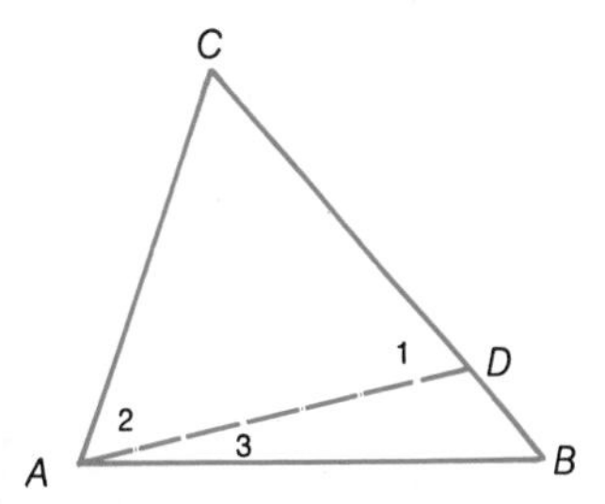

17. Prove Theorem 5-18.

Given: $m\angle B > m\angle A$

Prove: $AC > BC$

Plan: Use the indirect method. Either $AC < BC$ or $AC = BC$ or $AC > BC$. To prove that $AC > BC$, show that $AC < BC$ or $AC = BC$ leads to a contradiction. Use Theorem 5-17 to eliminate $AC < BC$, and the Isosceles Triangle Theorem to eliminate $AC = BC$. Then, $AC > BC$.

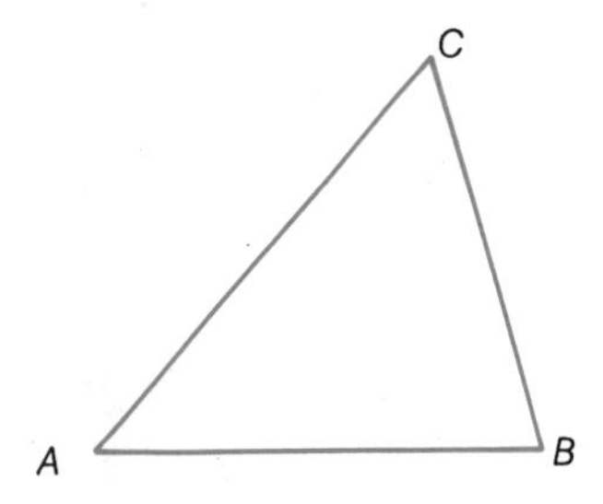

Prove each statement.

18. In a parallelogram that is not a rhombus, the diagonals do not bisect the angles of the parallelogram.

19. If two given lines are cut by a transversal so that the sum of the interior angles on one side of the transversal is less than 180, the lines will intersect on that side of the transversal.

20. The diagonals of parallelogram $FGHM$ in which $MH > GH$ intersect at K. Prove that $m\angle FKG > m\angle FGK$.

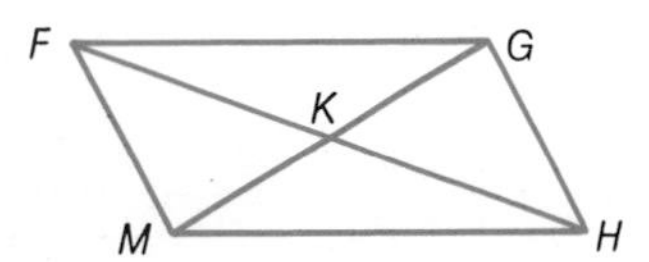

5-7 More Inequalities in Triangles

Try to draw a triangle with sides of 4 centimeters, 6 centimeters, and 10 centimeters. You will find that the 4-centimeter and 6-centimeter sides do not intersect to form a triangle.

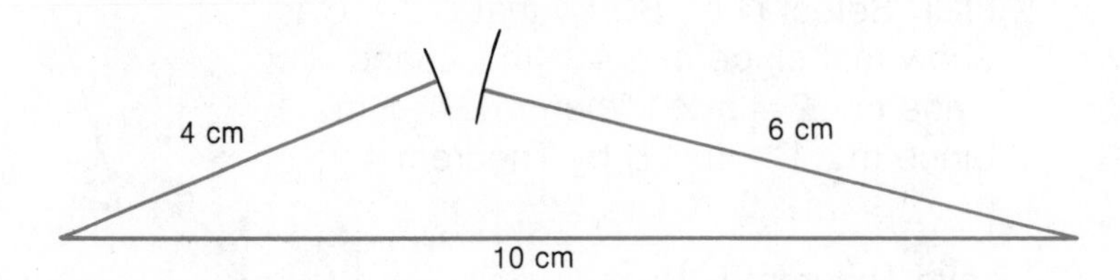

The reason for this is given in Theorem 5-20.

Theorem 5-20: Triangle Inequality Theorem

The sum of the lengths of two sides of a triangle is greater than the length of the third side.

Given: $\triangle RTQ$ is any triangle.

Prove: $RT + TQ > RQ$

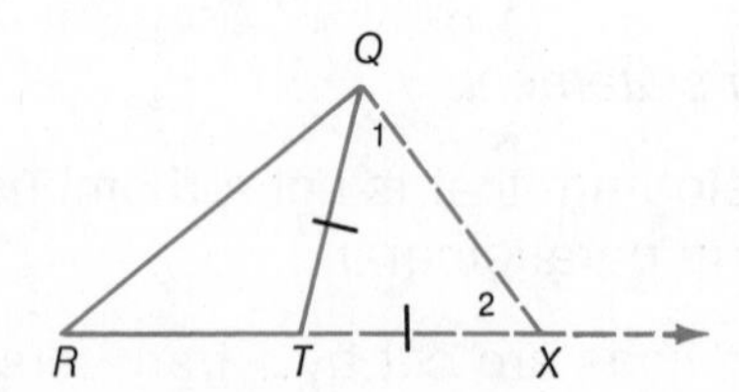

Plan: Extend $\overline{RT}$ to X so that $\overline{TX} \cong \overline{TQ}$. Draw $\overline{QX}$.

Proof: $\triangle QTX$ is isosceles with base QX, so $\angle 1 \cong \angle 2$. $RT + TX = RX$ and $RT + TQ = RX$ by substitution. Then $m\angle RQX > m\angle 1$, so $m\angle RQX > m\angle 2$. In $\triangle RQX$, $RX > RQ$ by Theorem 5-18. Thus, $RT + TQ > RQ$.

Example 1

In the figure, suppose that $\overline{BC}$ changes position from C_1 to C_2 to C_3. If the lengths of $\overline{AB}$ and $\overline{BC}$ do not change as the measure of the angle at B increases, does the length of $\overline{AC}$ increase or decrease?

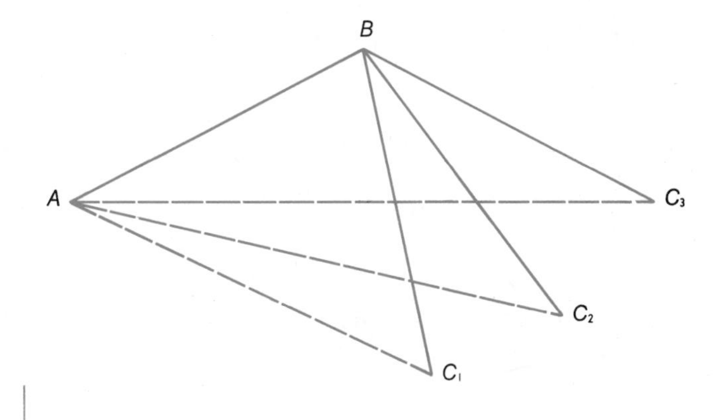

Answer:

As the measure of the angle at B increases, the length of $\overline{AC}$ increases.

Theorem 5-21

If two sides of one triangle are congruent to two sides of another triangle and if the included angles are not congruent, then the remaining sides are also not congruent, and the smaller side is opposite the smaller angle.

The converse of Theorem 5-21 is also a theorem.

Theorem 5-22

If two sides of one triangle are congruent to two sides of another triangle and if the third sides are not congruent, then the angles opposite the third sides are also not congruent, and the smaller angle is opposite the smaller side.

You are asked to prove both Theorem 5-21 and its converse in the Exercises.

Example 2

Use the figure and given information to replace ___?___ with >, <, or =.

a. Given: $m\angle F > m\angle C$

AB ___?___ DE

b. Given: $BC > FE$

$m\angle A$ ___?___ $m\angle D$

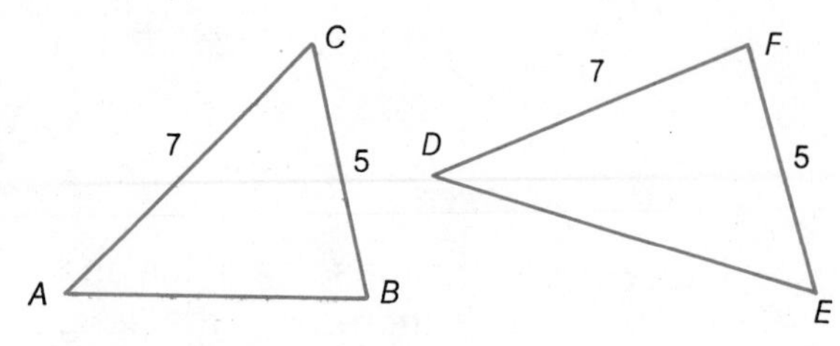

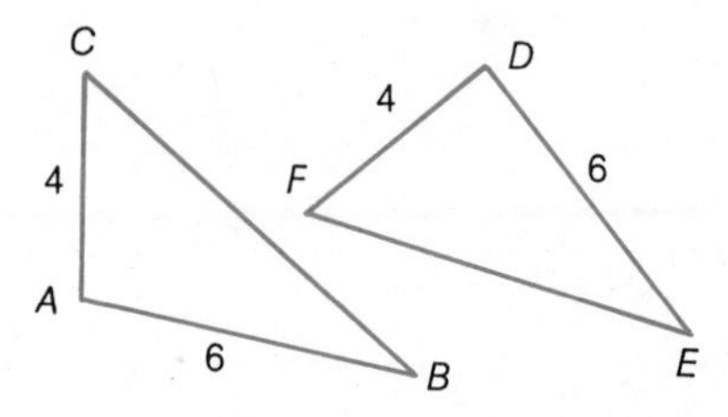

a. $AB < DE$

b. $m\angle A > m\angle D$

Try These

Write the letter of the response that completes each statement.

1. Two sides of a triangle measure 10 centimeters and 15 centimeters. The third side can measure

a. 5 cm **b.** 20 cm **c.** 25 cm **d.** 30 cm

2. In $\triangle DFE$, $DE = 4$ cm, $EF = 7$ cm, and $m\angle E = 70$. In $\triangle GJH$, $GH = 4$ cm, $HJ = 7$ cm, and $m\angle H = 60$. Then

a. $DF > GJ$ **b.** $DF < GJ$ **c.** $DF = GJ$ **d.** $DF = 11$ cm

3. In $\triangle KQM$, $KM = 4$, $MQ = 5$, and $KQ = 7$. In $\triangle NPO$, $NO = 4$, $OP = 5$, and $NP = 8$. Then

a. $m\angle M > m\angle O$ **b.** $m\angle M < m\angle O$

c. $m\angle M = m\angle O$ **d.** $m\angle M = 90$

4. In $\triangle ABC$, $\overline{AB} \cong \overline{BC}$ and $AC > AB$. Then

a. $m\angle B = 60$ **b.** $m\angle B < m\angle A$

c. $m\angle B > m\angle C$ **d.** $m\angle B = m\angle C$

5. The measures of two sides of a triangle are 22 and 34. The measure of the third side can be

a. 56 **b.** 5 **c.** 51 **d.** 12

Exercises

a

1. In triangle ABC, $AB + BC > AC$. Draw triangle ABC and write two other inequalities.

For each Exercise, write Yes if a triangle can have sides of the given measures. Otherwise, write No.

2. 2, 3, and 3 **3.** 2, 3, and 4 **4.** 2, 3, and 5

5. 5, 12, and 13 **6.** 12, 13, and 21 **7.** 100, 150, and 200

8. In $\triangle ABC$ at the left below, $\overline{CD}$ is an altitude. Prove that $BC > CD$.

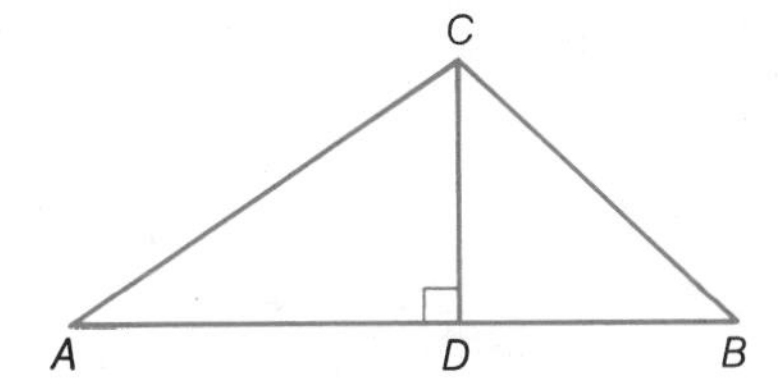

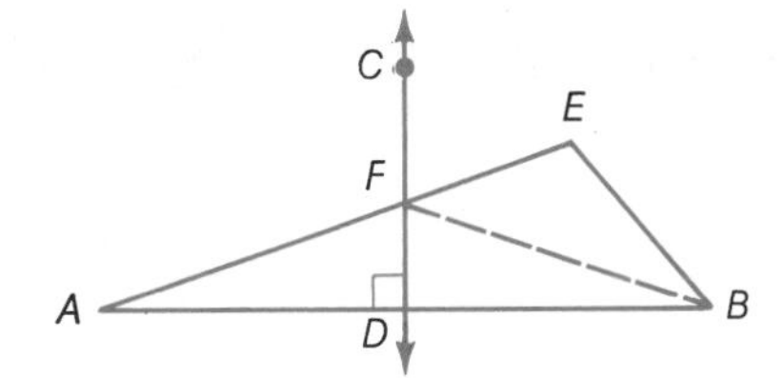

9. In the figure at the right above, $\overleftrightarrow{CD}$ is the perpendicular bisector of $\overline{AB}$, and E is not on $\overleftrightarrow{CD}$. Prove that $EA > EB$.

Write a proof for each statement in Exercises ***10–12.***

10. The difference between the lengths of any two sides of a triangle is less than the length of the third side.
11. If the alternate vertices A, C, and E of regular hexagon $ABCDEF$ are joined, the perimeter of the triangle formed is less than the perimeter of the hexagon.
12. The sum of the lengths of the altitudes of a triangle is less than the perimeter of the triangle.
13. In the figure at the right, O is the center of the circle, $\overline{OD} \cong \overline{OC} \cong \overline{OA} \cong \overline{OB}$, and $m\angle DOC > m\angle AOB$. Prove that $DC > AB$.
14. You are given that O is the center of the circle, $\overline{OD} \cong \overline{OC} \cong \overline{OB} \cong \overline{OA}$, and $DC > AB$. Prove that $m\angle COD > m\angle AOB$.

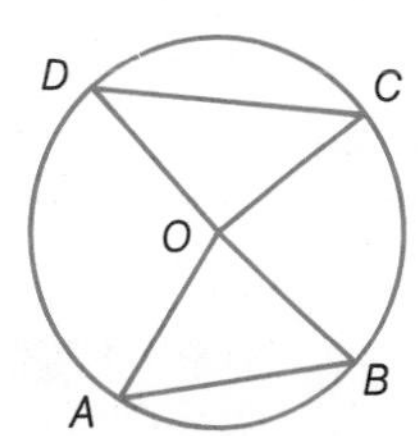

15. In the figure at the right, $\overline{XZ} \cong \overline{YZ}$ and $m\angle 1 > m\angle 2$. Prove that $XW < WY$.

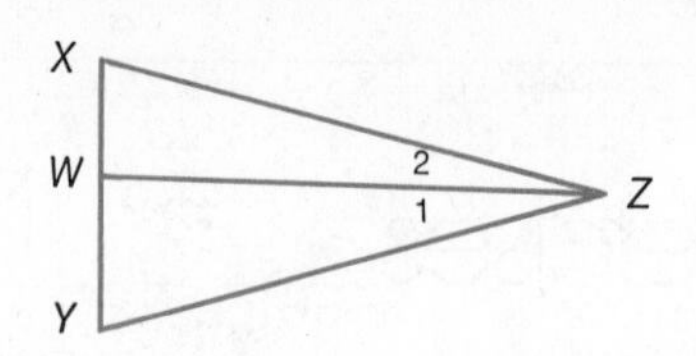

16. In the figure for Exercise 15, $\overline{XZ} \cong \overline{YZ}$ and $YW > XW$. Prove that $m\angle 1 > m\angle 2$.

17. The lengths of the sides of a triangle are 5 units and 7 units. The length of the third side, s, is such that $\underline{\ ?\ } < s < \underline{\ ?\ }$.

18. Suppose that x and y are the lengths of two sides of a triangle with $x < y$ and that the length of the third side is z. Then $\underline{\ ?\ } < z < \underline{\ ?\ }$.

b

19. Prove that for any quadrilateral whose sides have lengths a, b, c, and k and whose diagonals have lengths d_1 and d_2, the perimeter P of the quadrilateral is greater than $d_1 + d_2$.

20. Prove Theorem 5-21. (HINT: In triangles ABC and DEF below, $\overline{AC} \cong \overline{DF}$, $\overline{CB} \cong \overline{FE}$, and $m\angle ACB > m\angle F$. Draw $\overline{CH}$, $\overline{AH}$, $\overline{CG}$, and $\overline{GH}$ such that $\angle ACH \cong \angle F$, $\overline{CH} \cong \overline{FE}$, and $\overline{CG}$ bisects $\angle BCH$.)

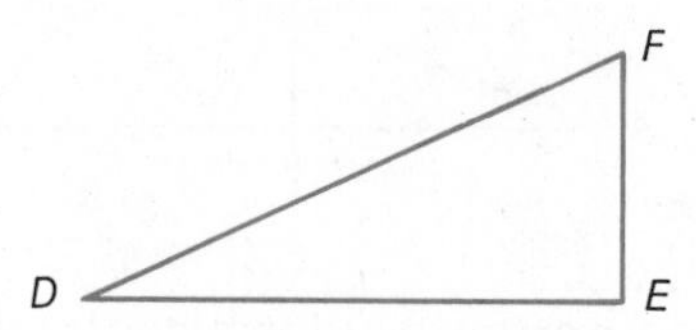

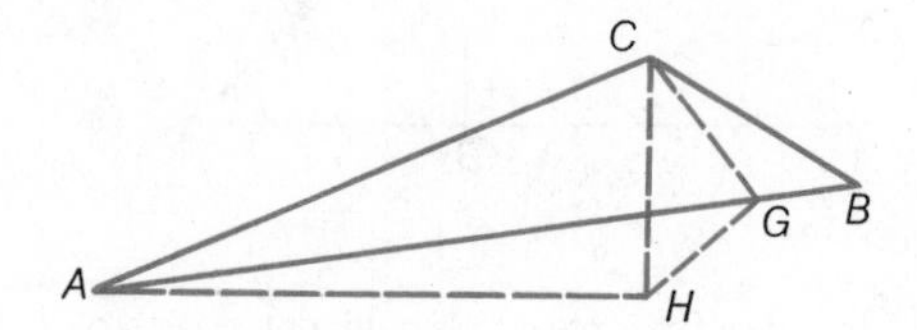

21. Prove Theorem 5-22 by the indirect method.

22. $\triangle RST$ below is isosceles with base $\overline{ST}$. If $TB > SB$, prove that $m\angle RSB < m\angle RTB$.

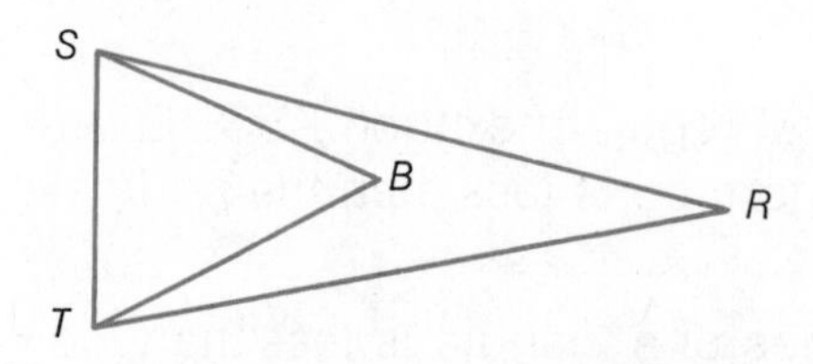

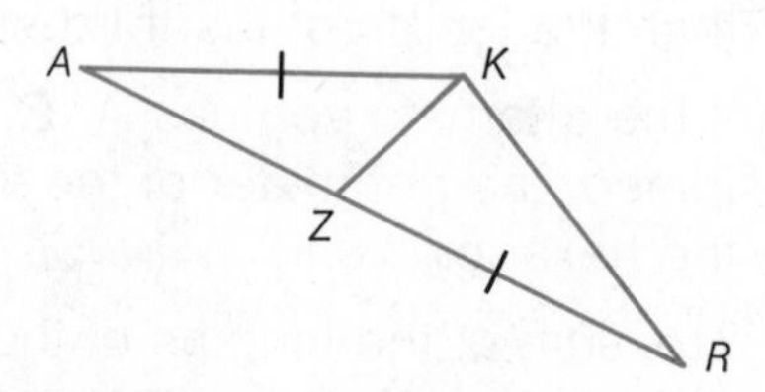

23. In $\triangle AKR$ above, $\overline{ZR} \cong \overline{AK}$. Prove that $KR > AZ$.

24. Given that P is a point in the interior of a triangle whose sides have lengths of a, b, and c. The distances of P from two of the vertices are d and e. Prove that $d + e < a + b$.

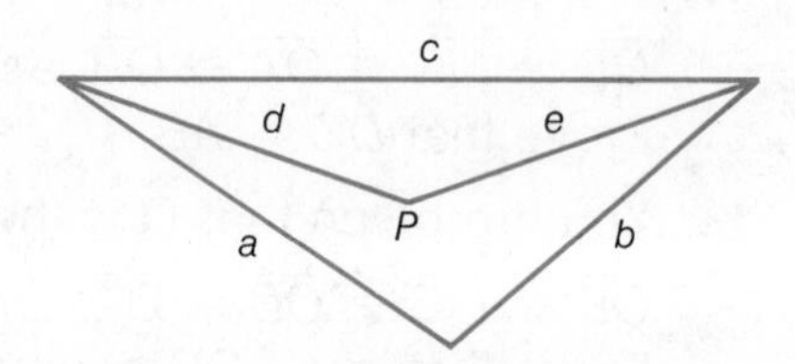

Remember

Choose the answer that completes each statement.

1. Three __?__ points determine a plane. (collinear, noncollinear)
2. If two planes intersect, then their intersection is a __?__. (point, line)
3. Two distinct intersecting lines determine a __?__. (line, point)
4. Plane I does not contain $\overleftrightarrow{AB}$. If $\overleftrightarrow{AB}$ and plane I intersect, then their intersection is a __?__. (point, line)

The answers are on page 248. If you need help, see pages 18, 23, 24, and 25.

5-8 Dihedral Angles

Fold a sheet of paper once. The result is a model of the figure formed by two intersecting half-planes. The crease *XY* represents a line, and the halves *ABYX* and *DCYX* represent half-planes. The line common to both half-planes is their intersection. It is the **edge** of each half-plane.

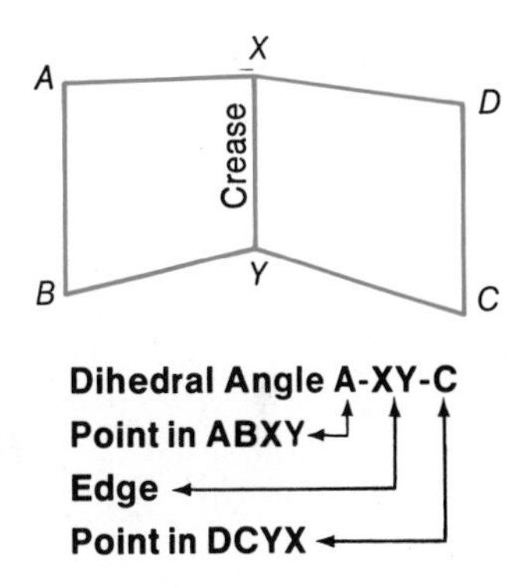

Definitions: A **dihedral angle** is the union of two noncoplanar half-planes whose edges are the same line. The line is the **edge** of the dihedral angle and the half-planes are its **faces.**

More than one dihedral angle may have the same edge, as shown at the right. Angles *A-CB-F* and *F-CB-D* are **adjacent dihedral angles.**

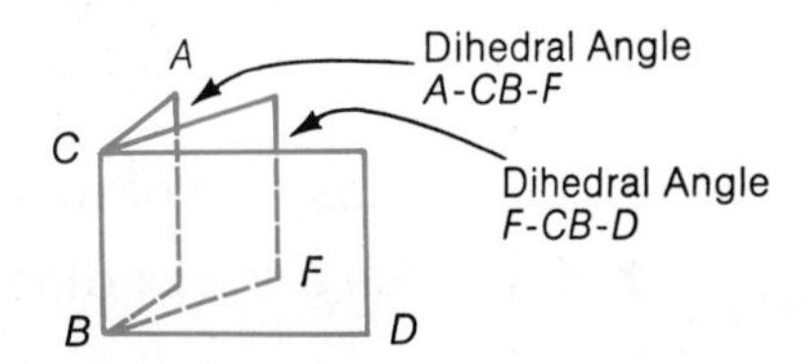

Example

Plane I is passed through dihedral angle EF so that it contains a point S on $\overleftrightarrow{EF}$ and is perpendicular to $\overleftrightarrow{EF}$. Describe the intersection of the plane and the angle.

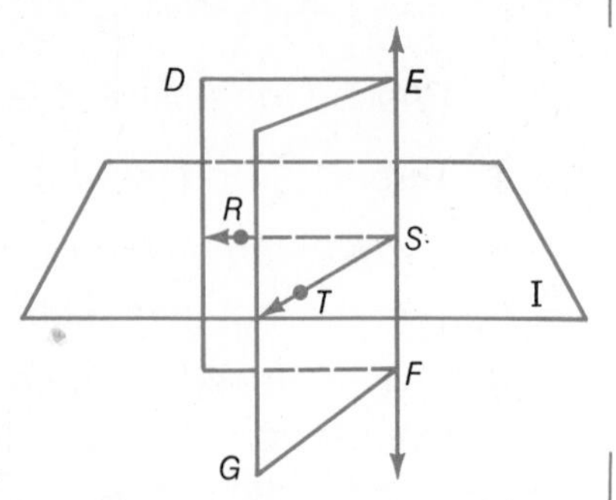

Answer: The intersection is $\angle RST$.

The angle in the Example is a plane angle. $\overleftrightarrow{ES}$ is perpendicular to plane I if it is perpendicular to every line in plane I that contains point S.

Definition: A **plane angle** of a dihedral angle is the intersection of the dihedral angle and a plane perpendicular to its edge.

All the plane angles of a given dihedral angle have the same measure and the measure of a dihedral angle is the measure of any of its plane angles. Dihedral angles that have the same measure are congruent.

Theorem 5-23: All plane angles of the same dihedral angle are congruent.

Since an angle contains three noncollinear points, any angle determines exactly one plane.

Try These

Complete each statement. In the figure, $\overline{AQ} \perp \overline{QB}$, $\overline{AQ} \perp \overline{QC}$, and $\overline{CQ} \perp \overline{QB}$.

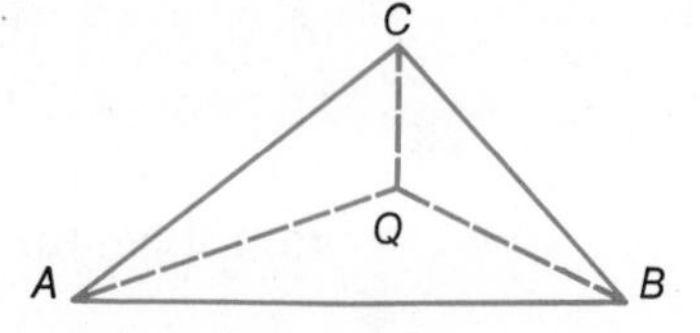

1. $\overline{CQ}$ is the edge of dihedral angle __?__.
2. $\overline{CB}$ is the edge of dihedral angle __?__.
3. $\overline{AB}$ is the edge of dihedral angle __?__.

4. $\angle AQB$ is a plane angle of dihedral angle __?__.
5. $\angle AQC$ is a plane angle of dihedral angle __?__.
6. $\angle BQC$ is a plane angle of dihedral angle __?__.

Exercises

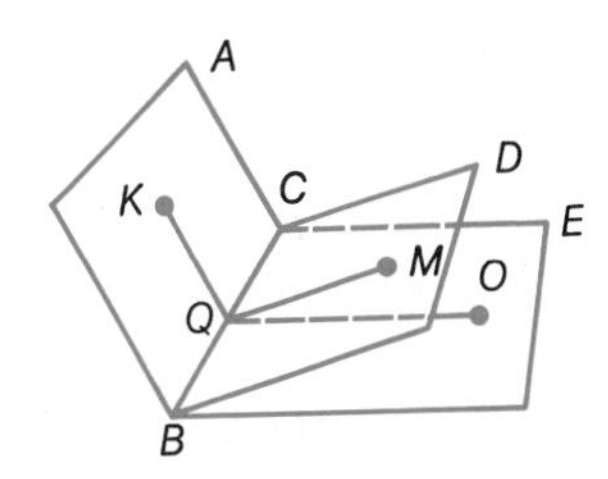

In the figure at the right, $\overleftrightarrow{BC}$ is the edge of half-planes AB, DB, and EB. Q is a point on $\overleftrightarrow{BC}$. $\overline{KQ}$, $\overline{MQ}$, and $\overline{OQ}$ lie in half-planes AB, DB, and EB respectively.

a

1. If $\angle KQM$ is a plane angle of dihedral angle *A-BC-D*, are $\overline{KQ}$ and $\overline{MQ}$ each perpendicular to $\overline{BC}$? Give a reason for your answer.
2. If $\overline{MQ}$ and $\overline{OQ}$ are each perpendicular to $\overleftrightarrow{BC}$ at Q, is $\angle MQO$ a plane angle of angle *D-BC-E*? Give a reason for your answer.
3. Is $\angle KQM \cong \angle MQO$? Give a reason for your answer.

Write the letter (or letters) of the response that answers each question or completes each statement in Exercises ***4–10.***

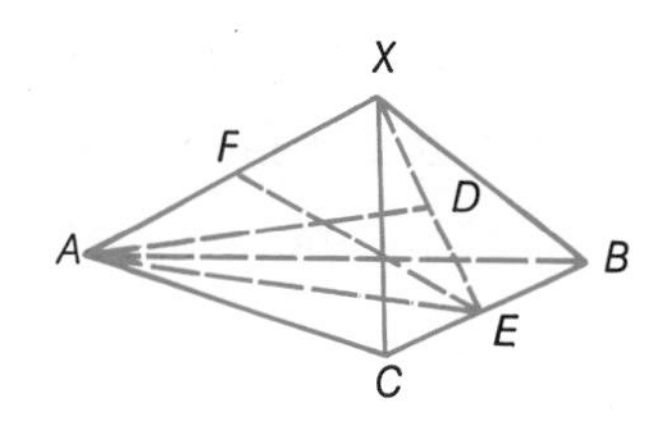

The figure at the right is a pyramid made up of four equilateral triangles. E and F are the midpoints of $\overline{BC}$ and $\overline{AX}$ respectively. $\overline{AE}$, $\overline{FE}$, and $\overline{XE}$ are drawn. $\overline{AD}$ is a median of $\triangle AXE$.

4. The number of dihedral angles in pyramid *X-ABC* is

   a. 4. **b.** 3. **c.** 6. **d.** 5.

5. The plane angle of dihedral angle *X-BC-A* is

   a. $\angle ACX$. **b.** $\angle XEB$. **c.** $\angle AEF$. **d.** $\angle AEX$.

6. A plane angle of dihedral angle *C-AE-X* is

   a. $\angle XEC$. **b.** Not shown. **c.** $\angle XAC$. **d.** $\angle CEF$.

7. Identify which of the following are right angles.

   a. $\angle BXE$. **b.** $\angle AEX$. **c.** $\angle AEC$. **d.** $\angle BEF$.

8. Identify the pairs that are congruent dihedral angles.

a. $\angle X\text{-}AB\text{-}C$, $\angle A\text{-}BC\text{-}X$
b. $\angle C\text{-}AX\text{-}E$, $\angle F\text{-}AE\text{-}C$
c. $\angle B\text{-}AE\text{-}D$, $\angle D\text{-}AX\text{-}C$
d. $\angle B\text{-}AE\text{-}X$, $\angle D\text{-}AE\text{-}C$

9. Identify the pairs that are congruent segments.

a. $\overline{CX}$, $\overline{AE}$ b. $\overline{ED}$, $\overline{DX}$ c. $\overline{EX}$, $\overline{EA}$ d. $\overline{AD}$, $\overline{FE}$

10. Identify the pairs that are congruent angles.

a. $\angle FAE$, $\angle FXE$
b. $\angle ADE$, $\angle BXA$
c. $\angle FEA$, $\angle BXE$
d. $\angle BXE$, $\angle EAC$

In the cube at the right, a plane is passed through the vertices A, C, and H forming $\triangle ACH$. In a cube, length, width, and height have the same measure, that is, $HG = GF = FB$. Use this figure for Exercises **11–24.**

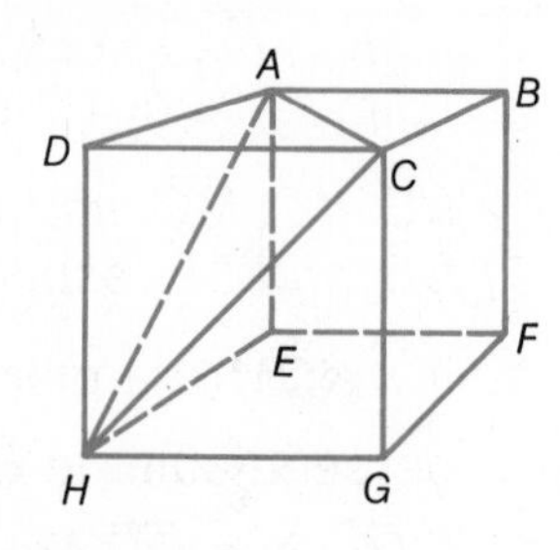

11. How many dihedral angles are there in the cube?

12. How many dihedral angles are there in pyramid $D\text{-}ACH$?

Find the measure of each angle.

13. $\angle DCH$ 14. $\angle CHD$ 15. $\angle CAD$ 16. $\angle DCA$

17. $\angle HAD$ 18. $\angle DHA$ 19. $\angle GHC$ 20. $\angle EHA$

21. What kind of triangle is $\triangle ACH$? Find the measure of each of its angles.

22. Find the measure of dihedral angle $C\text{-}DH\text{-}A$.

23. Find the measure of dihedral angle $A\text{-}BC\text{-}G$.

24. Explain how to get a plane angle of dihedral angle $D\text{-}HC\text{-}A$.

25. Prove that two dihedral angles are congruent if their plane angles are congruent.

26. Prove the converse of the statement in Exercise **25.**

The figure at the right shows two planes intersecting so that four dihedral angles are formed. Also, plane angle $CXD < 90$ and plane angle $DXE > 90$.

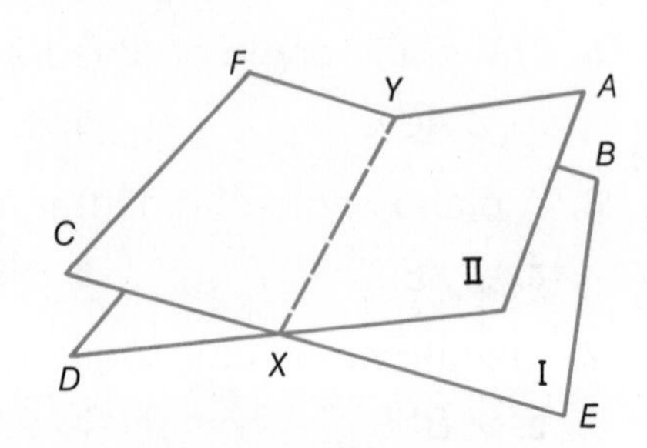

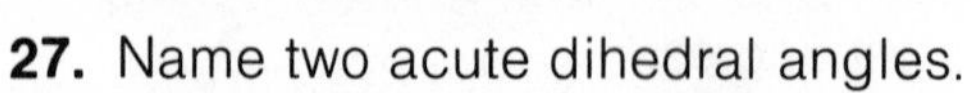

27. Name two acute dihedral angles.

28. Name two obtuse dihedral angles.

29. Name the dihedral angles that are supplementary to $\angle A\text{-}XY\text{-}B$.

30. Name two pairs of vertical dihedral angles.

*Use the figure below for Exercises **31–32.** Planes I and II are each perpendicular to plane III.*

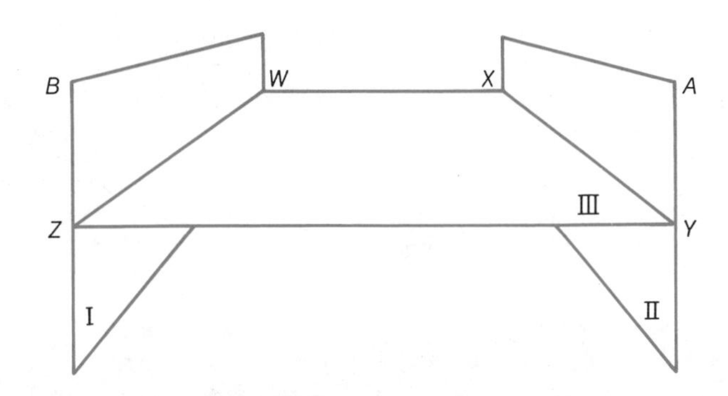

C

31. Name two right dihedral angles.

32. Are planes I and II necessarily parallel? Explain.

In the figure at the right, planes I and II are parallel. Angles 1 and 2 are the plane angles of their respective dihedral angles.

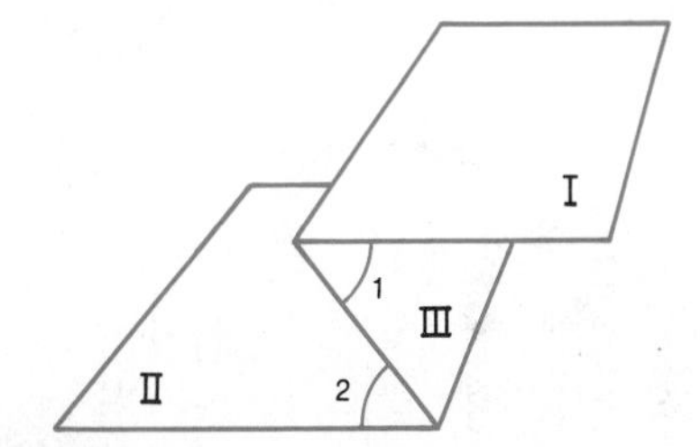

33. How would you describe plane III?

34. How would you describe $\angle 1$ and $\angle 2$?

35. What would you assume to be true of $\angle 1$ and $\angle 2$?

36. Write a definition for the interior of a dihedral angle.

PUZZLE

Given any triangle, draw 12 lines that divide the triangle into 25 congruent triangles.

Try to find 3 lines that divide a triangle into 3 pentagons and 4 congruent triangles.

Mathematics and Urban Planning

Urban planners assist communities in developing programs that plan for the most efficient use of land for streets, highways, water and sewer lines, housing, schools, libraries, playgrounds, and for business and industrial purposes. These plans are concerned with slum clearance, urban renewal, and pollution of the environment.

Two years of graduate work in city planning beyond the bachelors degree is often required for entry into this field. However, people with bachelor's degrees in architecture or engineering may qualify for beginning positions.

The invention of the **geodesic dome** may help to solve various urban problems that presently exist. Its use is also being considered as a possible solution to some future problems. In the geodesic dome, columns are not needed to support the structure. The dome is composed of triangular shapes that are usually framed with metal pipe and covered with plastic. The light and flexible construction of a geodesic dome provides for easy mobility and economy.

Because it is also strong and can resist high winds and heavy snow loads, a possible use of a transparent geodesic dome would be as an enclosure for cities as a protection against bad weather and air pollution.

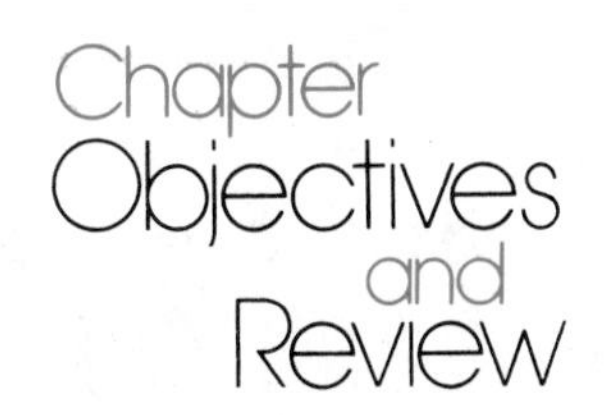

Objective: To recall, and give examples of, the important mathematical terms of this chapter.

1. Be sure that you know the meaning of these mathematical terms used in Chapter 5.

counterexample (p. 212)
dihedral angle (p. 239)
edge (p. 239)
face (p. 239)
plane angle (p. 240)
isosceles trapezoid (p. 206)
median of a trapezoid (p. 223)
parallelogram (p. 206)
rectangle (p. 206)
rhombus (p. 206)
square (p. 206)
trapezoid (p. 206)

Objective: To identify a quadrilateral as a trapezoid, parallelogram, rectangle, rhombus, or square. (Section 5-1)

Use the information about quadrilateral ABCD to identify it as a trapezoid, parallelogram, rectangle, rhombus, or square. If two names apply, state both.

2. $\overline{AB} \parallel \overline{CD}$, $\overline{AD} \parallel \overline{BC}$, $\angle A \cong \angle B \cong \angle C \cong \angle D$
3. $\overline{AB} \parallel \overline{CD}$, $\overline{AD} \parallel \overline{BC}$, $AB = BC = CD = DA$
4. $\overline{AB} \parallel \overline{CD}$, $\overline{BC}$ is not parallel to $\overline{AD}$.
5. $\overline{AB} \parallel \overline{CD}$, $\overline{BC} \parallel \overline{AD}$

Objective: To identify the properties of a parallelogram. (Section 5-1)

Refer to ▱QRST at the right to complete each statement.

6. If $m\angle QTS = 105$, then $m\angle$ __?__ $= 105$ also.
7. If $m\angle QTS = 120$, then $m\angle$ __?__ $= m\angle$ __?__ $= 60$.
8. If $m\angle 1 = 68$, then $m\angle$ __?__ $= 68$ also.
9. If $TW = 6$, then __?__ $= 12$.
10. If $QS = 15$, then __?__ $= 7.5$ and __?__ $= 7.5$.

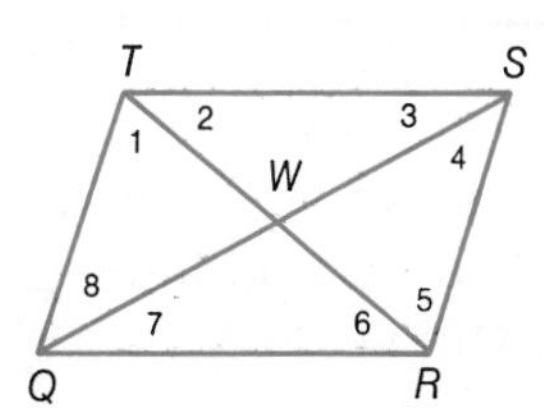

In Exercises **11–12,** *QRST is a parallelogram,* $TS = 4y + 2$, $QR = 2y + 10$, *and* $TQ = 3y$.

11. Find the value of y.

12. Find the perimeter of $\square QRST$.

Objective: To identify the conditions that determine a parallelogram. (Section 5-2)

For each exercise, determine whether quadrilateral ABCD is a parallelogram. Give a reason for each answer.

13.

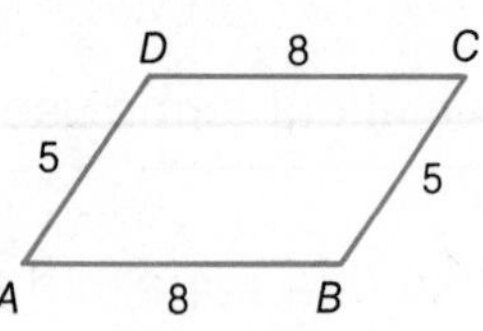

14.

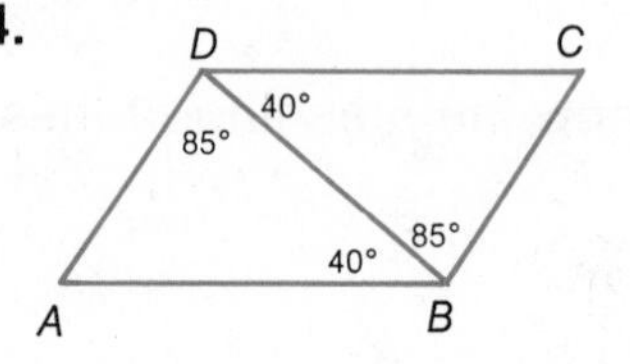

15.

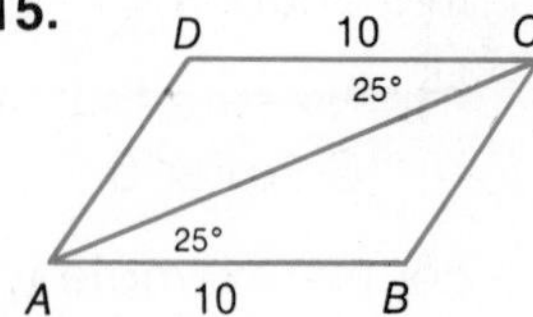

16.

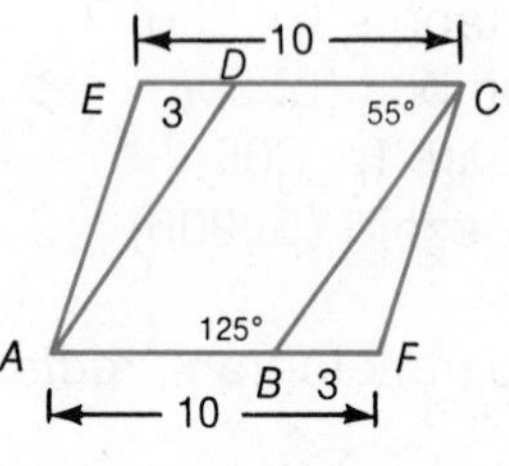

17.

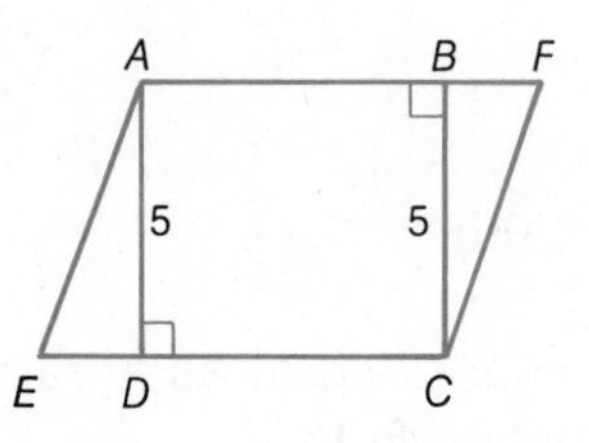

18.

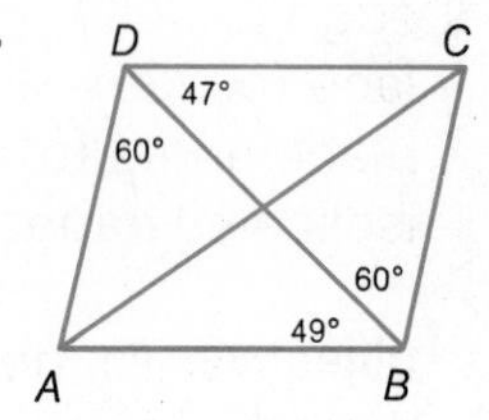

Objective: To identify the special properties of a rectangle, a rhombus, and a square. (Section 5-3)

In Exercises **19–23,** *match each property with all the quadrilaterals named in* **a–d** *to which it applies.*

19. The diagonals are perpendicular.
20. The diagonals are congruent.
21. The diagonals are congruent and perpendicular.
22. The diagonals bisect each other.
23. The diagonals bisect the angles.

a. Parallelogram
b. Rectangle
c. Rhombus
d. Square

Objective: To apply the theorem that relates midpoints and parallel lines. (Section 5-4)

24. In $\triangle ABC$, P, Q, and R are midpoints of the sides, $m\angle A = 72$ and $m\angle B = 25$. Find $m\angle C$ and the measure of each numbered angle.

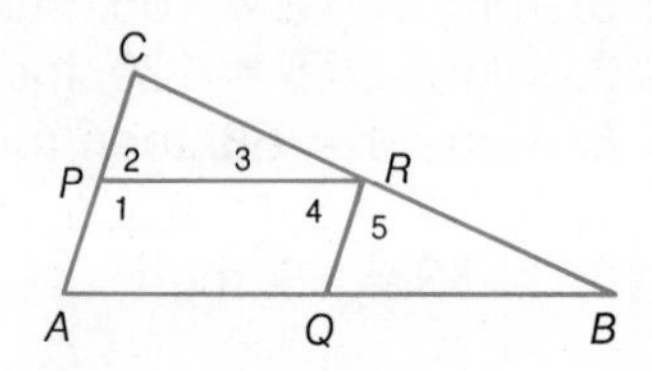

*For Exercises **25–27,** refer to $\triangle DEF$ with S, T, and W the midpoints of the sides.*

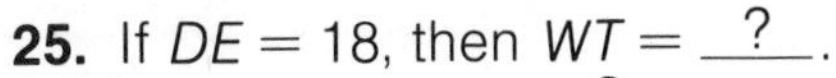

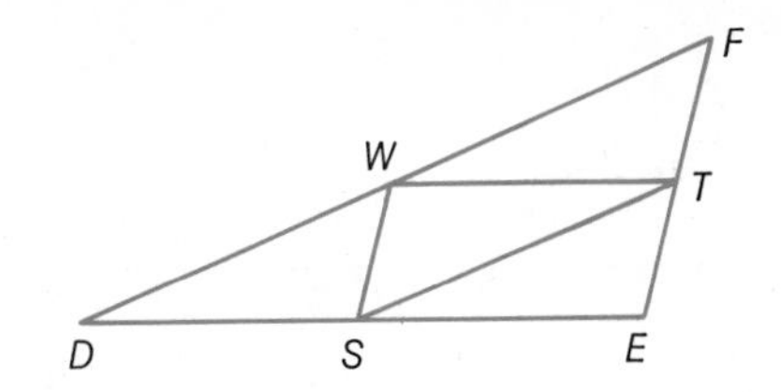

25. If $DE = 18$, then $WT = \underline{\ ?\ }$.
26. If $WS = 11$, then $\underline{\ ?\ } = 22$.
27. If $WT = 5$, $ST = 8$, and $SW = 7$, then the perimeter of $\triangle DEF = \underline{\ ?\ }$.

Objective: To apply theorems that relate to parallel lines cut by more than one transversal. (Section 5-5)

ADCB is a trapezoid with median RS. Complete each statement.

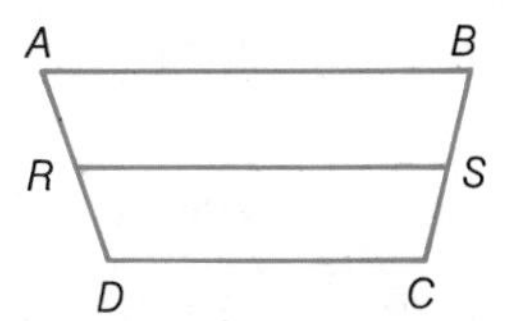

28. If $DC = 8$ and $AB = 14$, then $RS = \underline{\ ?\ }$.
29. If $DC = 18$ and $RS = 20$, then $AB = \underline{\ ?\ }$.
30. If $CD = x$ and $AB = y$, then $RS = \underline{\ ?\ }$.
31. If $DR = 3n$ and $RA = n + 6$, then $DA = \underline{\ ?\ }$.

Objective: To recognize inequality relationships in triangles. (Sections 5-6 and 5-7)

In $\triangle GHP$, $\overline{HG} \cong \overline{HP}$. Replace each $\underline{\ ?\ }$ with $<$, $>$ or $=$.

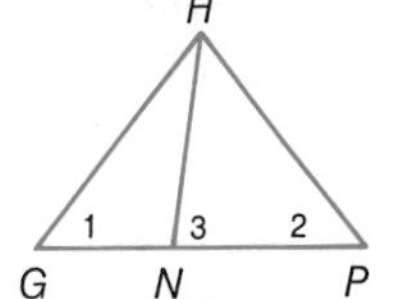

32. $m\angle 1 \ \underline{\ ?\ }\ m\angle 2$
33. $m\angle 3 \ \underline{\ ?\ }\ m\angle 1$
34. $m\angle 3 \ \underline{\ ?\ }\ m\angle 2$
35. $HN \ \underline{\ ?\ }\ HP$

In triangle ABC, $AB = 5$ and $BC = 9$. Classify each statement as True or False.

36. $AC = 14$
37. $AC > 14$
38. $AC < 14$
39. $AC = 4$
40. $AC > 4$
41. $AC < 4$

Objective: To recognize dihedral angles and their plane angles. (Section 5-8)

*In the figure at the right below, $\triangle ABC$ is in plane **I**, and $\overline{TA}$ is perpendicular to $\overline{AB}$, $\overline{AD}$, and $\overline{AC}$.*

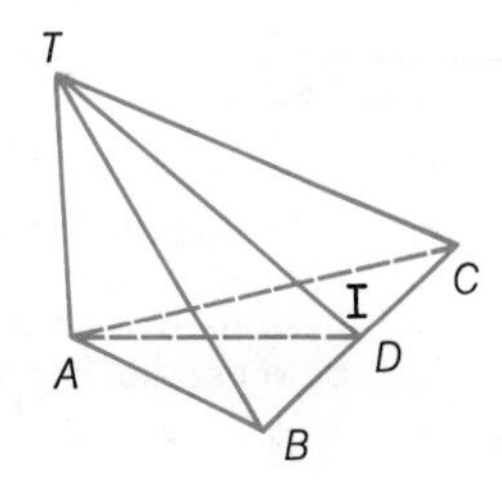

42. Name the dihedral angle formed by the planes containing $\triangle ABT$ and $\triangle ADT$.

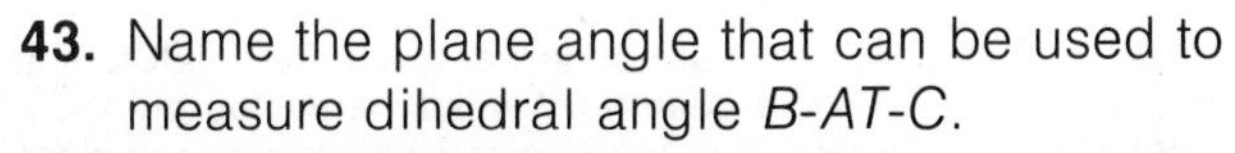

43. Name the plane angle that can be used to measure dihedral angle B-AT-C.
44. Name the two triangles whose planes form dihedral angle A-BT-D.

Chapter Test

Classify each statement as True or False.

1. The diagonals of a parallelogram bisect each other.
2. If a diagonal of a parallelogram bisects an angle of the parallelogram, then the parallelogram is a rhombus.
3. A parallelogram with perpendicular diagonals must be a square.
4. A quadrilateral with four congruent sides must be a rhombus.
5. A parallelogram with one right angle must be a rectangle.

Refer to quadrilateral ABCD to complete each statement.

A B D C

6. Quadrilateral $ABCD$ must be a parallelogram if $\overline{AB} \cong \overline{CD}$ and $\underline{\ ?\ } \parallel \underline{\ ?\ }$.
7. If diagonal AC is drawn and $\triangle ADC \cong \triangle \underline{\ ?\ }$, then $ABCD$ must be a parallelogram.

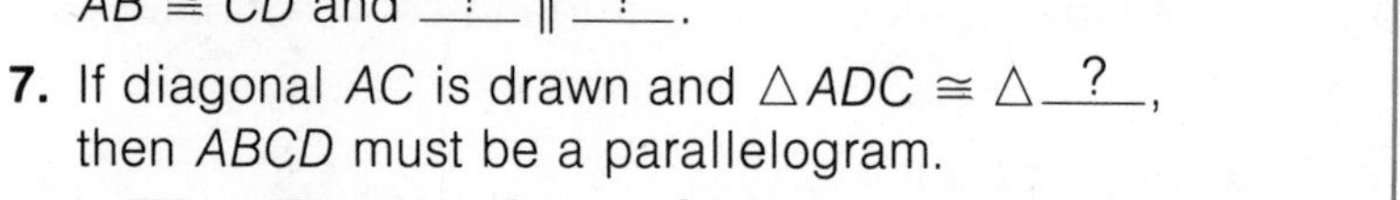

8. If $\overline{AB} \cong \overline{BC}$ and $\underline{\ ?\ } = \underline{\ ?\ }$, then diagonals AC and BD are perpendicular to each other.
9. In $\triangle RMP$, E is the midpoint of $\overline{RM}$, F is the midpoint of $\overline{RP}$, and $MP = 9$ centimeters. Find EF.

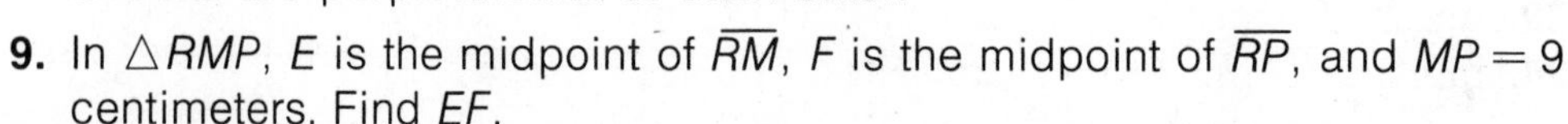

10. The lengths of the bases of a trapezoid are 7 and 16. Find the length of the median.
11. In isosceles triangle PRG, $PR = 6$ and $PG = 15$. Which side is the base?
12. In $\triangle KRM$, $KR > RM > KM$. Which angle of the triangle is the largest?
13. **Given:** Rectangle $RSTW$ with Q the midpoint of $\overline{RW}$.

    Prove: $\triangle QWT \cong \triangle QRS$.

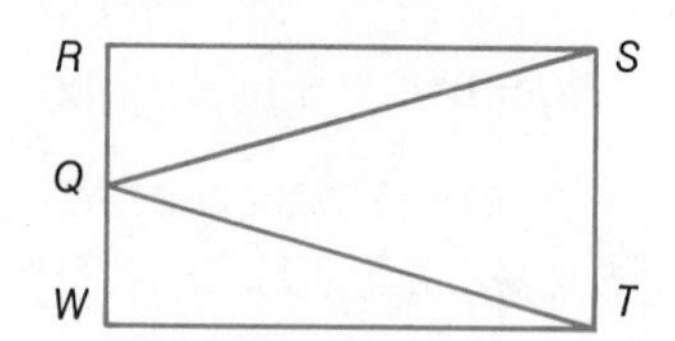

Answers to Remember

Page 213: **1.** b **2.** c **3.** d **4.** a

Page 229: **1.** If a quadrilateral is a rhombus then all of its sides are congruent; if a quadrilateral has all of its sides congruent then it is a rhombus. **2.** If a quadrilateral is a parallelogram then it has one pair of sides both parallel and congruent; if a quadrilateral has one pair of sides both parallel and congruent, then it is a parallelogram.

Page 239: **1.** Noncollinear **2.** Line **3.** Point **4.** Point

Chapter 6
Similarity

6-1 Ratio and Proportion

Numbers such as $\frac{2}{5}$, $\frac{9}{11}$, and $\frac{1}{3}$ are called ratios.

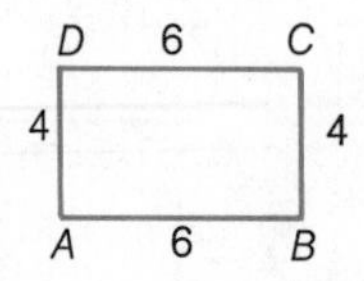

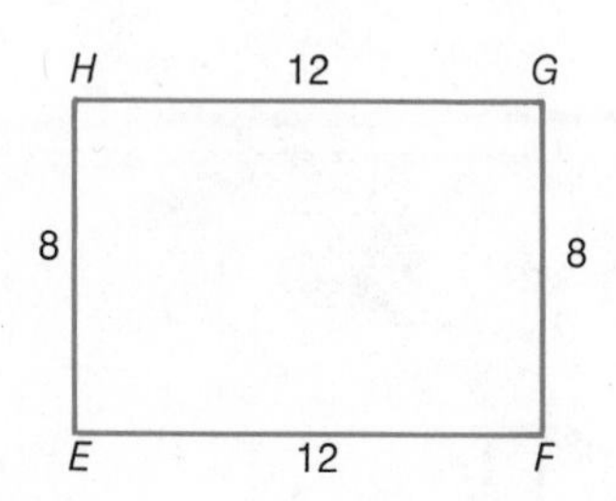

$$\frac{\text{Length of rectangle } ABCD}{\text{Length of rectangle } EFGH} = \frac{AB}{EF} = \frac{6}{12}, \text{ or } \frac{1}{2}$$ ← Ratio

$$\frac{\text{Length of rectangle } EFGH}{\text{Length of rectangle } ABCD} = \frac{EF}{AB} = \frac{12}{6}, \text{ or } \frac{2}{1}$$ ← Ratio

A **ratio** is the comparison of two numbers by division. Recall that division by zero is not defined.

Note that the ratio of 6 to 12, or $\frac{6}{12}$, is not the same as the ratio of 12 to 6, or $\frac{12}{6}$.

Example 1

Compare these ratios for the rectangles shown above.

a. $\frac{\text{Width of rectangle } EFGH}{\text{Width of rectangle } ABCD}$ **b.** $\frac{\text{Length of rectangle } EFGH}{\text{Length of rectangle } ABCD}$

a. $\frac{\text{Width of rectangle } EFGH}{\text{Width of rectangle } ABCD} = \frac{GF}{CB} = \frac{8}{4}, \text{ or } \frac{2}{1}$

b. $\frac{\text{Length of rectangle } EFGH}{\text{Length of rectangle } ABCD} = \frac{EF}{AB} = \frac{12}{6}, \text{ or } \frac{2}{1}$

← The ratios are equal.

An equation that shows that two ratios are equal is a **proportion.**

You can test whether two ratios can be written as a proportion by "cross-multiplying."

$$\frac{8}{4} \stackrel{?}{=} \frac{12}{6}$$

$$8 \times 6 \stackrel{?}{=} 4 \times 12$$

$$48 = 48$$

Example 2

Test whether each pair of ratios can be written as a proportion.

a. $\frac{4}{5}; \frac{16}{25}$ **b.** $\frac{12}{9}; \frac{4}{3}$

a.

$$\frac{4}{5} \stackrel{?}{=} \frac{16}{25}$$

$$4 \times 25 \stackrel{?}{=} 5 \times 16$$

$$100 \neq 80$$

b.

$$\frac{12}{9} \stackrel{?}{=} \frac{4}{3}$$

$$12 \times 3 \stackrel{?}{=} 9 \times 4$$

$$36 = 36$$

Only the ratios in **b** can be written as a proportion.

Theorem 6-1: $\frac{a}{b} = \frac{c}{d}$ if and only if $ad = bc$ $(b \neq 0, d \neq 0)$.

Note that Theorem 6-1 is a biconditional.

Example 3

Find x if $\frac{5}{6} = \frac{15}{x}$.

$$\frac{5}{6} = \frac{15}{x}$$

$5x = (6)(15)$ ← Theorem 6-1

$x = \frac{(6)(15)}{5}$ ← Solve for x.

$x = 18$

Try These

Write the ratios of the two given numbers in lowest terms.

1. 2 to 3

2. 8 to 24

3. $4x$ to $5x$

4. $10x^2$ to $4x$

5. 90 cm to 270 cm

6. 25 cm to 100 cm

7. 20 dm to 4 dm

8. 1 m to 10 m

9. Solve for y: $\frac{2}{y} = \frac{5}{20}$

10. State Theorem 6-1 as a conditional and its converse.

Exercises

In the figure at the right, $AB = 21$ and $BC = 7$. Write these ratios.

a

1. $\frac{AC}{AB}$ **2.** $\frac{BC}{AB}$ **3.** $\frac{BC}{AC}$ **4.** $\frac{AB}{AC}$

*In the figure for Exercises **1–4,** let $AC = 21$ and $CB = 7$. Write these ratios.*

5. $\frac{AC}{CB}$ **6.** $\frac{CB}{AC}$ **7.** $\frac{AC}{AB}$ **8.** $\frac{AC}{AC}$

9. $\frac{AB}{CB}$ **10.** $\frac{CB}{AB}$ **11.** $\frac{AB}{AC}$ **12.** $\frac{AB}{AB}$

In the figure at the right, $AB = 5a$ and $AC = 5b$. Find these ratios.

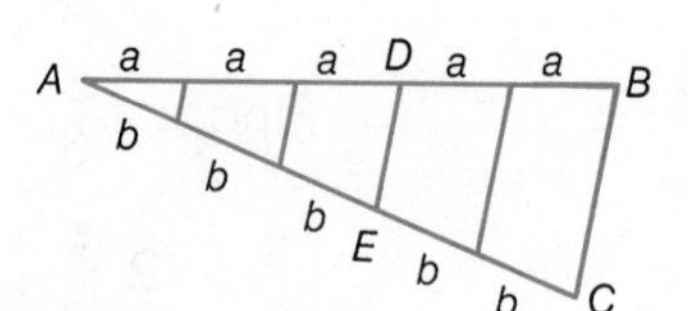

13. $\frac{AB}{AC}$ **14.** $\frac{AD}{DB}$ **15.** $\frac{AE}{EC}$

Test whether each pair of ratios can be written as a proportion.

16. $\frac{5}{8}; \frac{10}{16}$ **17.** $\frac{12}{27}; \frac{24}{54}$ **18.** $\frac{7}{19}; \frac{21}{57}$ **19.** $\frac{4}{11}; \frac{12}{32}$

20. $\frac{7}{21}; \frac{17}{51}$ **21.** $\frac{19}{18}; \frac{7}{6}$ **22.** $\frac{1}{5}; \frac{3}{15}$ **23.** $\frac{3}{2}; \frac{108}{72}$

For each exercise, use the equation to write three other proportions.

b

24. $\frac{2}{3}=\frac{10}{15}$ **25.** $\frac{3}{7}=\frac{9}{21}$ **26.** $\frac{AB}{BC}=\frac{RS}{ST}$

Solve for x. No denominator equals zero.

27. $\frac{3}{5}=\frac{4}{x}$ **28.** $\frac{2}{x}=\frac{3}{7}$ **29.** $\frac{4}{7}=\frac{x}{6}$

30. $\frac{x}{10}=\frac{6}{5}$ **31.** $\frac{21-x}{x}=\frac{1}{2}$ **32.** $\frac{20-x}{x}=\frac{2}{3}$

33. $\frac{a}{b}=\frac{c}{x}$ **34.** $\frac{2a}{3b}=\frac{5c}{2x}$ **35.** $\frac{a-x}{x}=\frac{b}{c}$

36. If $\frac{a}{m}=\frac{b}{r}$, write three other proportions using a, b, m, and r.

37. If $6x=5y$ then $\frac{x}{y}=\frac{?}{?}$. (HINT: Use Theorem 6-1.)

38. If $9x=2y$ then $\frac{y}{x}=\frac{?}{?}$.

If $\frac{a}{b}=\frac{c}{d}$, show that these are proportions. No denominator equals zero.

c

39. $\frac{b}{a}=\frac{d}{c}$ **40.** $\frac{a}{c}=\frac{b}{d}$ **41.** $\frac{c}{a}=\frac{d}{b}$

42. Prove Theorem 6-1. (HINT: Multiply both sides of $\frac{a}{b}=\frac{c}{d}$ by bd. For the converse, start with $ad=bc$ and divide both sides by bd.)

Remember

Use the Table of Squares and Square Roots on page 580 to approximate each number to the nearest hundredth.

1. $\sqrt{15}$ **2.** $\sqrt{8}$ **3.** $\sqrt{41}$ **4.** $\sqrt{50}$ **5.** $\sqrt{72}$ **6.** $\sqrt{133}$

Find x.

7. $x^2=36$ **8.** $x^2=81$ **9.** $x^2=8$

The answers are on page 302. If you need help, see page 565 in the Review: Topics From Algebra One.

6-2 Other Properties of Proportions

The examples in the table suggest Theorem 6-2. Start with the proportion $\frac{2}{5} = \frac{4}{10}$.

Addition	Subtraction
$\frac{2}{5} + 1 = \frac{4}{10} + 1$	$\frac{2}{5} - 1 = \frac{4}{10} - 1$
$\frac{2}{5} + \frac{5}{5} = \frac{4}{10} + \frac{10}{10}$	$\frac{2}{5} - \frac{5}{5} = \frac{4}{10} - \frac{10}{10}$
$\frac{2+5}{5} = \frac{4+10}{10}$	$\frac{2-5}{5} = \frac{4-10}{10}$

Theorem 6-2: If $\frac{a}{b} = \frac{c}{d}$, then $\frac{a+b}{b} = \frac{c+d}{d}$ and $\frac{a-b}{b} = \frac{c-d}{d}$.

If the numbers 4, 6, and 9 are related such that $\frac{4}{6} = \frac{6}{9}$, then 6 is the geometric mean (mean proportional) between 4 and 9.

Definition: If a, b, and x are positive numbers and $\frac{a}{x} = \frac{x}{b}$, then x is the **geometric mean** between a and b.

Example 1

Find the geometric mean between 2 and 8.

Let x = geometric mean.

$$\frac{2}{x} = \frac{x}{8}$$

$$x \cdot x = 2 \cdot 8$$

$$x^2 = 16$$

$$x = \sqrt{16}, \text{ or } 4$$ ← Geometric mean

You can write $\frac{a}{b} = \frac{c}{d}$ as $a : b = c : d$. The numbers a, b, c, and d are, respectively, the first, second, third and fourth terms of the proportion. The fourth term is called the **fourth proportional** to the other three.

Example 2

Find the fourth proportional to 3, 5, and 7.

$\frac{3}{5} = \frac{7}{x}$ ⟵ Write the proportion.

$3x = 35$ ⟵ Solve for x.

$x = \frac{35}{3}$, or $11\frac{2}{3}$ ⟵ Fourth proportional

Try These

Find the geometric mean for each pair of numbers.

1. 4 and 9

2. 2 and 18

3. $3a$ and $12a$

Find the fourth proportional to the three given numbers.

4. 3, 4, and 7

5. 8, 10, and 6

6. 2, 1, and 5

Exercises

Given that $\frac{a}{b} = \frac{c}{d}$, classify each statement as True or False. No denominator is zero.

a

1. $ad = bc$

2. $ac = bd$

3. $\frac{a}{d} = \frac{b}{c}$

4. $\frac{a}{c} = \frac{b}{d}$

5. $\frac{a-b}{c} = \frac{c-d}{d}$

6. $\frac{a+b}{b} = \frac{c+d}{d}$

Complete each statement.

7. If $\frac{2}{5} = \frac{x}{7}$, then $\frac{2+5}{5} = \frac{?}{7}$.

8. If $\frac{x}{3} = \frac{y}{7}$, then $\frac{?}{3} = \frac{y-7}{7}$.

Find the geometric mean between the given numbers.

9. 4 and 100 **10.** 16 and 14 **11.** 27 and 3
12. 2 and 50 **13.** $4a$ and $16a$ **14.** a and b

Find the geometric mean between the given numbers. Use the Table of Square Roots on page 580 to approximate the answers to the nearest hundredth.

15. 12 and 6 **16.** 19 and 7 **17.** 13 and 11

Find the fourth proportional to the given numbers.

18. 3, 4, 9 **19.** 8, 10, 6 **20.** $2a$, $3b$, $4a$
21. 2, 6, 5 **22.** a, b, c **23.** $\frac{1}{2}$, $\frac{2}{3}$, $\frac{3}{4}$

Find the geometric mean between each pair of numbers. Leave the answers in simplified radical form.

b

24. $\frac{2}{3}$, $\frac{3}{4}$ **25.** $\frac{1}{6}$, $\frac{5}{3}$ **26.** $\frac{3}{2}$, $\frac{1}{8}$
27. $5\sqrt{2}$, $3\sqrt{8}$ **28.** $\frac{3}{8}\sqrt{6}$, $\frac{2}{3}\sqrt{6}$ **29.** $\frac{1}{2}$, $\frac{1}{6}$

Solve for x ($x > 0$). Leave your answers in simplified radical form.

30. $\frac{3}{x} = \frac{2x}{5}$ **31.** $\frac{2x}{7} = \frac{4}{5x}$ **32.** $\frac{7}{3x} = \frac{x}{8}$
33. $\frac{7x}{3} = \frac{3}{4x}$ **34.** $\frac{5}{2x} = \frac{3x}{11}$ **35.** $\frac{3x^2 + 7}{3x} = \frac{5x}{4}$

In the figures below, $\frac{JT}{MO} = \frac{TK}{ON} = \frac{JK}{MN}$. *That is,* $\frac{JT}{MO} = \frac{TK}{ON}$, $\frac{TK}{ON} = \frac{JK}{MN}$, *and* $\frac{JT}{MO} = \frac{JK}{MN}$.

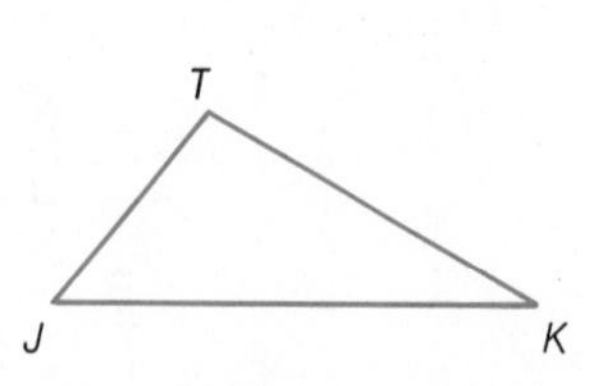

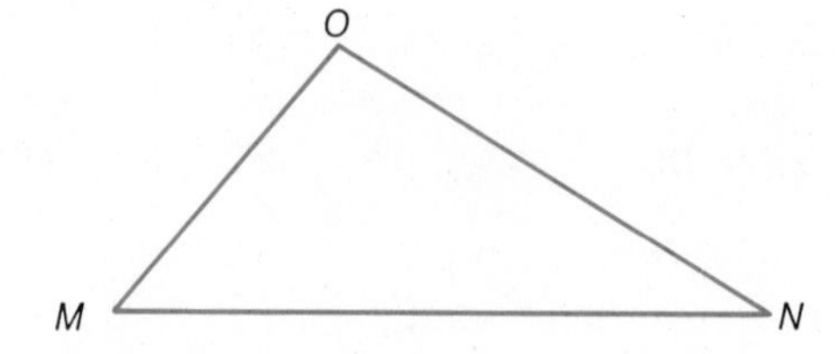

36. If $JT = 6$, $MO = 8$, and $TK = 9$, find ON.
37. If $JK = 10$, $MN = 20$, $TK = x + 3$ and $ON = 3x + 1$, find x, TK, and ON.
38. If $JT = x$, $MO = 2x$, $JK = x + 3$, and $MN = 4x - 2$, find x, JT, MO, JK, and MN.

In the figure at the right, CD is the geometric mean between AD and DB.

39. If $AD = 9$ cm and $DB = 4$ cm, find CD.

40. If $AD = 30$ mm and $DB = 10$ mm, find CD.

41. If $AD = 18$ and $CD = 12$, find DB.

C **42.** Find the measures of the angles of a triangle if they are in the ratio $2 : 3 : 4$. (HINT: Let $2x$, $3x$, and $4x$ be the measures of the angles.)

43. Find the measures of the angles of a triangle if they are in the ratio $5 : 7 : 8$.

44. Prove that if $\frac{a}{b} = \frac{c}{d} = \frac{e}{f} = \frac{g}{h}$, then $\frac{a+c+e+g}{b+d+f+h} = \frac{a}{b}$

PUZZLE

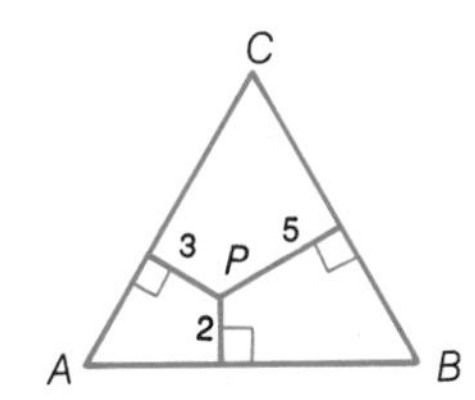

In an equilateral triangle, perpendicular segments are drawn from an interior point P to the sides of the triangle. The perpendicular segments are 2, 3, and 5 units long. Find the length of an altitude of the triangle.

think–draw–see

1. Draw $\triangle ABC$ with $AC = 4$ centimeters, $CD = 3$ centimeters, $AD = 1$ centimeter, and $CB = 8$ centimeters.
2. Construct $\overline{DE} \parallel \overline{AB}$.
3. Measure $\overline{CE}$ and $\overline{EB}$.
4. Compare the ratios $\frac{CD}{DA}$ and $\frac{CE}{EB}$.
5. Compare the ratios $\frac{CA}{CD}$ and $\frac{CB}{CE}$.

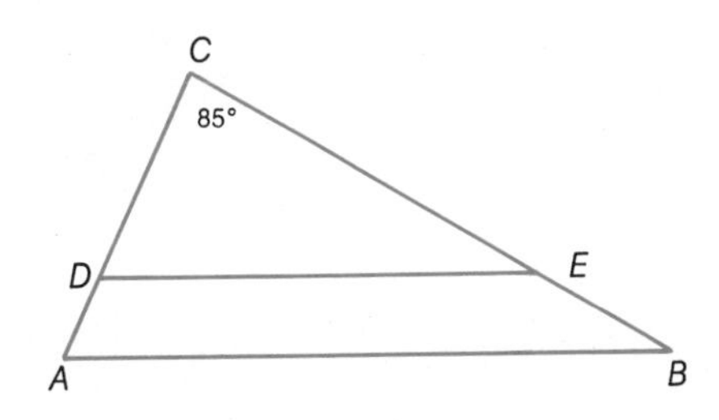

6-3 Proportional Segments

In the figure below, lines k, j, q, s, and w are parallel and $\overline{RP} \cong \overline{PM} \cong \overline{MN} \cong \overline{NT}$. Then $\overline{AB} \cong \overline{BC} \cong \overline{CD} \cong \overline{DE}$ by Theorem 5–14 on page 224.

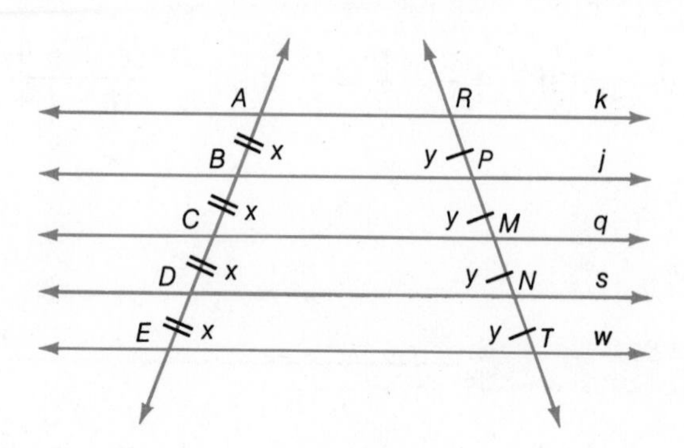

Example 1

In the figure above, $RP = y$ and $AB = x$.

Compare $\frac{RP}{PT}$ and $\frac{AB}{BE}$.

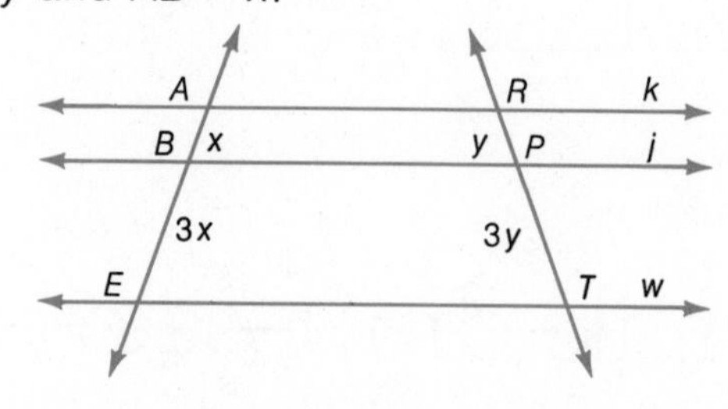

$$\frac{RP}{PT} = \frac{y}{3y} = \frac{1}{3} \qquad \frac{AB}{BE} = \frac{x}{3x} = \frac{1}{3}$$

$$\therefore \frac{RP}{PT} = \frac{AB}{BE}$$

In Example 1, you could have chosen any three parallel lines to write a proportion using the lengths of the line segments cut off on the transversals. The parallel lines are said to divide the transversals proportionally.

Theorem 6-3: If three parallel lines intersect two transversals, then the lines divide the transversals proportionally.

Example 2

In the figure below, lines r, s, and t are parallel. Complete each proportion.

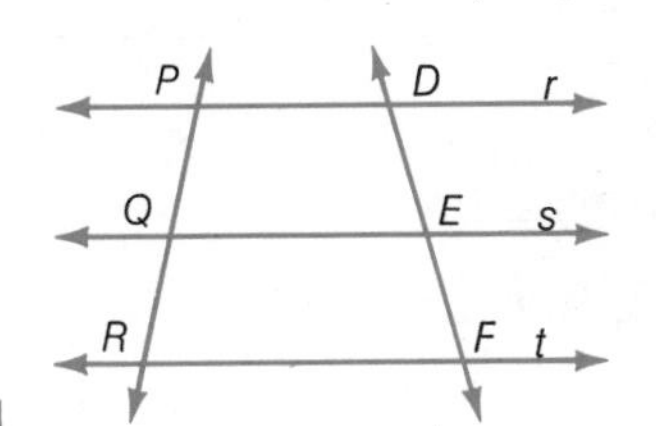

a. $\frac{PQ}{QR} = \frac{?}{EF}$ **b.** $\frac{PQ}{?} = \frac{DE}{DF}$ **c.** $\frac{QR}{PR} = \frac{?}{?}$

a. $\frac{PQ}{QR} = \frac{DE}{EF}$ **b.** $\frac{PQ}{PR} = \frac{DE}{DF}$ **c.** $\frac{QR}{PR} = \frac{EF}{DF}$

Two corollaries of Theorem 6-3 apply to triangles.

Corollary 6-4: If a line intersecting the interior of a triangle is parallel to one side, then the line divides the other two sides proportionally.

Corollary 6-5: If a line intersecting the interior of a triangle is parallel to one side, then either side intersected by the line is to one of its segments as the other side is to its corresponding segment.

Example 3

In $\triangle ABC$, $\overline{DE} \parallel \overline{AB}$, $AC = 12$, $EC = 10$ and $BE = 8$. Find DC and AD.

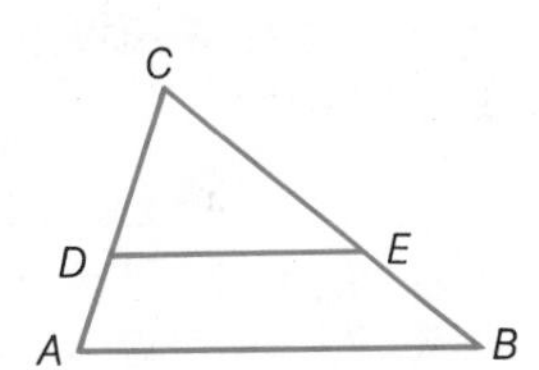

$\frac{AC}{DC} = \frac{BC}{EC}$ ← Corollary 6-5

$\frac{12}{DC} = \frac{18}{10}$ ← $BC = BE + EC = 8 + 10 = 18$

$18 \cdot DC = 12 \cdot 10$ ← Theorem 6-1 (Cross-multiply.)

$DC = \frac{12 \cdot 10}{18} = \frac{20}{3}$, or $6\frac{2}{3}$

$AC = AD + DC$ ← Definition of betweenness for points

$12 = AD + 6\frac{2}{3}$ ← Add $-6\frac{2}{3}$ to each side.

$AD = 5\frac{1}{3}$

Try These

In the figure at the right, $\overline{AB} \parallel \overline{CD}$. Complete each proportion.

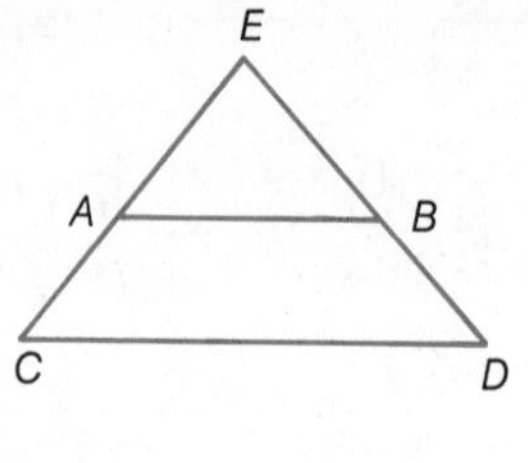

1. $\frac{EA}{AC} = \frac{EB}{?}$
2. $\frac{EC}{AC} = \frac{?}{?}$
3. $\frac{EB}{BD} = \frac{?}{?}$
4. $\frac{EB + BD}{EB} = \frac{?}{?}$
5. Use the figure to find AC if $EA = 24$, $EB = 21$, and $BD = 28$.
6. Use the figure to find BD if $EA + AC = 45$, $AC = 25$, and $EB + BD = 54$.

Exercises

*For Exercises **1–3**, $\overline{AB} \parallel \overline{CD}$, and the lengths of the other segments are marked. Find $\underline{x}$.*

a

1.

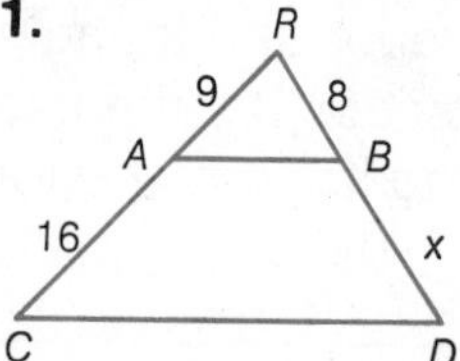

2.

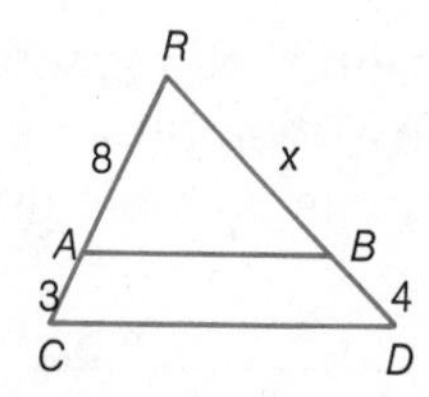

3.

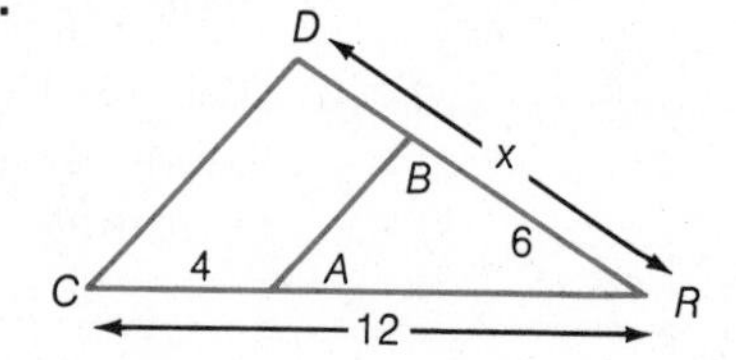

*For Exercises **4–9**, $\overline{RS} \parallel \overline{YZ}$, and three lengths are given. Find the missing length.*

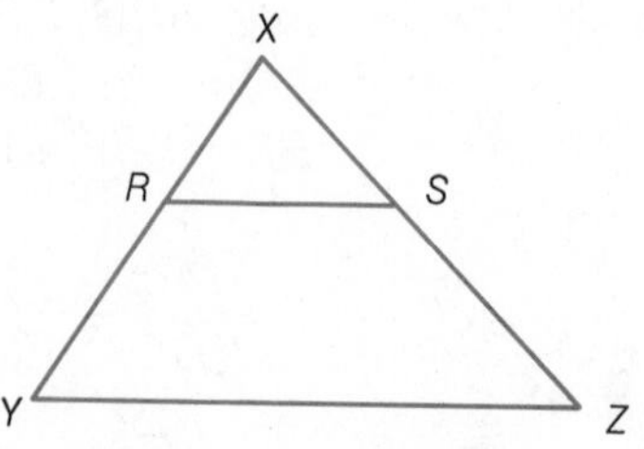

4. $XR = 2$, $RY = 4$, $XS = 3$, $SZ =$ __?__
5. $XS = 8$, $SZ = 16$, $RY = 8$, $XR =$ __?__
6. $RY = 5$, $SZ = 7$, $XR = 3$, $XS =$ __?__
7. $SZ = 9$, $XR = 5$, $XS = 4$, $RY =$ __?__
8. $XR = 5$, $XS = 4$, $SZ = 6$, $XY =$ __?__
9. $SZ = 24$, $XR = 12$, $RY = 21$, $XZ =$ __?__

*In $\triangle ABC$, $\overline{DE} \parallel \overline{AB}$. Find the missing lengths for Exercises **10–17**.*

	AD	DC	BE	EC
10.	3	2	6	?
11.	7	3	?	5
12.	2	?	3	4
13.	$\frac{4}{3}$	$\frac{1}{2}$	4	?

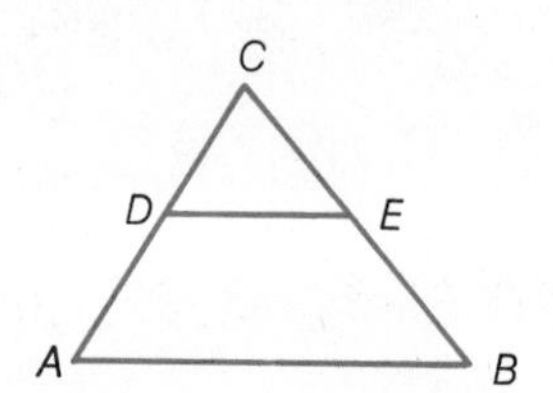

	AD	DC	AC	BE	EC	BC
14.	?	8	20	?	?	15
15.	12	?	30	9	?	?
16.	10	18	?	?	?	36
17.	?	?	48	16	28	?

18. Prove Corollary 6-4. (HINT: Through C, draw $\overleftrightarrow{CF} \parallel \overline{AB}$. Then use Theorem 6-3.)

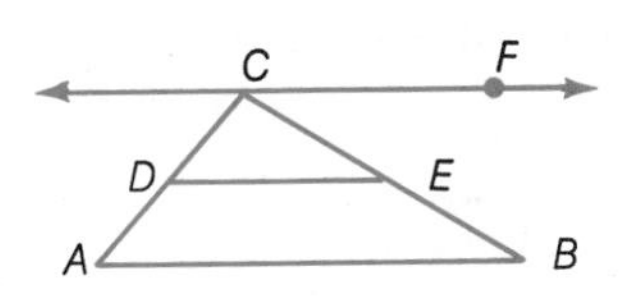

19. Prove Corollary 6-5.

In the figure at the right below, $\overline{DE} \parallel \overline{AB}$. Find the missing lengths in Exercises **20–24.**

	AD	DC	BE	EC
20.	a	b	c	?
21.	a	?	b	c
22.	$2a$	$3b$	$5b$	?
23.	$3a$	?	$4a$	$2b$
24.	$3m$	$7p$	?	$14q$

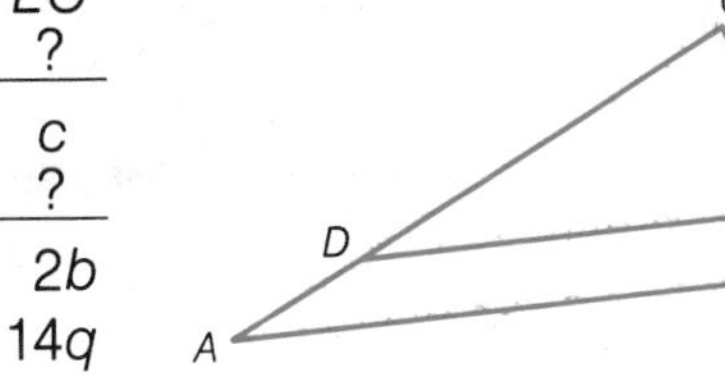

think–draw–see

1. Draw $\triangle JPN$ in which $PJ = 6$ centimeters, $JN = 4$ centimeters, and $PN = 7.5$ centimeters. Bisect $\angle J$ and extend the bisector to meet $\overline{PN}$ at K.
2. Measure $\overline{PK}$ and $\overline{KN}$.
3. Find the ratios $\frac{PK}{PJ}$ and $\frac{KN}{NJ}$.
4. Does $\frac{PK}{PJ} = \frac{KN}{NJ}$?
5. Repeat Steps **1–4** for $\triangle JPN$ in which $JP = 10$ centimeters, $PN = 9$ centimeters, and $JN = 5$ centimeters.

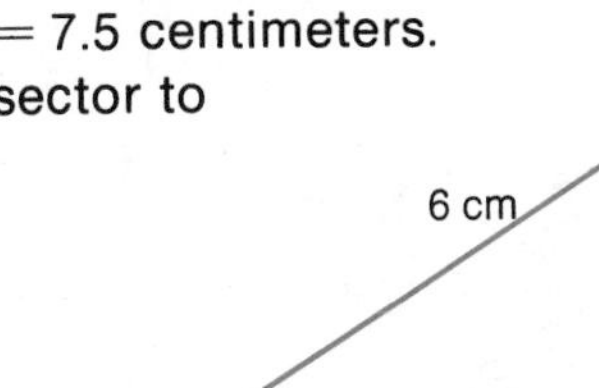

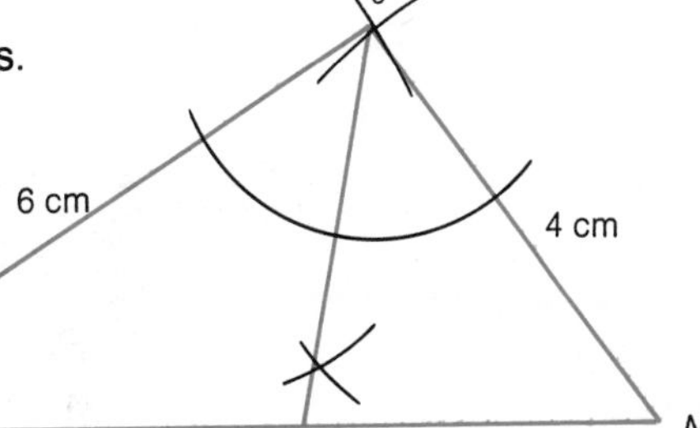

6-4 More Proportional Segments

Corollary 6-6: If a line divides two sides of a triangle proportionally, then the line is parallel to the third side.

Example 1

In $\triangle PTQ$, $PN = 6$, $NQ = 2$, $PR = 12$, and $RT = 4$. Is $\overline{NR} \parallel \overline{QT}$?

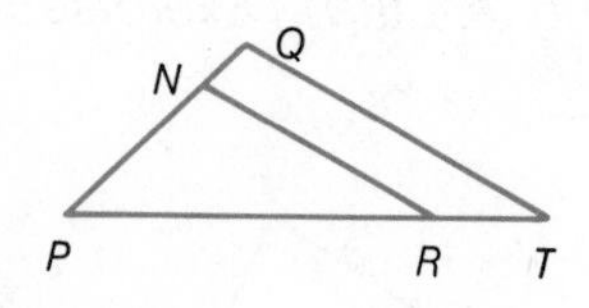

$$\frac{6}{2} \stackrel{?}{=} \frac{12}{4} \quad \longleftarrow \quad \frac{PN}{NQ} \stackrel{?}{=} \frac{PR}{RT}$$

$$6 \cdot 4 = 2 \cdot 12 \quad \longleftarrow \quad \text{Theorem 6-1 (Cross-multiply.)}$$

$$24 = 24$$

Since the ratios are equal, $\overline{NR} \parallel \overline{QT}$ by Corollary 6.6.

In Corollary 6-7, it is more convenient to refer to "segments that are proportional" rather than to "measures of segments that are proportional." Similar simplified phrasings will be used.

Corollary 6-7: The bisector of an angle of a triangle divides the opposite side into segments that are proportional to the adjacent sides of the triangle.

Example 2

In $\triangle ABC$, $\overrightarrow{CD}$ bisects $\angle C$ and meets $\overline{AB}$ at D.
If $AC = 12$, $BC = 10$, and $AD = 5$, find BD.

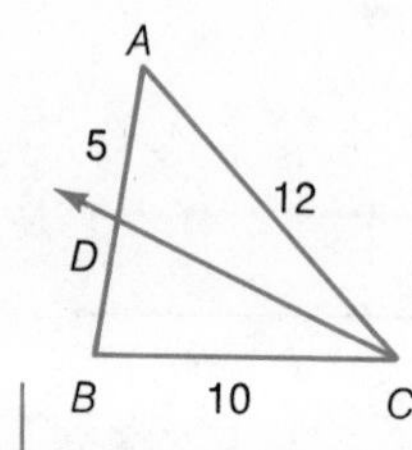

$$\frac{5}{12} = \frac{BD}{10} \quad \longleftarrow \quad \frac{AD}{AC} = \frac{BD}{BC} \text{ (Corollary 6-7)}$$

$$12 \cdot BD = 5 \cdot 10 \quad \longleftarrow \quad \text{Theorem 6-1 (Cross-multiply.)}$$

$$BD = \frac{50}{12} = 4\tfrac{1}{6}$$

Parallel planes can also cut off proportional segments.

Corollary 6-8: If two lines are cut by three parallel planes, the corresponding segments are proportional.

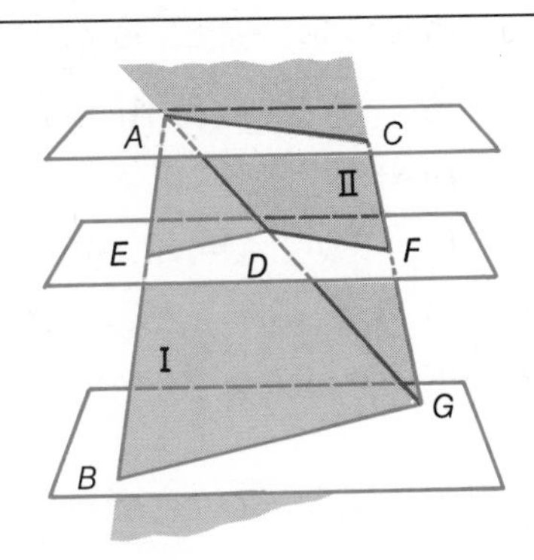

Plan of Proof: To show that $\frac{AE}{EB} = \frac{CF}{FG}$, draw $\overline{AG}$ intersecting the middle plane at D. Then draw $\overline{AC}$, $\overline{ED}$, $\overline{DF}$, and $\overline{BG}$.

In plane I (ABG), show that $\frac{AE}{EB} = \frac{AD}{DG}$.

In plane II (ACG), show that $\frac{AD}{DG} = \frac{CF}{FG}$.

Use the property of transitivity to complete the proof.

Try These

Use the figure at the right and the given information to classify each statement as True or False.

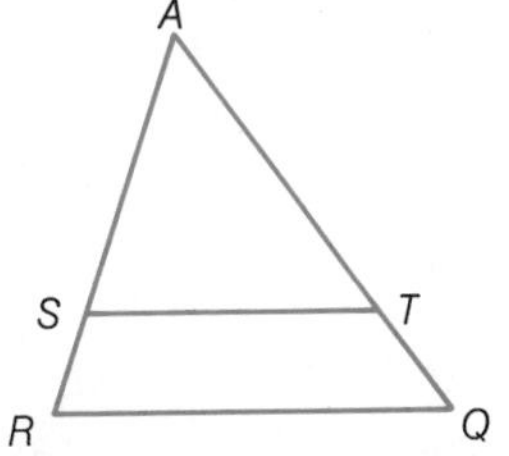

1. If $AS = 7$, $SR = 3$, $AT = 8$, and $TQ = 4$, then $\overline{ST} \parallel \overline{RQ}$.
2. If $SR = 4$, $SA = 12$, $QT = 5$ and $TA = 10$, then $\overline{ST} \parallel \overline{RQ}$.

In $\triangle RPQ$, $\overline{RS}$ bisects $\angle R$, and S is on $\overline{QP}$.

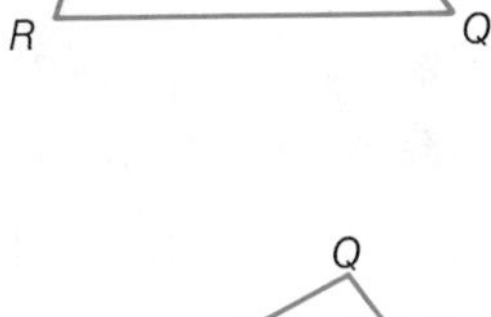

3. Find RQ if $PR = 10$, $PS = 6$ and $SQ = 3$.
4. Find PS if $PR = 12$, $RQ = 9$ and $SQ = 4$.

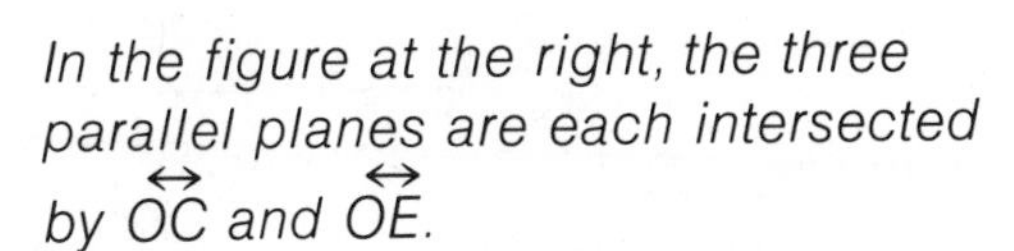

In the figure at the right, the three parallel planes are each intersected by $\overleftrightarrow{OC}$ and $\overleftrightarrow{OE}$.

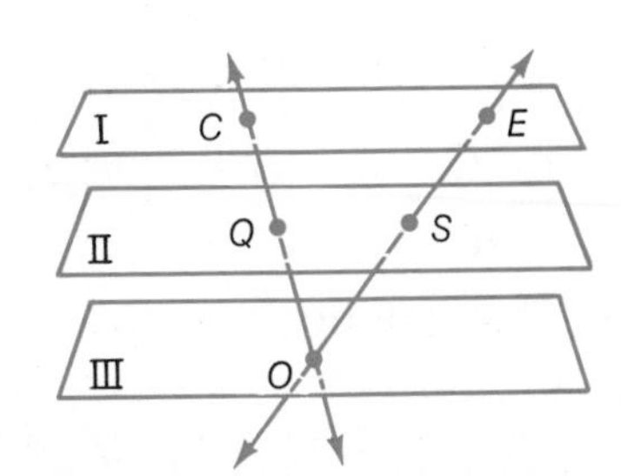

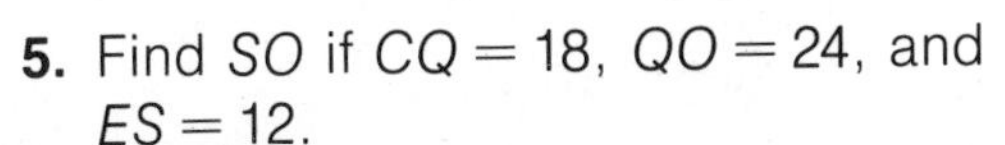

5. Find SO if $CQ = 18$, $QO = 24$, and $ES = 12$.
6. Find ES if $CQ = 5$, $CO = 20$, and $SO = 12$.
7. State Corollaries 6-4 and 6-6 as a biconditional.

Exercises

Use the figure and the given information to state whether $\overline{EF}$ is parallel to $\overline{HS}$. Answer Yes or No.

a

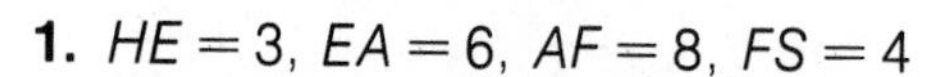

1. $HE = 3$, $EA = 6$, $AF = 8$, $FS = 4$
2. $HA = 14$, $HE = 4$, $SA = 21$, $FS = 7$
3. $HA = 18$, $EA = 12$, $AF = 20$, $FS = 10$
4. $HA = 15$, $SA = 25$, $HE = 5$, $AF = 8\frac{1}{3}$
5. $HE = 8$, $EA = 20$, $AS = 42$, $FS = 12$

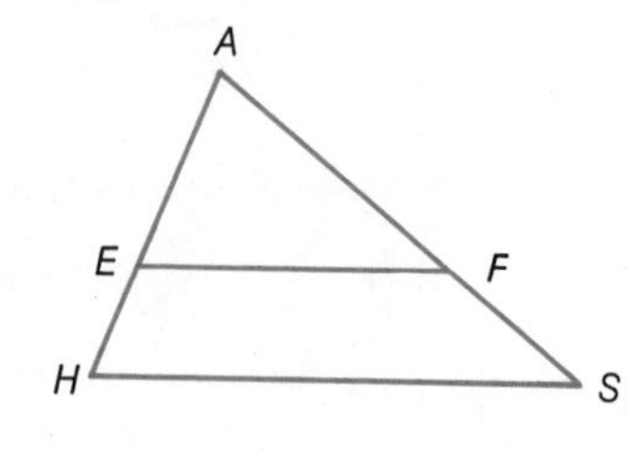

In $\triangle ABC$, $\overline{CD}$ bisects $\angle C$.

6. If $AC = 3$, $CB = 4$ and $AD = 2$, find DB.
7. If $AC = 5$, $CB = 9$ and $AD = 3$, find DB.
8. If AC is 3, $CB = 6$, and $AB = 7$, find AD and DB. (HINT: Let $AD = x$ and $DB = 7 - x$.)
9. If $AC = 16$, $CB = 20$ and $AB = 24$, find AD and DB.
10. If $AC = 12$, $CB = 15$ and $AB = 9$, find DB.

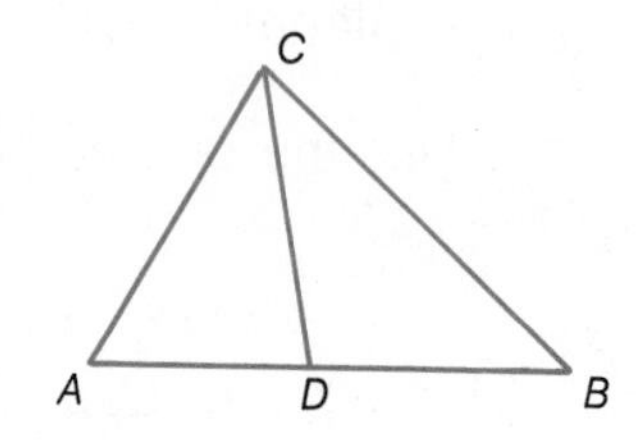

In the figure at the right, lines k and t intersect three parallel planes.

11. If $a = 6$, $b = 9$, and $c = 6\frac{1}{2}$, find d.
12. If $a = 8$, $c = 10$, and $d = 14$, find b.
13. If $b = 12$, $c = 5$, and $d = 8$, find a.
14. If $a = 2$, $b = 7$, and $d = 9$, find c.

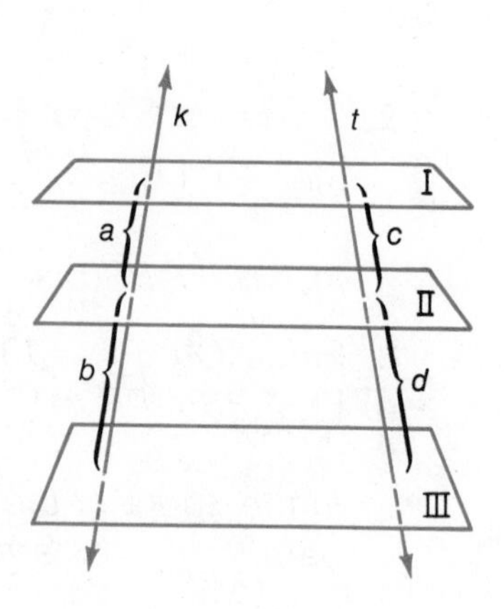

In $\triangle ABC$, $\overline{CD}$ bisects $\angle C$ and D is on $\overline{AB}$.

b

15. If $AC = b$, $CB = a$, and $AD = k$, find DB.
16. If $AC = b$, $CB = a$, and $AB = c$, find AD and DB.
17. The statement $a = b = c$ is actually three statements:

$$a = b,\ b = c, \text{ and } a = c.$$

Write three statements for $\frac{r}{s} = \frac{q}{t} = \frac{y}{z}$.

18. Write these three statements as one statement.

$$\frac{e}{f} = \frac{g}{h} \qquad \frac{e}{f} = \frac{k}{m} \qquad \frac{g}{h} = \frac{k}{m}$$

19. Prove Corollary 6-7.

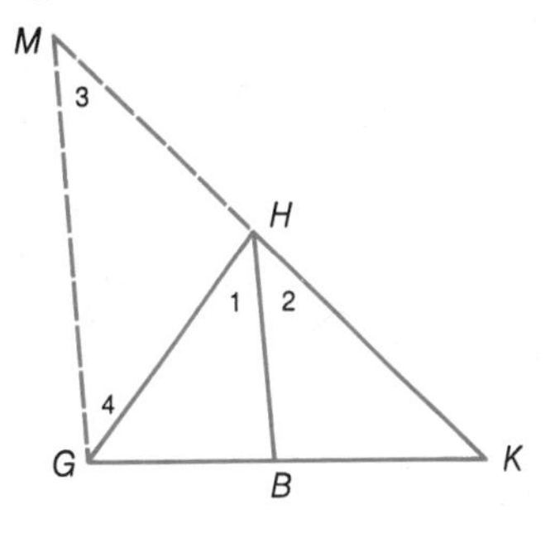

Given: $\overline{HB}$ bisects $\angle GHK$;
B is a point on $\overline{GK}$.

Prove: $\frac{KH}{HG} = \frac{KB}{BG}$

(HINT: Draw $\overline{GM} \parallel \overline{BH}$. Then show $\angle 3 \cong \angle 2$, $\angle 4 \cong \angle 1$, and $\angle 3 \cong \angle 4$. $\therefore \overline{MH} \cong \overline{HG}$. Complete the proof.)

20. Prove Corollary 6-6.

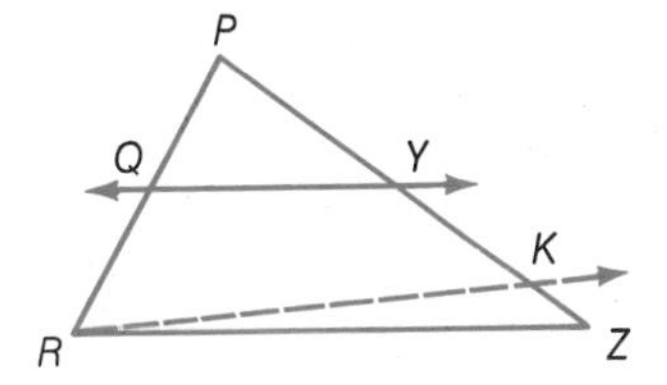

Given: $\frac{PQ}{QR} = \frac{PY}{YZ}$

Prove: $\overleftrightarrow{QY} \parallel \overline{RZ}$

(HINT: Use an indirect proof. Assume that $\overleftrightarrow{QY}$ is not parallel to $\overline{RZ}$ and draw $\overrightarrow{RK} \parallel \overleftrightarrow{QY}$. $\therefore \frac{PQ}{QR} = \frac{PY}{YK}$ and $YK = YZ$. Complete the proof.)

PUZZLE

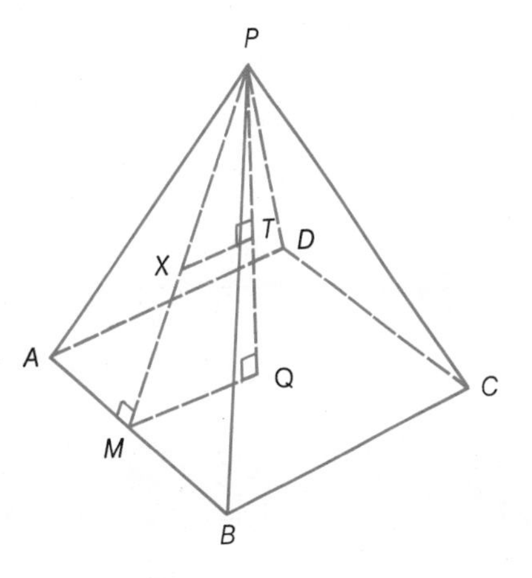

An explorer found a set of directions which tell where a treasure chest of jewels is hidden in a pyramid. The pyramid has a square base and a height of 80 meters. The treasure is at T which is on $\overline{PQ}$ and 48 meters from P. M is the midpoint of $\overline{AB}$; the distance on the outside from M to P is 100 meters. How far up from M toward P should the explorer go before digging along a horizontal line toward T?

Construction

Constructing Proportional Segments

Given: Segments with lengths a, b, and c

Required: To construct a segment of length x, such that $\frac{a}{b} = \frac{c}{x}$.

a

b

c

1. Draw any angle. Label it $\angle ABC$.

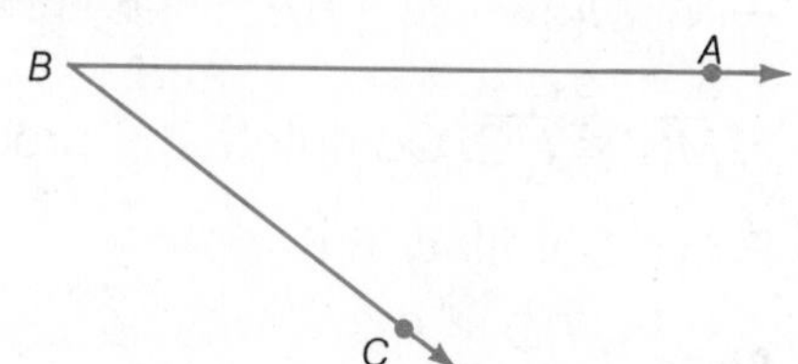

2. On $\overrightarrow{BC}$, mark off $BD = a$ and $DE = b$. On $\overrightarrow{BA}$, mark off $BF = c$.

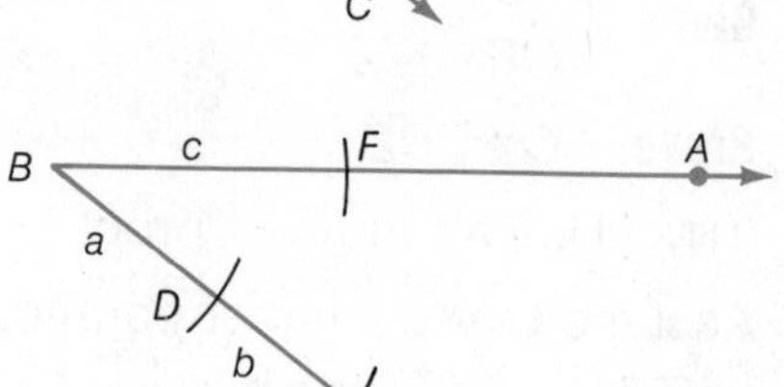

3. Draw $\overline{DF}$. Through E, construct a line parallel to $\overline{DF}$. Let G be the point where the line intersects $\overrightarrow{BF}$. Then $\overline{FG}$ is the required length x, such that $\frac{a}{b} = \frac{c}{x}$.

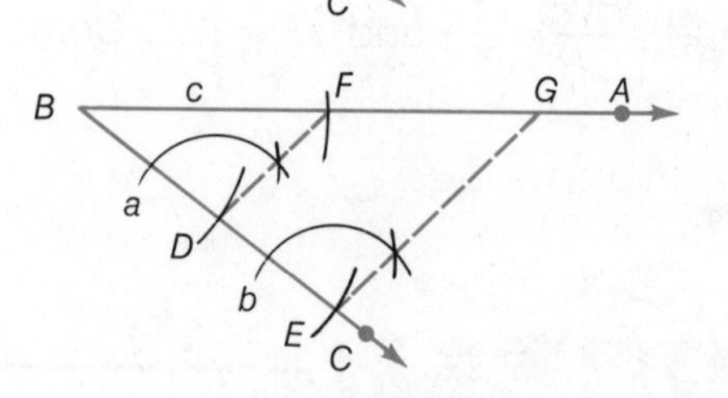

Exercises

1. Draw three segments x, z, and w with lengths 1, 2, and 3 centimeters respectively. Construct a segment with length y, such that $\frac{1}{2} = \frac{3}{y}$.

2. Draw three segments, a, b, and c, with lengths 3, 4, and 5 centimeters, respectively. Construct a segment with length x, such that $\frac{3}{4} = \frac{5}{x}$.

6-5 Similar Polygons

Similar polygons have the same shape. Polygons will have the same shape if corresponding angles are congruent and if the lengths of corresponding sides have the same ratio (are proportional).

Polygons	Similar?	Reason
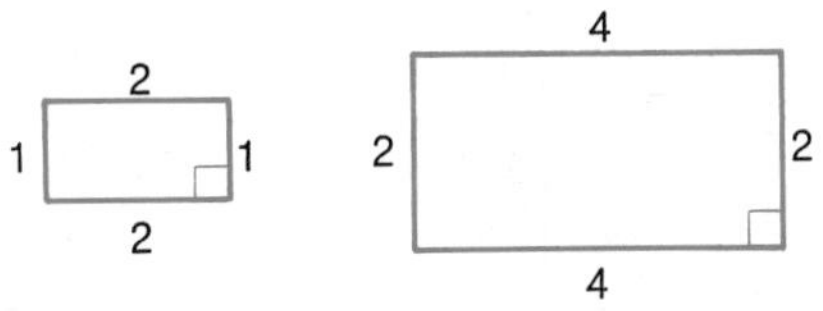	Yes	Corresponding angles are congruent and corresponding sides have the same ratio, $\frac{1}{2}$.
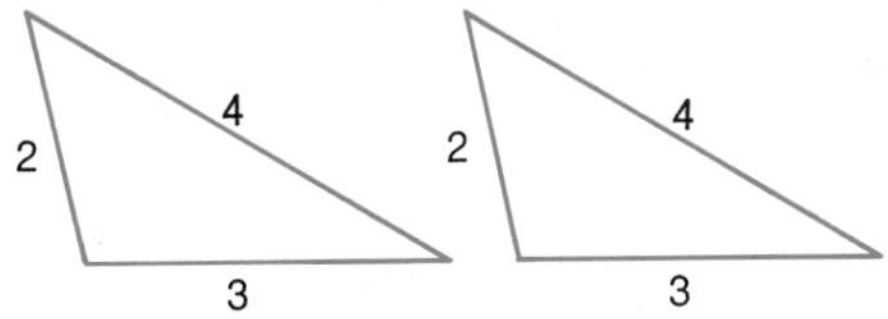	Yes	The triangles are congruent by s.s.s. The ratio of corresponding sides is $\frac{1}{1}$.
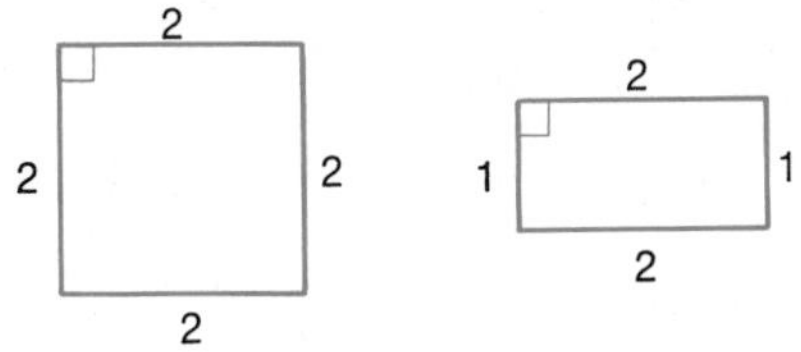	No	Corresponding sides do not have the same ratio. $\frac{2}{2} \neq \frac{2}{1}$
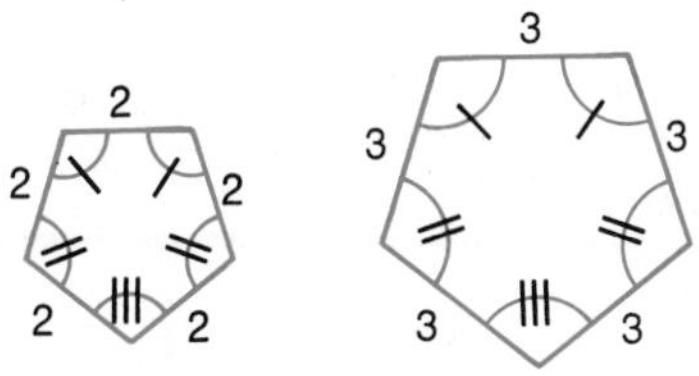	Yes	Corresponding angles are congruent and corresponding sides have the same ratio, $\frac{2}{3}$.
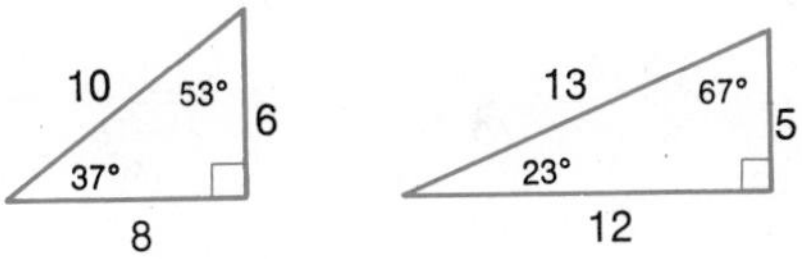	No	Corresponding angles are not congruent and corresponding sides do not have the same ratio.

Definition: Two polygons are similar if corresponding angles are congruent and corresponding sides are proportional.

The symbol ~ means "is similar to."

Example

For similar polygons *SRQP* and *YZTX*, the lengths of certain sides are given. Find *PQ*, *PS*, and *SR*.

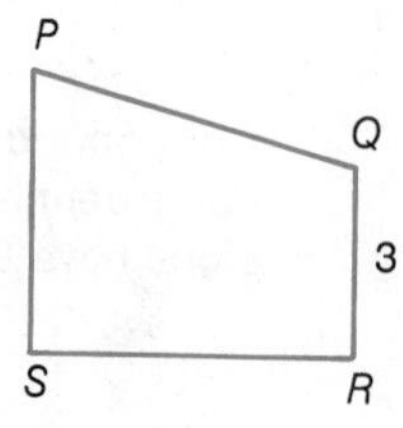

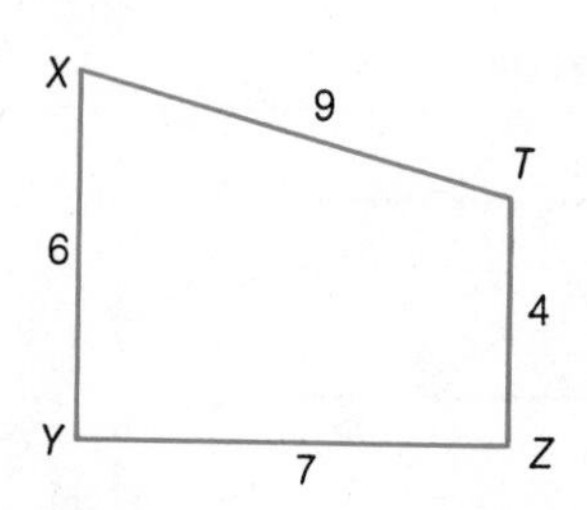

$$\frac{QR}{TZ} = \frac{PQ}{XT} \qquad \frac{3}{4} = \frac{PQ}{9} \qquad 4 \cdot PQ = 3 \cdot 9 \qquad PQ = \frac{27}{4} = 6\tfrac{3}{4}$$

$$\frac{QR}{TZ} = \frac{PS}{XY} \qquad \frac{3}{4} = \frac{PS}{6} \qquad 4 \cdot PS = 18 \qquad PS = \frac{18}{4} = 4\tfrac{1}{2}$$

$$\frac{QR}{TZ} = \frac{SR}{YZ} \qquad \frac{3}{4} = \frac{SR}{7} \qquad 4 \cdot SR = 21 \qquad SR = \frac{21}{4} = 5\tfrac{1}{4}$$

Try These

State whether each pair of polygons is similar. Give a reason for each answer.

1.

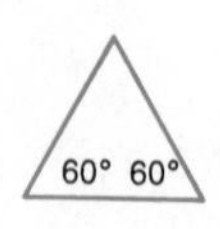

2.

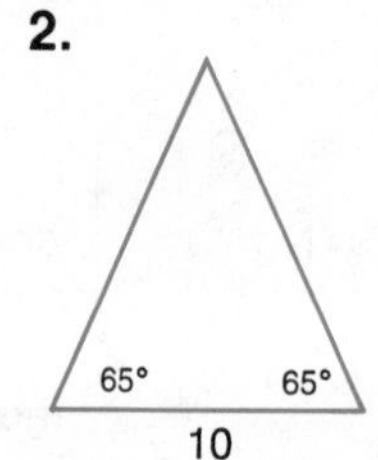

3.

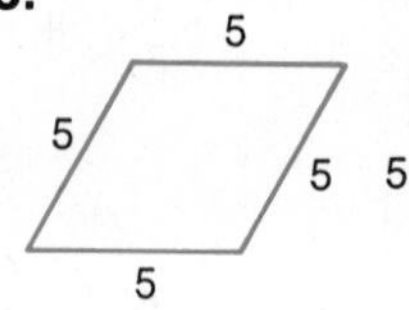

Exercises

a

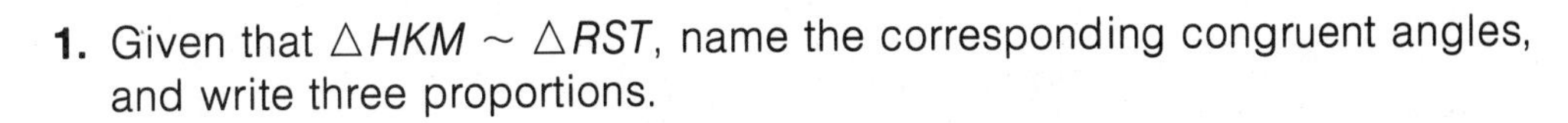

1. Given that $\triangle HKM \sim \triangle RST$, name the corresponding congruent angles, and write three proportions.

For Exercises **2** *and* **3,** $\triangle ABC \cong \triangle DEF$.

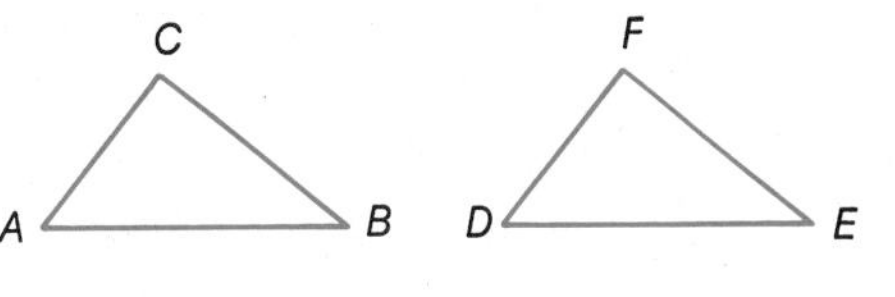

2. Is $\triangle ABC$ similar to $\triangle DEF$?

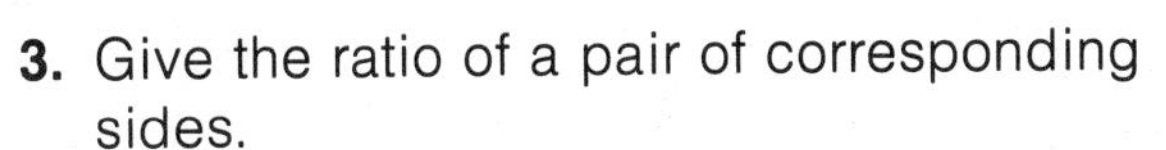

3. Give the ratio of a pair of corresponding sides.
4. If $\triangle MNQ \sim \triangle ABC$ and $\triangle ABC \sim \triangle DEF$, is $\triangle MNQ \sim \triangle DEF$?

In Exercises **5–8,** *the lengths of corresponding sides of two similar polygons are given. Write the ratio of the corresponding sides of the first polygon to the second.*

5. 5, 6, 8; 10, 12, 16
6. 3, 6, 8, 8; $4\frac{1}{2}$, 9, 12, 12
7. 9, 11, 14; $4\frac{1}{2}$, $5\frac{1}{2}$, 7
8. $8a$, $8b$, $8c$; $5a$, $5b$, $5c$

Classify each statement in Exercises **9–22** *as* True *or* False.

9. Any two squares are similar.
10. Any two triangles are similar.
11. Any two rectangles are similar.
12. Any two equilateral triangles are similar.
13. Any polygon is similar to itself.
14. If two polygons are congruent, then they are similar.
15. If two polygons are similar, then they are congruent.
16. Any two regular hexagons are similar.
17. Any two rhombuses are similar.
18. Any two rectangles with lengths three times their widths are similar.
19. Any two isosceles triangles are similar.
20. If $\triangle XYZ \sim \triangle DFT$, then $\overline{XY}$ corresponds to $\overline{FT}$.
21. If $\triangle XYZ \sim \triangle DFT$, then $\angle Y \cong \angle F$.
22. If $\triangle XYZ \sim \triangle DFT$, then $\frac{YZ}{FT} = \frac{ZX}{TD}$.

In the figure at the right, $\triangle HTR \sim \triangle HNS$.

23. If $m\angle H = 50$ and $m\angle HRT = 45$, find $m\angle N$.

24. If $HT = 5$, $TN = 3$, and $HR = 7$, find RS.

25. If $HR = 9$, $RS = 4$, and $NS = 12$, find TR.

26. The lengths of the sides of a triangle are 6, 4, 5. The lengths of the corresponding sides of a similar triangle are 9, x, and y. Find x and y.

The lengths of the corresponding sides of two similar triangles are given. Find the missing lengths.

27. 6, 9, 12; 9, x, y

28. 8, 12, 16; 6, a, b

29. 15, 18, e; 45, f, 60

30. 24, 30, 36; c, 40, d

31. 1.2, 1.6, 2.4; 1.8, g, h

32. .75, 1.25, 1.5; 2.25, p, q

The lengths of the corresponding sides of two similar polygons are given. Find the missing lengths.

33. 8, 10, 12, 16, 18; 12, k, p, m, r

34. 3, 5, 8, 12; 4, r, p, q

b

35. Is similarity between two polygons an equivalence relation? Give reasons for your answer.

PUZZLE

Draw $\triangle ABC$. Mark any point A_1 on $\overline{BC}$. Draw $\overline{A_1B_1}$ parallel to $\overline{BA}$ as shown, then $\overline{B_1C_1}$ parallel to $\overline{BC}$, and $\overline{C_1A_2}$ parallel to $\overline{AC}$. If you continue this way between points on the sides of the triangle, A_3 must equal A_1. Can you explain why?

What difference will it make if A_1 is the midpoint of $\overline{BC}$?

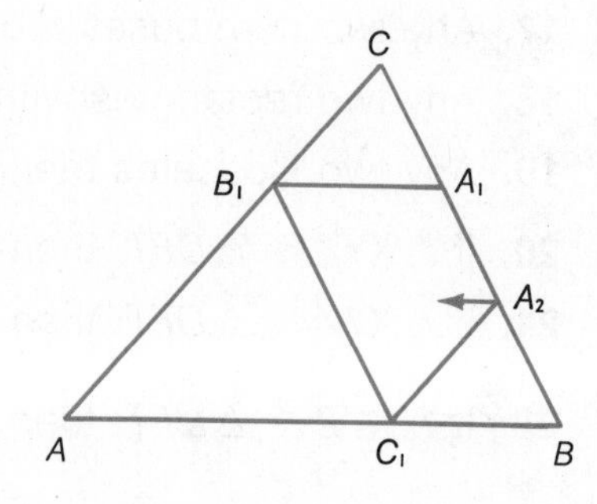

6-6 Similar Triangles

To prove that two triangles are similar, prove that corresponding angles are congruent or that corresponding sides are proportional.

Theorem 6-9: **A.A.A. Theorem**

If the angles of one triangle are congruent to the angles of another triangle, then the triangles are similar.

Given: In $\triangle ABC$ and $\triangle DEF$, $\angle A \cong \angle D$, $\angle B \cong \angle E$, and $\angle C \cong \angle F$.

Prove: $\triangle ABC \sim \triangle DEF$

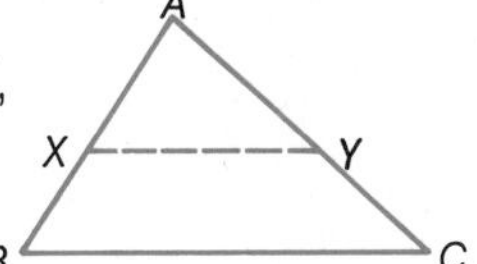

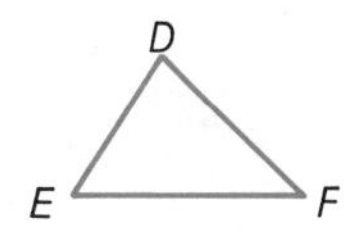

Statements	Reasons
1. $\angle A \cong \angle D$, $\angle B \cong \angle E$, $\angle C \cong \angle F$	1. Given
2. Let X be a point on $\overline{AB}$ such that $\overline{AX} \cong \overline{DE}$. Let Y be a point on $\overline{AC}$ such that $\overline{AY} \cong \overline{DF}$.	2. To every distinct pair of points there corresponds exactly one positive number. The number is the distance between the points.
3. Draw $\overline{XY}$.	3. (2). Postulate 4, page 23
4. $\triangle AXY \cong \triangle DEF$	4. (1). (2). (3). S.A.S.
5. $\angle AXY \cong \angle E$	5. (4). C.P.C.T.C.
6. $\angle AXY \cong \angle B$	6. (1). (5). Transitive property of $\cong$.
7. $\overline{XY} \parallel \overline{BC}$	7. Theorem 4-9, page 173
8. $\dfrac{AB}{AX} = \dfrac{AC}{AY}$	8. Corollary 6-5, page 259
9. $AX = DE$, $AY = DF$	9. (2). Congruent segments have equal measures.
10. $\dfrac{AB}{DE} = \dfrac{AC}{DF}$	10. (9). Substitution Principle

To complete the proof, use auxiliary segment RS and prove that $\triangle RBS \cong \triangle DEF$. Then prove that $\frac{AB}{DE} = \frac{CB}{FE}$.

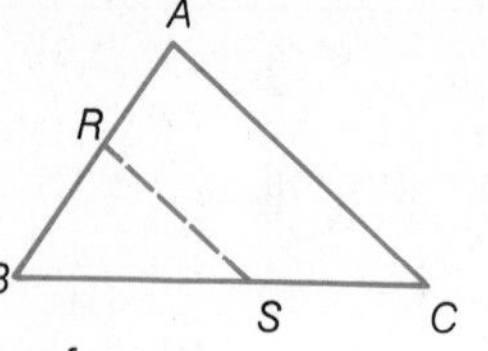

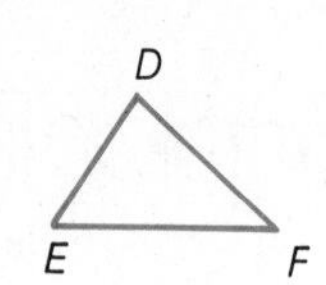

From this and Step 10 of the proof,

$$\frac{AB}{DE} = \frac{AC}{DF} = \frac{CB}{FE}.$$

Since corresponding angles are congruent and corresponding sides are proportional, $\triangle ABC \sim \triangle DEF$.

Example

Use the triangles at the right to show that $\triangle QGD \sim \triangle FCN$.

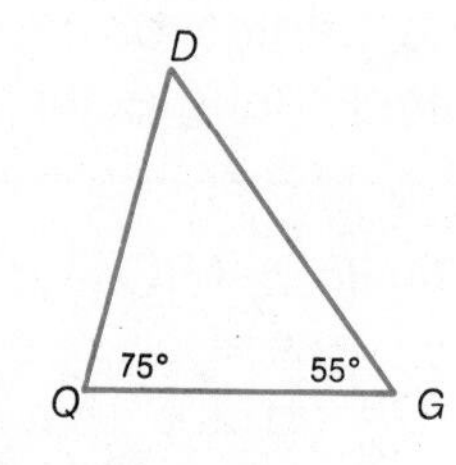

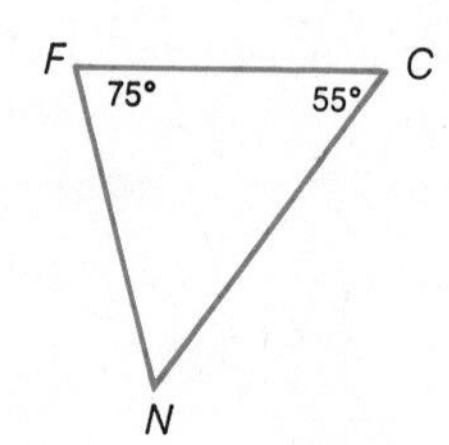

$\angle Q \cong \angle F$; $\angle G \cong \angle C$	←	**Given**
$\angle D \cong \angle N$	←	**Corollary 4-13, page 181**
$\therefore \triangle QGD \sim \triangle FCN$	←	**Theorem 6-9**

The example suggests this corollary.

Corollary 6-10: **A.A. Corollary**

If two angles of one triangle are congruent to two angles of a second triangle, then the triangles are similar.

A special case of Corollary 6-10 occurs with right triangles.

Corollary 6-11: If two right triangles have an acute angle of one congruent to an acute angle of the other, then the triangles are similar.

A line parallel to one side of a triangle may form another triangle with the given triangle. In these figures line YX is parallel to segment BC, and $\triangle ABC \sim \triangle AXY$ by the indicated congruence of angles.

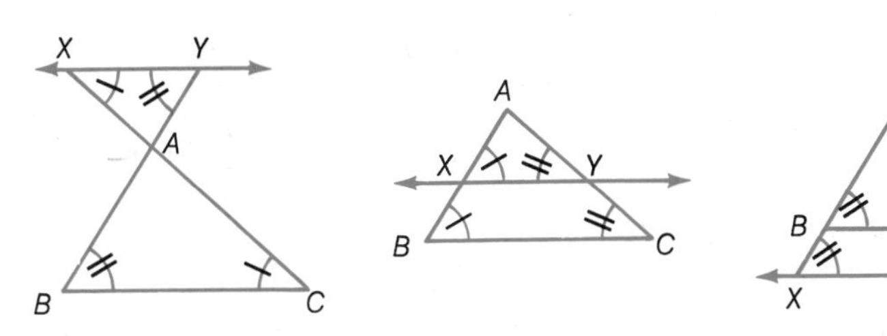

This suggests the following corollary which you are asked to prove in the Exercises.

Corollary 6-12: If a line parallel to one side of a triangle determines a second triangle, then the second triangle will be similar to the original triangle.

Try These

Use each figure and the given information to tell whether each pair of triangles is similar. Give a reason for each answer.

1.

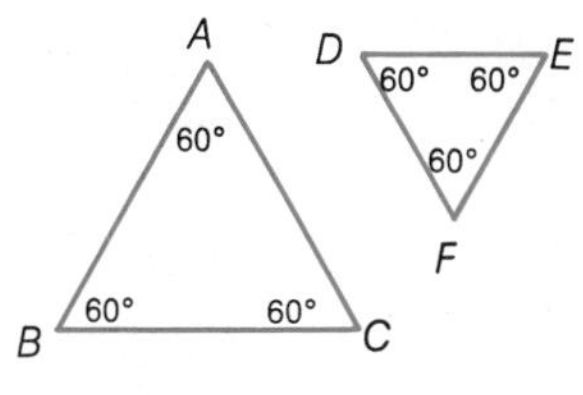

2. $\overline{KY} \parallel \overline{NO}$

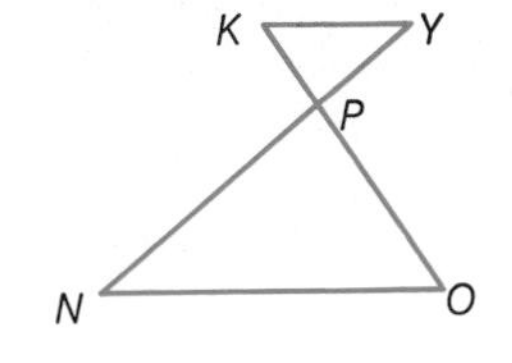

3.

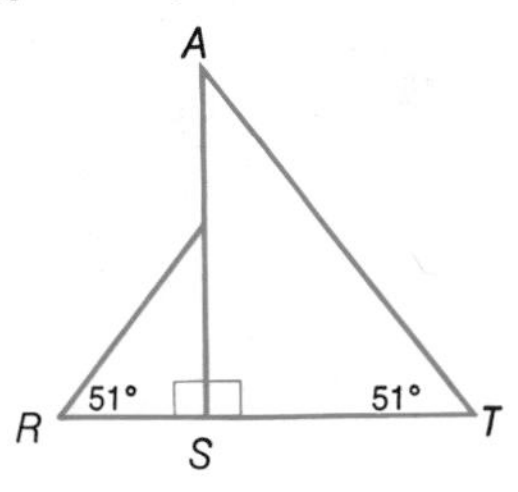

4. $\overline{KM} \parallel \overline{TS}$

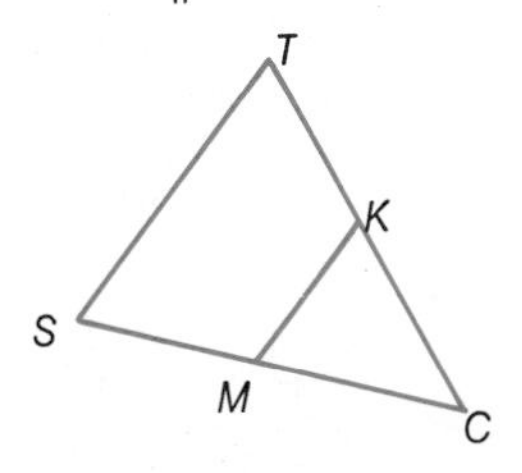

5.

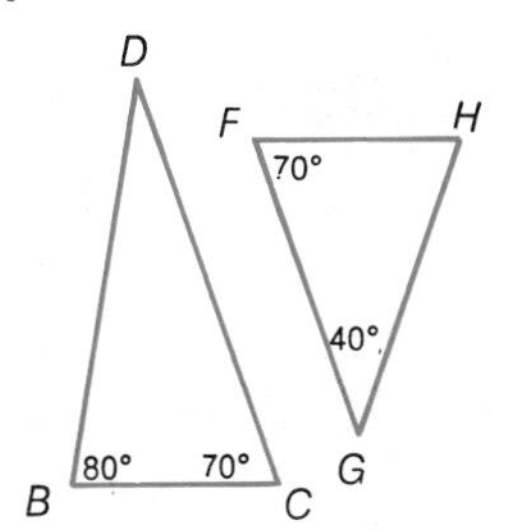

6.

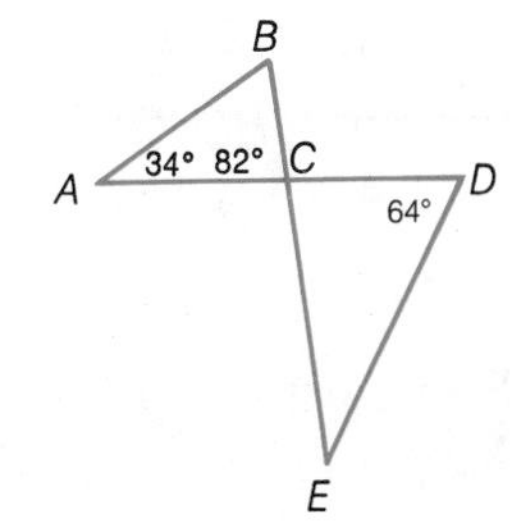

Exercises

*Exercises **1–4** refer to $\triangle ABC$ in which $\angle 1 \cong \angle 2$. Complete each statement.*

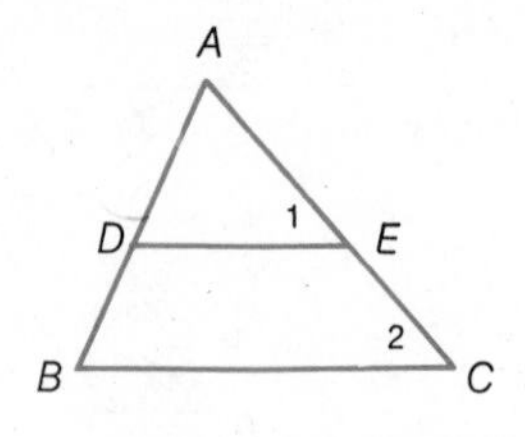

a

1. $\triangle ABC \sim \triangle$ _?_
2. $\frac{AD}{AB} = \frac{?}{AC} = \frac{?}{BC}$
3. If $AD = 3$, $DE = 4$, and $AB = 5$, $BC =$ _?_.
4. If $AE = 5$, $ED = 7$, and $BC = 21$, $AC =$ _?_.

5. **Given:** $\overline{TS} \parallel \overline{PQ}$
   Prove: $\triangle RTS \sim \triangle RPQ$

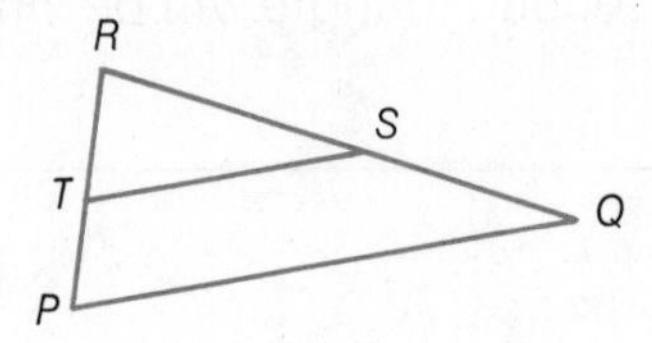

6. **Given:** $\triangle THE$; $\frac{EU}{UT} = \frac{ER}{RH}$
   Prove: $\triangle URE \sim \triangle THE$

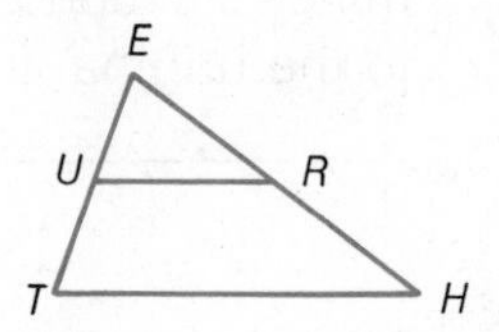

7. **Given:** In $\triangle MRO$, $\overline{TS} \perp \overline{MR}$ and $\overline{OR} \perp \overline{MR}$
   Prove: $\triangle MRO \sim \triangle MST$

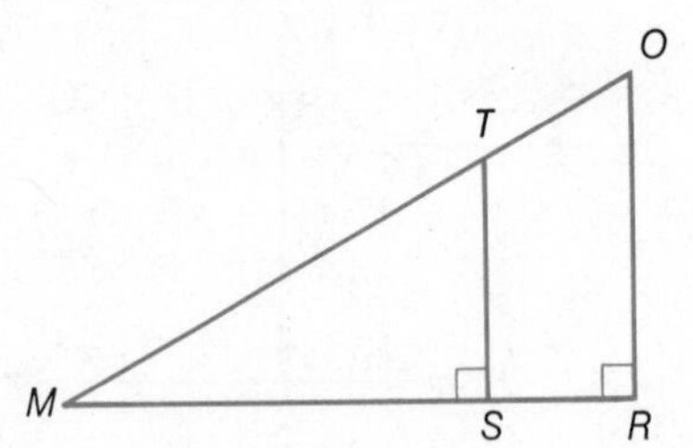

8. **Given:** $\triangle XYZ$, in which $m\angle Y = 90$ and $\overline{WU} \perp \overline{XZ}$
   Prove: $\triangle XYZ \sim \triangle XUW$

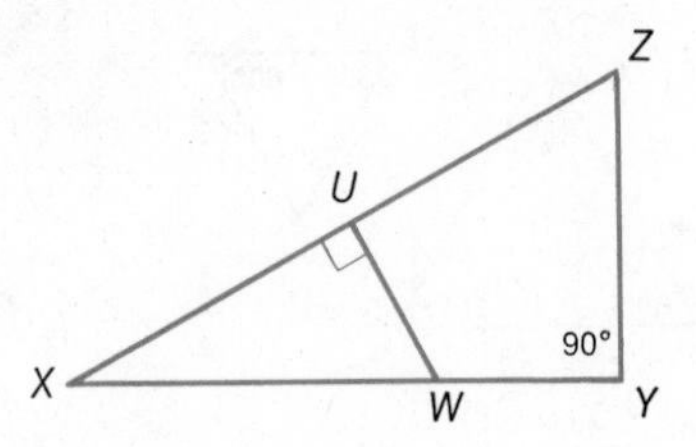

*Exercises **9–11** refer to the figure at the right. $\overline{BD}$ and $\overline{AE}$ are altitudes of $\triangle ABC$.*

9. Prove that $\triangle AEC \sim \triangle BDC$.
10. Prove that $\triangle BFE \sim \triangle AFD$.
11. Prove that $\triangle ADF \sim \triangle AEC$.

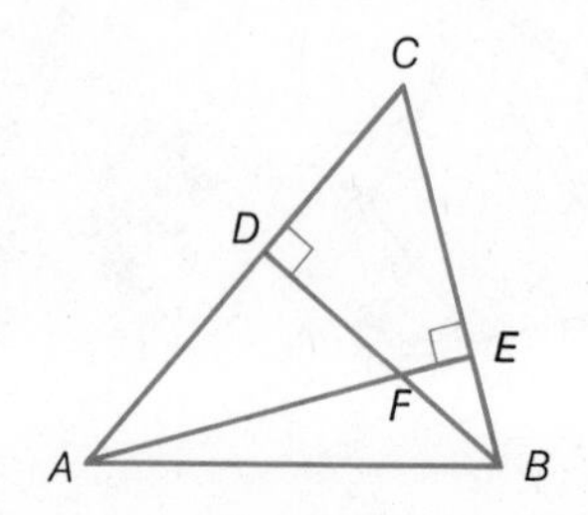

12. **Given:** Trapezoid $DRTC$ with bases DC and RT.
Prove: $\triangle DOC \sim \triangle TOR$

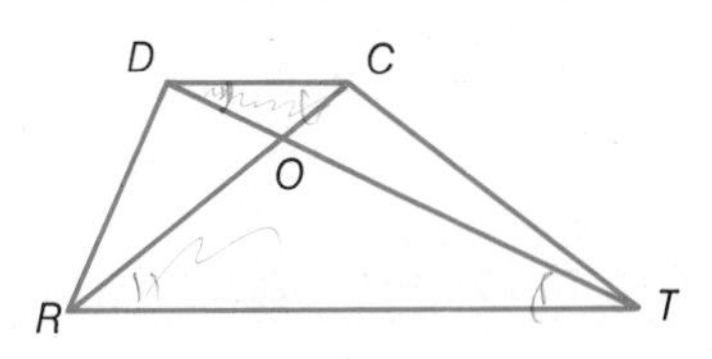

13. **Given:** $\triangle FDN$ in which $\angle F \cong \angle NDQ$
Prove: $\triangle NQD \sim \triangle NDF$

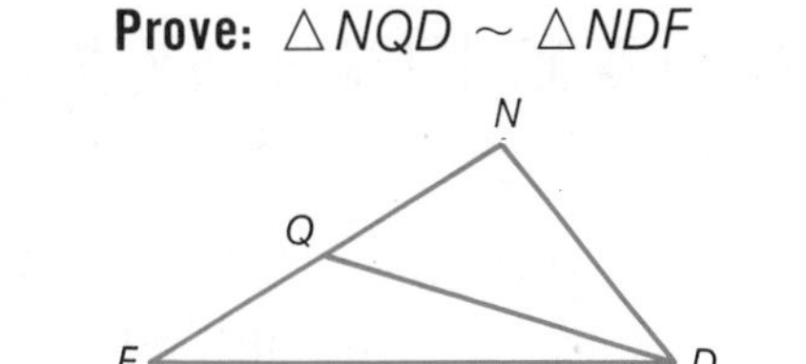

14. **Given:** $\triangle PMT \sim \triangle RGA$; $\overline{PS} \perp \overline{MT}$; $\overline{RQ} \perp \overline{GA}$
Prove: $\triangle STP \sim \triangle QAR$
$\triangle SPM \sim \triangle QRG$

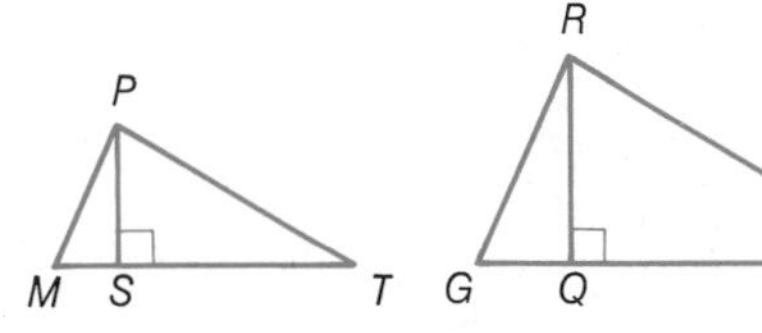

15. Prove Corollary 6-12.

16. A line is drawn parallel to the base of an isosceles triangle so that it forms a second triangle. Explain why this second triangle is also isosceles.

17. Two quadrilaterals have their corresponding angles congruent. Are the quadrilaterals similar? Explain.

18. Scalene triangle WEF has R, T, and A as the midpoints of its sides. Segments AR, RT, and TA are drawn. Explain why all four triangles formed are similar to triangle WEF.

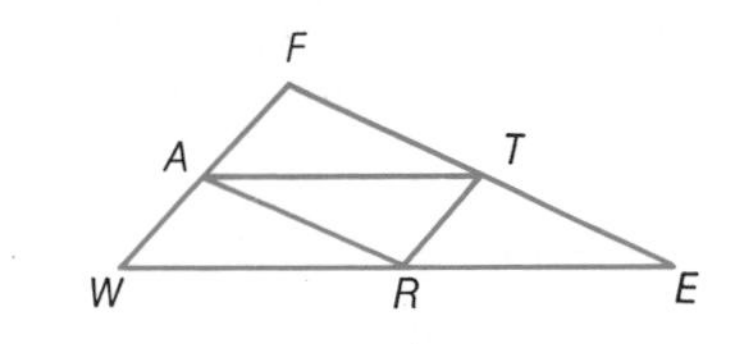

19. **Given:** $\triangle BCA \sim \triangle EFD$; $\overline{AR}$ and $\overline{DT}$ are angle bisectors.
Prove: $\triangle RCA \sim \triangle TFD$
$\triangle RAB \sim \triangle TDE$

20. Two triangles have five parts (angles and sides) of the first triangle congruent to five parts of the second triangle. The triangles are <u>not</u> congruent. Explain how this is possible.

Remember

1. In $\triangle ABC$, name the side opposite $\angle A$.

2. In $\triangle DEF$, name the side opposite $\angle F$.

3. $\triangle ABC \cong \triangle DEF$. Name the corresponding angles and sides.

The answers are on page 302. If you need help, see pages 94 and 230.

6-7 More on Similar Triangles

In similar triangles, corresponding sides are opposite congruent angles.

Example 1

In similar triangles ABC and DEF, $\angle A \cong \angle D$ and $\angle C \cong \angle F$. Complete each statement.

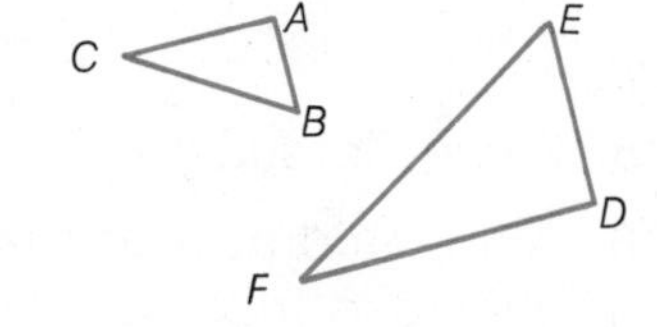

a. $\frac{AC}{DF} = \frac{?}{DE}$ **b.** $\frac{AB}{DE} = \frac{BC}{?}$

a. $\frac{AC}{DF} = \frac{AB}{DE}$ ← $\overline{DE}$ is opposite $\angle F$; $\overline{AB}$ is opposite $\angle C$.

b. $\frac{AB}{DE} = \frac{BC}{EF}$ ← $\overline{BC}$ is opposite $\angle A$; $\overline{EF}$ is opposite $\angle D$.

The S.A.S. Theorem for similarity corresponds to the S.A.S. Theorem for congruence. You are asked to prove it in the Exercises.

Theorem 6-13: S.A.S. Similarity Theorem

If an angle of one triangle is congruent to an angle of another, and the sides including these angles are proportional, then the triangles are similar.

There is also an S.S.S. theorem for similarity.

Theorem 6-14: S.S.S. Similarity Theorem

If the corresponding sides of two triangles are proportional, then the triangles are similar.

Example 2

Tell whether each pair of triangles is similar.

a.

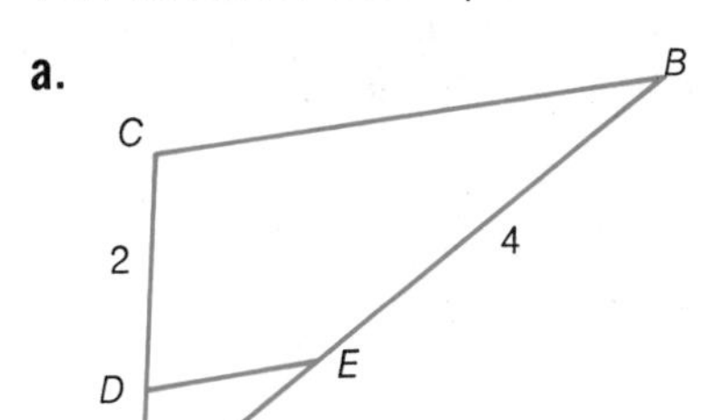

b.

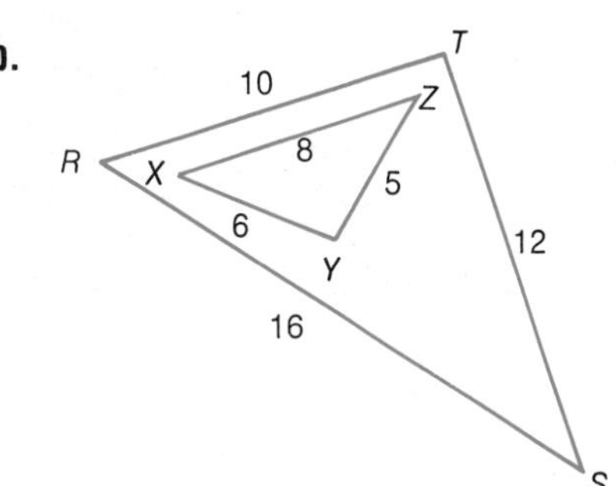

a. $\angle A \cong \angle A$ ← Identity

$\frac{AD}{AC} \stackrel{?}{=} \frac{AE}{AB}$ ← Test whether corresponding sides are proportional.

$\frac{1}{3} = \frac{2}{6}$ ← Each ratio equals $\frac{1}{3}$.

$\therefore \triangle ADE \sim \triangle ACB$ ← S.A.S. Similarity Theorem

b. $\frac{XY}{ST} \stackrel{?}{=} \frac{YZ}{TR} \stackrel{?}{=} \frac{ZX}{SR}$ ← Test whether corresponding sides are proportional.

$\frac{6}{12} = \frac{5}{10} = \frac{8}{16}$ ← Each ratio equals $\frac{1}{2}$.

$\therefore \triangle XYZ \sim \triangle STR$ ← S.S.S. Similarity theorem

The following corollaries also relate to similar triangles. Recall from page 262 that "segment" refers to the "measure of a segment" in theorems and corollaries about proportional segments.

Corollary 6-15: The perimeters of two similar triangles are proportional to any pair of corresponding sides.

Corollary 6-16: The altitudes of similar triangles are proportional to any pair of corresponding sides.

Corollary 6-17: The medians of similar triangles are proportional to any pair of corresponding sides.

Example 3

Two similar triangles have perimeters of 63 cm and 49 cm. Find the length of the altitude of the smaller triangle if the corresponding altitude of the larger triangle is 27 cm long.

$$\frac{\text{Perimeter of larger triangle}}{\text{Perimeter of smaller triangle}} = \frac{63}{49} = \frac{9}{7}$$ ← **Ratio of any pair of corresponding sides**

Let $x =$ the length of the altitude of the smaller triangle.

$$\frac{9}{7} = \frac{27}{x}$$ ← **Corollary 6-16**

$$x = \frac{7 \cdot 27}{9}$$

$$x = 21$$ ← **The length of the altitude is 21 cm.**

Try These

Use the given figure and information to find x.

1. $\triangle ABC \sim \triangle DEF$

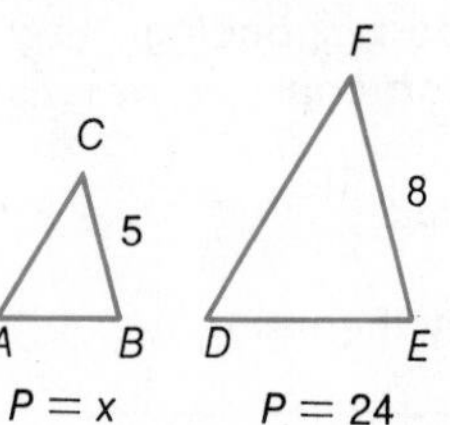

2. $\triangle PRQ \sim \triangle TRS$

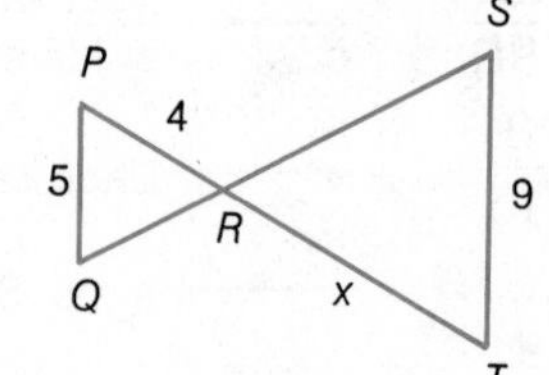

3. $\triangle PQR \sim \triangle WZT$

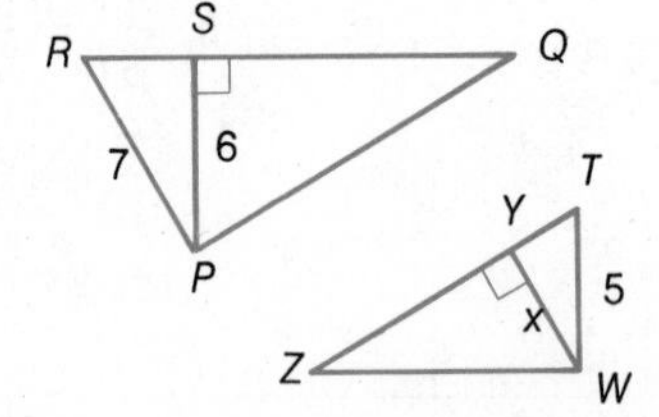

Exercises

Use the given information to tell whether each pair of triangles is similar. Give a reason for each answer.

a

1.

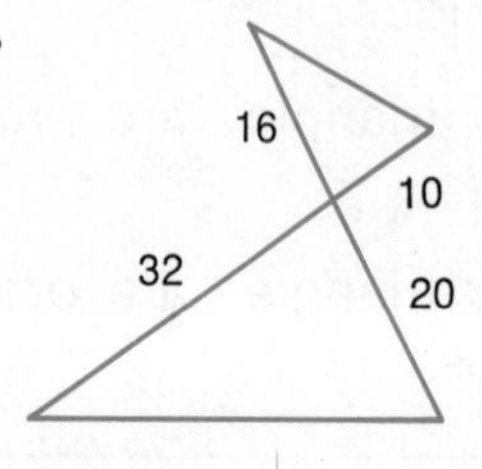

2.

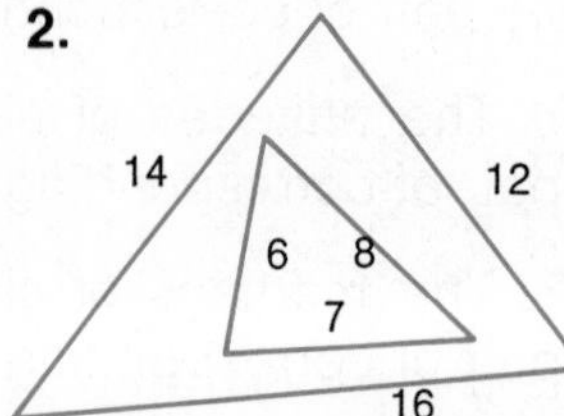

3.

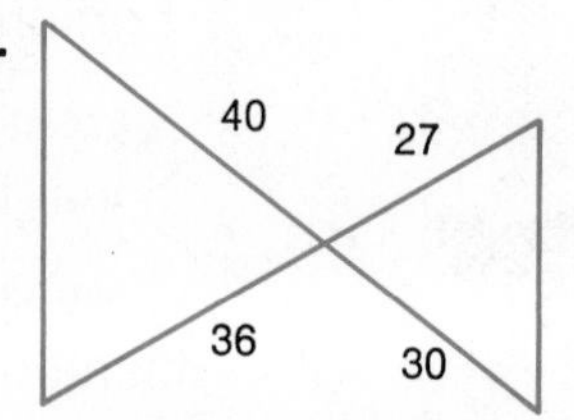

*In Exercises **4–8,** the lengths of the corresponding sides of two triangles are given. Tell whether each pair of triangles is similar. If the triangles are similar, give the ratio of the corresponding sides.*

4. Triangle I: 9, 5, $7\frac{1}{2}$ Triangle II: $4\frac{1}{2}$, $2\frac{1}{2}$, $3\frac{3}{4}$

5. Triangle I: 14, 17, 21 Triangle II: 5, 6, 7

6. Triangle I: $2\frac{2}{3}$, $4\frac{1}{2}$, 3 Triangle II: 8, $13\frac{1}{2}$, 9

7. Triangle I: .14, .19, .24 Triangle II: .7, .95, 1.2

8. Triangle I: 7, 8, 9 Triangle II: 17, 18, 19

9. Two similar triangles have perimeters of 35 cm and 65 cm. Find the length of the altitude of the larger triangle if the corresponding altitude of the smaller triangle is 10 cm long.

10. Two corresponding medians of two similar triangles are 9 cm and 15 cm long. One side of the larger triangle is 25 cm long. Find the length of the corresponding side of the smaller.

11. Two corresponding altitudes of two similar triangles are 12 dm and 16 dm long. A median of the larger triangle is 20 dm long. Find the length of the corresponding median of the smaller triangle.

In $\triangle SRT$, $\overline{RA} \perp \overline{ST}$, $\overline{AN} \perp \overline{TR}$, $\overline{SR} \perp \overline{TR}$, $\overline{NG} \perp \overline{TA}$, and $m\angle T = 25$.

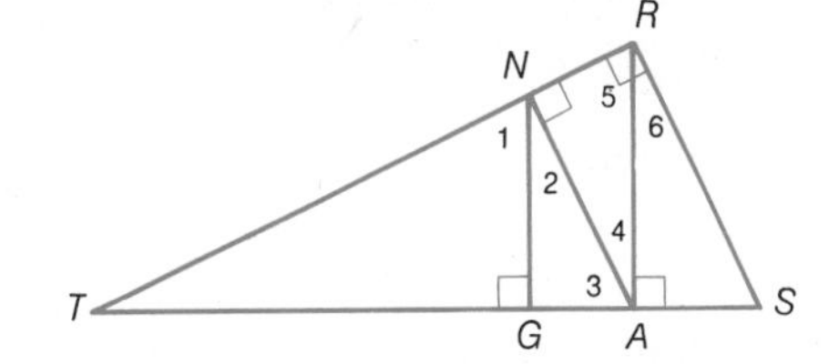

12. Find $m\angle S$, $m\angle 1$, $m\angle 2$, $m\angle 3$, $m\angle 4$, $m\angle 5$, and $m\angle 6$.

13. In the figure for Exercise 12, name all of the similar triangles.

14. Prove that two right triangles are similar if the sides adjacent to the right angles are proportional.

15. In the figure at the left below, the lengths of the sides of each triangle are given. Prove that $\overline{XY} \parallel \overline{WU}$.

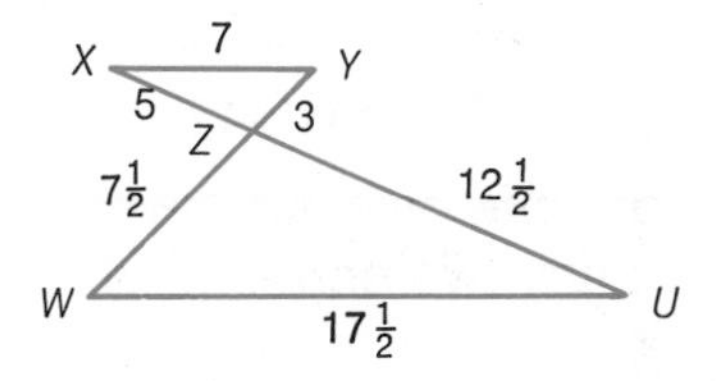

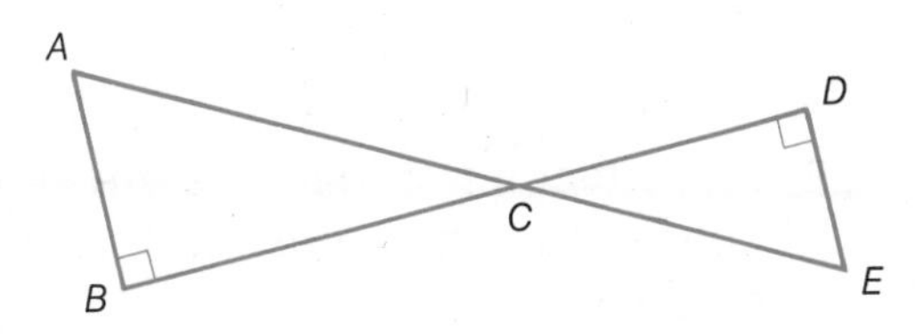

16. In the figure at the right above, $\overline{AB} \perp \overline{BD}$, $\overline{ED} \perp \overline{BD}$, and $\overline{AE}$ and $\overline{BD}$ intersect at C. Prove that $\triangle ABC \sim \triangle EDC$.

17. Write three proportions involving the sides of the triangles that you proved similar in Exercise **16.**

18. Given: $\triangle MOP$ in which $\frac{PM}{PQ} = \frac{PO}{PR}$

Prove: $\triangle PMO \sim \triangle PQR$

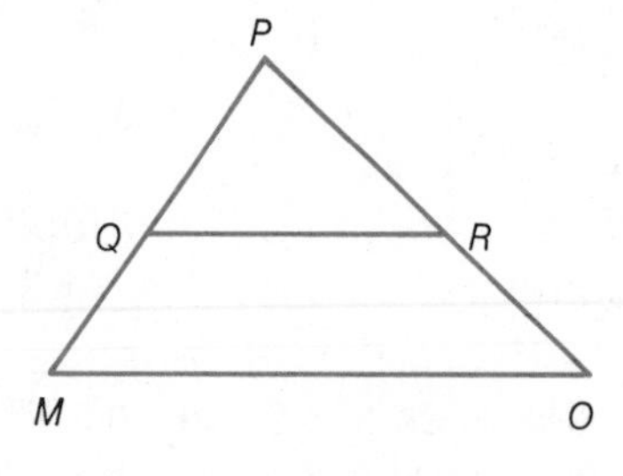

19. Given: $\angle A \cong \angle E$; $\angle B \cong \angle F$;

G is the midpoint of $\overline{AB}$;

H is the midpoint of $\overline{EF}$.

Prove: $\frac{AC}{ED} = \frac{CG}{DH}$.

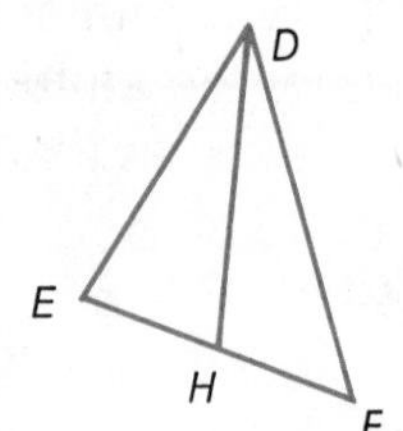

20. Given any triangle ABC and a segment DE with length equal to $\frac{2}{3}AB$, construct triangle DEF similar to triangle ABC. Prove your construction.

21. Prove Theorem 6-13.

Given: $\angle A \cong \angle D$;

$\frac{AB}{DE} = \frac{AC}{DF}$

Prove: $\triangle ABC \sim \triangle DEF$

Plan: Mark off Q and R on $\overline{AB}$ and $\overline{AC}$, respectively, such that $\overline{AQ} \cong \overline{DE}$ and

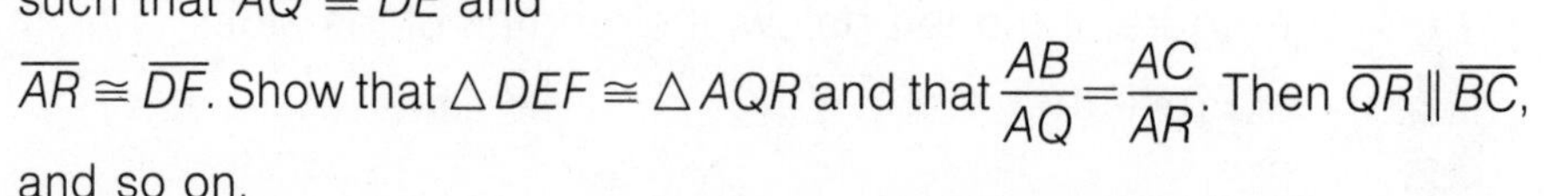

$\overline{AR} \cong \overline{DF}$. Show that $\triangle DEF \cong \triangle AQR$ and that $\frac{AB}{AQ} = \frac{AC}{AR}$. Then $\overline{QR} \parallel \overline{BC}$, and so on.

22. Prove Theorem 6-14.

23. Prove Corollary 6-15.

24. Prove Corollary 6-16.

25. Prove Corollary 6-17.

26. Prove that if two triangles are similar, the segments bisecting two corresponding angles have the same ratio as any two corresponding medians.

27. Prove that if two triangles are similar, their perimeters have the same ratio as any two corresponding altitudes.

28. Prove that two triangles are similar if their sides are parallel to each other.

6-8 Similar Right Triangles

When the altitude to the hypotenuse of a right triangle is drawn, the two triangles formed are similar to each other and both are similar to the original triangle.

Example 1

Triangle ABC has a right angle at C. $\overline{CD}$ is the altitude to $\overline{AB}$ and $m\angle A = 40$.

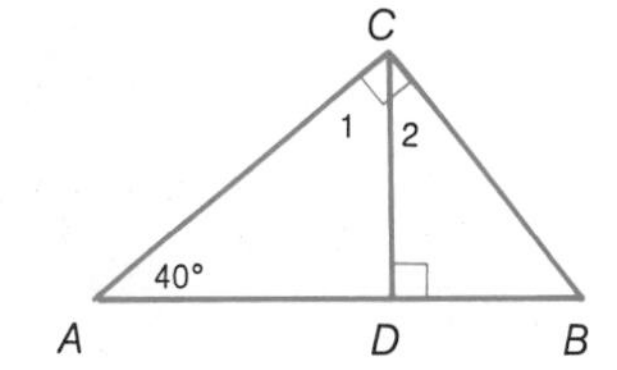

a. Find $m\angle 1$, $m\angle 2$, and $m\angle B$.
b. Tell which triangles are similar.

a. In $\triangle ADC$, $m\angle 1 = 50$. ⟵ $m\angle A + m\angle 1 = 90$
In $\triangle BDC$, $m\angle 2 = 40$, ⟵ $m\angle 1 + m\angle 2 = 90$
and $m\angle B = 50$. ⟵ $m\angle 2 + m\angle B = 90$

b. $\triangle ABC \sim \triangle ACD \sim \triangle CBD$ ⟵ If the angles of one triangle are congruent to the angles of another triangle, the triangles are similar.

The example suggests this theorem. You are asked to prove the theorem in the Exercises.

Theorem 6-18: The altitude to the hypotenuse of a right triangle determines two triangles that are similar to each other and to the original triangle.

Example 2

In $\triangle DEF$, $\angle D$ is a right angle, $\overline{DR}$ is the altitude to $\overline{EF}$, $ER = 9$, and $RF = 4$. Find DR.

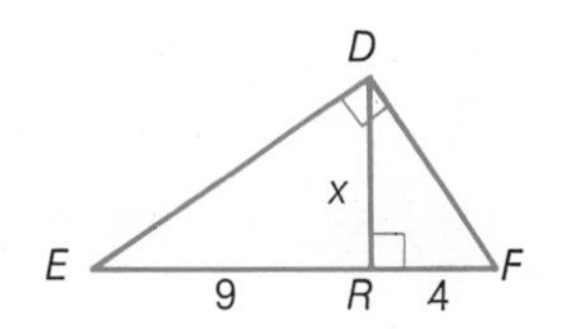

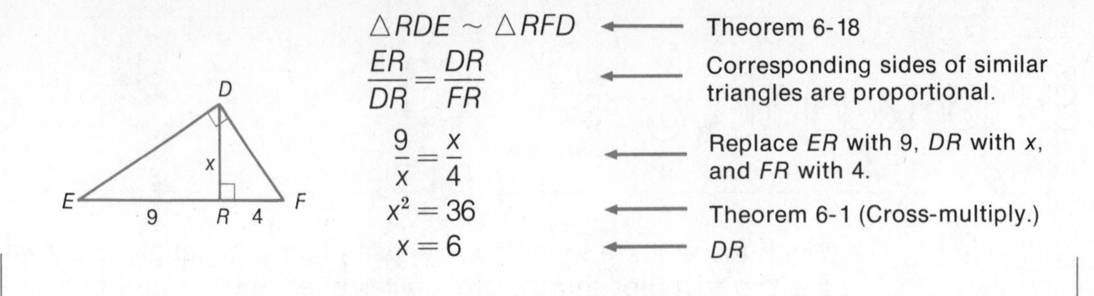

$\triangle RDE \sim \triangle RFD$ ← Theorem 6-18

$\frac{ER}{DR} = \frac{DR}{FR}$ ← Corresponding sides of similar triangles are proportional.

$\frac{9}{x} = \frac{x}{4}$ ← Replace *ER* with 9, *DR* with *x*, and *FR* with 4.

$x^2 = 36$ ← Theorem 6-1 (Cross-multiply.)

$x = 6$ ← *DR*

Example 2 suggests this corollary.

Corollary 6-19: The altitude to the hypotenuse of a right triangle is the geometric mean between the two segments of the hypotenuse.

Example 3

Right triangle *BNA* has altitude *AD* drawn to hypotenuse *BN*. If $AB = 8$ and $BN = 12$, find *BD*.

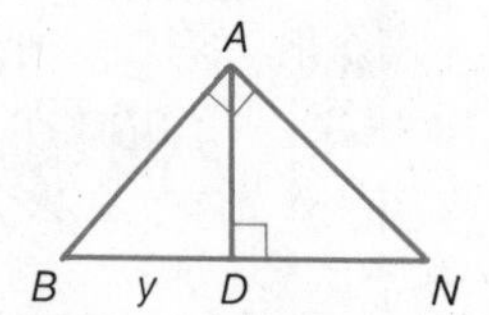

$\triangle ADB \sim \triangle NAB$ ← Theorem 6-18

$\frac{BD}{BA} = \frac{BA}{BN}$ ← Corresponding sides of similar triangles are proportional.

$\frac{y}{8} = \frac{8}{12}$ ← Replace *BA* with 8, *BN* with 12, and *BD* with *y*.

$12y = 64$ ← Theorem 6-1 (Cross-multiply.)

$y = 5\frac{1}{3}$ ← *BD*

Example 3 suggests this corollary.

Corollary 6-20: If the altitude to the hypotenuse of a right triangle is drawn, either leg of the triangle is the geometric mean between the hypotenuse and the segment of the hypotenuse adjacent to the leg.

Try These

Find the measure of each segment marked x or y.

1\. 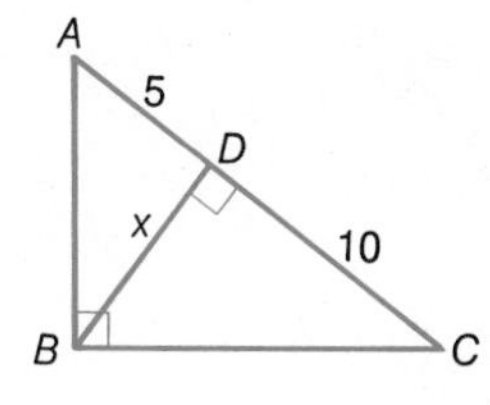

2\. 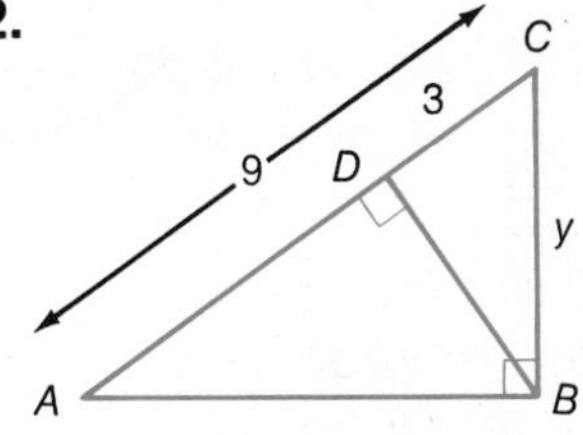

3\. 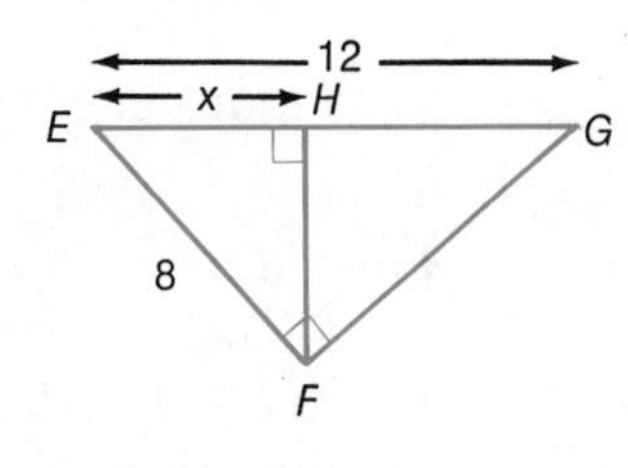

4\. 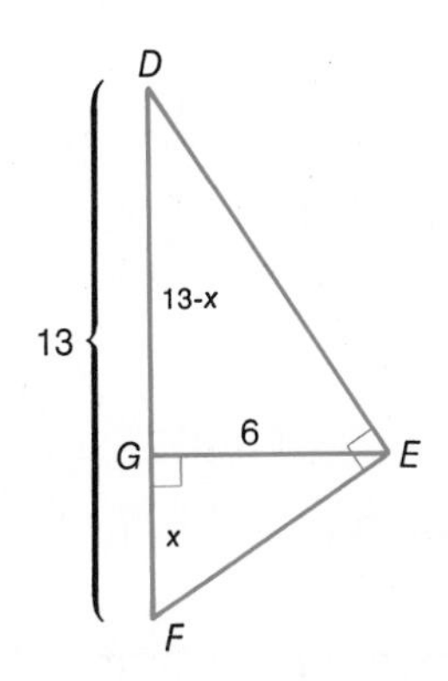

5\. 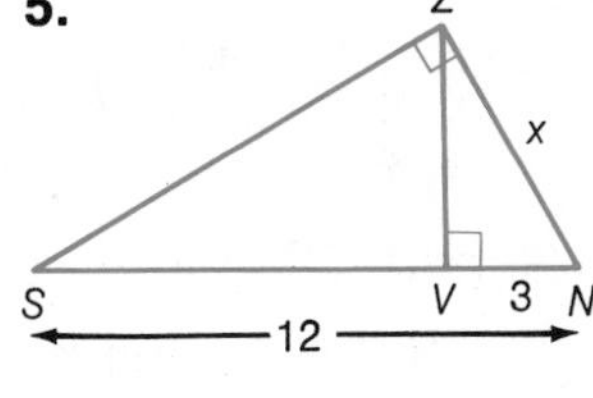

6\. 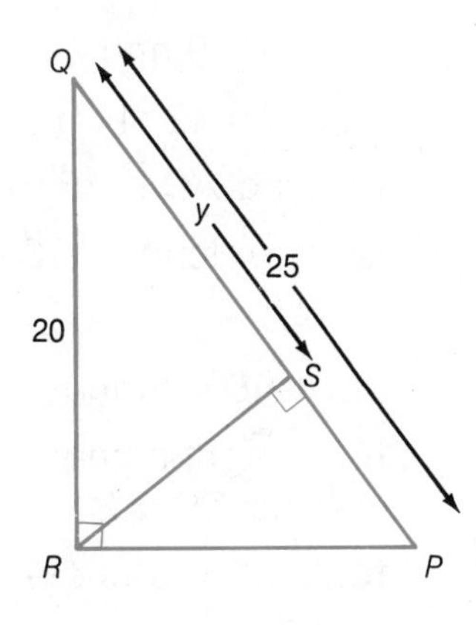

Exercises

*Use Figures 1–3 for Exercises **1–8.** Each figure represents a right triangle in which there is an altitude to the hypotenuse.*

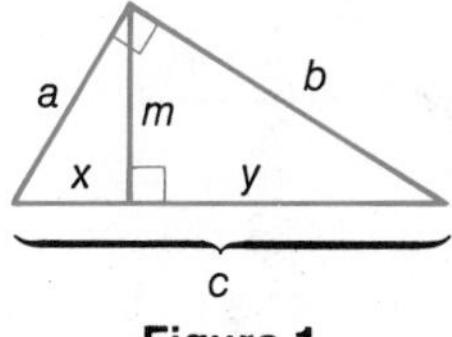

Figure 1

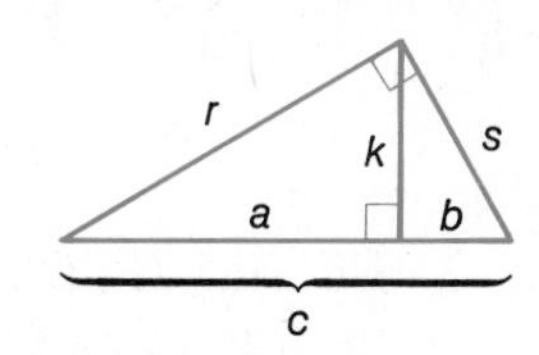

Figure 2

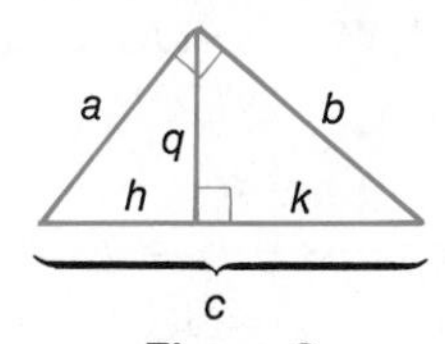

Figure 3

a

1. For each figure, write the proportion of Corollary 6-19.
2. For each figure, write both proportions of Corollary 6-20.

State the corollary that justifies each proportion.

3\. For Figure 1, $\frac{c}{b} = \frac{b}{y}$.

4\. For Figure 3, $\frac{h}{q} = \frac{q}{k}$.

5. For Figure 2, $\frac{c}{r} = \frac{r}{a}$.

6. For Figure 3, $\frac{h}{a} = \frac{a}{c}$.

7. For Figure 2, $\frac{b}{k} = \frac{k}{a}$.

8. For Figure 1, $\frac{c}{a} = \frac{a}{x}$.

*In right triangle ABC, $\overline{CD}$ is the altitude to base AB. Use this figure for Exercises **9–14.** Express any radicals in your answers in simplest form.*

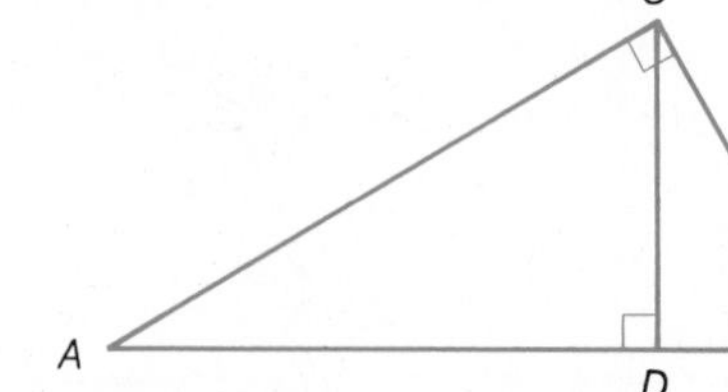

9. $AD = 9$ and $DB = 4$. Find DC.

10. $AB = 12$ and $DB = 3$. How long is $\overline{BC}$?

11. Find AC if $AB = 16$ and $AD = 4$.

12. How long is $\overline{DB}$ if $AD = 20$ and $DC = 10$?

13. $AD = 9$ and $AC = 16$. Find DB. (HINT: First find AB.)

14. If $AD = 9$ and $DB = 4$, find AC and BC.

15. In right triangle ABC, altitude CD is drawn to hypotenuse AB. If $DB = 10$ and $CD = 20$, find AB.

16. In right triangle ABC, altitude CD is drawn to hypotenuse AB. If $AD = 4.5$ and $DB = 13.5$, find AC.

17. The altitude to the hypotenuse, $\overline{DF}$, of right triangle DEF divides the hypotenuse into segments that are 4 centimeters and 5 centimeters long. Find the length of the shorter leg of $\triangle DEF$.

18. Prove Theorem 6-18.

Given: Right triangle ACB; $\angle ACB$ is a right angle; $\overline{CD} \perp \overline{AB}$

Prove: $\triangle ADC \sim \triangle ACB$
$\triangle CDB \sim \triangle ACB$
$\triangle ADC \sim \triangle CDB$

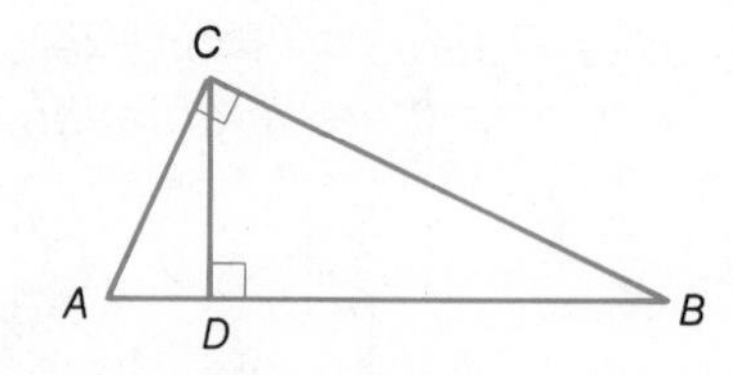

Plan: Prove $\triangle ADC \sim \triangle ACB$ and $\triangle CDB \sim \triangle ACB$ by the A.A. Corollary. Then $\triangle ADC \sim \triangle CDB$ by the transitive property of similarity.

19. Prove Corollary 6-19. (HINT: Follow the method of Example 2.)

20. Prove Corollary 6-20. (HINT: Follow the method of Example 3.)

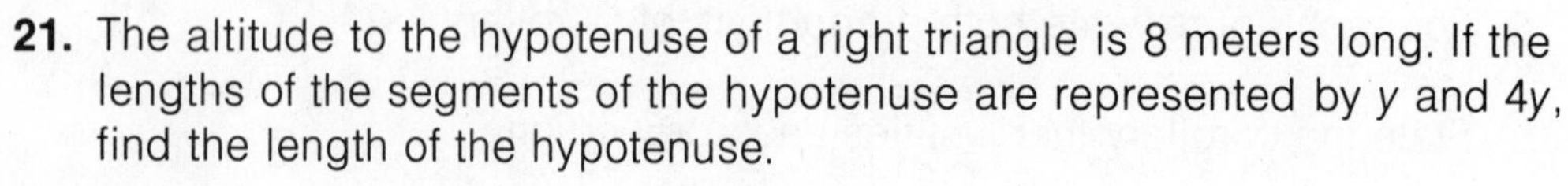

b

21. The altitude to the hypotenuse of a right triangle is 8 meters long. If the lengths of the segments of the hypotenuse are represented by y and $4y$, find the length of the hypotenuse.

22. ABC is a right triangle with $\overline{CD}$ the altitude to hypotenuse AB. If $AC = 20$ and $AB = 25$, find AD, CD, and BC.

23. In right triangle XYZ, the right angle is at Z and the altitude from Z meets the hypotenuse at F. If $ZF = 6$, $XF = 3$, and $FY = 5x - 3$, find x.

24. $\overline{CD}$ is the altitude to the hypotenuse of right triangle ABC. If $AC = 6$, $AD = 3$ and $BD = x$, write a proportion that can be used to find x. Solve the proportion for x.

25. In right triangle ABC, $\overline{BD}$ is the altitude to hypotenuse AC. If $BD = 2$, $AC = 5$, and $CD = x$, write a proportion that can be used to find x. Solve the proportion for x.

26. If x is the geometric mean between a and b, solve for x in terms of a and b.

C 27. If $\frac{a}{b} = \frac{b}{c}$, prove that $\frac{ac - 1}{b - 1} = \frac{b + 1}{1}$.

28. If $\frac{a}{b} = \frac{c}{d}$, prove that $\frac{a - 1}{b} = \frac{bc - d}{bd}$.

29. If $\frac{a}{b} = \frac{c}{d}$, prove that $\frac{a + 1}{1} = \frac{bc + d}{d}$.

30. Side BC of $\triangle ABC$ is extended to form exterior angle ACD. A ray bisects angle ACD and intersects side BA extended at point E. Prove that $\frac{AC}{CB} = \frac{EA}{EB}$.

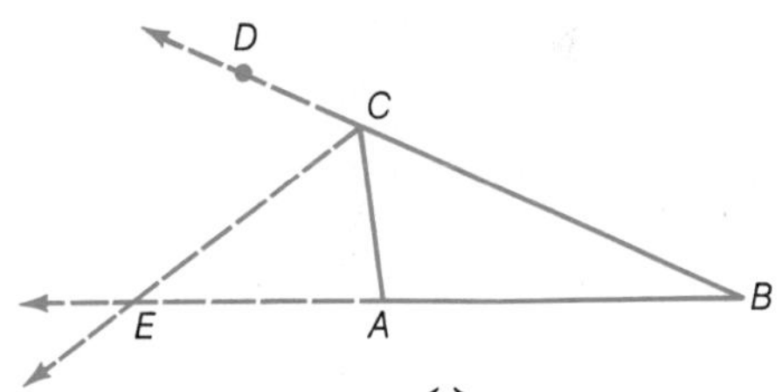

31. $\overline{BC}$ is the base in isosceles triangle ABC. D is a point on $\overleftrightarrow{BC}$ such that $\angle BAD \cong \angle B$. Prove that AB is the geometric mean between BC and BD.

32. Prove that if the lengths of two legs of a right triangle are in the ratio of one to two, then the altitude to the hypotenuse divides the hypotenuse into segments which are in the ratio of one to four.

Remember

Write the square of each number.

1. $\sqrt{2}$ 2. $\sqrt{13}$ 3. $\frac{\sqrt{2}}{2}$ 4. $\frac{\sqrt{3}}{2}$ 5. $3\sqrt{3}$ 6. $10\sqrt{2}$

The answers are on page 302. If you need help, see page 564 in the Review: Topics from Algebra One.

6-9 The Pythagorean Theorem

Example 1

Given: $\triangle ABC$ is a right triangle with right angle at C.

Prove: $c^2 = a^2 + b^2$

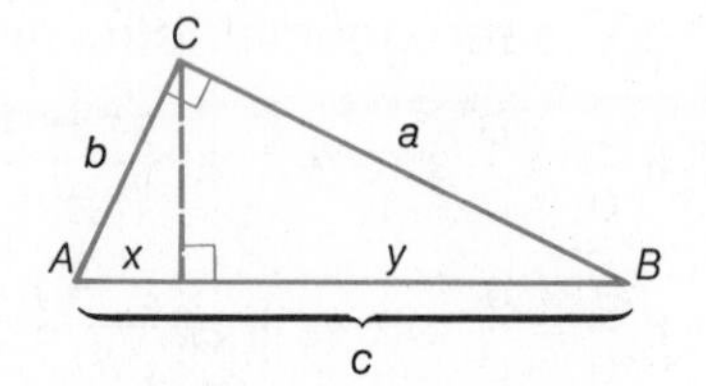

Statement	Reasons
1. Draw a perpendicular from C to $\overline{AB}$.	1. Through a given external point, there is exactly one line perpendicular to a given line.
2. $\frac{c}{a} = \frac{a}{y}$; $\frac{c}{b} = \frac{b}{x}$	2. (1). If the altitude to the hypotenuse of a right triangle is drawn, either leg of the triangle is the geometric mean between the hypotenuse and the segment of the hypotenuse adjacent to the leg.
3. $cy = a^2$; $cx = b^2$	3. (2). Theorem 6-1, page 251
4. $cy + cx = a^2 + b^2$	4. (3). Addition Property of Equations
5. $c(y + x) = a^2 + b^2$	5. (4). Distributive Property
6. $c^2 = a^2 + b^2$	6. (5). Substitution Principle

The example is a proof of the Pythagorean Theorem.

Theorem 6-21: Pythagorean Theorem

In any right triangle, the square of the length of the hypotenuse equals the sum of the squares of the lengths of the other two sides.

You can use the Pythagorean Theorem to find the measure of one side of a right triangle if the measures of the other two sides are known.

Example 2

In a right triangle, the hypotenuse is 26 centimeters long and one leg is 24 centimeters long.
Find the length of the other leg.

$$a^2 + b^2 = c^2$$
$$(24)^2 + b^2 = (26)^2$$
$$576 + b^2 = 676$$
$$b^2 = 100$$
$$b = 10$$

← Length in centimeters of side *AC*.

The converse of the Pythagorean Theorem is also a theorem. You are asked to prove the converse, Theorem 6–22, in the Exercises.

Theorem 6-22: If the square of the length of one side of a triangle equals the sum of the squares of the lengths of the other two sides, then the triangle is a right triangle.

Example 3

Determine whether the triangles with the given lengths for sides are right triangles.

a. 3, 4, 5 **b.** 5, 5, $5\sqrt{2}$ **c.** 6, 8, 9

a. $a^2 + b^2 = c^2$
$3^2 + 4^2 \stackrel{?}{=} 5^2$
$9 + 16 \stackrel{?}{=} 25$
$25 = 25$ Yes

b. $a^2 + b^2 = c^2$
$5^2 + 5^2 \stackrel{?}{=} (5\sqrt{2})^2$
$25 + 25 \stackrel{?}{=} 25 \cdot 2$
$50 = 50$ Yes

c. $a^2 + b^2 = c^2$
$6^2 + 8^2 \stackrel{?}{=} 9^2$
$36 + 64 \stackrel{?}{=} 81$
$100 \neq 81$ No

Try These

For Exercises **1–6,** *find x and y.*

1.

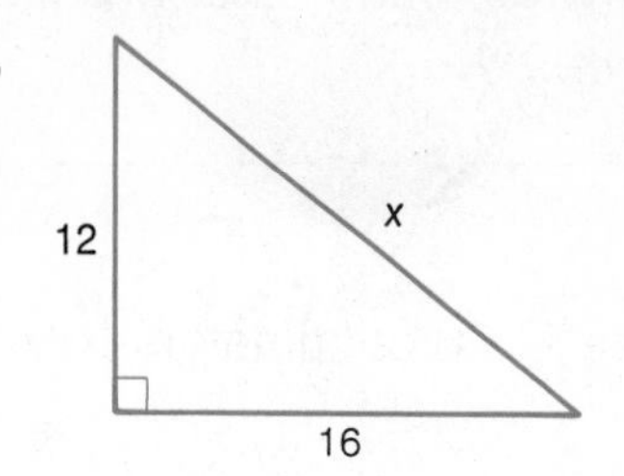

2.

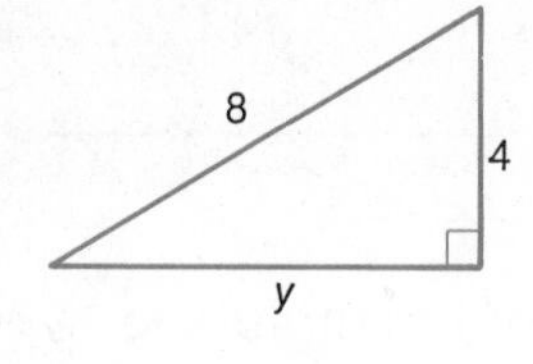

3.

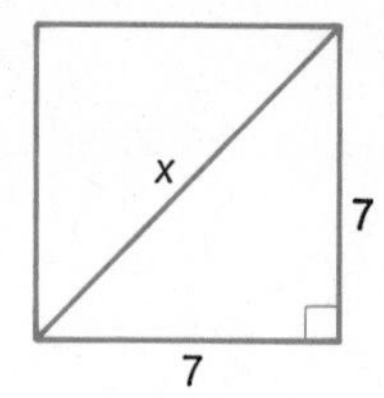

4.

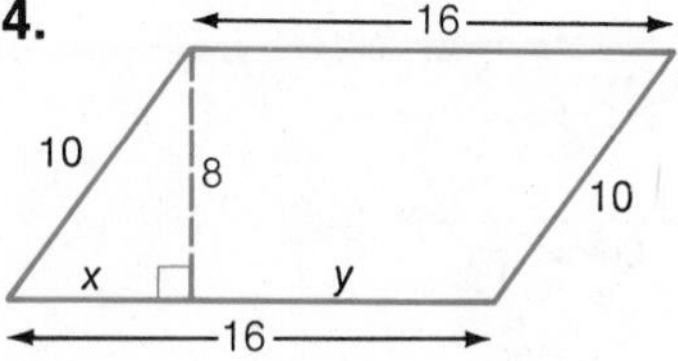

5.

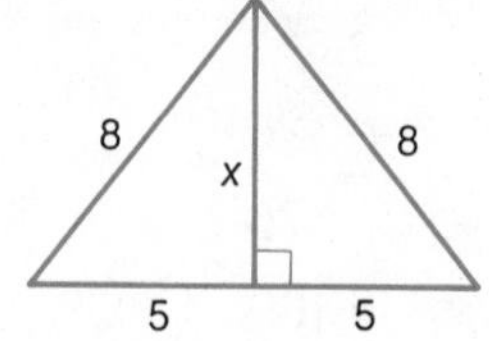

6.

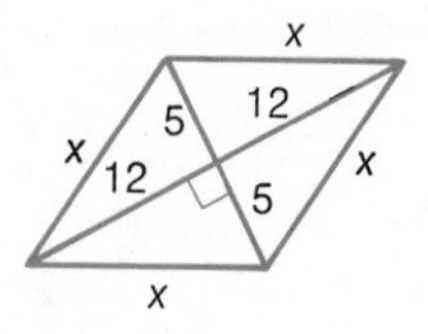

For Exercises **7–9,** *the lengths of three sides of a triangle are given. Determine whether the triangle is a right triangle.*

7. 30, 40, 50 **8.** 12, 16, 18 **9.** 10, 24, 26

10. State Theorems 6-21 and 6-22 as a biconditional.

Exercises

In these Exercises, express any radicals in your answers in simplest form.
For Exercises **1–8,** *refer to right triangle ABC to find c, the length of the hypotenuse.*

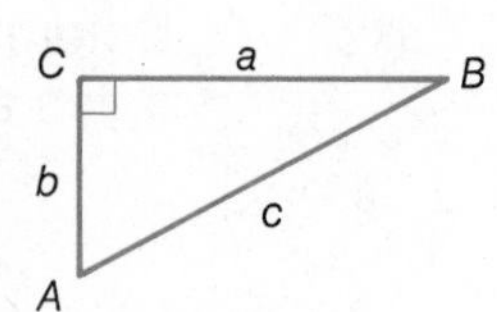

1. $a = 7, \quad b = 24$

2. $a = 8, \quad b = 15$

3. $a = \frac{3}{2}, \quad b = 2$

4. $a = 0.3, \quad b = 0.4$

5. $a = 0.6, \quad b = \frac{4}{5}$

6. $a = \sqrt{13}, \quad b = 6$

7. $a = 1, \quad b = \dfrac{\sqrt{21}}{2}$

8. $a = 3\sqrt{3}, \quad b = 3\sqrt{6}$

For Exercises **9–14,** *refer to right triangle ABC with hypotenuse c and legs a and b. Find the length of the missing leg.*

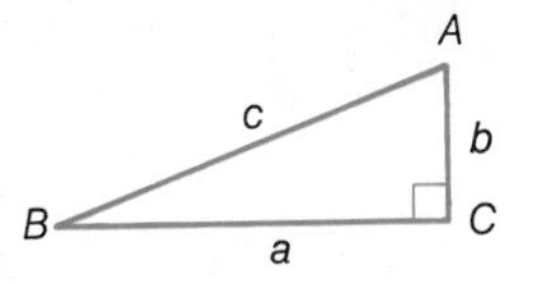

9. $c = 61, \quad a = 60$

10. $c = \frac{5}{12}, \quad b = \frac{1}{3}$

11. $c = 2.6, \quad a = 2.4$

12. $c = 2\sqrt{10}, \quad a = 5$

13. $c = 6\sqrt{5}, \quad b = 10$

14. $c = 10\sqrt{2}, \quad b = 5\sqrt{3}$

For Exercises **15–20,** *the lengths of the three sides of a triangle are given. Determine whether the triangle is a right triangle.*

15. 7, 8, 10

16. 5, 12, 13

17. 51, 24, 45

18. 24, 8, 25

19. 2, 4.8, 5.2

20. 4, 0.9, 4.1

21. Triangle JKM is isosceles with $JK = JM = 6$, and base $KM = 4$. Find the length of altitude JP. (HINT: The altitude to the base of an isosceles triangle bisects the base.)

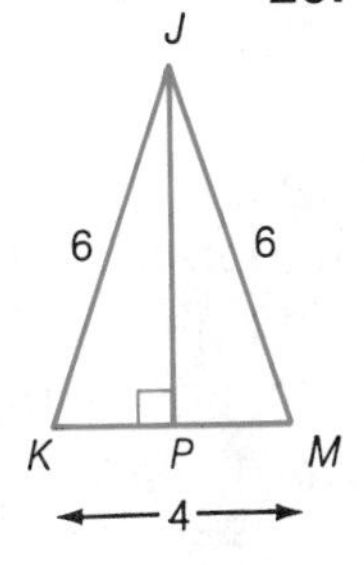

22. The two sides of a tent are each 2 meters long. If the tent is pitched so that the sides meet in a right angle at the top, find w, the width of the tent, and p, the height of the center pole.

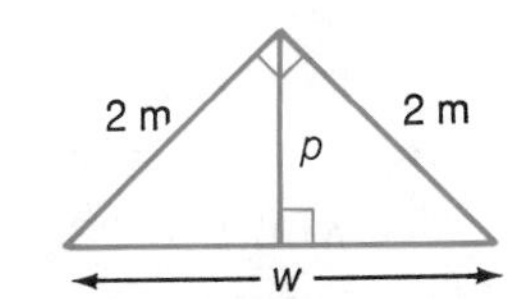

23. The base of an isosceles triangle is 24 centimeters long and the length of the altitude to the base is 5 centimeters. Find the length of the two congruent sides.

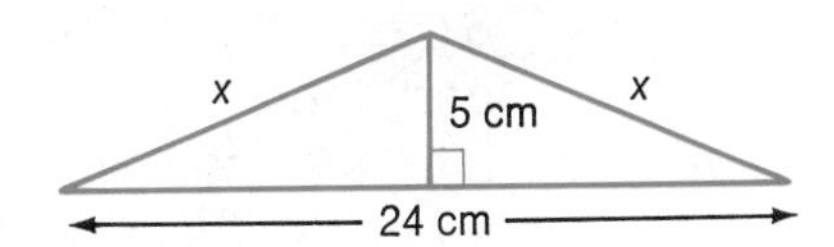

24. Each of the congruent sides of an isosceles triangle is 17 decimeters long. The length of the altitude to the base is 8 decimeters. Find the length of the base.

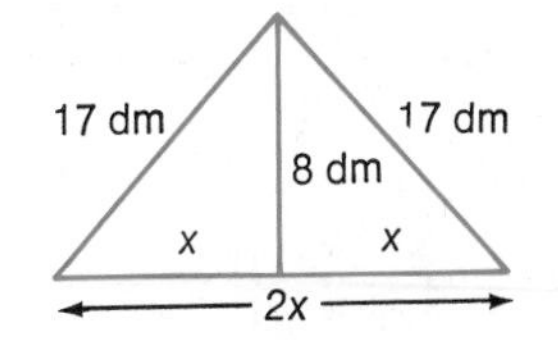

25. The length of a side of an equilateral triangle is 8 centimeters. Find the length of the altitude.

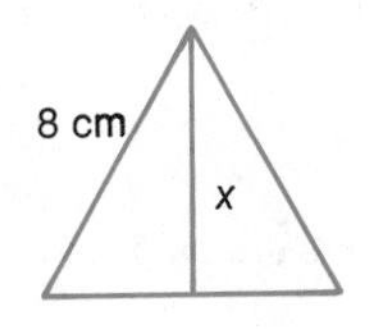

b

26. Compute the length of the altitude to the shortest side of a triangle whose sides are 17, 25, and 26 centimeters long.

27. Compute the length of the altitude to the longest side of a triangle whose sides are 10, 6, and 12 decimeters long.

28. Write a formula that can be used to find the altitude of an equilateral triangle with side s. Use the figure at the right to solve for h in terms of s.

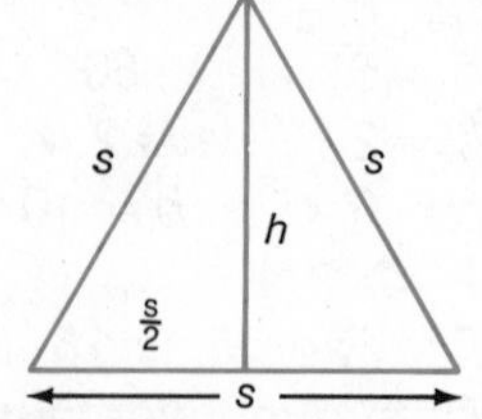

*For Exercises **29–31**, use the formula of Exercise **28** to find the altitude of an equilateral triangle with a side having the given measure.*

29. $s = 10$ **30.** $s = 12$ **31.** $s = 5$

32. There are many ways to prove the Pythagorean Theorem. Use the figure at the right and the given information to prove $c^2 = a^2 + b^2$.

Given: $\triangle ABC$ with right angle at C.
$\overline{BE} \cong \overline{BC}$, $\overline{DE} \perp \overline{AB}$, $\overline{BD}$ is drawn.

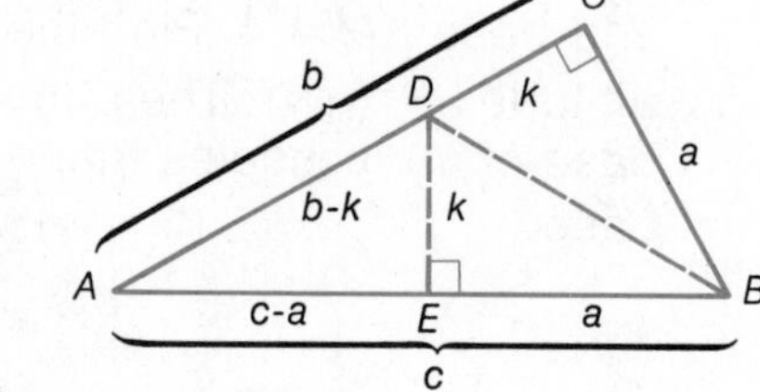

33. Prove the converse of the Pythagorean Theorem.

Given: In $\triangle ABC$, $c^2 = a^2 + b^2$

Prove: $\triangle ABC$ is a right triangle, with right angle at C.

Plan: Construct $\triangle RST$ with $m\angle T = 90$, $ST = a$, and $RT = b$. Show that $c = t$, and, therefore, that $\triangle ABC \cong \triangle RST$ by S.S.S. Then since $\angle T$ is a right angle, $\angle C$ is also a right angle.

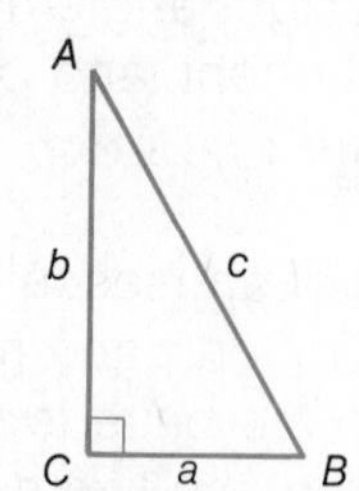

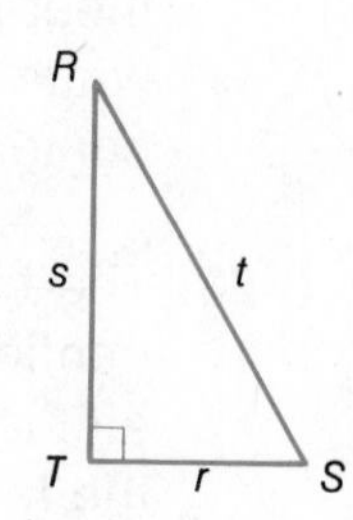

Remember

Simplify each radical.

1. $\sqrt{8}$ **2.** $\sqrt{40}$ **3.** $\sqrt{200}$ **4.** $\sqrt{125}$ **5.** $\sqrt{98}$ **6.** $2\sqrt{4}$

The answers are on page 302. If you need help, see page 566 in the Review: Topics From Algebra One.

-10 Special Right Triangles

You can use the Pythagorean Theorem to find useful relationships in a 45-45-90 triangle which is an isosceles triangle.

Triangle	Computation	Rule
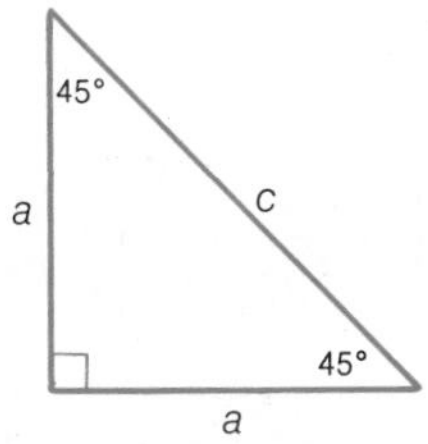	$c^2 = a^2 + a^2$ $c^2 = 2a^2$ $c = a\sqrt{2}$	Given the length of a leg of a 45-45-90 triangle, multiply the length by $\sqrt{2}$ to find the length of the hypotenuse.
	$a^2 + a^2 = c^2$ $2a^2 = c^2$ $a^2 = \frac{c^2}{2}$ $a = \frac{c}{2}\sqrt{2}$	Given the length of the hypotenuse of a 45-45-90 triangle, multiply the length by $\frac{\sqrt{2}}{2}$ to find the length of a leg.

Theorem 6-23: Isosceles Right Triangle Theorem

In an isosceles right triangle with legs of length *a* and hypotenuse of length *c*,

$$a = \frac{c}{2}\sqrt{2} \qquad \text{and} \qquad c = a\sqrt{2}.$$

Example 1

Find the length of the diagonal of a square with sides of 15 centimeters.

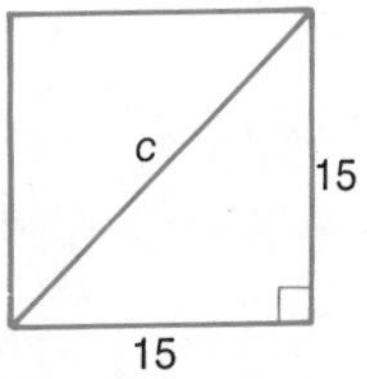

$c = a\sqrt{2}$ ← Theorem 6-23

$c = 15\sqrt{2}$ ← Replace *a* with 15.

You also use the Pythagorean Theorem to find useful relationships in a 30-60-90 triangle.

Start with an equilateral triangle with side of length s. Draw an altitude, h, of the triangle.

Triangle	Computation	Rule
	$\frac{1}{2} \cdot s = \frac{s}{2}$	In a 30-60-90 triangle, the length of the side opposite the 30°-angle is one half the length of the hypotenuse.
	$h^2 + \left(\frac{s}{2}\right)^2 = s^2$ $h^2 + \frac{s^2}{4} = s^2$ $h^2 = s^2 - \frac{s^2}{4}$ $h^2 = \frac{3s^2}{4}$ $h = \frac{s}{2}\sqrt{3}$	In a 30-60-90 triangle, the length of the side opposite the 60°-angle is one half the length of the hypotenuse multiplied by $\sqrt{3}$.

Theorem 6-24: 30-60-90 Triangle Theorem

In any right triangle with acute angle measures of 30 and 60 and with hypotenuse s, the length of the shorter leg (opposite the 30°-angle) is $\frac{s}{2}$, and the length of the longer leg (opposite the 60°-angle) is $\frac{s}{2}\sqrt{3}$.

Example 2

The length of the hypotenuse of a 30-60-90 triangle is 14. Find the lengths of the shorter leg and the longer leg.

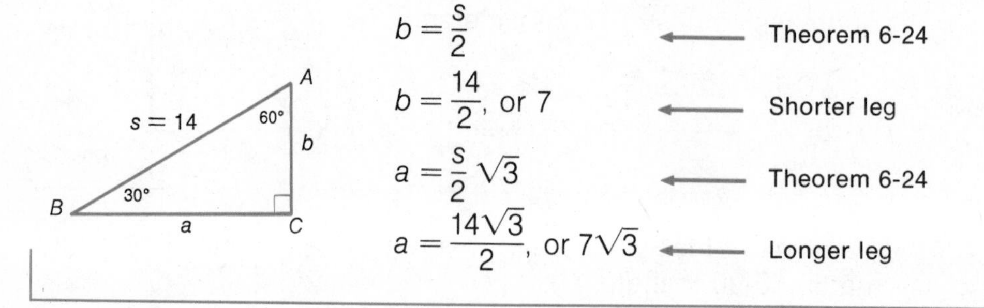

$b = \frac{s}{2}$ ← Theorem 6-24

$b = \frac{14}{2}$, or 7 ← Shorter leg

$a = \frac{s}{2}\sqrt{3}$ ← Theorem 6-24

$a = \frac{14\sqrt{3}}{2}$, or $7\sqrt{3}$ ← Longer leg

Try These

Refer to the figure below for Exercises **1–8.**

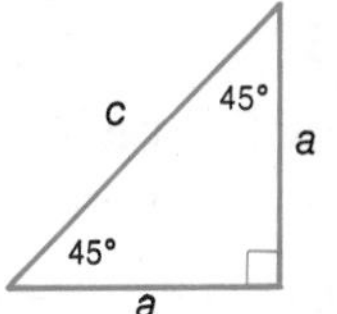

1. $a = 8$, $c = \underline{\ ?\ }$

2. $a = 15$, $c = \underline{\ ?\ }$

3. $a = \frac{3}{4}$, $c = \underline{\ ?\ }$

4. $a = 6\sqrt{2}$, $c = \underline{\ ?\ }$

5. $c = 10$, $a = \underline{\ ?\ }$

6. $c = 12$, $a = \underline{\ ?\ }$

7. $c = 5\frac{1}{4}$, $a = \underline{\ ?\ }$

8. $c = 18\sqrt{2}$, $a = \underline{\ ?\ }$

Exercises

a

Refer to the figure at the right to find c.

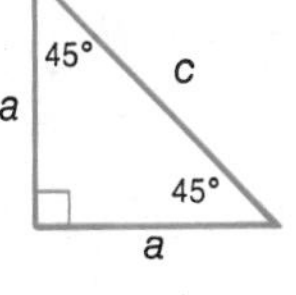

1. $a = 12$ **2.** $a = 17$ **3.** $a = 450$

4. $a = 4.63$ **5.** $a = 1\frac{3}{4}$ **6.** $a = 5\sqrt{2}$

Refer to the figure for Exercises **1–6** *to find a.*

7. $c = 24$ **8.** $c = 2.8$ **9.** $c = 35$

10. $c = 3\frac{1}{3}$ **11.** $c = \sqrt{3}$ **12.** $c = 16\sqrt{2}$

13. $c = 9\sqrt{2}$ **14.** $c = \sqrt{2}$ **15.** $c = 1$

Use the figure at the right to find the missing measures.

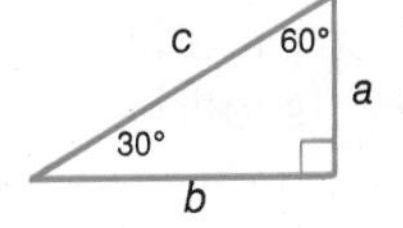

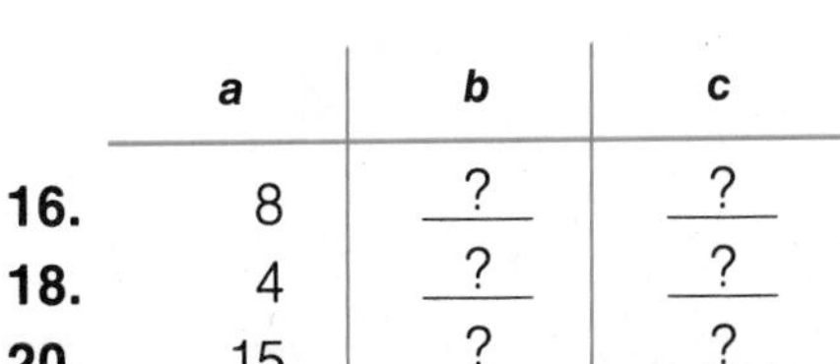

	a	b	c
16.	8	?	?
18.	4	?	?
20.	15	?	?
22.	2.75	?	?
24.	$4\sqrt{3}$	?	?
26.	?	$6\sqrt{3}$	?
28.	?	$11\sqrt{3}$	?
30.	?	$\frac{13}{4}\sqrt{3}$	?

	a	b	c
17.	?	9	?
19.	?	25	?
21.	?	?	18
23.	?	?	10
25.	?	?	5.6
27.	?	?	$12\sqrt{3}$
29.	?	?	$8\frac{1}{2}$
31.	?	?	1

32. Find the length of one side of a square that has a diagonal of 16 centimeters.

33. Find the perimeter of a square that has a diagonal of 10 meters.

34. Find the length of the diagonal of a square that has a side of 15 decimeters.

35. The perimeter of a square is 48 meters. Find the length of a side and the length of a diagonal.

For Exercises **36–41,** *refer to the figure at the right. $\triangle MED$ is a right triangle with the right angle at M. $\overline{MA}$ is an altitude, and $m\angle D = 30$.*

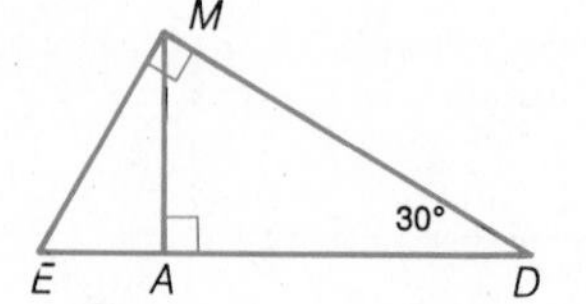

36. If $MD = 10$, find MA, AD, ME, EA, and ED.

37. If $MA = 6$, find MD, AD, ME, EA, and ED.

38. If $ME = 4$, find ED, MD, EA, AD, and MA.

39. If $MA = 8$, find MD, AD, EA, ED, and ME.

40. If $ED = 24$, find ME, MD, EA, AD, and MA.

41. If $EA = 6$, find ME, MA, AD, ED, and MD.

For Exercises **42–45,** *use $\sqrt{2} = 1.414$ and $\sqrt{3} = 1.732$. Express each answer to the nearest tenth.*

42. A baseball diamond is shaped like a square and each side is 90 feet long. How far is it from second base to home plate?

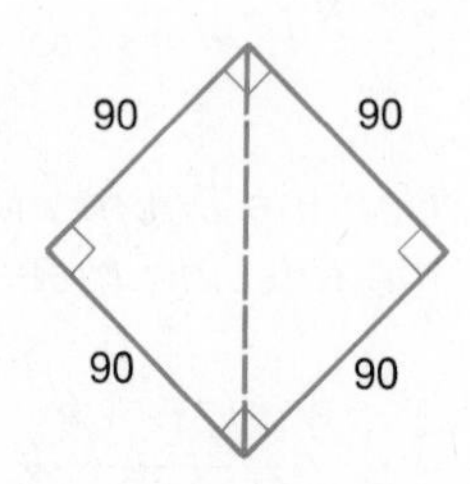

43. Albany is 250 kilometers north of New York City. and Syracuse is 250 kilometers west of Albany. How many kilometers is the air distance from New York City to Syracuse?

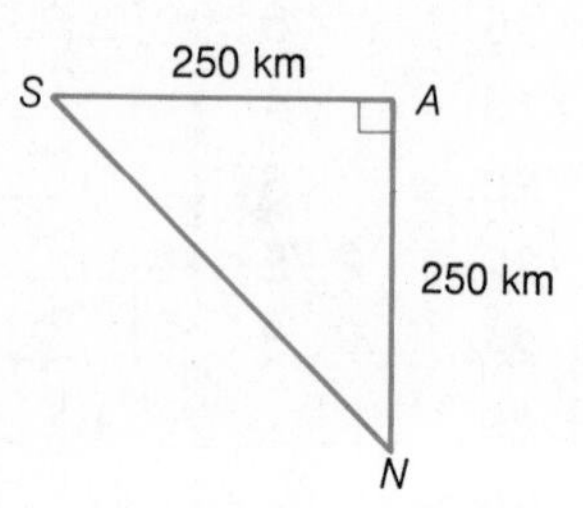

44. An equilateral triangle appears on a billboard as part of a symbol for a bank. How tall is the triangle if each side is 4 meters long?

b

45. A fence based on the design shown is being constructed to enclose a plot of land. Lumber is needed for the diagonal pieces only. The fence is 1.3 meters high and runs for 200 meters. If each section is a square, how many meters of lumber are needed?

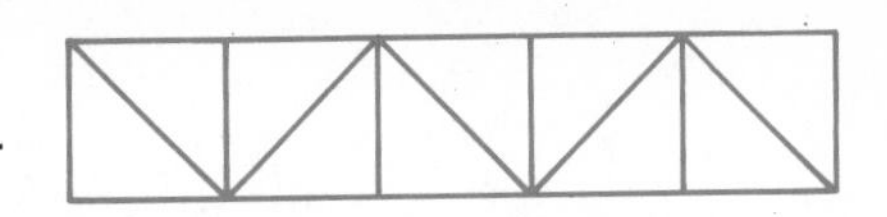

46. The front wall of an A-frame house is in the shape of an equilateral triangle. If the base of the house is 8 meters long from side to side, how tall is it?

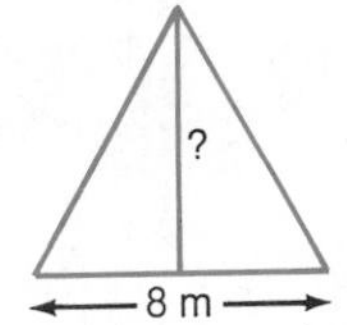

*For Exercises **47–49,** ▱WXYZ has ZY = 20 centimeters. Find the length of the altitude from Z for each measure of ∠Y.*

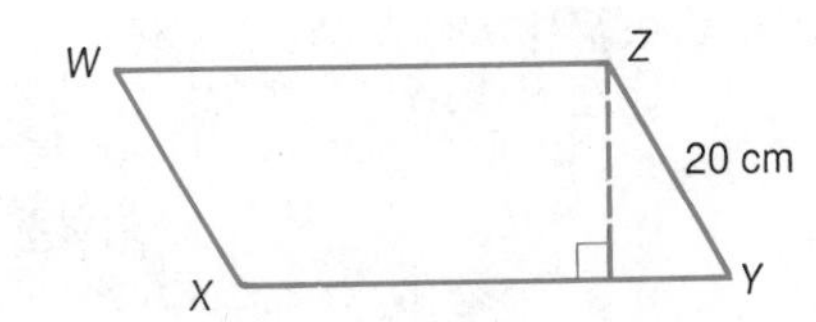

47. 30 **48.** 45 **49.** 60

*For Exercises **50–52,** isosceles triangle HJK has congruent sides that are 12 meters long and m∠K as given. Find the length of the altitude.*

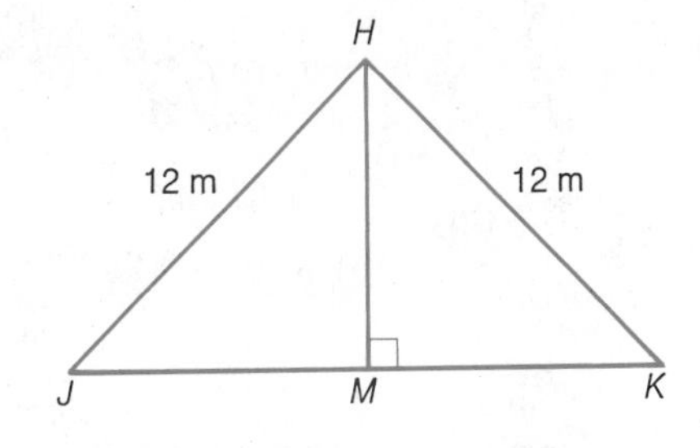

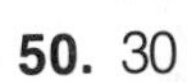

50. 30 **51.** 45 **52.** 60

*For Exercises **53–55,** the base of isosceles triangle FHJ is 18 and $\overline{FK}$ is the altitude to base HJ. Find FK for each measure of ∠H.*

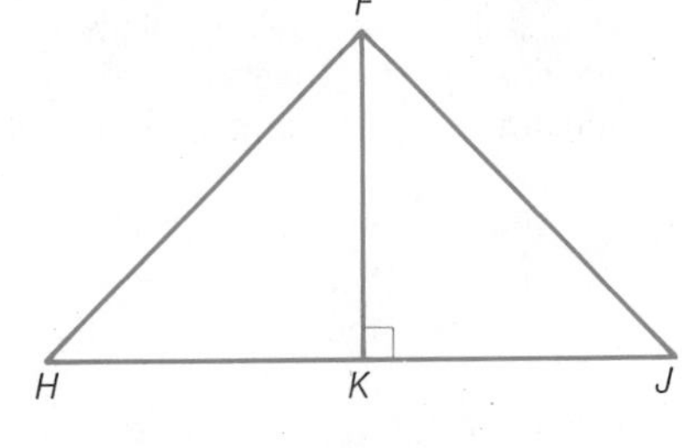

53. 30 **54.** 45 **55.** 60

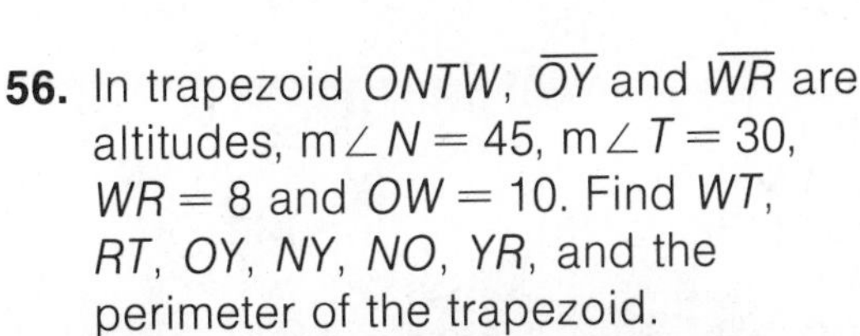

56. In trapezoid ONTW, $\overline{OY}$ and $\overline{WR}$ are altitudes, m∠N = 45, m∠T = 30, WR = 8 and OW = 10. Find WT, RT, OY, NY, NO, YR, and the perimeter of the trapezoid.

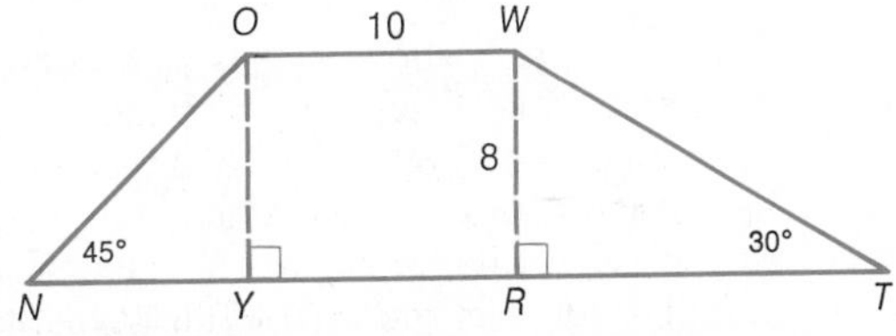

c

57. Derive a formula for the length *d* of a diagonal of a square in terms of *P*, the perimeter of the square.

Mathematics and Agricultural Engineering

Agricultural engineers are concerned with conservation and management of soil and water resources, as well as with designing farm machinery, equipment, and structures. A bachelor's degree in agricultural engineering is a requirement to enter this field. The first two years of college are usually spent on mathematics, physics, chemistry, and basic courses in engineering. The last two years are then devoted to the engineering specialty.

An important agricultural problem is the planning of the layout of the land for farming, particularly if the land is not flat. You know that lines are parallel if and only if they are coplanar lines and do not intersect. Laying out land that is not flat involves an understanding of parallel curves in three-space. The photograph above illustrates the concept of parallelism with regard to curves in three-space.

This photograph above shows **contour farming.** Each curve shown is parallel to every other curve, and each curve is in a different plane. Thus, each plane that contains a curve is parallel to every other plane that contains a curve. (See the figure at the right.) This layout takes into account such critical factors as rain fall, slope, water drainage, and soil erosion.

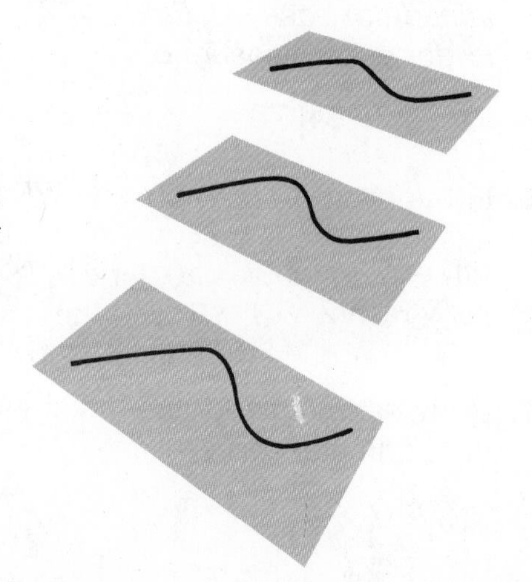

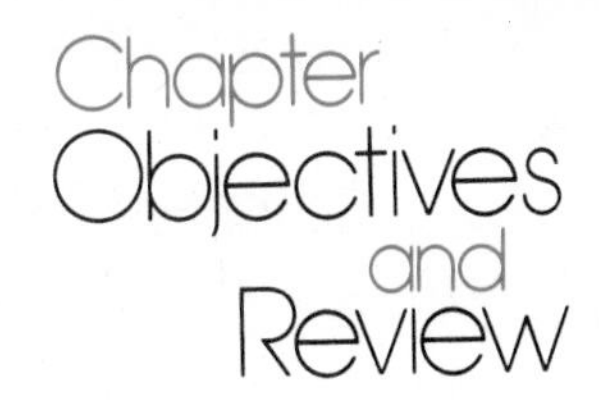

Objective: To recall, and give examples of, the important mathematical terms of the chapter.

1. Be sure that you know the meanings of these mathematical terms used in Chapter 6.

fourth proportional (p. 255)
geometric mean (p. 254)
proportion (p. 250)
ratio (p. 250)
similar polygons (p. 268)

Objective: To write a given proportion in three different ways. (Section 6-1)

2. If $\frac{r}{t}=\frac{2}{3}$ write three other proportions using r, t, 2, and 3.

Objective: To solve problems using proportions. (Section 6-1)

Solve for x. No denominator equals 0.

3. $\frac{3}{8}=\frac{4}{x}$
4. $\frac{5}{7}=\frac{1}{x}$
5. $\frac{x-2}{x}=\frac{9}{12}$
6. $\frac{x}{x+9}=\frac{5}{8}$

Objective: To find the geometric mean between two numbers. (Section 6-2)

7. Find the geometric mean between 4 and 25.
8. Find the geometric mean between $6n$ and $24n$.

Objective: To find the fourth proportional to three given numbers. (Section 6-2)

9. Find the fourth proportional to 5, 35, and 9.

Objective: To use proportional segments to solve problems. (Sections 6-3 and 6-4)

*For Exercises **10–12,** $\overline{EB} \parallel \overline{DC}$ and three lengths are given. Find the missing length.*

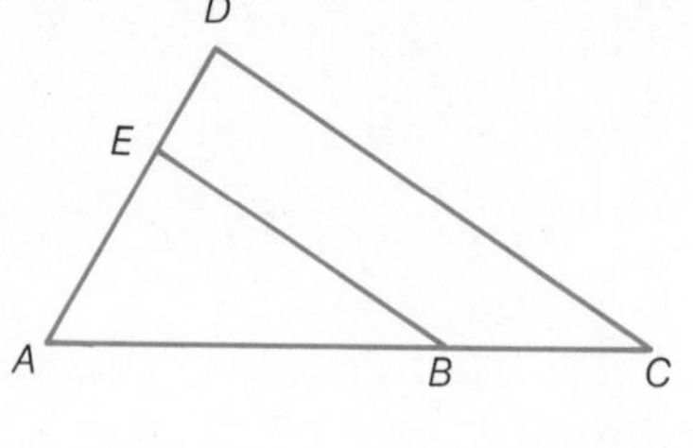

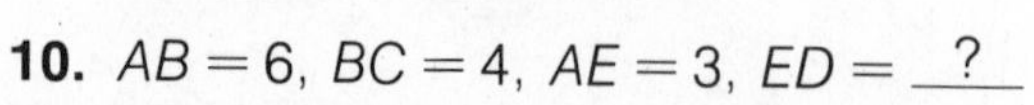

10. $AB = 6$, $BC = 4$, $AE = 3$, $ED = \underline{\quad ? \quad}$

11. $AB = 9$, $BC = 6$, $ED = 4$, $AE = \underline{\quad ? \quad}$

12. $BC = 3$, $AC = 10$, $AE = 2\frac{1}{3}$, $ED = \underline{\quad ? \quad}$

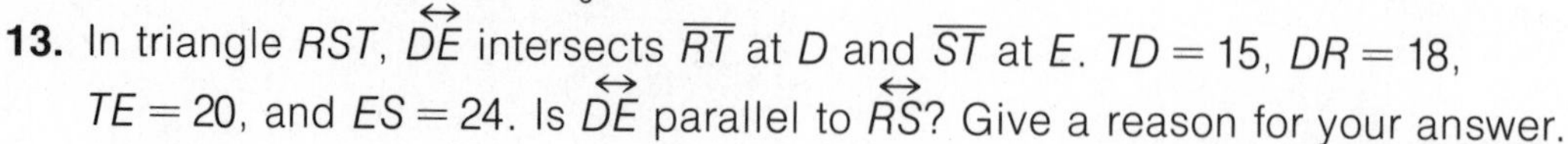

13. In triangle RST, $\overleftrightarrow{DE}$ intersects $\overline{RT}$ at D and $\overline{ST}$ at E. $TD = 15$, $DR = 18$, $TE = 20$, and $ES = 24$. Is $\overleftrightarrow{DE}$ parallel to $\overleftrightarrow{RS}$? Give a reason for your answer.

In the figure at the right, $\overline{HW}$ bisects $\angle H$.

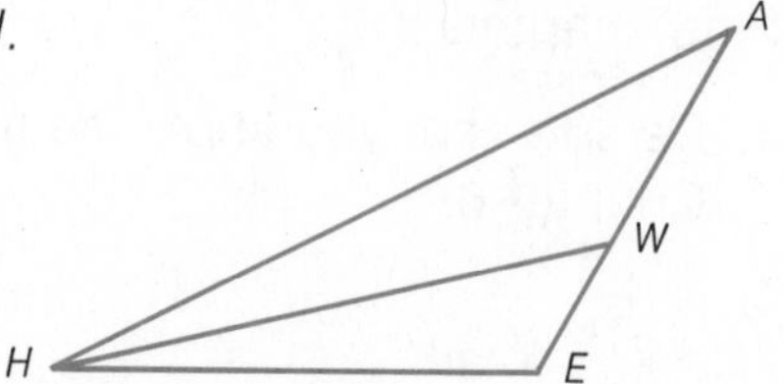

14. If $HE = 10$, $EW = 4$, $HA = 14$, find WA.

15. If $HE = 8$, $HA = 12$, and $EA = 10$, find EW and WA. (HINT: Let $EW = x$ and $WA = 10 - x$.)

Objective: To apply the definition of similar polygons. (Section 6-5)

16. Triangles MRT and QSH are similar with $MR = 7$, $RT = 6$, $MT = 4$, $m\angle M = 50$, $m\angle R = 30$, $QH = 12$, and $QS = 21$. Find $m\angle H$ and HS.

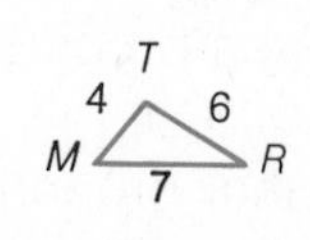

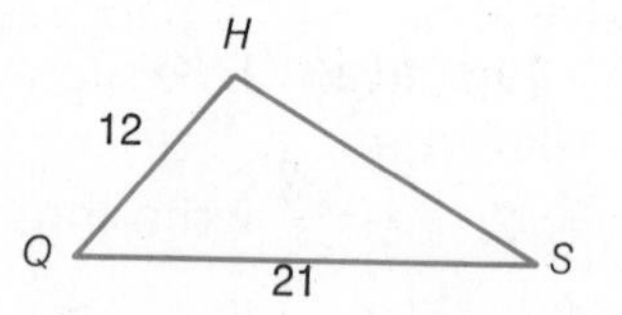

17. The sides of a pentagon are 10, 6, 20, 16, and 18. The corresponding sides of a similar pentagon are 35, a, b, c, and d. Find a, b, c, and d.

Objective: To use the A.A.A. theorem and its corollaries to determine whether two triangles are similar. (Section 6-6)

*For Exercises **18–20,** refer to the figure below. Triangle ABC is a right triangle with $\angle C$ the right angle. $\overline{DE} \perp \overline{AB}$, $AE = 4$, $ED = 3$, $AD = 5$, and $CD = 7$.*

18. State why $\triangle ADE$ is similar to $\triangle ABC$.

19. Complete the following statement.

$$\frac{AD}{AB} = \frac{AE}{?} = \frac{ED}{?}$$

20. Find AC, BC, and AB.

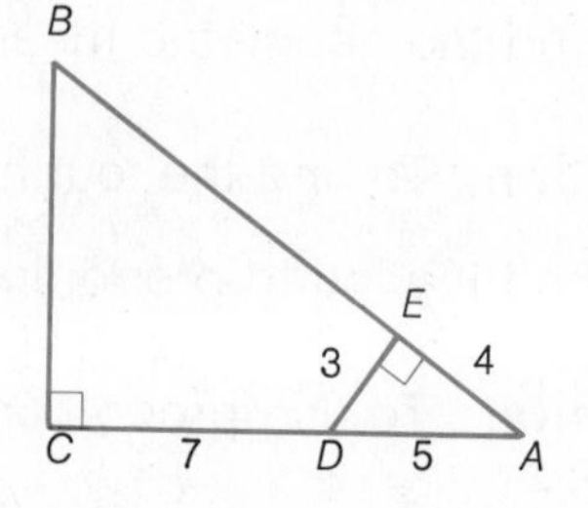

*For Exercises **21–22,** refer to triangle GHK below.*

21. Given: R is the midpoint of $\overline{GK}$.
T is the midpoint of $\overline{HK}$.
Prove: $\triangle RKT \sim \triangle GKH$.

22. Given: $RK = a$, $TK = b$, $GR = 2a$, and $HT = 2b$.
Prove: $\triangle RST \sim \triangle HSG$.

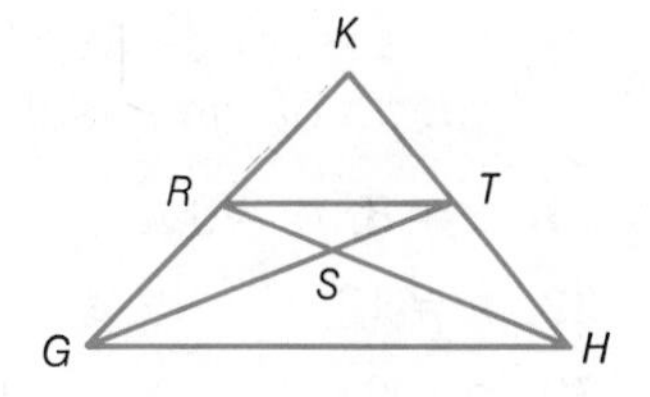

Objective: To apply the S.A.S. and S.S.S. Similarity theorems. (Section 6-7)

*For Exercises **23–24,** use the given information to tell why each pair of triangles is similar.*

23. $\triangle RSY$; $\triangle PTW$

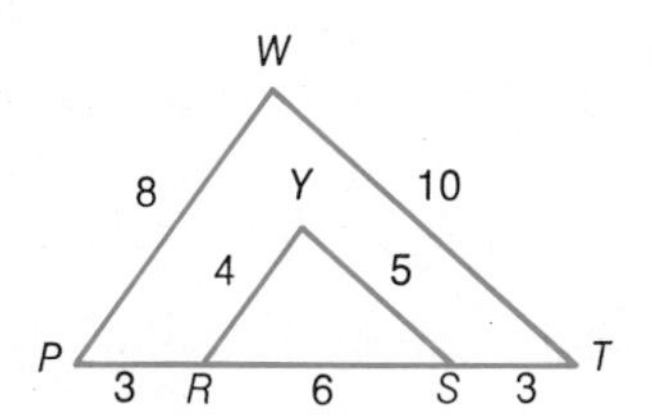

24. $\triangle AED$; $\triangle ACB$

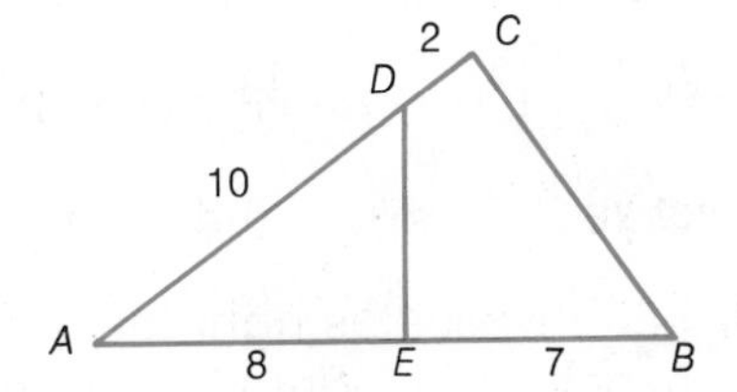

Objective: To apply the corollaries about corresponding perimeters, altitudes, angle bisectors, and medians of similar triangles. (Section 6-7)

25. The sides of a triangle are 8, 9, and 13 units long. The shortest side of a similar triangle is 12 units long. What is the perimeter of the second triangle?

26. Corresponding sides of two similar triangles have the ratio $\frac{3}{8}$. A median of the larger triangle is 24 centimeters long. How long is the corresponding median of the smaller triangle?

Objective: To apply the theorem and corollaries about similar right triangles. (Section 6-8)

*In right $\triangle ABC$, $\overline{AD}$ is the altitude to the hypotenuse $\overline{BC}$. Use this figure for Exercises **27–30.** Express any radicals in your answer in simplest form.*

27. $CD = 3$, $AD = 9$. Find BD.

28. $CD = 1$, $CB = 12$. Find AC.

29. $AB = 8$, $BD = 6$. Find BC.

30. $CD = 4$, $DB = 16$. Find AC, AD, and AB.

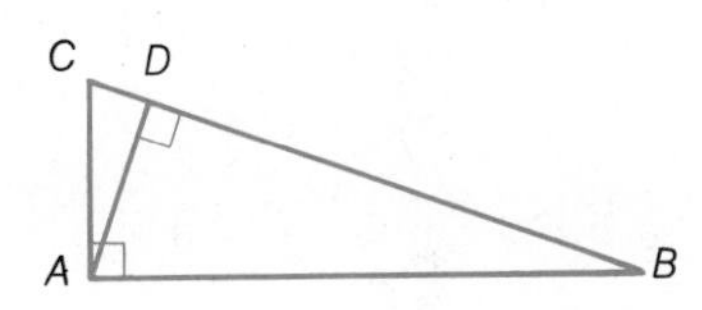

Objective: To apply the Pythagorean Theorem. (Section 6-9)

*For Exercises **31–34,** refer to right triangle ABC with hypotenuse c. Find the length of the missing side.*

31. $a = 8$, $b = 6$, $c =$ ___?___

32. $a = 12$, $c = 13$, $b =$ ___?___

33. $b = 2\sqrt{6}$, $c = 7$, $a =$ ___?___

34. $a = 35$, $c = 37$, $b =$ ___?___

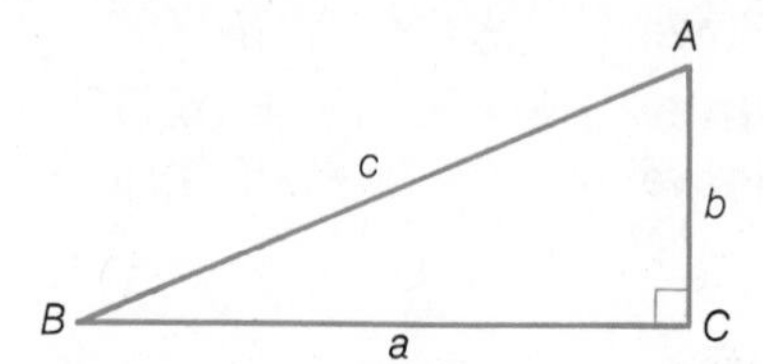

Objective: To use the converse of the Pythagorean Theorem to determine whether a triangle is a right triangle. (Section 6-9)

The lengths of three sides of a triangle are given. Determine whether the triangle is a right triangle.

35. 5, 10, 12 **36.** 16, 30, 34 **37.** 60, 80, 100 **38.** 0.7, 2.4, 2.5

Objective: To apply the relationships in special right triangles. (Section 6-10)

39. In an isosceles right triangle, a leg is 3 centimeters long. How long is the hypotenuse? Write the answer in simplest form.

40. The hypotenuse of a right isosceles triangle is 100 units long. How long is each leg? Write the answer in simplest form.

41. If the diagonal of a square is $5\sqrt{2}$ units long, how long is a side?

*For Exercises **42–46,** refer to right triangle ABC.*

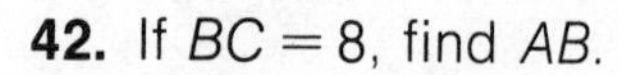

42. If $BC = 8$, find AB.

43. If $BC = 5$, find AC.

44. If $AC = 3\sqrt{3}$, find BC.

45. If $BC = 8\sqrt{3}$, find AC and AB.

46. If $AB = 18$, find BC and AC.

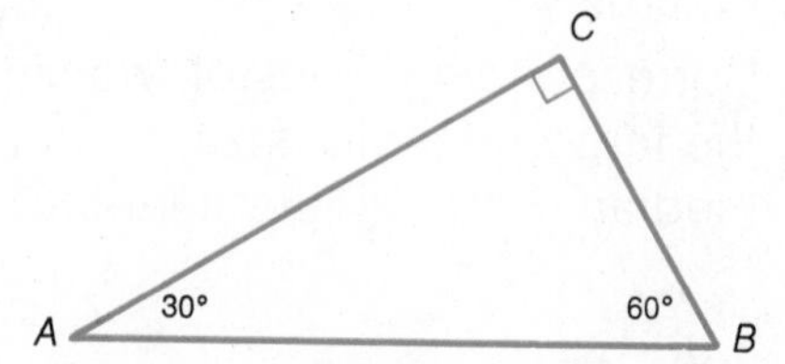

47. The altitude of an equilateral triangle is $9\sqrt{3}$ units long. Find the perimeter.

48. In the figure at the right, $ABCD$ is an isosceles trapezoid in which $m\angle A = 120$. How long is the altitude?

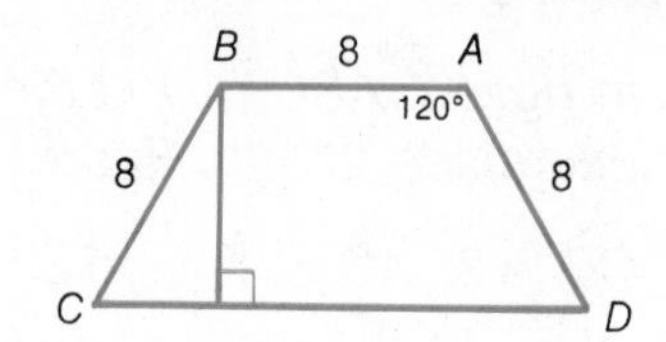

Chapter Test

Solve for x. No denominator is 0.

1. $\frac{3}{7} = \frac{4}{x}$

2. $\frac{x - 10}{x} = \frac{4}{9}$

3. Find the geometric mean between 4 and 25.

4. Find the fourth proportional to 2, 6, and 7.

For Exercises **5–7,** $\overline{DE} \parallel \overline{AB}$ *and the lengths of other segments are marked. Find x.*

5.

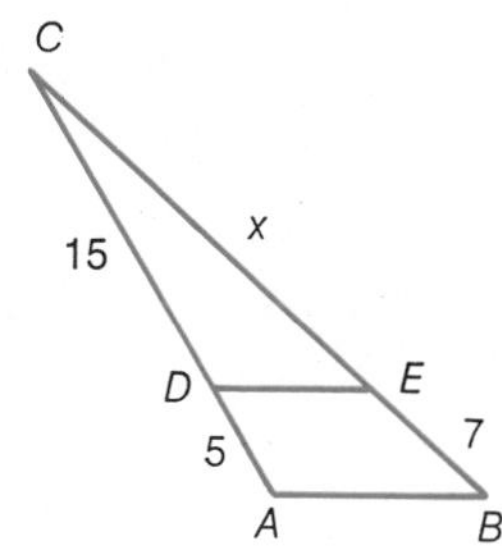

6.

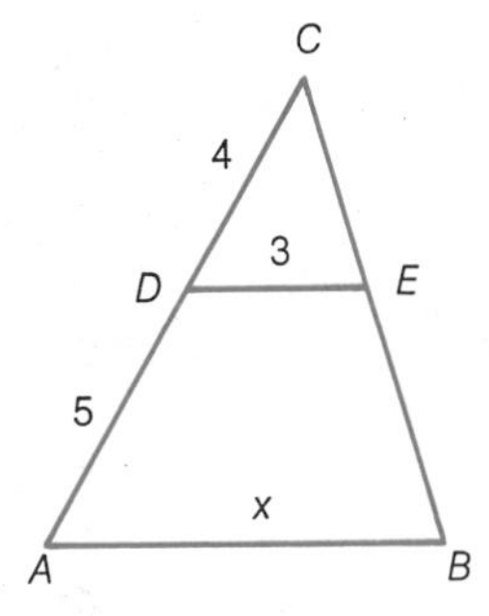

7.

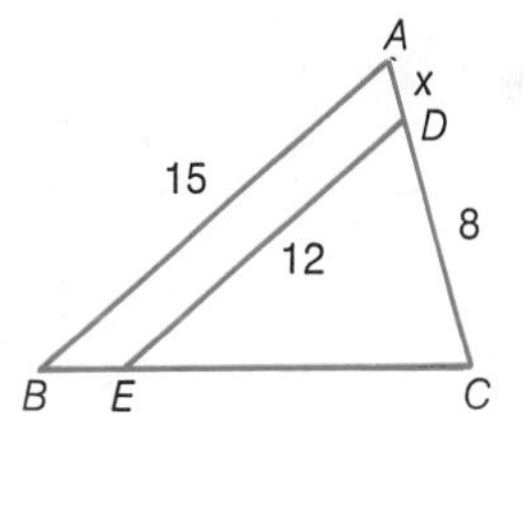

8. In $\triangle ABC$ at the right, $AC = 8$, $BC = 12$, and $AB = 10$. $\overline{CD}$ bisects $\angle C$, and D is between A and B. Find AD and DB. (HINT: Let $AD = x$ and $DB = 10 - x$.)

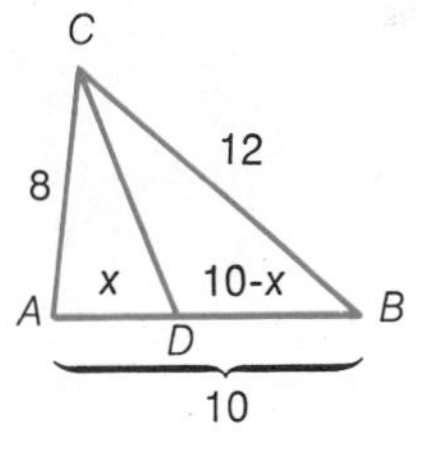

In Exercises **9–13,** *classify each statement as* True *or* False.

9. Any two isosceles triangles are similar.

10. All squares are similar.

11. Each side of pentagon *ABCDE* is 1 meter long and each side of pentagon *FGHIJ* is 3 meters long. These pentagons must be similar.

12. Any two regular hexagons are similar.

13. If a segment joins the midpoints of two sides of a triangle, it determines a triangle similar to the given triangle.

14. In the figure at the left below, $\overline{EA} \perp \overline{AB}$ and $\overline{DB} \perp \overline{AB}$. $\overline{EB}$ and $\overline{AD}$ intersect at C. Name two triangles that are similar.

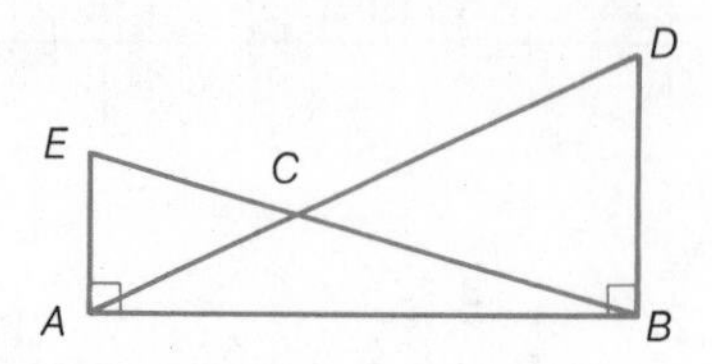

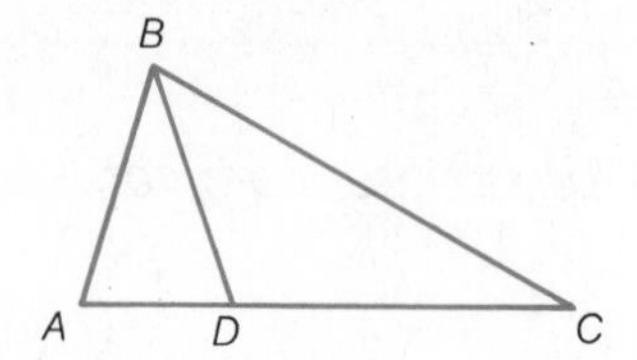

15. In the figure at the right above, $\overline{AC} \cong \overline{BC}$ and $\overline{AB} \cong \overline{BD}$. Name two triangles that are similar.

16. **Given:** $\square ABCD$ with $\overline{DE} \perp \overline{AB}$ and $\overline{DF} \perp \overline{BC}$.

Prove: $\triangle AED \sim \triangle CFD$

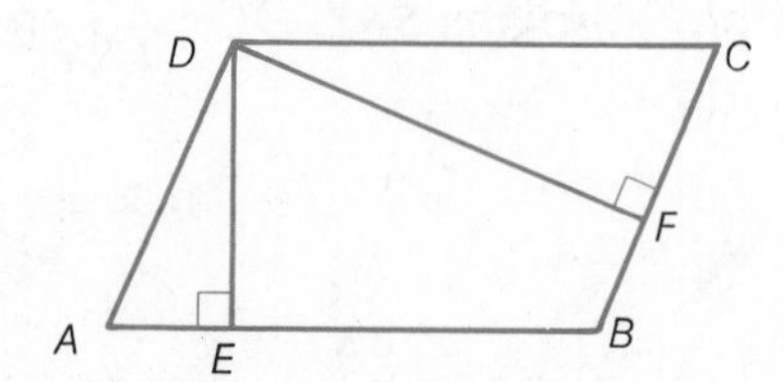

For Exercises ***17–20,*** *write each answer in simplest form.*

17. The adjacent sides of a rectangle are 5 and 12 units long. How long is a diagonal?

18. In an isosceles triangle, the base is 6 centimeters long and the altitude to the base is 6 centimeters long. How long is each of the congruent sides?

19. The perimeter of a square is 20 units long. How long is a diagonal?

20. A side of an equilateral triangle is $4\sqrt{3}$ units long. How long is an altitude?

Answers to Remember

Page 253: **1.** 3.87 **2.** 2.83 **3.** 6.40 **4.** 7.07 **5.** 8.49 **6.** 11.53 **7.** −6, 6 **8.** −9, 9 **9.** $-2\sqrt{2}$, $2\sqrt{2}$

Page 275: **1.** $\overline{BC}$ **2.** $\overline{DE}$ **3.** $\angle A \leftrightarrow \angle D$, $\angle B \leftrightarrow \angle E$, $\angle C \leftrightarrow \angle F$, $\overline{AB} \leftrightarrow \overline{DE}$, $\overline{BC} \leftrightarrow \overline{EF}$, $\overline{AC} \leftrightarrow \overline{DF}$

Page 285: **1.** 2 **2.** 13 **3.** $\frac{2}{4}$, or $\frac{1}{2}$ **4.** $\frac{3}{4}$ **5.** 27 **6.** 200

Page 290: **1.** $2\sqrt{2}$ **2.** $2\sqrt{10}$ **3.** $10\sqrt{2}$ **4.** $5\sqrt{5}$ **5.** $7\sqrt{2}$ **6.** 4

Chapter 7
Circles

7-1 The Circle: Related Lines and Segments

In the figure at the right, circle O is in plane I. Point O is the center of the circle and all points on the circle are 3 centimeters from O. $\overline{OP}$ is a radius of circle O.

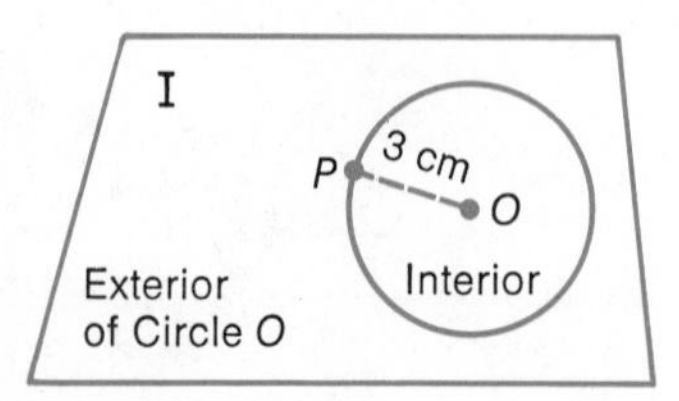

Definition: A **circle** is the set of all points in a plane at a given distance from a fixed point of the plane.

It follows from this definition that all radii (plural of radius) of the same circle are congruent. A line in the plane of a circle can intersect the circle in no points, one point, or two points.

No Points	One Point	Two Points
The line and the circle do not intersect.	A line that intersects the circle in exactly one point is a **tangent** to the circle. (Line p)	A line that intersects the circle in two points is a **secant.** (Line p)

Segments related to the circle have special names.

Segment	Name	Description
$\overline{OP}$	**Radius**	A segment joining the center of the circle with a point on the circle.
$\overline{CD}$	**Chord**	A segment with endpoints on the circle.
$\overline{AB}$	**Diameter**	A chord passing through the center of the circle.

Example

In circle A, all points of the circle are 2 centimeters from A.

a. Name two radii of the circle.
b. Find the length of the radius.
c. Why is $\overline{AC}$ congruent to $\overline{AB}$?
d. Find the length of a diameter of circle A.

Answers: **a.** $\overline{AC}$ and $\overline{AB}$.
b. $AC = AB = 2$ cm
c. Segments having the same measure are congruent.
d. Length of diameter $= 2AC = 4$ *cm*

Two or more coplanar circles that have the same center and different radii are **concentric** circles.

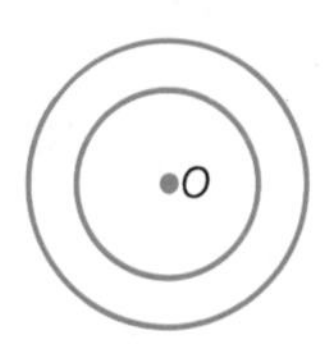

Try These

*Use the figure below to answer Exercises **1–6.***

1. Name the center of the circle.
2. Name two radii of the circle.
3. Name a diameter of the circle.
4. Name three chords of the circle.
5. Name a tangent to the circle.
6. Name a secant to the circle.

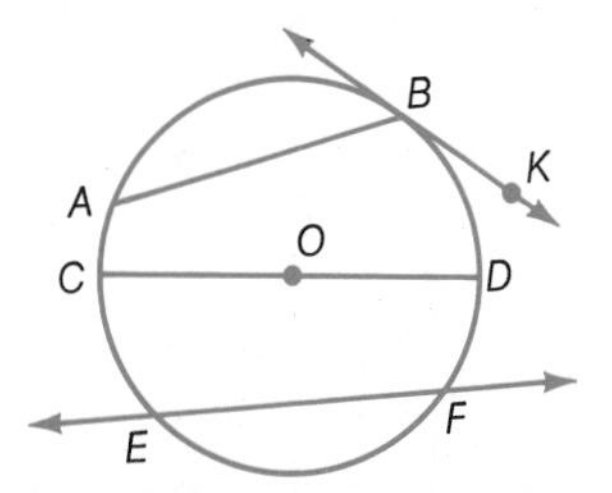

*A circle has a radius of 8 centimeters. If each measure in Exercises **7–10** is the distance of a line from the center of the circle, state whether the line intersects the circle in 0, 1, or 2 points.*

7. 6 cm **8.** 8 cm **9.** 8.5 cm **10.** 7.5 cm

Exercises

*Use the figure at the right to complete each statement in Exercises **1–12**. The radius of circle P is 3 centimeters; the radius of circle Q is 2 centimeters.*

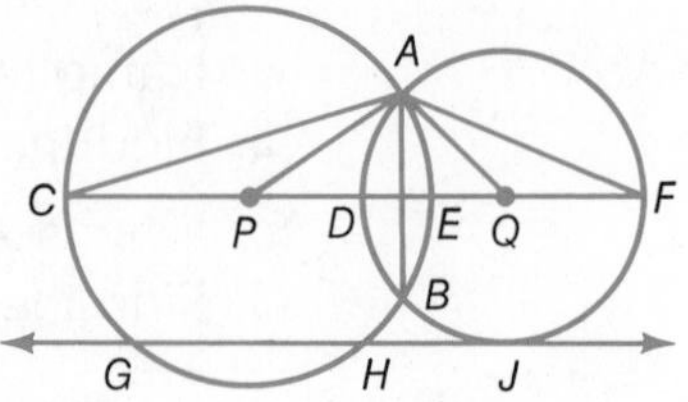

a

1. Three radii of circle P are $\overline{PA}$, _?_, and _?_.

2. Three radii of circle Q are _?_, _?_, and _?_.

3. $\overline{CE}$ is a _?_ of circle P; $\overline{DF}$ is a _?_ of circle Q.

4. If $DE = 1$ centimeter, then $CF =$ _?_.

5. $\overline{GH}$ is a _?_ of circle P.

6. $\overleftrightarrow{GH}$ is a _?_ of circle P.

7. $\overleftrightarrow{GH}$ is a _?_ to circle Q.

8. If $DE = 1$ centimeter and $AF = 3\frac{1}{2}$ centimeters, then the perimeter of $\triangle APQ =$ _?_ and the perimeter of $\triangle AQF =$ _?_.

9. $\overline{AB}$ is a _?_ of circle P and a _?_ of circle Q.

10. $DQ = \frac{1}{2}$ _?_ **11.** $PA = \frac{1}{2}$ _?_ **12.** $\overline{QA} \cong$ _?_ $\cong$ _?_

13. Circle Q has a radius of 8 cm, P is in the plane of the circle, and $QP = 6$ cm. State whether P is inside, on, or outside the circle.

14. A circle O has a radius of 8. Find the length of the longest chord of the circle.

Find the radius of a circle in which the longest chord has each given length.

15. 12 **16.** 9 **17.** 15.24 **18.** $2x$ **19.** y

20. Two concentric circles have a common center P and radii of 7 centimeters and 11 centimeters respectively. Points A, B, C, D are chosen such that $PA = 5$ cm, $PB = 8$ cm, $PC = 10$ cm, and $PD = 14$ cm. State whether each of the points A, B, C, and D is in the interior or exterior of each circle.

The figure at the right shows two circles with four common tangents. Lines p and q are common <u>*external tangents*</u>*; lines r and s are* <u>*common internal*</u> *tangents.*

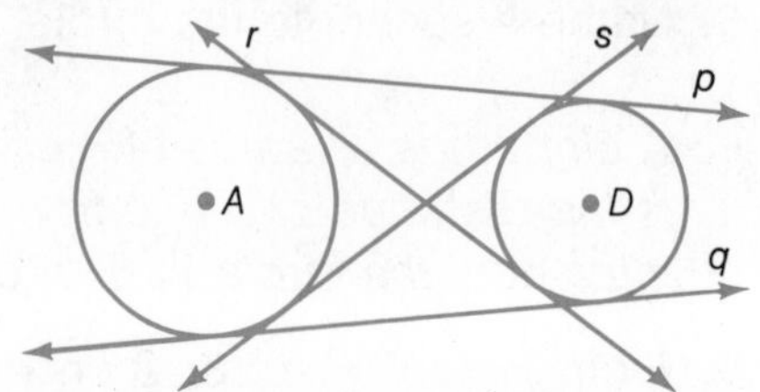

*If possible, draw two circles in such a position that each condition in Exercises **21–24** is satisfied.*

21. Exactly three common tangents can be drawn.
22. Exactly two common tangents can be drawn.
23. Exactly one common tangent can be drawn.
24. No common tangents can be drawn.

*For Exercises **25–32,** classify each statement as True or False.*

25. Every diameter of a circle is also a chord of the circle.
26. Every radius of a circle is also a chord of the circle.
27. Every chord of a circle contains exactly two points of the circle.
28. A line and a circle can have exactly one point in common.
29. A circle has exactly two radii.
30. A chord of a circle can be a segment of a tangent to the circle.
31. The union of any two radii of a circle is a diameter of the circle.
32. If a line intersects a circle in one point, then it intersects the circle in two points.

b

33. Circle O has a radius of 4 centimeters. If radii OA and OB form a right angle, find AB.
34. In circle Q, radii QX and QY form a right angle. If $XY = 128$, find QX.
35. Circle N has a radius of 10 meters, and radii NA and NB form an angle of 120°. Find AB.
36. $\overline{TP}$ and $\overline{TQ}$ are radii of a circle. If $m\angle PTQ = 120$ and $PQ = 18$, find TQ.

Remember

State each biconditional as a conditional and its converse.

1. A triangle is isosceles if and only if it has two congruent angles.
2. Two triangles are similar if and only if two pairs of corresponding angles are congruent.
3. Two lines cut by a transversal are parallel if and only if two alternate interior angles are congruent.
4. Two sides of a triangle are not congruent if and only if the angles opposite these sides are not congruent.

The answers are on page 363. If you need help, see page 78.

7-2 Central Angles and Arcs

In circle B, $\angle ABC$ is a central angle. A **central angle** has its vertex at the center of the circle.

Points A and C and all points of the circle in the interior of $\angle ABC$ form a minor arc, called $\overset{\frown}{AC}$ (arc AC).

Points A and C and all points of the circle in the exterior of $\angle ABC$ form a major arc, $\overset{\frown}{AFC}$. You use three letters to name a major arc.

A **semicircle** is the union of the endpoints of a diameter and all points of the circle lying on one side of the diameter. In the figure, $\overset{\frown}{ADB}$ and $\overset{\frown}{ACB}$ are semicircles.

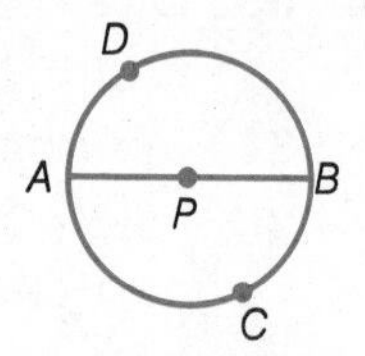

Example 1

Classify each arc as a major arc, minor arc, or a semicircle.

Arc	Classification
$\overset{\frown}{ST}$	minor
$\overset{\frown}{SQT}$	major
$\overset{\frown}{QTR}$	semicircle
$\overset{\frown}{QRT}$	major
$\overset{\frown}{QT}$	minor
$\overset{\frown}{QSR}$	semicircle

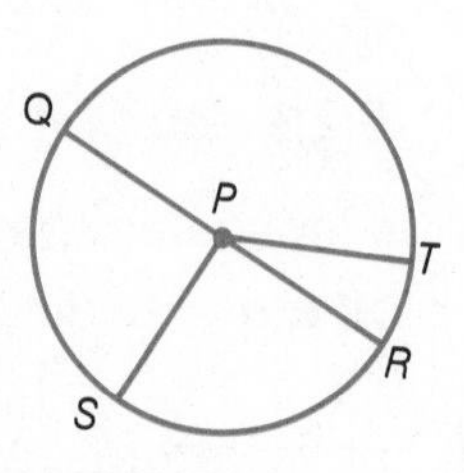

The measure of a major or minor arc of a circle is determined by the central angle of its minor arc.

Definitions: The **measure of a minor arc** equals the measure of its central angle.

The **measure of a major arc** equals 360 − m, where m is the measure of the central angle of its minor arc.

The **measure of a semicircle** is 180.

Example 2

In circle E, $m\angle TEN = 70$, $m\overset{\frown}{NR} = 80$, and $\overline{CN}$ is a diameter. Find $m\overset{\frown}{TN}$, $m\overset{\frown}{TC}$, $m\overset{\frown}{TR}$, and $m\overset{\frown}{CTR}$.

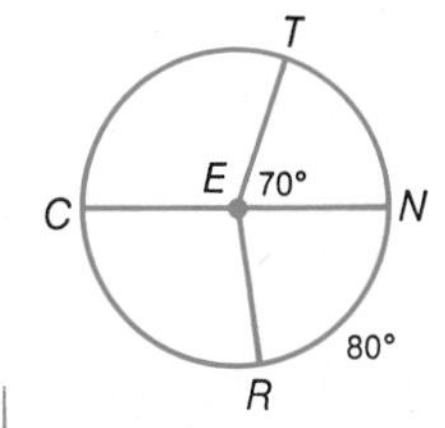

$m\overset{\frown}{TN} = 70$ ⟵ The measure of a minor arc equals the measure of its central angle.

$m\overset{\frown}{TC} = 110$ ⟵ $m\angle TEC = 180 - 70 = 110$

$m\overset{\frown}{TR} = 150$ ⟵ $m\angle TER = 70 + 80 = 150$

$m\overset{\frown}{CTR} = 260$ ⟵ $m\angle CET + m\angle TEN + m\angle NER = 260$

The example suggests the Arc-Addition Theorem. The theorem and definition that follow apply both to major and minor arcs.

Theorem 7-1: Arc-Addition Theorem

If B is a point on $\overset{\frown}{AC}$, then $m\overset{\frown}{AB} + m\overset{\frown}{BC} = m\overset{\frown}{AC}$.

The Arc-Addition Theorem suggests this definition.

Definition: B is the **midpoint of** $\overset{\frown}{AC}$ if B is a point on $\overset{\frown}{AC}$ and $m\overset{\frown}{AB} = m\overset{\frown}{BC}$.

All circles have the same shape. Two circles are congruent if their radii are congruent. Circles O and P are congruent if $\overline{OQ} \cong \overline{PR}$. Further, $\overset{\frown}{QS} \cong \overset{\frown}{RT}$ if $m\overset{\frown}{QS} = m\overset{\frown}{RT}$.

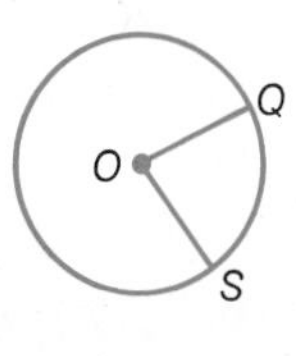

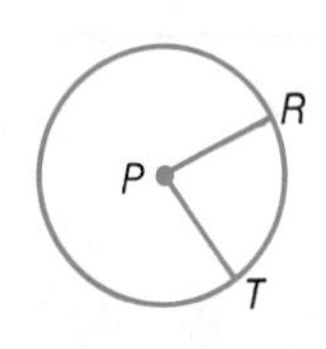

Definitions: Two **circles are congruent** if their radii are congruent.

In the same circle or in congruent circles, two **arcs are congruent** if they have the same measure.

Example 3

In the figure, O is the center of the concentric circles. $\overline{AB}$ and $\overline{CD}$ are diameters of the larger circle, and $m\angle DOB = 50$.

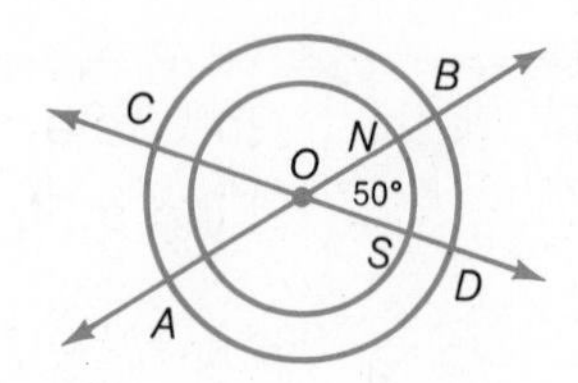

a. Find $m\widehat{NS}$ and $m\widehat{DB}$.

b. Does $\widehat{SN}$ appear congruent to $\widehat{BD}$?

Answers: **a.** $m\widehat{NS} = 50$; $m\widehat{DB} = 50$ ⟵ Definition

b. No, $\widehat{SN}$ does not appear congruent to $\widehat{DB}$.

Example 3 suggests that arcs with equal measures are not necessarily congruent. Arcs with equal measures can be proved congruent if they are in the same or congruent circles.

Theorem 7-2: In the same circle or in congruent circles, two arcs are congruent if and only if their central angles are congruent.

The theorem is left for you to prove in the Exercises.

Try These

*Use circle P at the right to answer Exercises **1–6.** $\overline{CD}$ and $\overline{AB}$ are diameters.*

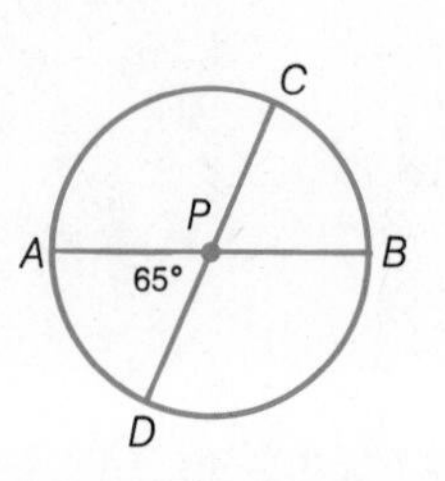

1. Name 4 central angles in the figure.
2. Name 1 diameter in the figure.
3. Name 2 pairs of congruent minor arcs.

4. Name 4 semicircles in the figure.

5. Name a major arc for each of the minor arcs $\overset{\frown}{AC}$, $\overset{\frown}{BC}$, and $\overset{\frown}{BD}$.

6. Find $m\overset{\frown}{AD}$, $m\overset{\frown}{DB}$, $m\overset{\frown}{BC}$, $m\overset{\frown}{CA}$, and $m\overset{\frown}{ADB}$.

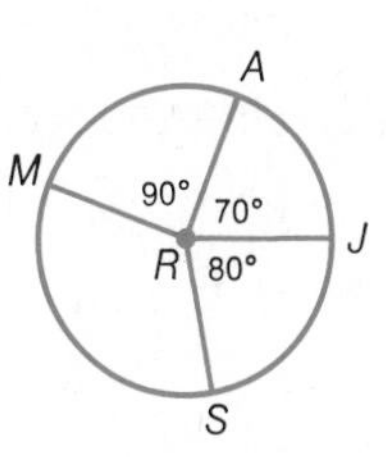

7. In circle R at the right, the central angles have the measures shown. Find $m\angle MRS$, $m\overset{\frown}{MA}$, $m\overset{\frown}{AJ}$, $m\overset{\frown}{JS}$, $m\overset{\frown}{JSM}$, and $m\overset{\frown}{MAS}$.

8. State Theorem 7-2 as a conditional and its converse.

Exercises

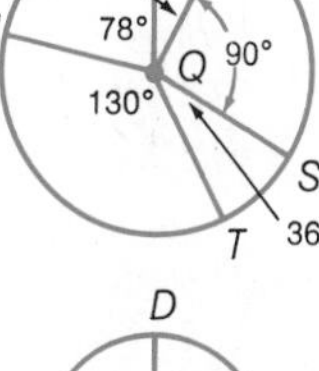

The measures of the angles in circle Q are given in the figure. Find the measure of each arc.

1. $\overset{\frown}{RT}$ **2.** $\overset{\frown}{UR}$ **3.** $\overset{\frown}{VS}$ **4.** $\overset{\frown}{US}$

5. $\overset{\frown}{RSU}$ **6.** $\overset{\frown}{SUV}$ **7.** $\overset{\frown}{TVR}$ **8.** $\overset{\frown}{VTR}$

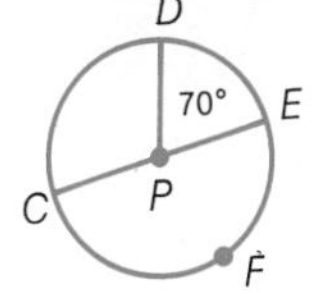

In circle P, $\overline{CE}$ is a diameter and $m\angle DPE = 70$. Find each of the following.

9. $m\overset{\frown}{DE}$ **10.** $m\overset{\frown}{DFE}$ **11.** $m\angle CPD$ **12.** $m\overset{\frown}{CD}$

13. $m\overset{\frown}{CED}$ **14.** $m\overset{\frown}{CFD}$ **15.** $m\overset{\frown}{CDE}$ **16.** $m\overset{\frown}{EFC}$

17. Points A, B, C and D, are placed in succession on a circle so that $\overset{\frown}{AB} \cong \overset{\frown}{CD}$ and $\overset{\frown}{BC} \cong \overset{\frown}{DA}$. Is $\overline{AC}$ a diameter? Give a reason for your answer.

18. Make a drawing to show how two arcs can have the same measure but not be congruent.

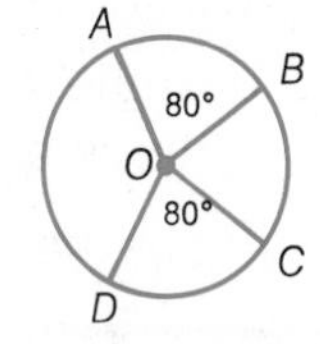

19. In the figure at the right, O is the center of the circle, and $m\angle AOB = m\angle DOC = 80$. Which arcs are congruent? Give reasons for your answers.

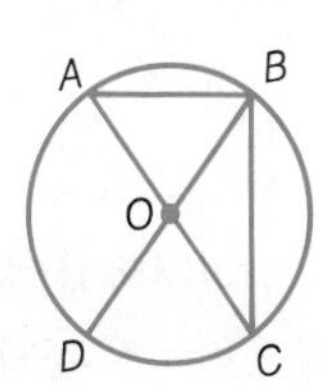

In the figure at the right, $\overline{AC}$ and $\overline{BD}$ are diameters of circle O, and $m\overset{\frown}{DC} = 71$. Find each of the following.

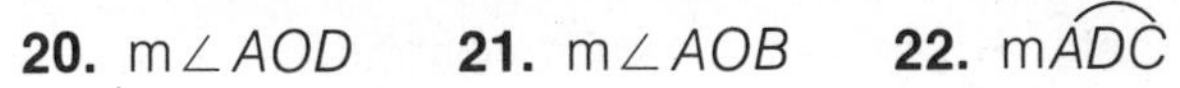

20. $m\angle AOD$ **21.** $m\angle AOB$ **22.** $m\overset{\frown}{ADC}$ **23.** $m\overset{\frown}{BC}$

24. In the figure at the right, polygon $MNPQRS$ is a regular hexagon. Explain why each small arc, such as $\widehat{MN}$, $\widehat{NP}$, and $\widehat{PQ}$, has a measure of 60.

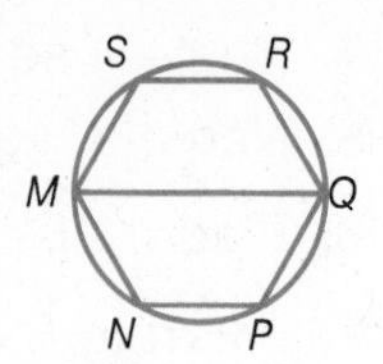

25. Use the figure and the information for Exercise **24** to find $m\widehat{MSR}$, $m\widehat{SRQ}$, $m\widehat{SRP}$, and $m\widehat{NRP}$.

26. In the same circle, is the chord of a central angle of 120 twice as long as the chord of a central angle of 60? (Use a drawing to help you find the answer.)

27. Find the measure of the central angle of a chord with length equal to the length of the radius of the circle.

28. Prove Theorem 7-2. (HINT: This theorem is a biconditional. See Exercise 8 in the Try These on page 311.)

In the figure at the right, H is the center of concentric circles with radii HM and HT. If $m\angle JHK = 51$ and $m\angle KHT = 77$, find each of the following.

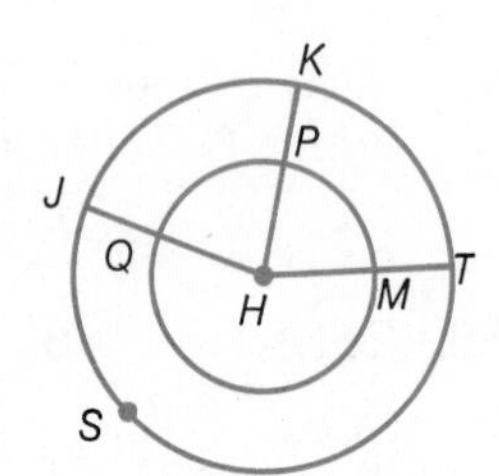

29. $m\widehat{JK}$	**30.** $m\widehat{QP}$	**31.** $m\widehat{KT}$	**32.** $m\widehat{PM}$
33. $m\widehat{JSK}$	**34.** $m\widehat{QMP}$	**35.** $m\widehat{JST}$	**36.** $m\widehat{KST}$

37. In the figure for Exercises **29–36,** which arcs have the same measure?

38. **Given:** $\overline{AB}$ and $\overline{CD}$ are diameters.
Prove: $\widehat{AD} \cong \widehat{BC}$

39. **Given:** $\overline{AB}$ and $\overline{CD}$ are diameters.
Prove: $\widehat{AC} \cong \widehat{DB}$

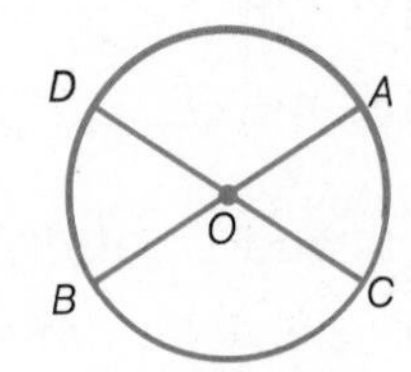

40. A circle is divided into three congruent arcs. Chords join the endpoints of the arcs. Prove that the triangle formed is equilateral.

41. Triangle ABC is inscribed in a circle (all three vertices are on the circle) and has $\angle A \cong \angle C$. Prove that $\widehat{AB} \cong \widehat{BC}$.

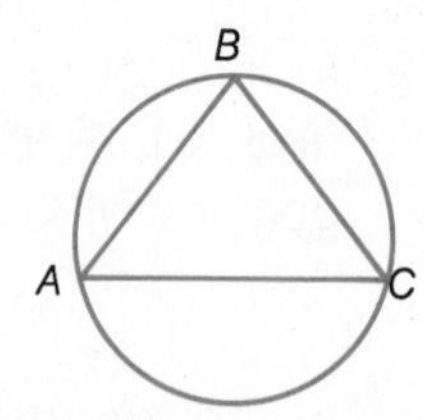

42. Point P on $\widehat{AB}$ is equidistant from the radii OA and OB. Prove that P is the midpoint of arc AB.

43. $\overline{AB}$ and $\overline{BC}$ are congruent chords in circle O, and A and C are distinct points. If $\overline{BD}$ is a diameter, prove $\angle ABD \cong \angle CBD$.

44. Chord AB is parallel to diameter RS in circle Q. Prove that $\widehat{RA} \cong \widehat{SB}$.

think–draw–see

1. Draw two circles, each with a radius of 2 centimeters. In each circle draw a chord 3 centimeters long. Draw the radii to the endpoints of both chords.
2. Measure the central angles with your protractor.
3. How do the measures of the central angles compare? How do the measures of the arcs compare?
4. Repeat Steps 1–3, making the chords both 1.5 centimeters long.

7-3 Congruent Chords and Arcs

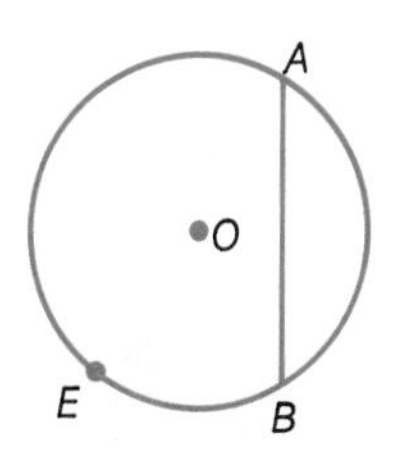

In circle *O* at the right, there are two arcs with endpoints *A* and *B*, $\overset{\frown}{AB}$ and $\overset{\frown}{AEB}$. Unless otherwise stated, the arc of chord *AB* is $\overset{\frown}{AB}$, the smaller of the two arcs with endpoints *A* and *B*.

Theorem 7-3: In the same or in congruent circles, two chords are congruent if their arcs are congruent.

The converse of Theorem 7-3 is Theorem 7-4. You are asked to prove both theorems in the Exercises.

Theorem 7-4: In the same or in congruent circles, two arcs are congruent if their chords are congruent.

Now consider two chords that intersect in the interior of a circle.

When any two of the conditions outlined in the table exist, then the other two can be proved. Cases II and III lead to Theorem 7-5.

Case I: One chord bisects the other.	**Case II: One chord is perpendicular to the other.**	**Case III: One chord is a diameter.**	**Case IV: One chord bisects the arc of the other.**
$CE = ED$	$\overline{AB} \perp \overline{CD}$	$\overline{AB}$ is a diameter.	$\overset{\frown}{CA} \cong \overset{\frown}{DA}$

Theorem 7-5: If a diameter of a circle is perpendicular to a chord, then it bisects the chord and its arc.

Given: $\overline{RQ}$ is a diameter or circle O;
$\overline{RQ} \perp \overline{PT}$ at S.

Prove: **a.** S is the midpoint of $\overline{PT}$.
b. Q is the midpoint of $\overset{\frown}{PT}$.

Plan: Draw $\overline{OP}$ and $\overline{OT}$.

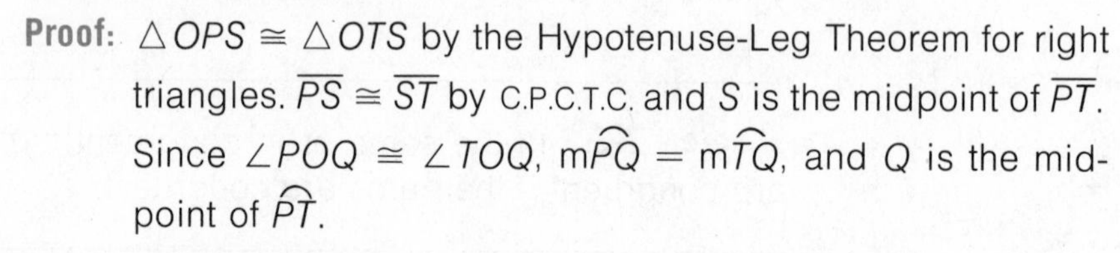

Proof: $\triangle OPS \cong \triangle OTS$ by the Hypotenuse-Leg Theorem for right triangles. $\overline{PS} \cong \overline{ST}$ by C.P.C.T.C. and S is the midpoint of $\overline{PT}$. Since $\angle POQ \cong \angle TOQ$, $m\overset{\frown}{PQ} = m\overset{\frown}{TQ}$, and Q is the midpoint of $\overset{\frown}{PT}$.

Cases I and IV lead to Theorem 7–6.

Theorem 7-6: If one chord of a circle intersects a second chord so that it bisects both the second chord and its arc, then the first chord is a diameter and is perpendicular to the second chord.

Theorem 7-7: If a diameter bisects a chord that is not a diameter, then it is perpendicular to the chord and bisects its arc.

You are asked to prove Theorems 7-6 and 7-7 in the Exercises.

Try These

*For Exercises **1–10,** give reasons to justify each statement.*

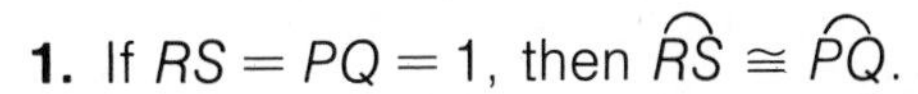

1. If $RS = PQ = 1$, then $\overset{\frown}{RS} \cong \overset{\frown}{PQ}$.
2. If $\overset{\frown}{RS} \cong \overset{\frown}{PQ}$ and $RS = 5$, then $PQ = 5$.
3. If $\angle ROS \cong \angle POQ$, then $\overset{\frown}{RS} \cong \overset{\frown}{PQ}$.
4. If $\overset{\frown}{RS} \cong \overset{\frown}{PQ}$, then $m\angle ROS = m\angle POQ$.

In circle O at the right, $\overline{OC} \perp \overline{AB}$, $AB = 24$, and $OC = 5$.

5. $\overline{AC} \cong \overline{CB}$
6. $AC = 12$
7. $(AO)^2 = (AC)^2 + (OC)^2$
8. $AO = 13$

In the figure at the right, $AE = EB$, and $m\overset{\frown}{AD} = m\overset{\frown}{DB}$.

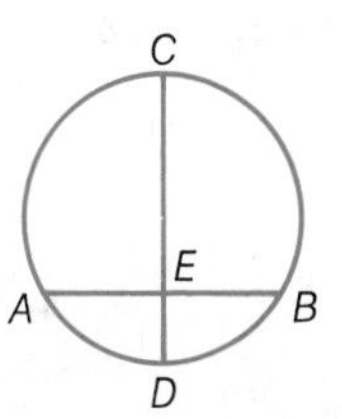

9. $m\angle CEA = 90$
10. $\overline{CD}$ is a diameter.
11. State Theorems 7-3 and 7-4 as a biconditional.

Exercises

Use the given information and figure to state conclusions that can be drawn. Give a reason for each conclusion.

a

1. $\overline{AB} \cong \overline{CD}$

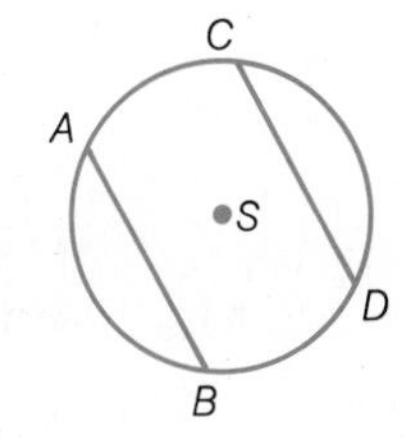

2. $\overline{AB}$ is a diameter; $\overline{AB} \perp \overline{PQ}$

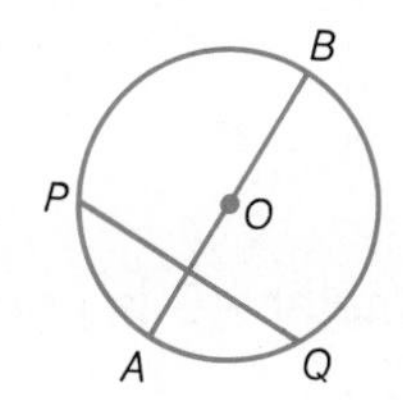

3. $\overline{AP} \cong \overline{BR}$; $\overset{\frown}{PQ} \cong \overset{\frown}{RS}$

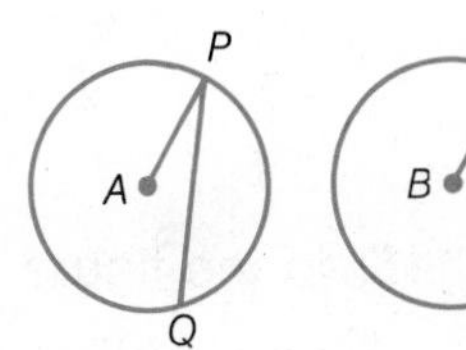

4. $\overline{PQ}$ is a diameter; $AE = EB$

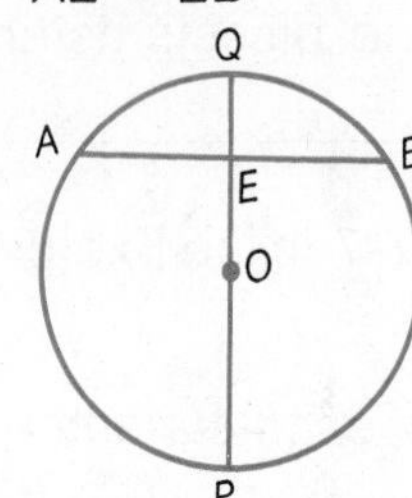

5. $TW = WV$; $m\widehat{TS} = m\widehat{SV}$

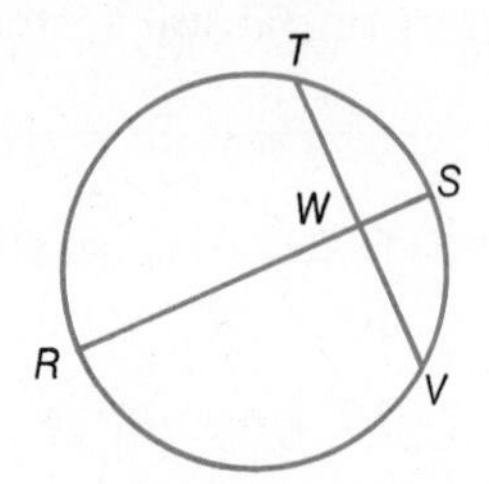

6. $\overline{PD} \perp \overline{AB}$; $AP = 5$; $PD = 4$

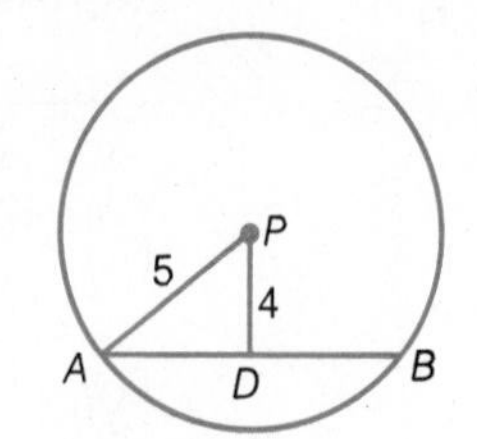

7. In semicircle O at the right, $\overline{OB}$ bisects $\angle AOC$ and $\angle 1 \cong \angle 2$. Explain why $\overline{BC} \cong \overline{DE}$.

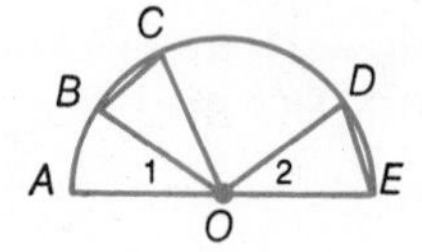

8. Five points on a circle divide it into five congruent arcs. Explain why the chords of these arcs form an equilateral pentagon.

9. Prove Theorem 7-3. (HINT: Draw the radii to the endpoints of the chords.)

10. Prove Theorem 7-4.

11. Given: $\overline{AD} \perp \overline{AB}$; $\overline{DC} \perp \overline{BC}$; $\overline{BD}$ bisects $\angle ABC$.

Prove: $m\widehat{AB} = m\widehat{BC}$

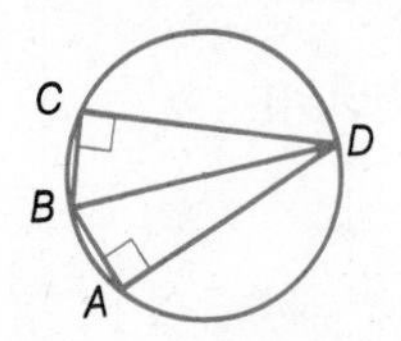

12. Given: $\overline{PQ} \cong \overline{RS}$

Prove: $m\widehat{PQR} = m\widehat{SRQ}$

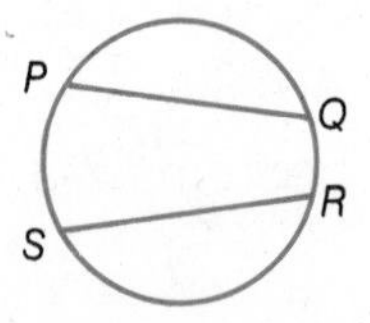

13. In circle O, diameter QR is perpendicular to chord AC. Prove that $\angle RAC \cong \angle RCA$ without proving triangles congruent.

14. In circle S below, $\overline{AB}$ and $\overline{BC}$ are congruent chords, $\overline{SV} \perp \overline{AB}$, and $\overline{SU} \perp \overline{BC}$. Prove that B is the midpoint of $\widehat{VU}$.

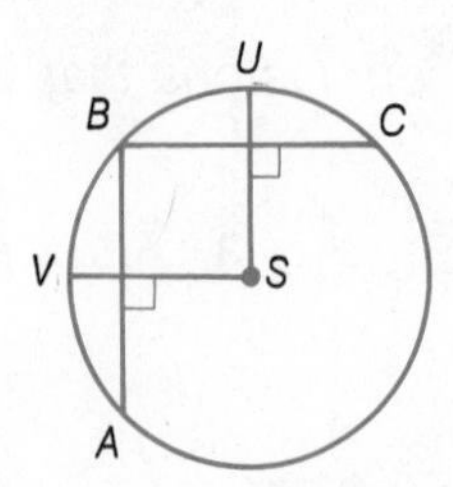

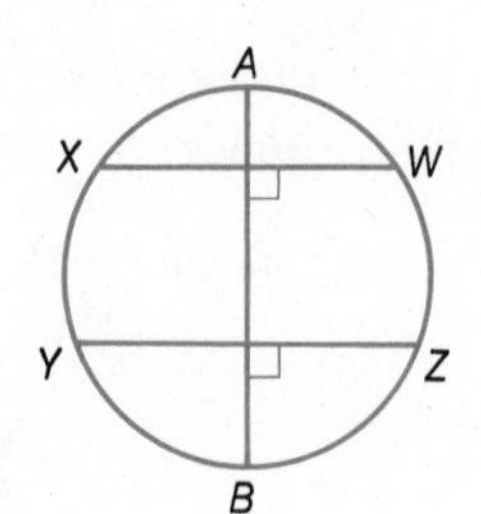

15. In the figure at the right above, diameter AB is perpendicular to chords XW and YZ. Prove that $\widehat{XB} \cong \widehat{WB}$.

16. Prove Theorem 7-6.

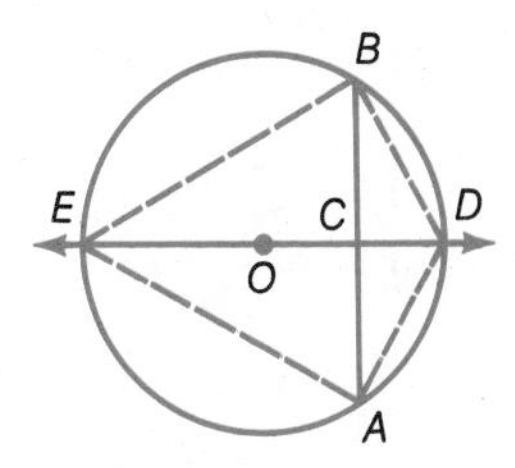

Given: In circle O, $\overleftrightarrow{DE}$ intersects chord AB and arc AB such that $\overline{AC} \cong \overline{CB}$ and $\overset{\frown}{AD} \cong \overset{\frown}{DB}$.

Prove: $\overleftrightarrow{DE} \perp \overline{AB}$; $\overleftrightarrow{DE}$ contains O.

Plan: Draw $\overline{DA}$, $\overline{DB}$, $\overline{EA}$, and $\overline{EB}$. Show that C and D are equidistant from A and B. Then C and D must lie on the perpendicular bisector of $\overline{AB}$ and $\overleftrightarrow{ED} \perp \overline{AB}$. Then show that $\overset{\frown}{DAE} \cong \overset{\frown}{DBE}$, and that $\overset{\frown}{DAE}$ and $\overset{\frown}{DBE}$ are semicircles. Complete the proof.

17. Prove Theorem 7-7. (HINT: Draw the radii to the endpoints of the chord.)

18. Given: Diameter AB bisects chord CD.

Prove: $\triangle ABC \cong \triangle ABD$

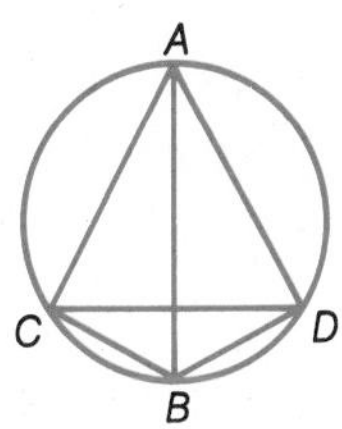

19. In circle O at the left below, $\overline{GK}$ and $\overline{HM}$ are intersecting congruent chords. Prove that $\overset{\frown}{KH} \cong \overset{\frown}{MG}$.

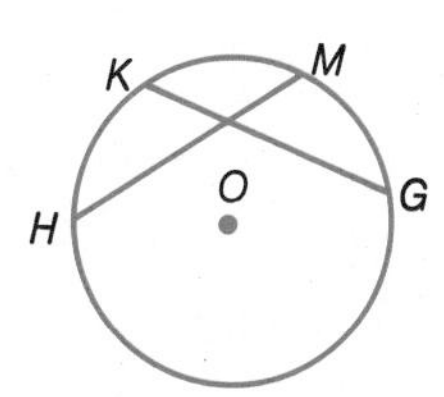

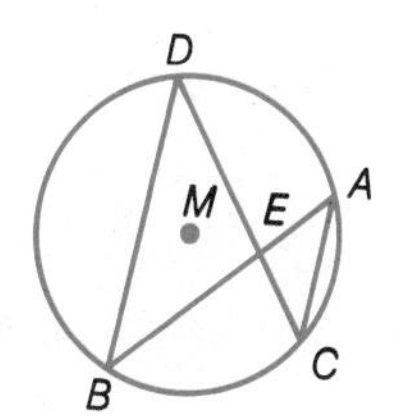

20. In circle M at the right above, chords AB and CD are congruent. Prove that $\triangle DBE$ is isosceles with base $\overline{BD}$. (HINT: Draw $\overline{AD}$ and $\overline{BC}$.)

21. Given any circle, locate its center by construction. (HINT: Draw two chords.)

Remember

Simplify each radical.

1. $\sqrt{36}$	**2.** $\sqrt{8}$	**3.** $\sqrt{27}$	**4.** $\sqrt{50}$
5. $\sqrt{12}$	**6.** $\sqrt{63}$	**7.** $\sqrt{75}$	**8.** $\sqrt{32}$

The answers are on page 365. If you need help, see page 566 in the Review: Topics From Algebra One.

7-4 Chords and Inscribed Polygons

Recall that the distance from a point to a line is the length of the perpendicular segment from the point to the line.

Example 1

Circle O has a radius of 5 centimeters. Chords ST and RP are each 3 centimeters from O. Compare the lengths of $\overline{ST}$ and $\overline{RP}$.

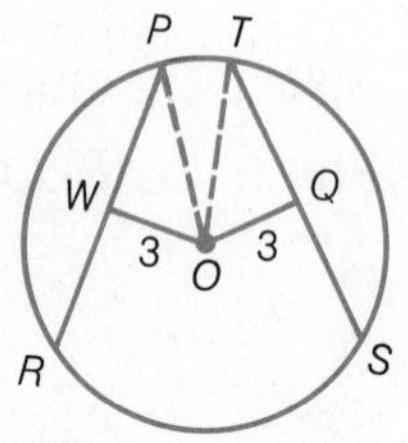

Draw $\overline{OT}$ and $\overline{OP}$. ⟵ $\overline{OT}$ and $\overline{OP}$ are radii of circle O.

$OT = OP = 5$ ⟵ Radii of the same circle have the same measure.

$$(OW)^2 + (WP)^2 = (OP)^2 \qquad (OQ)^2 + (QT)^2 = (OT)^2$$
$$3^2 + (WP)^2 = 5^2 \qquad 3^2 + (QT)^2 = 5^2$$
$$(WP)^2 = 25 - 9 \qquad (QT)^2 = 25 - 9$$
$$(WP)^2 = 16 \qquad (QT)^2 = 16$$
$$WP = 4 \qquad QT = 4$$

$RP = 2(WP) = 8$ ← Theorem 7-7 → $ST = 2(QT) = 8$

Chords ST and RP are congruent.

The example suggests this theorem. Note that Theorem 7-8 is a biconditional that you are asked to prove in the Exercises.

Theorem 7-8: In the same circle or in congruent circles, two chords are congruent if and only if they are equidistant from the center.

Example 2

Circle C has a radius of 10. Chord QT is 5 units from C and chord PR is 8 units from C.

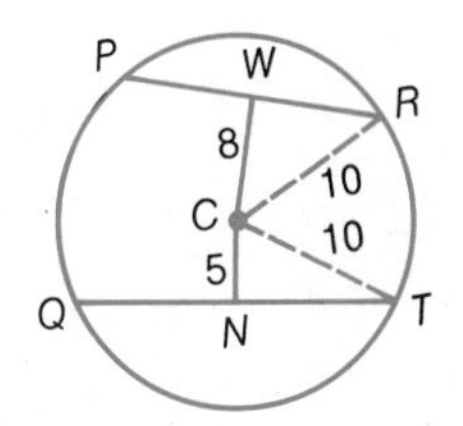

a. Compare the lengths of $\overline{PR}$ and $\overline{QT}$.

b. Compare the distances of $\overline{PR}$ and $\overline{QT}$ from C.

a.

$$(NT)^2 + (NC)^2 = (CT)^2 \qquad (WR)^2 + (WC)^2 = (RC)^2$$
$$(NT)^2 + (5)^2 = (10)^2 \qquad (WR)^2 + (8)^2 = (10)^2$$
$$(NT)^2 = 100 - 25 \qquad (WR)^2 = 100 - 64$$
$$(NT)^2 = 75 \qquad (WR)^2 = 36$$
$$NT = 5\sqrt{3} \qquad WR = 6$$
$$QT = 2(NT) = 10\sqrt{3} \qquad PR = 2(WR) = 12$$

Since $10\sqrt{3} > 12$, $QT > PR$.

b. Since $CW > CN$, $\overline{PR}$ is farther from C than $\overline{QT}$.

Example 2 suggests these theorems.

Theorem 7-9: In the same or in congruent circles, if two chords are not congruent then their distances from the center of the circle are not equal, and the longer chord is closer to the center of the circle.

Theorem 7-10: In the same or in congruent circles, if the distances of two chords from the center of the circle are not equal, then the chords are not congruent, and the chord that is closer to the center of the circle is the longer chord.

Note that Theorems 7-9 and 7-10 can be stated as a biconditional.

Polygons are sometimes drawn with their vertices on a circle. Polygon $ABCD$ at the right is an inscribed quadrilateral. Polygon $KEFGHJ$ is an inscribed hexagon.

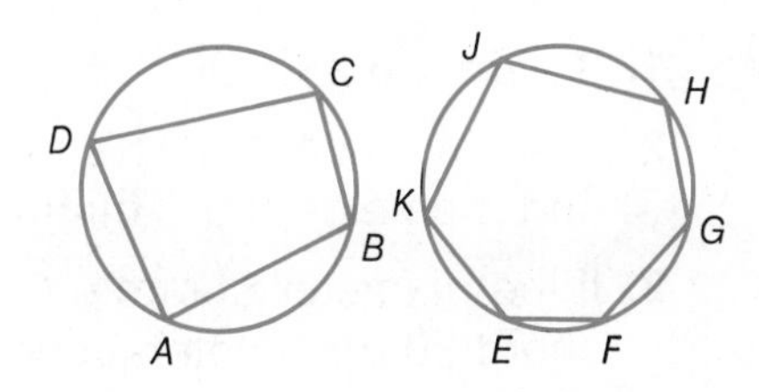

Definition: A polygon is **inscribed in a circle** if all its vertices are on the circle.

Try These

Choose the letter of the response that makes each statement true.

1. In a circle, two chords are equally distant from the center of the circle. The chords are
   a. congruent. b. not congruent. c. parallel.
2. $\overline{AB}$ and $\overline{CD}$ are two chords of the same circle O and $AB < CD$. Then
   a. $\overline{AB}$ is closer to O. b. $\overline{CD}$ is closer to O.
3. A chord is 5 centimeters from the center of a circle of radius 13 centimeters. The length of the chord is
   a. 6 centimeters. b. 12 centimeters. c. 24 centimeters.
4. A chord 40 units long is contained in a circle of radius 25. The distance of the chord from the center of the circle is
   a. 15 units. b. 31.2 units. c. 47.1 units.
5. A chord $8\sqrt{3}$ units long is 4 units from the center of a circle. The length of the radius of the circle is
   a. 14.4 units. b. 8 units. c. $4\sqrt{2}$ units.
6. State Theorem 7-8 as a conditional and its converse.

Exercises

In circle O, $\overline{AB}$ is a chord, $\overline{OA}$ is a radius, and $\overline{AB} \perp \overline{OC}$. Use this figure for Exercises **1–6.** *Leave radicals in your answers in simplest form.*

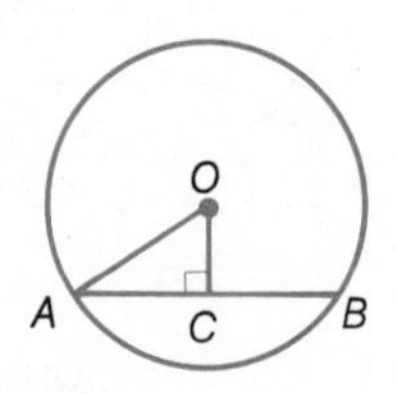

a

1. If $AO = 13$ and $OC = 5$, find AC and AB.
2. If $\overline{AB}$ is 16 centimeters long and is 6 centimeters from O, find the radius and diameter of the circle.
3. If the diameter of circle O is 34 centimeters, how far from the center is a chord 30 centimeters long?

4. The radius of circle O is 25 units long. How long is $\overline{AB}$ if it is 7 units from point O?

5. If $m\angle AOC = 60$ and $AO = 12$, find OC, AC, and AB.

6. Chord AB is 10 meters long and is 5 meters from O. Find OA.

7. In circle Q, $\overline{QW} \perp \overline{XY}$, $\overline{QT} \perp \overline{YZ}$, $QW = 5$, $QT = 5$, and $YT = 12$. Find XY.

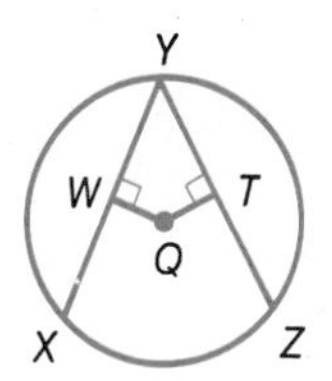

An equilateral triangle is inscribed in a circle of radius 12 centimeters.

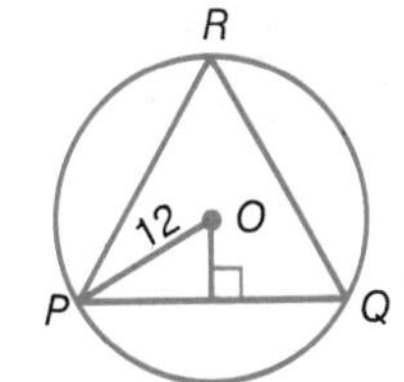

8. Find the distance from the center of the circle to each side of the triangle.

9. Find the length of each side of the triangle.

Square ABCD is inscribed in a circle with center O and radius 8 centimeters.

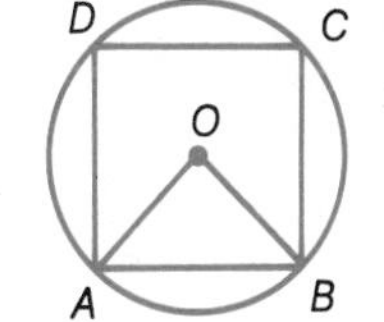

10. Find $m\angle AOB$.

11. What kind of triangle is $\triangle AOB$?

12. Find the length of $\overline{AB}$.

13. How far is $\overline{AB}$ from O?

14. A square whose side is 20 centimeters is inscribed in a circle. Find the radius of the circle. (Use the figure for Exercises **10–13.**)

A regular hexagon is inscribed in a circle of radius 14.

15. Find the length of each side of the hexagon.

16. Find the distance of each side of the hexagon from the center of the circle.

17. A regular hexagon is inscribed in a circle. Each side of the hexagon is $5\sqrt{3}$ units from the center of the circle. Find the radius of the circle.

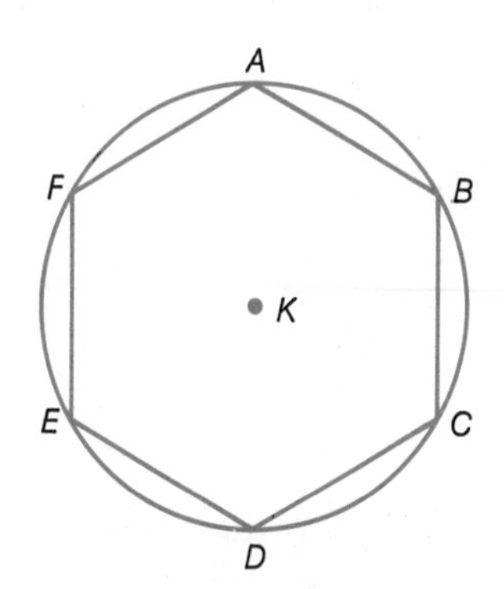

18. A, B, and C are three points on circle T. A, B, and C are joined to form $\triangle ABC$ and $m\angle A < m\angle C$. Prove that the distance from T to $\overline{AB}$ is less than the distance from T to $\overline{BC}$.

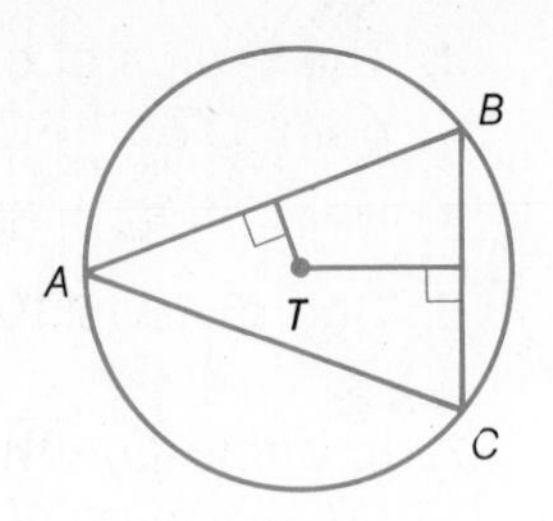

19. Prove Theorem 7-8.

Part 1.

Given: In circle O, $\overline{AB} \cong \overline{CD}$, $\overline{OE} \perp \overline{AB}$, and $\overline{OF} \perp \overline{CD}$.

Prove: $\overline{OE} \cong \overline{OF}$

Plan: Draw $\overline{OA}$ and $\overline{OC}$. Prove that $\triangle AEO \cong \triangle CFO$.

Part 2. The figure for Part 1 may be used.

Given: In circle O, $\overline{OE} \perp \overline{AB}$, $\overline{OF} \perp \overline{CD}$, and $\overline{OE} \cong \overline{OF}$.

Prove: $\overline{AB} \cong \overline{CD}$

Plan: Draw $\overline{OA}$ and $\overline{OC}$. Prove that $\triangle AEO \cong \triangle CFO$, and $\overline{AE} \cong \overline{CF}$ by C.P.C.T.C. Use Theorem 7-5 to show that $AB = 2AE$ and $CD = 2CF$. Thus, $\overline{AB} \cong \overline{CD}$.

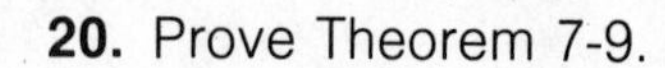

20. Prove Theorem 7-9.

Given: In circle O, $AB > CD$, $\overline{OG} \perp \overline{AB}$, and $\overline{OH} \perp \overline{CD}$.

Prove: $OG < OH$

Plan: Draw chord AE so that $\overline{AE} \cong \overline{CD}$. Let $\overline{OF}$ be perpendicular to $\overline{AE}$ and draw $\overline{FG}$. Show that $AB > AE$ and that $AG > AF$. It follows that $m\angle 2 > m\angle 4$ and, by subtraction, $m\angle 1 < m\angle 3$, which makes $OG < OF$. Since $OH = OF$, $OG < OH$.

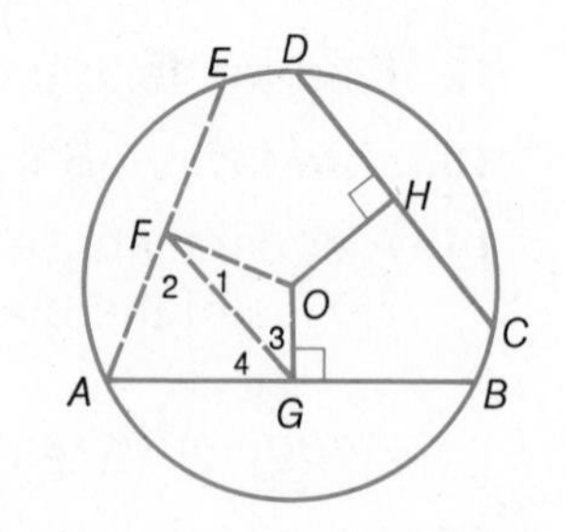

21. Prove Theorem 7-10. (Use the figure for Exercise 20.)

Given: In circle O, $OG < OH$, $\overline{OG} \perp \overline{AB}$, and $\overline{OH} \perp \overline{CD}$.

Prove: $AB > CD$

Plan: Draw the same auxiliary segments as in Exercise 20. Reverse the order of the reasons given in the proof of Exercise 20.

22. Prove that if the vertices of a square are on a circle, then the diagonals of the square intersect at the center of the circle.

Construction

Constructing an Inscribed Regular Hexagon

Given: Circle O

Required: To inscribe a regular hexagon in the circle.

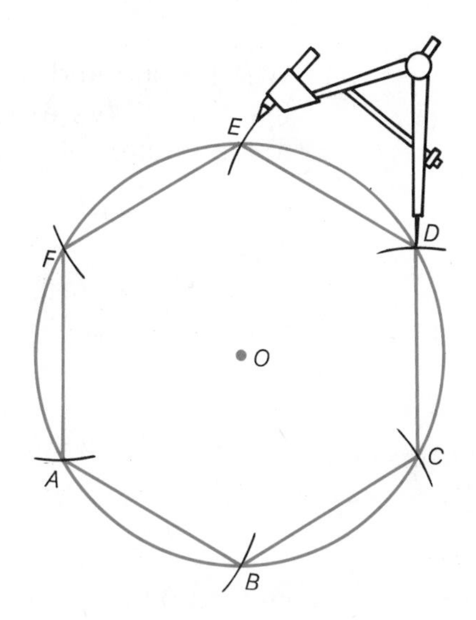

1. With the radius of the circle as the length of the opening of the compass, mark off six congruent arcs.
2. Connect the points in order.
3. Polygon $ABCDEF$ is an inscribed regular hexagon.

Exercises

1. Construct an equilateral triangle inscribed in a circle. (HINT: Start with the procedure for inscribing a hexagon. Then join alternate points.)
2. Construct a square inscribed in a circle. (HINT: First draw a diameter through C, the center of the circle. Then construct the perpendicular bisector of the diameter.)
3. Explain why polygon $ABCDEF$ as constructed above is a regular hexagon.

PUZZLE

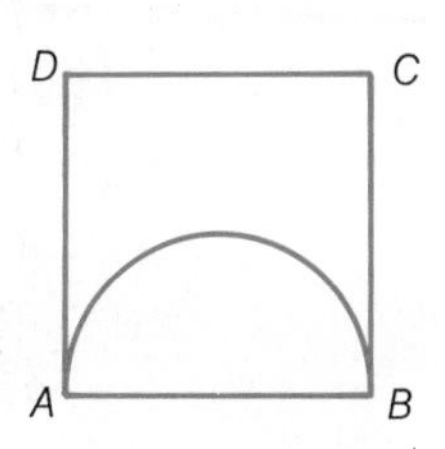

$\overline{AB}$ is a side of square $ABCD$. It is also the diameter of a semicircle.

Locate the vertices of a square with base on $\overline{AB}$ inscribed in the semicircle. Prove your answer.

7-5 Tangents to a Circle

When a line and a circle lie in the same plane and the line and the circle have exactly one point in common, the line is tangent to the circle.

Theorem 7-11: In the plane of a given circle O, a line is perpendicular to radius OC at C if and only if the line is tangent to the circle at C.

Note that Theorem 7-11 is a biconditional.

Example 1

From point X, two tangents are drawn to circle T. The tangents meet the circle at Y and Z. $\overline{TY}$, $\overline{TZ}$, and $\overline{TX}$ are drawn. Explain why $\overline{YX} \cong \overline{ZX}$.

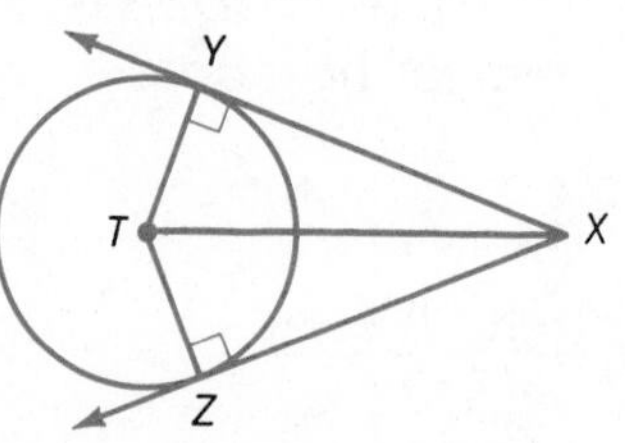

$\overline{TY} \cong \overline{TZ}$	←	Radii of the same circle are congruent.
$\overline{TX} \cong \overline{TX}$	←	Identity.
$\angle TYX \cong \angle TZX$	←	Both are right angles by Theorem 7-11; all right angles are congruent.
$\triangle TYX \cong \triangle TZX$	←	Hypotenuse-Leg Theorem
$\overline{YX} \cong \overline{ZX}$	←	C.P.C.T.C.

In Example 1, $\overline{XY}$ and $\overline{XZ}$ are called tangent segments.

Definition: A **tangent segment** is a segment from a point in the exterior of a circle to the point of tangency.

Example 1 suggests Theorem 7-12.

Theorem 7-12: The two tangent segments from the same exterior point of a circle are congruent.

You are asked to prove Theorem 7-12 in the Exercises.

Example 2

$\overline{QT}$ and $\overline{QS}$ are tangent segments to circle R, $TR = 5$, and $RQ = 13$. Find QT and QS.

$\triangle QRT$ is a right triangle ⟵ **Theorem 7-11**

$(QR)^2 = (QT)^2 + (TR)^2$

$(13)^2 = (QT)^2 + 5^2$

$169 = (QT)^2 + 25$

$(QT)^2 = 169 - 25$

$QT = 12$

$QT = QS = 12$ ⟵ $\overline{QT} \cong \overline{QS}$ **by Theorem 7-12**

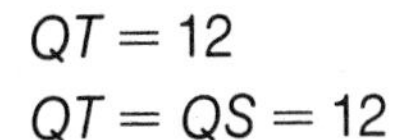

In Example 2, $\triangle QTR \cong \triangle QSR$, and $\angle 1 \cong \angle 2$. Thus, $\overline{QR}$ bisects $\angle TQS$. This suggests the following corollary.

Corollary 7-13: Two tangents to a circle from a given point in the exterior of the circle determine an angle that is bisected by the segment joining the given point to the center of the circle.

You are asked to prove this corollary in the Exercises.

Try These

*Use the figure at the right for Exercises **1** and **2**.*

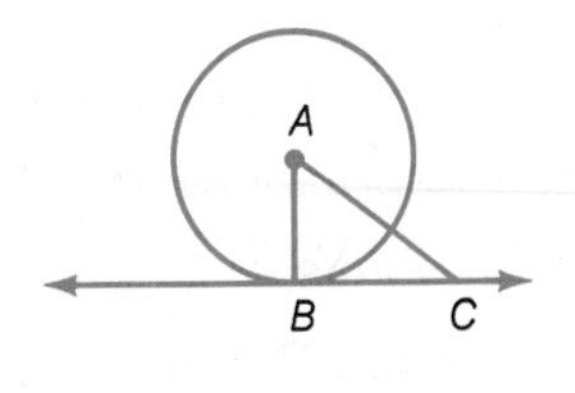

1. Given that $\overline{AB}$ is a radius and $\overleftrightarrow{BC}$ is a tangent, classify triangle ABC as an acute, obtuse, or right triangle.
2. Given that $\overline{AB}$ is a radius and $\overline{AB} \perp \overleftrightarrow{BC}$, what conclusion can be drawn? Give a reason for your answer.

3. Theorem 7-11 is stated as a biconditional. Rewrite the theorem as a conditional and its converse.

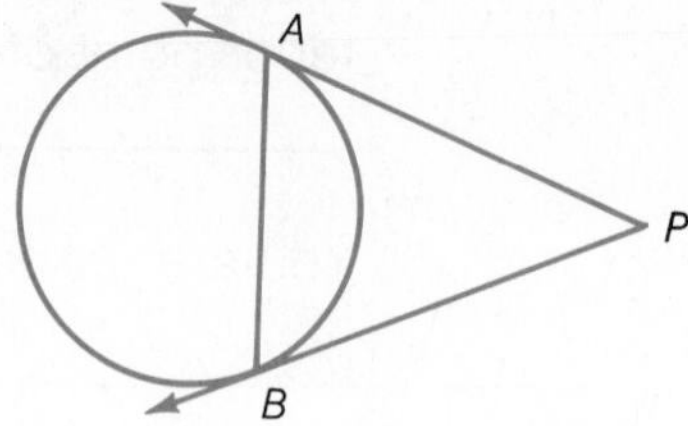

4. In the figure at the right, $\overrightarrow{PA}$ and $\overrightarrow{PB}$ are tangents. Classify $\triangle PAB$ as a scalene, isosceles, or equilateral triangle.

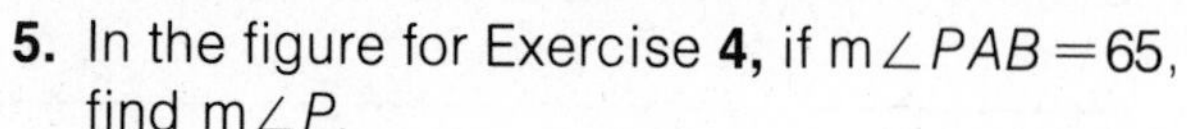

5. In the figure for Exercise **4,** if $m\angle PAB = 65$, find $m\angle P$.

Exercises

a

1. In the figure at the left below, $m\angle C = 40$ and $\overleftrightarrow{AC}$ is a tangent to circle O. Find $m\angle O$.

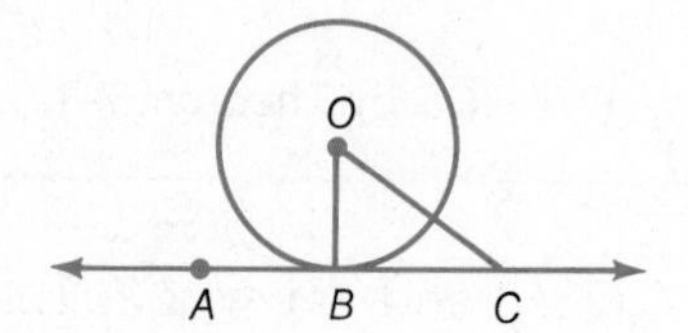

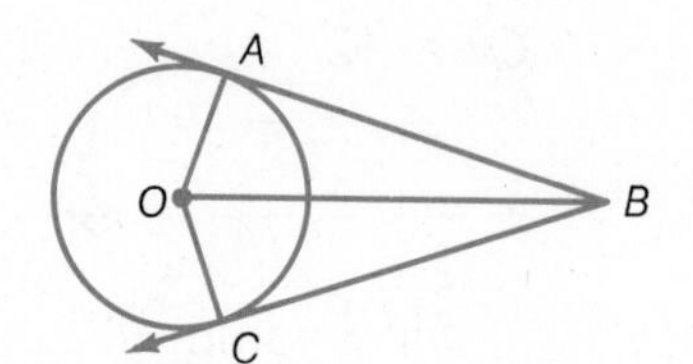

2. In the figure at the right above, $\overline{AB}$ and $\overline{CB}$ are tangent segments to circle O. Prove that $\triangle ABO \cong \triangle CBO$.
3. In the figure for Exercise **1,** if B is a point on circle O and $\overline{AC} \perp \overline{OB}$, is $\overleftrightarrow{AC}$ a tangent? Why?
4. Prove Theorem 7-12. (See Example 1.)
5. Prove Corollary 7-13.
6. Prove the following statement: *Two tangents to a circle from a given external point form an isosceles triangle with the segment joining their points of tangency.*

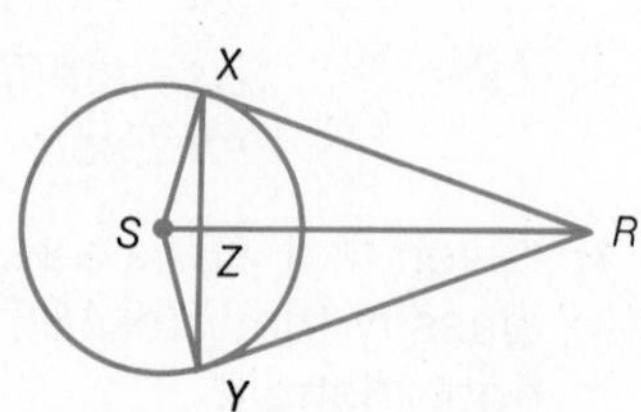

In the figure at the right, $\overline{RX}$ and $\overline{RY}$ are tangent segments to circle S. $\overline{XY}$ joins the points of tangency and $\overline{SR}$ is drawn. Classify each triangle as right, isosceles, equilateral, right isosceles, or right scalene.

7. $\triangle SXZ$
8. $\triangle RZY$
9. $\triangle SXY$
10. $\triangle RXY$

In the figure below, $\overline{CD}$ is a tangent segment to circle T, $\overline{CE} \perp \overline{TD}$, and $m\angle T = a$. Find the measure of each angle.

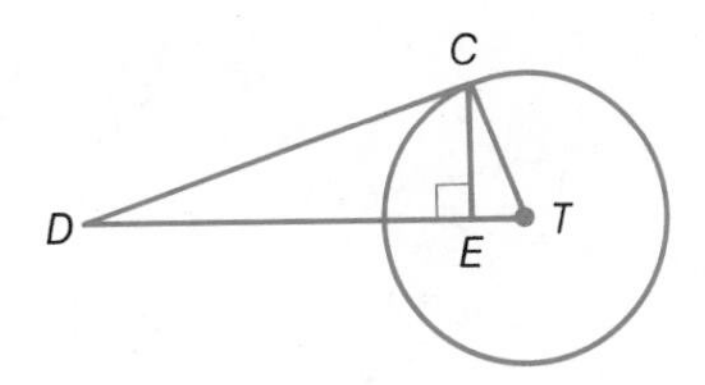

11. $\angle TCE$ **12.** $\angle ECD$ **13.** $\angle D$

Use the figure for Exercises **7–10** *and $m\angle RSX = 80$ to find the measure of each angle.*

14. $\angle RSY$ **15.** $\angle SXZ$ **16.** $\angle SYZ$

17. $\angle XZR$ **18.** $\angle ZXR$ **19.** $\angle XRZ$

20. Use the figure for Exercises **11–13** and $m\angle DCE = 56$ to find $m\angle T$.

21. In the figure at the right, $\overline{AP}$ and $\overline{BP}$ are tangent segments to circle O from P, and $m\angle ABO = 12$. Find $m\angle P$.

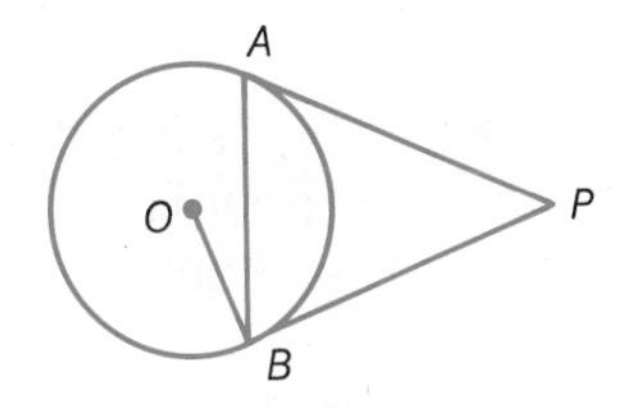

22. In the figure for Exercise **21,** prove that $m\angle P = 2m\angle ABO$.

23. The distance from a point to a circle is measured along the line that contains the point and the center of the circle. In the figure at the left below, the distance from point C to circle A is BC, where points A, B, and C are collinear. Prove that if any other point D of the circle is chosen, then $CD > CB$.

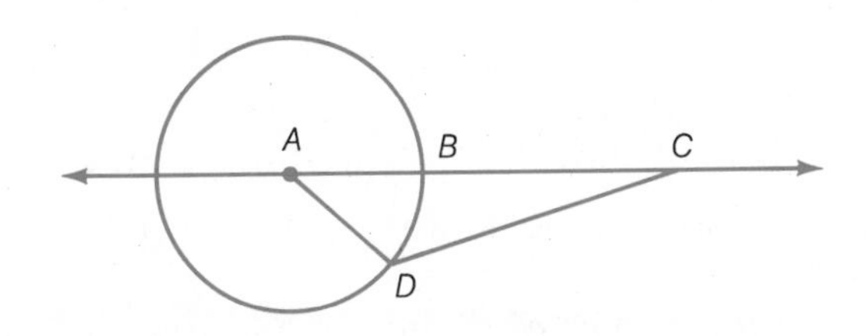

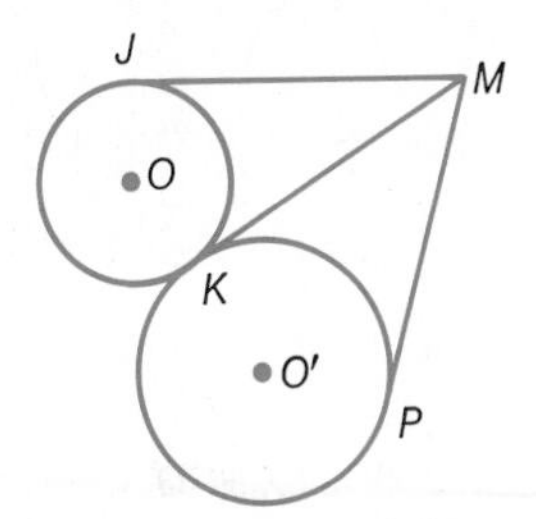

24. Segments MJ, MK, and MP are each tangent to circles O and O' as shown at the right above. Prove that $\overline{MJ} \cong \overline{MP}$.

25. Prove that if the vertices of a quadrilateral lie on a circle, then the opposite angles of the quadrilateral are supplementary.

26. In the figure at the left below, $\overline{CE}$ and $\overline{NE}$ are tangent segments to circle O. Prove that $\angle CON$ and $\angle E$ are supplementary.

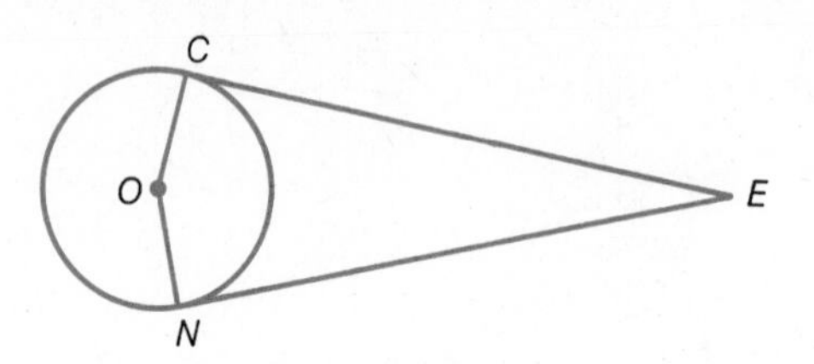

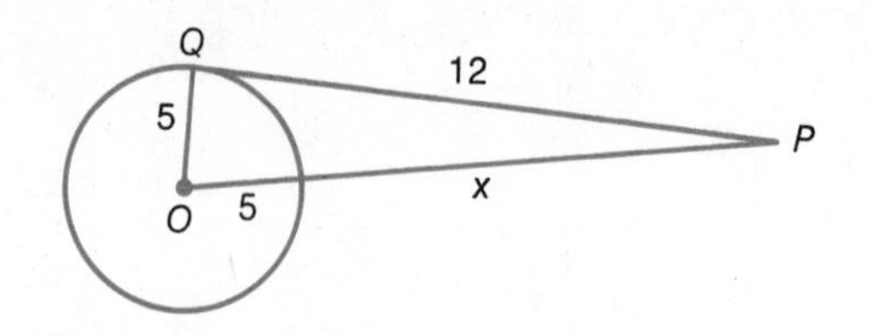

27. In the figure at the right above, the tangent segment from a point is 12 units and the radius of the circle is 5 units. Find the distance from the point to the circle.

28. In the figure at the right, A is the center of the smaller circle, and $\overline{AB}$ is a diameter of the larger circle. The circles intersect at C. $\overline{AC}$ and $\overleftrightarrow{BC}$ are drawn. Prove that $\overleftrightarrow{BC}$ is tangent to circle A.

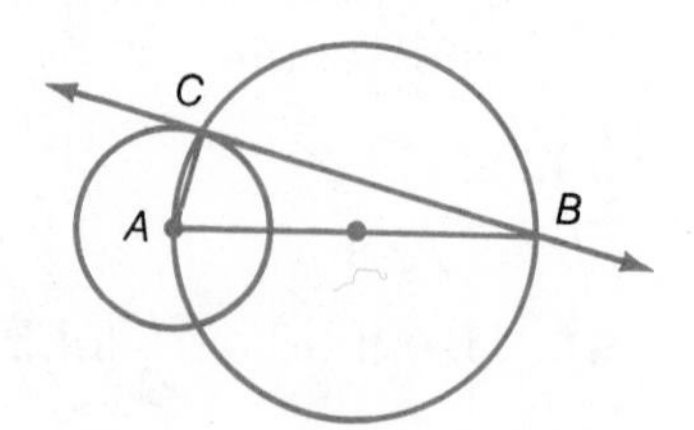

C **29.** **Prove:** If $\overline{OC}$ is a radius of circle O, then a line perpendicular to a tangent will contain C if and only if it contains O.

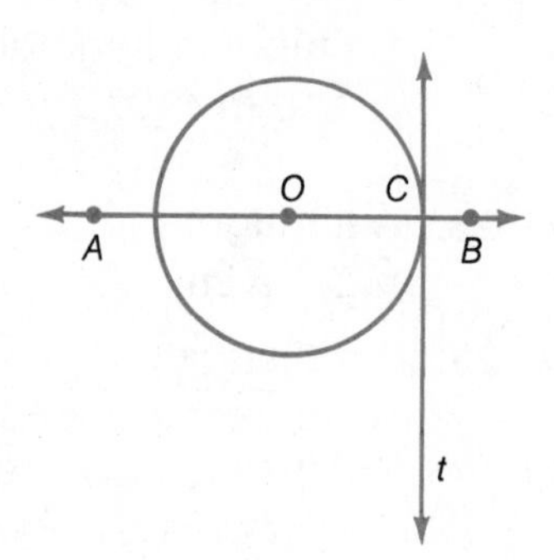

Plan: Part 1

If $\overleftrightarrow{AB}$ is perpendicular to tangent t at C, then point O is on $\overleftrightarrow{AB}$. In an indirect proof, if O is not on $\overleftrightarrow{AB}$, then draw $\overline{OC}$. $\overline{OC}$ and $\overleftrightarrow{AB}$ are both perpendicular to line t at C, which is not possible.

Part 2

If O is on $\overleftrightarrow{AB}$ and $\overleftrightarrow{AB} \perp t$, then C is on $\overleftrightarrow{AB}$. In an indirect proof, draw $\overline{OC}$. Then $\overline{OC} \perp t$ and $\overleftrightarrow{AB} \perp t$, which is impossible.

Points O and O' trisect $\overline{AB}$. O is the center of a circle with radius AO, and O' is the center of a circle with radius $O'B$. The circles intersect at points X and Y. Prove these statements.

30. $AXBY$ is a rhombus with $m\angle A = 60$.

31. $\overline{AX}$ and $\overline{AY}$ are tangent segments to circle O' from A.

7-6 Inscribed Angles

In each figure below, $\angle BAC$ is an inscribed angle. $\overset{\frown}{BC}$ is the intercepted arc.

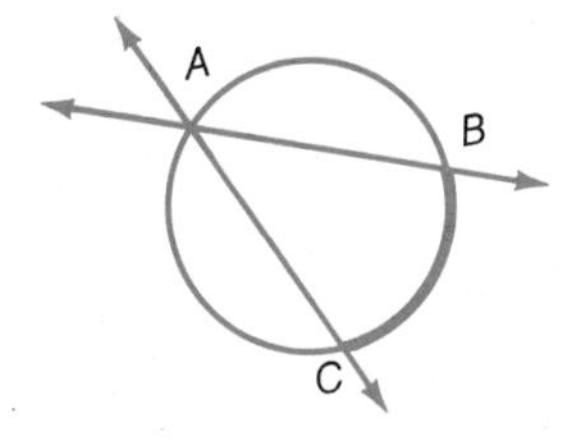

Secants *AB* and *AC* intersect at *A*.

Chords *AB* and *AC* intersect at *A*.

Definition: An **inscribed angle** is an angle whose vertex lies on the circle and whose sides contain chords of the circle.

Example 1

In circle *O*, $\overline{DE}$ is a diameter and $m\angle FOE = 80$.

a. Find $m\overset{\frown}{FE}$, $m\angle DOF$, and $m\angle D$.

b. Compare $m\angle D$ with $m\overset{\frown}{FE}$.

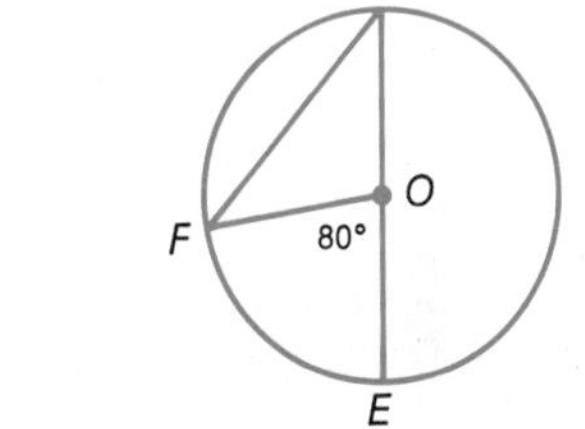

a. $m\overset{\frown}{FE} = 80$ ⟵ An arc has the same measure as its central angle.

$m\angle DOF = 100$ ⟵ $180 - 80 = 100$

$m\angle D = 40$ ⟵ $\overline{OD} \cong \overline{OF}$; $\therefore m\angle D = m\angle F = 40$.

b. $m\angle D = \frac{1}{2}m\overset{\frown}{FE}$ ⟵ $40 = \frac{1}{2}(80)$

The example suggests this theorem.

Theorem 7-14: The measure of an inscribed angle is one half the measure of its intercepted arc.

To prove Theorem 7-14, you consider three possible cases.

Given: $\angle ABC$ inscribed in circle O. **Prove:** $m\angle ABC = \frac{1}{2}m\overset{\frown}{AC}$

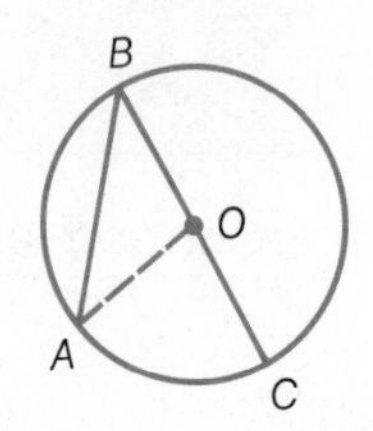

1. Point O lies on $\angle ABC$.

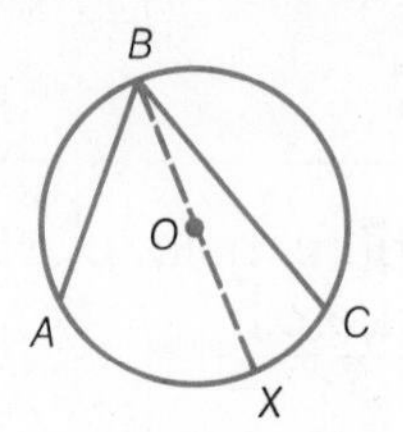

2. Point O lies in the interior of $\angle ABC$.

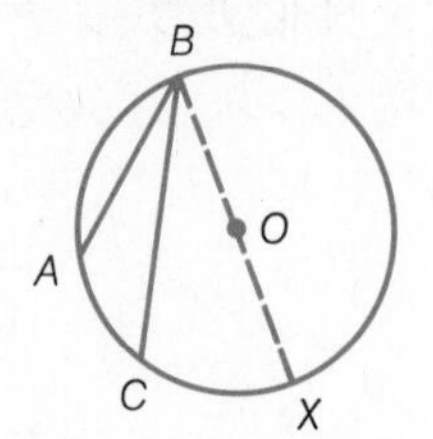

3. Point O lies in the exterior of $\angle ABC$.

Proof of Case 1: (Cases 2 and 3 are left for the Exercises.)

Statements	Reasons
1. Draw $\overline{OA}$.	1. Two points determine a line.
2. $\overline{OB} \cong \overline{OA}$	2. (1). Radii of the same circle are congruent.
3. $\angle A \cong \angle B$	3. (2). Theorem 3-1, page 116
4. $m\angle A = m\angle B$	4. (3). Definition of congruent angles
5. $m\angle A + m\angle B = m\angle AOC$	5. The measure of an exterior angle of a triangle equals the sum of the measures of the nonadjacent interior angles.
6. $m\angle B + m\angle B = m\angle AOC$, or $2m\angle B = m\angle AOC$	6. (4). (5). Substitution Principle
7. $m\angle B = \frac{1}{2}m\angle AOC$	7. (6). Multiplication Postulate for Equations
8. $m\overset{\frown}{AC} = m\angle AOC$	8. Definition, page 309
9. $m\angle B = \frac{1}{2}m\overset{\frown}{AC}$	9. (7). (8). Substitution Principle

Example 2

In the circle at the right, $m\overset{\frown}{TN} = 120$. Find $m\angle TAN$, $m\angle TEN$, and $m\angle TON$.

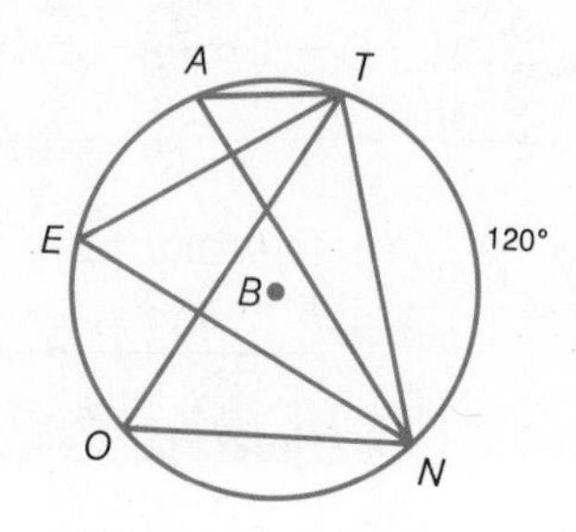

$m\angle TAN = \frac{1}{2}(120) = 60$ ← Theorem 7-14

$m\angle TEN = \frac{1}{2}(120) = 60$

$m\angle TON = \frac{1}{2}(120) = 60$

In Example 2, inscribed angles A, E, and O intercept the same arc. Thus, angles A, E, and O are congruent.

Theorem 7-15: If inscribed angles intercept the same arc or congruent arcs, the angles are congruent.

Try These

Use circle O for Exercises **1–3.** *$\overline{BC}$ is a diameter and $m\angle A = 22$.*

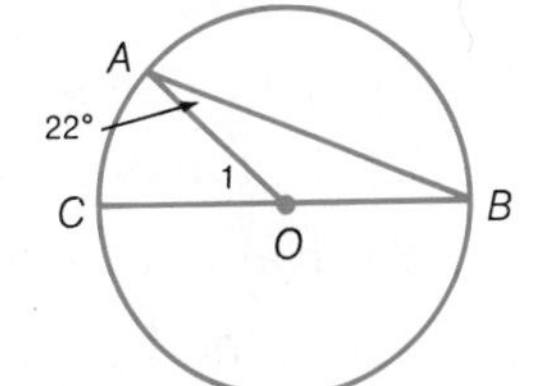

1. Find $m\angle 1$.
2. Find $m\widehat{AC}$.
3. Name an inscribed angle in circle O.

Use the circle at the right below for Exercises **4–7.**

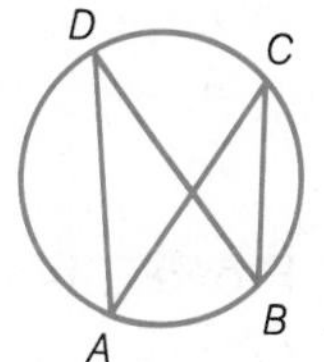

4. $m\widehat{AB} = 60$ $\quad m\angle C = $ __?__ $\quad m\angle D = $ __?__
5. $m\angle D = 22$ $\quad m\widehat{AB} = $ __?__ $\quad m\angle C = $ __?__
6. $m\widehat{CD} = 85$ $\quad m\angle B = $ __?__ $\quad m\angle A = $ __?__
7. $m\angle B = a$ $\quad m\widehat{DC} = $ __?__ $\quad m\angle A = $ __?__

Exercises

For Exercises **1–23,** *refer to the figures below. For Exercises* **1–6,** *name the arc intercepted (cut off) by each angle.*

a

1. $\angle A$

2. $\angle B$
3. $\angle C$
4. $\angle D$
5. $\angle E$
6. $\angle F$

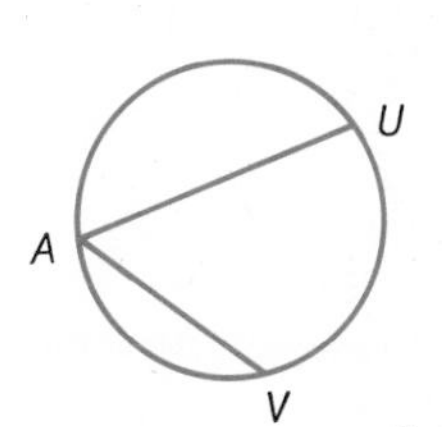

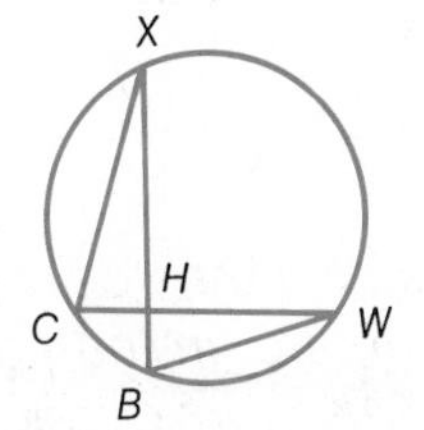

For Exercises **7–12,** *$m\widehat{UV} = 80$, $m\widehat{XW} = 170$, and $m\widehat{YZ} = 36$. Find the measure of each angle.*

7. $\angle A$ **8.** $\angle B$ **9.** $\angle C$ **10.** $\angle D$ **11.** $\angle E$ **12.** $\angle F$

13. If $m\widehat{UAV} = 236$, find $m\angle A$.

14. If $m\widehat{UAV} = 5(m\widehat{UV})$, find $m\angle A$.

15. Is $\angle C$ congruent to $\angle B$? Is $\angle X$ congruent to $\angle W$? Is $\triangle XHC$ similar to $\triangle WHB$?

*For Exercises **16–20**, $m\widehat{CX} = 100$, $m\widehat{CB} = 40$, and $m\widehat{BW} = 55$. Find each of the following.*

16. $m\widehat{WX}$ 17. $m\angle X$ 18. $m\angle C$ 19. $m\angle B$ 20. $m\angle W$

21. Are angles D, E, and F congruent? Why or why not?

22. Name two inscribed angles that intercept $\widehat{DE}$. Are they congruent?

23. Name two inscribed angles that intercept $\widehat{EF}$. Are they congruent?

24. In the figure at the right, angles X and Y are inscribed angles and $\widehat{AB} \cong \widehat{CD}$. Is $\angle X$ congruent to $\angle Y$? Give a reason for your answer.

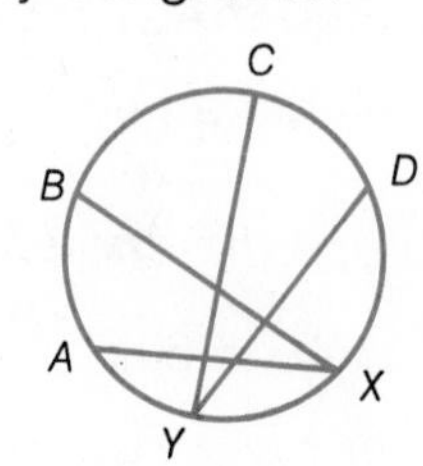

25. Prove Case 2 for Theorem 7-14.
Case 2: Point O lies in the interior of $\angle ABC$.
(HINT: Draw diameter BX.)

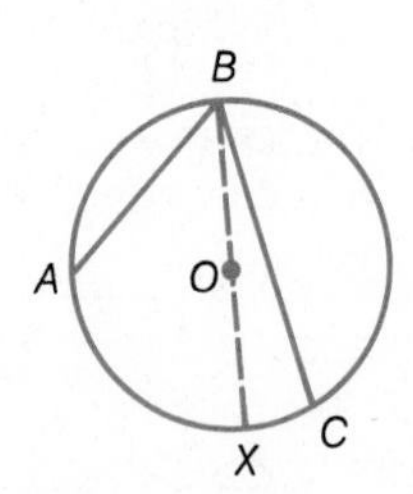

26. Prove Case 3 for Theorem 7-14.
Case 3: The center of the circle lies in the exterior of $\angle ABC$.
(HINT: Draw diameter BX.)

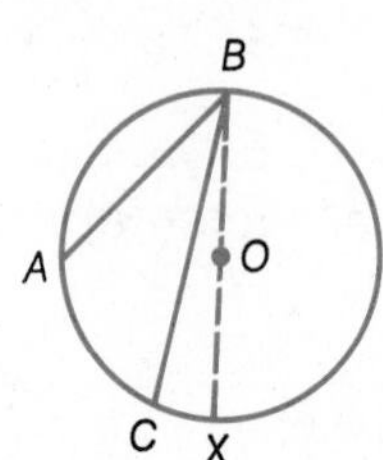

An angle is sometimes described as being inscribed in an arc. In the figure at the right, $\angle MAK$ is <u>inscribed in</u> major arc MAK. The angle <u>intercepts</u> $\widehat{MK}$.

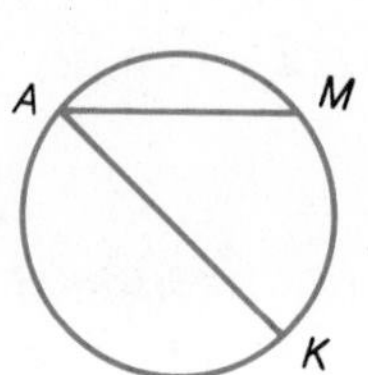

*Use the figures for Exercises **1–23** to name the arc in which each angle is inscribed.*

27. $\angle A$ 28. $\angle B$ 29. $\angle C$ 30. $\angle D$ 31. $\angle E$ 32. $\angle F$

*In the figures for Exercises **1–23,** name the angles inscribed in each given major arc.*

33. $\widehat{XBW}$ **34.** $\widehat{YEZ}$ **35.** $\widehat{DZE}$

In the figure at the right, $\overline{AB}$, $\overline{BC}$, and $\overline{CD}$ are chords, $m\widehat{ADC} = 136$, and $m\widehat{BAD} = 148$.

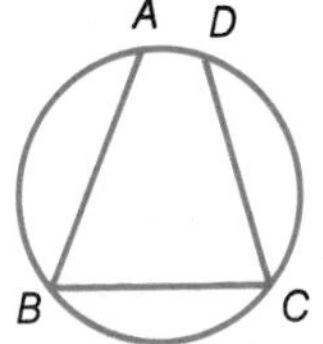

36. Find $m\angle B$. **37.** Find $m\angle C$.

38. In the figure at the left below, E is not the center of the circle. Find $m\angle B$, $m\angle C$, and $m\angle AEC$.

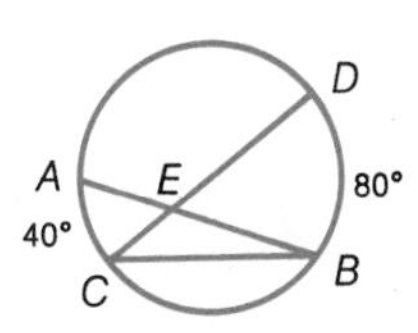

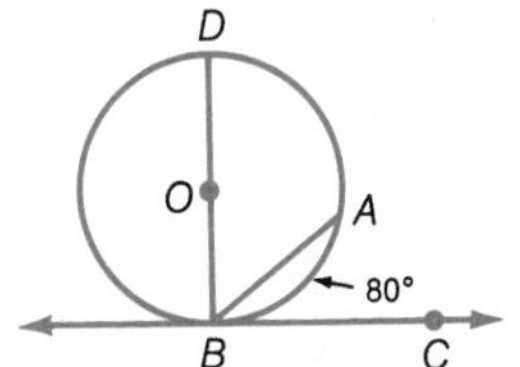

39. In the figure at the right above, $\overline{DB}$ is a diameter, $\overleftrightarrow{BC}$ is a tangent, and $m\widehat{AB} = 80$. Find $m\widehat{BAD}$, $m\widehat{AD}$, $m\angle DBA$, $m\angle DBC$, and $m\angle ABC$.

40. In the figure at the left below, $m\widehat{PT} = 40$ and $m\widehat{MQ} = 100$. Find $m\angle MTQ$, $m\angle M$, and $m\angle R$.

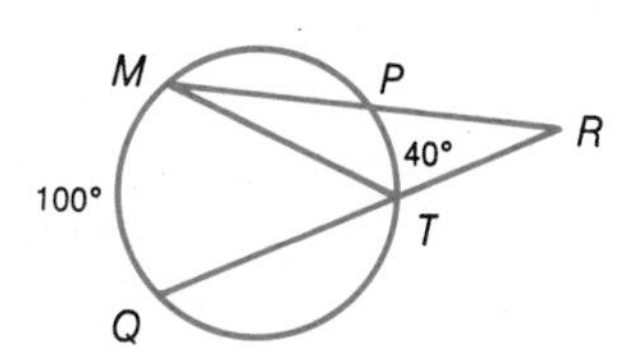

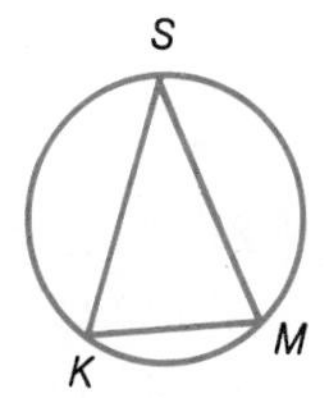

41. In the figure at the right above, $m\widehat{KM} = 2x + 8$, $m\widehat{KS} = 4x - 20$, and $m\widehat{SM} = 3x + 12$. Find $m\angle K$, $m\angle S$, and $m\angle M$.

42. In circle R below, $\overline{TP}$, $\overline{JM}$, $\overline{MP}$, and $\overline{JT}$ are chords. Prove that $\angle T \cong \angle M$, $\angle J \cong \angle P$, and $\triangle JAT \sim \triangle PAM$.

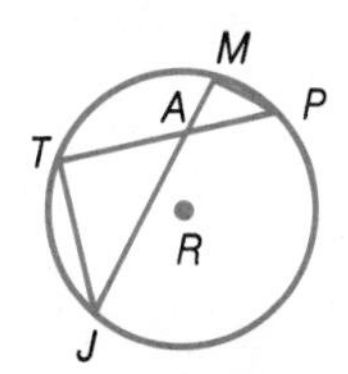

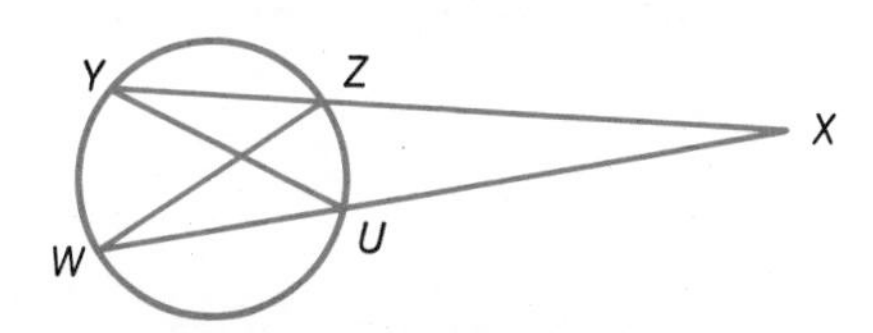

43. Use the figure at the right above to prove $\triangle XYU \sim \triangle XWZ$.

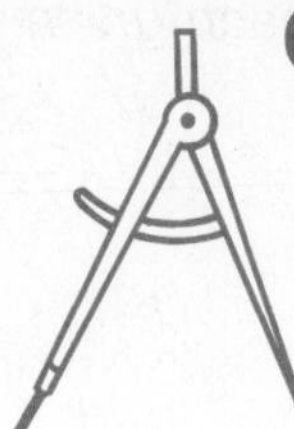

Constructions

Constructing a Tangent to a Circle at a Point on the Circle

Given: Circle O and P, a point on circle O.

Required: To construct a tangent to circle O at P.

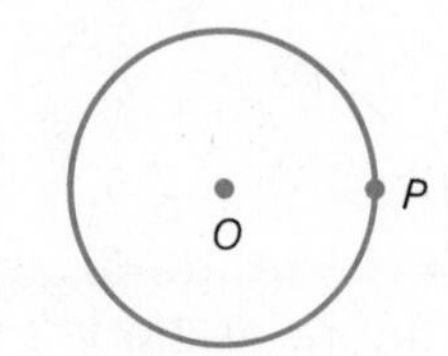

1. Draw $\overrightarrow{OP}$.

2. At P on $\overrightarrow{OP}$, construct line PQ perpendicular to $\overrightarrow{OP}$.

Then $\overleftrightarrow{PQ}$ is tangent to circle O at P.

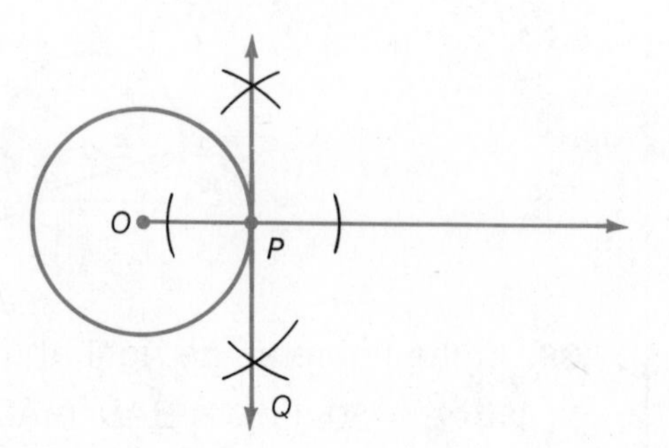

Constructing a Tangent to a Circle From a Point Outside the Circle

Given: Circle O and P, a point outside circle O.

Required: To construct two tangents to circle O from P.

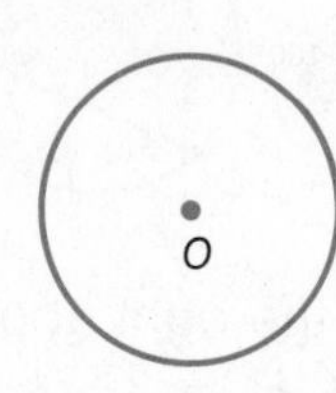

1. Draw $\overline{OP}$. Construct the perpendicular bisector of $\overline{OP}$. Label the midpoint of $\overline{OP}$ point Q.

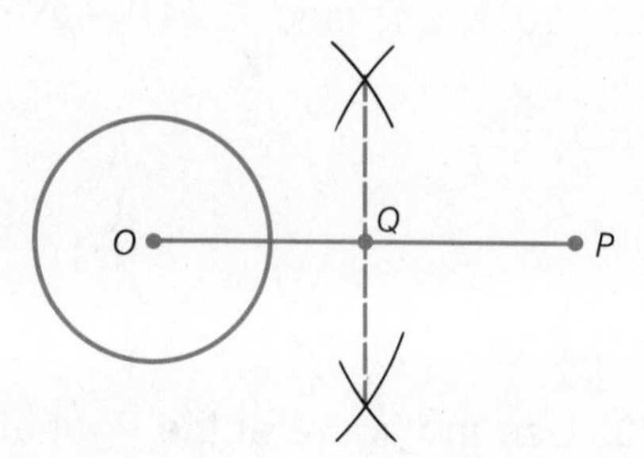

2. With Q as center and radius OQ, construct a circle intersecting the given circle at points X and Y.

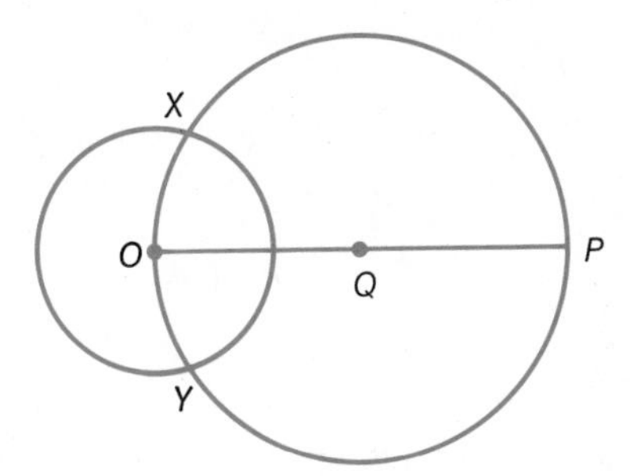

3. Draw $\overrightarrow{PX}$ and $\overrightarrow{PY}$.

Then $\overrightarrow{PX}$ and $\overrightarrow{PY}$ are tangents to circle O from P.

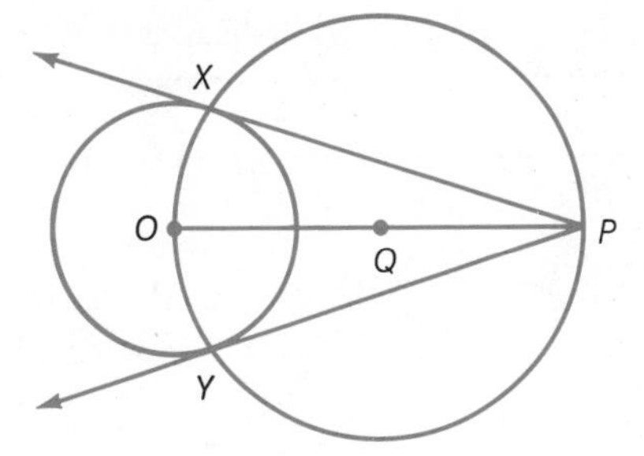

Exercises

1. A circle of radius 2 centimeters has a point R located on its circumference. Construct a tangent to the circle at R.
2. A circle of radius 2 centimeters has point R located 5 centimeters from its center. From R, construct two tangents to the circle.
3. Prove the construction of Exercise 1.
4. Prove the construction of Exercise 2.
5. Draw a circle and place a point A outside the circle. Construct an isosceles triangle with vertex angle at A so that all three sides of the triangle will be tangent to the circle.

Remember

Identify each statement as True or False. If a statement is false, tell why it is false.

1. A diameter of a circle contains the center of the circle.
2. A diameter of a circle is a chord of the circle.
3. Parallel chords in a circle are equidistant from the center of the circle.
4. The opposite angles of a parallelogram are congruent.
5. The opposite angles of a parallelogram are supplementary.

The answers are on page 365. If you need help, see pages 207, 208, 304, and 318.

7-7 More Inscribed Angles

Example 1

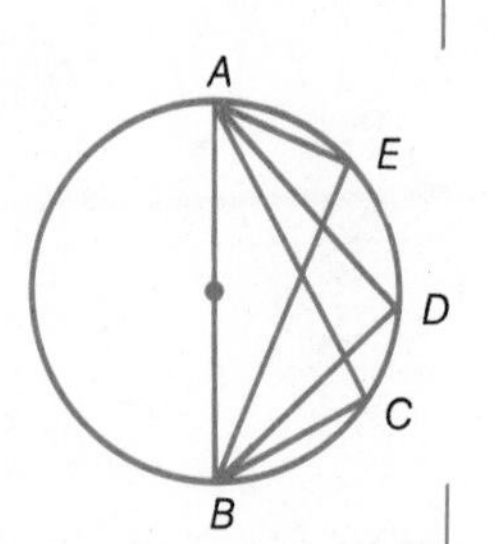

In the circle at the right, $\overline{AB}$ is a diameter. Find $m\angle E$, $m\angle D$, and $m\angle C$.

$m\angle E = \frac{1}{2}(m\widehat{AB}) = \frac{1}{2}(180) = 90$ ⟵ **Theorem 7-14**

$m\angle D = \frac{1}{2}(m\widehat{AB}) = 90$

$m\angle C = \frac{1}{2}(m\widehat{AB}) = 90$

The example suggests this corollary which is a biconditional.

Corollary 7-16: An inscribed angle is a right angle if and only if it is inscribed in a semicircle.

Example 2

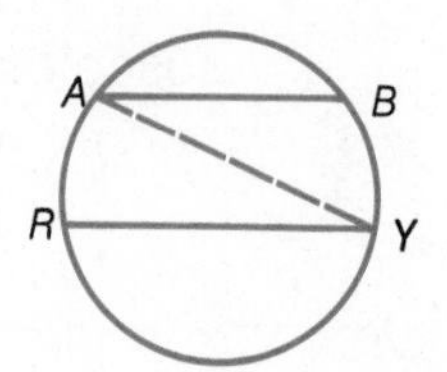

In circle O, chords AB and RY are parallel. Explain why $\widehat{AR} \cong \widehat{BY}$.

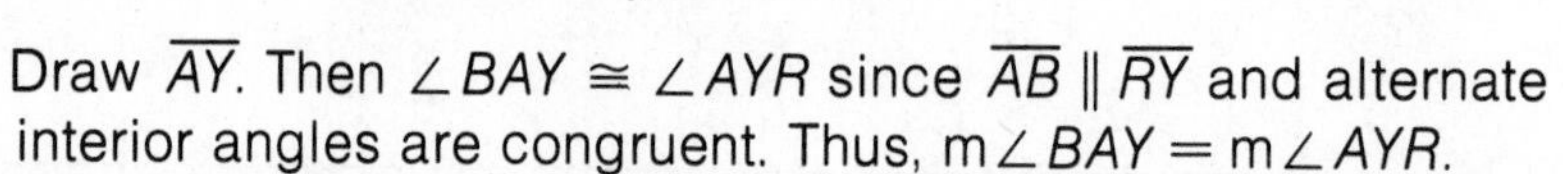

Draw $\overline{AY}$. Then $\angle BAY \cong \angle AYR$ since $\overline{AB} \parallel \overline{RY}$ and alternate interior angles are congruent. Thus, $m\angle BAY = m\angle AYR$.

Let the measure of each angle equal x. Then $m\widehat{BY} = 2x$ and $m\widehat{AR} = 2x$. Thus, $m\widehat{BY} = mAR$ and $\widehat{BY} \cong \widehat{AR}$.

Example 2 suggests Corollary 7-17.

Corollary 7-17: If two secants of the same circle are parallel, then the arcs between them are congruent.

A third corollary follows from the theorem about inscribed angles. The proof is left for you in the Exercises.

Corollary 7-18: The opposite angles of an inscribed quadrilateral are supplementary.

Example 3

Quadrilateral $ABCD$ is inscribed in a circle, $\overline{AB} \parallel \overline{CD}$, $m\widehat{AB} = 130$, and $m\angle D = 110$.
Find $m\widehat{BC}$, $m\widehat{AD}$, $m\angle B$, $m\angle C$, and $m\angle A$.

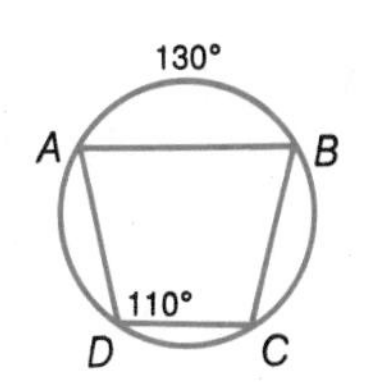

Arc or Angle	Measure	Reason
$\widehat{BC}$	90	Since $m\angle D = 110$, $m\widehat{ABC} = 220$. Since $m\widehat{BC} = m\widehat{ABC} - m\widehat{AB}$, $m\widehat{BC} = 220 - 130 = 90$.
$\widehat{AD}$	90	Since $\overline{AB} \parallel \overline{CD}$, $m\widehat{AD} = m\widehat{BC}$ by Corollary 7-17.
$m\angle B$	70	By Corollary 7-18, $\angle B$ is supplementary to $\angle D$, and $m\angle D = 110$.
$m\angle C$	110	$m\angle C = \frac{1}{2}m\widehat{DAB} = \frac{1}{2}(220) = 110$
$m\angle A$	70	By Corollary 7-18, $\angle C$ and $\angle A$ are supplementary.

Try These

*In the figure for Exercises **1–8,** $\overline{XZ}$ is a diameter and $\overline{YZ} \parallel \overline{XR}$. Classify each statement as True or False. Explain each answer.*

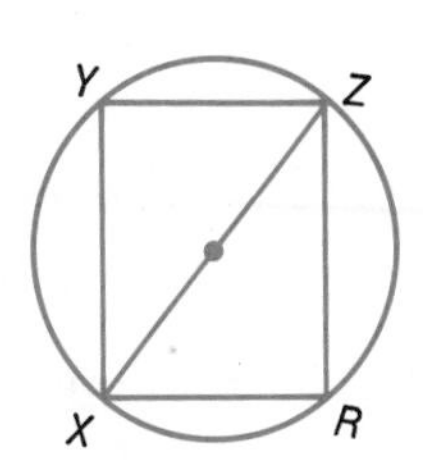

1. $m\angle XYZ = 90$.
2. $\triangle XRZ$ is an obtuse triangle.
3. $m\widehat{XY} = m\widehat{ZR}$
4. $m\angle YZX = m\angle ZXR$
5. $m\angle YXZ + m\angle RZX = 180$
6. $m\angle Y + m\angle R = 180$
7. $m\angle YZR + m\angle YXR = 180$
8. If $m\angle RZX = 58$, then $m\angle YXZ = 58$.
9. State Corollary 7-16 as a conditional and its converse.

Exercises

In circle O, $\overline{WT}$ is a diameter, points Q and S are on the circle, $m\widehat{ST} = 60$, and $m\angle QWT = 50$. Find each measure.

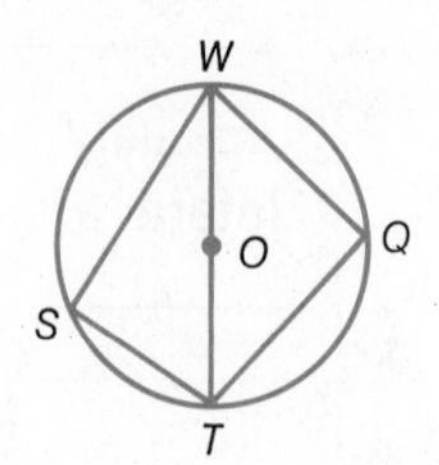

a

1. $\angle S$
2. $\angle Q$
3. $\widehat{WS}$
4. $\angle SWT$
5. $\angle WTS$
6. $\widehat{QT}$
7. $\widehat{WQ}$
8. $\angle WTQ$

For Exercises **9–12,** *O is the center of the circle and $\overline{ZY} \parallel \overline{TR}$. Find x.*

9.

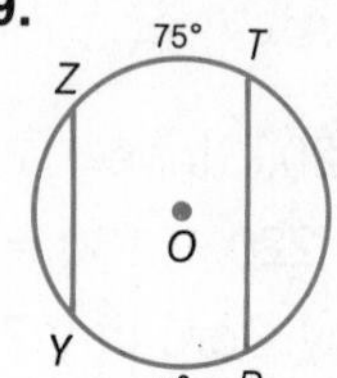

10.

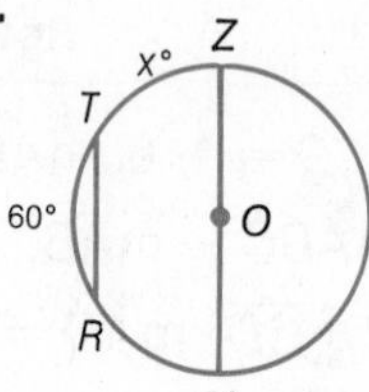

11.

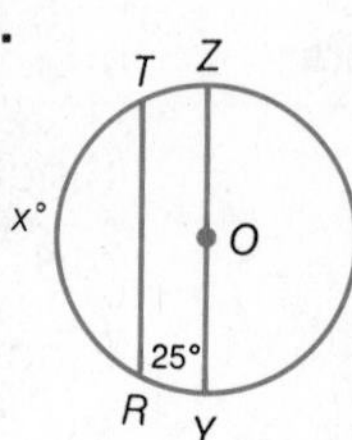

12.

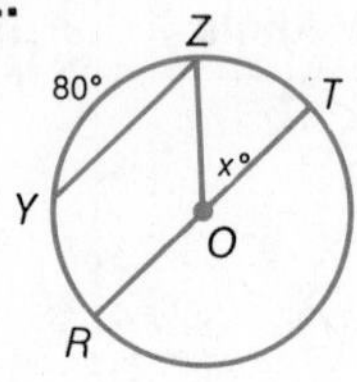

13. In the figure at the right, *PQRS* is an inscribed quadrilateral, and $m\widehat{RSP} = 206$. Find $m\angle PST$.

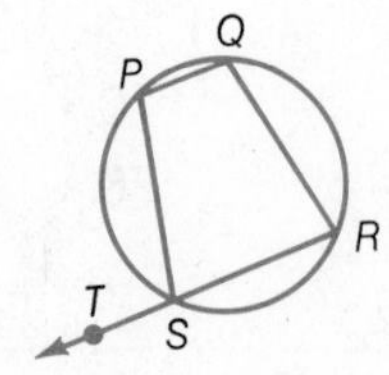

14. In inscribed quadrilateral *ABCD*, $m\widehat{AB} = 90$, $m\widehat{BC} = 110$, and $m\widehat{CD} = 70$. Find the measures of the angles of the quadrilateral.

15. Use the figure at the left below to prove that $\widehat{CAB} \cong \widehat{DBA}$ if $\overleftrightarrow{AB} \parallel \overleftrightarrow{CD}$.

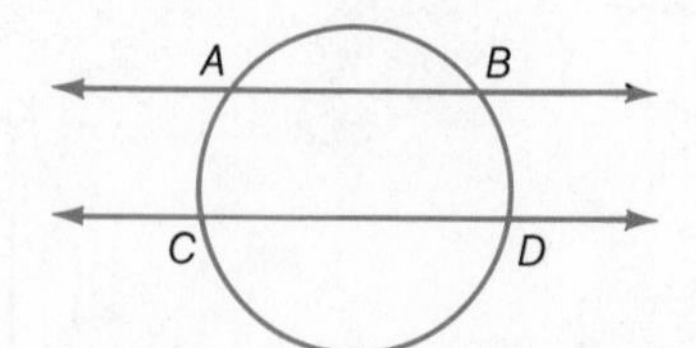

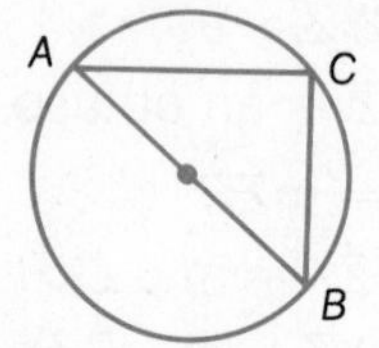

16. In the figure at the right above, $\overline{AB}$ is a diameter of the circle and $m\widehat{AC} = \frac{1}{2}m\widehat{AB}$. Find $m\angle C$, $m\angle A$, and $m\angle B$.

17. Prove that if a right triangle is inscribed in a circle, then the hypotenuse of the triangle is a diameter of the circle.

18. Prove Corollary 7-18.

Given: $m\widehat{AB} = w$, $m\widehat{BC} = x$,
$m\widehat{CD} = y$, $m\widehat{DA} = z$.

Prove: $m\angle B + m\angle D = 180$
$m\angle A + m\angle C = 180$

Plan: Show that $m\angle B = \frac{1}{2}(z + y)$ and $m\angle D = \frac{1}{2}(w + x)$. Then show that $m\angle B + m\angle D = \frac{1}{2}(z + y + w + x) = \frac{1}{2}(360)$. Follow a similar plan to prove that $m\angle A + m\angle C = 180$.

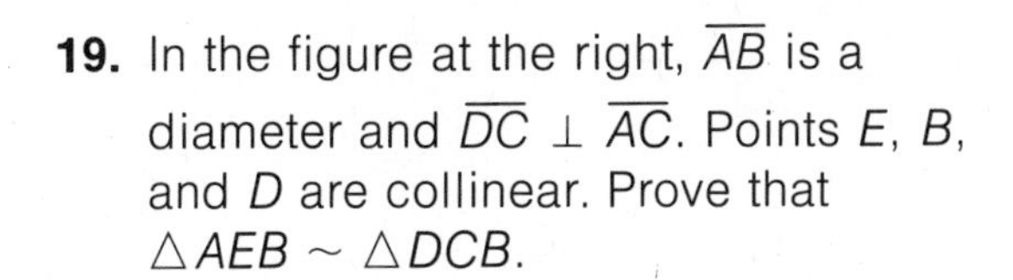

19. In the figure at the right, $\overline{AB}$ is a diameter and $\overline{DC} \perp \overline{AC}$. Points E, B, and D are collinear. Prove that $\triangle AEB \sim \triangle DCB$.

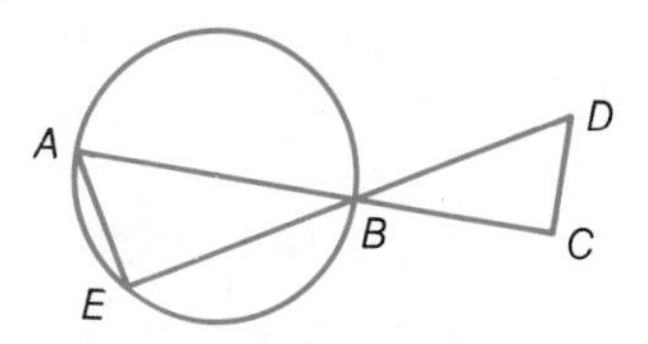

20. Quadrilateral $ABCD$ is inscribed in a circle, $m\angle A + m\angle B = 180$, and $AD \neq BC$. Prove that the quadrilateral is an isosceles trapezoid.

21. In the figure at the left below, $\overline{CD}$ is a diameter, X is the midpoint of $\overline{EF}$ and Y is the midpoint of $\overline{GH}$. Prove that $\widehat{EG} \cong \widehat{FH}$.

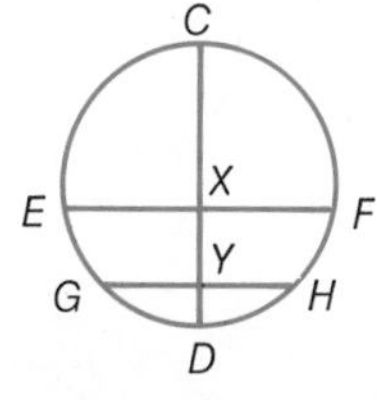

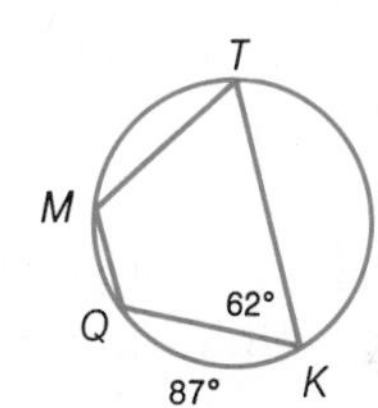

22. In the figure at the right above, $\overline{QM} \parallel \overline{KT}$, $m\widehat{QK} = 87$, and $m\angle K = 62$. Find $m\angle Q$, $m\angle T$, $m\angle M$, $m\widehat{QM}$, $m\widehat{MT}$, and $m\widehat{TK}$.

23. Prove that if a tangent and a chord are parallel, then the chords of the intercepted arcs determine an isosceles triangle.

24. Use the figure at the right to prove that the three angles of $\triangle ABC$ are congruent to three angles of $\triangle EBD$.

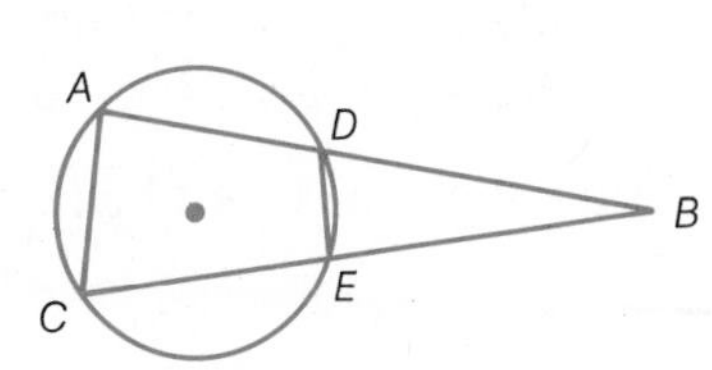

In the figure at the right, $\overline{BE}$ bisects $\angle ABC$ of inscribed $\triangle ABC$.

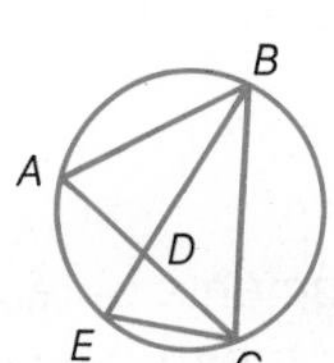

25. Prove $\triangle ABD \sim \triangle EBC$.

26. Prove $\triangle EDC \sim \triangle ECB$.

Construction

Constructing the Geometric Mean

Given: Segments with lengths r and s

Required: To construct a segment of length x such that x is the geometric mean between r and s.

1. Draw any ray AE. On $\overrightarrow{AE}$, mark off $AB = r$ and $BC = s$.

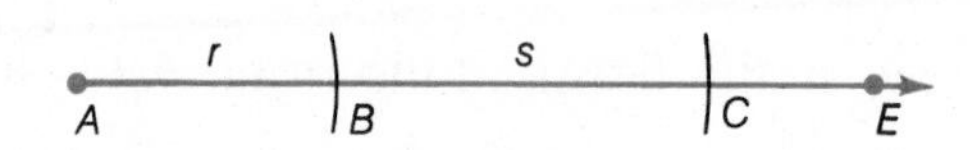

2. Construct the perpendicular bisector of $\overline{AC}$. With M, the midpoint of $\overline{AC}$, as center and AM as radius, construct a semicircle.

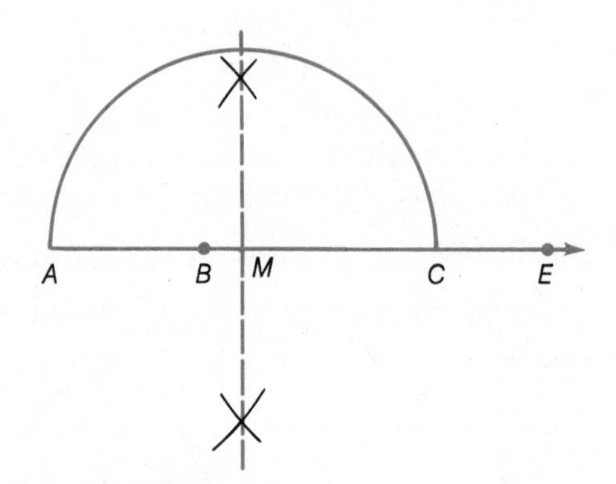

3. At B, construct $\overline{BD} \perp \overline{AC}$ so that D is a point on the semicircle. Draw $\overline{AD}$ and $\overline{CD}$.

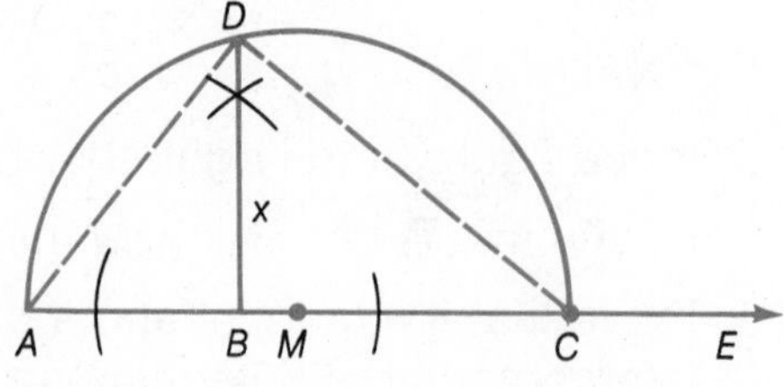

4. $\angle ADC$ is a right angle since it is inscribed in a semicircle, and $\triangle ADC$ is a right triangle. $\overline{BD}$ is the altitude to the hypotenuse, and BD is the geometric mean between AB and BC by Theorem 6-20.

Thus, the measure of $\overline{BD}$, or x, is the required geometric mean.

Exercises

1. Given segments of length 3 centimeters and 5 centimeters. Construct the geometric mean between the two segments.

2. Draw segments with length 2.5 centimeters and 3 centimeters. Construct the geometric mean between the two segments.

3. Given two segments with lengths s and t. Construct a segment equal to $\sqrt{st}$.

4. Given two segments with lengths s and t. Construct a segment equal to $\sqrt{6st}$.

Given two segments with lengths r and s, construct segments equal to each of the following.

5. $\frac{\sqrt{rs}}{3}$

6. $\sqrt{\frac{rs}{3}}$

PUZZLE

Tunnels join the twelve buildings shown in the diagram. Each tunnel joining two buildings is 1 kilometer long.

Can you find where to start and what route to follow to satisfy these conditions?

1. Each tunnel is traversed <u>at least</u> once.
2. The total distance traveled is 19 kilometers.

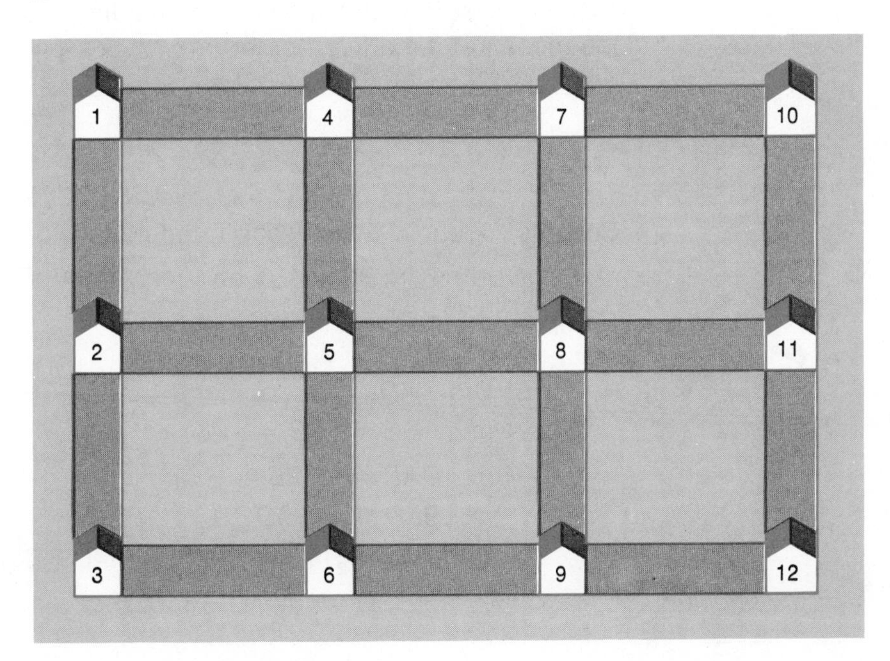

7-8 More Angles and Arcs

Example 1

Tangent AB and secant AC intersect at A, and $m\overset{\frown}{AC} = 140$. Find $m\angle CAB$ and compare it with $m\overset{\frown}{AC}$.

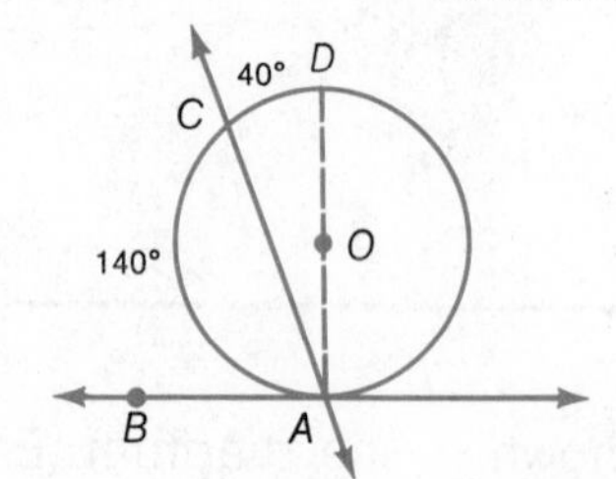

Draw diameter AD.

Since $m\overset{\frown}{ACD} = 180$, $m\overset{\frown}{CD} = (180 - 40)$, or 40.

Since $\overline{DA} \perp \overleftrightarrow{BA}$, $m\angle DAB = 90$.

Since $m\angle CAD = 20$, $m\angle CAB = 90 - 20 = 70$.

Since $m\overset{\frown}{AC} = 140$, $m\angle CAB = \frac{1}{2}m\overset{\frown}{AC}$.

Example 1 suggests this theorem.

Theorem 7-19: If a tangent and a secant (or chord) intersect in a point on a circle, the measure of the angle formed is one half the measure of the intercepted arc.

Example 2

Secants AB and CD intersect in the interior of a circle at E, $m\overset{\frown}{DB} = 60$, $m\overset{\frown}{BC} = 150$, and $m\overset{\frown}{CA} = 40$. Find $m\angle BED$. Compare $m\angle BED$ with $m\overset{\frown}{AC} + m\overset{\frown}{DB}$.

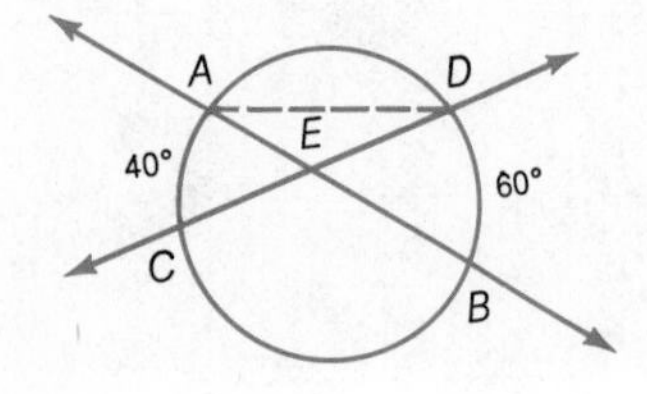

Draw $\overline{AD}$.

$m\angle ADC = \frac{1}{2}\overset{\frown}{AC} = \frac{1}{2}(40)$

$m\angle DAB = \frac{1}{2}m\overset{\frown}{DB} = \frac{1}{2}(60)$

$m\angle BED = m\angle ADC + m\angle DAB$ ← Corollary 4-18, page 186

$m\angle BED = \frac{1}{2}(40) + \frac{1}{2}(60) = \frac{1}{2}(40 + 60)$, or 50

$\therefore m\angle BED = \frac{1}{2}(m\overset{\frown}{AC} + m\overset{\frown}{DB})$

Example 2 suggests the following theorem.

Theorem 7-20: If two secants (or chords) intersect in the interior of a circle, the measure of an angle formed is one half the sum of the measures of the arcs intercepted by the angle and its vertical angle.

Example 3

Chords ST and RQ intersect at P, $\overleftrightarrow{RN}$ is tangent to the circle at R, $m\widehat{SQ} = 112$, $m\widehat{RT} = 38$, and $m\widehat{QT} = 135$. Find $m\angle QRN$ and $m\angle SPQ$.

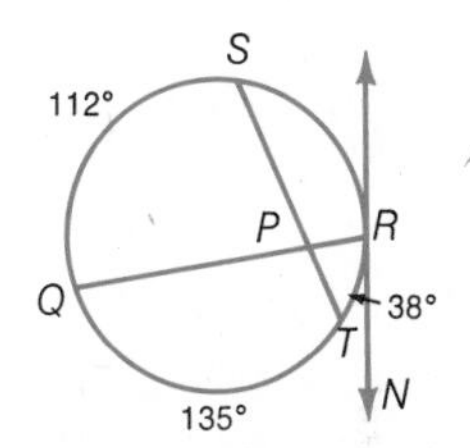

By Theorem 7-19:

$$m\angle QRN = \tfrac{1}{2}(m\widehat{QTR})$$
$$= \tfrac{1}{2}(m\widehat{QT} + m\widehat{TR})$$
$$= \tfrac{1}{2}(135 + 38)$$
$$= \tfrac{1}{2}(173), \text{ or } 86\tfrac{1}{2}$$

By Theorem 7-20:

$$m\angle SPQ = \tfrac{1}{2}(m\widehat{SQ} + m\widehat{RT})$$
$$= \tfrac{1}{2}(112 + 38)$$
$$= \tfrac{1}{2}(150), \text{ or } 75$$

Try These

Use the figure at the right to complete each statement in Exercises ***1–4.***

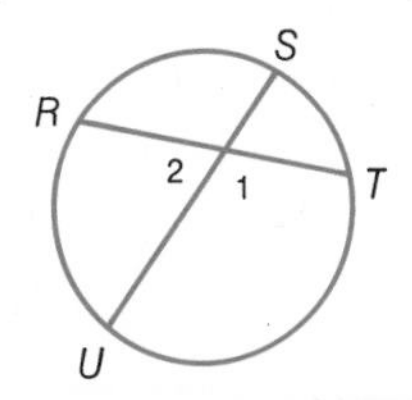

1. If $m\widehat{RS} = 140$ and $m\widehat{TU} = 96$, then $m\angle 1 =$ __?__.
2. If $m\widehat{ST} = 70$ and $m\widehat{RU} = 88$, then $m\angle 2 =$ __?__.
3. If $m\widehat{RU} = 95$ and $m\widehat{ST} = 63$, then $m\angle 2 =$ __?__.
4. If $m\widehat{RS} = 157$ and $m\widehat{TU} = 106$, then $m\angle 1 =$ __?__.

Use the figure at the right to complete each statement in Exercises ***5–7.***

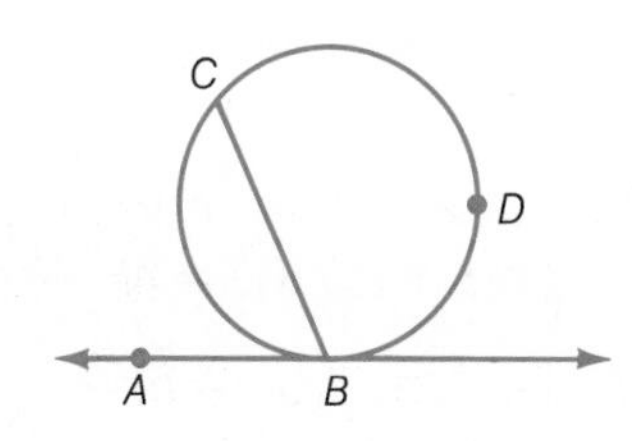

5. If $m\widehat{BC} = 82$, then $m\angle ABC =$ __?__.
6. If $m\widehat{BC} = 148$, then $m\angle ABC =$ __?__.
7. If $m\widehat{BDC} = 226$, then $m\angle ABC =$ __?__.

Exercises

a

1. In circles O, P, and Q below, $\overleftrightarrow{AB}$, $\overleftrightarrow{BC}$, $\overleftrightarrow{FY}$, and $\overleftrightarrow{RS}$ are tangents. Name the angles that are formed by a tangent and a secant or by a tangent and a chord intersecting on the circle.

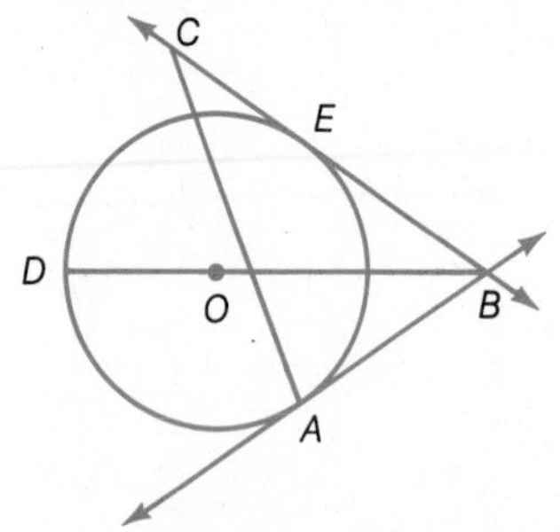

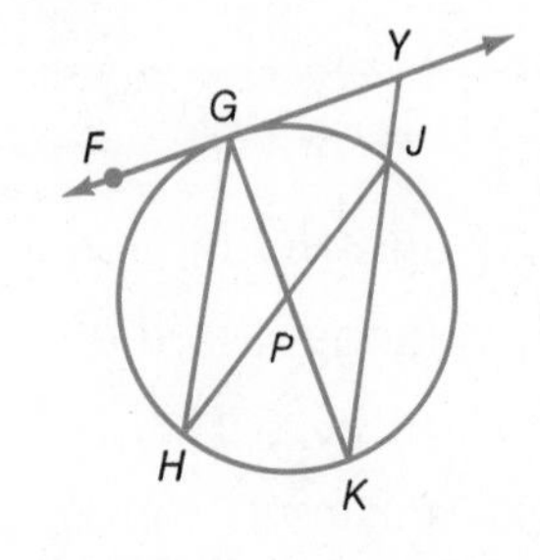

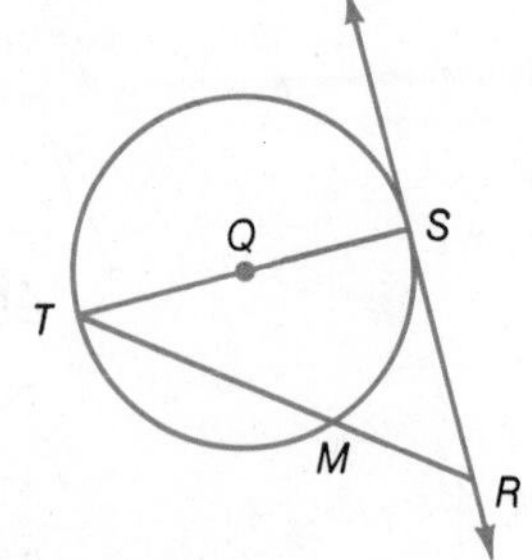

Use circle P above to name the arcs intercepted by each angle.

2. $\angle HJK$ **3.** $\angle HGK$ **4.** $\angle FGH$ **5.** $\angle JPK$

6. $\overline{AZ}$ is a chord in circle O, and $\overleftrightarrow{ST}$ is tangent at Z. If $m\widehat{AZ} = 146$, find $m\angle AZT$, $m\widehat{AYZ}$, and $m\angle AZS$.

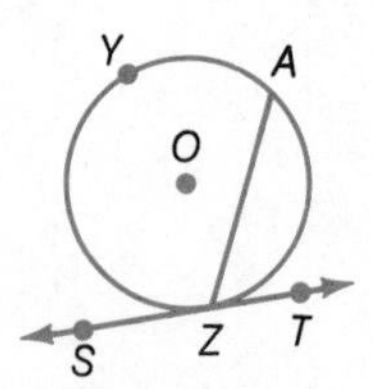

7. In the figure for Exercise 6, if $m\angle AZT = 81$, find $m\widehat{AZ}$, $m\widehat{AYZ}$, and $m\angle AZS$.

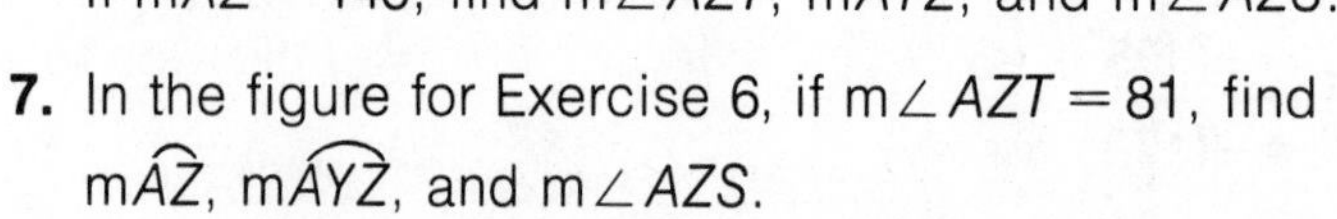

8. In the figure at the left below, $\overleftrightarrow{VU}$ is tangent to circle A at Y, $\overline{WY}$ and $\overline{XY}$ are chords such that $m\widehat{WY} = 72$ and $m\widehat{XW} = 88$. Find $m\angle UYW$, $m\angle UYX$, and $m\angle WYX$.

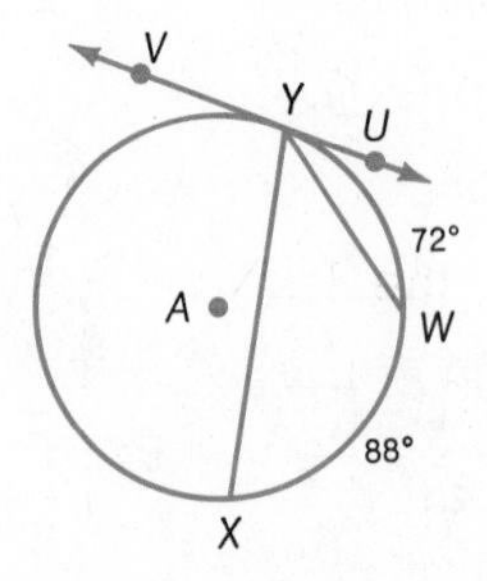

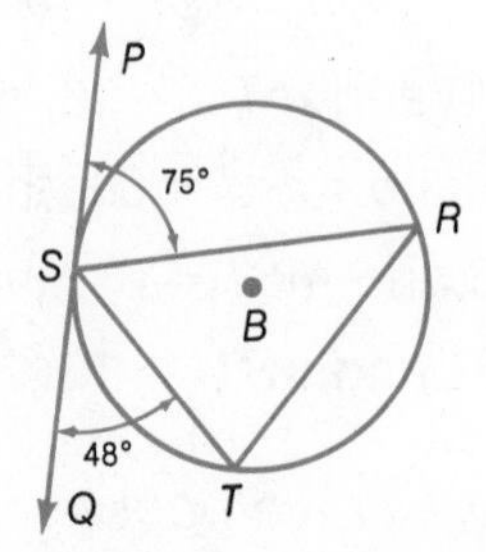

9. In the figure at the right above, $\overleftrightarrow{PQ}$ is tangent at S to circle B, $m\angle RSP = 75$, and $m\angle TSQ = 48$. Find the measure of each angle of $\triangle RST$.

10. Use the figure and <u>Given</u> for Exercise **8** to find $m\angle VYX$ and $m\angle VYW$.

*For Exercises **11–14,** use the figure below to complete each statement.*

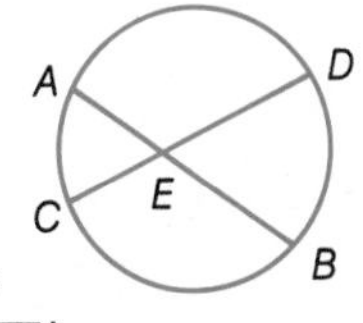

11. If $m\widehat{AC} = 50$ and $m\widehat{DB} = 80$, $m\angle AEC = \underline{\ ?\ }$.

12. If $m\widehat{AC} = 40$ and $m\widehat{DB} = 80$, $m\angle AEC = \underline{\ ?\ }$.

13. If $m\widehat{AC} = 60$ and $m\widehat{DB} = 100$, $m\angle AED = \underline{\ ?\ }$.

14. If $m\widehat{AC} = 70$, $m\widehat{AD} = 100$, and $m\widehat{DB} = 90$, $m\angle BEC = \underline{\ ?\ }$.

*In the figure at the right, $\overline{AB}$ and $\overline{CD}$ intersect at E. Find $m\widehat{BD}$ in Exercises **15–17.***

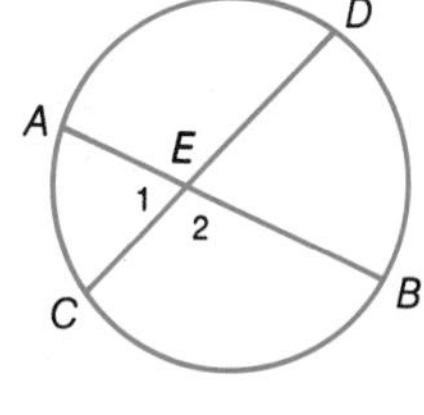

15. $m\angle 1 = 80$, $m\widehat{AC} = 100$

16. $m\angle 1 = 67$, $m\widehat{AC} = 98$

17. $m\angle 1 = 46\frac{1}{2}$, $m\widehat{AC} = 62\frac{3}{4}$

18. Prove Theorem 7-20. (See Example 2.)

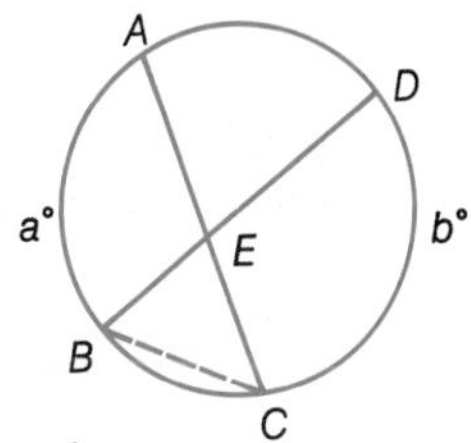

Given: Chords AC and BD intersect at E.

Prove: $m\angle AEB = \frac{1}{2}(m\widehat{AB} + m\widehat{CD})$

Plan: Let $m\widehat{AB} = a$ and $m\widehat{CD} = b$.
Draw $\overline{BC}$. Then $m\angle C = \frac{1}{2}a$, $m\angle B = \frac{1}{2}b$, and $m\angle AEB = m\angle B + m\angle C$. Complete the proof.

19. Prove Theorem 7-19. (See Example 1.)

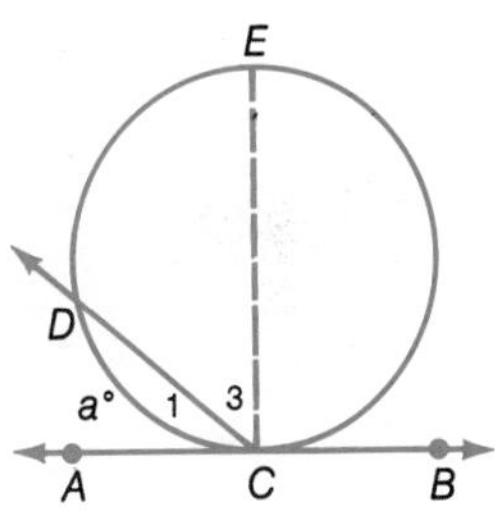

Given: $\overleftrightarrow{AB}$ is tangent to the circle at C; $\overleftrightarrow{CD}$ is a secant.

Prove: $m\angle ACD = \frac{1}{2}m\widehat{CD}$

Plan: Let $m\widehat{CD} = a$. Draw diameter CE.
Then $m\widehat{CD} + m\widehat{DE} = 180$, or $a + m\widehat{DE} = 180$.
Thus, $m\angle 3 = \frac{1}{2}(180 - a)$. Since $\overline{CE} \perp \overleftrightarrow{AB}$, $m\angle 1 + m\angle 3 = 90$, and $m\angle 1 = 90 - m\angle 3$.
Complete the proof.

*For Exercises **20–23,** refer to the figure below to find $m\widehat{BD}$.*

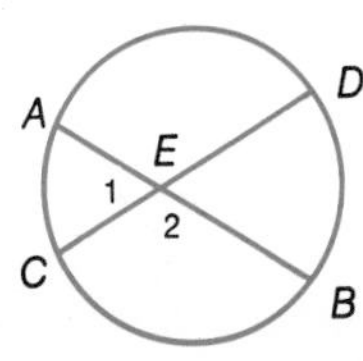

20. $m\angle 1 = a$, $m\widehat{AC} = b$

21. $m\angle 1 = 3a$, $m\widehat{AC} = a$

22. $m\angle 2 = a$, $m\widehat{AC} = b$

23. $m\angle 1 = 180 - a$, $m\widehat{AC} = \frac{a}{2}$

Remember

Complete each statement.

1. The sum of the measures of the angles of a triangle is __?__.
2. The measure of a semicircle is __?__.
3. The measure of a minor arc of a circle equals the measure of __?__.
4. The measure of a major arc of a circle equals __?__.
5. The sum of the measures of the angles of a quadrilateral is __?__.

The answers are on page 365. If you need help, see pages 179, 190, and 309.

7-9 Angles Formed by Secants and Tangents

Example 1

Secants DF and DH intersect at D, $m\widehat{FH} = 120$, and $m\widehat{GE} = 60$. Find $m\angle D$ and compare $m\angle D$ with $m\widehat{FH} - m\widehat{EG}$.

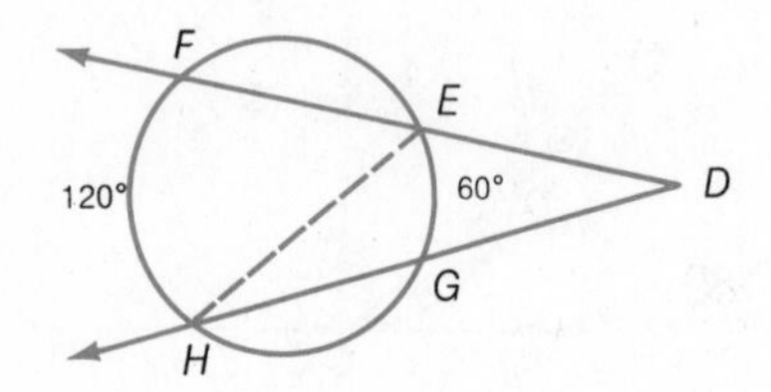

Draw $\overline{EH}$.

$m\angle FEH = \frac{1}{2}m\widehat{FH} = \frac{1}{2}(120)$

$m\angle GHE = \frac{1}{2}m\widehat{EG} = \frac{1}{2}(60)$

$m\angle D + m\angle GHE = m\angle FEH$ ⟵ Corollary 4-18, page 186

$m\angle D = m\angle FEH - m\angle GHE$

$m\angle D = \frac{1}{2}(120) - \frac{1}{2}(60) = \frac{1}{2}(120 - 60)$, or 30

$\therefore m\angle D = \frac{1}{2}(m\widehat{FH} - m\widehat{EG})$

Example 1 suggests the following theorem.

Theorem 7-21: If two secants intersect in the exterior of a circle, the measure of the angle formed by the secants is one half the difference of the measures of the intercepted arcs.

Example 2

Secant PT intersects tangent PM at P; $m\overset{\frown}{QM} = 80$, and $m\overset{\frown}{TM} = 150$. Find $m\angle P$ and compare $m\angle P$ with $m\overset{\frown}{TM} - m\overset{\frown}{QM}$.

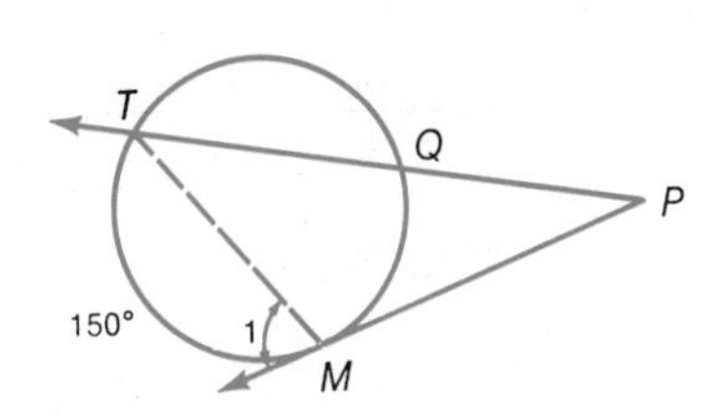

Draw $\overline{TM}$.

$m\angle 1 = \frac{1}{2}m\overset{\frown}{TM} = \frac{1}{2}(150)$

$m\angle PTM = \frac{1}{2}m\overset{\frown}{QM} = \frac{1}{2}(80)$

$m\angle P + m\angle PTM = m\angle 1$

$m\angle P = m\angle 1 - m\angle PTM$

$m\angle P = \frac{1}{2}(150) - \frac{1}{2}(80) = \frac{1}{2}(150 - 80)$, or 35

$\therefore m\angle P = \frac{1}{2}(m\overset{\frown}{TM} - m\overset{\frown}{QM})$

Example 2 suggests this theorem. Its proof is asked for in the Exercises.

Theorem 7-22: If a tangent and a secant intersect in the exterior of a circle, the measure of the angle formed is one half the difference of the measures of the intercepted arcs.

Example 3

Tangents QP and QR meet at Q and $m\overset{\frown}{PSR} = 250$. Find $m\angle Q$ and compare it with $m\overset{\frown}{PSR} - m\overset{\frown}{PR}$.

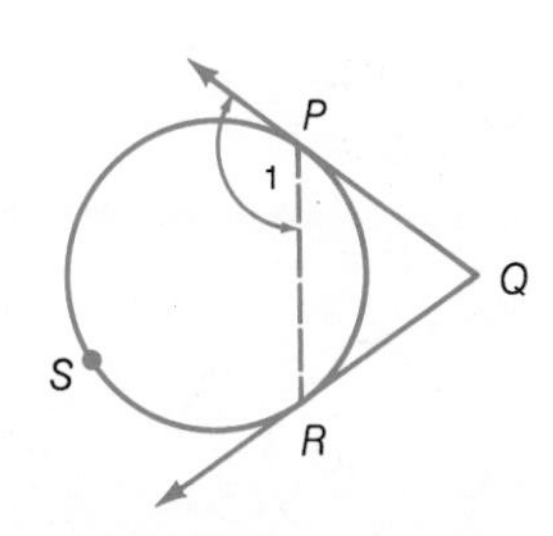

Draw $\overline{PR}$.

$m\overset{\frown}{PR} = (360 - 250) = 110$

$m\angle 1 = \frac{1}{2}m\overset{\frown}{PSR} = \frac{1}{2}(250)$

$m\angle PRQ = \frac{1}{2}m\overset{\frown}{PR} = \frac{1}{2}(110)$

$m\angle Q + m\angle PRQ = m\angle 1$

$m\angle Q = m\angle 1 - m\angle PRQ$

$m\angle Q = \frac{1}{2}(250) - \frac{1}{2}(110) = \frac{1}{2}(250 - 110)$, or 70

$\therefore m\angle Q = \frac{1}{2}(m\overset{\frown}{PSR} - m\overset{\frown}{PR})$

Example 3 suggests this theorem. Its proof is asked for in the Exercises.

Theorem 7-23: If two tangents intersect in the exterior of a circle, the measure of the angle formed is one half the difference of the intercepted arcs.

Try These

*For Exercises **1–3,** use the given information to find x.*

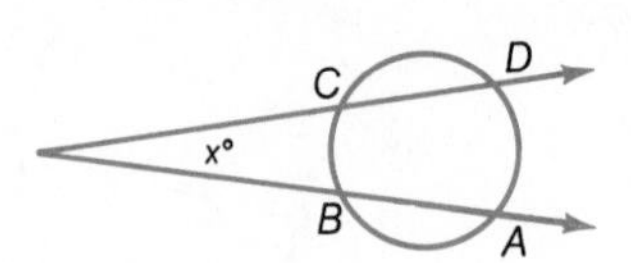

1. $m\widehat{AD} = 108$ and $m\widehat{BC} = 42$
2. $m\widehat{AD} = 130$ and $m\widehat{BC} = 28$
3. $m\widehat{AD} = 117$ and $m\widehat{BC} = 35$

$\overline{FE}$ and $\overline{FG}$ are tangent segments. Find each measure.

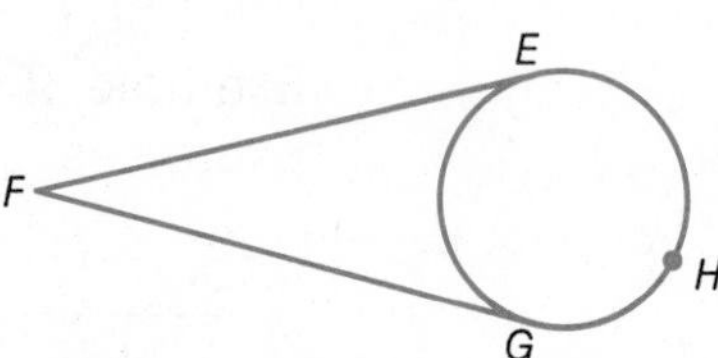

4. $m\widehat{EG} = 100$, $m\widehat{GHE} =$ _?_, $m\angle F =$ _?_
5. $m\widehat{EHG} = 250$, $m\widehat{EG} =$ _?_, $m\angle F =$ _?_
6. $m\widehat{EHG} = 3x$, $m\widehat{EG} = x$, $x =$ _?_, $3x =$ _?_, $m\angle F =$ _?_

Exercises

*Use the figure below for Exercises **1–4.***

a

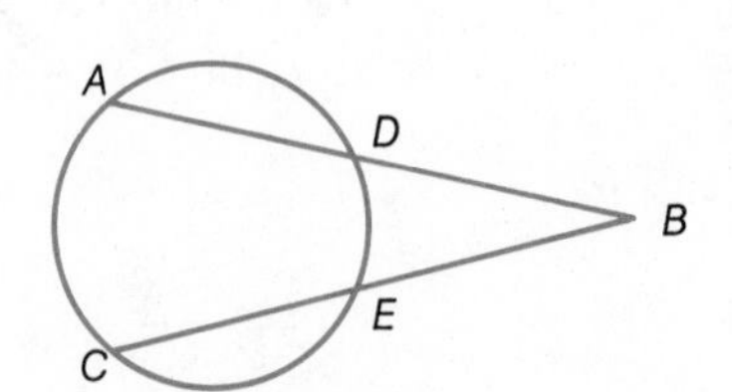

1. $m\widehat{AC} = 80$, $m\widehat{DE} = 50$, $m\angle B =$ _?_
2. $m\widehat{AC} = 94$, $m\widehat{DE} = 57$, $m\angle B =$ _?_
3. $m\angle B = 20$, $m\widehat{AC} = 100$, $m\widehat{DE} =$ _?_
4. $m\angle B = 31$, $m\widehat{DE} = 40$, $m\widehat{AC} =$ _?_

In the figure at the right, $\overleftrightarrow{MS}$ and $\overleftrightarrow{QS}$ are tangents that intersect at S.

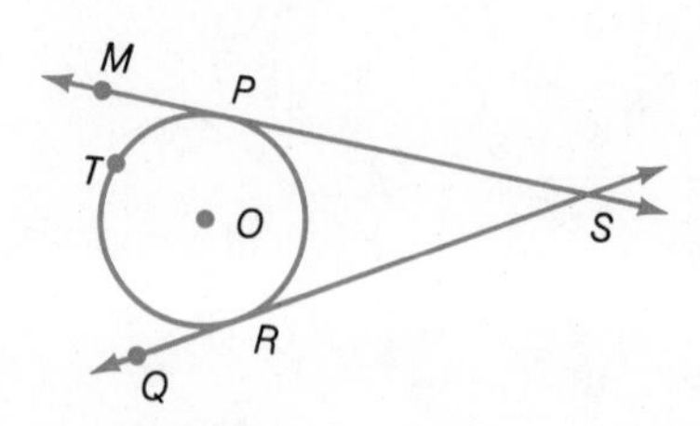

5. $m\widehat{PTR} = 220$, $m\widehat{PR} =$ _?_, $m\angle S =$ _?_
6. $m\widehat{PR} = 78$, $m\widehat{PTR} =$ _?_, $m\angle S =$ _?_
7. $m\widehat{PTR} = b$, $m\widehat{PR} =$ _?_, $m\angle S =$ _?_

*In Exercises **8–11**, use the figure below to find m$\widehat{AC}$.*

8. $m\angle B = 30$, $m\widehat{DE} = 40$

9. $m\angle B = 37$, $m\widehat{DE} = 64$

10. $m\angle B = \frac{3a}{4}$, $m\widehat{DE} = a$

11. $m\angle B = 90 - a$, $m\widehat{DE} = 90 + a$

12. Prove Theorem 7-21.

Given: Secants BA and BC

Prove: $m\angle B = \frac{1}{2}(m\widehat{AC} - m\widehat{DE})$

Plan: Let $m\widehat{AC} = a$ and $m\widehat{DE} = b$. Draw $\overline{AE}$. Then $m\angle 1 = \frac{1}{2}a$, and $m\angle 1 = m\angle A + m\angle B$. Also, $m\angle BAE = \frac{1}{2}b$. Thus, $\frac{1}{2}a = \frac{1}{2}b + m\angle B$. Complete the proof.

13. Prove Theorem 7-22. (HINT: Follow the plan outlined in Exercise **12.**)

14. Prove Theorem 7-23. (HINT: Follow the plan for Exercise **12.**)

In the figure, $\overrightarrow{EA}$ is tangent to circle O at A and secant ED intersects the circle at B and D. Diameter AC intersects $\overline{BD}$ at F, $m\angle E = 26$ and $m\widehat{AD} = 108$. Find each of the following.

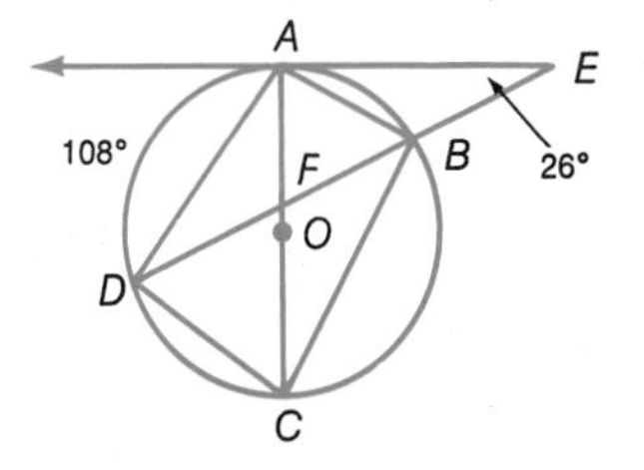

15. $m\widehat{AB}$

16. $m\widehat{BC}$

17. $m\angle DFC$

18. $m\angle EAB$

19. $m\angle ABE$

20. $m\angle DOC$

In the figure, secant AC passes through the center of circle O and $\overrightarrow{CE}$ is tangent to the circle at D. The ratio of $m\widehat{BD}$ to $m\widehat{AFD}$ is 1:4. $\overline{BD}$ and $\overline{AD}$ are chords. Find each of the following.

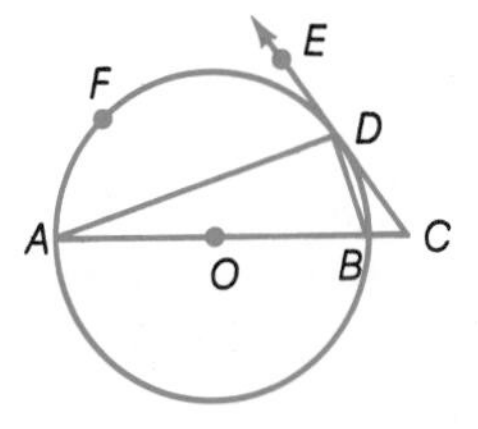

21. $m\widehat{BD}$

22. $m\angle BAD$

23. $m\angle ADE$

24. $m\angle C$

25. $m\angle DBC$

26. $m\angle ADB$

C **27.** In the figure at the right, $\overleftrightarrow{AB}$ is tangent to circle Q at B, $\overline{AE} \perp \overline{AD}$, and segment DE contains B. Prove that $\triangle AEB$ is isosceles with base BE.

*Prove Exercises **28** and **29** by algebraic methods.*

28. In the figure at the right, $\overline{BA}$, $\overline{BC}$, $\overline{BE}$, $\overline{CA}$ and $\overline{CE}$ are chords, and $\overline{BE}$ bisects angle ABC. Prove that three angles of $\triangle ABD$ are congruent to three angles of $\triangle EBC$.

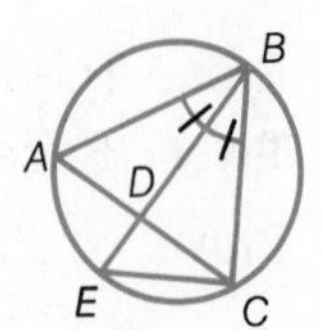

29. Prove that three angles of $\triangle EDC$ in the figure for Exercise 28 are congruent to three angles of $\triangle EBC$.

PUZZLE

Triangle ABC below is drawn incorrectly.

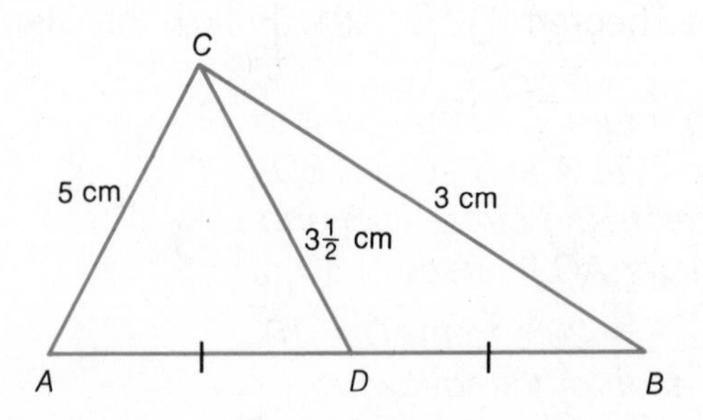

Can you construct the triangle correctly so that $AC = 5$ centimeters, $BC = 3$ centimeters, and $\overline{CD}$, the median to $\overline{AB}$, is $3\frac{1}{2}$ centimeters long?

Remember

Find the geometric mean between each pair of numbers.

1. 3 and 27

2. 16 and 4

3. 25 and 4

4. 3 and 8

5. $8a$ and $6a$

6. a and b

The answers are on page 365. If you need help, see page 254.

7-10 Lengths of Segments

When the endpoints of two chords that intersect in the interior of a circle are joined, two similar triangles are formed.

Example 1 Chords AB and CD intersect at E; $\overline{AC}$ and $\overline{BD}$ are drawn.

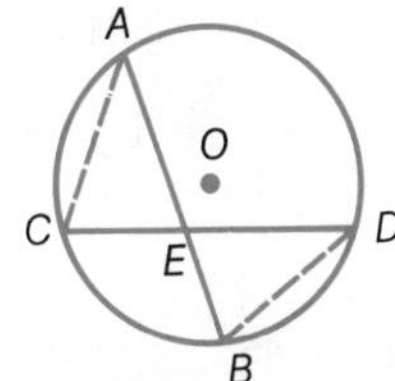

a. Explain why $\triangle AEC \sim \triangle DEB$.
b. Explain why $AE \cdot EB = CE \cdot ED$.

a. Since $m\angle A = \frac{1}{2}m\widehat{BC}$ and $m\angle D = \frac{1}{2}m\widehat{BC}$, $m\angle A = m\angle D$ and $\angle A \cong \angle D$.
Since $m\angle C = \frac{1}{2}m\widehat{AD}$ and $m\angle B = \frac{1}{2}m\widehat{AD}$, $m\angle C = m\angle B$ and $\angle C \cong \angle B$.
$\therefore \triangle AEC \sim \triangle DEB$ ← A.A. Similarity Corollary

b. Since $\triangle AEC \sim \triangle DEB$, $\frac{AE}{DE} = \frac{CE}{BE}$. ← Corresponding sides of similar triangles are proportional.

$\therefore AE \cdot EB = CE \cdot ED$ ← Theorem 6-1, page 251

Example 1 suggests this theorem.

Theorem 7-24: If two chords of a circle intersect in the interior of a circle, the product of the lengths of the segments of the first chord equals the product of the lengths of the segments of the second chord.

In the figure at the right, $\overleftrightarrow{AC}$ and $\overleftrightarrow{AE}$ are secants, and $\overline{AB}$ and $\overline{AD}$ are <u>external secant segments.</u>

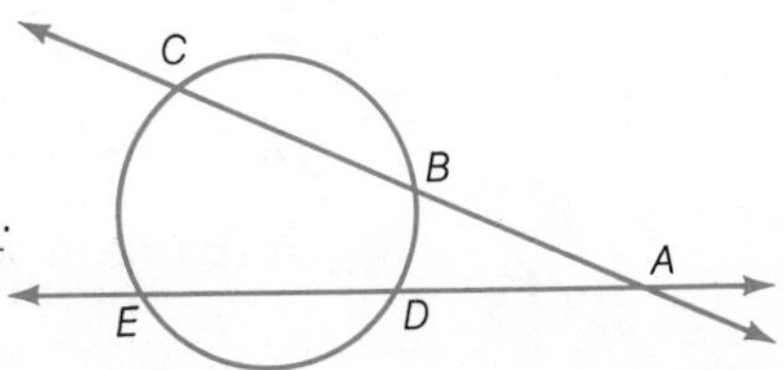

Example 2

Secant segments NT and NG intersect at N, $NE = 6$, $ET = 4$ and $NA = 5$. Find AG and NG.

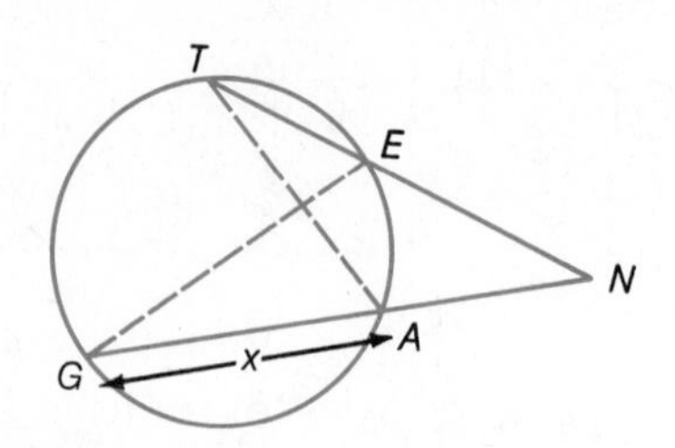

Draw $\overline{GE}$ and $\overline{TA}$.

Since $m\angle T = \frac{1}{2}m\widehat{EA}$ and $m\angle G = \frac{1}{2}m\widehat{EA}$, $m\angle T = m\angle G$.

Since $m\angle N = m\angle N$ and $m\angle T = m\angle G$, $\triangle TNA \sim \triangle GNE$.

Since $\triangle TNA \sim \triangle GNE$, $\frac{NA}{NE} = \frac{NT}{NG}$, or $NA \cdot NG = NE \cdot NT$.

Since $NA \cdot NG = NE \cdot NT$, $5(5 + x) = 6(6 + 4)$.

$$25 + 5x = 60$$
$$5x = 35$$
$$x = 7 \longleftarrow AG$$
$$x + 5 = 12 \longleftarrow NG$$

Example 2 suggests the following theorem. The proof is left for you in the exercises.

Theorem 7-25: If two secant segments are drawn to a circle from the same exterior point, the product of the lengths of one secant segment and its external segment equals the product of the lengths of the other secant segment and its external segment.

Now consider a tangent segment and a secant segment.

Example 3

Tangent segment QP and secant segment QR intersect at Q.

$\overline{PS}$ and $\overline{PR}$ are drawn.

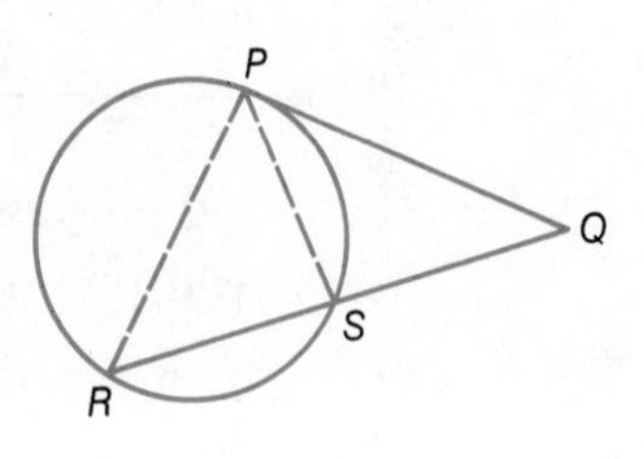

a. Explain why $\triangle QPS \sim \triangle QRP$.

b. Explain why $\frac{QS}{QP} = \frac{QP}{QR}$.

c. Explain why $(QP)^2 = QS \cdot QR$

Answers: **a.** Since $m\angle R = \frac{1}{2}m\widehat{PS}$ and $m\angle QPS = \frac{1}{2}m\widehat{PS}$, $m\angle R = m\angle QPS$. Since $m\angle Q = m\angle Q$ and $m\angle R = m\angle QPS$, $\triangle QPS \sim \triangle QRP$.

b. Since $\triangle QPS \sim \triangle QRP$, $\frac{QS}{QP} = \frac{QP}{QR}$.

c. Since $\frac{QS}{QP} = \frac{QP}{QR}$, $QS \cdot QR = QP \cdot QP$, or $(QP)^2 = QS \cdot QR$.

Example 3 suggests this theorem.

Theorem 7-26: If a tangent and a secant are drawn to a circle from the same exterior point, the tangent segment is the geometric mean between the secant segment and its external segment.

Example 4

In the figure, $WZ = 5$, and $WT = 4$. Find TE.

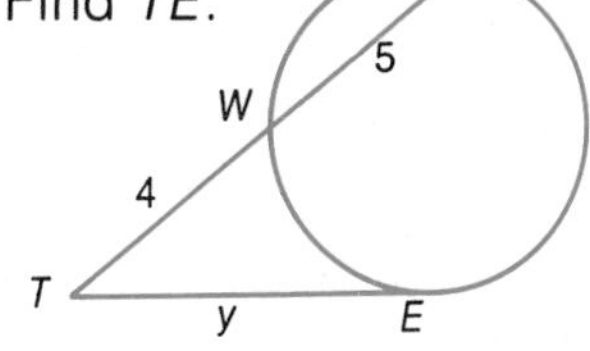

$\frac{9}{y} = \frac{y}{4}$ ⟵ Theorem 7-26

$y^2 = 36$

$y = 6$ ⟵ TE

Try These

Use the figure at the right for Exercises ***1–3.***

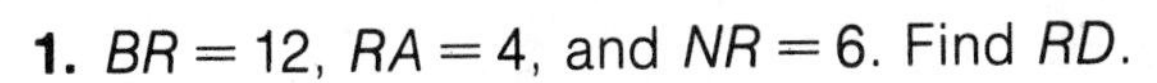

1. $BR = 12$, $RA = 4$, and $NR = 6$. Find RD.

2. $NR = 4$, $RD = 5$, and $BR = 8$. Find RA.

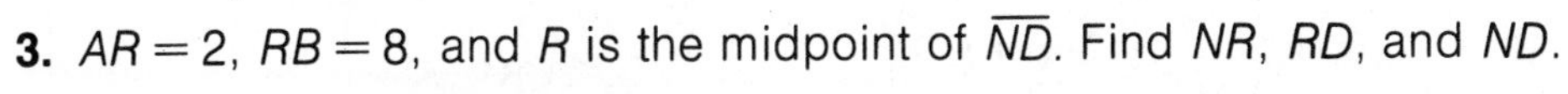

3. $AR = 2$, $RB = 8$, and R is the midpoint of $\overline{ND}$. Find NR, RD, and ND.

Use the figure at the right for Exercises ***4–6.***

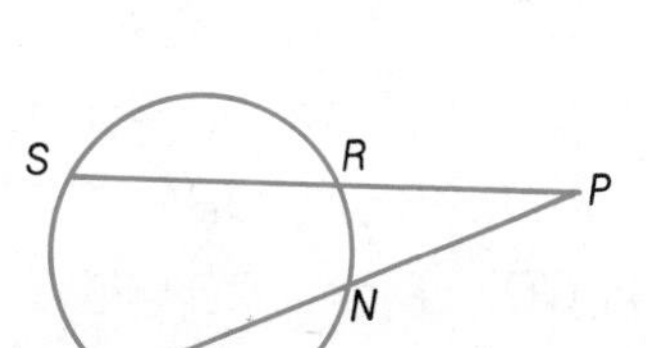

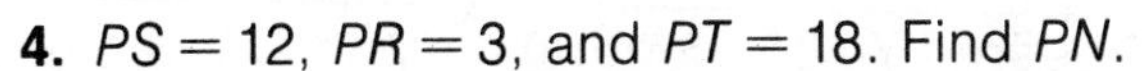

4. $PS = 12$, $PR = 3$, and $PT = 18$. Find PN.

5. $PN = 3$, $NT = 7$, and $PR = 4$. Find RS.

6. $PR = 4$, $RS = 8$, and $PN = 3$. Find NT.

Use the figure at the right for Exercises **7–9.**

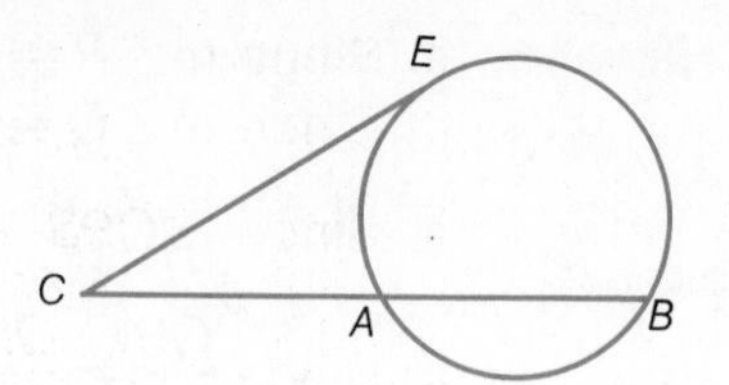

7. $CA = 5$ and $BA = 15$. Find CE.
8. $CA = 4$ and $BA = 12$. Find CE.
9. $CE = 6$ and $CA = 4$. Find AB.

Exercises

Use the figure at the right for Exercises **1–4.**

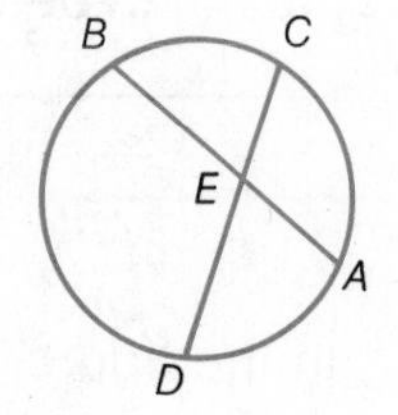

a

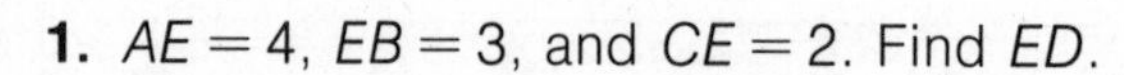

1. $AE = 4$, $EB = 3$, and $CE = 2$. Find ED.
2. $AE = 5$, $EB = 4$, and $ED = 10$. Find CE.
3. $AE = 2\frac{1}{2}$, $EB = 3\frac{1}{3}$, and $ED = 6$. Find CE.
4. $AE = 6.4$, $EB = 5.3$, and $CE = 3.2$. Find ED.

Use the figure at the right for Exercises **5–9.**

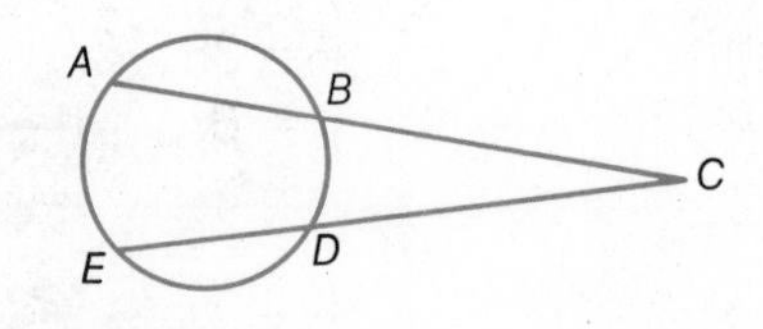

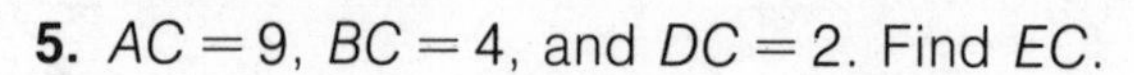

5. $AC = 9$, $BC = 4$, and $DC = 2$. Find EC.
6. $AC = 9$, $BC = 3$, and $EC = 12$. Find DC.
7. $AB = 5$, $BC = 4$, and $DC = 2$. Find EC. (HINT: $AC =$ __?__)
8. $AB = 6$, $BC = 3$, and $DC = 2$. Find ED. (HINT: First find EC.)
9. $AB = 8$, $BC = 6$, and $DC = 4$. Find ED.

Use the figure at the right for Exercises **10–14.**

A
B
D
C

10. $AB = 8$ and $CB = 16$. Find BD.
11. $CB = 9$ and $DB = 4$. Find AB.
12. $CD = 5$ and $DB = 4$. Find AB.

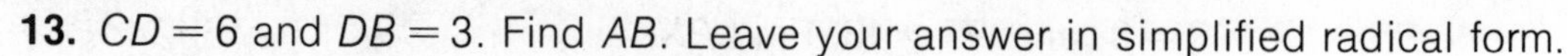

13. $CD = 6$ and $DB = 3$. Find AB. Leave your answer in simplified radical form.
14. $CD = 2$ and $DB = 3$. Find AB to the nearest hundredth.
15. Write a formal proof for Theorem 7-24. (Follow the method of Example 1.)

16. Write a formal proof for Theorem 7-25. (Follow the method of Example 2.)

17. Write a formal proof for Theorem 7-26. (Follow the method of Example 3.)

18. In the figure at the left below, $\triangle ABC$ is inscribed in a circle, $\overline{BE}$ is a diameter, and $\overline{BD} \perp \overline{AC}$. Prove that $AB \cdot BC = DB \cdot BE$.

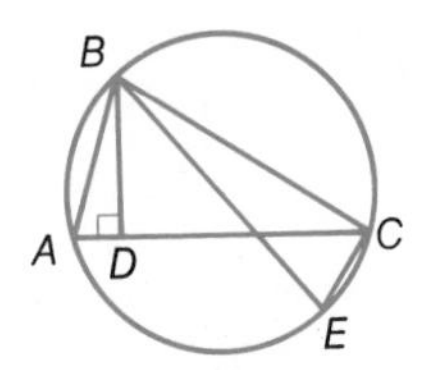

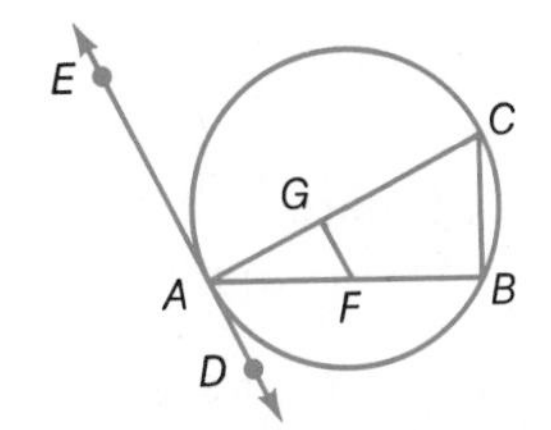

19. In the figure at the right above, $\overleftrightarrow{DE}$ is tangent to the circle at A and $\overline{FG} \parallel \overleftrightarrow{DE}$. Prove that $AF \cdot AB = AG \cdot AC$.

Prove the statements in Exercises ***20–22.***

20. In any triangle, the product of the measures of any altitude and the side to which it is drawn is equal to the product of the measures of any other altitude and the side to which it is drawn.

21. In any parallelogram, the product of the measures of any altitude and the side to which it is drawn is equal to the product of the measures of any other altitude and the side to which it is drawn.

22. The product of the measures of the two legs of a right triangle is equal to the product of the measures of the hypotenuse and the altitude to the hypotenuse.

23. In the figure at the right, $AE = 8$, $EB = 3$, and $CD = 10$. Find CE and ED.

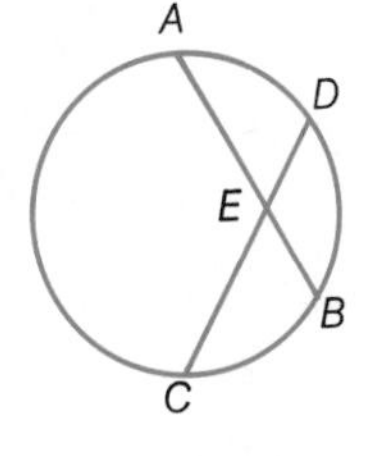

24. When the product of two quantities is a constant, they are said to vary inversely. For example, if $xy = k$, where k is a constant, then x varies inversely as y and y varies inversely as x. Restate Theorems 7-24 and 7-25 in terms of inverse variation.

25. Triangle ABC is inscribed in a circle and $\overline{CD}$ is drawn to D, the midpoint of $\widehat{AB}$. Prove that

$$AC:CD = AE:BD.$$

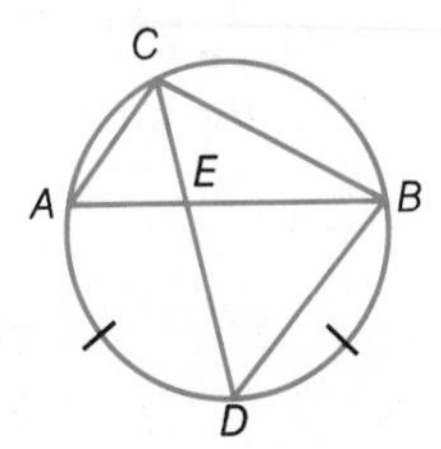

7-11 The Sphere

A **sphere** is the set of all points in space at a given distance from a fixed point in space.

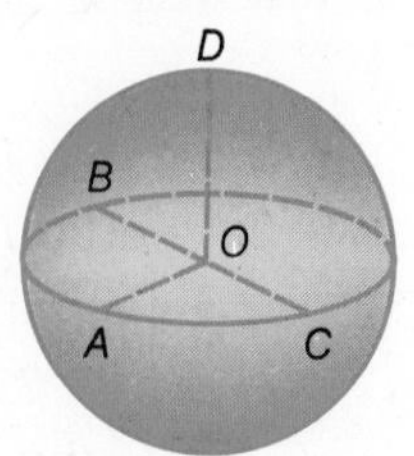

In the figure at the right, $\overline{AO}$ and $\overline{DO}$ are radii of the sphere and O, the center of the sphere, is the fixed point in space. $\overline{BC}$ is a diameter of the sphere. It is a chord of the sphere that also passes through its center. A chord is a segment whose endpoints are points of the sphere.

Example 1

A sphere has a radius of 10 centimeters. Describe the intersection of the sphere with a plane for each given distance of the center of the sphere from the plane.

a. 12 cm **b.** 10 cm **c.** 6 cm

a.

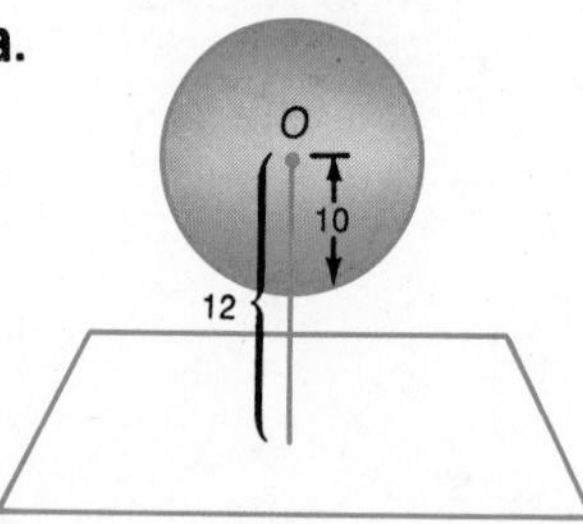

They do not intersect. Thus, the intersection is the empty set.

b.

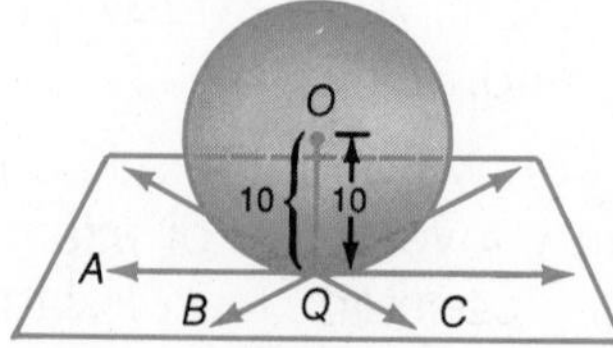

They intersect in one point. That is, the plane is tangent to the sphere.

c.

They intersect in a circle.

The example illustrates the following theorem. Its proof is asked for in the exercises.

Theorem 7-27: If a plane intersects a sphere, the intersection is either a point or a circle.

Many of the terms connected with circles are also used with spheres. Thus, in the figure at the right, C is the center of the sphere, A and B are points on the sphere, and $\angle ACB$ is a central angle. Points A, B, and C determine a plane that intersects the sphere in a great circle. $\widehat{AB}$ of this great circle is a minor arc.

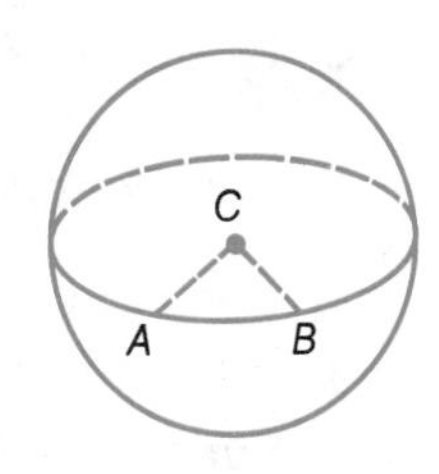

Definition: A **great circle** of a sphere is a circle formed by the intersection of a sphere and a plane passing through its center.

On the surface of a sphere, the shortest distance from any point A to any other point B is along $\widehat{AB}$, an arc of a great circle.

Try These

The figure below shows a sphere with center Q. Identify each of the following.

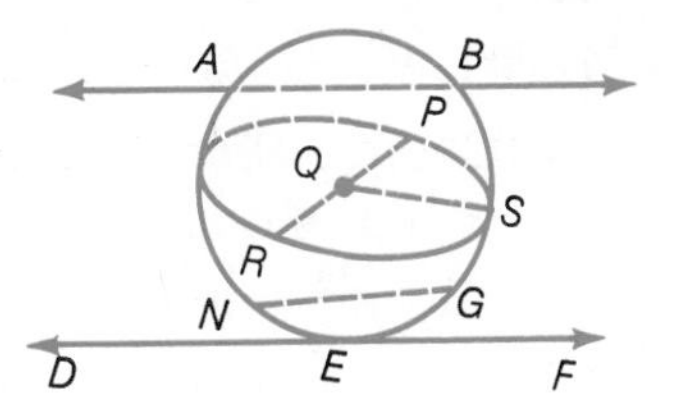

1. Eight points that lie on the sphere
2. Two points that lie in the exterior of the sphere
3. One point that lies in the interior of the sphere
4. Three radii of the sphere
5. A diameter of the sphere
6. Three chords of the sphere
7. A secant of the sphere
8. A line tangent to the sphere
9. A great circle of the sphere
10. Two minor arcs of the sphere
11. Two central angles of the sphere

Exercises

a

1. Describe the three regions into which a sphere separates space.
2. Under what conditions are two spheres congruent?

*For Exercises **3–9,** classify each statement as True or False.*

3. All great circles of a sphere are congruent.
4. All radii of a sphere are congruent.
5. Every diameter of a sphere is a diameter of a great circle.
6. A secant of a sphere intersects the sphere in exactly one point.
7. Two spheres always intersect in exactly one point.
8. A line tangent to one endpoint of a diameter of a sphere is parallel to a line tangent to the other endpoint of the diameter.
9. If a plane is tangent to a sphere, it is perpendicular to a radius of the sphere drawn to the point of tangency.

Two spheres have radii of 4 centimeters and 8 centimeters. Describe their intersection for each distance (given in centimeters) between their centers.

10. 16 **11.** 12 **12.** 10 **13.** 4 **14.** 2 **15.** 0

Two spheres have radii of 3 centimeters and 5 centimeters and their centers are 12 centimeters apart.

16. How many lines can be tangent to both spheres?
17. How many planes can be tangent to both spheres?
18. Chord AB of a sphere is shorter than chord CD of the same sphere. Which chord is closer to the center of the sphere?
19. Two arcs lie on the surface of the sphere. When are the arcs congruent?
20. Two tangent segments are drawn to a sphere from the same point in the exterior of the sphere. Compare the lengths of the tangent segments.
21. A diameter of a sphere is perpendicular to a chord of the sphere. Does the diameter bisect the chord?
22. A diameter of a sphere bisects a chord of the sphere. Is the diameter always perpendicular to the chord?
23. A plane intersects a sphere and a diameter of the sphere is perpendicular to the plane. Does the diameter pass through the center of the circle formed by this intersection?

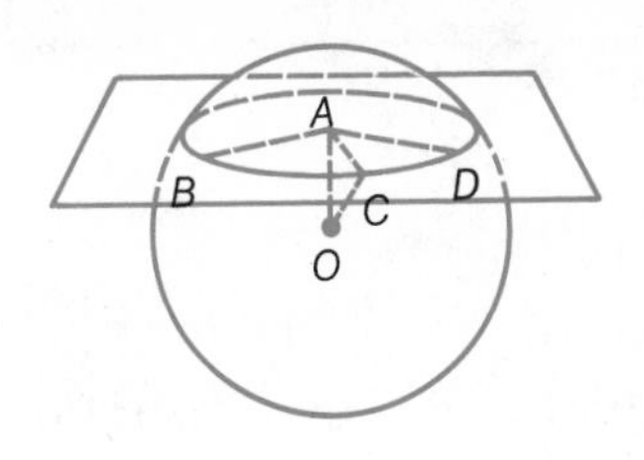

*In the figure at the right, a plane intersects sphere O in circle A. Points B, C, and D are on circle A and $\overline{OA}$ is perpendicular to the plane. Tell which statements in Exercises **24–32** are always true.*

24. $\overline{AB} \cong \overline{AD}$
25. $\overline{AB} \cong \overline{AO}$
26. $\overline{AB} \cong \overline{OB}$
27. $\overline{AC} \cong \overline{AB}$
28. $\overline{OA} \perp \overline{AD}$
29. $\overline{AB} \perp \overline{AD}$
30. $\triangle ADO \cong \triangle ABO$
31. $\overline{OA} \cong \overline{AC}$
32. $\overline{AC} \cong \overline{AD}$

33. If a sphere is inscribed in a cube, how many faces of the cube are tangent to the sphere?

34. If a cube is inscribed in a sphere, how many points do the cube and the sphere have in common?

35. A plane is passed through a sphere 6 centimeters from its center. The radius of the sphere is 10 centimeters. Find the radius of the circle formed by the intersection of the plane and the sphere. (HINT: Use the figure for Exercises **24–32** with $CO = 10$ cm and $AO = 6$ cm. Find AC.)

36. A sphere has a radius of 26 centimeters. How far from the center of the sphere must a plane pass for the circle formed by the intersection to have a radius of 24 centimeters? Use the figure for Exercise **35.**

b

37. Describe the figure you would get by drawing all possible tangent lines to a sphere from an external point. What figure is determined by all of the points of tangency?

38. Spheres *A* and *B* are tangent externally at *C*. Prove that the lengths of any two tangents to each of the two spheres from a common point in the plane that is the common internal tangent are congruent.

39. In circle *O*, $\widehat{ABC}$ is a semicircle, and point *D* on $\widehat{ABC}$ is so located that $\widehat{BD} \cong \widehat{DC}$. Prove that $\overline{AB} \parallel \overline{OD}$.

40. Prove Theorem 7-27.

Given: Sphere *O* and plane I intersect in Section *BCD*.
Prove: Section *BCD* is a circle.

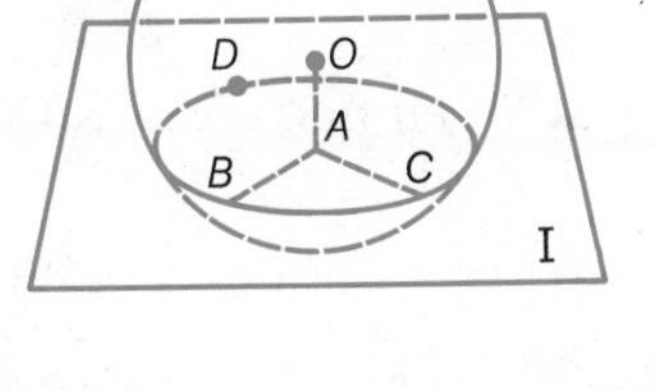

Plan: If center *O* is not in plane I, then let *C* and *B* be any two distinct points of section *BCD*. Prove that $\overline{AB} \cong \overline{AC}$ and that all points of section *BCD* are equidistant from *A*. If center *O* is in plane I, $\overline{OB} \cong \overline{OC}$.

Non-Euclidean Geometry

The geometry you are studying is **Euclidean**; that is, it is based on the postulates of Euclid (about 300 B.C.). In a **non-Euclidean geometry,** Euclid's Parallel Postulate (Postulate 15, page 159) does not hold. The following example of **hyperbolic geometry** illustrates this.

Model	Description
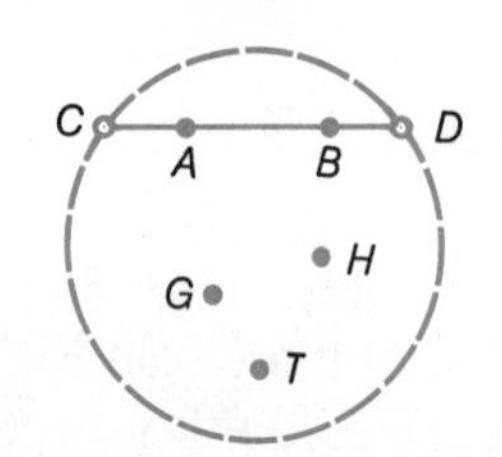	The plane consists of points in the interior of a circle, such as A and B but not C and D. Two points in the interior determine a chord, and each chord is thought of as a "line", such as "line" AB.

In hyperbolic geometry, lines TG and TH are parallel to line AB because they do not intersect line AB. (Recall that points C and D are not in the interior of the circle.) Further, there are infinitely many lines through T that are parallel to line AB; that is, they do not intersect line AB, but they are coplanar with line AB. One of these is line TK.

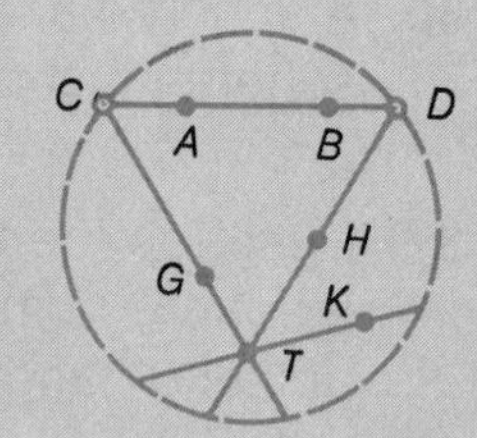

Can You Solve These?

1. Write a parallel postulate for hyperbolic geometry.
2. The model for **elliptic geometry** is a sphere. In this geometry, a "line" is a great circle of the sphere, such as line AB. Can a line be drawn through G that will be parallel to line AB? Explain.
3. Write a parallel postulate for elliptic geometry.
4. Are postulates 1, 2, and 4 on page 23 true in hyperbolic geometry? In elliptic geometry?

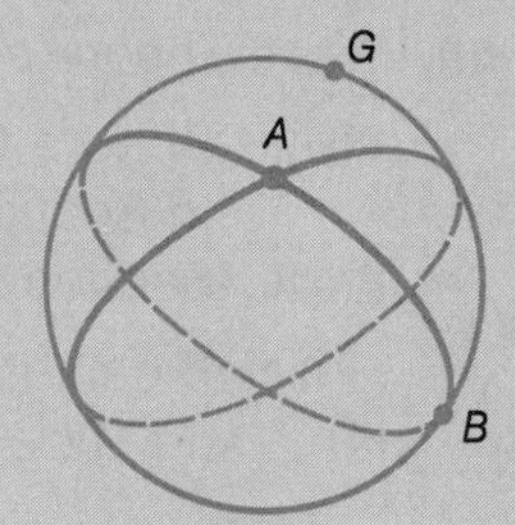

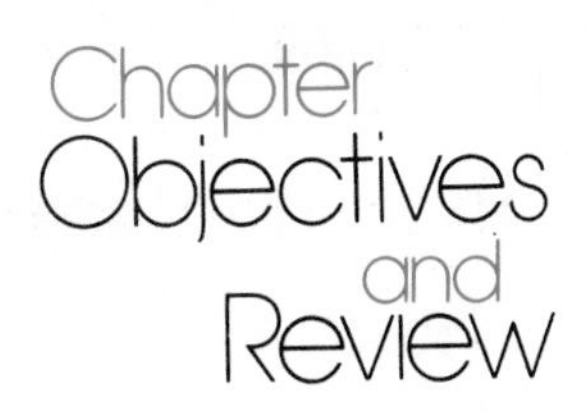

Objective: To recall, and give examples of, the important mathematical terms of the chapter.

1. Be sure that you know the meaning of these mathematical terms used in the chapter.

central angle (p. 308)
chord (p. 304)
circle (p. 304)
concentric circles (p. 305)
congruent arcs (p. 310)
congruent circles (p. 310)
diameter (p. 304)
great circle (p. 357)
inscribed angle (p. 329)
inscribed polygon (p. 320)
major arc (p. 308)
midpoint of an arc (p. 309)
minor arc (p. 308)
radius (p. 304)
secant (p. 304)
semicircle (p. 308)
sphere (p. 356)
tangent (p. 304)
tangent segment (p. 324)

Objective: To identify the special points, lines, and line segments associated with a circle. (Section 7-1)

Use the figure at the right to identify each of the following.

2. A secant of O
3. A diameter of circle P
4. A radius of circle O
5. A chord of circle P
6. A common external tangent to circles O and P
7. A common internal tangent to circles O and P

Objective: To find the measures of a central angle and its major and minor arcs. (Section 7-2)

In circle A, $\overline{BD}$ is a diameter and $m\angle DAE = 85$. Find each of the following.

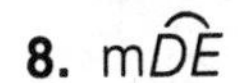

8. $m\widehat{DE}$ **9.** $m\widehat{DBE}$ **10.** $m\angle BAE$ **11.** $m\widehat{EB}$ **12.** $m\widehat{DFB}$

Objective: To identify congruent chords and the relationships between chords and arcs. (Section 7-3)

Classify each statement as True *or* False.

13. If two arcs of a circle are congruent, the chords of these arcs are congruent.

14. The perpendicular bisector of a chord of a circle never passes through the center of the circle.

15. A line passing through the midpoint of a chord of a circle always passes through the center of the circle.

16. Two chords of the same circle intersect at M, and M is the midpoint of each chord. Then the chords are perpendicular to each other and one chord is a diameter of the circle.

Objective: To identify the relationship between the length of a chord and its distance from the center of a circle. (Section 7-4)

17. Chords AB and CD are in the same circle and $AB > CD$. Which chord is closer to the center of the circle?

18. An equilateral triangle is inscribed in a circle of radius 10. Find x, the distance of a side of the triangle from the center of the circle, and find the perimeter of the triangle.

Objective: To identify and apply tangent relationships. (Section 7-5)

19. In the figure at the right, $\overline{PX}$ and $\overline{PY}$ are tangent segments to circle O and $m\angle XYO = 20$. Find $m\angle P$.

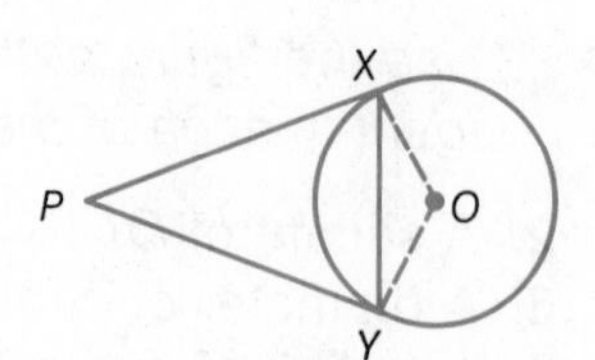

Objective: To identify and apply relationships between inscribed angles and their intercepted arcs. (Sections 7-6 and 7-7).

Use the figure at the right for Exercises ***20–21.***

20. If $m\widehat{BAD} = 260$, find $m\angle BAD$.

21. $ABCD$ is an inscribed quadrilateral. If $m\angle A = 45$, find $m\angle C$.

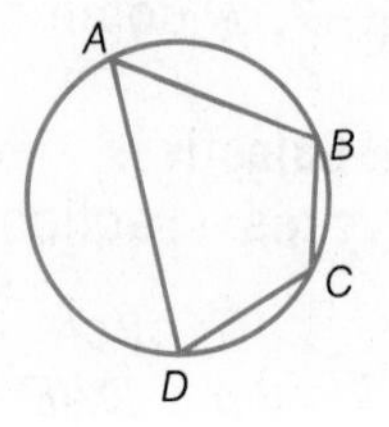

Objective: To find the measures of angles formed by a tangent and a secant or by two secants (or chords) intersecting in the interior of a circle. (Section 7-8)

22. In the circle at the left below, $\overleftrightarrow{AY}$ is a tangent at A and $\overleftrightarrow{XA}$ is a secant. If $m\angle XAY = 50$, find $m\widehat{AX}$.

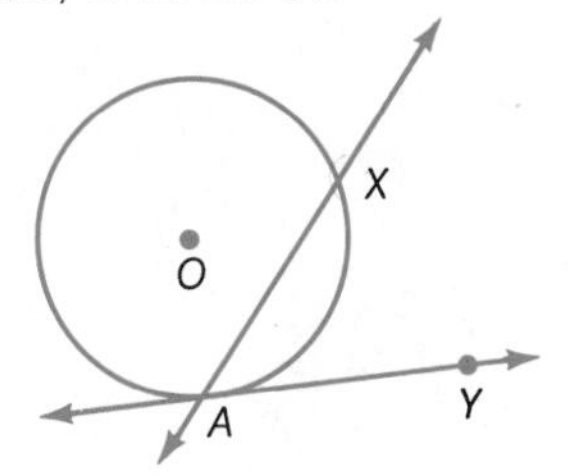

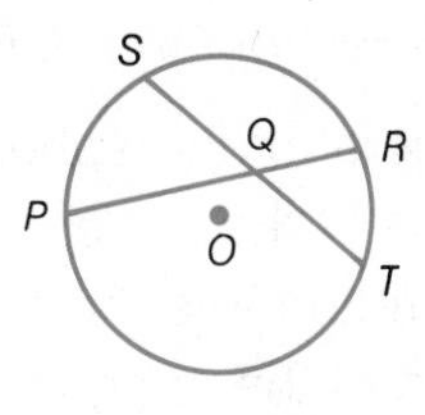

23. In circle O at the right above, $m\widehat{PS} = 60$ and $m\widehat{RT} = 40$. Find $m\angle SQR$.

Objective: To find the measures of angles formed by two secants or a tangent and a secant. (Section 7-9)

24. In Figure 1 below, $\overleftrightarrow{PQ}$ is a tangent, $\overleftrightarrow{PS}$ is a secant, R is the midpoint of $\widehat{QRS}$, and $m\widehat{QS} = 160$. Find $m\angle P$.

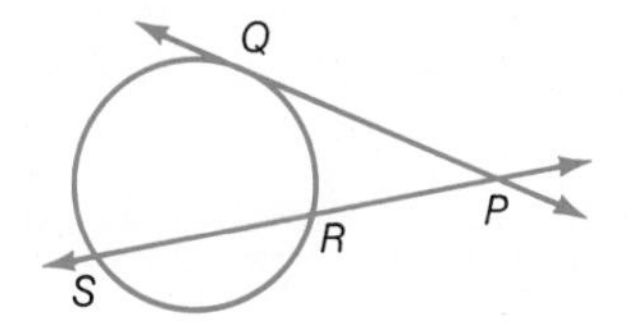

Figure 1

V
T
W

Figure 2

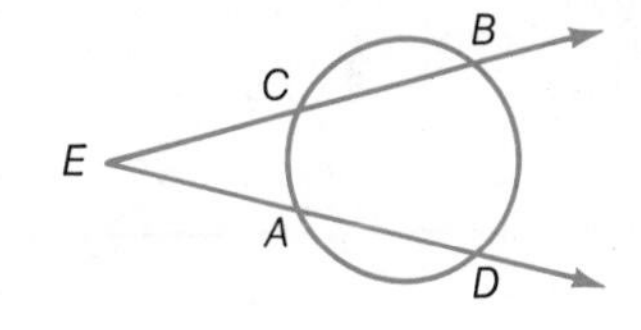

Figure 3

25. In Figure 2 above, $\overrightarrow{TV}$ and $\overrightarrow{TW}$ are tangents, and $m\widehat{VW} = 95$. Find $m\angle T$.

26. In Figure 3 above, $m\widehat{DB} = 110$ and $m\widehat{AC} = 44$. Find $m\angle E$.

Objective: To find the lengths of segments formed by intersecting chords, secant segments, and tangent segments. (Section 7-10)

Use the given information and figure to find x.

27. $AE = 5$, $EB = 4$, $CE = 2$

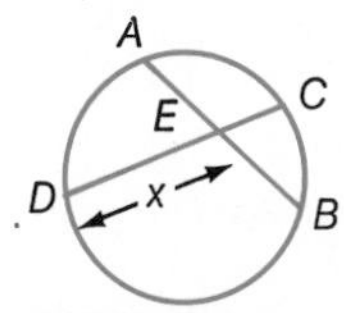

28. $ST = 6$, $TV = 4$, $SQ = 5$

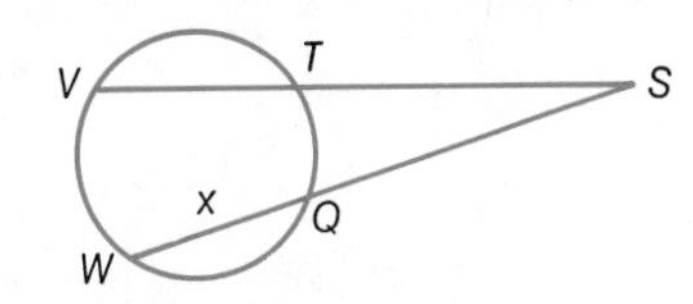

Answers to Remember

Page 307: **1.** If a triangle is isosceles then it has two congruent adjacent angles; If a triangle has two congruent adjacent angles then it is isosceles. **2.** If two triangles are similar then two pairs of corresponding angles are congruent; In two triangles, if two pairs of corresponding angles are congruent then the triangles are similar. **3.** If two lines cut by a transversal are parallel then two alternate interior angles are congruent; If two alternate interior angles are congruent then the two lines cut by the transversal are parallel. **4.** If two sides of a triangle are not congruent then the angles opposite these sides are not congruent; If two angles of a triangle are not congruent then the sides opposite these angles are not congruent.

Objective: To identify the special points, lines, and line segments associated with a sphere. (Section 7-11)

Identify each of the following.

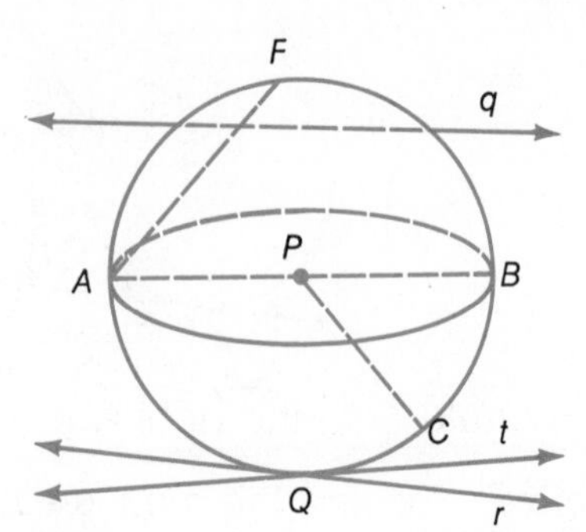

29. A diameter of the sphere
30. A radius of the sphere
31. A secant to the sphere
32. A chord of the sphere
33. A great circle of the sphere
34. A minor arc of the sphere
35. A central angle of the sphere
36. Two intersecting lines tangent to the sphere

Chapter Test

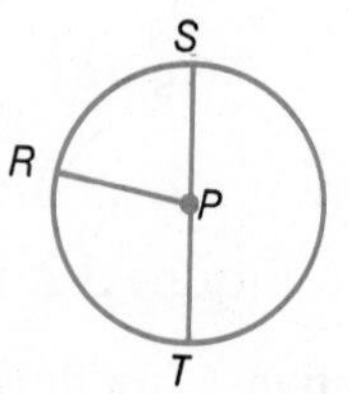

1. In the figure at the right, $\overline{ST}$ is a diameter of the circle and $m\widehat{TR} = 105$. Find $m\angle RPS$.
2. An equilateral triangle is inscribed in a circle whose radius is 8 centimeters. Find the length of a side of the triangle.
3. In circle O, chord ST measures 7 and chord QR measures 5. Which chord is closer to the center of the circle?
4. In circle O at the left below, $\overline{PX}$ and $\overline{PY}$ are tangent segments, $OX = 5$ and $OP = 13$. Find PX.

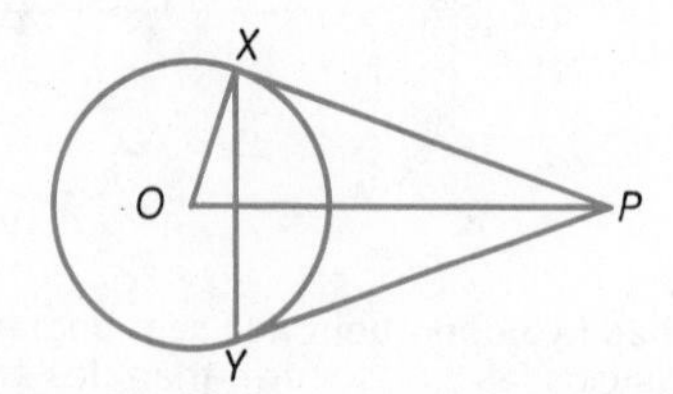

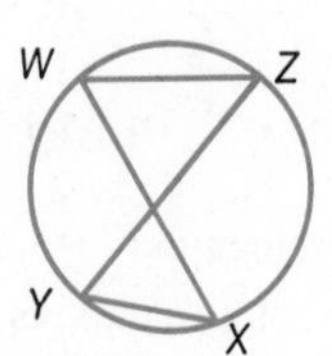

5. Use the figure at the right above to name two inscribed angles that intercept $\widehat{ZX}$.
6. In the figure for Exercise **5,** $m\widehat{WY} = 190$. Find $m\angle X$.

7. In the figure at the left below, circles S and T are tangent at A, and $\overline{AT}$ is a diameter of circle S. $ST = 2.4$ cm and $MT = 3$ cm. Find AB.

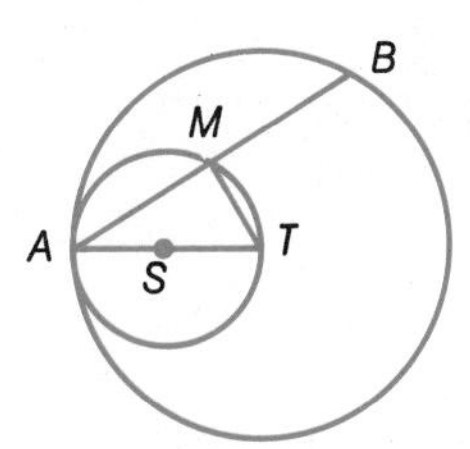

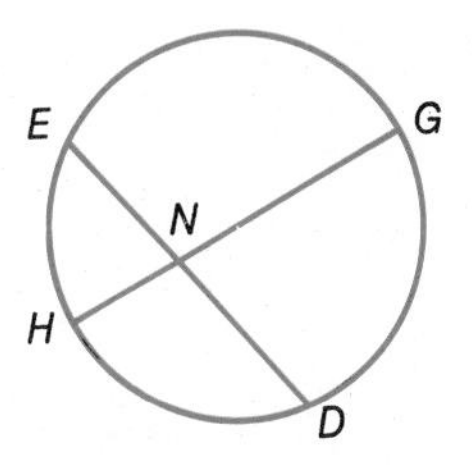

8. In the figure at the right above, chords ED and HG intersect at N, $m\widehat{EG} = 126$, and $m\widehat{HD} = 86$. Find $m\angle ENG$.

9. In the figure for Exercise 8, $ED = 13$, $HN = 12$, and $NG = 3$. Find DN and NE.

10. In the figure at the left below, $\overleftrightarrow{TN}$ is tangent to circle O at A, and $m\angle BAN = 50$. Find $m\widehat{BA}$.

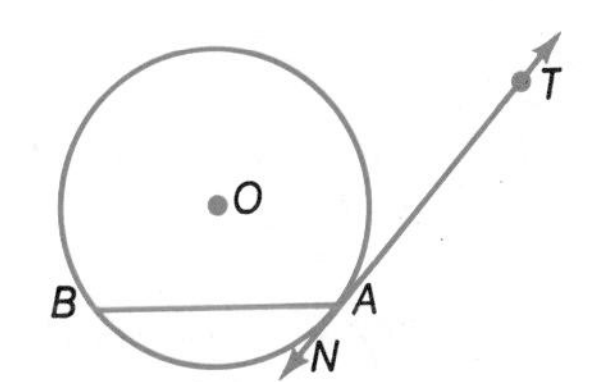

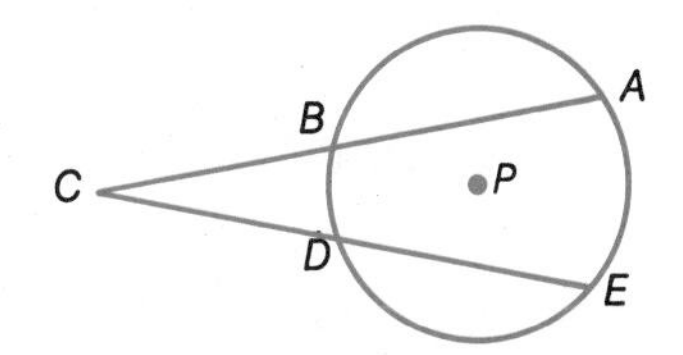

11. In the figure at the right above, $CB = 4$, $CD = 6$, and $DE = 7$. Find BA.

12. In the circle at the left below, PT is a tangent segment, $PR = 4$, and $RS = 12$. Find PT.

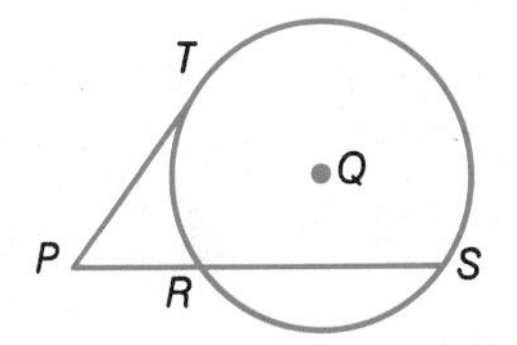

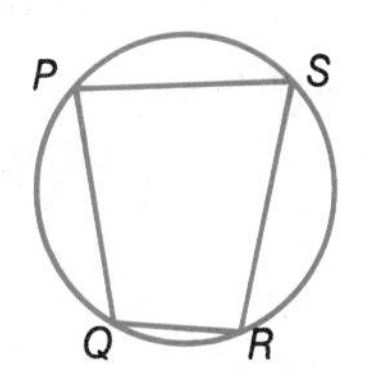

13. In the figure at the right above, quadrilateral $PQRS$ is inscribed in a circle, $m\angle P = 85$, and $m\angle Q = 100$. Find $m\angle S$ and $m\angle R$.

14. Two spheres have radii of 5 centimeters and 9 centimeters and the distance between their centers is 11 centimeters. Describe the figure determined by their intersection.

Answers to Remember

Page 317: **1.** 6 **2.** $2\sqrt{2}$ **3.** $3\sqrt{3}$ **4.** $5\sqrt{2}$ **5.** $2\sqrt{3}$ **6.** $3\sqrt{7}$ **7.** $5\sqrt{3}$ **8.** $4\sqrt{2}$

Page 335: **1.** True **2.** True **3.** False; congruent chords are equidistant from the center of a circle. **4.** True **5.** False; the opposite angles of a parallelogram are congruent.

Page 346: **1.** 180 **2.** 180 **3.** its central angle. **4.** $360 - m$, where m is the measure of the central angle of its minor arc. **5.** 360

Page 350: **1.** 9 **2.** 8 **3.** 10 **4.** $2\sqrt{6}$ **5.** $4a\sqrt{3}$ **6.** $\sqrt{ab}$

Cumulative Review

Write the letter of the response that best answers each question.

*For Exercises **1–4,** refer to quadrilateral ABCD.*

1. Given that $ABCD$ is a parallelogram, state the correct conclusion.

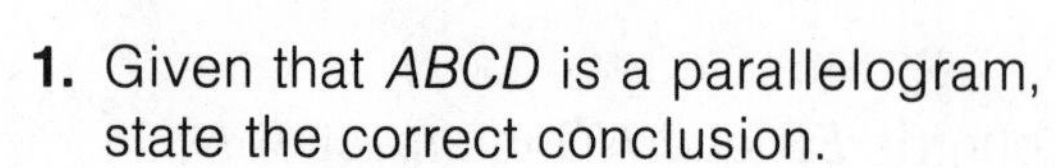

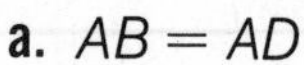

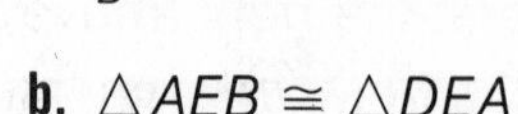

a. $AB = AD$ **b.** $\triangle AEB \cong \triangle DEA$
c. $BD = AC$ **d.** $\angle ADB \cong \angle CBD$

2. Given that $ABCD$ is a rectangle, state the correct conclusion.

a. $AD = DC$ **b.** $\angle DAC \cong \angle BAC$
c. $BD = AC$ **d.** $\overline{BD} \perp \overline{AC}$

3. Given that $ABCD$ is a rhombus, state the correct conclusion.

a. $m\angle ABC = 90$ **b.** $\overline{AC} \cong \overline{BD}$
c. $\overline{AC} \perp \overline{BD}$ **d.** $\angle BCD \cong \angle CDA$

4. Given that $ABCD$ is an isosceles trapezoid with bases $\overline{AD}$ and $\overline{BC}$, state the false conclusion.

a. $AB = DC$ **b.** $\overline{AD} \parallel \overline{BC}$ **c.** $\angle ABC \cong \angle DCB$ **d.** $AE = EC$

5. The perimeter of $\triangle ABC$ is 20. Find the perimeter of the triangle formed by connecting the midpoints of the sides of $\triangle ABC$.

a. 20   **b.** 10   **c.** $6\frac{2}{3}$ **d.** 5

6. The measures of two sides of a triangle are 13 and 24. Choose the number that could be the length of the third side.

a. 35   **b.** 11   **c.** 40   **d.** 8

7. Find the geometric mean between 1 and 9.

a. 3   **b.** 4   **c.** 5   **d.** 6

*Use the figure at the right for Exercises **8** and **9.***

8. Given that $AD = 2$, $DB = 4$, $CE = 3$ and $EB = 6$, state the correct conclusion.

a. $DE = \frac{1}{2}AC$ **b.** $\overline{DE} \parallel \overline{AC}$ **c.** $DE = BE$ **d.** $DE = DB$

9. Given that $AB = 6$, $CB = 9$, $AF = 3$, and $\overrightarrow{BF}$ bisects $\angle ABC$, find FC.

a. 4 **b.** $4\frac{1}{2}$ **c.** 5 **d.** $5\frac{1}{2}$

*For Exercises **10–16,** classify each statement as one of the following.*

a. Always true **b.** Sometimes true **c.** Never true

10. Two congruent polygons are similar.

11. Two regular polygons are similar.

12. Two rectangles are similar.

13. If one of two similar triangles is obtuse and scalene, then the second triangle could be a right triangle.

14. Two isosceles triangles with congruent vertex angles are similar.

15. A rhombus and a rectangle are similar.

16. If one pentagon is equiangular and another is not, then the two pentagons could be similar.

C

A D B

*In the figure at the right, $\angle ACB$ and $\angle BDC$ are right angles. Refer to this figure for Exercises **17–19.***

17. Name the triangles that are similar to $\triangle ACB$.

a. $\triangle ADC$ only **b.** Both $\triangle ADC$ and $\triangle CDB$
c. $\triangle CDB$ only **d.** None of these

18. Given that $AC = 5$ and $AB = 13$, find CB.

a. 5 **b.** 8 **c.** 10 **d.** 12

19. If $AD = x$ and $DB = 4x$, find CD.

a. $3x$ **b.** $2x$ **c.** $x\sqrt{5}$ **d.** $x\sqrt{2}$

20. Find the length of a diagonal of a square whose perimeter is 20 centimeters.

a. 5 cm **b.** $\sqrt{10}$ cm **c.** $5\sqrt{2}$ cm **d.** 10 cm

21. Find the length of an altitude of an equilateral triangle if each side is 7 centimeters long.

a. $\frac{7}{2}$ cm **b.** $7\sqrt{2}$ cm **c.** $\frac{7}{2}\sqrt{3}$ cm **d.** $\frac{7}{2}\sqrt{2}$ cm

22. The measure of a minor arc of a circle is x. Find the measure of its major arc.

a. $x + 180$ **b.** $180 - x$ **c.** $360 - x$ **d.** $2x$

23. In circle O, the midpoint of minor arc AB is M. Tell which statement is false.

a. $\widehat{AM} \cong \widehat{MB}$ **b.** $\overline{AM} \cong \overline{MB}$

c. $m\widehat{AB} = 2m\widehat{AM}$ **d.** $AB = 2AM$

24. Quadrilateral $ABCD$ is inscribed in circle O. Tell which statement is true.

a. The quadrilateral is a rectangle.
b. The opposite angles of the quadrilateral are congruent.
c. The quadrilateral is a trapezoid.
d. The opposite angles of the quadrilateral are supplementary.

In the figure at the right, P is the center of the circle, $\overleftrightarrow{HA}$ *is tangent to the circle at A,* $m\angle BPC = 50$*, and* $\overline{BD} \perp \overline{AC}$*. Use this figure for Exercises* ***25–32.***

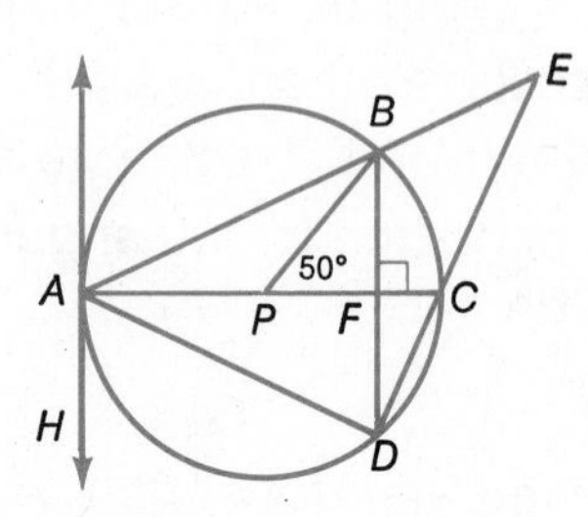

25. Name a chord of the circle.

a. $\overline{PB}$ **b.** $\overline{AB}$ **c.** $\overline{DE}$ **d.** $\overline{PA}$

26. Name a semicircle.

a. $\widehat{BCD}$ **b.** $\widehat{ACB}$ **c.** $\widehat{BDA}$ **d.** $\widehat{ABC}$

27. Find $m\widehat{BC}$.

a. 50 **b.** 25 **c.** 100 **d.** 90

28. Find $m\angle BAC$.

a. 50 **b.** 25 **c.** 40 **d.** 30

29. Find $m\angle FAH$.

a. 100 **b.** 90 **c.** 60 **d.** 50

30. Find $m\angle CDA$.

a. 135 **b.** 100 **c.** 90 **d.** 60

31. Find $m\widehat{DC}$.

a. 50 **b.** 90 **c.** 40 **d.** 130

32. Find $m\angle E$.

a. 50 **b.** 25 **c.** 40 **d.** 30

Chapter 8
Area

8-1 Polygonal Regions

Each figure below shows a polygonal region. The figure at the left shows a triangular region.

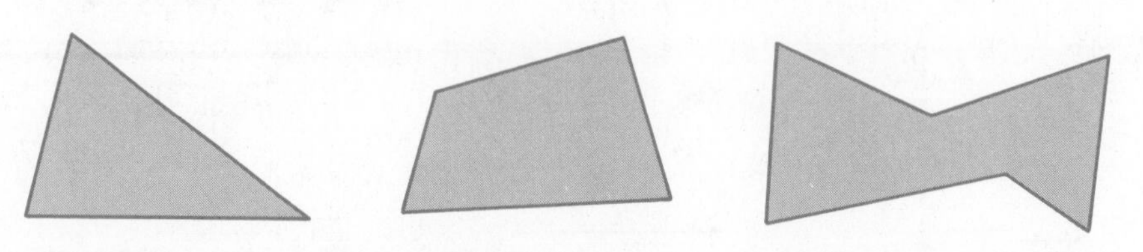

Definitions: A **triangular region** is the union of a triangle and its interior.

In a plane, a **polygonal region** is the union of a finite number of triangular regions which intersect only in a segment or a point.

Example 1

Tell whether each shaded region is a polygonal region. Begin by drawing auxiliary segments that separate the figure into triangular regions that do not overlap.

a.

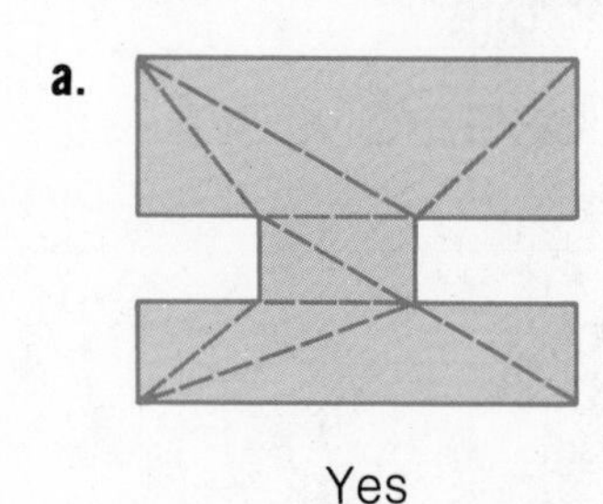

Yes

b.

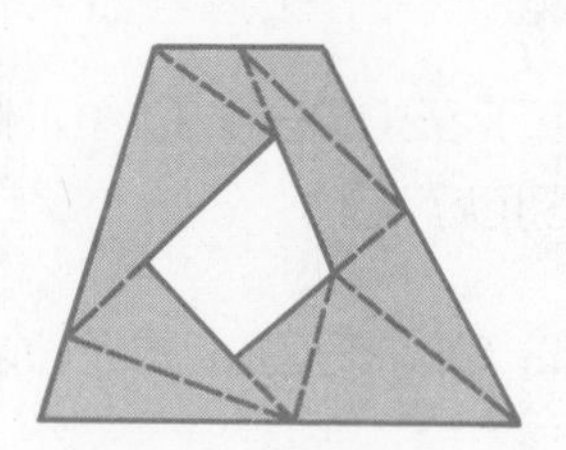

Yes

c.

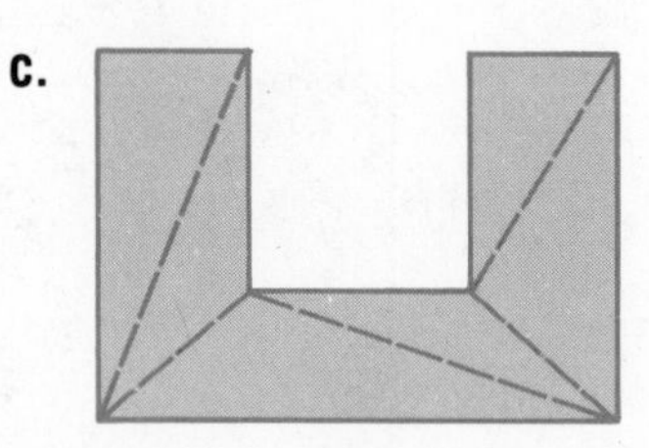

Yes

For convenience, area of a triangle will mean area of a triangular region. Similar phrases will be used when discussing the areas of other polygonal regions.

To compute areas of polygons, you use the Area Postulates.

Postulate 16: To each polygon (polygonal region), there corresponds a positive number which is its area.

Postulate 17: Regions of congruent triangles have the same area.

Postulate 18: The area of a polygon is the sum of the areas of the triangular regions into which it is separated.

Postulate 19: The area A of a rectangle is the product of its length, ℓ, and its width, w. That is, $A = \ell w$.

Area is measured in square units. If measures are given in centimeters, abbreviated cm, the area is stated in terms of square centimeters, abbreviated sq. cm or cm^2. A **square centimeter** is the area of a square which measures one centimeter on a side.

1 sq. cm
or
1 cm^2

Example 2

In rectangle $ABCD$, the area of $\triangle ACD$ is 36 square units.

a. Find the area of $\triangle CAB$.
b. Find the area of rectangle $ABCD$.

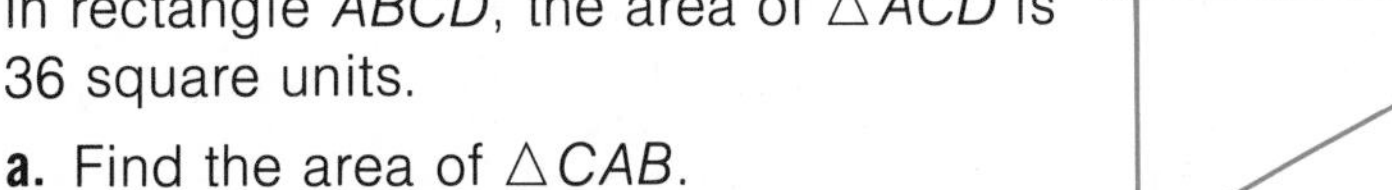

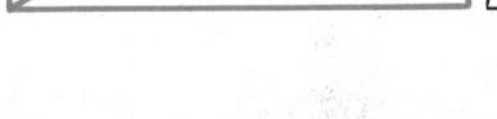

a. Since $\triangle ACD \cong \triangle CAB$, area $\triangle CAB = 36$ sq. units. ← **Postulate 17**

b. Since area rectangle $ABCD =$ area $\triangle ACD +$ area $\triangle CAB$,
area rectangle $ABCD = 72$ square units. ← **Postulate 18**

Example 3

The length of a rectangle is 9 centimeters and its area is 31.5 square centimeters. Find its width.

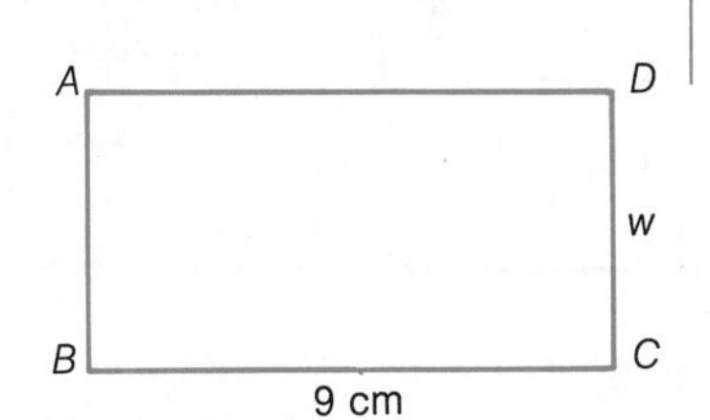

$A = \ell w$ ← **Postulate 19**

$31.5 = 9w$ ← **Replace A with 31.5 and ℓ with 9.**

$w = 3.5$ ← **The width is 3.5 centimeters.**

Try These

*In Exercises **1–3,** tell whether each shaded region is a polygonal region. Begin by drawing auxiliary segments that separate the figure into triangular regions that do not overlap.*

1.

2.

3.

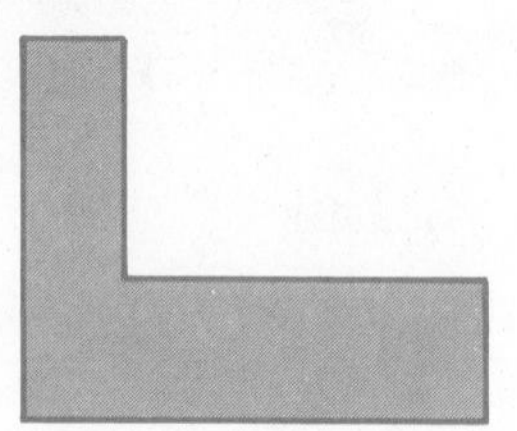

4. The area of $\triangle ABD$ is 12 square units and the area of $\triangle BCD$ is 50 square units. Find the area of polygon $ABCD$.

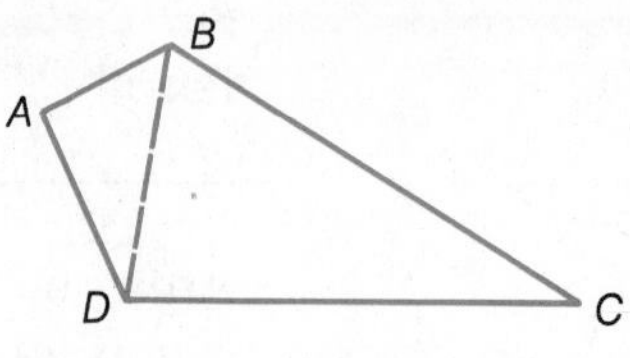

5. Find the area of rectangle $STPQ$ if $ST = 12$ cm and $TP = 5$ cm.

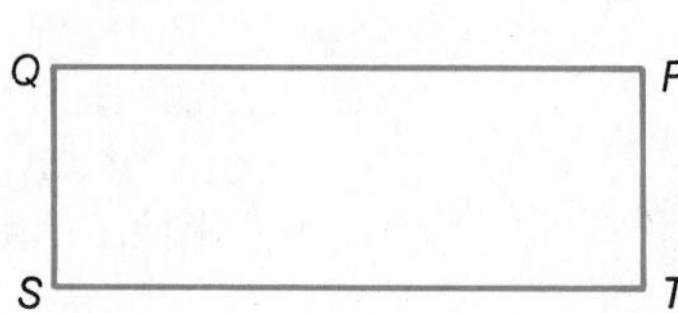

6. Find the length of $\overline{ST}$ if the area of $STPQ$ is 36 and $TP = 5$.

Exercises

Copy each figure. Then try to draw auxiliary segments that separate the figure into triangular regions that do not overlap. If this cannot be done, explain why.

1.

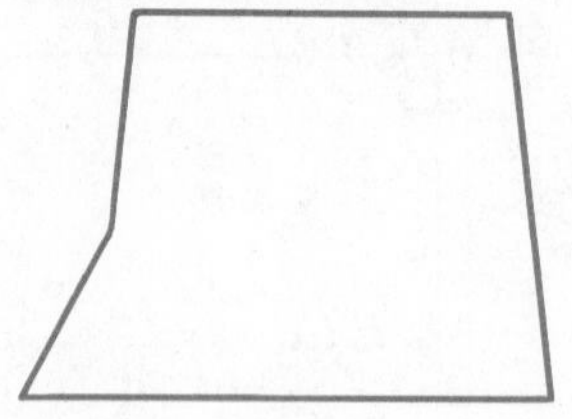

2.

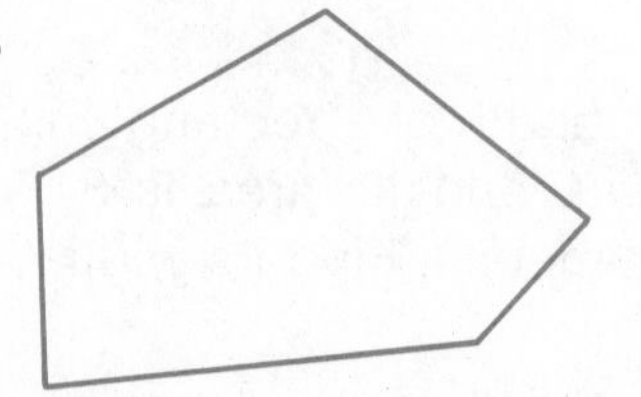

3.

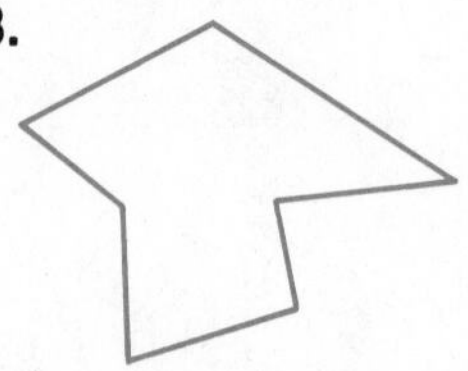

4. The polygon in Exercise **1** can be separated into triangles in several ways. Is there a limit to the number of ways? Explain.

5. Try to find the minimum number of triangular regions into which each of the figures of Exercises **1–3** can be separated. What advantage is there in finding the minimum number of triangular regions in a polygonal region?

6. The figure *ABGFED* in Figure 1 shows the shape that results when triangles *ABC* and *DEF* intersect as shown in Figure 2. Is the union of $\triangle ABC$ and $\triangle DEF$ the same as *ABGFED*? Make a copy of *ABGFED* in Figure 1 and separate it into triangular regions.

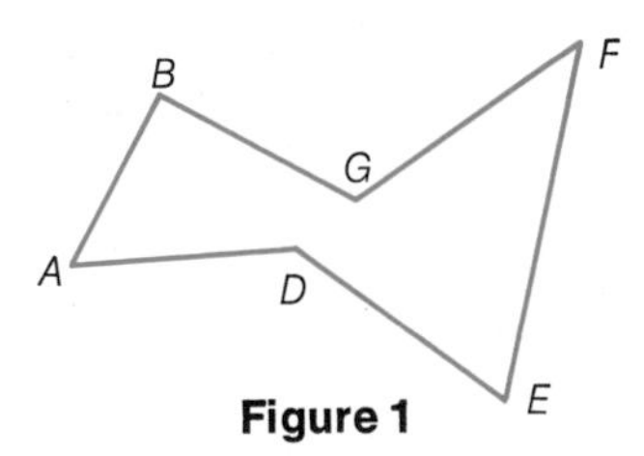

Figure 1

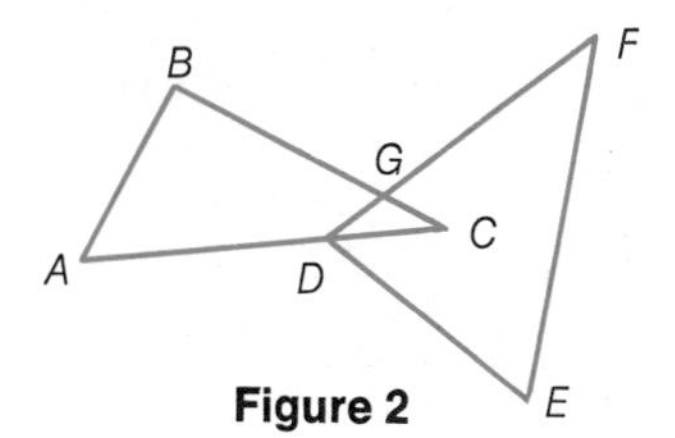

Figure 2

7. In Figure 1 and Figure 2, if the area of $\triangle ABC$ is 12 and the area of $\triangle DEF$ is 15, can you find the area of *ABGFED*? Why?

Exercises ***8–10*** *refer to the figure at the right. Quadrilateral GHKR is divided into triangles by diagonals GK and HR, which intersect at M.*

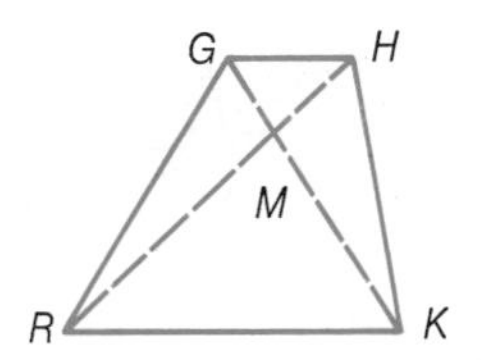

8. What is the intersection of $\triangle GHK$ with $\triangle GHR$?

9. If you know that the area of triangles *GHK*, *GHR*, and *KRM* are 5, 6, and 9 square centimeters, respectively, will the area of *GHKR* be $(5+6+9)$ square centimeters? Why?

10. The area of $\triangle MQP$ is 12, the area of $\triangle SRT$ is 10, and the area of $\triangle PSR$ and $\triangle RPQ$ are each 15. Find the area of polygon *MTSP*.

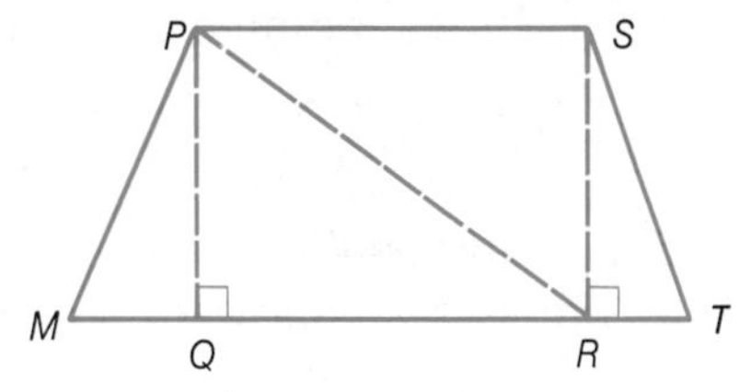

Find each missing measure.

	ℓ	w	Area
11.	5 cm	3.28 cm	?
12.	3 cm	?	30 cm^2
13.	?	6.25 m	1250 m^2
14.	$2\sqrt{5}$	?	$12\sqrt{5}$
15.	?	0.6 k	0.42 k^2

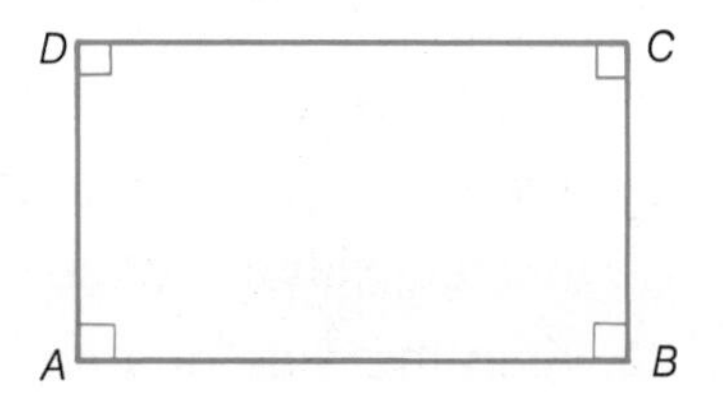

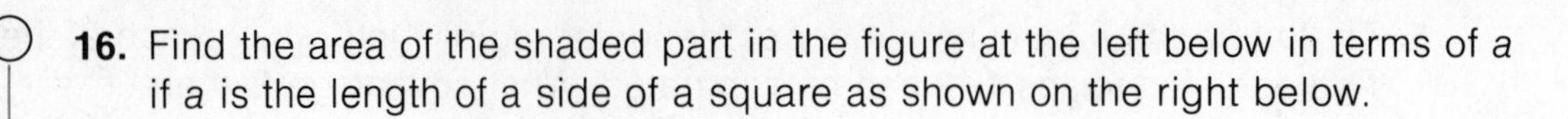

16. Find the area of the shaded part in the figure at the left below in terms of a if a is the length of a side of a square as shown on the right below.

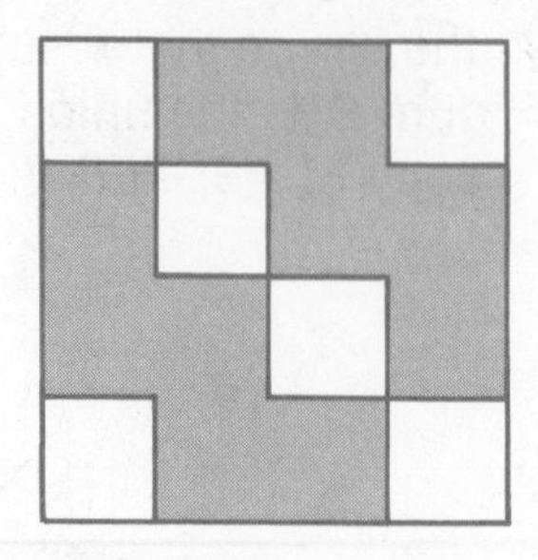

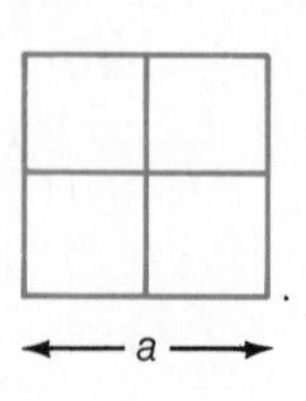

17. The area of a rectangle is 56. The length of the rectangle is $x + 5$ and its width is $x - 5$. Find the dimensions of the rectangle.

18. Polygon $ABCDE$ at the left below is a regular pentagon with side of length s and with perimeter p. Express the area of $ABCDE$ in terms of p and h if the area of $\triangle ABO$ is $\frac{sh}{2}$.

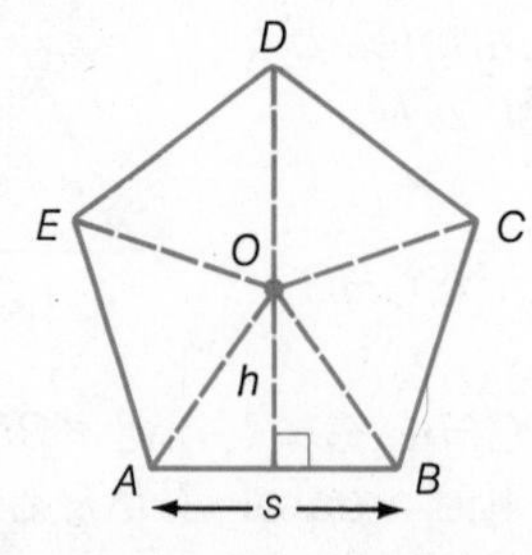

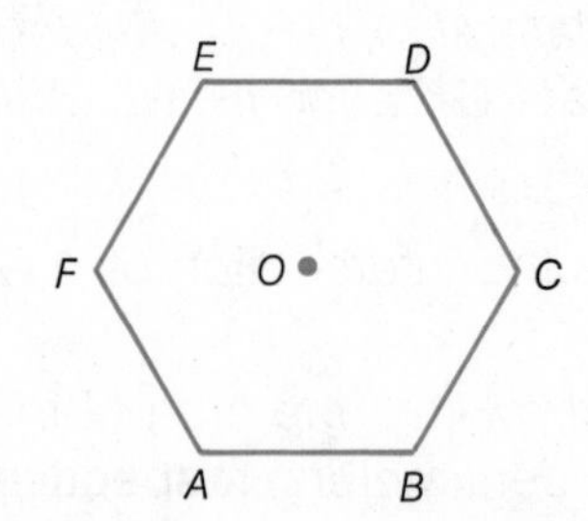

19. Express the area of the regular hexagon $ABCDEF$ above in terms of the length s of one side. Assume the area of a triangle is one half the product of the measures of the base and altitude.

20. A diagonal of a rectangle is 60 meters long and makes an angle of 30° with the base. Find the area of the rectangle.

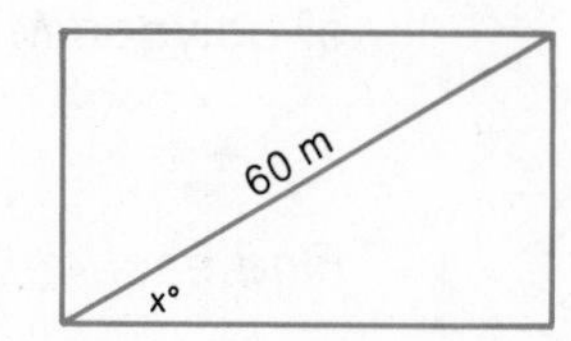

21. Find the area of the rectangle in Exercise **20** if the angle that the diagonal makes with the base measures 45°.

22. Find the area of the rectangle in Exercise **20** if the angle that the diagonal makes with the base measures 60°.

23. Find the area of a square whose diagonal measures 25.

Remember

Write a definition for each of the following.

1. Altitude of a triangle **2.** Parallelogram

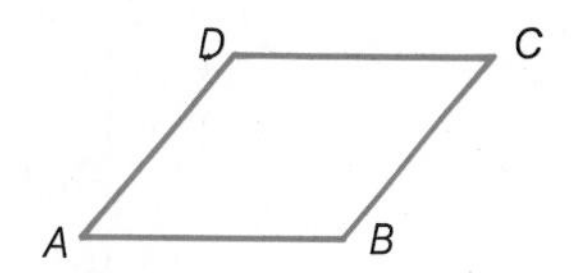

3. $ABCD$ is a parallelogram with $m\angle A = 47$. Find $m\angle B$ and $m\angle C$.

4. Triangle RST is a right triangle with $m\angle S = 30$, $m\angle T = 60$ and $RS = 6\sqrt{3}$. Find TR and ST.

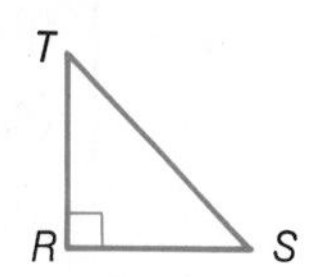

5. Triangle RST is a right triangle with $m\angle S = m\angle T = 45$ and $RS = 7$. Find RT and TS.

The answers are on page 412. If you need help, see pages 82, 206–208, 286, and 291–292.

8-2 Area/Parallelogram and Triangle

Any side of a parallelogram may be called the base of the parallelogram. For each base, there is a corresponding altitude.

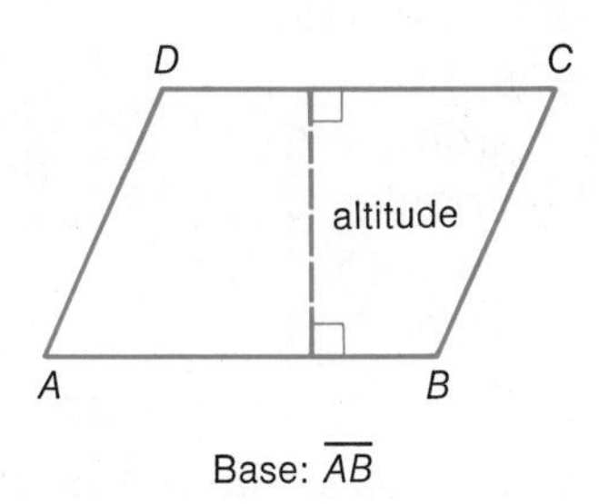

Base: $\overline{AB}$

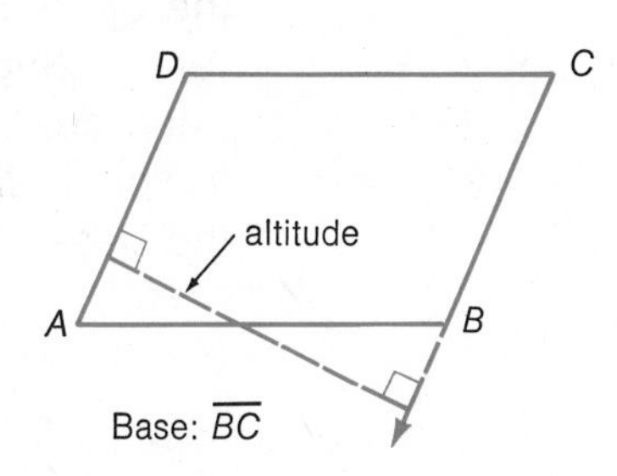

Base: $\overline{BC}$

Definition: The **altitude of a parallelogram** is a perpendicular segment whose endpoints lie on the line that contains the base and on the line that contains the opposite side.

In the theorems that follow, base and altitude will refer to the lengths of these segments.

Theorem 8-1: The area A of a parallelogram is the product of a base b and its corresponding altitude h.

$$A = bh$$

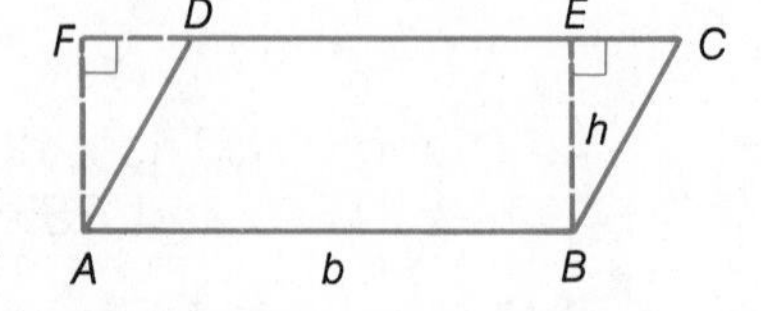

Given: ▱$ABCD$ has base b and altitude h.

Prove: Area of ▱ $ABCD$ is bh.

Plan: With $\overline{EB}$ as the given altitude, $\overline{AF}$ can be constructed to intersect $\overrightarrow{CD}$ so that $ABEF$ is a rectangle whose area is bh. Prove that the area of $\triangle CBE$ equals the area of $\triangle DAF$. The area A of ▱ $ABCD$ is the sum of the areas of regions $ABED$ and CBE. The area of rectangle $ABEF$ is the sum of the areas of regions $ABED$ and DAF. In this way, show that the area of ▱$ABCD$ equals the area, bh, of rectangle $ABEF$.

Corollary 8-2: Parallelograms with equal bases and equal altitudes have equal areas.

Any side of a triangle may be the base of a triangle. The corresponding altitude is the perpendicular segment from one vertex to the line that contains the base.

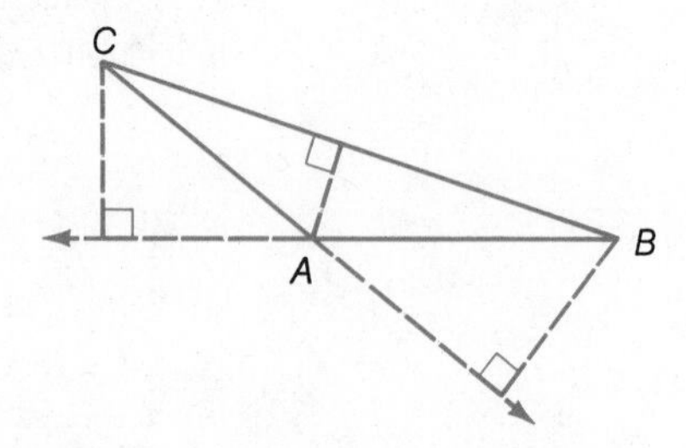

Theorem 8-3: The area A of a triangle is one half the product of a base b and its corresponding altitude h.

$$A = \frac{1}{2}bh$$

Given: $\triangle ABC$ has base b and altitude h.

Prove: $A = \frac{1}{2}bh$

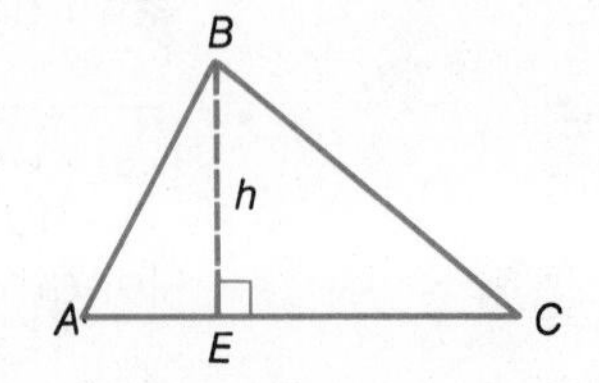

Plan: Through B construct a line parallel to $\overline{AC}$. Through C construct a line parallel to $\overline{AB}$ and intersecting the first line at D. Prove $\triangle ABC \cong \triangle DCB$. Use Theorem 8-1 and Postulates 17 and 18.

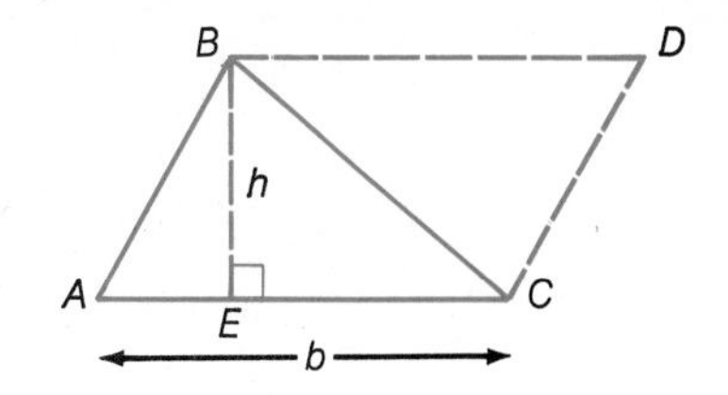

Corollary 8-4: Triangles with equal bases and equal altitudes have equal areas.

Any altitude of an equilateral triangle forms two 30-60-90 triangles. Recall the following relationship between the lengths of the side opposite the 60°-angle, h, and the hypotenuse, s.

$$h = \frac{s}{2}\sqrt{3}$$

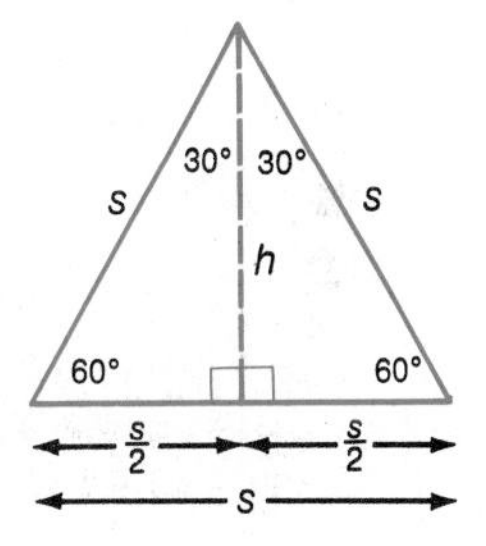

Replacing h with $\frac{s}{2}\sqrt{3}$ and b with s in $A = \frac{1}{2}bh$ leads to the following corollary.

Corollary 8-5: The area A of an equilateral triangle with side of length s is $\frac{s^2\sqrt{3}}{4}$.

$$A = \frac{s^2\sqrt{3}}{4}$$

Example

Find the area of $\triangle ABC$ and of $\triangle EFG$.

a.

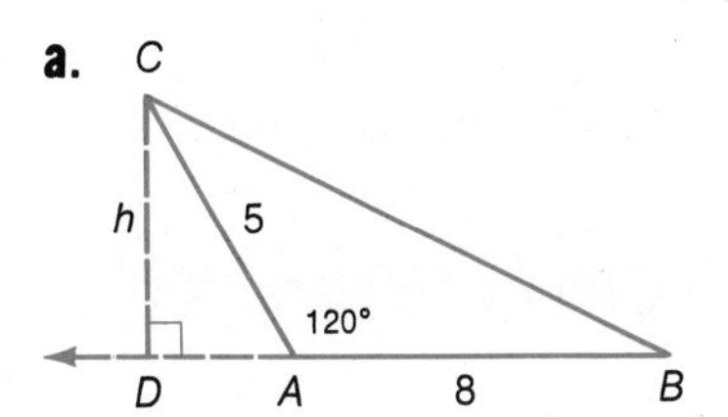

b.

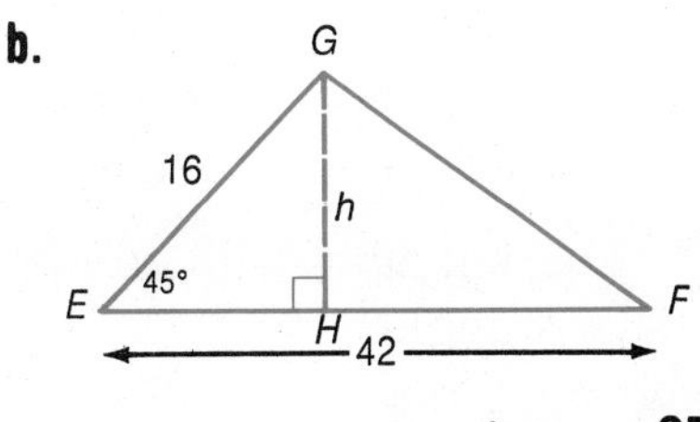

In each triangle, you must first find h.

a. $m\angle DAC = 60$ ⟵ $m\angle BAC = 120$, and $180 - 120 = 60$.

$\therefore \triangle CDA$ is a 30-60-90 triangle.

$$h = \frac{s}{2}\sqrt{3}$$ ⟵ Relationship in a 30-60-90 triangle

$$= \frac{5}{2}\sqrt{3}$$

$$A = \frac{1}{2}bh$$

$$= \frac{1}{2}(8)\left(\frac{5}{2}\sqrt{3}\right) = 10\sqrt{3}$$ ⟵ Area is $10\sqrt{3}$ square units.

b. $\triangle EHG$ is a 45-45-90 triangle.

$$h = \frac{\sqrt{2}}{2}c$$ ⟵ Relationship in a 45-45-90 triangle

$$= \frac{\sqrt{2}}{2} \cdot 16 = 8\sqrt{2}$$ ⟵ The hypotenuse measures 16.

$$A = \frac{1}{2}bh$$

$$= \frac{1}{2}(42)(8\sqrt{2}) = 168\sqrt{2}$$ ⟵ Area is $168\sqrt{2}$ square units.

Try These

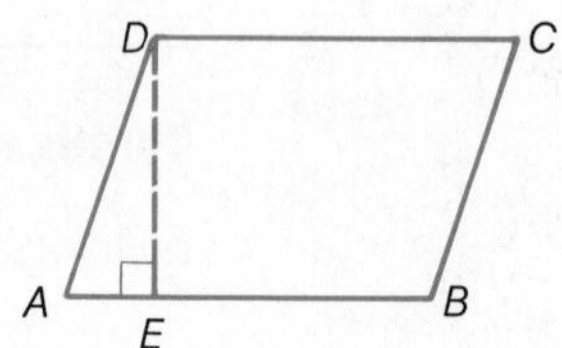

1. In parallelogram $ABCD$, $AB = 10$ centimeters and $DE = 6$ centimeters. Find the area of the parallelogram.

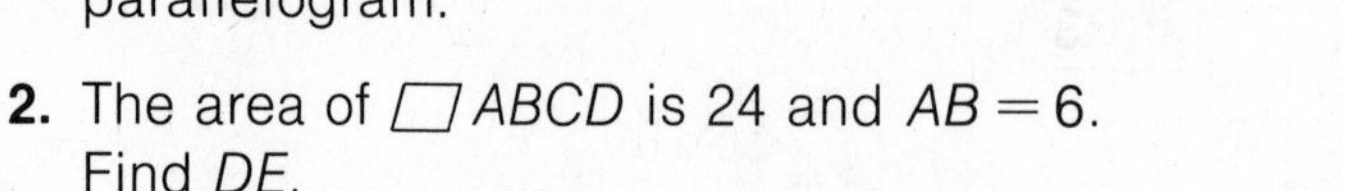

2. The area of ▱$ABCD$ is 24 and $AB = 6$. Find DE.

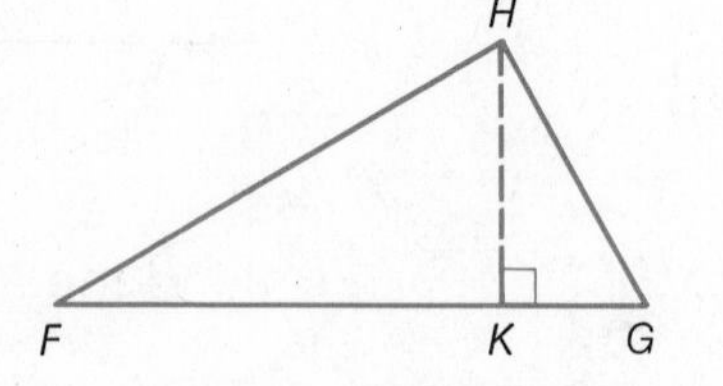

3. In triangle FGH, $FG = 15$ centimeters and $HK = 6$ centimeters. Find the area of the triangle.

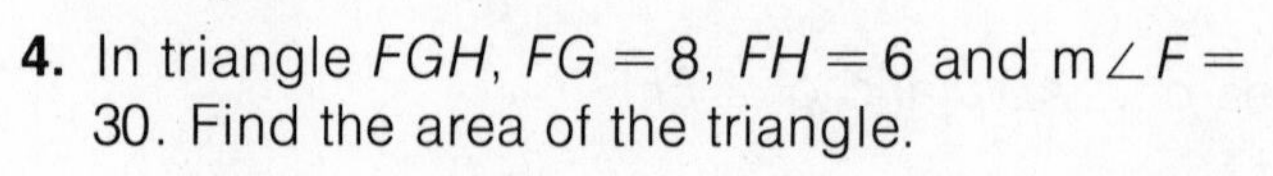

4. In triangle FGH, $FG = 8$, $FH = 6$ and $m\angle F = 30$. Find the area of the triangle.

5. The legs of a right triangle are 14 centimeters and 12 centimeters long. Find the area of the triangle.

6. Each side of an equilateral triangle is 12 meters long. Find the area of the triangle.

Exercises

For Exercises **1–4,** *refer to parallelogram ABCD. Find each missing measure.*

a

	b	h	Area
1.	12 cm	4.32 cm	___?___
2.	4 cm	___?___	36 cm^2
3.	___?___	3.75 m	19.5 m^2
4.	$5\sqrt{2}$ cm	___?___	$40\sqrt{2}$ cm^2

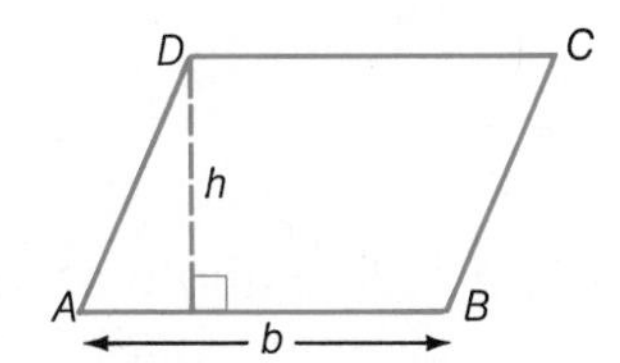

5. In parallelogram $ABCD$ above, $AB = 12$, $AD = 4$ and $m\angle A = 45$. Find the area of the parallelogram.

For Exercises **6–9,** *refer to triangle RST below. Find each missing measure.*

	b	h	Area
6.	9 cm	4.26 cm	___?___
7.	8 cm	___?___	40.25 cm^2
8.	___?___	$3\frac{1}{4}$ m	$8\frac{15}{16}$ m^2
9.	1 cm	___?___	$\frac{5}{4}$ cm^2

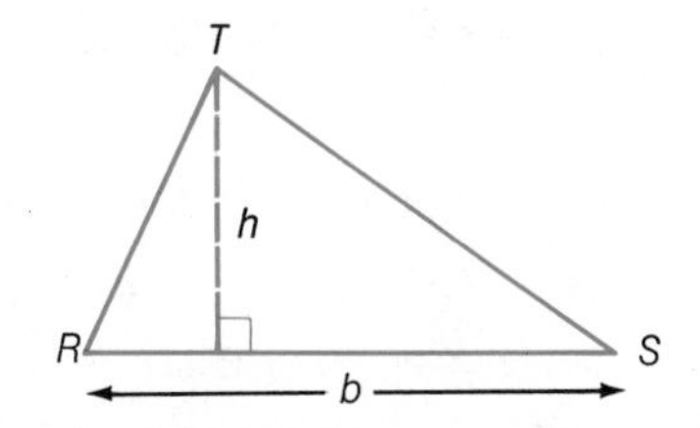

10. In $\triangle RST$ above, $RS = 12$, $RT = 9$ and $m\angle R = 60$. Find the area of the triangle. (Leave your answer in radical form.)

Classify each statement as True or False. If a statement is false, give an example to show why it is false.

11. If two triangles are congruent, then they have equal areas.

12. If two triangles have equal areas, then they are congruent.

13. If two parallelograms have equal bases and equal altitudes, then they have equal areas.

14. If two parallelograms have equal areas, then they have equal bases and equal altitudes.

15. If two triangles have equal areas, then they have equal bases and equal altitudes.

16. In triangles HKL and JGF, the altitudes from H and from J are equal. $\overline{FG}$ joins the midpoints of sides JL and JK in $\triangle KLJ$. What is the ratio of the area of $\triangle HKL$ to the area of $\triangle JGF$? Give a reason for your answer.

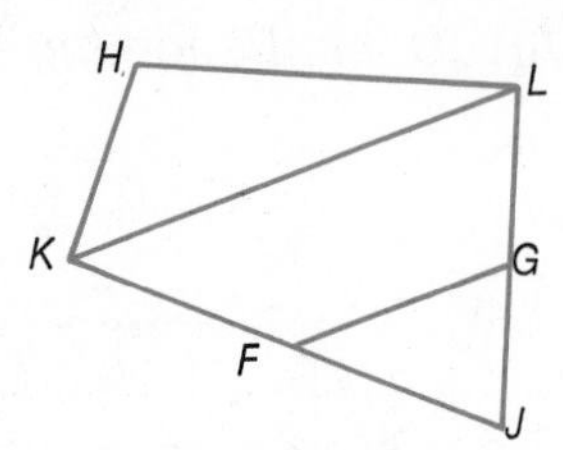

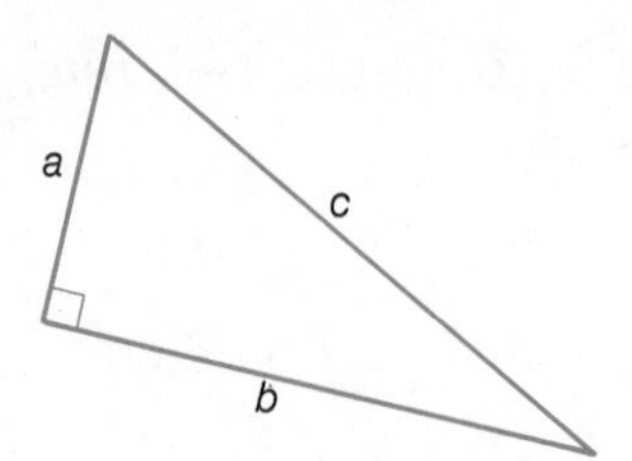

In the right triangle above, the sides have lengths a, b, and c. Find the area, given the following information.

17. $a = 4$; $b = 12$

18. $a = 6.2$; $b = 5.4$

19. $c = 10$; $a = 8$

20. $c = 16$; $a = b$

21. $c = 20$; $b = 12$

22. $c = 41$; $a = 9$

23. Find the area of an equilateral triangle with a side of 20 centimeters.

24. Find the area of an equilateral triangle with an altitude of 9 millimeters.

25. The area of an equilateral triangle is $25\sqrt{3}$ square units. Find the length of one side of the triangle.

In $\square ABCD$, E is the midpoint of $\overline{AB}$, and $\overline{BD}$ is a diagonal. Find the ratio of the following areas.

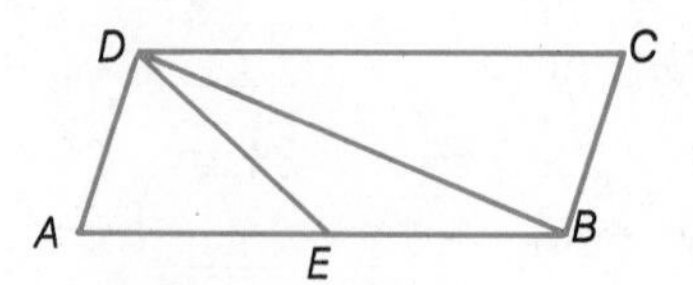

26. $\triangle ABD$ to $\square ABCD$

27. $\triangle AED$ to $\triangle ABD$

28. $\triangle AED$ to $\square ABCD$

29. $\triangle AED$ to $\triangle EBD$

30. In $\triangle ABC$, $AB = 10$, $AC = 7$, and $m\angle A = 135$. Find the area of $\triangle ABC$.

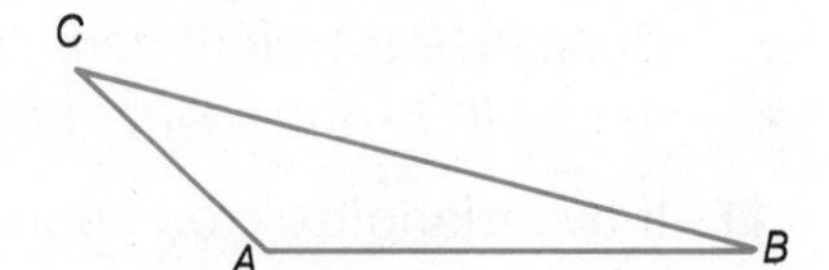

31. Prove Theorem 8-1.

32. Prove Theorem 8-3.

33. Prove Corollary 8-5.

*For Exercises **34–37,** find the area of $\triangle ABC$. Begin by sketching each triangle.*

b

34. $AC = 15$, $AB = 10$, $m\angle A = 30$

35. $AC = 10$, $AB = 8$, $m\angle A = 60$

36. $AC = 4$, $AB = 3$, $m\angle A = 45$

37. $AC = 12$, $AB = 8$, $m\angle A = 150$

*For Exercises **38–39**, find the area of ▱ABCD. Begin by sketching each parallelogram.*

38. $AD = 16$, $AB = 5$, $m\angle A = 30$

39. $AD = 14$, $AB = 5$, $m\angle A = 135$

40. The perimeter of an equilateral triangle is $5x$ centimeters. Express the altitude of the triangle in terms of x.

Remember

Classify each statement as True or False.

1. A parallelogram with all four sides congruent is a rectangle.
2. A quadrilateral with exactly one pair of parallel sides is a trapezoid.
3. The bases of a trapezoid are the nonparallel sides.
4. The diagonals of a rhombus are congruent.

The answers are on page 412. If you need help, see pages 206 and 215.

8-3 Area / Rhombus and Trapezoid

In a rhombus, all sides are congruent and the diagonals are perpendicular bisectors of each other.

Example 1

Find the area of the rhombus, where $AC = d_1$ and $DB = d_2$.

D C E A B

Area of $\triangle ADC = \frac{1}{2}bh$

$= \frac{1}{2}(d_1)(\frac{1}{2}d_2)$ ← $AC = d_1$ and $DE = \frac{1}{2}d_2$.

$= \frac{1}{4}d_1\,d_2$

Area of $\triangle ABC$ = area of $\triangle ADC = \frac{1}{4}d_1\,d_2$ ← $\triangle ABC \cong \triangle ADC$

∴ Area of rhombus = area of $\triangle ADC$ + area of $\triangle ABC$

$= \frac{1}{4}d_1\,d_2 + \frac{1}{4}d_1\,d_2 = \frac{1}{2}d_1\,d_2$

This example suggests the following corollary.

Corollary 8-6: The area A of a rhombus is one half the product of the lengths of its diagonals, d_1 and d_2.

$$A = \frac{1}{2} d_1 \, d_2$$

Example 2

Find the area of the rhombus, where $GM = d_1 = 32$ and $AM = 20$.

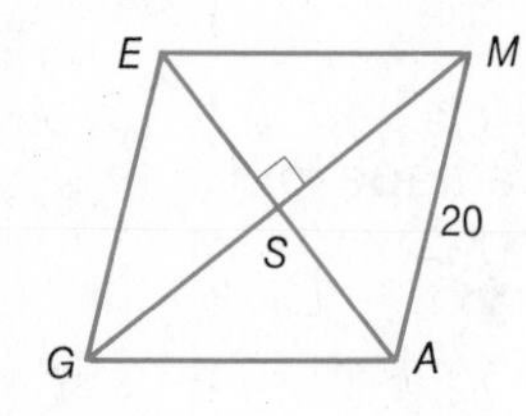

To find d_2, or EA, first find ES, which is $\frac{1}{2}d_2$.

$$\begin{aligned}
(ES)^2 + (SM)^2 &= (EM)^2 \\
(ES)^2 + (16)^2 &= (20)^2 \quad \longleftarrow \; SM = \tfrac{1}{2}GM \text{ and } EM = MA = 20 \\
(ES)^2 + 256 &= 400 \\
(ES)^2 &= 144 \\
ES &= 12 \\
\therefore d_2 &= 24 \quad \longleftarrow \; d_2 = 2(ES) \\
A &= \tfrac{1}{2} d_1 \, d_2 \\
&= \tfrac{1}{2}(32)(24) \\
&= 384 \text{ square units}
\end{aligned}$$

The formula for the area of a trapezoid can be derived by finding the areas of the triangles formed by a diagonal.

Theorem 8-7: The area, A, of a trapezoid is one half the product of its altitude and the sum of its bases b and b' (read: b prime).

$$A = \frac{1}{2}h(b + b')$$

Given: Trapezoid $ABCD$ has bases b and b', altitude h, and area A.

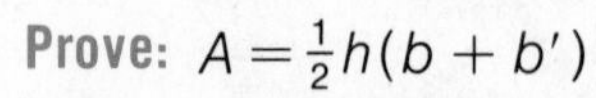

Prove: $A = \frac{1}{2}h(b + b')$

Plan: Draw $\overline{BD}$.
Then, Area of $ABCD$ = area of $\triangle ABD$ + area of $\triangle BCD$.
Since h is the altitude of each triangle,

$$\text{Area of } ABCD = \tfrac{1}{2}bh + \tfrac{1}{2}b'h = \tfrac{1}{2}h(b + b').$$

Try These

1. The diagonals of rhombus are 32 centimeters and 20 centimeters long. Find the area.
2. The area of a rhombus is 48 and one diagonal is 12. Find the other diagonal.
3. In trapezoid $ABCD$, $AB = 32$ meters, $DC = 18$ meters, and $DE = 20$ meters. Find the area.
4. In trapezoid $ABCD$, $AB = 27$, $DC = 13$, and the area of $ABCD$ is 140. Find altitude DE.

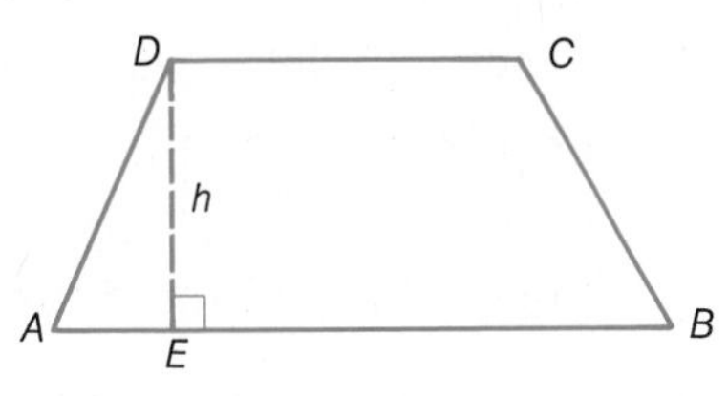

5. In trapezoid $ABCD$, $AB = 12$ centimeters, $DC = 8$ centimeters, $AD = 6$ centimeters, and $m\angle A = 30$. Find the area.

Exercises

*For Exercises **1–5** refer to rhombus KATH. Find each missing measure.*

a

	KT	AH	Area
1.	20	8	?
2.	?	15	60
3.	4	?	$10\sqrt{3}$
4.	10.2	16.4	?
5.	?	$6\frac{2}{3}$	30

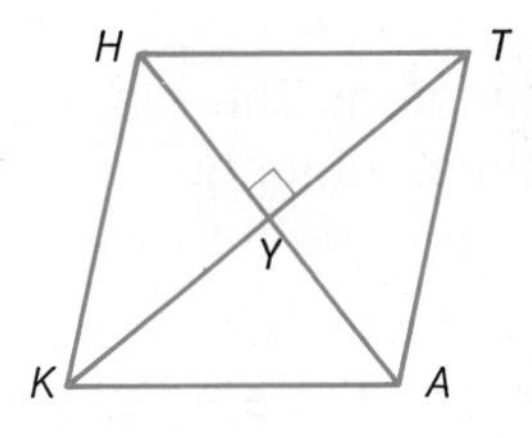

*For Exercises **6–10,** refer to trapezoid WXYZ. Find each missing measure.*

	h	b	b′	Area
6.	2	6	4	?
7.	5	3	2	?
8.	?	10	8	45
9.	5	10	?	$32\frac{1}{2}$
10.	?	$5\sqrt{2}$	$3\sqrt{2}$	$4\sqrt{6}$

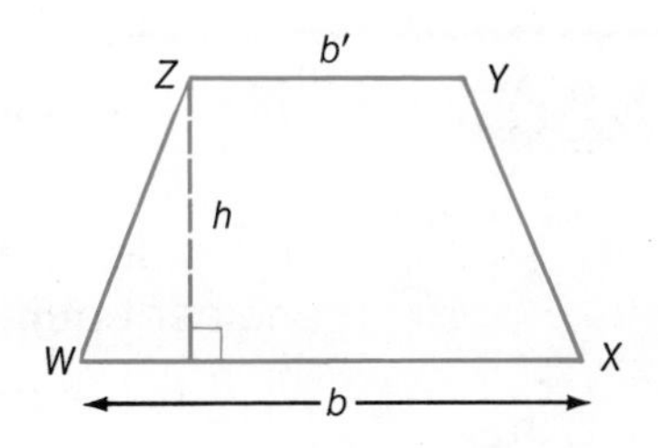

Compute the areas of the figures below.

11.

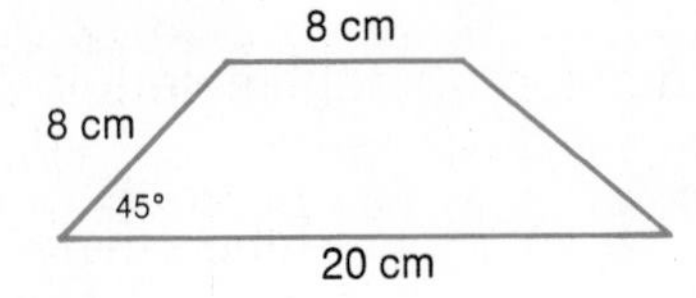

12.

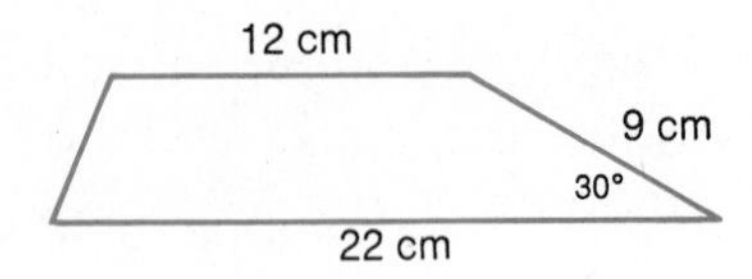

13. Prove Corollary 8-6. (HINT: Follow the method of Example 1.)

14. Prove Theorem 8-7.

15. In rhombus $NEXT$, $NX = 24$ and $EX = 13$. Find the area of the rhombus.

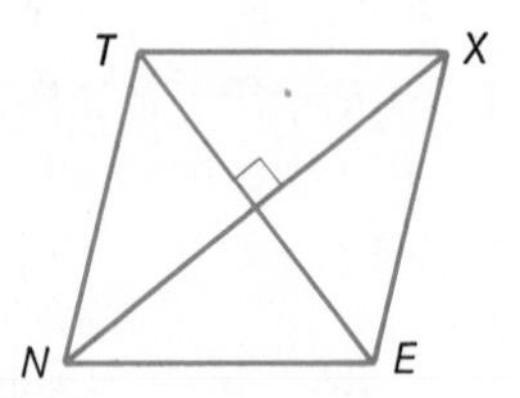

16. In rhombus $NEXT$, $NX = 10$ centimeters and the area is 120 square centimeters. Find the length of one side of the rhombus.

17. In rhombus $NEXT$, $m\angle ENT = 60$ and $NE = 20$. Find the area.

18. In isosceles trapezoid $ABCD$, $DC = 6$, $AB = 12$ and $m\angle B = 30$. Find the area.

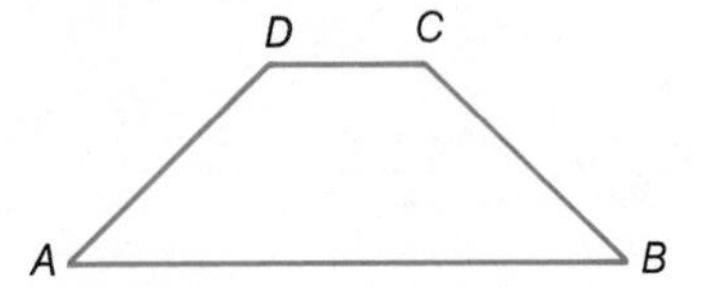

19. Find a side of a square equal in area to a rhombus with diagonals of 10 and 12.

20. The perimeter of a rhombus is 60 and one of its diagonals is 18. Find tte area of the rhombus.

21. A rhombus is equal in area to a trapezoid with an altitude of length 10 centimeters. The diagonals of the rhombus are 15 centimeters and 20 centimeters long. Find the measures of the bases of the trapezoid if one base is twice the length of the other.

22. The length of one diagonal of a rhombus is three times the length of the other and the area of the rhombus is 54. Find the lengths of the diagonals.

PUZZLE

One side of an equilateral triangle is congruent to an altitude of another equilateral triangle.

What is the ratio of their areas?

Remember

1. One side of a regular polygon has a length of 6 centimeters. Find the length of an adjacent side.
2. One angle of a regular polygon is 120°. Give the measures of the other angles of the polygon.

Identify each regular polygon.

3. 

4. 

5. 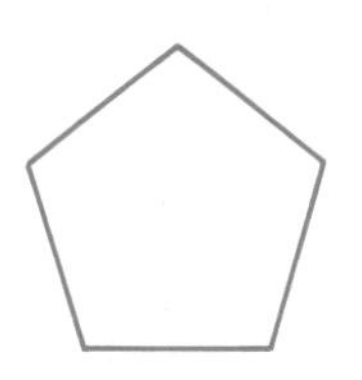

6. 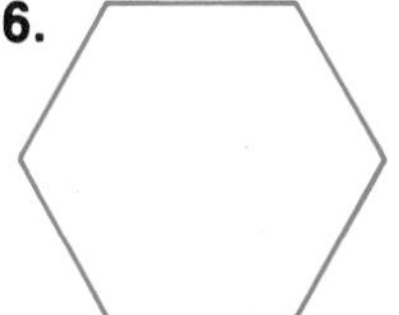

The answers are on page 412. If you need help, see pages 81 and 192.

8-4 Circumscribed and Inscribed Polygons

A circle **circumscribed** about a polygon contains each vertex of the polygon. The **radius of a regular polygon** is the radius of the circumscribed circle. The radii of pentagon *ABCDE* are $\overline{AO}$, $\overline{BO}$, $\overline{CO}$, $\overline{DO}$, and $\overline{EO}$.

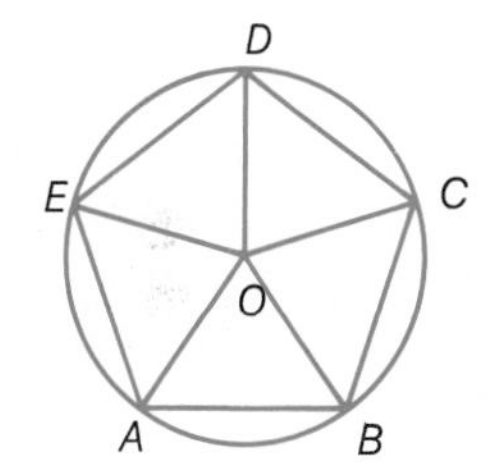

A circle **inscribed** in a polygon is tangent to each side of the polygon. The **apothem** of a regular polygon is the radius of its inscribed circle. The apothems of pentagon *ABCDE* are $\overline{FO}$, $\overline{GO}$, $\overline{HO}$, $\overline{JO}$, and $\overline{KO}$.

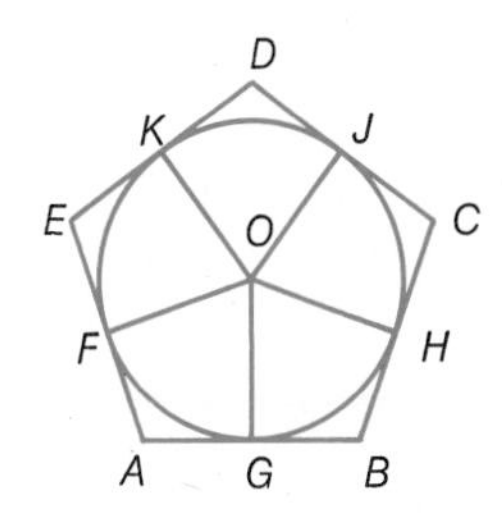

The **center of a regular polygon** is the common center of its inscribed and circumscribed circles.

If a polygon is <u>not</u> regular, <u>both</u> a circumscribed and inscribed circle with a common center cannot be drawn. Try it.

Theorem 8-8: A polygon is regular if and only if a circle with a common center can be inscribed in and circumscribed about it.

Each of the triangles formed by two consecutive radii and a side of a regular polygon are congruent. Thus, the central angles are congruent. A **central angle** of a regular polygon is determined by two consecutive radii.

Example 1

a. Name each pair of consecutive radii and the central angle each pair determines.

b. Find the measure of each central angle.

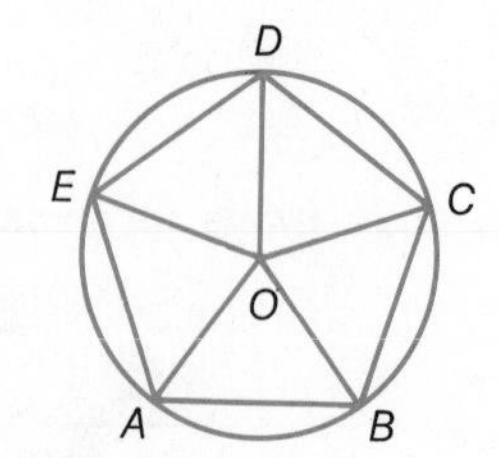

a.

Consecutive radii	$\overline{AO}, \overline{BO}$	$\overline{BO}, \overline{CO}$	$\overline{CO}, \overline{DO}$	$\overline{DO}, \overline{EO}$	$\overline{EO}, \overline{AO}$
Central angles	$\angle AOB$	$\angle BOC$	$\angle COD$	$\angle DOE$	$\angle EOA$

b. $m\angle AOB + m\angle BOC + m\angle COD + m\angle DOE + m\angle EOA = 360$

$m\angle AOC = m\angle BOC = m\angle COD = m\angle DOE = m\angle EOA$ ← **The central angles are congruent.**

$\therefore x + x + x + x + x = 360$ ← **Let x represent the measure of each central angle.**

$5x = 360$

$x = 72$ ← **The measure of each central angle.**

Example 1 suggests the following corollary.

Corollary 8-9: The measure of each central angle of a regular polygon of n sides is $\frac{360}{n}$.

By the S.S.S. Postulate, triangles formed by two consecutive radii and a side of a regular polygon are congruent.

Example 2

a. Find the measure of a base angle of one of the isosceles triangles.

b. Find the measure of an angle of the regular polygon.

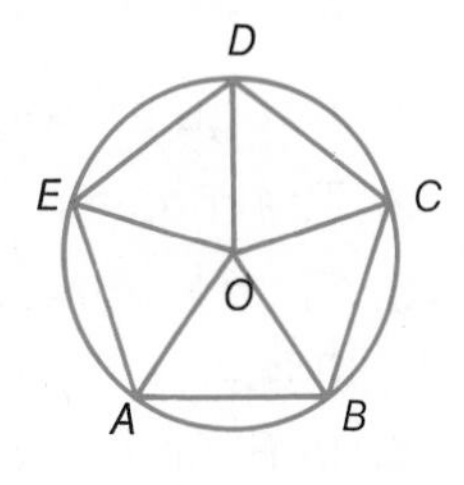

a. In $\triangle AOB$, $m\angle OAB + m\angle OBA + m\angle AOB = 180$

$m\angle AOB = 72$ ⟵ From Example 1

$m\angle OAB = m\angle OBA$ ⟵ Since $\angle OAB \cong \angle OBA$

$y + y + 72 = 180$ ⟵ Let $y = m\angle OAB = m\angle OBA$.

$2y = 108$

$y = 54$ ⟵ $m\angle OAB$ and $m\angle OBA$

b. $m\angle EAB = m\angle OAE + m\angle OAB$

$m\angle OAE = m\angle OAB$ ⟵ Since $\triangle OAE \cong \triangle OAB$

$m\angle OAE = 54$

$\therefore m\angle EAB = m\angle OAE + m\angle OAB = 54 + 54 = 108$

Example 2 suggests that each radius of a regular polygon bisects an angle of the polygon.

Corollary 8-10: A radius of a regular polygon bisects an angle of the polygon.

In this figure, $\overline{AB}$ is a tangent to the inscribed circle, and apothem OG is perpendicular to $\overline{AB}$. Further, $\overline{AB}$ is a chord of the circumscribed circle. Therefore, apothem OG also bisects $\overline{AB}$. (Theorem 7-7)

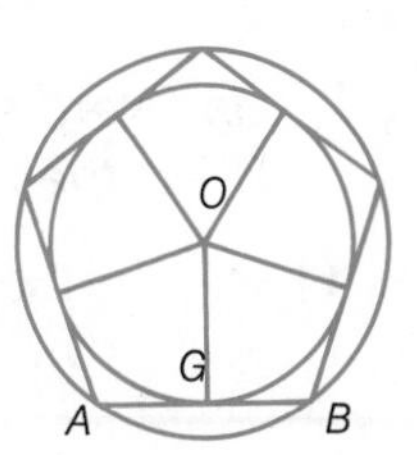

Corollary 8-11: The apothem of a regular polygon is the perpendicular bisector of a side of the polygon.

Try These

Complete each statement.

1. A regular polygon of n sides has ___?___ central angles.
2. The measure of each central angle of a regular polygon of nine sides is ___?___.
3. Each central angle of a regular polygon has a measure of 45. The polygon has ___?___ sides.
4. In Exercise **3,** the name of the regular polygon is ___?___.
5. The central angles of a regular polygon are ___?___.
6. A central angle of a regular polygon is formed by two ___?___.
7. The radii of a regular hexagon are drawn and the length of each radius is 9. Then the length of a side of the regular hexagon is ___?___.
8. Apothem OG is drawn to side AB of regular pentagon $ABCDE$. Then, $\overline{OG}$ ___?___ $\overline{AB}$ and $\overline{OG}$ bisects ___?___.

Exercises

*In Exercises **1–5,** the number of sides of a regular polygon is given. Find the measure of a central angle of the polygon.*

a

1. 5 **2.** 8 **3.** 10 **4.** 12 **5.** 20

*In Exercises **6–10,** the measure of a central angle of a regular polygon is given. Find the number of sides of the polygon.*

6. 18° **7.** 40° **8.** 120° **9.** 30° **10.** 72°

*In Exercises **11–15,** the number of sides of a regular polygon is given. Find the measure of each angle of the polygon.*

11. 18 **12.** 12 **13.** 20 **14.** 30 **15.** 10

16. The radius of a regular hexagon is 4 centimeters. What is the length of one side of the hexagon?

17. A regular hexagon is inscribed in a circle whose radius is 10 centimeters. What is the length of the apothem?

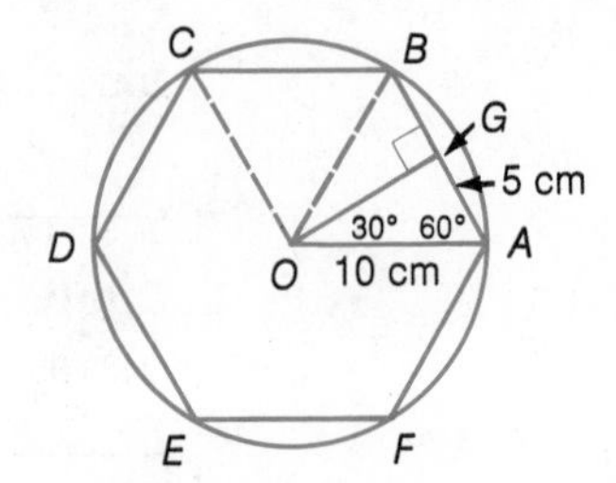

*In Exercises **18–23,** the radius of a regular hexagon is given. Find the length of the apothem.*

18. 2 meters

19. 3 meters

20. 4 decimeters

21. 6 centimeters

22. 5.5 millimeters

23. y meters

24. In the figure at the left below, an equilateral triangle is inscribed in a circle whose radius is 12. Find the length of the apothem.

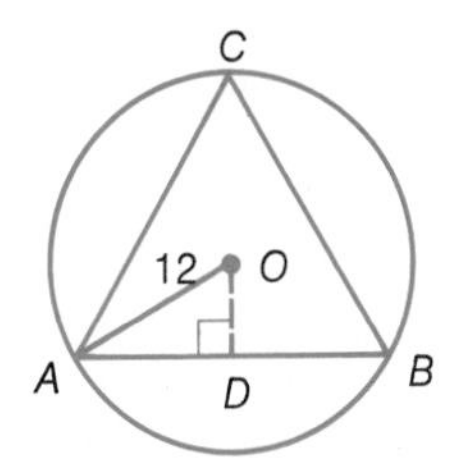

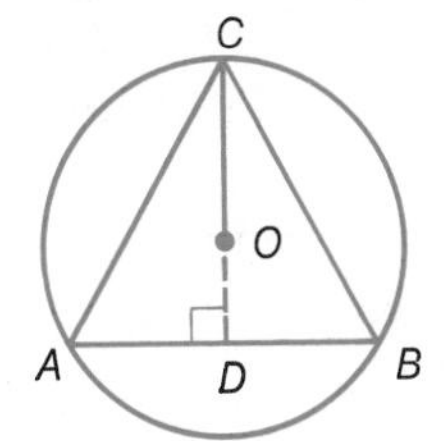

25. In the figure at the right above, equilateral triangle ABC is inscribed in circle O whose radius is 8. Find the length of altitude CD. (HINT: Draw $OA = 8$ and find apothem OD. Then $CO + OD = CD$.)

26. Repeat Exercise **24** if the radius of the circle is x units.

27. Use Exercise **25** to find AD and AB.

28. An equilateral triangle is inscribed in a circle whose radius is 14. Find the length of one side of the triangle. (HINT: See Exercises **25** and **27.**)

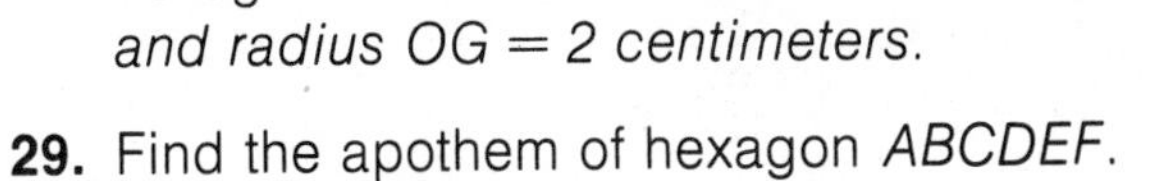

*In Exercises **29–31,** ABCDEF is a regular hexagon circumscribed about circle O and radius OG = 2 centimeters.*

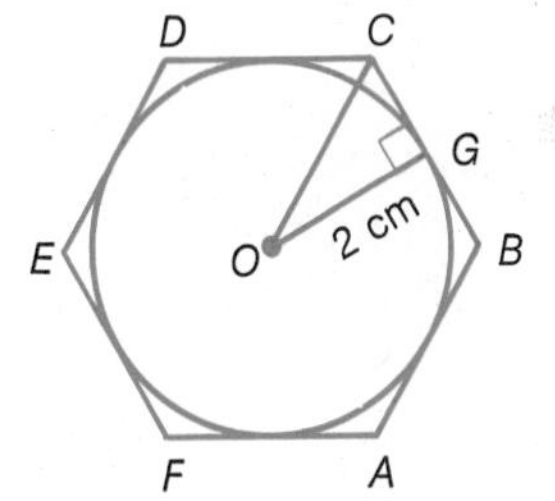

29. Find the apothem of hexagon $ABCDEF$.

30. Find the length of radius OC.

31. Find the area of the hexagon. (HINT: First find the area of $\triangle BOC$. Then area of hexagon $ABCDEF = 6$ (area $\triangle BOC$).

32. The radius of regular hexagon $ABCDEF$ is 7. Find the area of the hexagon.

33. The radius of regular hexagon $ABCDEF$ is a. Find the area of the hexagon.

34. Find the ratio of the apothem of an equilateral triangle to the radius of its circumscribed circle.

35. For a circle whose radius is x, find the ratio of the area of the inscribed equilateral triangle to the area of the circumscribed equilateral triangle.

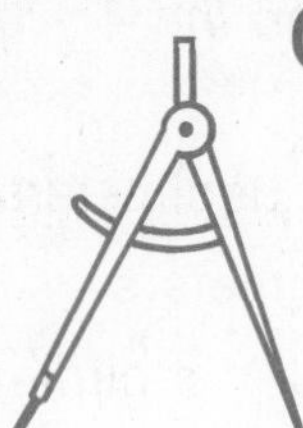

Constructions

Circumscribing a Circle about a Triangle

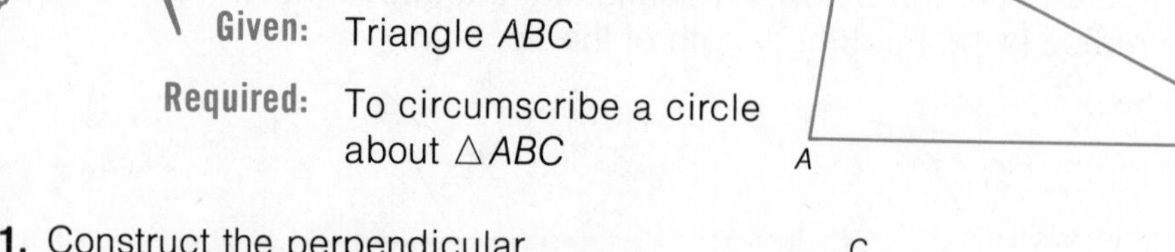

Given: Triangle ABC

Required: To circumscribe a circle about $\triangle ABC$

1. Construct the perpendicular bisectors of any two sides of $\triangle ABC$. Let P be the point of intersection of the perpendicular bisectors.

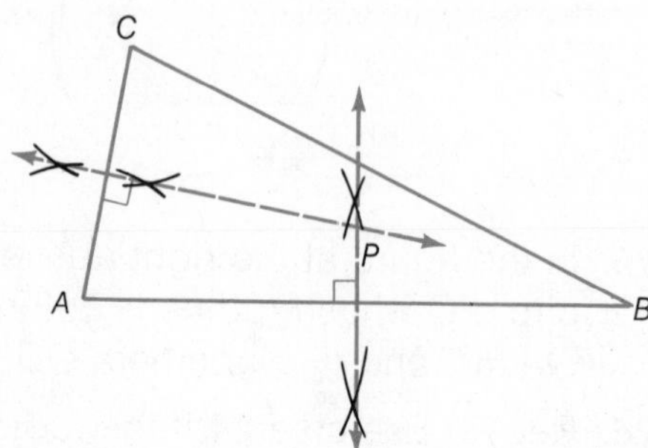

2. With P as center, and radius $r = PA$, construct a circle.

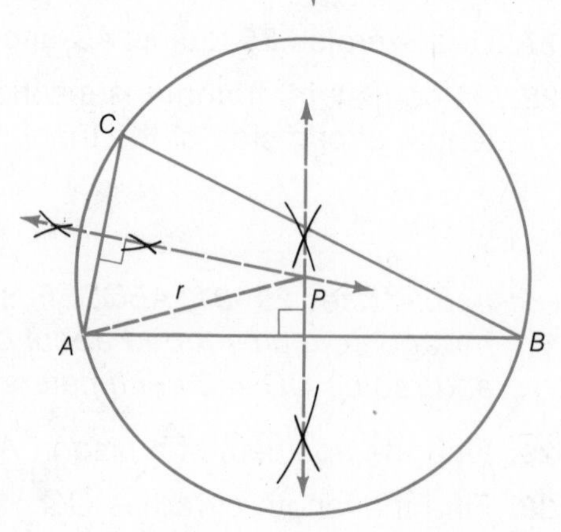

Since $PC = PB = PA = r$, the circle contains A, B, and C. Then circle P is the required circle.

Inscribing a Circle in a Triangle

Given: Triangle ABC

Required: To inscribe a circle in $\triangle ABC$

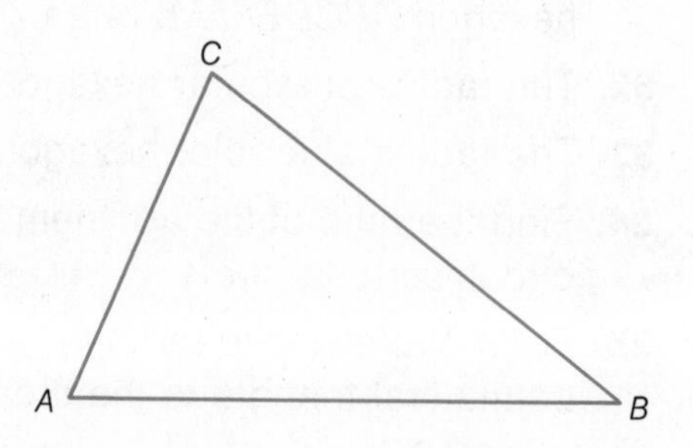

1. Construct the bisectors of any two angles of $\triangle ABC$. Let T be the point of intersection of the angle bisectors.

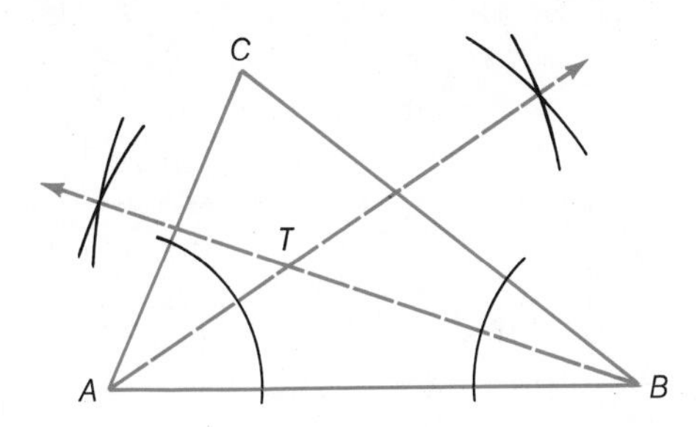

2. Construct a perpendicular to $\overline{AB}$ from T. Label the point of intersection Y.

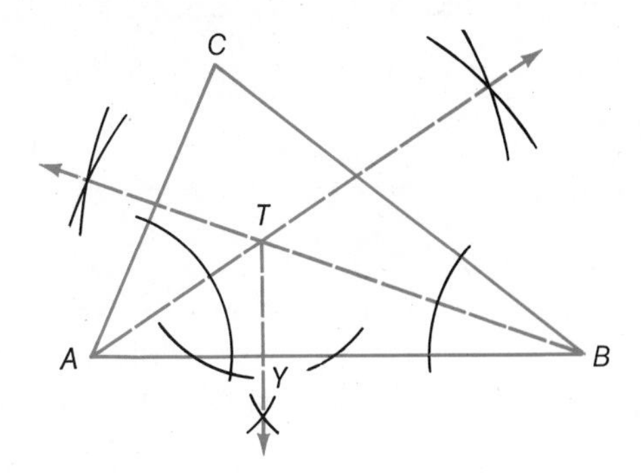

3. With T as center and TY as radius, construct a circle.

Circle T is tangent to $\overline{AB}$ at Y, because $\overline{AB}$ is perpendicular to the radius, $\overline{TY}$. Similarly, the circle is tangent to the other two sides of the triangle.

Thus, circle T is the required circle.

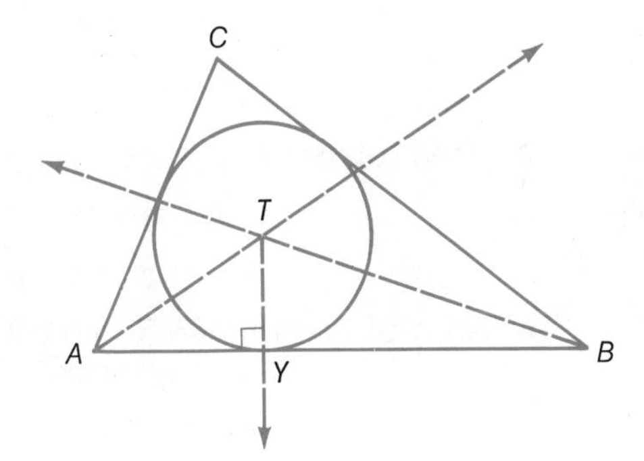

Exercises

In Exercises **1–2,** *complete each statement.*

1. The perpendicular bisectors of the sides of a triangle meet at a point equidistant from the __?__ of the triangle.
2. The bisectors of the angles of a triangle meet at a point equidistant from the __?__ of the triangle.
3. Draw a triangle and construct the circumscribed circle.
4. Draw a triangle and construct the inscribed circle.
5. Draw an equilateral triangle. Construct the circumscribed and the inscribed circle.

8-5 Areas of Regular Polygons

Example 1

Each side of a regular hexagon is 14 centimeters long and the length of its apothem is $7\sqrt{3}$ centimeters.

a. Find the area of one triangle formed by consecutive radii of the hexagon.

b. Find the area of the regular hexagon.

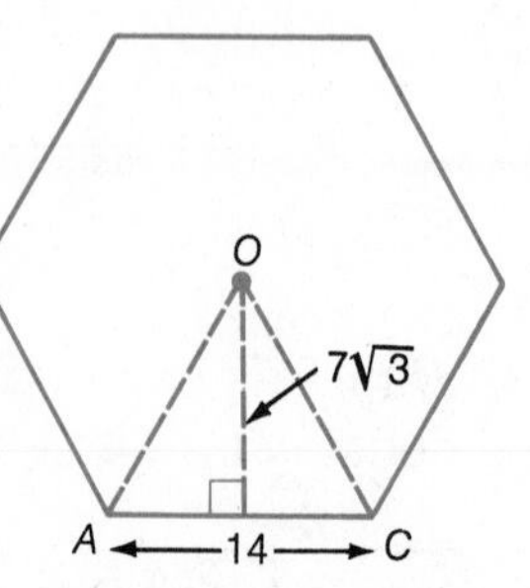

a. Area of triangle $= \frac{1}{2}bh$

$A = \frac{1}{2} \cdot 14 \cdot 7\sqrt{3}$ ⟵ The apothem is an altitude of $\triangle AOC$.

$= 49\sqrt{3}$ ⟵ Area of one triangle is $49\sqrt{3}$ sq. cm.

b. Area of hexagon $= 6 \cdot 49\sqrt{3}$ ⟵ The consecutive radii form 6 triangles.

$= 294\sqrt{3}$ ⟵ Area of hexagon is $294\sqrt{3}$ sq. cm.

This example suggests the following formula, where a is the apothem, b is the base, and n is the number of triangles formed by consecutive radii in a regular polygon.

$$A = \frac{1}{2}abn$$

Example 2

Find the perimeter of the regular hexagon in Example 1.

$P = bn$

$= 14 \cdot 6 = 84$ ⟵ Perimeter of hexagon is 84 cm.

These examples lead to the following formulas for the area of a regular polygon.

$A = \frac{1}{2}abn$ ⟵ Since $P = bn$, replace bn with P.

$= \frac{1}{2}aP$

Theorem 8-12: The area, A, of a regular polygon is one half the product of its perimeter, P, and the length, a, of the apothem.

$$A = \frac{1}{2}aP$$

Example 3

Find the area of a regular hexagon if its apothem is $8\sqrt{3}$.

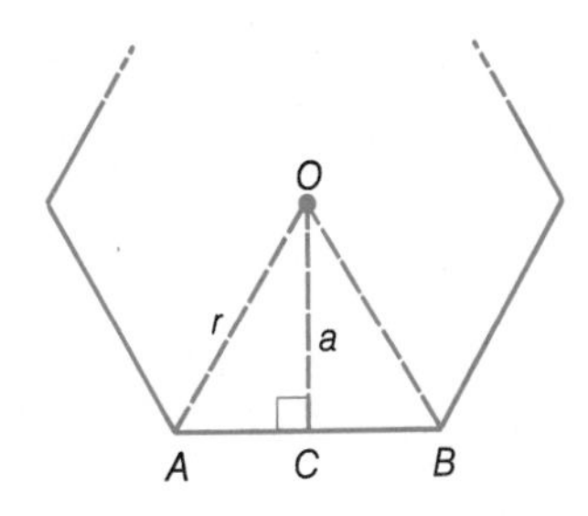

$m\angle AOB = 60$ ⟵ $\frac{360}{n}$, $n = 6$

$\therefore \triangle AOB$ is equilateral.

$\triangle AOC$ is a 30-60 right triangle. ⟵ **Corollary 8-11**

$\therefore AO = 16$ and $AC = 8$.

$\therefore AB = 16$

$$P = bn = 16 \cdot 6$$
$$= 96$$

$$A = \frac{1}{2}aP = \frac{1}{2}(8\sqrt{3})(96)$$
$$= 384\sqrt{3}$$

Try These

*For Exercises **1–6,** use the given information to replace the ? with the correct measure.*

	Figure	Side	Apothem	Perimeter	Area
1.	Regular hexagon	10 cm	$5\sqrt{3}$	?	?
2.	Regular polygon	___	12	$48\sqrt{3}$	?
3.	Regular polygon	___	$\frac{10}{3}\sqrt{3}$	60	?
4.	Regular pentagon	x	y	?	?
5.	Square	?	10 dm	?	?
6.	Equilateral triangle	12 mm	?	?	?

Exercises

*In Exercises **1–4,** the perimeter P and the apothem a of a regular polygon are given. Find the area of each polygon.*

a

1. $P = 40$; $a = 5$

2. $P = 80\sqrt{3}$; $a = 10\sqrt{2}$

3. $P = 30\sqrt{3}$; $a = 5$

4. $P = 54$; $a = 3\sqrt{3}$

5. Find the apothem of a regular polygon with area of 144 square meters and perimeter of 48 meters.

6. Find the perimeter of an equilateral triangle with an apothem of 2 centimeters.

7. Find the perimeter of a regular hexagon with an apothem of 3 meters.

8. Find the apothem of a square with a side of 8 meters.

9. Find the apothem of a regular hexagon with a perimeter of 48 centimeters.

10. Find the area of a regular octagon with apothem of 7 millimeters and side of 5.8 millimeters.

11. Find the apothem of a square with radius of 10 decimeters.

An equilateral triangle has a side of 20 centimeters. Find each measure.

12. The radius

13. The apothem

14. The area

A square has a diagonal of $18\sqrt{2}$. Find each measure.

15. A side of the square

16. The apothem

17. The area

18. Find the area of a regular hexagon with a side 4 centimeters long.

19. Find the area of an equilateral triangle with a radius of $4\sqrt{3}$.

20. Find the area of a square with an apothem of $4\sqrt{2}$ decimeters.

b

21. An equilateral triangle has an area of $300\sqrt{3}$. Find the apothem of the triangle.

One side of a square is x units. Find each of the following in terms of x.

22. The apothem

23. The perimeter

24. The area

8-6 Similarity and Polygons

You know that two polygons are similar if corresponding angles are congruent and correspooding sides are proportional.

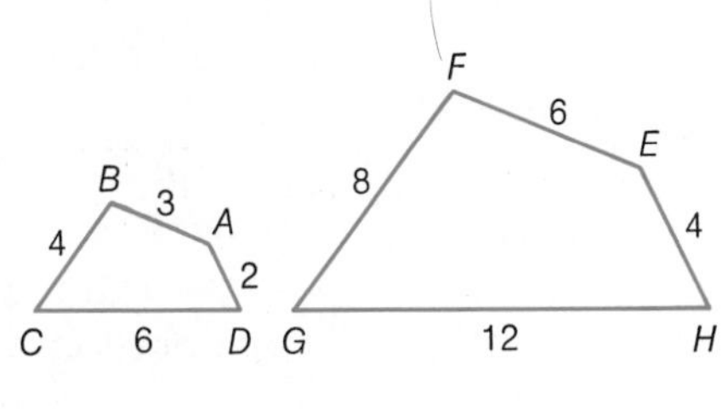

This suggests the following theorem for regular polygons.

Theorem 8-13: Regular polygons of the same number of sides are similar.

Example 1

Use the similar polygons above to find each ratio.

a. The ratio of the measures of the corresponding sides

b. The ratio of the perimeters

a. $\frac{6}{12}=\frac{4}{8}=\frac{3}{6}=\frac{2}{4}=\frac{1}{2}$ ⟵ Ratio of corresponding sides

b. $2+3+4+6=15$ ⟵ Perimeter of *ABCD*

$4+6+8+12=30$ ⟵ Perimeter of *EFGH*

$\frac{15}{30}=\frac{1}{2}$ ⟵ Ratio of the perimeters

Corollary 8-14: The perimeters of similar polygons have the same ratio as the measures of any two corresponding sides.

Corollary 8-15 can be similarly illustrated.

Corollary 8-15: The perimeters of two regular polygons of the same number of sides have the same ratio as their radii or as their apothems.

Other ratio relationships exist between similar polygons.

Theorem 8-16: The areas of two similar polygons have the same ratio as the squares of the measures of any two corresponding sides.

Corollary 8-17: The areas of two regular polygons of the same number of sides have the same ratio as the squares of their radii or as the squares of their apothems.

Example 2

Two similar polygons have areas of $54\sqrt{3}$ and $96\sqrt{3}$. The radius of the smaller polygon is 6. Find the radius of the larger.

$\frac{54\sqrt{3}}{96\sqrt{3}} = \frac{9}{16}$ ← Ratio of the smaller area to the larger area

$\frac{9}{16} = \left(\frac{6}{r}\right)^2$ ← By Corollary 8-17

$\frac{9}{16} = \frac{36}{r^2}$ ← $16 \cdot 36 = 576$

$9r^2 = 576$

$r^2 = 64$

$r = 8$ ← Radius of the larger polygon

Try These

1. Find the ratio of the perimeters of two regular pentagons whose sides are 3 centimeters and 7 centimeters.
2. Find the ratio of the areas of two regular octagons whose sides are 4 millimeters and 6 millimeters.

3. The areas of two regular decagons are 64 square units and 81 square units. Find the ratio of their apothems.
4. The areas of two regular hexagons are in the ratio of 4:7. Find the ratio of their radii.

Exercises

The radii of two regular pentagons are 5 centimeters and 7 centimeters. Give the ratio of:

a

1. Their sides.
2. Their apothems.
3. Their perimeters.
4. Their areas.

The areas of two regular hexagons are 100 and 144. Give the ratio of:

5. Their sides.
6. Their apothems.
7. Their radii.
8. Their perimeters.
9. Two similar polygons have apothems of 15 units and 18 units. Find the ratio of their areas.
10. Two regular decagons are inscribed in two circles whose radii are 5 inches and 10 inches. Find the ratio of the areas of the decagons.
11. The areas of two similar polygons are $27\sqrt{2}$ and $48\sqrt{2}$ and the radius of the smaller polygon is 6. Find the radius of the larger polygon.
12. The areas of two similar pentagons are in the ratio of 12:25 and the apothem of the larger pentagon is 5. Find the apothem of the smaller pentagon.
13. Two regular octagons have apothems of 4 centimeters and 6 centimeters and the area of the smaller octagon is 52 square centimeters. Find the area of the larger octagon.
14. The perimeters of two similar polygons are 48 and 72, and the area of the larger is 270. Find the area of the smaller.

b

15. Three regular polygons have apothems in the ratio of 2:3:7. What is the ratio of the areas of these polygons?
16. The measure of each side of a regular polygon is doubled to make another polygon. Find the ratio of the area of the original polygon to the new polygon.
17. The radii of two similar polygons are in the ratio of 2:3 and the sum of their perimeters is 40. Find the perimeters of the two polygons.

8-7 Circumference/Length of Arc

The distance around a polygon is the perimeter. The distance around a circle is the **circumference,** C. As the number of sides of a regular polygon is increased, the perimeter approximates the circumference of the circumscribed circle.

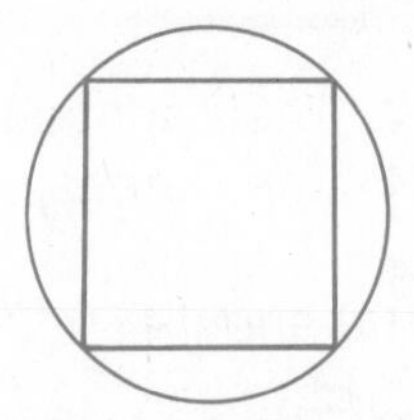

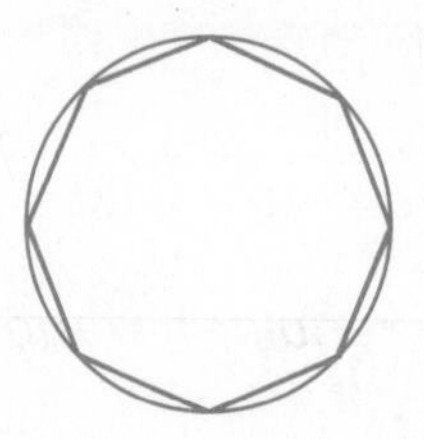

The ratio of the perimeter, P, to the radius, r, is the same (constant) for all regular polygons that are similar. Since all circles are similar, the ratio of the circumference, C, to the radius, r, is a constant.

Therefore, the ratio of C to $2r$, or d, is also a constant. This suggests the following theorem.

Theorem 8-18: The ratio $\frac{C}{d}$ of the circumference, C, of a circle to the measure of the diameter, d, is the same for all circles.

This table shows a method for approximating $\frac{C}{d}$, or π (pi).

$\frac{C}{d} = \pi$, or

$C = \pi d$ or

$C = 2\pi r$

Number of sides	$\frac{C}{d}$
16	3.121445
32	3.136548
64	3.140331
128	3.141277
256	3.141513
512	3.141572
1024	3.141587
2048	3.141591
4096	3.141592

Example 1

Find the circumference of a circle with $d = 20$. Express your answer in terms of π.

$C = \pi d = 20\pi$

The proof of the following corollary is asked for in the exercises.

Corollary 8-19: The circumferences of two circles have the same ratio as their radii.

If you think of a circle as an arc, then its arc has a degree measure of 360. Thus, $2\pi r = 360$.

Example 2

Find the length of $\widehat{AB}$ (arc AB), where 90 is its degree measure.

B
90°
O
6
A

$2\pi r = 360$

$12\pi = 360$ ⟵ $r = 6$

$\frac{90}{360} = \frac{1}{4}$ ⟵ $\frac{\text{Degree measure of } \widehat{AB}}{\text{Degree measure of a circle}}$

$\therefore \frac{1}{4} \cdot 12\pi = 3\pi$ ⟵ Length of $\widehat{AB}$

Example 2 suggests the following corollary.

Corollary 8-20: In a circle, the ratio of the length ℓ of an arc to the circumference C is equal to the ratio of the degree measure m of the arc to 360.

$$\frac{\ell}{C} = \frac{m}{360}, \quad \text{or} \quad \frac{\ell}{2\pi r} = \frac{m}{360}$$

Example 3 Find the degree measure of $\widehat{CD}$.

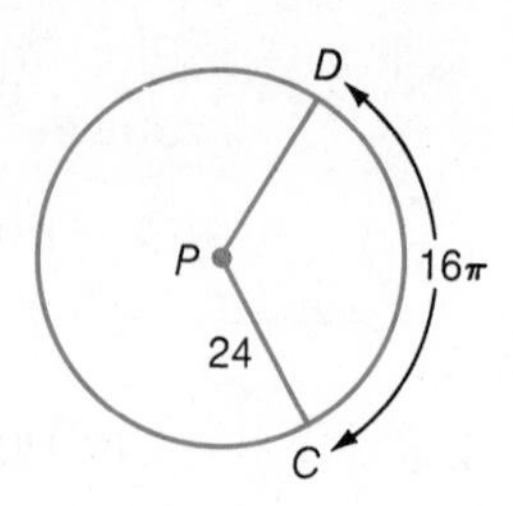

$$\frac{\ell}{2\pi r} = \frac{m}{360}$$
$$\frac{16\pi}{48\pi} = \frac{m}{360}$$
$$\frac{1}{3} = \frac{m}{360}$$
$$360 = 3m$$
$$120 = m$$

Try These

Express answers in terms of π.

1. Find the circumference of a circle whose radius is 14 centimeters.

2. Find the radius of a circle whose circumference is 34π units.

3. Find the length of an arc whose degree measure is 60 in a circle of radius 4.

4. In circle O, the length of $\widehat{AB}$ is 4π meters and the length of radius $\overline{OB}$ is 10 meters. Find the degree measure of $\widehat{AB}$.

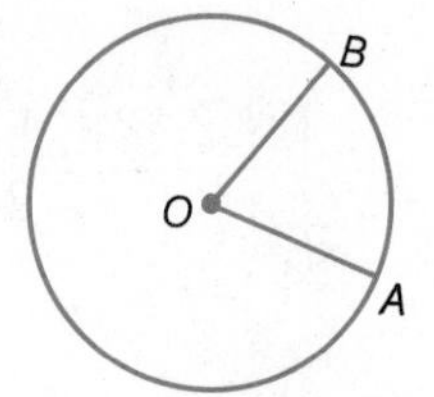

Exercises

*In Exercises **1–6**, find the missing measures. Express answers in terms of π.*

a

	Radius	Diameter	Circumference
1.	?	8	8π
2.	6	?	?
3.	?	?	48π
4.	?	6.4	?
5.	?	?	$\frac{15}{8}\pi$
6.	4.7	?	?

7. Prove Corollary 8-19. (HINT: Let the radii of the circles equal r and r' respectively. Find the circumference of each circle and compare the ratios.)

8. The radii of two circles are 2 meters and 8 meters. Find the ratio of their circumferences.

9. The circumferences of two circles are 6π units and 12π units. Find the ratio of the radii.

10. The ratio of the circumferences of two circles is 5:8 and the radius of the smaller circle is 10 centimeters. Find the radius of the larger circle.

*In Exercises **11–16,** the radius, r, and the degree measure, m, of an arc of a circle are given. Find the length of each arc of the circle.*

11. $r = 18$; $m = 135$

12. $r = 12$; $m = 45$

13. $r = 24$; $m = 90$

14. $r = 36$; $m = 12$

15. $r = 4$; $m = 60$

16. $r = 8$; $m = 36$

17. In circle O, $\overline{AB}$ is a chord that is 4 centimeters from the center of the circle and radius OA is 8 centimeters. Find the length of $\widehat{AB}$.

*In Exercises **18–23,** the arc length, ℓ, and the radius, r, of a circle are given. Find the degree measure of each arc.*

18. $r = 6$; $\ell = 2\pi$

19. $r = 15$; $\ell = 10\pi$

20. $r = 16$; $\ell = 4\pi$

21. $r = 35$; $\ell = 14\pi$

22. $r = 32$; $\ell = 40\pi$

23. $r = 6$; $\ell = \frac{8}{3}\pi$

24. An arc of a circle has a measure of 45 and a length of 3π centimeters. Find the radius of the circle.

25. The radius of a circle is x inches and the circumference is y inches. Find the radius of a circle whose circumference is $2y$ inches in terms of x.

26. Circles O and O' below have equal radii and each circle passes through the center of the other. Find the sum of the lengths of arcs BCD and DAB in terms of a radius r.

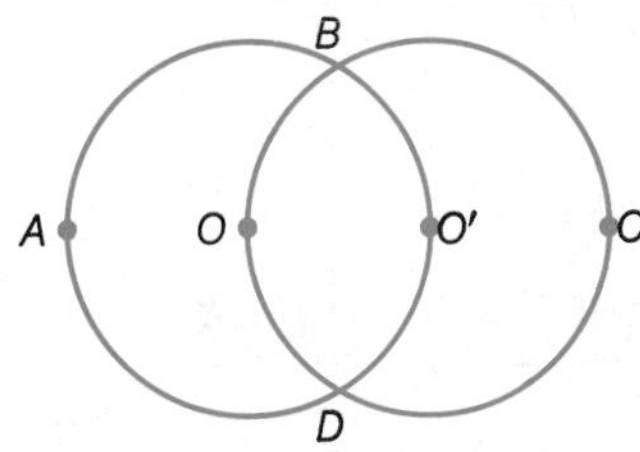

27. Triangle EFG at the right is an equilateral triangle one of whose sides has length a. Each side is a diameter of a semicircle. Find the distance around the entire figure.

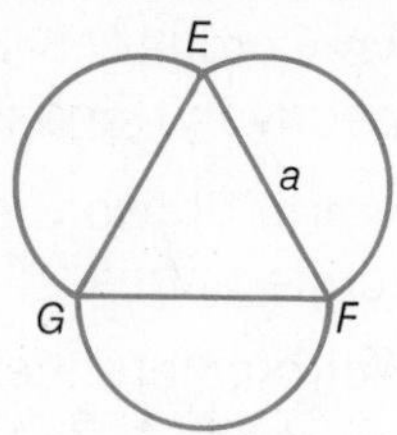

C **28.** Triangle ABC below is equilateral with one side of length s. D, E, and F are the midpoints of the sides. An arc is drawn with each vertex as center and one half the length of a side as radius. Find, in terms of s, the distance around region DEF.

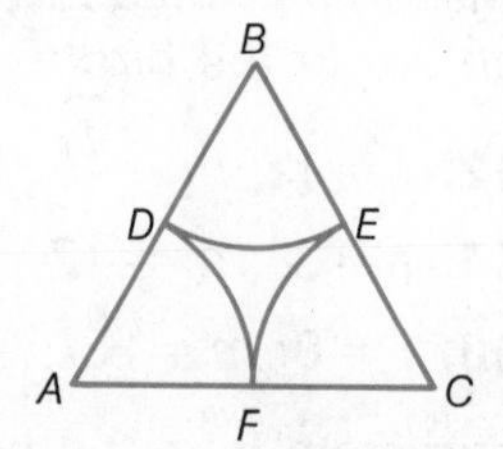

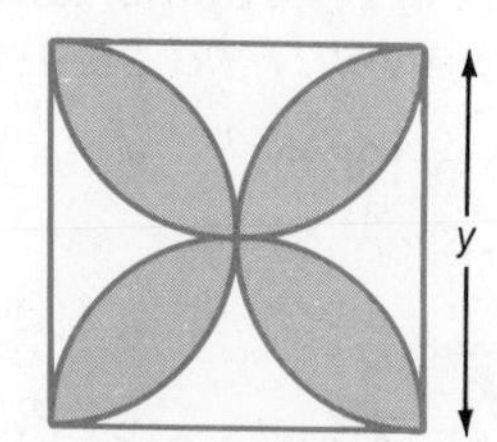

29. In the figure at the right above, semicircles are drawn on each side of a square. Find, in terms of y, the total distance around the four petals that are formed.

8-8 Areas of Circles, Sectors, and Segments

As these figures suggest, the area of a regular polygon approximates the area of a circle as the number of sides increases.

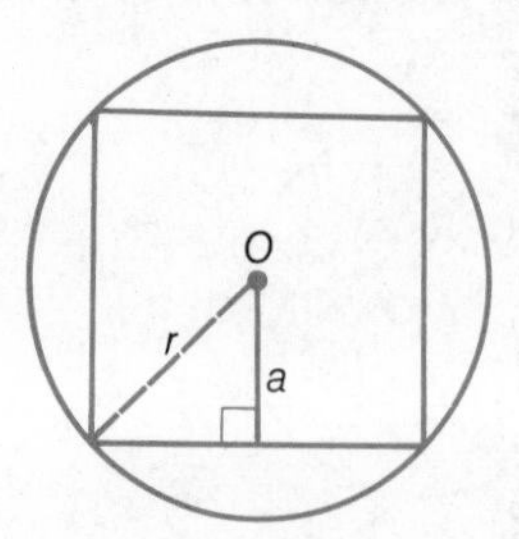

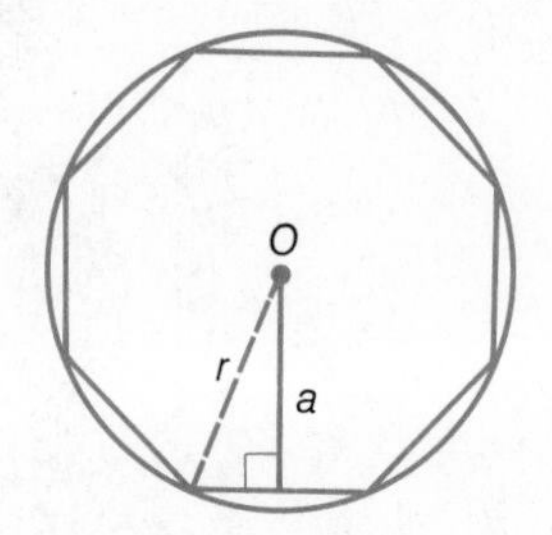

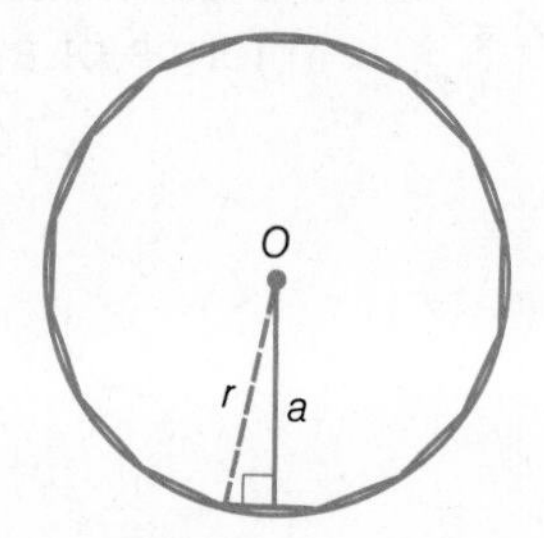

Further, as the number of sides increases, the apothem a approximates the radius r and the perimeter P approximates the circumference C.

$A = \frac{1}{2}aP$ ⟵ Area of a regular polygon

$A = \frac{1}{2}rC$ ⟵ The apothem, a, approximates r and P approximates C.

or

$A = \frac{1}{2}r \cdot 2\pi r$

$A = \pi r^2$

Theorem 8-21: The area A of a circle of radius r is πr^2.

$$A = \pi r^2$$

Corollary 8-22: The areas of two circles have the same ratio as the squares of their radii.

Example 1

Find the area of the shaded part of the circle.

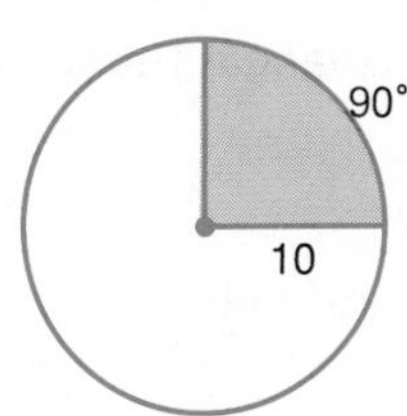

$A = \pi r^2$

$= \pi(10)^2 = 100\pi$ ⟵ Area of the circle.

$\frac{90}{360} = \frac{1}{4}$ ⟵ Ratio of the area of the shaded region to the area of the circle

$\therefore \frac{1}{4} \cdot \frac{100\pi}{1} = 25\pi$

The shaded region in the figure for Example 1 is a sector.

Definition: A **sector of a circle** is a region bounded by an arc of a circle and two radii to the endpoints of the arc.

Example 1 suggests the following corollary.

Corollary 8-23: In a circle with radius r, the ratio of the area, A, of a sector to the area of the circle equals the ratio of the degree measure, m, of its arc to 360.

$$\frac{A}{\pi r^2} = \frac{m}{360}, \quad \text{or} \quad A = \frac{m}{360}\pi r^2$$

Example 2

Find the area of the shaded part of the circle, where $m\angle AOB = 90$.

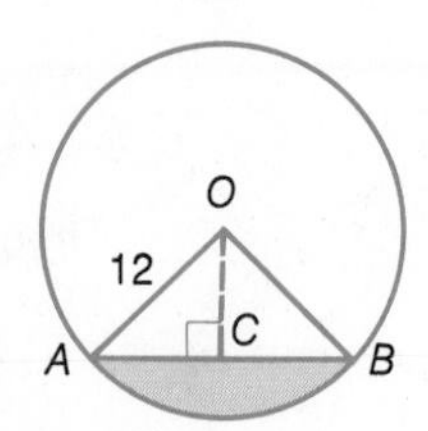

Area of shaded part = Area of sector OAB − area of $\triangle OAB$

Area of sector OAB:
$$A = \frac{m}{360}\pi r^2$$
$$= \frac{90}{360}\pi(12)^2$$
$$= \frac{90}{360} \cdot \frac{144}{1}\pi = 36\pi \text{ square units}$$

Area of $\triangle OAB$:

$AC = OC$ ← $\triangle AOC$ is a 45-45-90 triangle.

$OC = \frac{12}{2}\sqrt{2} = 6\sqrt{2}$ ← Isosceles Right Triangle Theorem

$\therefore AB = 12\sqrt{2}$ ← $AB = 2AC$

$A = \frac{1}{2}bh$

$= \frac{1}{2}(12\sqrt{2})(6\sqrt{2})$ ← $b = AB$ and $h = OC$.

$= 72$ square units

Area of shaded part = $(36\pi - 72)$ square units.

The shaded region in the figure of Example 2 is a <u>segment of a circle</u>.

Definition: A **segment of a circle** is a region bounded by an arc and its chord.

Try These

Express your answers in terms of π.

1. Find the area of a circle whose diameter is 12 centimeters.
2. Two circles have radii of 2 cm and 3 cm. Find the ratio of their areas.
3. Find the radius of a circle whose area is 25π square units.
4. Find the area of a sector with a 30°-arc and a radius of 6 centimeters.

Exercises

In Exercises **1–5,** *find the missing measures. Express answers in terms of π.*

	Radius	Diameter	Area
1.	?	16	64π
2.	30	?	?
3.	?	?	256π
4.	$4\frac{3}{4}$	?	?
5.	?	?	$\frac{81}{64}\pi$

6. Find the circumference of a circle whose area is 121π square units.
7. The radii of two circles are 3 centimeters and 5 centimeters. Find the ratio of their areas.
8. The areas of two circles are 25π and 75π. Find the ratio of their radii.
9. The radius of one circle is twice the radius of a second circle. Find the ratio of their areas.
10. The region bounded between two concentric circles is an annulus, or ring, as in the figure at the right. Find the area of the annulus bounded by two circles whose radii are 6 and 8.

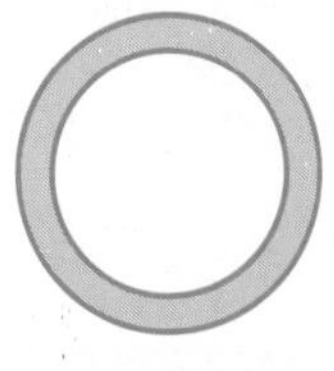

11. Triangle *DEF* at the right has sides of 6, 8, and 10. Show that the area of the semicircle on the hypotenuse equals the sum of the areas of the semicircles on the legs.

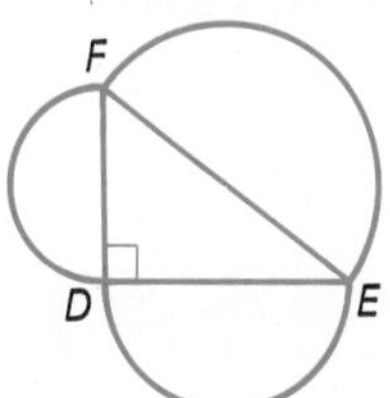

12. Point B is the midpoint of $\overline{AC}$ and $AC = 10$. Find the area bounded by $\overline{AC}$ and the two semicircles.

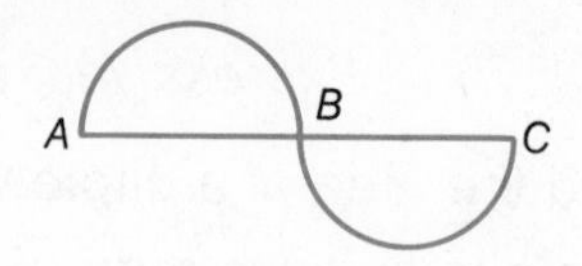

*In Exercises **13–15**, the radius, r, and the degree measure, m, of an arc of a circle are given. Find the area of the sector that is determined.*

13. $r = 2$; $m = 60$ **14.** $r = 3$; $m = 90$ **15.** $r = 4$; $m = 120$

16. Find the area of each segment in Exercises **13–15.**

*In Exercises **17–19**, the radius, r, and the area, A, of a sector are given. Find the degree measure of the arc.*

17. $r = 4$; $A = 4\pi$ **18.** $r = 12$; $A = 24\pi$ **19.** $r = 20$; $A = 40\pi$

b

20. Write a formula for the area of a circle in terms of d, the diameter of the circle.

21. A regular hexagon is inscribed in a circle whose radius is 8 centimeters. Find the difference in the areas of the circle and the hexagon.

22. Write a formula for the area of a sector of a circle in terms of the length, ℓ, of its arc and a radius, r.

23. Find the area of a ring bounded by circles with radii of $\frac{1}{2}x$ and x.

24. A circle of radius y is inscribed in an equilateral triangle. Find the area of the shaded part of the triangle.

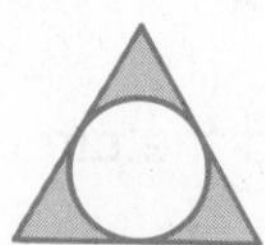

25. A circle of radius z is circumscribed about an equilateral triangle. Find the area of the shaded part of the circle.

C

26. Three circles are tangent to each other and each has a radius of 4 centimeters. Find the area of the region between the circles. (HINT: Draw $\triangle ABC$.)

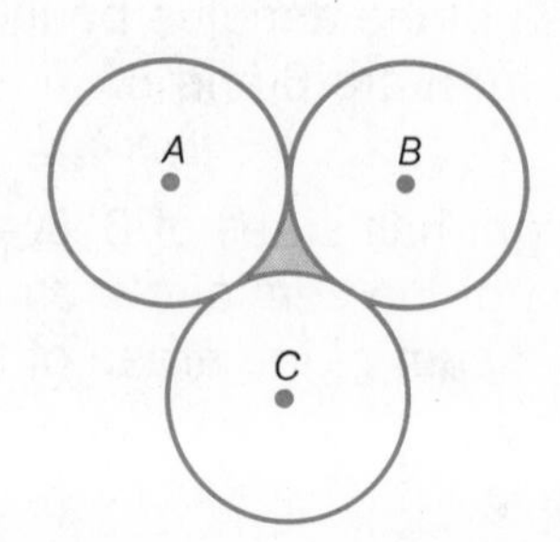

Mathematics and Cartography

The problem that map making presents is one of *projecting* a sphere (the earth's globe) upon a plane (a sheet of paper). Specifically, the problem is one of finding a method of projecting the *meridians* and the *parallels of latitude* of the earth's globe to a plane. Each **meridian** is a great circle that contains the north pole, N, and the south pole, S. Each **parallel of latitude** is a circle whose plane is perpendicular to the *polar axis*, $\overline{NS}$.

Cartography is a specialized branch of geography. Cartographers compile data that is then used to design and construct maps. Many cartographers begin by majoring in geography in college. They then specialize while in graduate school working toward a master's or a doctor's degree. Courses in advanced mathematics and computer science are required in graduate work.

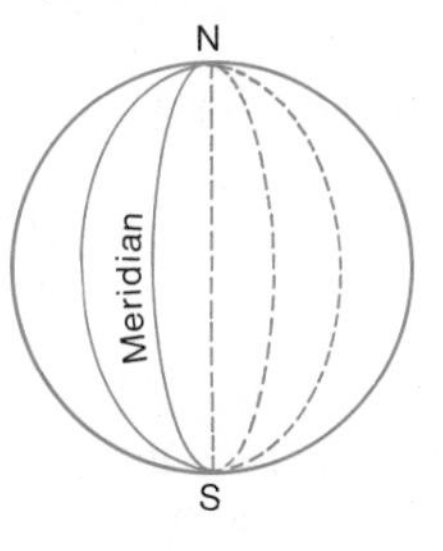

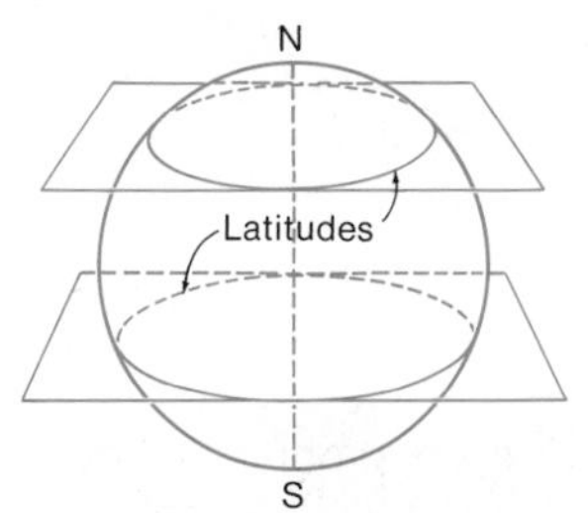

In this method, the entire sphere is projected as an *ellipse*. The parallels of latitude and the meridians are projected as curved lines. This type of map is used for the plotting of stars in astronomical work.

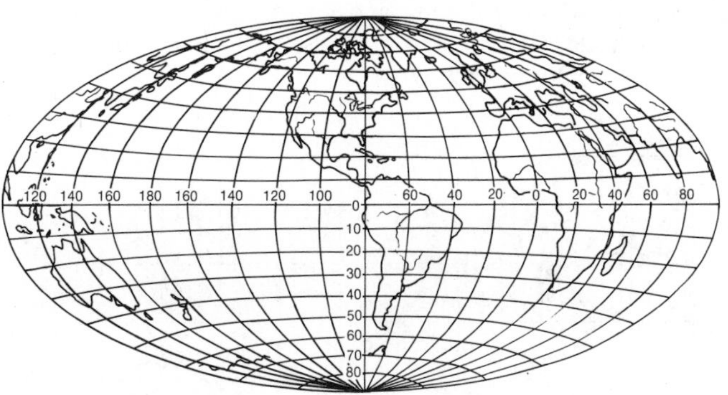

AITOFF-EQUAL-AREA PROJECTION

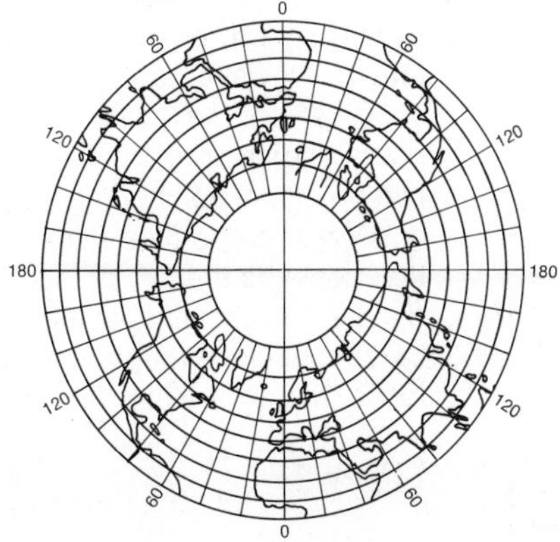

LAMBERT PROJECTION OF THE NORTHERN HEMISPHERE

In this method, the parallels of latitude on the sphere are projected as circles, whereas the meridians are projected as line segments. By repeating this projection for the southern hemisphere and making the two hemispheres tangent at some appropriate point, sailing routes between any two continents can be determined.

Mathematics and Marine Engineering

The surest way to become an officer of an ocean-going ship is by attending a merchant marine academy. Some of the major courses of study are mathematics, electronics, electrical engineering, and navigation. **Marine engineering** candidates must also pass Coast Guard examinations for entry into the career.

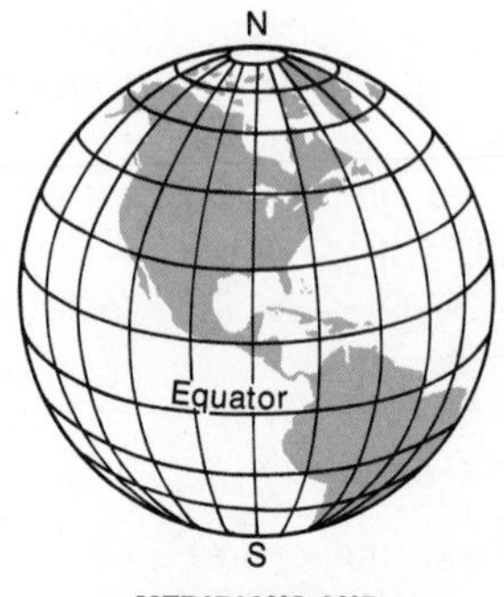

MERIDIANS AND PARALLELS OF LATITUDE

A major problem in navigating a ship is the plotting of the shortest course between two points on the earth. The **mercator map** (a portion of which is shown below) is used for this purpose. On this type of map, the **meridians** (great circles through the north and south poles) and **parallels of latitude** (circles that are parallel to the equator) are perpendicular to each other.

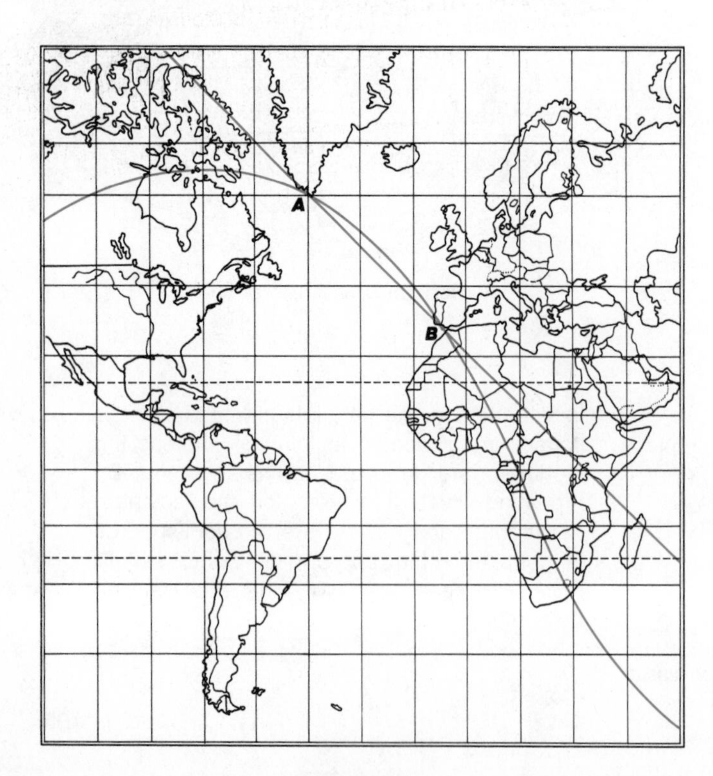

A straight line on the mercator map is the *simplest* course between any two points, such as A and B. However, this is not the *shortest* course. The shortest course (distance) between any two points on a sphere is the arc of a *great circle* (see page 357) that contains the two points. The curved line shows what the great circle course through A and B looks like on the mercator map.

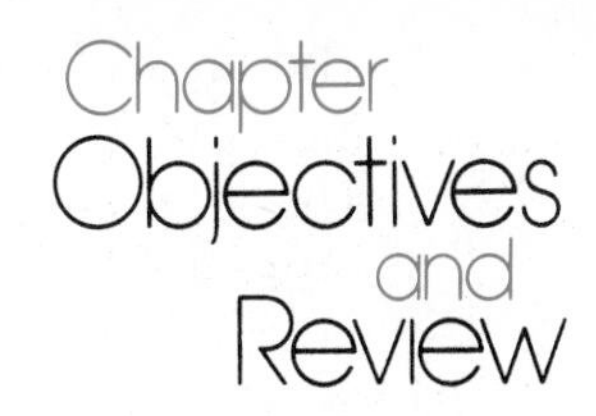

Objective: To recall, and give examples of, the important mathematical terms of the chapter.

1. Be sure that you know the meanings of these mathematical terms used in Chapter 8.

altitude (p. 375)
apothem (p. 385)
base (p. 375)
center (regular polygon) (p. 385)
central angle (p. 386)
circumference (p. 398)
circumscribed circle (p. 385)
inscribed circle (p. 385)
polygonal region (p. 370)
radius (regular polygon) (p. 385)
sector (p. 403)
segment (p. 404)
square centimeter (p. 371)
triangular region (p. 370)

Objective: To find the areas of polygonal regions by using the Area Postulates. (Section 8-1)

2. *ABCDE* is a polygonal region in which the area of $\triangle ABE$ is 7, the area of $\triangle EBD$ is 9, and the area of $\triangle DBC$ is 4. Find the area of polygonal region *ABCDE*.

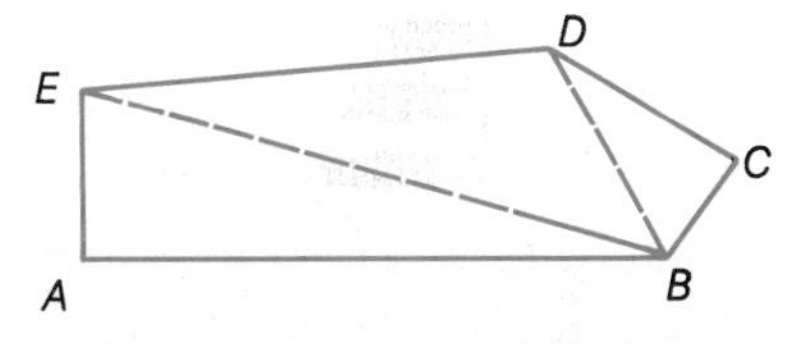

3. A rectangle has a length of 17.4 centimeters and a width of 14.2 centimeters. Find the area of the rectangle.

Objective: To apply the formulas for the area of a parallelogram and the area of a triangle. (Section 8-2)

4. In parallelogram *GRAM* at the left below, $GR = 8$ centimeters and $MO = 5$ centimeters. Find the area.

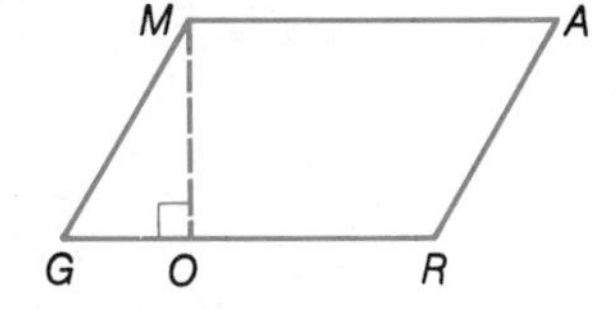

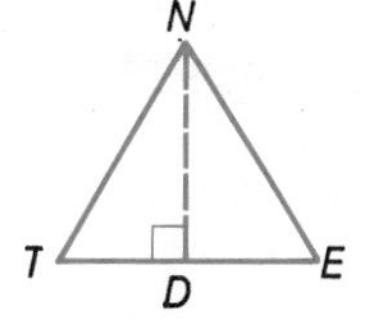

5. In triangle *TEN* at the right above, $\overline{ND} \perp \overline{TE}$, $m\angle T = 60$, $TE = 9$ and $TN = 8$. Find the area.

6. The area of an equilateral triangle is $9\sqrt{3}$ square units. Find the length of a side of the triangle.
7. The legs of a right triangle are 6 centimeters and 9 centimeters. Find the area of the triangle.

Objective: To apply the formulas for the area of a rhombus and the area of a trapezoid. (Section 8-3)

8. Find the area of a rhombus with diagonals of 5 and 8.
9. The bases of a trapezoid are 10 units and 16 units and the area is 117 square units. Find the altitude.

Objective: To find the measures of angles and the lengths of segments related to a regular polygon. (Section 8-4)

10. Find the measure of a central angle of a regular polygon with 20 sides.
11. The radius of a regular hexagon is 6 centimeters. Find the length of one side of the hexagon.
12. A regular hexagon is inscribed in a circle whose radius is 8 decimeters. Find the length of the apothem.

Objective: To apply the formula for the area of a regular polygon. (Section 8-5)

13. Find the area of a regular decagon with an apothem of 4.2 centimeters and a side of 2.73 centimeters.
14. Find the area of an equilateral triangle with a radius of $6\sqrt{3}$.

Objective: To apply the ratios related to area, perimeter, and segments that are parts of regular polygons. (Section 8-6)

Two similar polygons have apothems of length $2\sqrt{3}$ and $5\sqrt{3}$. Give the ratio of:

15. Their sides.
16. Their perimeters.
17. Their areas.

Objective: To apply the formulas for circumference of a circle and length of an arc of a circle. (Section 8-7)

18. Find the radius of a circle whose circumference is 36π units.
19. In circle O, $m\angle AOB = 36$ and radius $OA = 8$. Find the length of $\widehat{AB}$.

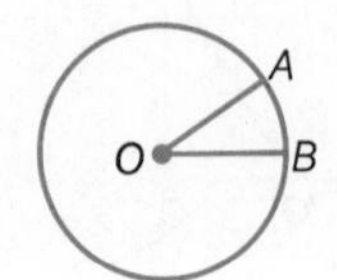

20. The circumferences of two circles are 4π units and 8π units. Find the ratio of the radii.

Objective: To apply the formulas for the area of a circle, area of a sector, and area of a segment. (Section 8-8)

21. Find the area of a circle with circumference of 24π centimeters.

22. The radii of two circles are 4 centimeters and 7 centimeters. Find the ratio of their areas.

23. Find the area of a sector of a circle with a radius of 4 and a degree measure of 120.

24. In circle O, $OB = 6$ and $m\angle AOB = 60$. Find the area of segment ACB.

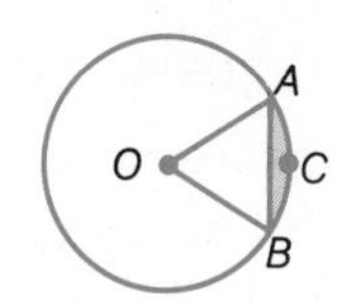

Chapter Test

1. In parallelogram $ABCD$, $DE = 8$ and $AB = 12$. Find the area of the parallelogram.

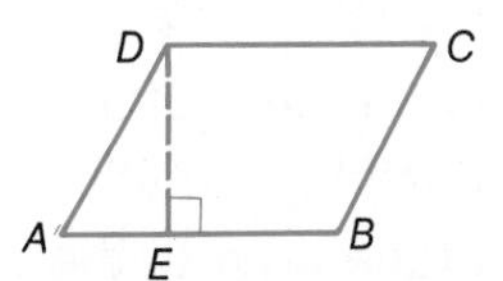

2. In triangle RST at the left below, $m\angle R = 120$, $TR = 8$ and $RS = 9$. Find the area of the triangle.

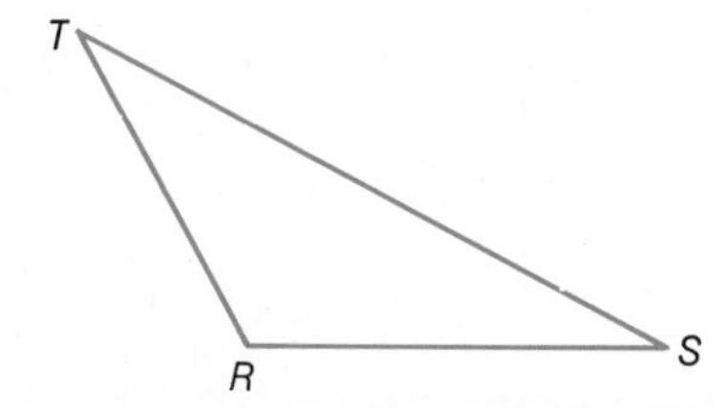

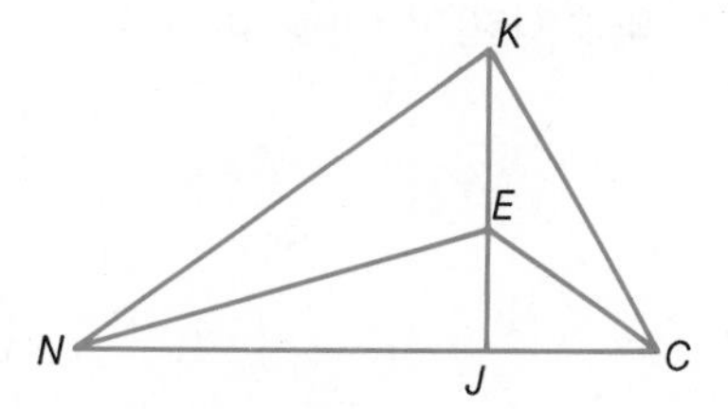

3. In the figure at the right above, $KJ = 7$ centimeters and $EJ = 3$ centimeters. Find the ratio of the area of $\triangle NCE$ to the area of $\triangle NCK$.

4. Find the area of an equilateral triangle with a side 3 units long.

5. The length of the hypotenuse of a right triangle is 13 and the length of one leg is 12. Find the area of the triangle.

6. The area of a rhombus is 28 square centimeters and the length of one diagonal is 8 centimeters. Find the length of the other diagonal.

7. In trapezoid $TRAP$, $PA = 6$, $TR = 10$, $\overline{AR} \perp \overline{TR}$, and $m\angle T = 45$. Find the area of the trapezoid.

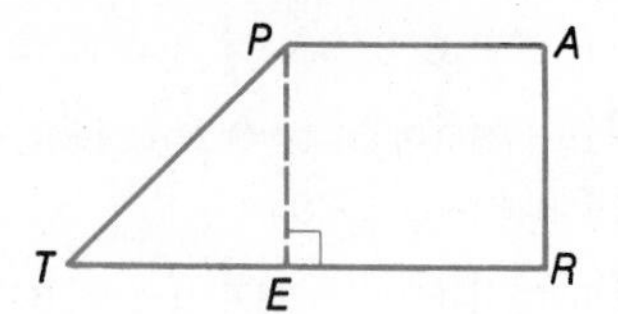

8. Find the measure of each central angle of a regular polygon with 12 sides.

9. The measure of one central angle of a regular polygon is 40. Find the number of sides of the polygon.

10. Find the length of the apothem of a regular hexagon whose radius is 8 centimeters.

11. Find the area of a regular decagon with apothem of 4 millimeters and side of 2.6 millimeters.

12. The areas of two regular pentagons are in the ratio of 4:49. Find the ratio of their apothems.

13. Find the circumference of a circle whose radius is 7 meters.

14. In circle O, the length of radius OA is 7 meters and $m\angle AOB = 16$. Find the length of $\overset{\frown}{AB}$.

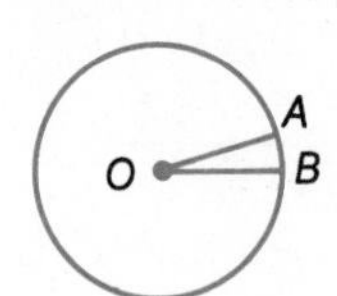

15. Find the area of a circle whose diameter is 10 centimeters.

16. Find the area of the shaded part of the circle at the right.

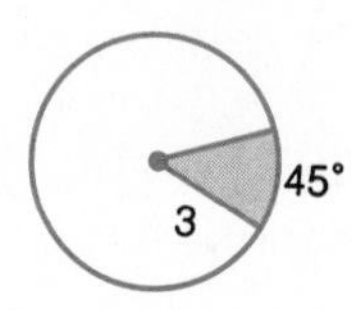

17. Find the area of the segment of a circle with radius of 12 centimeters and degree measure of 60.

Answers to Remember

Page 375: **1.** An altitude of a triangle is a segment from one vertex perpendicular to the opposite side. **2.** A parallelogram is a quadrilateral with both pairs of opposite sides parallel. **3.** $m\angle B = 133$; $m\angle C = 47$ **4.** $TR = 6$; $ST = 12$ **5.** $RT = 7$; $TS = 7\sqrt{2}$

Page 381: **1.** False **2.** True **3.** False **4.** False

Page 385: **1.** Six centimeters **2.** 120 **3.** Equilateral triangle **4.** Square **5.** Regular pentagon **6.** Regular hexagon

Chapter 9
Surface Area and Volume

9-1 The Prism

The solids shown below are prisms. The parts of intersecting planes that determine each prism are its **faces.** Two faces, B and B', are **bases** of each prism. The other faces are **lateral faces.** The intersections of the faces are called **edges.**

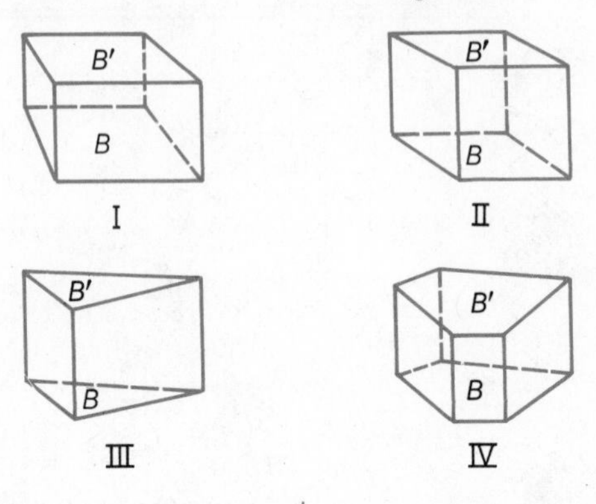

Prism	Name	Description
I	**Rectangular solid**	All six faces are rectangles.
II	**Cube**	A rectangular solid in which all edges are congruent.
III	**Triangular prism**	The bases are triangles.
IV	**Pentagonal prism**	The bases are pentagons.

The four prisms named in the table are **right prisms** because a lateral edge is perpendicular to the plane of a base. A prism that does not have this property is oblique. A **regular prism** is a right prism whose bases are regular congruent polygons.

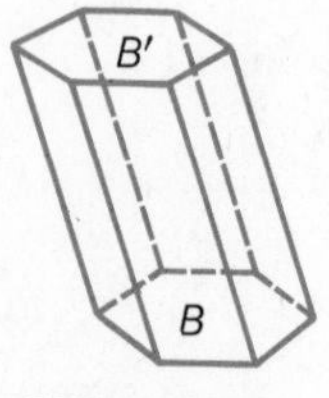

Oblique Prism

An **altitude of a prism** is a segment that is perpendicular to the planes of the bases and that has an endpoint in each plane. In a right prism, any lateral edge is an altitude.

The **lateral surface area** of a prism is the sum of the areas of its lateral faces.

Example 1

Find the lateral surface area of the triangular prism at the left below. The bases are equilateral triangles.

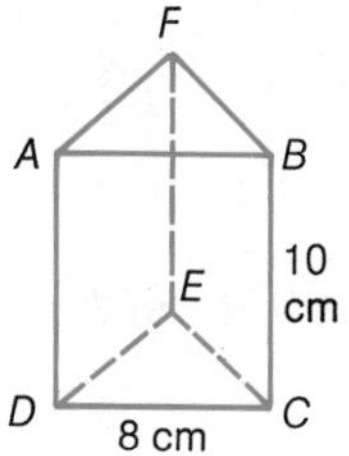

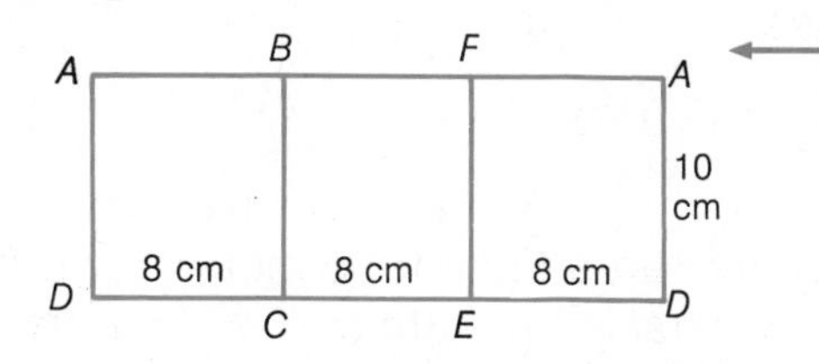

The lateral surface has three rectangular faces.

Lateral surface area $= (8 + 8 + 8) \cdot 10 = (24)10$, or 240 sq. cm.

Example 1 suggests this theorem.

Theorem 9-1: The lateral surface area L of a right prism is the product of the perimeter of its base P and its lateral edge e.

$$L = Pe$$

The **total area** of a prism is the sum of its lateral surface area and the areas of its two bases.

Example 2

Find the total area of the regular hexagonal prism.

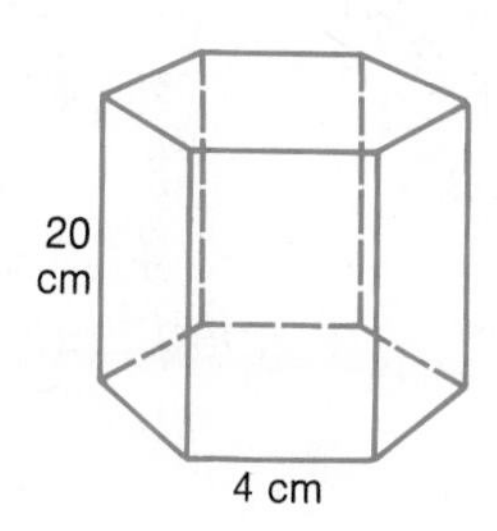

$L = P \cdot e$ ← Lateral surface area

$= (6 \cdot 4)20$

$= 480$ sq. cm.

Area of base $= \frac{1}{2}aP$ ← Theorem 8-12

$= \frac{1}{2} \cdot 2\sqrt{3} \cdot 24$

$= 24\sqrt{3}$ sq. cm.

Lateral surface area + Area of bases = Total area

$480 + 2 \cdot 24\sqrt{3} = 480 + 48\sqrt{3}$ sq. cm

Try These

Refer to the regular figure at the right below for Exercises **1–4.**

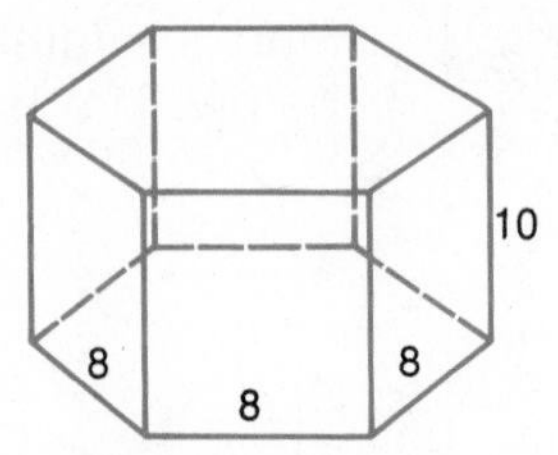

1. Find P, the perimeter of the base.
2. Find L, the lateral surface area.
3. Find the area of one base.
4. Find the total area.

A right pentagonal prism has an altitude of 6 meters, and bases with sides of 3 meters, 4 meters, 2 meters, 3.4 meters and 4.6 meters.

5. Find the perimeter of the base.
6. Find the lateral surface area.

Exercises

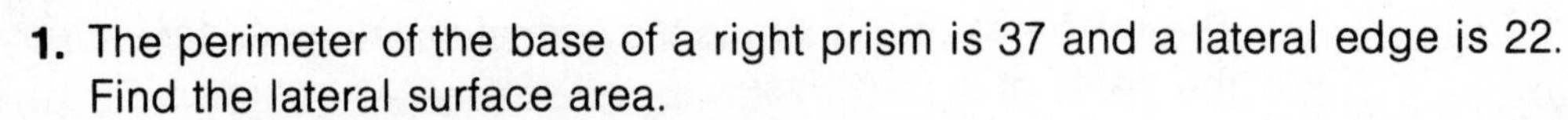

a

1. The perimeter of the base of a right prism is 37 and a lateral edge is 22. Find the lateral surface area.
2. Find the lateral surface area and the total area of the rectangular solid at the right.
3. The base of a right prism is a rectangle whose width is 6 meters and whose length is 9 meters. The altitude of the prism is 12 meters long. Find the lateral surface area.

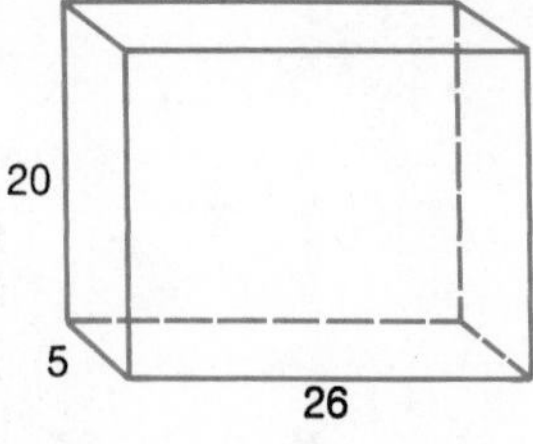

4. Find the total area of a cube with an edge of 5 millimeters.

For Exercises **5–9,** *the measure of an edge of a cube is given. Find the total area.*

5. 9 **6.** 3 **7.** $4\frac{1}{2}$ **8.** $4x$ **9.** e

10. Use Exercise **9** to write a formula for the lateral surface area L of a cube in terms of its edge e.
11. Use Exercise **9** to write a formula for the total area T of a cube in terms of its edge e.

The diagonal of one face of a cube is $5\sqrt{2}$ centimeters long.

12. Find the area of one face.

13. Find the total area.

For Exercises **14–18,** *the measure of a diagonal of a face of a cube is given. Find the total area.*

14. $6\sqrt{2}$ **15.** $4\sqrt{3}$ **16.** 16 **17.** $x\sqrt{2}$ **18.** d

19. Use Exercise **18** to write a formula for the total area T of a cube in terms of a diagonal d of one face.

Classify each statement as Always true, Sometimes true, or Never true.

20. The lateral edges of a right prism are perpendicular to both bases.

21. The lateral faces of a prism are rectangles.

22. In any prism the lateral edges are congruent and parallel.

23. The bases of a prism are regular polygons.

24. The lateral faces of a prism are parallelograms.

25. In an oblique prism, any lateral edge is an altitude of the prism.

26. The bases of any prism are congruent polygons.

27. If two parallel planes intersect a prism, the intersections form two congruent polygons.

28. The lateral faces of a prism are squares.

Use the cube at the right for Exercises **29–37.** *$\overline{BD}$ and $\overline{FH}$ are diagonals of two of the faces and $\overline{DF}$ is a diagonal of the cube. Express any radicals in simplest form.*

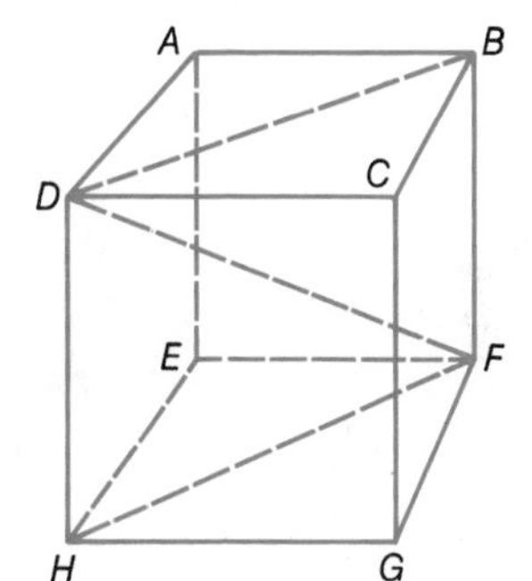

29. What kind of triangle is $\triangle ABD$?

30. What kind of triangle is $\triangle FGH$?

31. Is $\triangle DFH$ a right triangle? Explain.

32. Is $\triangle DFH$ isosceles? Explain.

33. If $CD = 5$, find BD.

34. If $GC = 7$, find BD and FH.

35. If $BD = 6$, find BF. Then use the Pythagorean Theorem to find DF.

36. If $AD = 8$, find BD and DF.

37. If $BF = x$, find BD and DF.

b **38.** Find the measure of one edge of a cube if the measure of a diagonal of the cube is $4\sqrt{3}$.

*For Exercises **39–46,** the measure of a diagonal of a cube is given. Find the total area.*

39. $12\sqrt{3}$ **40.** $\sqrt{12}$ **41.** $\sqrt{27}$ **42.** 24
43. $\sqrt{8}$ **44.** $3x$ **45.** $x\sqrt{3}$ **46.** d

In the figure at the right, $\overline{AB}$ is perpendicular to the plane of $\triangle BCD$ and $\overline{BD} \perp \overline{CD}$.

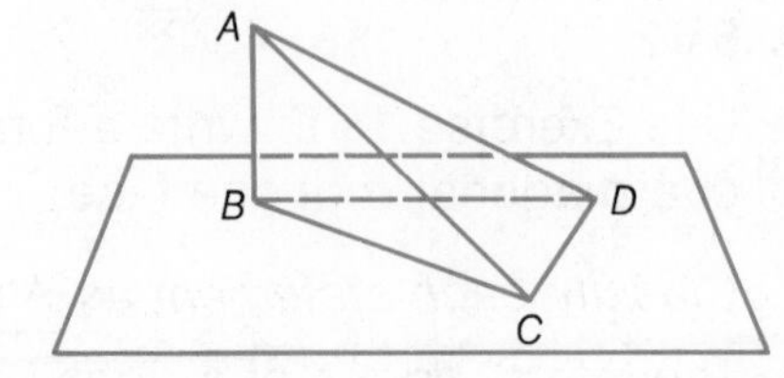

47. Name the right triangles in the figure and the hypotenuse of each.

48. If $AB = 16$, $BD = 10$, and $CD = 4$, find AC.

49. If $AD = 12$, $m\angle DBC = 30$ and $m\angle ADB = 30$, find AC.

PUZZLE

The six faces of a cube are numbered with "dots" from 1 to 6. Three views of this cube are shown below.

How many "dots" are there on the bottom face of the cube in Figure 1?

Figure 1

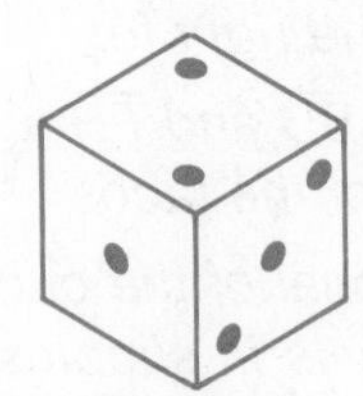
Figure 2

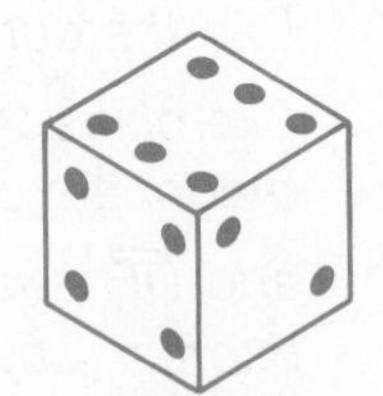
Figure 3

Remember

Find the area of each polygon.

1.

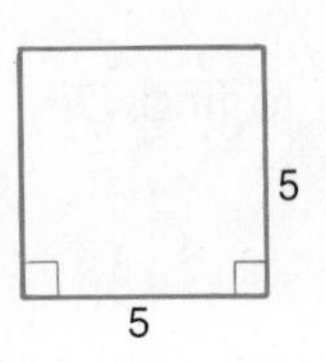

2.

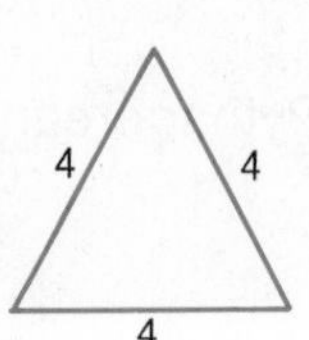

3.

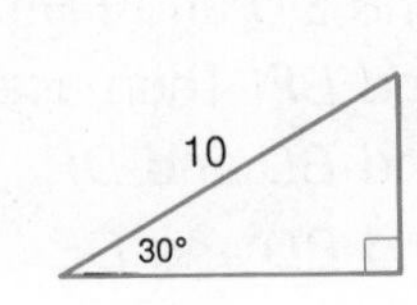

4.

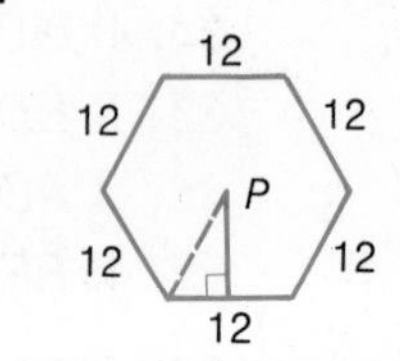

The answers are on page 442. If you need help, see pages 371, 376, and 393.

9-2 The Pyramid

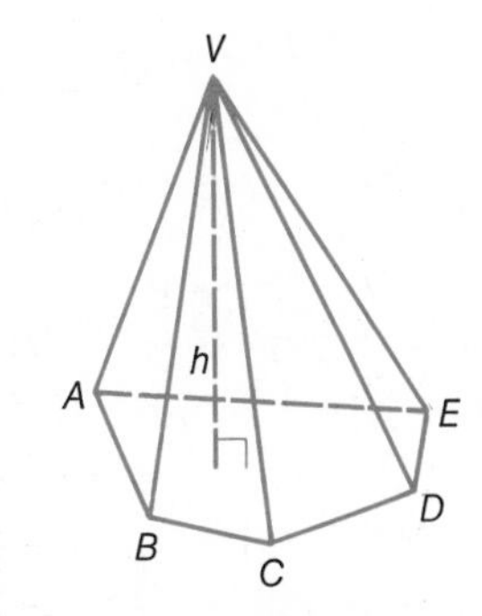

Pyramid *V-ABCDE* has its vertex at *V* and pentagon *ABCDE* is its base. The five triangular faces that have *V* as a common point are **lateral faces.** The intersections of the lateral faces, such as $\overline{AV}$, $\overline{BV}$, and $\overline{CV}$, are **edges.** The **altitude** of a pyramid is the segment drawn perpendicular to the base from the vertex of the pyramid.

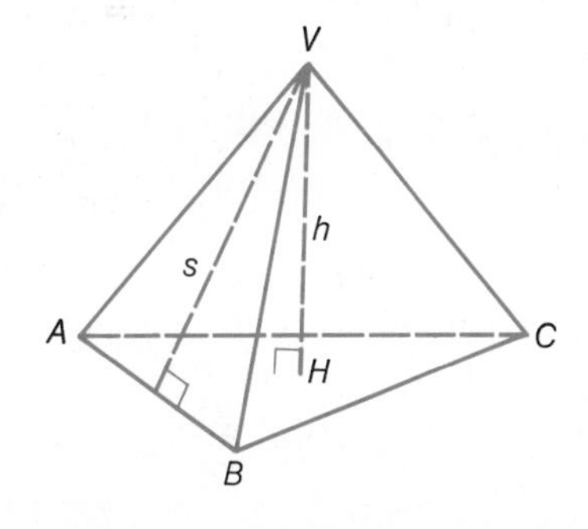

A **regular pyramid** is one whose base is a regular polygon and whose altitude, $\overline{VH}$, passes through the center of the base. The **slant height,** *s*, of a regular pyramid is the length of the altitude of one of its faces.

The **lateral surface area** of a pyramid is the sum of the areas of its lateral faces.

Example 1

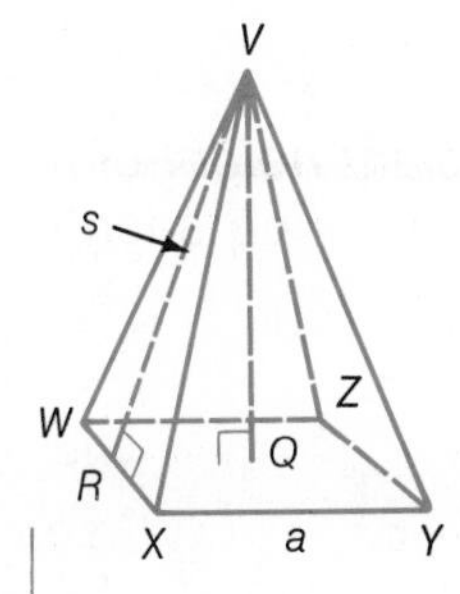

Find the lateral surface area of regular pyramid *V-WXYZ*.

NOTE: The lateral faces are four congruent isosceles triangles.

$$
\begin{aligned}
\text{Lateral surface area} &= 4(\text{Area } \triangle VWX) \\
&= 4(\tfrac{1}{2} \cdot b \cdot h) \\
&\qquad\ \ \downarrow \quad \downarrow \\
&= 4(\tfrac{1}{2} \cdot a \cdot s) \\
&= \tfrac{1}{2}(4a \cdot s) \longleftarrow \text{Perimeter of base: } 4a \\
&= \tfrac{1}{2}Ps
\end{aligned}
$$

Example 1 suggests this theorem.

Theorem 9-2: The lateral area L of a regular pyramid is one half the product of its slant height s and the perimeter P of its base.

$$L = \frac{1}{2}sP$$

Example 2

Find the total area of the regular hexagonal pyramid.

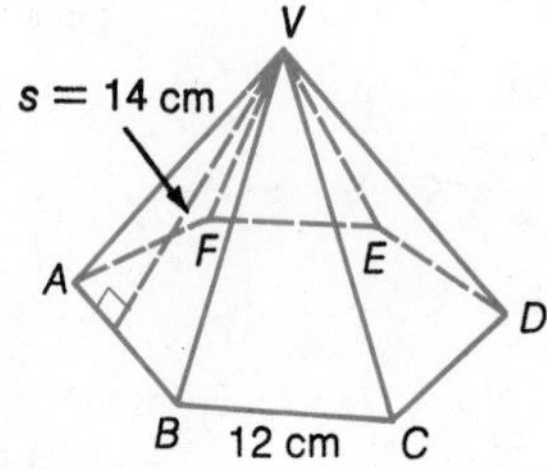

$L = \frac{1}{2}sP$ ← **Lateral surface area**

$= \frac{1}{2} \cdot 14 \cdot (12 \cdot 6)$

$= 7 \cdot 72$

$= 504$ sq. cm

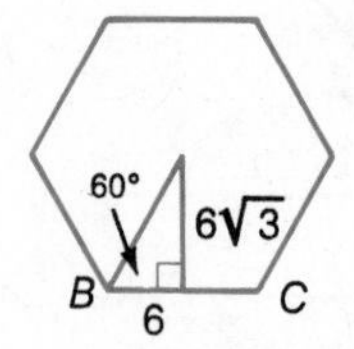

Area $= \frac{1}{2}aP$ ← **Area of hexagonal base**

$= \frac{1}{2} \cdot 6\sqrt{3} \cdot 72$ ← $a = 6\sqrt{3}$; $P = 72$

$= 216\sqrt{3}$ sq. cm

Total area $= 504 + 216\sqrt{3}$ sq. cm ← **Lateral surface area + Area of base**

Try These

A regular pyramid with a triangular base has a slant height of 14 meters. Each side of the base is 12 meters long. Find each area.

1. Lateral surface area

2. Area of the base

3. Total area

Exercises

A regular pyramid with a hexagonal base has a slant height of 9. Each side of the base measures 8. Find each area.

a

1. Lateral surface area

2. Area of the base

3. Total area

Refer to the triangular pyramid at the right to complete Exercises **4–8.** *The lateral faces and base are equilateral triangles.*

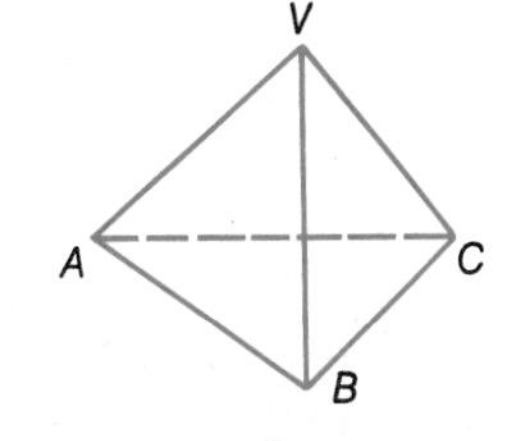

4. If edge BC is 8 centimeters long, then the area of one face is __?__ and the total area is __?__.

5. If edge BC measures 6 centimeters, then the slant height is __?__, the perimeter of the base is __?__, and the lateral surface area is __?__.

6. If the slant height of the regular pyramid is $5\sqrt{3}$, the length of an edge is __?__, the perimeter is __?__, and the lateral surface area is __?__.

7. If an edge of the regular pyramid is e, the slant height is __?__, the perimeter is __?__, and the lateral surface area is __?__.

8. If an edge of the regular pyramid is e, the area of one face is __?__, and the total surface area is __?__.

Classify each statement as Always true, Sometimes true, or Never true.

9. All lateral faces of a regular pyramid are triangles.

10. The lateral edges of a regular pyramid are congruent segments.

11. The slant height of a regular pyramid is greater than its altitude.

12. A pyramid with a regular polygon for a base is a regular pyramid.

13. A pyramid has two bases which are congruent polygons.

A regular hexagonal pyramid has a slant height of 20 and a base whose edge is 6. Find each area.

14. Lateral surface area

15. Area of the base

16. Total area

17. A regular pyramid has a slant height of 8 centimeters. Its base is a decagon with sides of 5 centimeters. Find the lateral surface area.

18. The base of a regular pyramid is an octagon with sides of 12 centimeters. The lateral surface area is 768 sq. cm. Find the slant height.

One side of the base of regular pyramid A-XYZT is 12 and altitude AC of the pyramid is 8. Find each of the following.

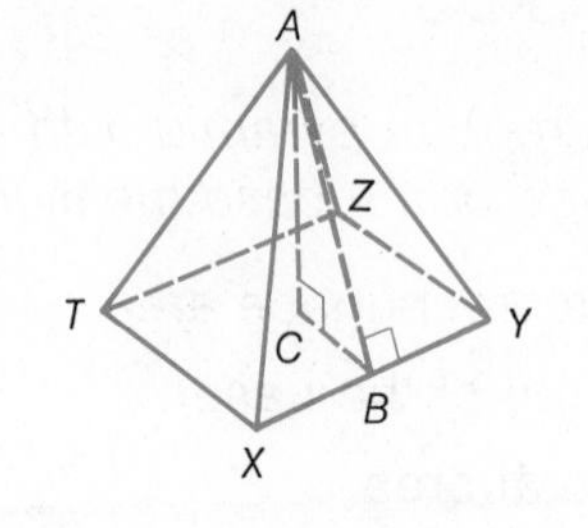

19. *CB*

20. *AB*

21. Lateral surface area

22. Total area

The base of a regular pyramid is a hexagon whose edge is 30 units and whose altitude is $10\sqrt{3}$ units. Find each of the following.

23. Slant height

24. Lateral surface area

A pyramid with a square base has $s = 8$ and a lateral surface area of 144. Find each of the following.

25. Perimeter of the base

26. Area of the base

27. The base of a regular pentagonal pyramid has a perimeter of 45 inches. Find the lateral area if the slant height is 10 inches.

28. The area of the base of a regular quadrangular pyramid is 100 square meters. The altitude of the pyramid is 12 meters. Compute the lateral area and the total area.

29. A regular pyramid has an equilateral triangle for each face. If one edge of the pyramid is 18, find the lateral area and the total area.

Remember

1. Write the formula for the circumference of a circle.

2. Write the formula for the area of a circle.

3. Find the area of a circle with radius 1.5.

4. Find the diameter of a circle with circumference of 15π units.

5. Find the radius of a circle with area of 1.69π square units.

The answers are on page 442. If you need help, see pages 398 and 403.

9-3 Cylinders and Cones

The figures below are cylinders with circular bases.

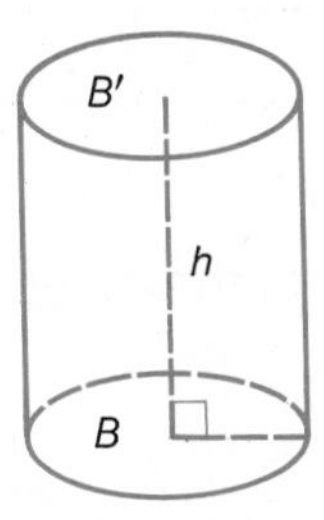

Right Circular Cylinder

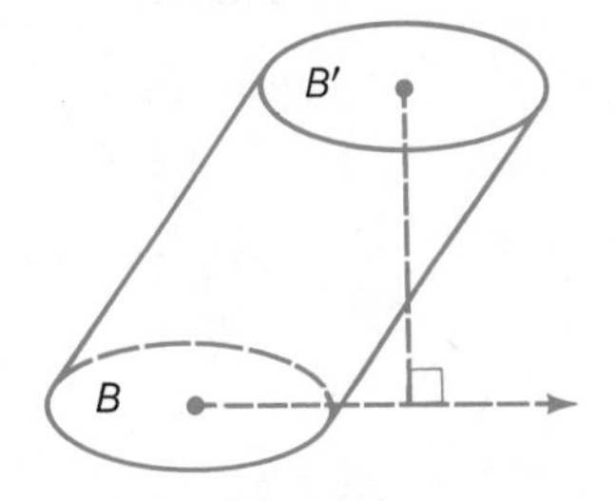

Oblique Circular Cylinder

In a **right circular cylinder** or in an oblique circular cylinder, the distance between the bases is the **altitude** of the cylinder. The **bases** B and B' are congruent circles.

The **lateral area** of a right circular cylinder is the area of its curved surface. The **total area** is the sum of the lateral area and the area of the two bases.

Example 1

Find the total area of a right circular cylinder of radius r and altitude h.

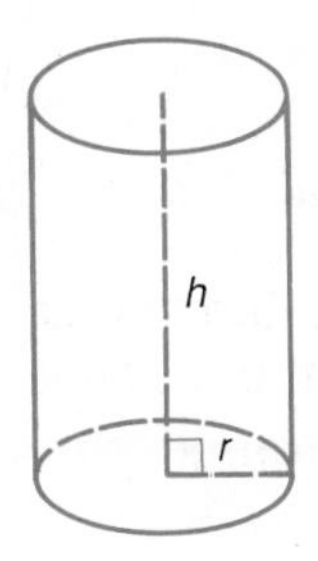

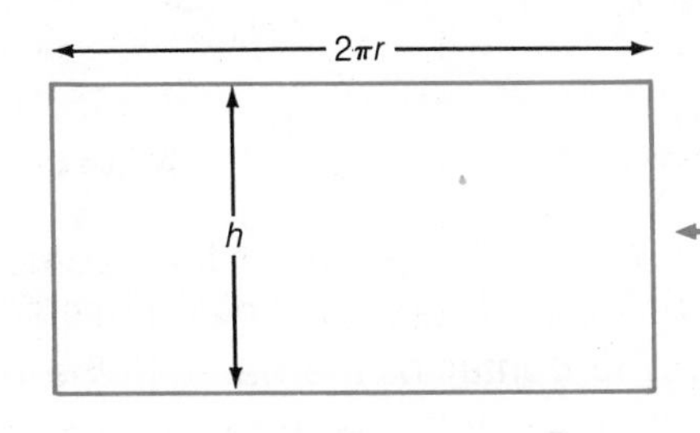

A rectangle with dimensions h and $2\pi r$ has the same lateral area as the cylinder.

Total area = Lateral Surface Area + Area of Bases

$= 2\pi rh + 2\pi r^2$ ← Area of circle: πr^2

$= 2\pi r(h + r)$ ← Common factor: $2\pi r$

Example 1 suggests Theorem 9-3.

Theorem 9-3: The lateral area L of a right circular cylinder with altitude h and base radius r is $2\pi rh$. The total area T is $2\pi rh + 2\pi r^2$. That is,

$$L = 2\pi rh \quad \text{and} \quad T = 2\pi r(h + r).$$

Example 2

Find the lateral area and the total area of the right circular cylinder.

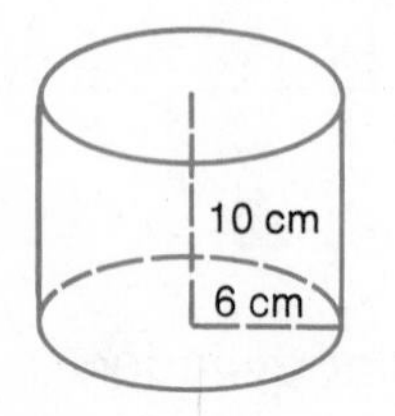

$L = 2\pi rh$
$L = 2\pi(6)(10)$
$L = 120\pi$ sq. cm

$T = 2\pi r(h + r)$
$T = 2\pi(6)(16)$
$T = 192\pi$ sq. cm

The figures below are cones with circular bases.

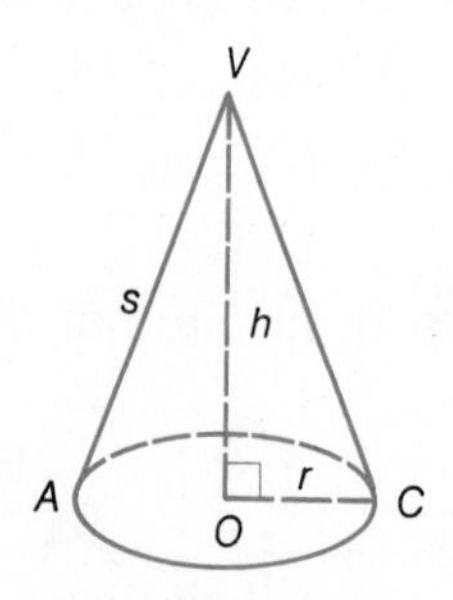

Right Circular Cone

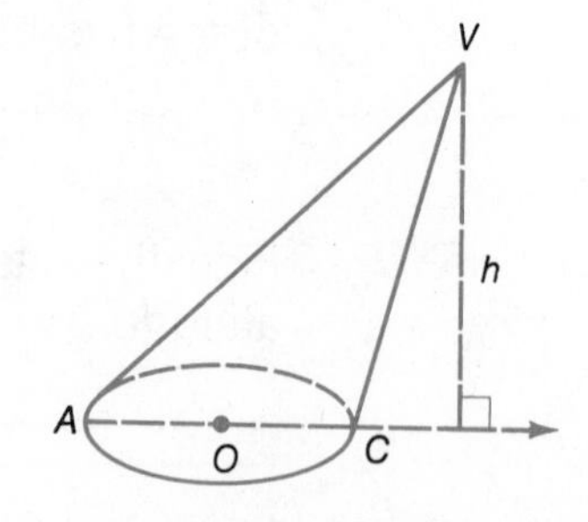

Oblique Circular Cone

The **altitude of a cone** is the length of the segment from the **vertex,** V, perpendicular to the base. In a **right circular cone,** the altitude passes through the center of the base. In the right circular cone above, h is the altitude and s is the slant height.

The **lateral area of a cone** is the area of its curved surface. The **total area** is the sum of the lateral area and the area of the base.

NOTE: Since we will only deal with right circular cones, any reference to a cone will mean a right circular cone.

Theorem 9-4: The lateral area L of a right circular cone is one half the product of its slant height s and the circumference $2\pi r$ of its base. The total area T is $\pi rs + \pi r^2$. That is,

$$L = \pi rs \quad \text{and} \quad T = \pi r(s + r).$$

Example 3

Find the lateral area and the total area of the cone at the right.

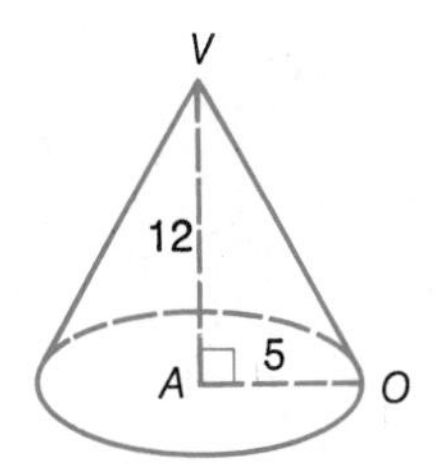

In $\triangle VAO$, $(VO)^2 = (VA)^2 + (AO)^2$ ← $\triangle VAO$ is a right $\triangle$; VO, the slant height, is the hypotenuse.

$(VO)^2 = 12^2 + 5^2$

$(VO)^2 = 144 + 25$

$(VO)^2 = 169$

$VO = 13$ ← The slant height

$L = \pi rs$

$= \pi \cdot 5 \cdot 13$

$= 65\pi$ sq. m

$T = \pi r(s + r)$

$= \pi \cdot 5(13 + 5)$

$= 90\pi$ sq. m

Try These

For Exercises **1–4,** *find the lateral area and the total area.*

1.

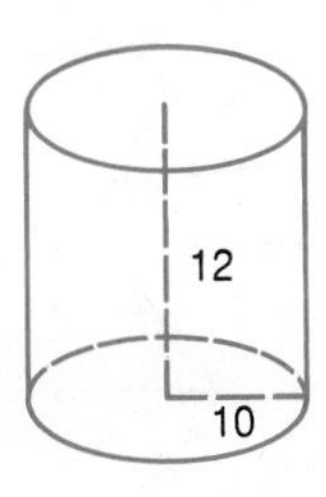

2.

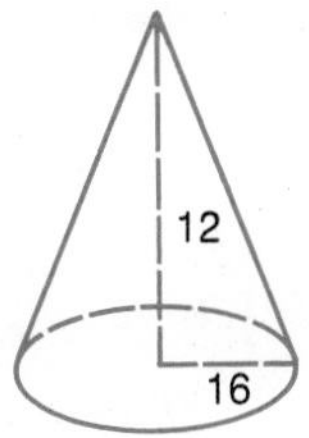

3.

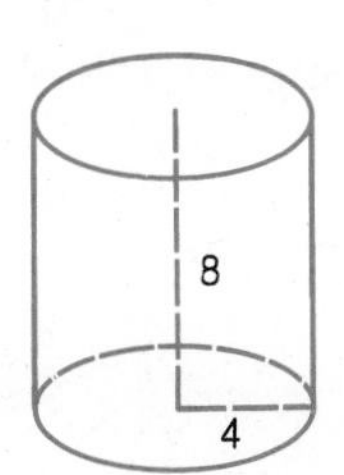

4.

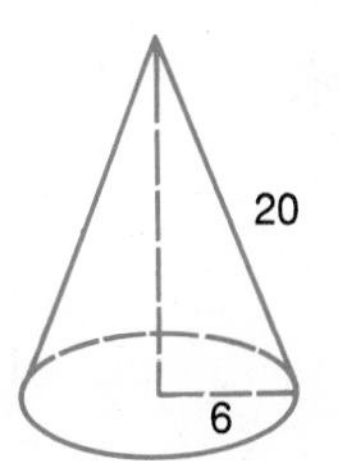

Exercises

Find the lateral area and the total area. Express answers in terms of π.

a

1.

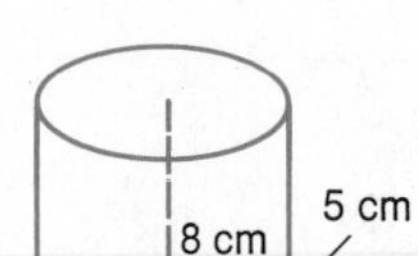

2.

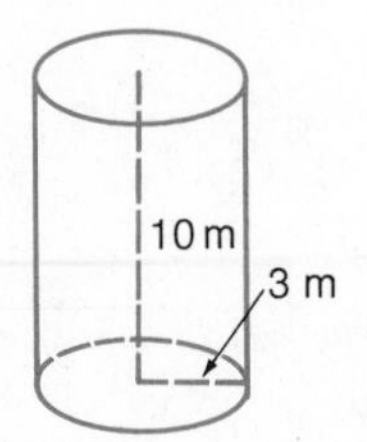

3.

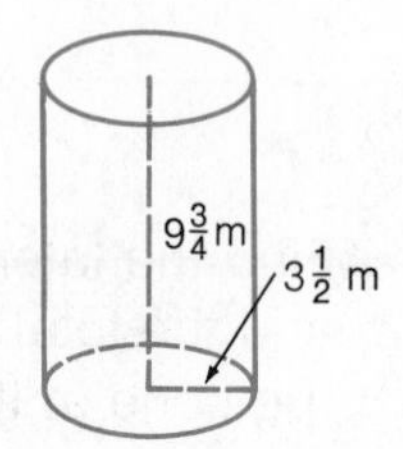

4.

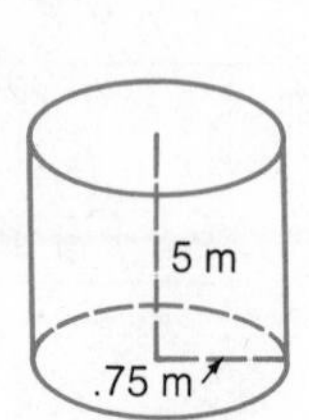

5.

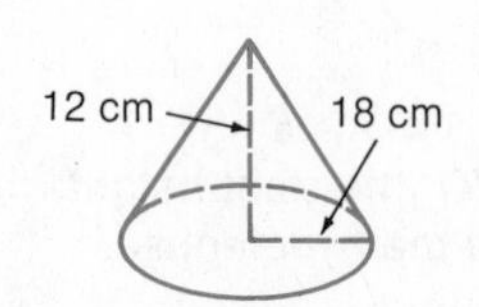

6.

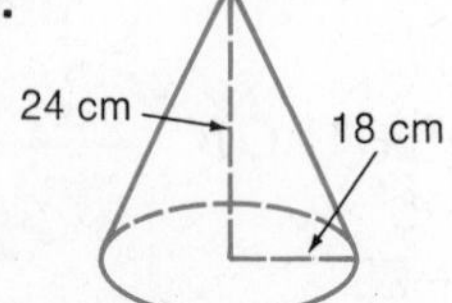

7.

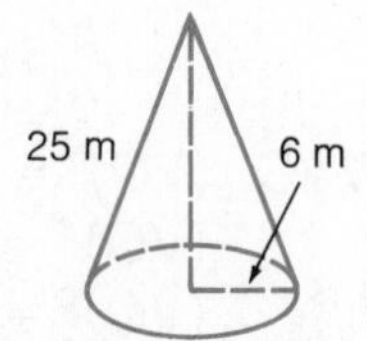

8.

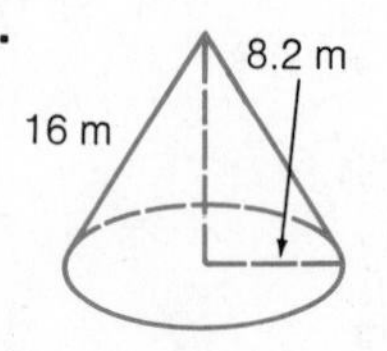

9. The altitude of a right circular cylinder is 6 meters and the total area is 110π square meters. Find the radius.

10. Find the lateral area of a right circular cone with a slant height of 12 and base radius of 4.

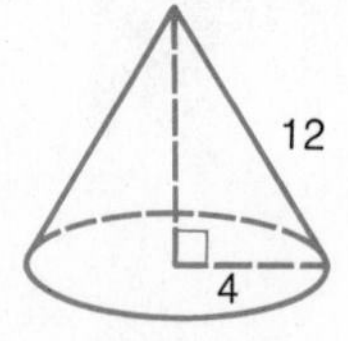

11. Find the total area of the cone in Exercise **10.**

b

12. A right circular cone has an altitude of 8 centimeters and a base radius of 6 centimeters. Find the lateral area and the total area.

13. Write the formulas $L = 2\pi rh$ and $T = 2\pi r(h + r)$ in terms of h when $r = h$.

14. Write the formulas in Exercise 13 in terms of h when $2r = h$.

15. Rectangle $EFGH$ is revolved about $\overline{EH}$ as an axis generating a right circular cylinder. Let $HG = x$ and $GF = y$. Find the lateral area of the cylinder in terms of x and y.

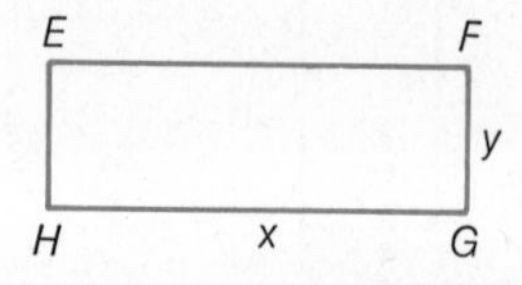

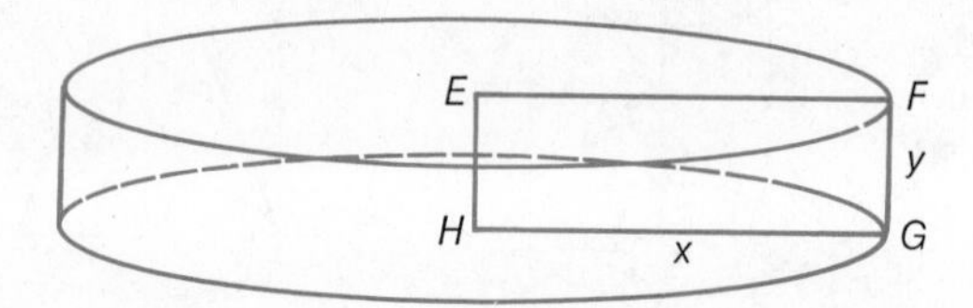

16. Right triangle ABC is revolved about $\overline{BC}$ as an axis. Name the figure generated.

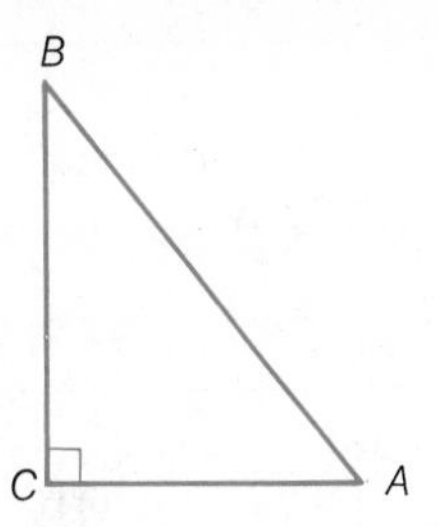

17. The radius of the base of a cone of revolution (see Exercise **16**) is 3.2 meters and the lateral area is 38.4π square meters. Find the slant height.

18. The slant height of a cone of revolution (see Exercise **16**) is 5 centimeters and the total area is 24π square centimeters. Find the radius of the base.

19. A right circular cylinder and a right circular cone each have altitude h and a base of radius r. Find the ratio of the lateral area of the cone to the lateral area of the cylinder.

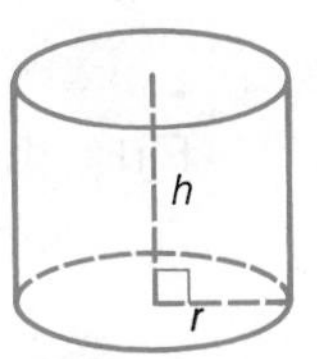

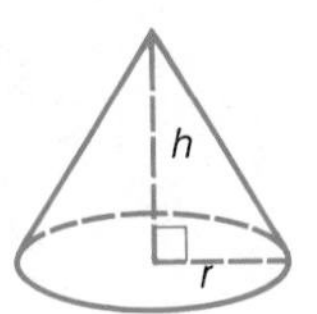

think–draw–see

1. Copy the figure below 3 times. Fold on the interior lines to obtain three pyramids with square bases.

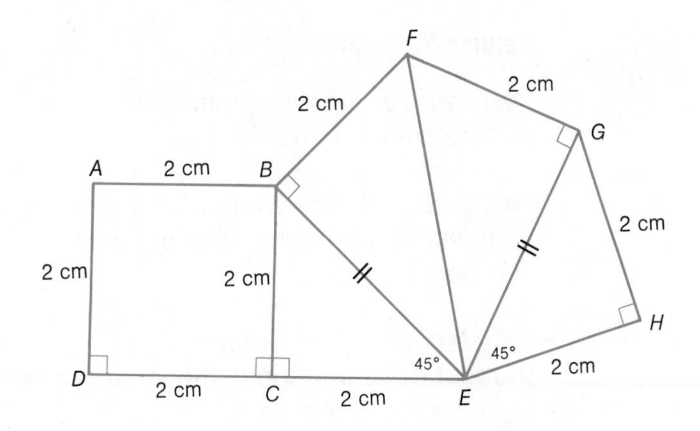

2. Fit the three pyramids together to form a cube.
3. Find the volume of the cube. (HINT: The volume of a cube equals e^3, where e is the measure of an edge.)
4. What is the volume of each pyramid?

9-4 Volume

The **volume of a solid** is the number of cubic units contained in the solid. If measures are given in centimeters, the volume is stated in terms of cubic centimeters, abbreviated cu. cm or cm^3.

Example 1 Find the volume of a rectangular solid 4 centimeters long, 2 centimeters wide, and 3 centimeters high.

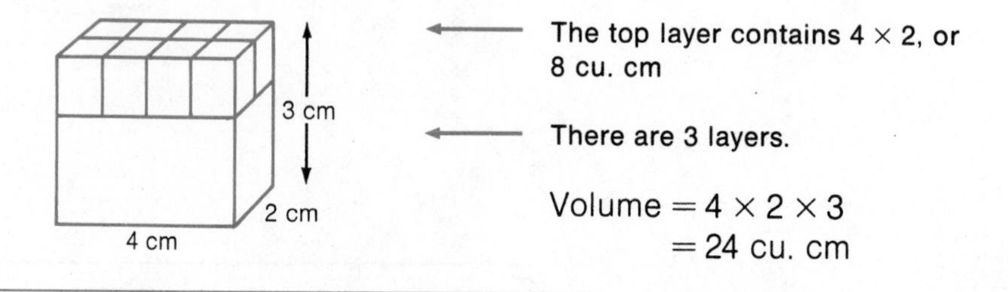

3 cm
2 cm
4 cm
The top layer contains 4 × 2, or 8 cu. cm
There are 3 layers.

$$\text{Volume} = 4 \times 2 \times 3$$
$$= 24 \text{ cu. cm}$$

The Example suggests the Volume Postulates.

Volume Postulates

Postulate 20: Every geometric solid corresponds to a positive number which is its volume.

Postulate 21: The volume of a solid figure is the sum of the volumes of a finite number of nonoverlapping figures of which it is composed.

Postulate 22: The volume V of a rectangular prism is the product of its altitude h, the length of its base, ℓ, and the width of its base, w. That is, $V = \ell wh$.

In $V = \ell wh$, ℓw represents the area of the base of the rectangular solid. Formulas for the volume of a prism and of a right circular cylinder can be given in terms of the base area, B.

These formulas could be stated as theorems.

Name	Model	Volume Formula
Cube		$V = Bh$ $= (e \cdot e) \cdot e$ $= e^3$
Prism		$V = Bh$ (B: Base Area)
Cylinder		$V = Bh$ (B: Base Area) or $V = \pi r^2 h$

Example 2 Find the volume of each solid.

a.

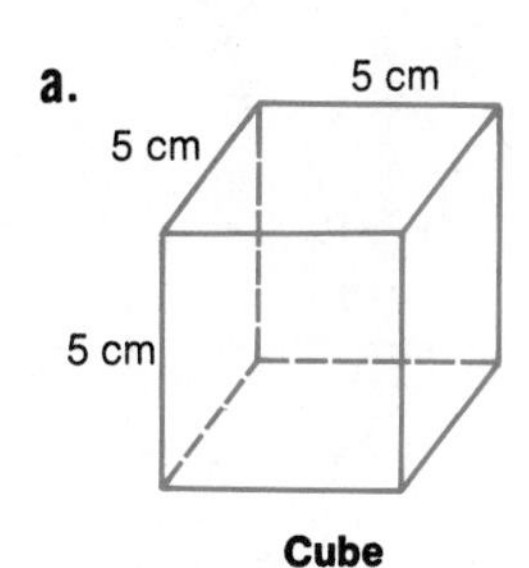

Cube

b.

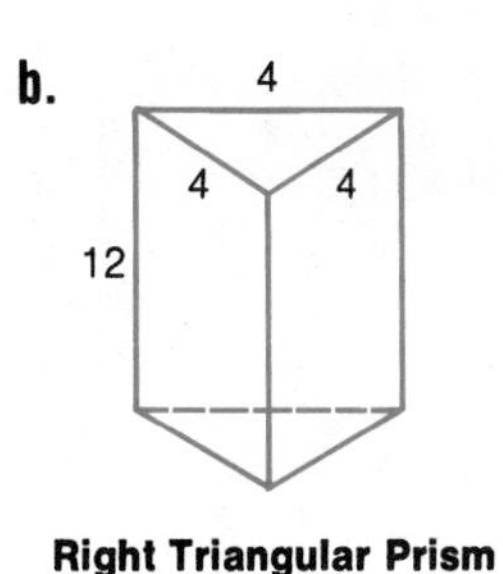

Right Triangular Prism

c.

Cylinder

a. $V = e^3$

$V = 5 \cdot 5 \cdot 5$

$V = 125$ cu. cm

b. $V = B \cdot h$

$V = \left(\frac{s^2}{4}\sqrt{3}\right) \cdot h$

$V = \frac{4^2}{4}\sqrt{3} \cdot 12$

$V = 48\sqrt{3}$ cu. cm

c. $V = \pi r^2 h$

$V = \pi \cdot 5^2 \cdot 8$

$V = 200\pi$ cu. cm

If a prism and a pyramid have equal altitudes and their bases have equal areas, the volume of the prism is three times the volume of the pyramid.

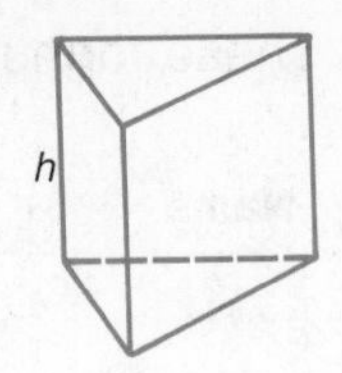

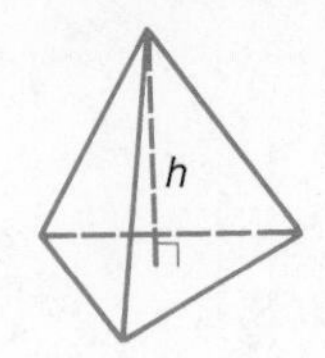

Since the area of the base of a pyramid approximates the area of a circle as the number of sides of the base of the pyramid increases, the formula for the volume of a cone resembles the formula for the volume of a pyramid.

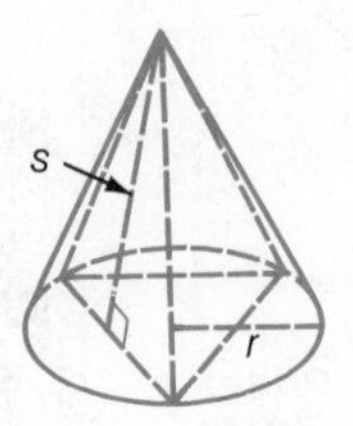

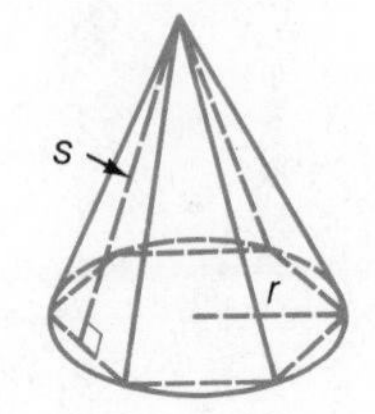

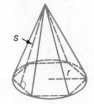

Name	Model	Volume Formula
Pyramid		$V = \frac{1}{3}Bh$ (B: Base Area)
Cone		$V = \frac{1}{3}Bh$ (B: Base Area) or $V = \frac{1}{3}\pi r^2 h$

Example 3

Find the volume of each solid.

a.

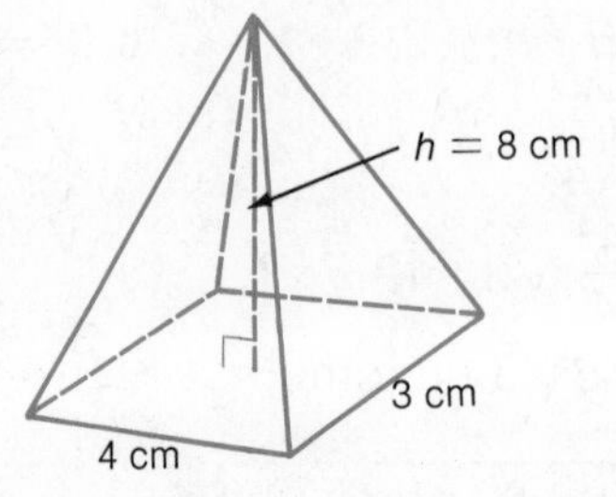

b.

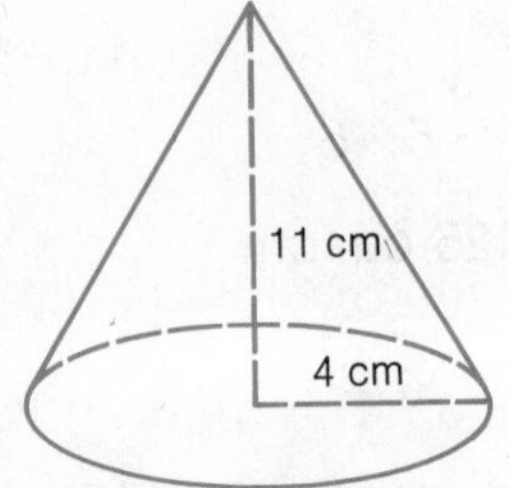

Solutions: **a.** $V = \frac{1}{3}Bh$

$V = \frac{1}{3}(4 \cdot 3)8$ ⟵ Area of base (rectangle): $\ell \cdot w$

$V = 32$ cu. cm

b. $V = \frac{1}{3}\pi r^2 h$

$V = \frac{1}{3}\pi \cdot 4^2 \cdot 11$ ⟵ Area of base (circle): πr^2

$V = 58.6\pi$ cu. cm

Try These

Find the volume of each solid.

1.

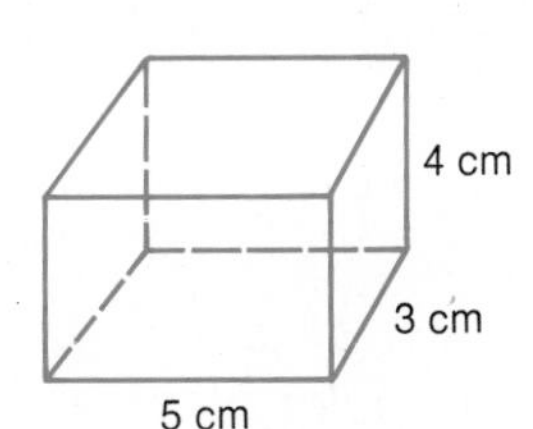

Rectangular Solid

2.

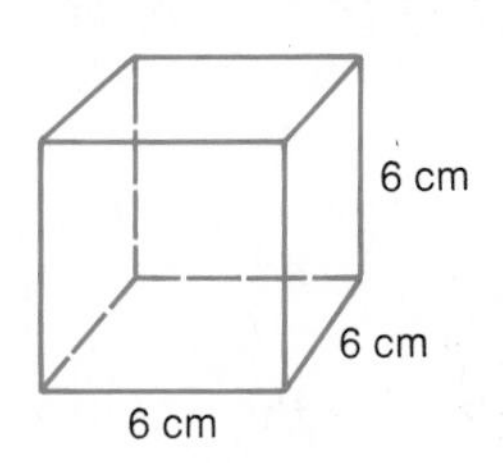

Cube

3.

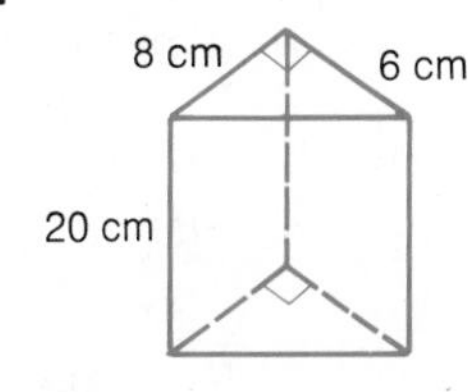

Right Triangular Prism

4.

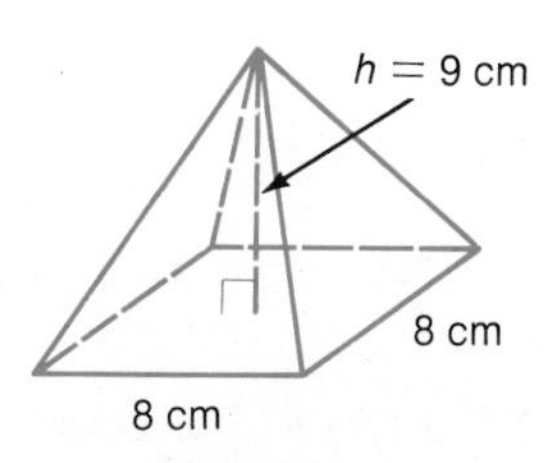

Pyramid

5.

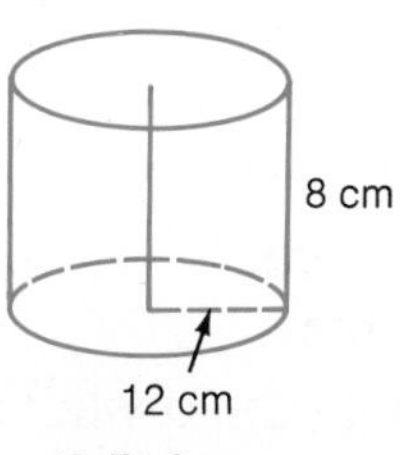

Cylinder

6.

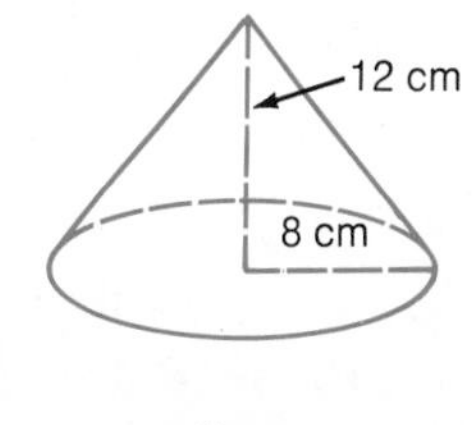

Cone

Exercises

In these Exercises, express radicals in simplest form. Also, express your answers in terms of π, where π occurs.

In Exercises **1–4,** *find the volumes of the rectangular solids with the given dimensions.*

a

1. $7 \times 9 \times 5$

2. $3.24 \times 2.64 \times 1.34$

3. $2\frac{1}{3} \times 1\frac{3}{4} \times 5\frac{1}{2}$

4. $8\sqrt{3} \times 5\sqrt{6} \times 7\sqrt{2}$

5. Find the volume of a prism whose base contains 24 square meters and whose altitude is 8 meters.
6. Find the volume of a right triangular prism whose base is an equilateral triangle 10 centimeters on a side and whose altitude is 6 centimeters.
7. The altitude of a right triangular prism is 6 and its base is an isosceles right triangle whose congruent sides are each 8. Find the volume of the prism.
8. The base of a right prism is an equilateral triangle 16 millimeters on a side. The altitude of the prism is 10 millimeters long. Find the volume.
9. Find the volume of a cube that has an edge of 10 meters.

Find the altitude of each rectangular solid having the given volume and area of the base.

10. 64 cu. m; 15 sq. m
11. 25.75 cu. cm; 5.5 sq. cm

In Exercises **12–17,** *find the volume of each right circular cylinder with the given radius and altitude.*

12. $r = 6$; $h = 10$
13. $r = 5$; $h = 10$
14. $r = 3$; $h = 15$
15. $r = 2\sqrt{3}$; $h = 6$
16. $r = 1.25$; $h = 18$
17. $r = \sqrt{20}$; $h = \sqrt{8}$
18. Find the volume of a pyramid whose base area is 12 sq. cm and whose altitude is 5 centimeters.
19. Find the volume of a pyramid whose altitude is $3\frac{1}{2}$ and whose base has an area of 6.
20. Find the volume of a triangular pyramid whose base is a right triangle with legs of 3 and $4\frac{1}{2}$ and whose altitude is 9.
21. Pyramid *V-RST* has an altitude of 5. Its base is an equilateral triangle of side 3. Find its volume.
22. Find the volume of a quadrangular pyramid whose altitude is 8 and whose base is a square each of whose sides is 4.

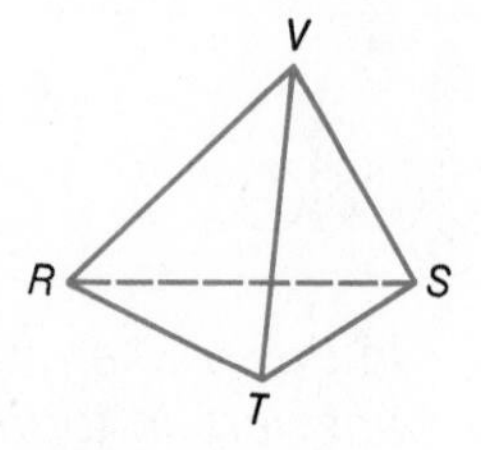

Find the altitude of each pyramid with the given volume and area of the base.

23. $V = 50$ cu. m; $B = 25$ sq. m
24. $V = 3$ cu. cm; $B = 2$ sq. cm

*In Exercises **25–28,** find the volume of each right circular cone with the given radius of the base and altitude.*

25. $r = 5$ cm; $h = 12$ cm

26. $r = 3.4$ m; $h = 8.9$ m

27. $r = 3.5$ mm; $h = 7$ mm

28. $r = 2\sqrt{10}$ cm; $h = 3.5$ cm

29. The volume of a right circular cylinder is 75π cubic units and the radius of its base is $\frac{5}{2}$ units. Find the altitude of the cylinder.

30. The volume of a right circular cone is 48π cubic units and its altitude is 4 units. Find the radius of the base.

31. Solve $V = \frac{1}{3}Bh$ for B.

32. Solve $V = \frac{1}{3}Bh$ for h.

33. Solve $V = \pi r^2 h$ for h.

34. Solve $V = \pi r^2 h$ for r.

35. Find the ratio of the volumes of two rectangular solids whose dimensions are $4 \times 3 \times 2$ units and $5 \times 6 \times 2$ units.

36. The base of a prism is an isosceles triangle whose congruent sides are each 5 centimeters and whose base is 4 centimeters. The altitude of the prism is 4 centimeters. Find the volume.

37. What is the effect upon the volume of a rectangular solid when one dimension is doubled and the two other dimensions remain the same? When two dimensions are doubled and the third remains the same? When all three are doubled?

38. In pyramid V-RST, $\overline{VR}$, $\overline{VT}$, and $\overline{VS}$ each have a length of 4 centimeters. The base is an equilateral triangle each of whose sides is 2 centimeters long. Find the volume.

In the figure at the right, a regular quadrangular prism is circumscribed about a circular cylinder. The altitude of the prism is 5. The radius of the base of the cylinder is 2.

39. Find the volume of the cylinder.

40. Find the volume of the prism.

41. Find the ratio of the volume of the cylinder to the volume of the prism.

42. Find the volume of a right circular cone whose altitude is h units and whose slant height is s units.

43. Find the slant height of the cone at the left below whose volume is 30π cubic inches and whose altitude is 10 inches.

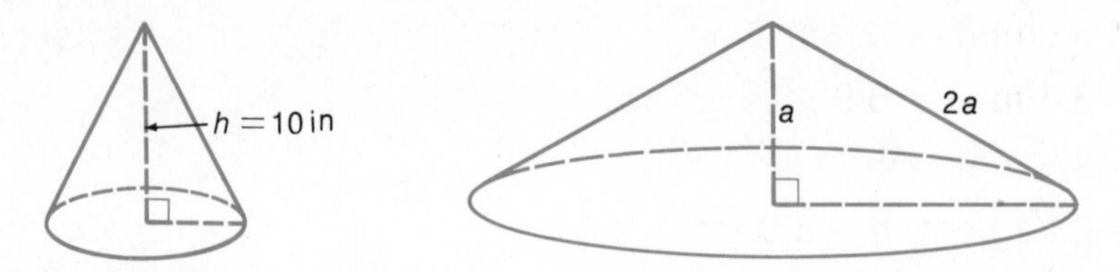

44. Find the volume of the right circular cone at the right above whose altitude is a units and whose slant height is $2a$ units.

45. If $V = \pi r^2 h$ and $T = 2\pi rh + \pi r^2$, find T in terms of r and V.

A regular quadrangular pyramid has as its base a square with sides of 3 inches. The altitude of the pyramid is 4 inches.

46. Find the volume of the pyramid.

47. Find the volume of the cone that circumscribes this pyramid.

48. Find the ratio of the volume of the pyramid to the volume of the cone.

For Exercises **49–55,** *refer to the similar rectangular solids at the right.*

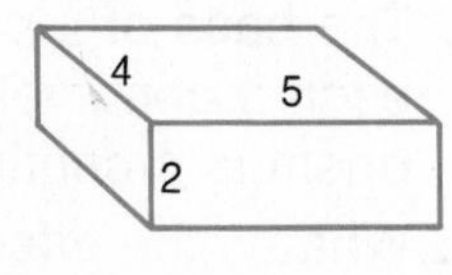

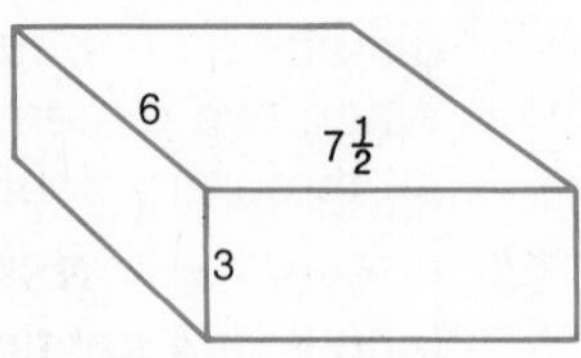

49. Find the ratio of each side of the smaller solid to the corresponding side of the larger.

50. Find the lateral surface area of each solid.

51. Find the ratio of the lateral surface area of the smaller solid to the lateral surface area of the larger.

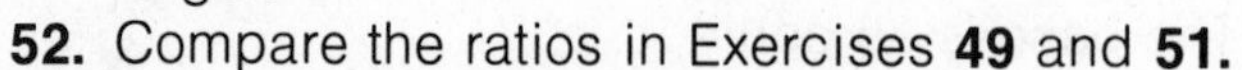

52. Compare the ratios in Exercises **49** and **51.**

53. Find the volume of each solid.

54. Find the ratio of the volume of the smaller solid to the larger.

55. Compare the ratios in Exercises **49** and **54.**

For Exercises **56–63,** *refer to the similar right circular cylinders at the right.*

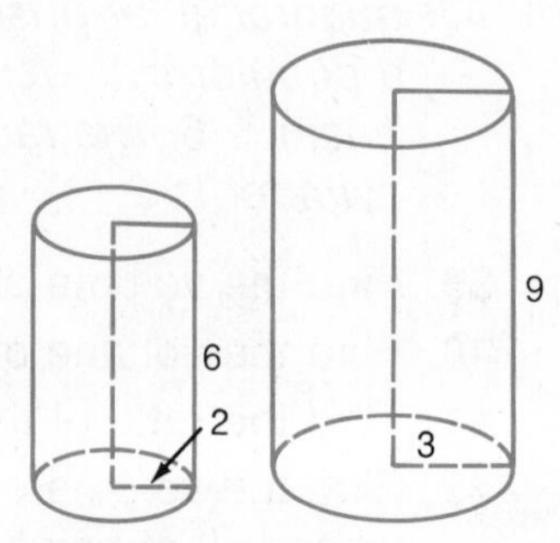

56. Find the ratio of the radius of the smaller cylinder to the radius of the larger.

57. Find the ratio of the altitude of the smaller cylinder to the altitude of the larger.

58. Find the total area of each cylinder.

59. Find the ratio of the total area of the smaller cylinder to the total area of the larger.

60. Compare the ratios in Exercises **56, 57,** and **59.**

61. Find the volume of each cylinder.

62. Find the ratio of the volume of the smaller cylinder to the volume of the larger.

63. Compare the ratios in Exercises **56, 59,** and **62.**

*Use Exercises **49–63** to complete these Corollaries.*

64. In similar solids, the lengths of corresponding segments have the same __?__.

65. In similar solids, the total areas, or any two corresponding areas, have the same ratio as the __?__ of the lengths of any two corresponding segments.

66. In similar solids, the volumes have the same ratio as the __?__ of the lengths of any two corresponding segments.

C 67. Find the volume of a triangular prism whose base is an equilateral triangle a units on a side and whose altitude is b units.

68. Find the volume of a triangular prism whose base is an isosceles right triangle whose congruent sides are each a units in length and whose altitude is b units.

69. The base of a prism is an isosceles triangle whose congruent sides are each a units and whose base is b units in length. The altitude of the prism is c units. Find the volume.

Remember

The figure at the right below shows a sphere with center T. Identify each of the following.

1. A radius of the sphere
2. A diameter of the sphere
3. A great circle of the sphere
4. Two central angles of the sphere
5. A chord of the sphere

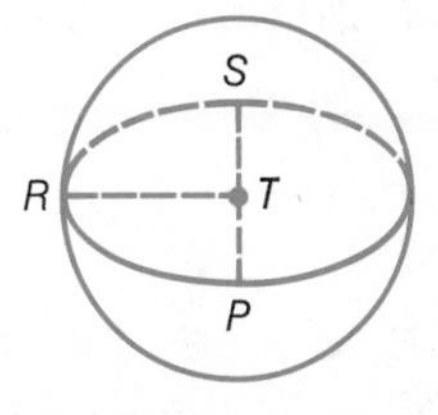

The answers are on page 442. If you need help, see pages 356 and 357.

9-5 Surface Area and Volume of a Sphere

One way to obtain a spherical surface is to revolve semicircle ACB about diameter AB as an axis. The formulas for the surface area and volume of a sphere are given below.

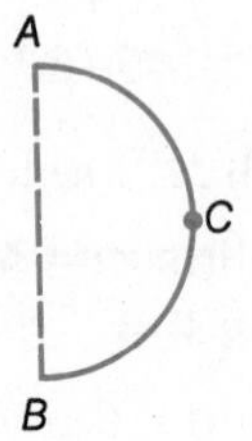

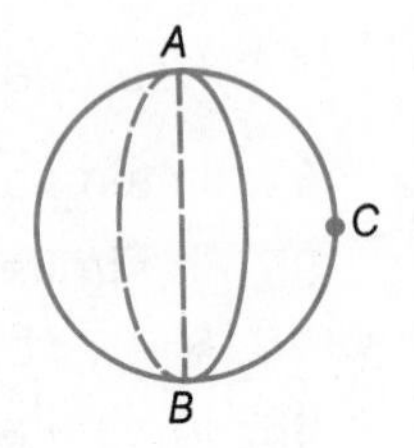

Solid	Model	Surface Area	Volume
Sphere		$A = 4\pi r^2$	$V = \frac{4}{3}\pi r^3$

Example

Find the surface area and the volume of a sphere that has a radius of 12 centimeters.

$$\begin{aligned} A &= 4\pi r^2 \\ &= 4\pi \cdot 12^2 \\ &= 4\pi \cdot 144 \\ &= 576\pi \text{ sq. cm} \end{aligned}$$

$$\begin{aligned} V &= \frac{4}{3}\pi r^3 \\ &= \tfrac{4}{3}\pi \cdot 12^3 \\ &= \tfrac{4}{3}\pi \cdot 1728 \\ &= 2304\pi \text{ cu. cm} \end{aligned}$$

Try These

1. Find the surface area of a sphere with a radius of 5 centimeters.
2. Find the radius of a sphere with surface area of 36π sq. units.
3. Find the volume of a sphere with a radius of 6 centimeters.

Exercises

In these exercises, express your answers in terms of π when finding area and volume. Simplify any radicals.

*In Exercises **1–5,** find the surface area of a sphere with the given radius.*

a

1. 5 **2.** 8.2 **3.** $4\frac{1}{2}$ **4.** $9\sqrt{2}$ **5.** $\frac{5}{2}\sqrt{30}$

*In Exercises **6–10,** find the volume of a sphere with the given radius.*

6. 6 **7.** 5.5 **8.** $6\frac{7}{8}$ **9.** $\frac{3}{4}$ **10.** $\frac{1}{2}\sqrt{3}$

*In Exercises **11–13,** find the radius of a sphere for each given surface area.*

11. $\frac{36}{25}\pi$ sq. cm **12.** $\frac{49}{16}\pi$ sq. m **13.** 1764π sq. m

14. Find the volume of a sphere whose diameter is $\frac{3}{4}$.

15. Find the radius of a sphere whose volume is 288π.

16. Find the volume of a sphere if the circumference of a great circle of the sphere is 3π units.

17. Solve $V = \frac{4}{3}\pi r^3$ for r.

18. The volume of a sphere is $\frac{32}{3}\pi$. Find its radius.

A cube whose edge is 20 is circumscribed about a sphere.

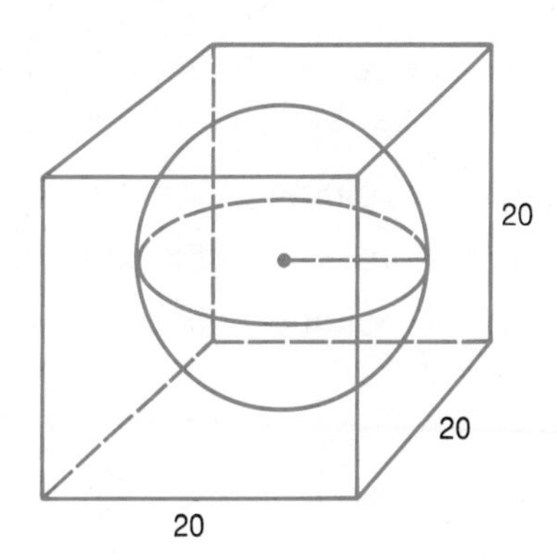

19. Find the total surface area of the cube.

20. Find the surface area of the sphere.

21. Find the ratio of the area of the sphere to the area of the cube.

*In Exercises **22–24,** find the volume of a sphere inscribed in a cube with the given dimensions.*

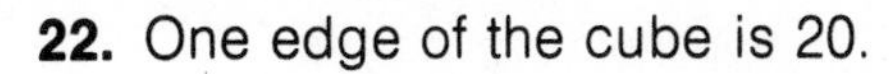

22. One edge of the cube is 20.

b

23. One edge of the cube is e.

24. A diagonal of one face is 4.

25. What is the ratio of the radii of two spheres if the area of one is twice the area of the other?

26. Find the surface area of one half of a sphere with radius 16.

27. Compare the volumes of two spheres whose radii are 1 centimeter and two centimeters.

A scoop of ice cream is in the shape of a ***hemisphere*** *(half a sphere) of diameter 7.5 cm. It is on a cone of diameter 7.5 cm and altitude 12 cm.*

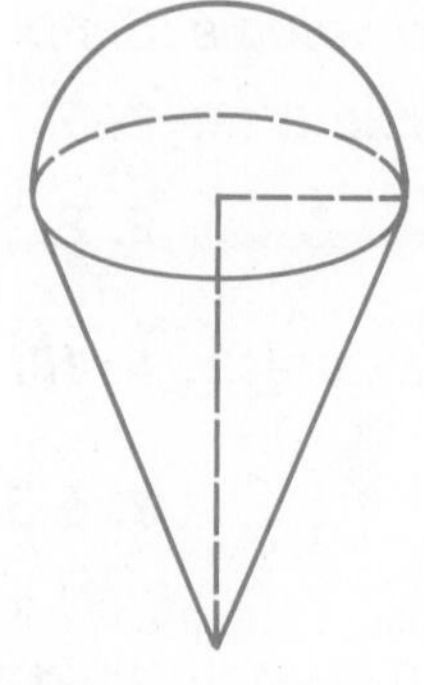

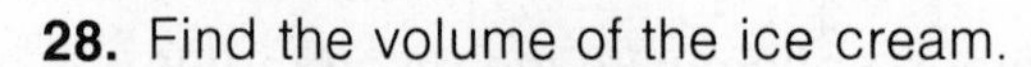

28. Find the volume of the ice cream.

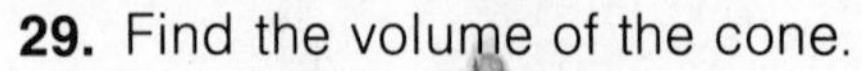

29. Find the volume of the cone.

30. If the ice cream melts into the cone, will it overflow?

A cube is inscribed in a sphere of radius 8.

31. Find the total surface area of the cube.

32. Find the ratio of the total surface area of the cube to the surface area of the sphere.

A cube is circumscribed about a sphere and the measure of one edge of the cube is e.

33. Find the total surface area of the cube.

34. Find the surface area of the sphere.

A cube is circumscribed about a given sphere and a cube is inscribed in the same sphere. Find each ratio.

C

35. The volume of the circumscribed cube to the volume of the sphere.

36. The volume of the sphere to the volume of the inscribed cube.

37. The volume of the circumscribed cube to the volume of the inscribed cube.

Cavalieri's Principle

Bonaventura Cavalieri, an Italian mathematician, pictured a solid as being made up of a large number of thin "slices." He used this idea to express a relationship between area and volume. Think of the solids in Figures 1 and 2 as being two decks of thin cards.

1. Each card has the same thickness.
2. The bottom card in Figure 1 is equal in area to the bottom card in Figure 2.
3. The two cards (one from each deck) next to the bottom are also equal in area but are smaller than the bottom cards, and so on, up to the top cards.
4. The two decks are equal in height.

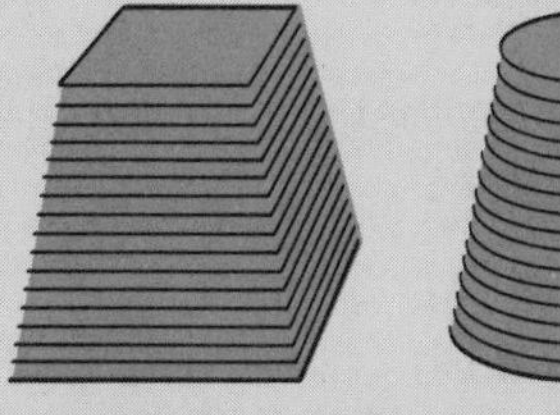
Figure 1

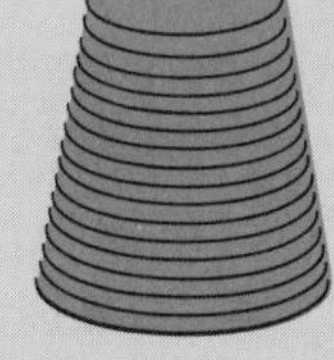
Figure 2

Conclusion: By Cavalieri's Principle, the decks have equal volumes.

Cavalieri's Principle
Let S and T be solids with their bases in plane I. If every plane that intersects S or T and is parallel to plane I intersects S and T in figures that have the same area, then

Volume S = Volume T.

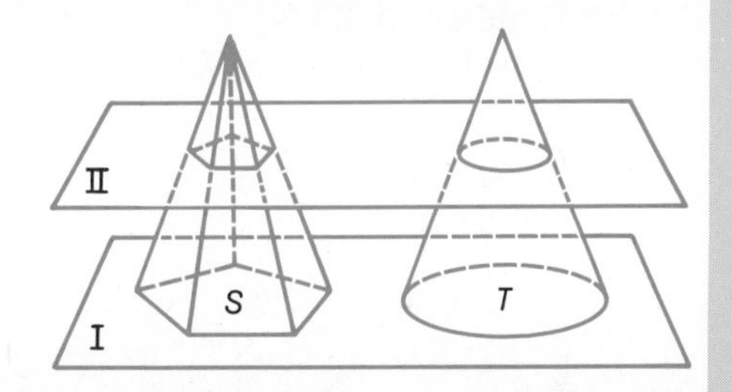

Can You Solve These?

For each exercise, the figures shown have bases that are equal in area. Use Cavalieri's Principle to tell under what conditions the figures will have equal volumes.

1.

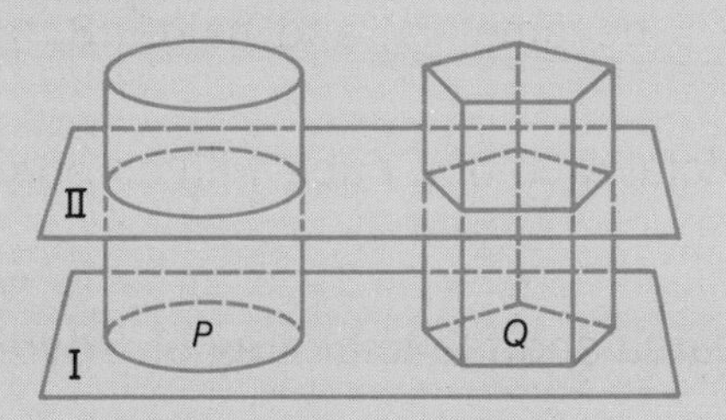

2.

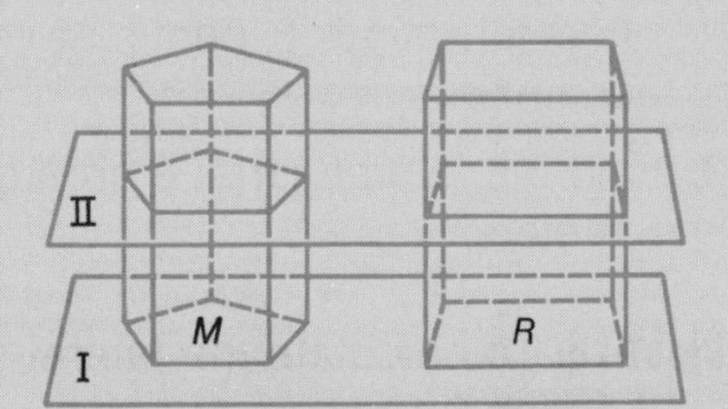

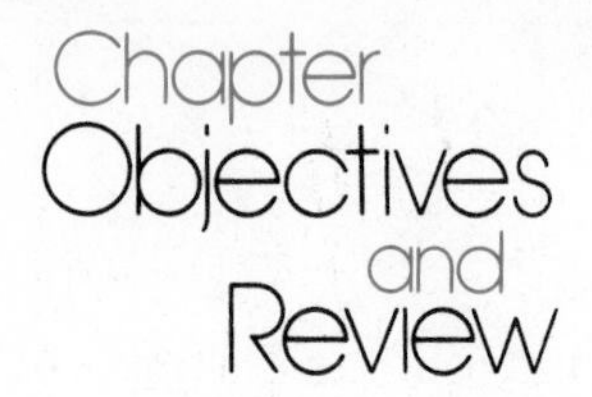

Objective: To recall, and give examples of, the important mathematical terms of the chapter.

1. Be sure that you know the meanings of these mathematical terms used in Chapter 9.

cube (p. 414)
prism (p. 414)
  altitude (p. 414)
  bases (p. 414)
  edges (p. 414)
  faces (p. 414)
  lateral faces (p. 414)
  lateral surface area (p. 414)
  oblique (p. 414)
  regular (p. 414)
  right (p. 414)
  total area (p. 415)
pyramid (p. 419)
  altitude (p. 419)
  edges (p. 419)
  faces (p. 419)
  lateral area (p. 419)
  regular (p. 419)
  slant height (p. 419)
right circular cone (p. 424)
  altitude (p. 424)
  lateral surface area (p. 424)
  total area (p. 424)
  vertex (p. 424)
right circular cylinder (p. 423)
  altitude (p. 423)
  lateral area (p. 423)
  total area (p. 423)

Objective: To calculate the lateral surface area and total area of a right prism. (Section 9-1)

2. Find the lateral surface area and the total area of a right rectangular prism of length 3 centimeters, width 5 centimeters, and height 8 centimeters.

3. Find the lateral surface area and the total area of a cube with an edge of 5 meters.

Objective: To calculate the lateral surface area and the total area of a pyramid. (Section 9-2)

4. Find the lateral surface area and the total area of a regular pyramid whose base is an equilateral triangle with a side of 6 centimeters and whose slant height is 4 centimeters.
5. The lateral surface area of a regular pyramid is 160 square units and the perimeter of its base is 40 units. Find the slant height.

Objective: To calculate the lateral area and the total area of a right circular cylinder and a right circular cone. (Section 9-3)

6. Find the lateral area and the total area of a right circular cylinder with a radius of 7 centimeters and an altitude of 10 centimeters.
7. Find the lateral area and the total area of a right circular cone with radius 2 millimeters and height 5 millimeters.

Objective: To calculate the volume of a right prism, pyramid, a right circular cylinder, and a right circular cone. (Section 9-4)

8. Find the volume of a right triangular prism whose base is a right triangle with legs of 3 centimeters and 4 centimeters and whose height is 9 centimeters.
9. Find the volume of a regular pyramid with a square base 5 meters on a side and with an altitude of 9 meters.
10. The radius of the base of a right circular cylinder is 6 centimeters and its altitude is 9 centimeters. Find the volume.
11. The base of a cone has an area of 49π square meters and its altitude is 12 meters. Find the volume.

Objective: To calculate the surface area and volume of a sphere. (Section 9-5)

12. Find the surface area of a sphere with a radius of 3 meters.
13. Find the volume of a sphere with a radius of 6 millimeters.

Chapter Test

Classify each statement as True or False. If a statement is false, tell why it is false.

1. The lateral faces of a pyramid are triangles.

2. The bases of a prism are congruent polygons.

3. The altitude of a pyramid is the same as the slant height.

4. The total area of a cone equals the lateral area.

5. In a right circular cone, the altitude passes through the center of the base.

Find the total area of each of the following.

6. A cube with an edge of 4.5 centimeters

7. A pyramid with a slant height of 10 meters and whose base is an equilateral triangle with a side of 6 meters

8. A right circular cylinder with radius 4 and altitude 7

Find the volume of each of the following.

9. A triangular prism whose base is an equilateral triangle with a side of 8 centimeters and whose altitude is 10 centimeters

10. A regular pyramid with a square base of side 12 meters and a slant height of $6\sqrt{5}$ meters.

11. A right circular cone whose base has a radius of 5 centimeters and whose altitude is 8 centimeters

12. A sphere with a diameter of 30 meters

Answers to Remember

Page 418: **1.** 25 **2.** $4\sqrt{3}$ **3.** $\frac{25\sqrt{3}}{2}$ **4.** $216\sqrt{3}$

Page 422: **1.** $C = 2\pi r$ or $C = \pi d$ **2.** $A = \pi r^2$ **3.** 2.25π **4.** 15 **5.** 1.3

Page 435: **1.** $\overline{TR}$, $\overline{TS}$, or $\overline{TP}$ **2.** $\overline{SP}$ **3.** SRP **4.** $\angle STR$; $\angle RTP$ **5.** SP

Chapter 10
Coordinate Geometry

10-1 The Coordinate Plane

To locate points on a plane, you use two number lines that are perpendicular to each other. The horizontal number line is the **x axis;** the vertical number line is the **y axis.** The axes separate the plane into four **quadrants.**

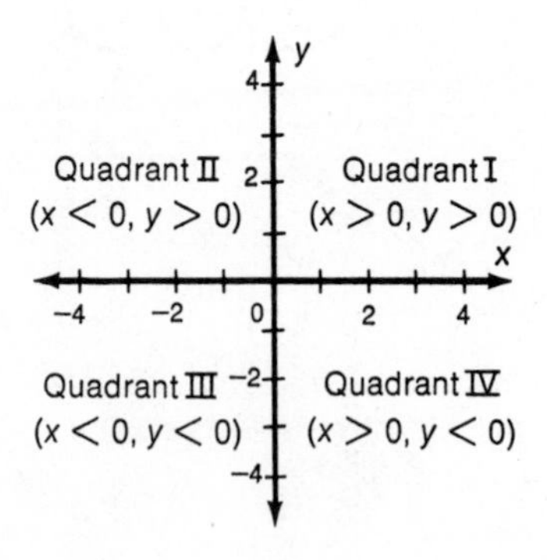

To locate a point in the plane, you use an ordered pair of real numbers called the **coordinates** of the point.

Number of units from the y axis. ⟶ (x, y) ⟵ Number of units from the x axis.

As the figure above shows, x is negative in Quadrants II and III; y is negative in Quadrants III and IV.

Example 1

Name the coordinates of points A, B, C, D, and E.

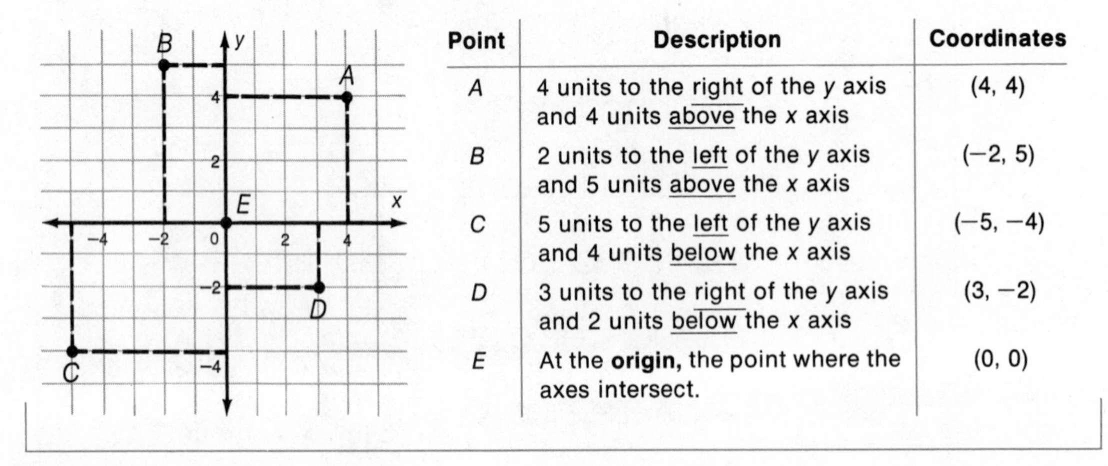

Point	Description	Coordinates
A	4 units to the right of the y axis and 4 units above the x axis	(4, 4)
B	2 units to the left of the y axis and 5 units above the x axis	(−2, 5)
C	5 units to the left of the y axis and 4 units below the x axis	(−5, −4)
D	3 units to the right of the y axis and 2 units below the x axis	(3, −2)
E	At the **origin,** the point where the axes intersect.	(0, 0)

Example 2

Graph these coordinates. Draw a line through each set of points. Describe each line.

a. $A(4, 4)$; $B(4, 2)$; $C(4, 0)$; $D(4, -1)$
b. $E(-3, -3)$; $F(0, -3)$; $G(2, -3)$; $H(5, -3)$

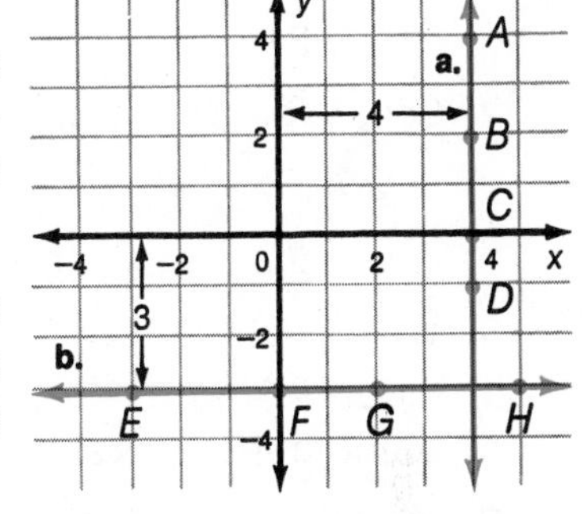

a. The line is vertical. Since each point on the line is 4 units to the right of the y axis, the x coordinate of each point is 4. Thus, the equation for the line is $x = 4$.

b. The line is horizontal. Since each point on the line is below the x axis, the y coordinate for each point is -3. Thus, the equation for the line is $y = -3$.

Example 2 suggests the general forms of the equations for a vertical line and for a horizontal line.

Vertical line: $x = a$, where a is a real number
Horizontal line: $y = b$, where b is a real number

Because there is a one-to-one correspondence between the points in the plane and ordered pairs of real numbers, the plane is called the **coordinate plane.**

Try These

*In Exercises **1–3,** name the quadrant in which each point is located.*

1. $(-2, -5)$ **2.** $(3, -6)$ **3.** $(-8, 4)$

4. Point D has coordinates $(-3, 4)$ and point E has coordinates $(-3, -1)$. Find the length of $\overline{DE}$.

*In Exercises **5–7,** complete each statement by inserting the word parallel or perpendicular.*

5. The graph of $x = 4$ is _?_ to the y axis and _?_ to the x axis.

6. The graph of $y = 6$ is _?_ to the graph of $y = 4$.

7. The graph of $x = 5$ is _?_ to the graph of $y = -2$.

Exercises

a

*In Exercises **1–6,** name the quadrant in which each point is located.*

1. $A(5, 7)$ **2.** $B(8, -2)$

3. $C(-2, 9)$ **4.** $D(-1, -4)$

5. $E(7, -3)$ **6.** $F(-\frac{1}{2}, 4)$

7. On the same set of axes, graph and label each point in Exercises **1–6.**

*Use the figure at the right below for Exercises **8–17.***
Name the quadrant in which each point lies.

8. W **9.** S **10.** U

11. Find the coordinate of each labeled point in the figure.

12. Find the length of $\overline{SR}$.

13. Find the length of $\overline{RX}$.

14. Find the length of $\overline{UX}$.

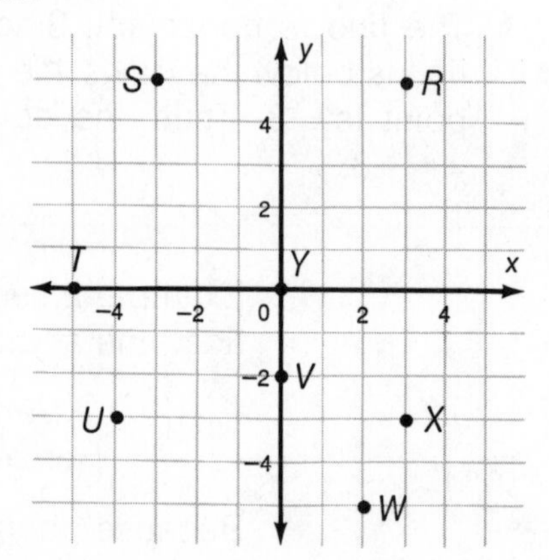

Write the equation for each line.

15. $\overleftrightarrow{SR}$ **16.** $\overleftrightarrow{XU}$ **17.** $\overleftrightarrow{RX}$

Graph on the same set of axes.

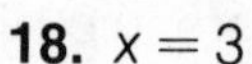

18. $x = 3$

19. $y = -4$

20. $x = -\frac{5}{2}$

21. Graph $A(2, -1)$, $B(2, 2)$, $C(-3, 2)$ and $D(-3, -1)$ on the same axes.

*Refer to the graph in Exercise **21** to answer Exercises **22–26.***

22. Write the equation of $\overleftrightarrow{BC}$.

23. Write the equation of $\overleftrightarrow{CD}$.

24. Find the length of each segment: $\overline{AB}$, $\overline{BC}$, $\overline{CD}$, $\overline{DA}$.

25. Name two pairs of parallel segments in quadrilateral $ABCD$.

26. Name the perpendicular lines determined by quadrilateral $ABCD$.

b

27. Rectangle $RQST$ has coordinates $R(-2, -3)$, $S(3, 5)$, and $T(3, -3)$. Find the coordinates of point Q.

28. Square $EFHG$ has coordinates $E(2, 3)$, $F(2, 6)$ and $G(5, 3)$. Find the coordinates of point H.

Remember

*In Exercises **1–6,** two points on a number line have the given coordinates. Find the distance between the points.*

1. 8; 3 **2.** 2; 5 **3.** 0; −7

4. −3; 10 **5.** 6; −3 **6.** −2; −8

The answers are on page 469. If you need help, see page 557 in the Review: Topics From Algebra One.

10-2 The Midpoint Formula

Example

Find the coordinates of the midpoint $M(x_m, y_m)$ of $\overline{AB}$.

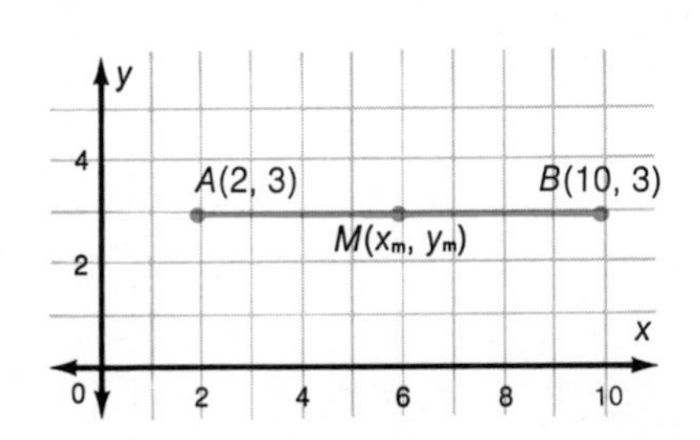

Since $\overline{AB}$ is horizontal, the y coordinate of M is 3, the same as for any point on $\overline{AB}$. Since $2 < x_m < 10$,

$$MA = x_m - 2 \text{ and } BM = 10 - x_m.$$

Since M is the midpoint of $\overline{AB}$, $MA = BM$. Thus,

$$x_m - 2 = 10 - x_m$$ ⟵ Replace MA with $x_m - 2$ and BM with $10 - x_m$.

$$2x_m = 10 + 2$$

$$x_m = \frac{10 + 2}{2}$$ ⟵ $\frac{\text{Sum of } x \text{ coordinates of endpoints}}{2}$

$$= \frac{12}{2} = 6$$

$\therefore M(x_m, y_m) = M(6, 3)$

This suggests that the x coordinate of the midpoint of a horizontal segment with endpoints $P_1(x_1, y_1)$ and $P_2(x_2, y_2)$ is

$$x_m = \frac{x_1 + x_2}{2}$$ ⟵ $\frac{\text{Sum of } x \text{ coordinates of endpoints}}{2}$

It can also be shown that the y coordinate of the midpoint of a vertical segment with endpoints $P_1(x_1, y_1)$ and $P_2(x_2, y_2)$ is:

$$y_m = \frac{y_1 + y_2}{2} \longleftarrow \frac{\text{Sum of } y \text{ coordinates of endpoints}}{2}$$

This suggests the following theorem.

Theorem 10-1: The Midpoint Formula

The coordinates (x_m, y_m) of the midpoint M of the segment whose endpoints are $P_1(x_1, y_1)$ and $P_2(x_2, y_2)$ are

$$x_m = \frac{x_1 + x_2}{2} \quad \text{and} \quad y_m = \frac{y_1 + y_2}{2}$$

Given: $\overline{P_1P_2}$ with endpoints (x_1, y_1) and (x_2, y_2). Point $M(x_m, y_m)$ is the midpoint of $\overline{P_1P_2}$ and $x_1 < x_m < x_2$.

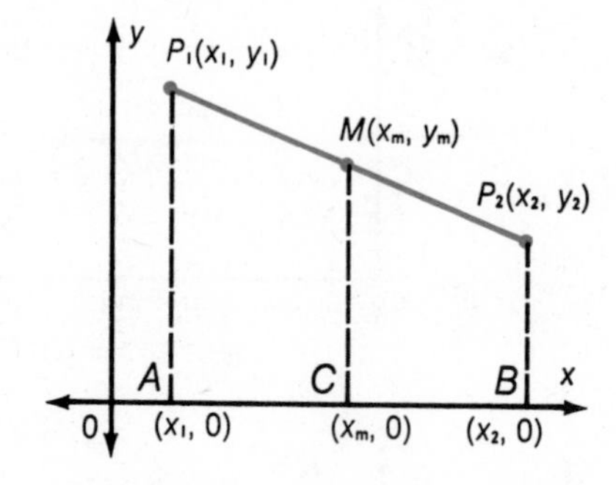

Prove: $x_m = \frac{x_1 + x_2}{2}$, and

$y_m = \frac{y_1 + y_2}{2}$

Outline of proof for x_m:

$\overline{P_1A}$, $\overline{MC}$, and $\overline{P_2B}$ are perpendicular to the x axis.

$\therefore \overline{P_1A} \parallel \overline{MC} \parallel \overline{P_2B}$. The coordinates of A, C, and B are $(x_1, 0)$, $(x_m, 0)$ and $(x_2, 0)$, respectively. Since M is the midpoint of $\overline{P_1P_2}$, $P_1M = MP_2$. $\therefore AC = BC$. Since $AC = x_m - x_1$ and $BC = x_2 - x_m$,

$$x_m - x_1 = x_2 - x_m$$
$$2x_m = x_1 + x_2$$
$$x_m = \frac{x_1 + x_2}{2}$$

The proof that $y_m = \frac{y_1 + y_2}{2}$ is similar.

Try These

Find the coordinates of the midpoint of a segment whose endpoints have the following coordinates.

1. (2, 5) and (6, 11)

2. (3, 7) and (−4, 1)

3. One endpoint of $\overline{AB}$ is $A(-3, 2)$, and the midpoint of $\overline{AB}$ is $M(-1, 5)$. Find the coordinates of point B.

Exercises

*In Exercises **1–6**, the coordinates of the endpoints of a segment are given. Find the midpoint of each segment.*

a

1. (6, 1)(4, 2)

2. (3, −2)(7, 8)

3. (4, −1)(−3, 7)

4. (−1, −8)(−5, −2)

5. $(a, 0)(0, b)$

6. $(2a, 2b)(2c, 2d)$

7. One endpoint of $\overline{RS}$ is $R(-3, 7)$, and the midpoint of $\overline{RS}$ is (3, 5). Find the coordinates of point S.

8. The endpoints of $\overline{XY}$ are $X(-5, 8)$ and $Y(r, 1)$. The midpoint of $\overline{XY}$ is $M(2, s)$. Find the values of r and s.

9. The midpoint of $\overline{EF}$ is $M(2, 3)$ and point E is at the origin. Find the coordinates of point F.

*Quadrilateral ABCD has coordinates A(0, 0), B(5, 1), C(7, 4) and D(2, 3). Use this information for Exercises **10–16**.*

10. Graph quadrilateral $ABCD$.

Find each midpoint.

11. Side AB

12. Side BC

13. Side CD

14. Side AD

15. Diagonal AC

16. Diagonal BD

Remember

Simplify each expression.

1. 2 − 5

2. 3 − (−2)

3. −6 − 3

4. −9 − (−4)

5. 0 − 10

6. 0 − (−2)

The answers are on page 469. If you need help, see page 557 in the Review: Topics From Algebra One.

10-3 Slope of a Line

The steepness of a line is a ratio called slope.

Definition: For any two points on a line, (x_1, y_1) and (x_2, y_2),

$$\textbf{slope} = m = \frac{\text{vertical change}}{\text{horizontal change}} = \frac{y_2 - y_1}{x_2 - x_1},\ (x_2 \neq x_1).$$

Example 1

Find the slope of the line containing the points (2, 3) and (6, 5).

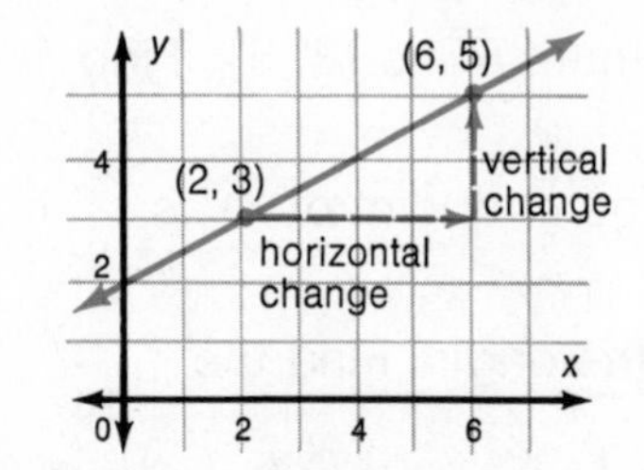

$$m = \frac{y_2 - y_1}{x_2 - x_1} \longleftarrow \frac{\text{Difference of } y \text{ coordinates}}{\text{Difference of } x \text{ coordinates}}$$

$$= \frac{5-3}{6-2} \quad \begin{array}{l} \longleftarrow \text{Replace } y_2 \text{ with 5 and } y_1 \text{ with 3.} \\ \longleftarrow \text{Replace } x_2 \text{ with 6 and } x_1 \text{ with 2.} \end{array}$$

$$= \frac{2}{4}, \text{ or } \frac{1}{2} \longleftarrow \text{Simplify.}$$

NOTE: You could let $(x_1, y_1) = (6, 5)$ and $(x_2, y_2) = (2, 3)$ to find m.

Example 2

Find the slope of line AB containing $A(-3, 5)$ and $B(4, -2)$.

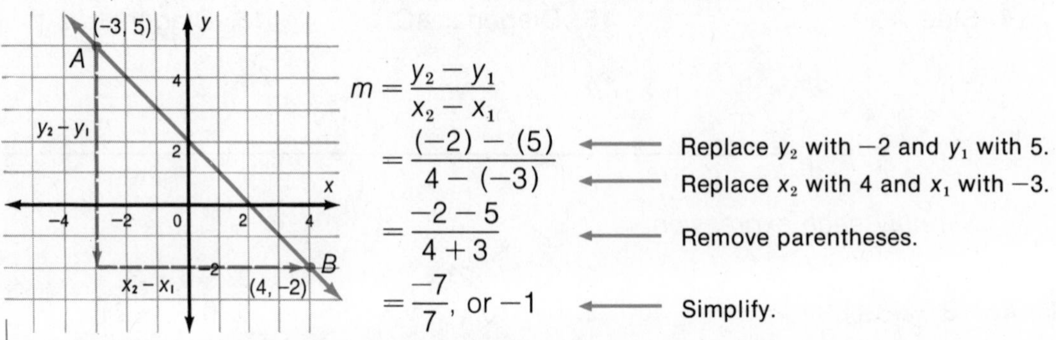

$$m = \frac{y_2 - y_1}{x_2 - x_1}$$

$$= \frac{(-2) - (5)}{4 - (-3)} \quad \begin{array}{l} \longleftarrow \text{Replace } y_2 \text{ with } -2 \text{ and } y_1 \text{ with 5.} \\ \longleftarrow \text{Replace } x_2 \text{ with 4 and } x_1 \text{ with } -3. \end{array}$$

$$= \frac{-2-5}{4+3} \longleftarrow \text{Remove parentheses.}$$

$$= \frac{-7}{7}, \text{ or } -1 \longleftarrow \text{Simplify.}$$

Lines with a positive slope slant upward to the right as in Example 1. Lines with a negative slope slant upward to the left as in Example 2.

Example 3

Find the slope of the line containing each pair of points.

a. (−3, 4) and (4, 4)　　**b.** (2, −4) and (2, 3)

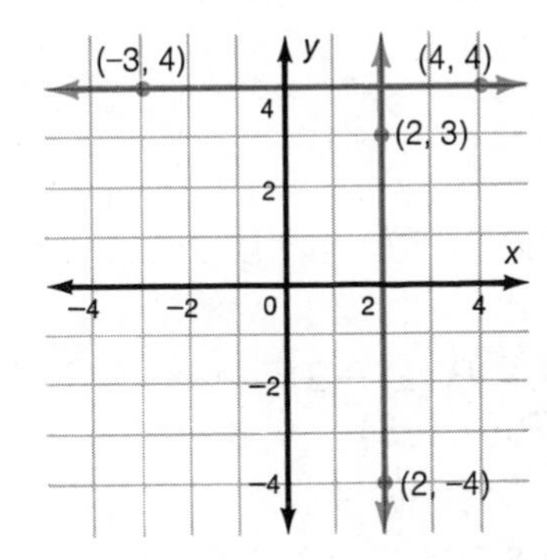

a. Let $(x_1, y_1) = (-3, 4)$ and $(x_2, y_2) = (4, 4)$.

$$m = \frac{4-4}{4-(-3)}$$

$$= \frac{0}{4+3} = 0$$ ← Zero divided by any nonzero number is zero.

b. Let $(x_1, y_1) = (2, -4)$ and $(x_2, y_2) = (2, 3)$.

$$m = \frac{3-(-4)}{2-2}$$

$$= \frac{7}{0}$$ ← The slope is <u>undefined</u>, since division by zero is undefined.

The slope of a horizontal line is 0. The slope of a vertical line is undefined. This is why the slope formula states that $x_2 \neq x_1$.

Try These

Find the slope of a line passing through the given points.

1. $A(3, 1)$; $B(4, 5)$
2. $C(5, -6)$; $D(-2, -4)$
3. $E(2, 5)$; $F(7, 9)$
4. $X(5, 2)$; $Y(-1, 2)$

Complete each statement.

5. The slope of line parallel to the x axis is _?_.
6. The slope of a _?_ (horizontal, vertical) line is undefined.

Exercises

*In Exercises **1–4,** state whether the slope is positive, negative, zero, or undefined.*

a

1. 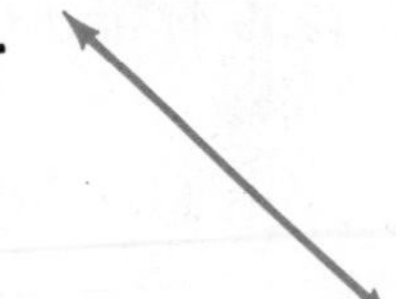

2. 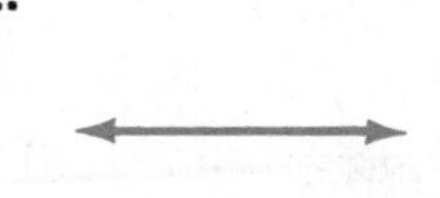

3. **4.** 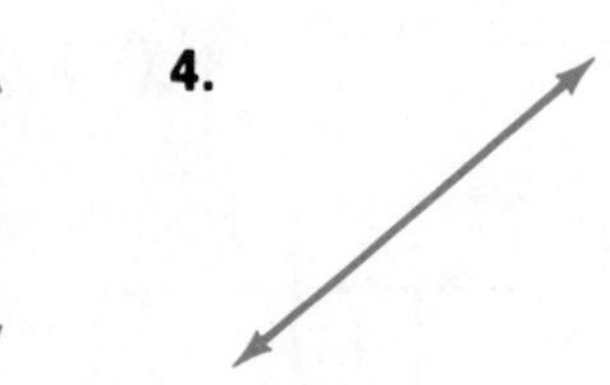

*In Exercises **5–10,** find the slope, m, of a line containing the two given points. If the line is vertical, write* Undefined.

5. $P_1(6, 3)$; $P_2(4, 1)$

6. $P_1(-4, -6)$; $P_2(2, -3)$

7. $P_1(-2, 6)$; $P_2(-1, 9)$

8. $P_1(4, 6)$; $P_2(4, -5)$

9. $P_1(\frac{3}{4}, -2)$; $P_2(\frac{1}{4}, 4)$

10. $P_1(a, b)$; $P_2(c, d)$

b

11. A line through the points $A(4, 3)$ and $B(x, 8)$ has a slope of -4. Find x.

12. A line passing through the points $A(-2, -7)$ and $B(2, y)$ has a slope of $\frac{3}{2}$. Find y.

13. A line passes through the points $P_1(2a, 3b)$ and $P_2(a, -b)$. Find the slope of the line.

Triangle ABC has vertices A(2, 4), B(6, −4), and C(−4, −2).

14. Find the midpoint of each side of the triangle.

15. Find the slope of each side of the smaller triangle formed by joining the midpoints.

c

16. Points $A(-3, -4)$, $B(1, -2)$ and $C(x, 3)$ are collinear. Find x.

Remember

Solve each equation for y in terms of x.

1. $2x + y = 4$

2. $y - 2x = -4$

3. $2y = 6x - 2$

4. $2y + 4x + 6 = 0$

5. $3x = y + 6$

6. $9 - 3y = 4x$

The answers are on page 469. If you need help, see pages 558 and 568 in the Review: Topics From Algebra One.

0-4 Slope and Linear Equations

You can draw the graph of a line if you know its slope and the coordinates of a point on the line.

Example 1

Draw the graph of the line that contains $P(3, -2)$ and has a slope of $\frac{2}{3}$.

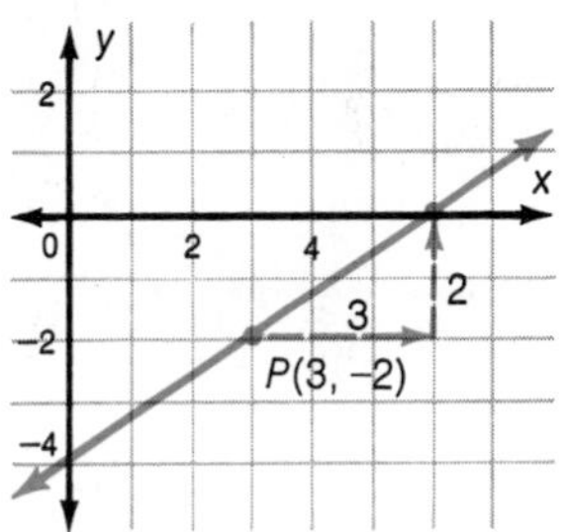

Graph the point $(3, -2)$.

Since the slope is $\frac{2}{3}$, another point is 2 units up from (vertical change), and 3 units to the right of (horizontal change), $(3, -2)$.

Plot this point, and draw the line.

The algebraic model of a line is a **linear equation.** If you know the slope of a line and a point on the line, the equation can be written in the **point-slope form,**

$$\mathbf{y - y_1 = m(x - x_1)},$$

where m is the slope and (x_1, y_1) is a point on the line.

Example 2

Write an equation of the line in Example 1.

$$y - y_1 = m(x - x_1)$$

$$y - (-2) = \frac{2}{3}(x - 3) \longleftarrow \text{Replace } y_1 \text{ with } -2 \text{ and } x_1 \text{ with } 3.$$

$$y + 2 = \frac{2}{3}(x - 3) \longleftarrow \text{Point-slope form}$$

The equation in Example 2 can be simplified.

$$y + 2 = \frac{2}{3}(x - 3)$$

$$y + 2 = \frac{2}{3}x - 2 \longleftarrow \text{Add } -2 \text{ to both sides.}$$

$$y = \frac{2}{3}x - 4$$

The equation $y = \frac{2}{3}x - 4$ is in the **slope-intercept form,**

$$\mathbf{y = mx + b,}$$

where m is the slope and $(0, b)$ is the ***y* intercept,** the point at which the line crosses the y axis. Any linear equation can be written in slope-intercept form.

Example 3

Write these equations in slope-intercept form. Then give the slope and the y intercept.

a. $3y - 2x = 7$ **b.** $x = \frac{2}{3}y - 1$

a. $3y - 2x = 7$

$3y = 2x + 7$

$y = \frac{1}{3}(2x + 7)$

$y = \frac{2}{3}x + \frac{7}{3}$ ⟵ $y = mx + b$

m: $\frac{2}{3}$

y intercept: $(0, \frac{7}{3})$

b. $x = \frac{2}{3}y - 1$

$x + 1 = \frac{2}{3}y$, or $\frac{2}{3}y = x + 1$

$y = \frac{3}{2}(x + 1)$

$y = \frac{3}{2}x + \frac{3}{2}$ ⟵ $y = mx + b$

m: $\frac{3}{2}$

y intercept: $(0, \frac{3}{2})$

Try These

1. Draw the graph of the line that contains the point $(-3, 2)$ and has a slope of $\frac{1}{2}$.

Use the given point P and slope m to write the equation of the line.

2. $P(0, 5)$; $m = -3$ **3.** $P(-3, 2)$; $m = -\frac{3}{5}$ **4.** $P(1, -1)$; $m = 2$

Rewrite the equation in slope-intercept form. Then give the slope and y intercept of each line.

5. $x + 2y = 5$ **6.** $2x - 6y = 2$ **7.** $3x - y - 5 = 0$

Exercises

Use the given point P and slope m to write the equation of the line.

a

1. $P(5, 2)$; $m = 3$

2. $P(3, -5)$; $m = -2$

3. $P(0, 3)$; $m = \frac{2}{3}$

4. $P(3, -4)$; $m = 0$

5. $P(-1, -5)$; $m = \frac{3}{4}$

6. $P(-2, 4)$; $m = -\frac{4}{3}$

Rewrite each equation in slope-intercept form. Give the slope and y intercept of each line.

7. $2x + y = 4$

8. $x = \frac{3}{2}y + 2$

9. $3x + 4y = 12$

10. $3x = y + 8$

11. $2x + 3y = -6$

12. $x - 2y = 0$

Write the equation of a line passing through the given points.

13. $A(3, 1)$; $B(5, 6)$

14. $R(-5, -2)$; $S(7, 5)$

15. $E(-5, -3)$; $F(0, 0)$

16. $X(0, 0)$; $Y(-5, 1)$

Graph each equation. Use only the slope and y intercept.

17. $y = \frac{3}{2}x + 1$

18. $y - 2x = -7$

19. $5y + 2x = 10$

The vertices of $\triangle ABC$ are $A(3, -1)$, $B(-5, 5)$, and $C(2, 6)$.

20. Find the equations of $\overleftrightarrow{AB}$, $\overleftrightarrow{BC}$, $\overleftrightarrow{AC}$.

21. Find the equation of the median from vertex C to side AB.

c

22. Show that the equation of a line with x intercept $(a, 0)$ and y intercept $(0, b)$ is $\frac{x}{a} + \frac{y}{b} = 1$, $a \neq 0$, $b \neq 0$.

Remember

Complete each equation.

1. $\frac{2}{3} \cdot \underline{\quad ? \quad} = 1$

2. $\frac{2}{3} \cdot \underline{\quad ? \quad} = -1$

3. $-\frac{3}{5} \cdot \frac{5}{3} = \underline{\quad ? \quad}$

The answers are on page 469. If you need help, see Example 1 on page 558 in the Review: Topics From Algebra One.

10-5 Parallel and Perpendicular Lines

Example 1

Line AB is parallel to line CD. Find the slope of each line. Compare the slopes.

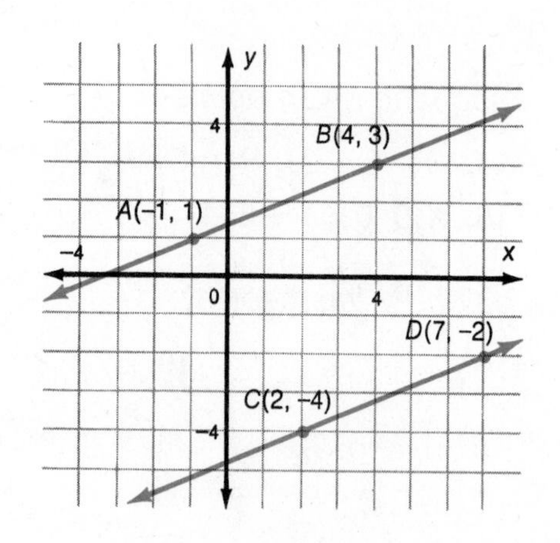

For $\overleftrightarrow{AB}$, let $(-1, 1) = (x_1, y_1)$ and $(4, 3) = (x_2, y_2)$.

$$m = \frac{3-1}{4-(-1)} \quad \longleftarrow \quad m = \frac{y_2 - y_1}{x_2 - x_1}$$

$$= \frac{3-1}{4+1} = \frac{2}{5} \quad \longleftarrow \quad \text{Slope of } \overleftrightarrow{AB}$$

For $\overleftrightarrow{CD}$, let $(2, -4) = (x_1, y_1)$ and $(7, -2) = (x_2, y_2)$.

$$m = \frac{-2-(-4)}{7-2}$$

$$= \frac{-2+4}{5} = \frac{2}{5} \quad \longleftarrow \quad \text{Slope of } \overleftrightarrow{CD}$$

$\therefore$ Slope of $\overleftrightarrow{AB}$ = Slope of $\overleftrightarrow{CD}$

This suggests that nonvertical parallel lines have the same slope. It can also be shown that lines having the same slope are parallel. This leads to the following biconditional.

Theorem 10-2: Two nonvertical lines are parallel if and only if they have the same slope.

Recall that the slope of vertical lines is not defined. However, any two vertical lines are parallel to each other.

Example 2

Line EF is perpendicular to line GF at F. Find the slope of each line. Find the product of the slopes.

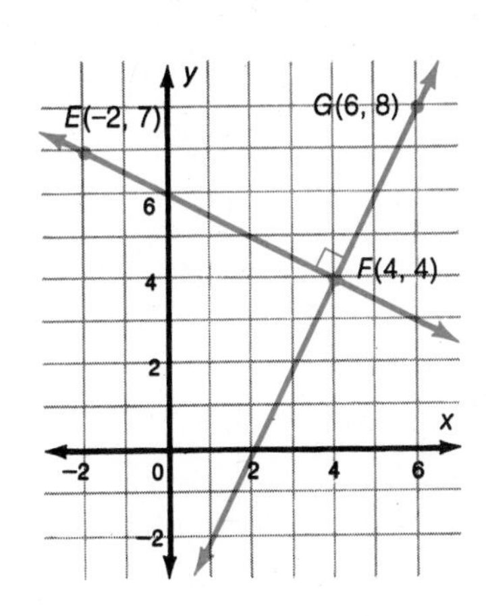

For $\overleftrightarrow{EF}$, let $(-2, 7) = (x_1, y_1)$ and $(4, 4) = (y_2, y_1)$.

$$m = \frac{4-7}{4-(-2)} \longleftarrow m = \frac{y_2 - y_1}{x_2 - x_1}$$

$$= \frac{4-7}{4+2} = \frac{-3}{6} = -\frac{1}{2}$$

For $\overleftrightarrow{GF}$, let $(6, 8) = (x_1, y_1)$ and $(4, 4) = (y_2, y_1)$.

$$m = \frac{4-8}{4-6} = \frac{-4}{-2} = 2$$

$$-\frac{1}{2} \cdot \frac{2}{1} = -1 \longleftarrow \text{Product of slopes}$$

The slopes 2 and $-\frac{1}{2}$ are negative reciprocals of each other, since their product is -1. This suggests the following biconditional.

Theorem 10-3: Two nonvertical lines are perpendicular if and only if their slopes are negative reciprocals.

By writing a linear equation in the slope-intercept form, $y = mx + b$, you can tell if the lines they represent are parallel, perpendicular, or neither.

Example 3

Classify the graphs of the equations listed below as parallel, perpendicular, or neither parallel nor perpendicular, to the graph of $3y - 2x = 7$.

a. $4x - 6y = 9$ **b.** $3x - 2y = 11$ **c.** $4y + 6x = 12$

Slope of $3y - 2x = 7$: $3y = 2x + 7$

$$y = \tfrac{2}{3}x + \tfrac{7}{3} \quad \therefore m = \tfrac{2}{3}$$

a. $4x - 6y = 9$
$-6y = -4x + 9$
$y = \frac{4}{6}x - \frac{9}{6}$, or
$y = \frac{2}{3}x - \frac{3}{2}$
$m = \frac{2}{3}$
$\therefore$ Parallel

b. $3x - 2y = 11$
$-2y = -3x + 11$
$y = \frac{3}{2}x - \frac{11}{2}$
$m = \frac{3}{2}$
$\therefore$ Neither

c. $4y + 6x = 12$
$4y = -6x + 12$
$y = -\frac{6}{4}x + 3$, or
$y = -\frac{3}{2}x + 3$
$m = -\frac{3}{2}$
$\therefore$ Perpendicular

Try These

Complete each statement.

1. Line k has a slope of $-\frac{2}{3}$. The slope of a line parallel to k is __?__. The slope of a line perpendicular to k is __?__.

2. Line q contains the points (7, −3) and (4, 2). The slope of a line parallel to q is __?__. The slope of a line perpendicular to q is __?__.

3. Find the slope of a line parallel to the graph of $y = 3x + 4$.

4. Find the slope of a line perpendicular to the graph of $3x + 6y = 7$.

Classify the graphs of the two given equations as parallel, perpendicular, or neither.

5. $2x - 3y = 6$; $10x - 15y = 6$

6. $2x + 3y = 0$; $x = \frac{2}{3}y + 3$

Exercises

*In Exercises **1–4,** find the slope of $\overleftrightarrow{AB}$ and $\overleftrightarrow{CD}$. State whether the two lines are parallel, perpendicular, or neither.*

a

1. $A(-2, 7)$, $B(3, 6)$; $C(4, 2)$, $D(9, 1)$

2. $A(0, 0)$, $B(-5, 3)$; $C(5, 2)$, $D(0, 5)$

3. $A(2, 5)$, $B(8, 7)$; $C(-3, 1)$, $D(-2, -2)$

4. $A(5, 3)$, $B(-5, -2)$; $C(6, -2)$, $D(4, 5)$

Classify the graphs of each pair of equations as parallel, perpendicular, or neither.

5. $2x - 3y = 6$; $10x - 15y = 16$

6. $3x - 10y = 7$; $5x + 4y = 0$

7. $x = \frac{2}{3}y$; $3y + 2x = 0$

8. $4y + x = 17$; $2x + 4y = 1$

9. $y = 2x + 8$; $y - 2x = 5$

10. $3x + y = 4$; $x - 3y = 4$

11. Which of the following equations have graphs that are parallel to the graph of $5y - 3x = 17$?

a. $y = -\frac{3}{5}x + 4$ **b.** $10y = 6x + 7$ **c.** $y = \frac{5}{3}x - 6$

12. Which of the following equations have graphs that are perpendicular to the graph of $x + y = 7$?

a. $y = x - 4$ **b.** $x + y = 6$ **c.** $2x + 2y = -12$

13. The line that contains $E(a, 3)$ and $F(2, 0)$ is parallel to the line that contains $D(2, 8)$ and $C(-3, -4)$. Find a.

14. The line through $R(5, -3)$ and $S(0, k)$ is perpendicular to the line through $T(-3, 2)$ and $V(-2, -5)$. Find k.

15. Show that a triangle with vertices $A(2, 5)$, $B(8, 1)$ and $C(-2, -1)$ is a right triangle. (HINT: Show that two of its sides are perpendicular.)

16. Write Theorem 10-2 as a conditional and its converse.

b

17. Write an equation of the line that contains the point $(0, -3)$ and is parallel to the graph of $4x - y = -7$.

18. Write an equation of the line that contains the point $(-4, -7)$ and is perpendicular to the graph of $2x - 3y = 6$.

The vertices of triangle RST are $R(-4, -2)$, $S(5, -5)$ and $T(3, 5)$.

19. Write an equation of the line parallel to $\overleftrightarrow{RS}$ and passing through point T.

20. Write an equation of the line perpendicular to $\overleftrightarrow{ST}$ and passing through point R.

21. Find the slope of each of the three altitudes of $\triangle RST$.

C

22. The vertices of quadrilateral $ABCD$ are $A(0, 0)$, $B(a, 0)$, $C(b, c)$ and $D(d, e)$. Prove the quadrilateral formed by joining the midpoints of consecutive sides is a parallelogram.

10-6 The Distance Formula

Example 1

Find the distance between points A and B.

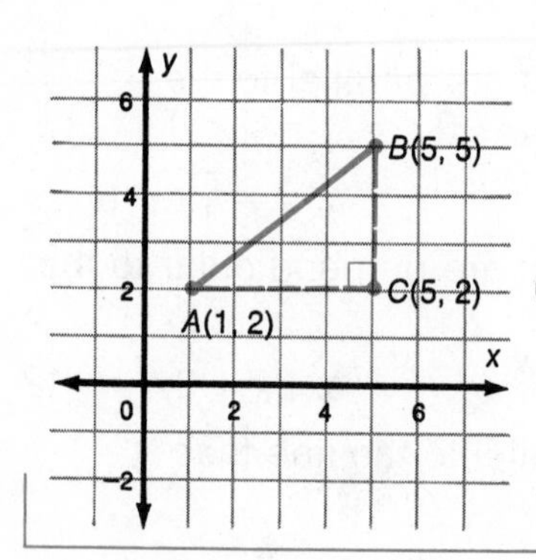

Form a right triangle by drawing the horizontal segment, $\overline{AC}$, and the vertical segment, $\overline{BC}$. Thus, $\overline{AB}$ is the hypotenuse of a right triangle. Therefore,

$$\begin{aligned}(AB)^2 &= (AC)^2 + (BC)^2 \quad \longleftarrow \text{ Pythagorean Theorem}\\ &= |5-1|^2 + |5-2|^2\\ &= 4^2 + 3^2\\ &= 25\\ AB &= 5\end{aligned}$$

This procedure can be generalized.

Example 2

Find the distance between P_1 and P_2.

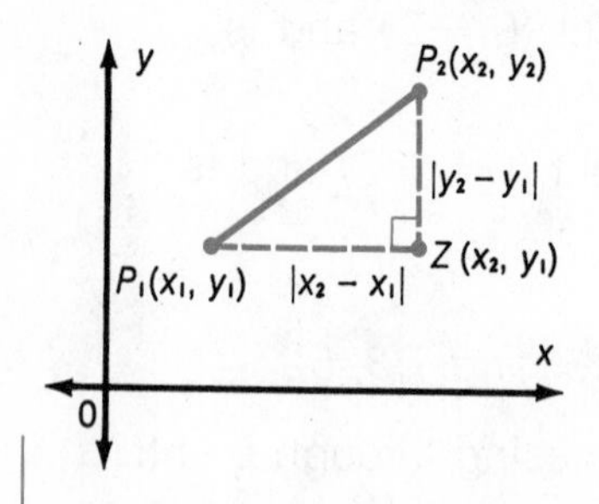

Form a right triangle by drawing the horizontal segment, $\overline{P_1Z}$, and the vertical segment, $\overline{P_2Z}$. Therefore,

$$(P_1P_2)^2 = (P_1Z)^2 + (P_2Z)^2$$

$$P_1P_2{}^2 = |x_2 - x_1|^2 + |y_2 - y_1|^2 \quad \longleftarrow \quad P_1Z = |x_2 - x_1|;\ P_2Z = |y_2 - y_1|$$

$$P_1P_2 = \sqrt{|x_2 - x_1|^2 + |y_2 - y_1|^2}$$

Theorem 10-4: The Distance Formula

The distance, d, between two points $P_1(x_1, y_1)$ and $P_2(x_2, y_2)$ is

$$d = \sqrt{(x_2 - x_1)^2 + (y_2 - y_1)^2}.$$

In Example 2, P_1P_2 is in the first quadrant. However, the formula holds for points in any quadrant. Since

$$|x_2 - x_1|^2 = (x_2 - x_1)^2 \text{ and } |y_2 - y_1|^2 = (y_2 - y_1)^2,$$

it is not necessary to use absolute value.

Example 3

Show that a triangle with vertices $A(3, -1)$, $B(8, 4)$ and $C(4, 6)$ is isosceles. (HINT: Show that the lengths of two sides are equal.)

$$AB = \sqrt{(8-3)^2 + (4-(-1))^2} = \sqrt{5^2 + 5^2} = \sqrt{50}, \text{ or } 5\sqrt{2}$$

$$BC = \sqrt{(4-8)^2 + (6-4)^2} = \sqrt{(-4)^2 + 2^2} = \sqrt{20}, \text{ or } 2\sqrt{5}$$

$$CA = \sqrt{(3-4)^2 + (-1-6)^2} = \sqrt{(-1)^2 + (-7)^2} = \sqrt{50}, \text{ or } 5\sqrt{2}$$

Since $AB = CA$, $\triangle ABC$ is isosceles.

Try These

Find the distance between points A and B.

1. $A(-2, 5)$; $B(-2, 0)$
2. $A(7, -1)$; $B(-3, -1)$
3. $A(7, -1)$; $B(-3, -11)$
4. $A(a, b)$; $B(3, 3)$

Exercises

Find the distance between each pair of points.

a

1. $A(4, 3)$; $B(1, 2)$
2. $A(-4, 1)$; $B(-5, 4)$
3. $R(7, -5)$; $S(2, -6)$
4. $R(-1, -2)$; $S(3, 6)$
5. $C(4, -3)$; $D(-4, 3)$
6. $E(-3, 3)$; $F(0, -4)$
7. $A(7, 1)$; $B(6, 2)$
8. $C(2, 2)$; $D(5, 2)$
9. $P(-2, 4)$; $Q(-2, -5)$
10. $M(-1, -3)$; $N(4, -3)$
11. $R(a, b)$; $S(c, d)$
12. $T(a, b)$; $U(c, b)$

13. Find the perimeter of triangle ABC with vertices $A(-1, -2)$, $B(2, -2)$ and $C(-1, -6)$.

14. Use the distance formula to show that $A(-4, 1)$, $B(5, 4)$ and $C(2, -2)$ are vertices of an isosceles triangle.

15. Use the distance formula and the Pythagorean theorem to show that $D(2, -2)$, $E(5, 4)$ and $F(-4, 1)$ are the vertices of a right triangle.

16. Describe another method that could be used in Exercise **15** to show that $\triangle DEF$ is a right triangle.

17. Determine whether the triangle with vertices $R(-3, 2)$, $S(6, 5)$ and $T(3, -1)$ is isosceles, equilateral or scalene.

18. Show that the triangle with vertices $A(1, -1)$, $B(7, 1)$ and $C(5, -3)$ is an isosceles right triangle.

19. Find the length of the radius of a circle that has its center at $O(-3, 4)$ and passes through the point $P(2, -5)$.

20. Find the lengths of the diagonals of a rectangle with vertices $R(-6, -8)$, $S(5, -8)$, $T(5, -5)$ and $Q(-6, -5)$.

b

21. Use the distance formula to show that $A(0, 2)$, $B(7, 1)$, $C(12, 4)$ and $D(5, 5)$ are the vertices of a parallelogram.

22. Use the distance formula to show that the points $A(-5, 7)$, $B(-3, 4)$ and $C(-1, 1)$ are collinear. (HINT: Show that the longest distance is the sum of the two shorter distances.)

The vertices of isosceles trapezoid ABCD are A(0, 0), B(a, 0), C(a − c, b), and D(c, b).

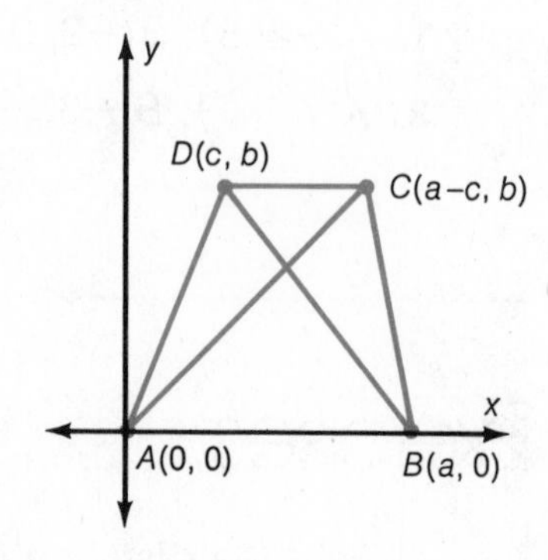

23. Show that $\overline{AB}$ is parallel to $\overline{CD}$ and that $\overline{AD}$ is <u>not</u> parallel to $\overline{BC}$.

24. Show that diagonals AC and BD are congruent.

25. Show that sides AD and BC are equal in length.

The vertices of $\triangle ABC$ are A(0, 0), B(a, 0) and C(b, c).

c

26. Prove that the line segment joining the midpoints of any two sides of the triangle is parallel to the third side.

27. Prove that the line segment joining the midpoints of any two sides of the triangle is one half as long as the third side.

)-7 Coordinate Proofs

You can prove theorems using the methods of coordinate geometry.

Example 1

Prove that the midpoint of the hypotenuse of a right triangle is equidistant from the vertices.

Draw the right triangle so that its right angle, $\angle C$, is at the origin, and its legs lie on the x and y axes. Let the coordinates of A be $(2a, 0)$ and of B be $(0, 2b)$, where a and b are positive numbers. The coefficient 2 is used to avoid fractions.

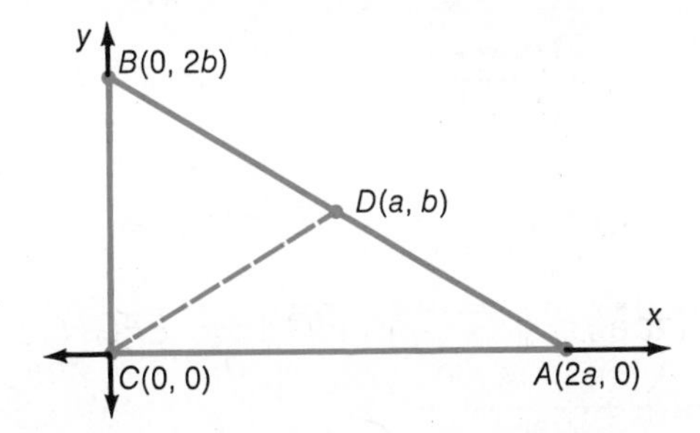

Find the coordinates of D, the midpoint of $\overline{AB}$.

x coordinate: $\dfrac{2a+0}{2} = a$ y coordinate: $\dfrac{0+2b}{2} = b$

Thus, D has coordinates (a, b).

Show that $DB = DA = DC$.

$DB = \sqrt{(a-0)^2 + (b-2b)^2} = \sqrt{a^2+b^2}$

$DA = \sqrt{(2a-a)^2 + (0-b)^2} = \sqrt{a^2+b^2}$

$DC = \sqrt{(a-0)^2 + (b-0)^2} = \sqrt{a^2+b^2}$

$\therefore D(a, b)$ is equidistant from the vertices.

Example 2

Prove that the segments joining the midpoints of the sides of any quadrilateral, taken in order, form a parallelogram.

Given quadrilateral $ABCD$, place the vertex A at the origin and $\overline{AB}$ on the x axis. Designate B, C, and D as $(2a, 0)$, $(2d, 2e)$ and $(2b, 2c)$, respectively. Thus, the midpoints are

$E(a, 0)$ $\quad$ $F(a + d, e)$

$H(b, c)$ $\quad$ $G(b + d, c + e)$

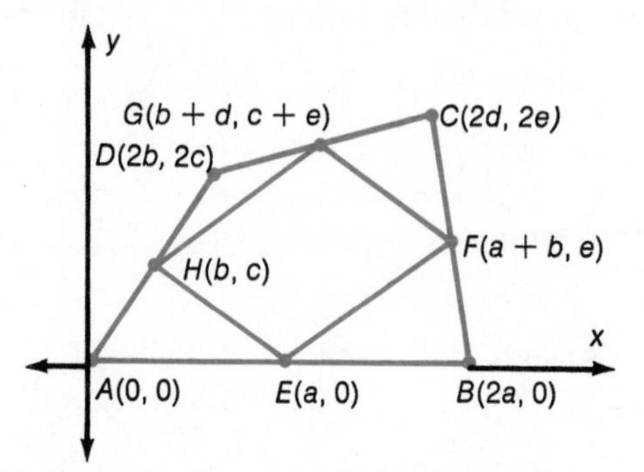

$EFGH$ is a parallelogram if the opposite sides are parallel; that is, have the same slope.

$$m \text{ of } \overline{HE} = \frac{c - 0}{b - a} = \frac{c}{b - a} \qquad m \text{ of } \overline{GF} = \frac{(c + e) - e}{(b + d) - (a + d)} = \frac{c}{b - a}$$

$$m \text{ of } \overline{HG} = \frac{c - (c + e)}{b - (b + d)} \qquad m \text{ of } \overline{EF} = \frac{0 - e}{a - (a + d)}$$

$$= \frac{-e}{-d} = \frac{e}{d} \qquad = \frac{-e}{-d} = \frac{e}{d}$$

Since $\overline{HE} \parallel \overline{GF}$ and $\overline{HG} \parallel \overline{EF}$, $EFGH$ is a parallelogram.

A key step in doing a coordinate proof is placing the geometric figure in the coordinate plane. Whenever possible, use the origin as a vertex, and let at least one side coincide with a coordinate axis.

Try These

Name the coordinates of the vertices that you would use in placing each of the following figures in the coordinate plane.

1. Square
2. Rectangle
3. Parallelogram
4. Right triangle
5. Isosceles triangle
6. Equilateral triangle

Exercises

Prove each of the following using the methods of coordinate geometry.

a

1. Prove that the diagonals of any rectangle are congruent.

2. Prove that the diagonals of a square are perpendicular to each other.

3. Prove that in any triangle the segment joining the midpoint of two sides is parallel to the third side and its length is half the length of the third side. (HINT: Let the vertices be (0, 0), ($2a$, 0), and ($2b$, $2c$).)

4. Prove that the diagonals of a parallelogram bisect each other.

5. Prove that the opposite sides of a parallelogram are congruent.

6. Prove that the diagonals of a rhombus are perpendicular to each other. (HINT: Let the vertices be (0, 0), (b, c), (a, 0), ($b + a$, c).)

7. If two sides of a quadrilateral are parallel and congruent, then the figure is a parallelogram.

8. If the diagonals of a parallelogram are perpendicular to each other, then the parallelogram is a rhombus.

9. If a trapezoid is isosceles, then the diagonals are congruent.

b

10. Prove that the altitudes of a triangle are concurrent. (Three or more lines are **concurrent** if they have a point in common.)

11. Prove that the medians of a triangle are concurrent in a point that is two thirds of the distance from each vertex to the midpoint of the opposite side.

c

12. Show that an equation of the perpendicular bisector of the segment with endpoints (a, b) and (c, d) is

$$2(c - a)x + 2(d - b)y + a^2 + b^2 - c^2 - d^2 = 0.$$

13. Given that a line k has the equation $ax + by + c = 0$ and that a given point has coordinates (x_1, y_1). Find an equation of a line containing the given point and perpendicular to k. Write an expression for the distance d of the given point from k.

A Coordinate System in Three-Space

You can set up a coordinate system in three-space by constructing a line perpendicular to the x axis and y axis at their point of intersection.

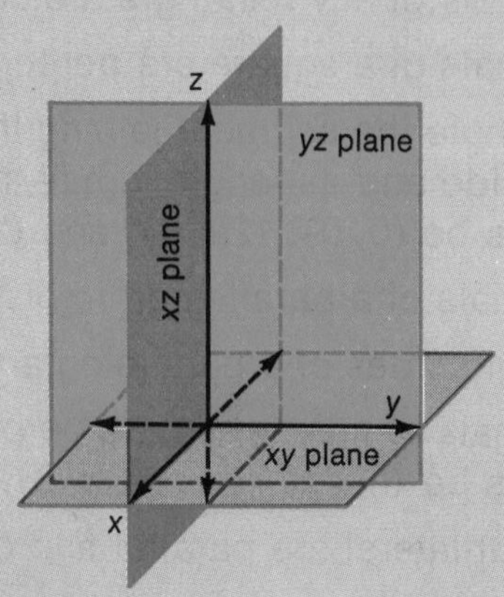

You use an ordered triple, (x, y, z) to locate a point in three-space. To locate point A in the figure, follow these steps.

$$A(-4, -3, 2)$$

1. Move 4 units along the negative x axis.
2. Move 3 units in the direction of the negative y axis.
3. Move 2 units in the direction of the positive z axis.

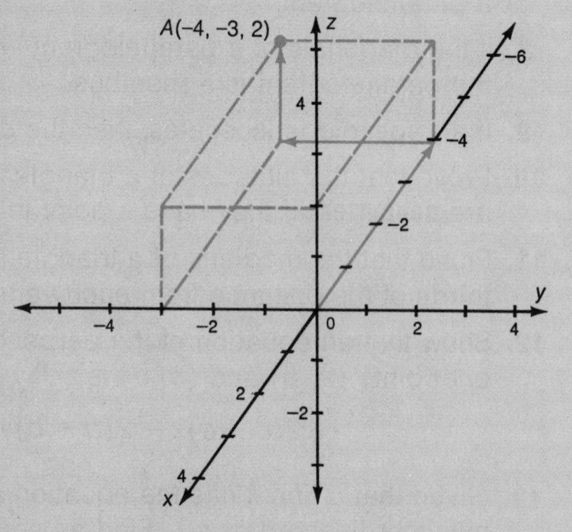

Can You Solve These?

Graph the following points in three-space.

1. $C(2, 3, 5)$
2. $D(-1, 0, 2)$
3. $E(5, -3, -4)$
4. In the xz plane, which coordinate is always zero?
5. In the yz plane, which coordinate is always zero?

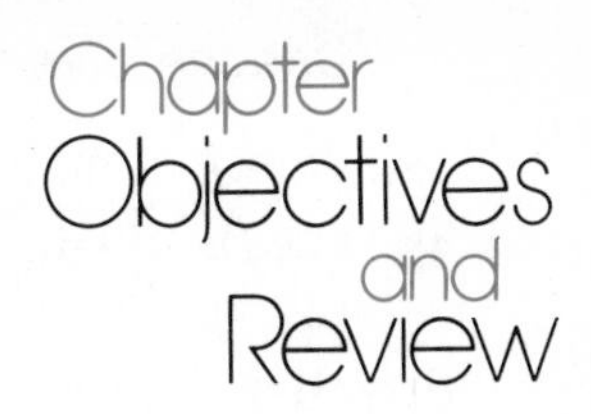

Objective: To recall, and give examples of, the important mathematical terms of this chapter.

1. Be sure that you know the meaning of these mathematical terms used in Chapter 10.

coordinates of a point (p. 444)
distance formula (p. 460)
midpoint formula (p. 448)
linear equation (p. 453)
ordered pair (p. 444)
point-slope form (p. 453)
quadrant (p. 444)
slope (p. 450)
slope-intercept form (p. 454)
y intercept (p. 454)

Objectives: To name and graph the coordinates of a point in the coordinate plane. (Section 10-1)

Graph on the same set of axes.

2. $R(-5, 3)$ 3. $S(-2, 4)$ 4. $T(-3, -4)$ 5. $Q(2\frac{1}{2}, 4)$

Objective: To find the coordinates of the midpoint of a segment. (Section 10-2)

The coordinates of the endpoints of a segment are given. Find the midpoint of each segment.

6. $(4, 7)$; $(-2, 5)$ 7. $(-1, -2)$; $(0, -3)$ 8. $(-3, 2)$; $(-3, 5)$
9. One endpoint of $\overline{AB}$ is $A(-1, 5)$ and the midpoint of $\overline{AB}$ is $(1, 3)$. Find the coordinates of point B.

Objective: To find the slope of a line given two points on the line. (Section 10-3)

Find the slope of a line passing through the given points.

10. $A(3, 2)$; $B(-7, 2)$ 11. $C(5, -7)$; $D(-3, 2)$

Objective: To write the equation of a line. (Section 10-4)

Use the given information to write the equation of line k.

12. Line k contains the point $P(2, -3)$ and has a slope of $\frac{3}{2}$.

13. Line k contains the points $A(4, 2)$ and $B(6, 7)$.

Objective: To graph a line using its slope and y intercept. (Section 10-4)

Rewrite each equation in slope-intercept form. Then graph the equation.

14. $2x + y = 7$

15. $3x + 2y = 6$

16. $3x - y = 9$

Find an equation of the line passing through the given points.

17. $A(6, 1)$; $B(-4, 3)$

18. $E(-4, 1)$; $F(8, 0)$

Objective: To use slope to identify parallel and perpendicular lines. (Section 10-5)

Classify the graphs of each pair of equations as parallel, perpendicular, or neither.

19. $2y = 4x + 8$; $y - 2x = 5$

20. $x + 2y = 12$; $2x + 2y = 3$

Objective: To find the distance between two points in the coordinate plane. (Section 10-6)

Find the distance between each pair of points.

21. $A(1, 2)$; $B(4, 6)$

22. $C(-1, -3)$; $D(7, 3)$

23. Use the distance formula to show that $A(5, 5)$, $B(-1, 7)$ and $C(-2, -6)$ are the vertices of an isosceles triangle.

Objective: To use coordinate geometry to prove theorems. (Section 10-7)

Use the methods of coordinate geometry to prove each statement.

24. The median of a trapezoid is parallel to the bases of the trapezoid.

25. The median of a trapezoid is equal in length to half the sum of the bases of the trapezoid.

Chapter Test

*In Exercises **1–4,** complete each statement.*

1. The point $A(2, -3)$ is located in the __?__ quadrant.
2. The graph of $y = 4$ is __?__ (perpendicular, parallel) to the x axis.
3. The slope of a line defined by $y = -4x + 7$ is __?__, and the coordinates of the y intercept are (__?__, __?__).
4. The slope of a line that contains the points $A(2, -3)$ and $B(-6, 5)$ is __?__.
5. The endpoints of $\overline{AB}$ are $A(-5, 2)$ and $B(3, 6)$. Find the midpoint of $\overline{AB}$.
6. Find the distance between the points $C(-3, 2)$ and $D(5, -2)$.
7. Find the slope of a line that is parallel to the graph of $2x - y + 5 = 0$.
8. Find the slope of a line that is perpendicular to the graph of $3x + 2y = 9$.
9. Write the equation of the line that passes through the points $(2, -3)$ and has a slope of $\frac{1}{2}$.
10. Write the equation of a line that passes through the points $A(4, 10)$ and $B(2, 6)$.

Classify the graphs of each pair of equations as parallel, perpendicular, or neither.

11. $x = \frac{3}{2}y$; $3y + 2x = 7$
12. $3y - 2x = 10$; $4x - 6y = 3$
13. Use the distance formula to show that $A(-4, 1)$, $B(5, 4)$ and $C(2, -2)$ are the vertices of an isosceles triangle.
14. Use the formula for slope to show that $D(2, -2)$, $E(11, 3)$ and $F(-3, 7)$ are the vertices of a right triangle.
15. Use the methods of coordinate geometry to prove that the diagonals of an isosceles trapezoid are congruent.

Answers to Remember

Page 447: **1.** 5 **2.** 3 **3.** 7 **4.** 13 **5.** 9 **6.** 6

Page 449: **1.** -3 **2.** 5 **3.** -9 **4.** -5 **5.** -10 **6.** 2

Page 452: **1.** $y = -2x + 4$ **2.** $y = 2x - 4$ **3.** $y = 3x - 1$ **4.** $y = -2x - 3$ **5.** $y = 3x - 6$ **6.** $y = -\frac{4}{3}x + 3$

Page 455: **1.** $\frac{3}{2}$ **2.** $-\frac{3}{2}$ **3.** -1

Cumulative Review

Write the letter of the response that best answers each question.

1. The area of a rectangle is 3.9 square centimeters and its length is 2.6 centimeters. Find its width.

   a. 1.3 cm b. 1.5 cm c. 1.7 cm d. 1.9 cm

2. Each side of an equilateral triangle is 6 centimeters long. Find the area.

   a. $9\sqrt{3}$ cm² b. $6\sqrt{3}$ cm² c. $18\sqrt{3}$ cm² d. 9 cm²

3. The area of a rhombus is 10 square centimeters and the length of one diagonal is 5 centimeters. Find the length of the other diagonal.

   a. 5 cm b. 10 cm c. 4 cm d. 2 cm

4. Write a formula for the area *A* of a trapezoid whose bases are *x* and *y* and whose altitude is *h*.

   a. $A = \frac{1}{2}x(h + y)$ b. $A = \frac{1}{2}h(x - y)$

   c. $A = \frac{1}{2}h(x \cdot y)$ d. $A = \frac{1}{2}h(x + y)$

5. Find the measure of each central angle of a regular octagon.

   a. 30 b. 45 c. 60 d. 90

6. The radius of a regular hexagon is 2 meters. Find the length of the apothem.

   a. 2 meters b. 1 meter c. $\sqrt{3}$ meters d. $2\sqrt{3}$ meters

7. Two similar polygons have apothems of 1 centimeter and 3 centimeters. Find the ratio of their areas.

   a. $\frac{1}{3}$ b. $\frac{1}{6}$ c. $\frac{1}{9}$ d. $\frac{1}{\sqrt{3}}$

8. The radius of a circle is 5 centimeters. Find its area.

   a. 25π cm² b. 10π cm² c. 5π cm² d. 3π cm²

9. Give the name of the region bounded by a chord and its arc.

   a. Sector b. Segment c. Secant d. Apothem

10. A right prism whose altitude is 6 centimeters has a base that is an equilateral triangle with sides of 4 centimeters each. Find the lateral surface area of the prism.

    a. 84 cm² b. $24\sqrt{3}$ cm² c. 72 cm² d. 48 cm²

11. Find the measure of an edge of a cube if a diagonal is 3 centimeters long.

a. $\sqrt{3}$ cm **b.** 1 cm **c.** $\sqrt{6}$ cm **d.** 2 cm

12. Find the total area of a right circular cylinder with base of radius 3 and height 7.

a. 21π **b.** 42π **c.** 60π **d.** 28π

13. Find the volume of the cylinder in Exercise 12.

a. 42π **b.** 49π **c.** $\frac{63}{4}\pi$ **d.** 63π

14. Two pyramids have congruent bases, and the altitude of one pyramid is twice the altitude to the other. Find the ratio of their volumes.

a. $\frac{2}{1}$ **b.** $\frac{3}{2}$ **c.** $\frac{4}{1}$ **d.** $\frac{8}{1}$

15. Find the volume of a sphere whose radius is 3 centimeters long.

a. 12π cm^3 **b.** 8π cm^3 **c.** 36π cm^3 **d.** 72π cm^3

16. Name the quadrant in which the point $(-1, 3)$ is located.

a. I **b.** II **c.** III **d.** IV

17. Find the midpoint of the line segment whose endpoints are $(4, 3)$ and $(-6, 0)$.

a. $(-2, 3)$ **b.** $(-1, 0)$ **c.** $(-1, 1.5)$ **d.** $(1, 3)$

18. Lines p and q are parallel. The slope of line p is $-\frac{2}{3}$. Find the slope of line q.

a. $\frac{2}{3}$ **b.** $-\frac{2}{3}$ **c.** $\frac{3}{2}$ **d.** $-\frac{3}{2}$

19. Line m has a slope of $\frac{1}{2}$. Tell which equation represents a line perpendicular to line m.

a. $y = -\frac{1}{2}x$ **b.** $y = \frac{1}{2}x$ **c.** $y = -2x$ **d.** $y = 2x$

20. Find the distance between $(3, 4)$ and $(4, 5)$

a. 1 **b.** $\sqrt{2}$ **c.** 2 **d.** $\sqrt{3}$

21. Three vertices of a parallelogram are $(5, 2)$, $(-1, 2)$, and $(-2, -3)$. Find the fourth vertex.

a. $(4, -3)$ **b.** $(-4, 3)$ **c.** $(-4, -3)$ **d.** $(4, 3)$

*For Exercises **22–34,** classify each statement as one of the following.*

a. Always true **b.** Sometimes true **c.** Never true

22. Two isosceles triangles that have the same area are congruent.

23. Two regular pentagons that have the same area are congruent.

24. Circle O is inscribed in triangle ABC. The area of circle O is greater than the area of triangle ABC.

25. The radius of a regular polygon is greater than its apothem.

26. For all circles, the ratio of the circumference to the diameter is the same.

27. A rectangular solid is a prism.

28. The two bases of a cylinder are congruent.

29. Two rectangular solids that have the same total surface area have the same volume.

30. If a cube is circumscribed about a sphere, then the cube and the sphere intersect in exactly six points.

31. Let $ABCD$ be a rhombus with A, B, and C in Quadrants I, II, and III respectively. Then D is in Quadrant IV.

32. If the endpoints of the base of an isosceles triangle are $(3, 1)$ and $(-3, 1)$, then the vertex is on the y axis.

33. If the midpoints of a quadrilateral are joined in succession, then a parallelogram is formed.

Write the letter of the response that best answers each question.

34. For any positive number k, the distance from $(k, 0)$ to $(0, k)$ is $k\sqrt{2}$.

35. Let $\triangle ABC$ be an isosceles right triangle with $A = (-2, 1)$ and $B = (2, 1)$. Name the point that cannot be point C.

a. $(2, -3)$ **b.** $(-2, -3)$ **c.** $(0, 3)$ **d.** $(2, 4)$

36. If the area of $\triangle PQR$ is 6 and $P = (1, 2)$ and $Q = (5, 2)$, tell what you can conclude about the location of point R.

a. R must be somewhere on the line $y = 5$.

b. R must be somewhere on the line $x = 5$.

c. R must be on either the line $y = 5$ or the line $y = -1$.

d. R must be somewhere on the y axis.

Chapter 11
Introduction to Locus

11-1 Drawing and Describing a Locus

A **locus** is a set of points (geometric figure) that is determined by certain conditions. In the first three sections of this chapter, we shall deal with locus only as it applies to a plane.

You have already solved two locus problems in a plane.

1. Constructing the perpendicular bisector of a segment: The locus of points equidistant from two fixed points is the perpendicular bisector of the segment joining the two fixed points.

2. Constructing the bisector of an angle: The locus of points equidistant from the sides of an angle is the angle bisector.

Example 1

Draw the locus of points that are one centimeter from P. Describe the locus.

• P

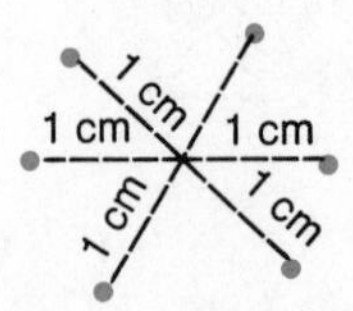

Find as many points as necessary to give you a "picture" of the locus.

•P

Then draw the figure—a circle.

Description: The locus of points one centimeter from P is a circle with its center at P and a radius of one centimeter.

Example 2

Draw the locus of points that are two meters from line k. Describe the locus.

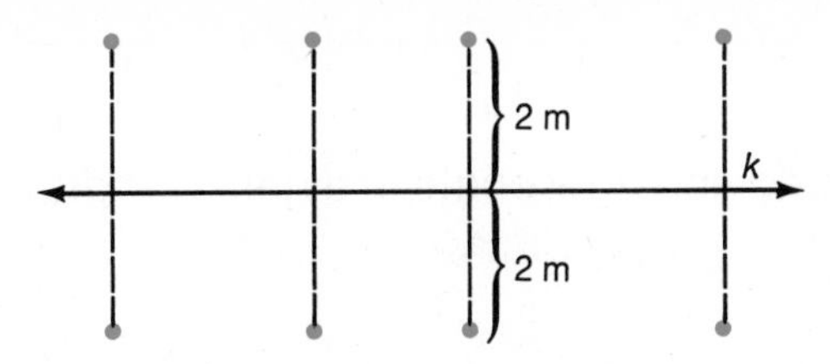

Find as many points as necessary to give you a "picture" of the locus.

Draw the figure—two parallel lines.

Description: The locus is a pair of lines, one on each side of k, parallel to k and 2 meters from k.

Example 3

Draw the locus of points equidistant from two parallel lines. Describe the locus.

Since each point on the locus is equidistant from lines k and m, each point is the midpoint of a segment perpendicular to lines k and m.

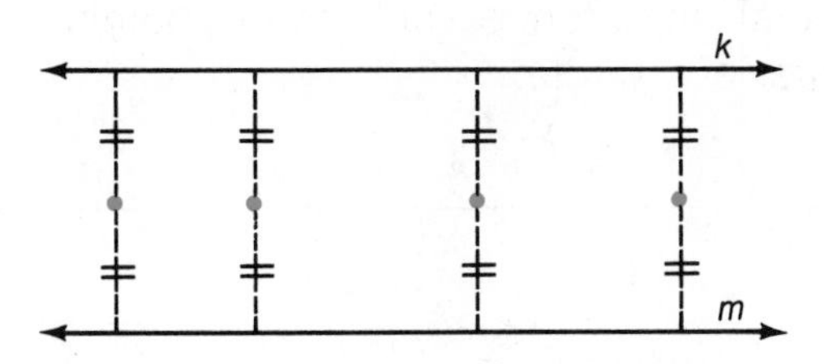

Find as many points as necessary to give you a picture of the locus.

Draw the figure—a line parallel to lines k and m.

Description: The locus is a line parallel to lines k and m and midway between them.

To solve a locus problem, begin by locating one point. This often helps to clarify what it is you are to find.

Example 4

Draw the locus of the vertex of the right angle of a right triangle with a fixed hypotenuse AB.

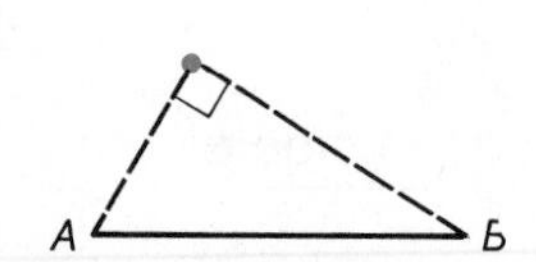

Find one point that is a vertex of a right triangle.

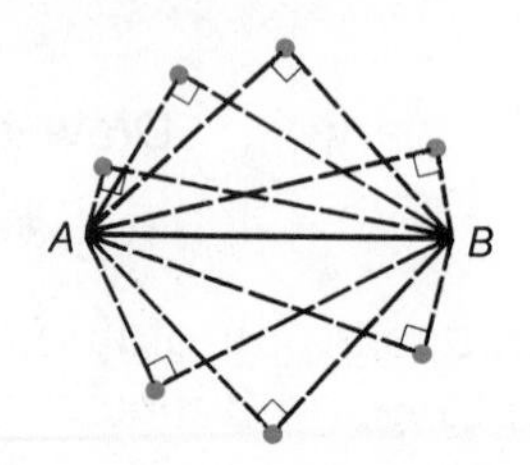

Find as many points as necessary to give you a picture.

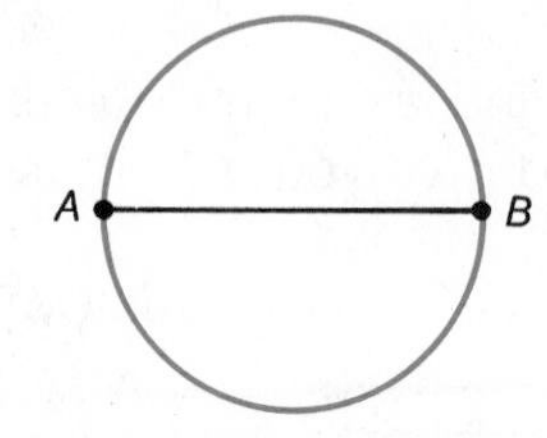

Draw the locus—a circle without points A and B.

Description: The locus is two arcs of the circle having $\overline{AB}$ as a diameter that contain all points of the circle except points A and B.

Steps in Finding and Describing a Locus

1. Decide what information is given or fixed.
2. Locate one of the points of the locus.
3. Locate several other points and see whether they form a familiar shape, such as a circle or line.
4. Locate points of special importance such as endpoints of a segment or the center of a circle.
5. Describe the locus.

Try These

Classify each statement as True or False.

1. A circle is determined if a given segment is its diameter.
2. A segment EF is determined if points E and G are given and G is between E and F.
3. A segment PR is determined if points P and Q are given and Q is the midpoint of $\overline{PR}$.
4. One line is determined if it is tangent to a given circle.
5. One line is determined if it is tangent to a given circle at a given point A on the circle.

6. Two parallel lines are determined if they are each perpendicular to a given segment GH at G and at H.
7. A line is determined if it is perpendicular to a given line.
8. A line b is determined if it is parallel to a given line a.
9. A line k is determined if it contains A and is parallel to $\overleftrightarrow{BC}$ in a given triangle ABC.

Exercises

Draw the locus. Then write its description.

a

1. The locus of points equidistant from R and from S in a given triangle RST.
2. The locus of vertices R and T in rectangle $QRST$ if diagonal QS is fixed in length and position.
3. The locus of points $1\frac{1}{2}$ centimeters from a given circle whose radius is 1 centimeter.
4. The locus of points 1 centimeter from a given circle whose radius is 1 centimeter.
5. The locus of the vertices, C, of all isosceles triangles that have a fixed base AB.
6. The locus of the midpoints of all chords of length 4 in a given circle with radius of length 3.
7. The locus of the centers of circles with radii 2 centimeters and that pass through a given point Q.
8. The locus of the center of a circle that is tangent to a given circle O at a given point A on circle O.
9. The locus of the midpoints of all segments in a given circle if one of the endpoints is on the circle, and the other endpoint is the center of the circle.
10. The locus of the centers of circles each of which is tangent to a given line at a given point of the line.
11. The locus of the centers of circles each of which is tangent to both sides of a given angle.
12. The locus of points whose distance from a given point P is less than a given distance, r.

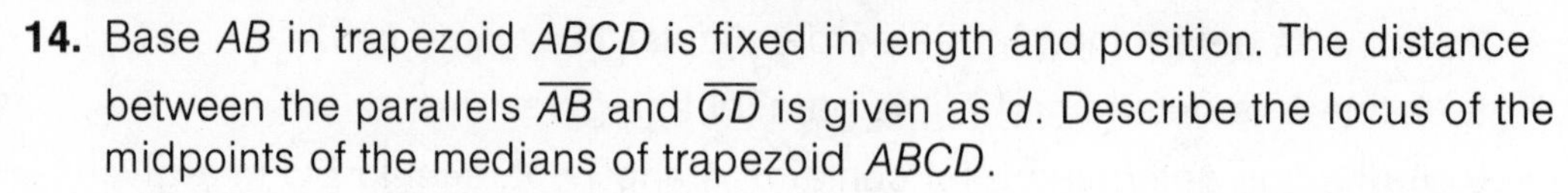

13. The locus of vertex K in a given triangle KLM if $\overline{LM}$ is fixed in length and position and the altitude from K is 2.75 centimeters.

b

14. Base AB in trapezoid $ABCD$ is fixed in length and position. The distance between the parallels $\overline{AB}$ and $\overline{CD}$ is given as d. Describe the locus of the midpoints of the medians of trapezoid $ABCD$.

15. For a given point Q and a given line k not containing Q, describe the locus of the endpoints of segments whose midpoints lie on k and whose other endpoint is Q.

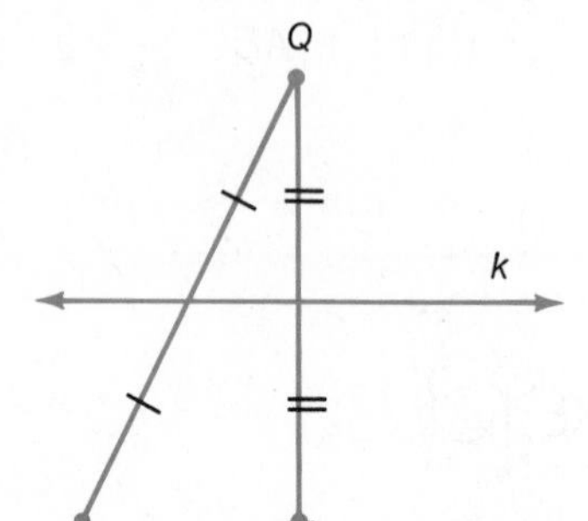

16. Describe the locus of points equidistant from each of three given noncollinear points.

17. Describe the locus of the midpoint of a segment of given length s, having one endpoint on each ray of a given right angle.

18. Segments AB and CD are segments of given lengths, and d is a given distance; $\overline{AB}$ is fixed in position, and $\frac{1}{2}AB < CD < AB$. For a trapezoid with base AB and median CD, when $\overline{AB}$ and $\overline{CD}$ are a distance d apart, describe the locus of the other base of the trapezoid.

PUZZLE

Show that the area of the shaded triangle in the figure below is $\frac{1}{3}$ the area of triangle ABC.

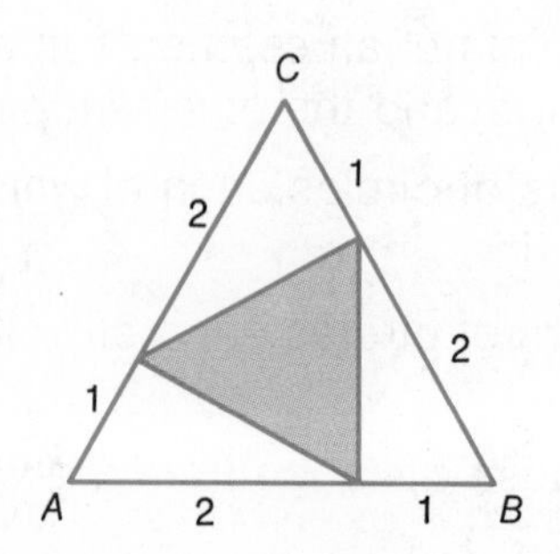

11-2 Intersection of Loci

When a set of points must satisfy each of two conditions, its location can be found from the intersection of two loci (plural of locus and pronounced LOW SIGH).

Example 1

Find the locus of points 2 centimeters from a circle O whose radius is 3 centimeters. The locus is also 1 centimeter from a line that is tangent to the circle.

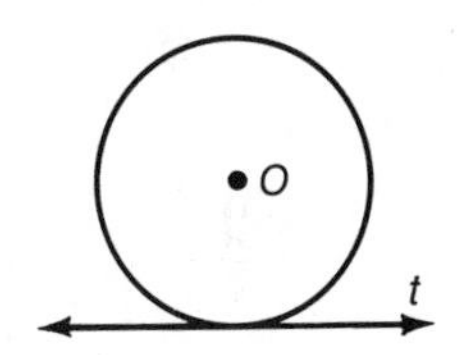

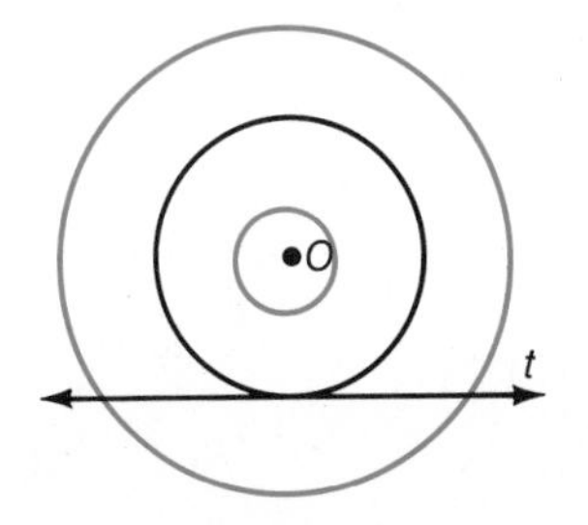

First Condition

Locus: Two circles with center O, each 2 cm from circle O

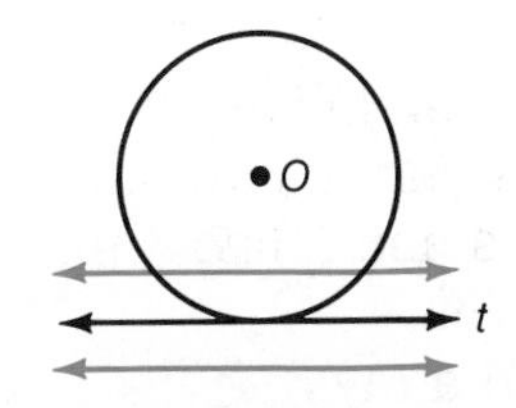

Second Condition

Locus: Two lines parallel to t and 1 cm from t

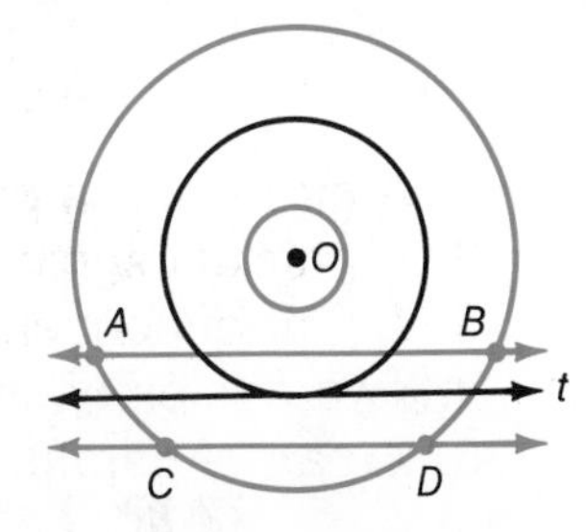

Both Conditions

Locus: Points A, B, C, and D.

Example 2

Given $\triangle ABC$, find the locus of points that are equidistant from A and B. The locus is also the same distance from $\overleftrightarrow{AC}$ that B is from $\overleftrightarrow{AC}$.

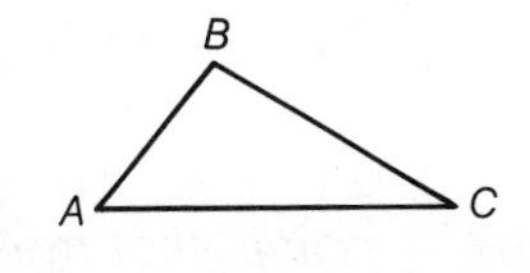

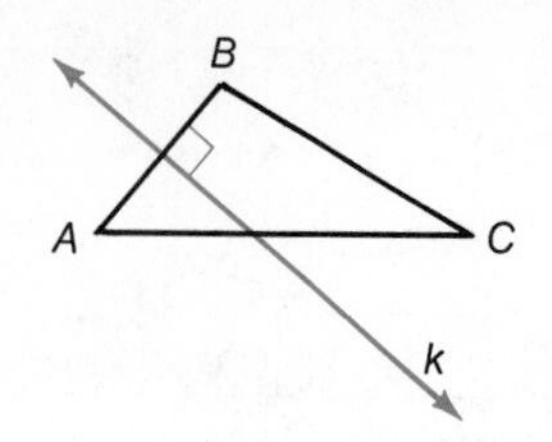

First Condition

Locus: Perpendicular bisector of $\overline{AB}$

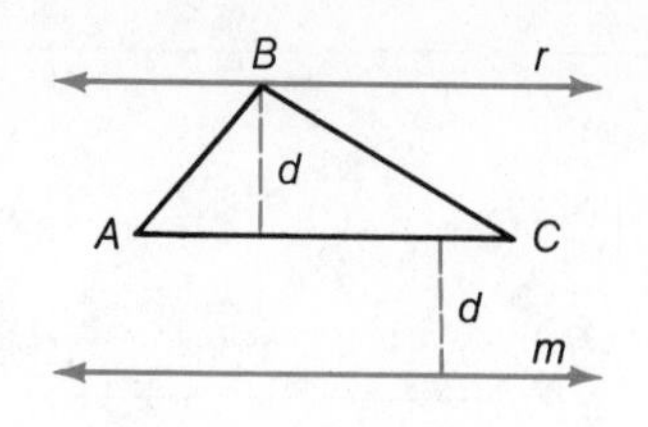

Second Condition

Locus: Pair of lines, one on each side of $\overline{AC}$, parallel to $\overline{AC}$ and d units from $\overleftrightarrow{AC}$

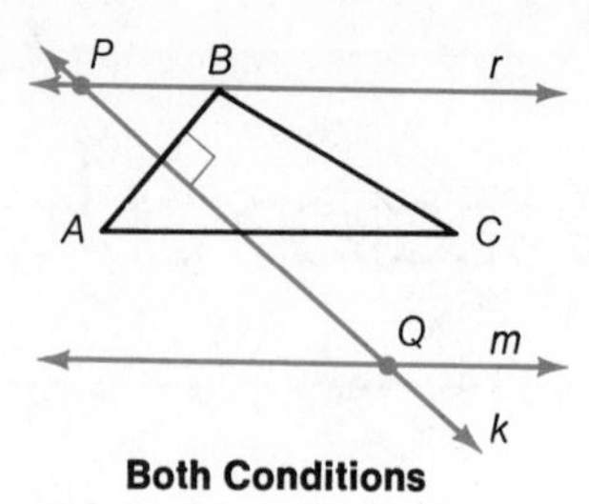

Both Conditions

Locus: P and Q

NOTE: If $\angle A$ in $\triangle ABC$ is a right angle, then the figure at the right results. In this special case, the loci do not intersect. The solution is the empty set.

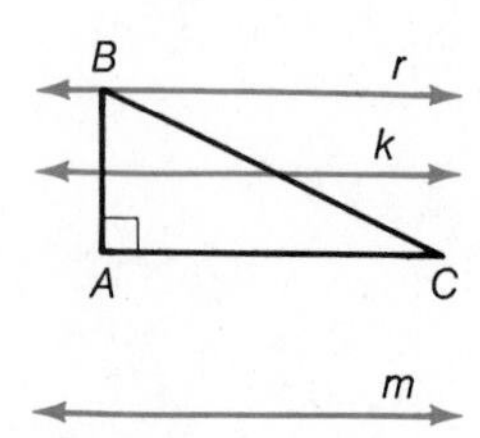

Try These

Give the number of possible intersections of these loci.

1. A circle and a pair of parallel lines
2. A pair of intersecting lines and a third line
3. A pair of concentric circles and a line
4. Two circles of unequal radii
5. A pair of parallel lines and a ray

Exercises

*In Exercises **1–19** consider only coplanar points and draw a separate figure for each exercise.*

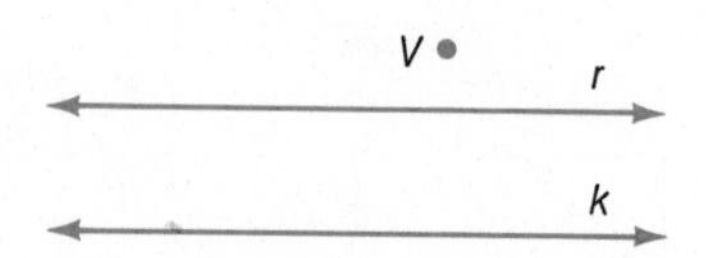

*For Exercises **1–4,** r and k are two parallel lines 1 cm apart, V is a point such that V and k are on opposite sides of r and V is $\frac{1}{2}$ cm from r. Find the locus of points that meets the given condition and is also equidistant from k and r.*

a

1. 1.75 cm from V **2.** 1 cm from V **3.** 1.5 cm from V **4.** .75 cm from V

*For Exercises **5–8,** point X is 2 cm from the given line m. Find the locus of points that meets the given condition and is also 1 cm from m.*

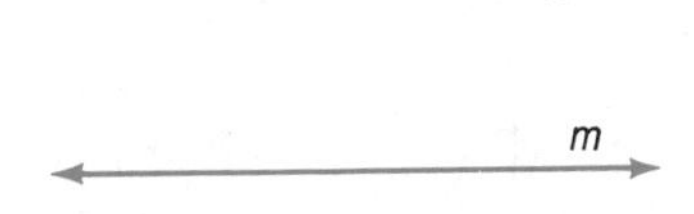

5. 3 cm from X **6.** 3.5 cm from X **7.** 1.75 cm from X **8.** 1 cm from X

9. Find the locus of points $\frac{1}{2}$ inch from a given line h and equidistant from the sides of a given angle ABC. (See the figure at the left below.)

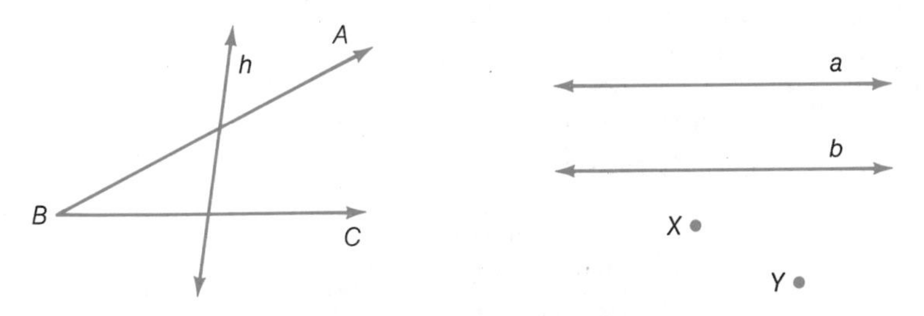

10. Find the locus of points equidistant from two given parallel lines a, b, and from two given points X, Y. (See the figure at the right above.)

11. Find the locus of points one centimeter from the vertex of a given right angle and in the interior of the angle.

12. Points A and B are 2 meters apart. Find the locus of points 3 meters from A and 2.5 meters from B.

13. Point T is 1 cm from line g. Find the locus of points 3 cm from T and 2 cm from g.

14. Find the locus of points at a given distance d from a given circle O with radius r and the same distance from a secant containing O. Discuss the special cases.

15. Find the locus of points equidistant from two given concentric circles and also equidistant from two given parallel lines. Consider special cases.

b **16.** A, B, C, and D are collinear points such that $\overline{AC}$ measures $1\frac{1}{2}$ cm and $\overline{CD}$ measures 1 cm. Base AC of $\triangle XAC$ is fixed in length and position. $\overline{BX}$ is a median of length $1\frac{1}{2}$ cm. Triangle YBD is a right triangle with right angle at Y and base BD fixed in length and position. Locate a point Z that will serve as X in $\triangle XAC$ and also as Y in $\triangle YBD$.

17. Find the locus of points on a given line q and at a given distance d from a circle with radius r. Discuss the special cases.

18. Find the locus of points equidistant from two given parallel lines and a given distance d from a third line. Discuss the special cases.

19. Find the locus of points equidistant from two intersecting lines.

11-3 Constructions and Loci

Sometimes constructions are used to solve locus problems.

Example 1

Find the locus of points equidistant from the three vertices of $\triangle ABC$ below.

Since any point on the perpendicular bisector of a segment is equidistant from the endpoints of the segment, construct the perpendicular bisector of each side of $\triangle ABC$.

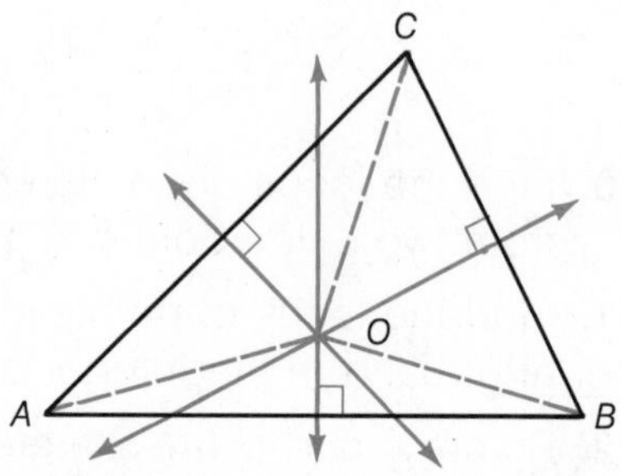

$AO = BO$ ⟵ Since O is on the perpendicular bisector of $\overline{AB}$

$AO = CO$ ⟵ Since O is on the perpendicular bisector of $\overline{AC}$

$BO = CO$ ⟵ Since O is on the perpendicular bisector of $\overline{BC}$

Since $AO = BO = CO$, the locus of points equidistant from the vertices of $\triangle ABC$ is O. Point O is the **circumcenter** of the triangle.

NOTE: To show that $AO = BO = CO$, it is sufficient to construct perpendicular bisectors of only two sides of $\triangle ABC$.

The perpendicular bisectors in $\triangle ABC$ are concurrent. Three or more lines are **concurrent** if they have a point in common.

Example 1 suggests Theorem 11-1.

Theorem 11-1: The perpendicular bisectors of the sides of a triangle are concurrent in a point that is equidistant from the vertices of the triangle.

Example 2

Find the locus of points equidistant from the three sides of $\triangle ABC$.

Since any point on the bisector of an angle is equidistant from the sides of the angle, construct the angle bisector of each angle of $\triangle ABC$.

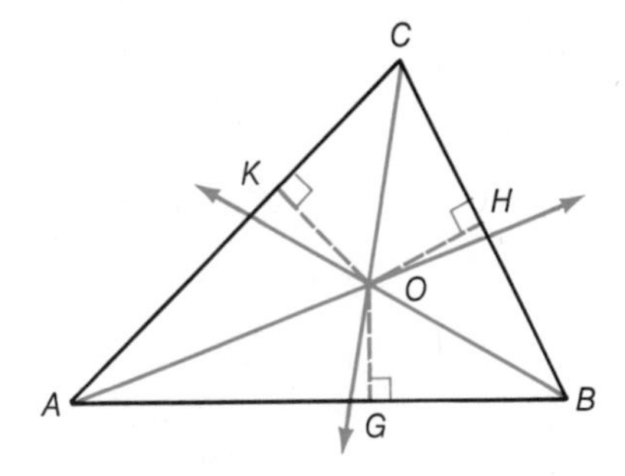

$GO = KO$ ⟵ Since O is on the bisector of $\angle A$

$GO = HO$ ⟵ Since O is on the bisector of $\angle B$

$KO = HO$ ⟵ Since O is on the bisector of $\angle C$

Since $GO = KO = HO$, the locus of points equidistant from the sides of $\triangle ABC$ is O. Point O is the **incenter** of the triangle.

NOTE: To show that $GO = HO = KO$, it is sufficient to construct the bisectors of only two angles of $\triangle ABC$.

Example 2 suggests Theorem 11-2.

Theorem 11-2: The bisectors of the angles of a triangle are concurrent in a point that is equidistant from the sides of the triangle.

Other constructions can lead to theorems about concurrent lines. For example, constructing the altitudes and the medians of a triangle suggests the following theorems.

Theorem 11-3: The altitudes of a triangle are concurrent.

The point of concurrency of the altitudes is the **orthocenter.**

Theorem 11-4: The medians of a triangle are concurrent in a point that is two thirds of the distance from each vertex to the midpoint of the opposite side.

The point of concurrency of the medians is the **centroid.**

Try These

Classify each statement as True or False.

1. Concurrent lines are parallel.
2. The altitudes of a triangle meet at the circumcenter of the triangle.
3. The medians of a triangle meet at the centroid of the triangle.
4. The bisectors of the angles of a triangle meet at the incenter of the triangle.
5. The incenter of a triangle is equidistant from the sides of the triangle.

Exercises

*For each of Exercises **1–4,** copy the acute triangle shown at the right. Then perform the indicated constructions.*

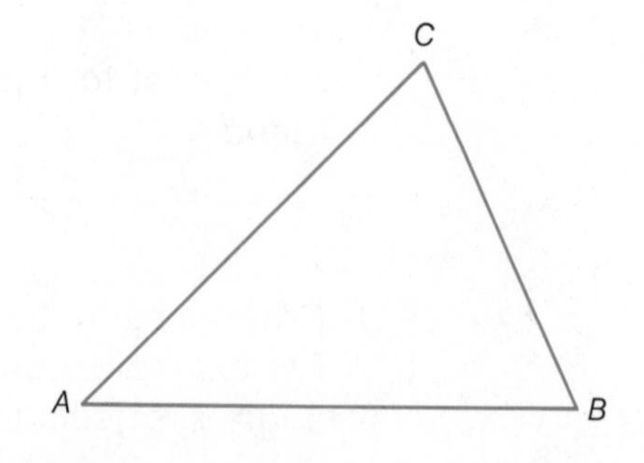

a

1. Construct the perpendicular bisectors of two sides. Label the point of intersection P. Construct the circle with center P and radius AP. The circle should circumscribe $\triangle ABC$.
2. Construct two angle bisectors. Label the point of intersection Q. Construct $\overline{QF} \perp \overline{AB}$. Then construct the circle with center Q and radius QF. The circle should be inscribed in $\triangle ABC$.

3. Construct the three altitudes. Label the point of concurrence T.

4. Construct the three medians. Label the point of concurrence R.

5. Repeat the steps of Exercises **1–4** but with a triangle in which $\angle C$ is a right angle.

6. Repeat the steps of Exercises **1–4** but with a triangle in which $\angle C$ is obtuse.

Use the results of Exercises **1–6** *to complete the table below. Write* *<u>inside</u>, <u>outside</u>, <u>at the vertex</u>, or <u>on a side of</u>, the triangle.*

	Acute	Right	Obtuse
7. Circumcenter	inside	?	?
8. Incenter	?	?	?
9. Orthocenter	?	?	?
10. Centroid	?	?	?

In the figure below, G is the midpoint of $\overline{OA}$ *and H is the midpoint of* $\overline{OB}$. $\overline{AE}$, $\overline{BF}$, *and* $\overline{CD}$ *are medians.*

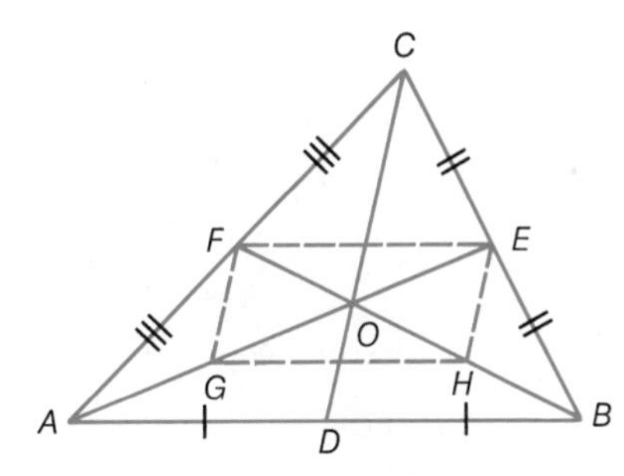

11. $AE = 6$; $AO =$? ; $OG =$?

12. $AO = 8$; $AE =$?

13. $BF = 7$; $BO =$? ; $OF =$?

14. $DO = 3$; $OC =$?

C **15.** Prove Theorem 11-4. Use the figure given for Exercises **11-14,** where G is the midpoint of $\overline{AO}$ and H is the midpoint of $\overline{BO}$. (HINT: Show that $EFGH$ is a parallelogram and that $\overline{AE}$ and $\overline{BF}$ are trisected. To show that $\overline{CD}$ contains O, assume that the intersection is another point. Then show that this is impossible.)

11-4 Locus in Three Dimensions

The locus problems in the preceding sections dealt only with points in a plane. If the same conditions are applied to points in space, a different locus often results.

Example 1

Find the locus of points at a given distance from point O.

In a plane: A circle with the given distance as radius and the given point as center.

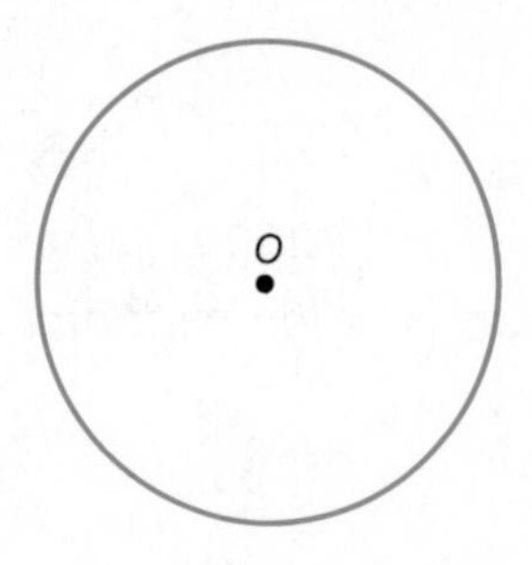

In space: A sphere with the given distance as radius and given point as center.

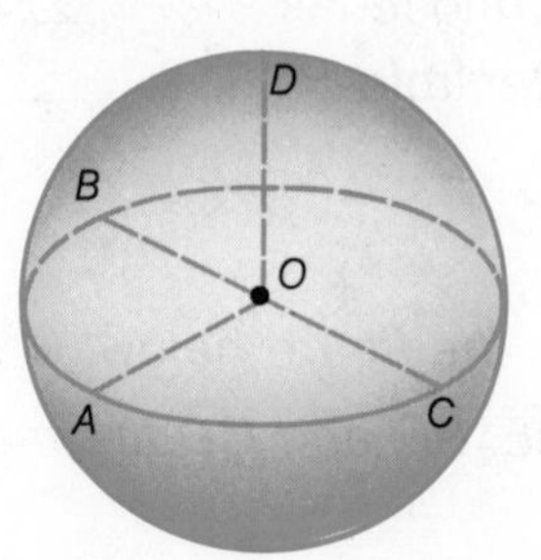

Example 2

Find the locus of points at a given distance from line m.

In a plane: Two lines, one on each side of the given line and parallel to the given line at the given distance from it.

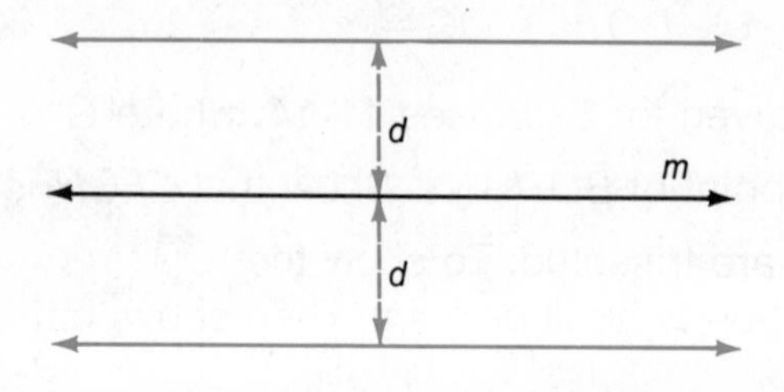

In space: A cylindrical surface with the given line as axis and the given distance as radius.

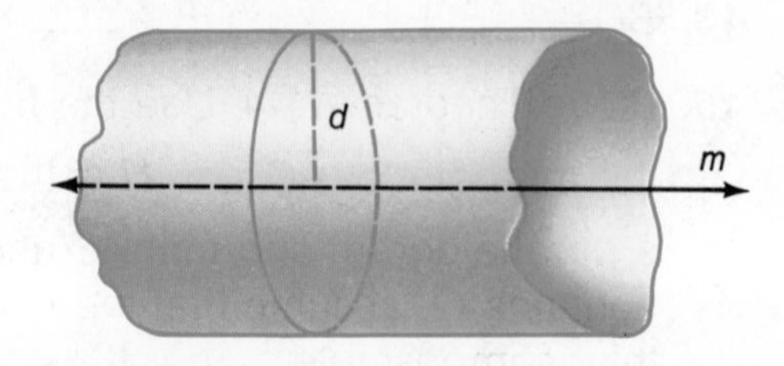

Example 3 Find the locus of points equidistant from points A and B.

In a plane: The perpendicular bisector of the segment joining the two given points.

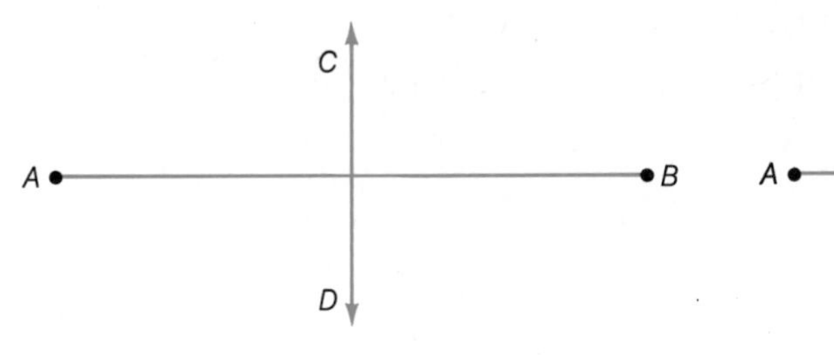

In space: The plane perpendicular to the segment joining the two given points at its midpoint.

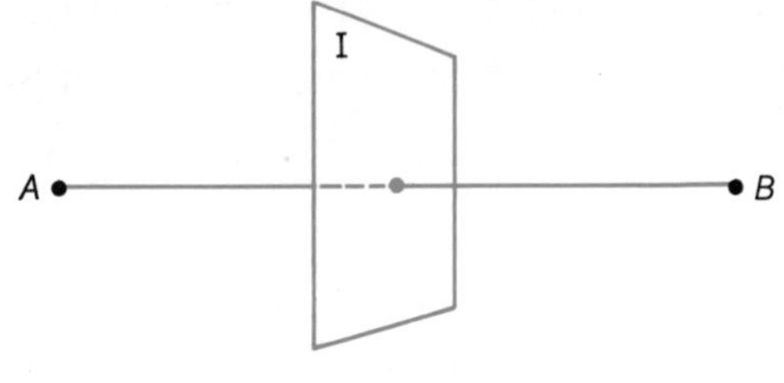

Example 4 Find the locus of points that are on line k and in plane I.

In a plane

Case 1: If the plane contains the line, then the locus consists of all of line k.

In space

Case 2: If the plane neither contains the plane nor is parallel to it, then the locus is the <u>one</u> point of intersection.

Case 3: If the plane and the line are parallel, then there are <u>no</u> points that are in both the plane <u>and</u> the line. The locus is the empty set.

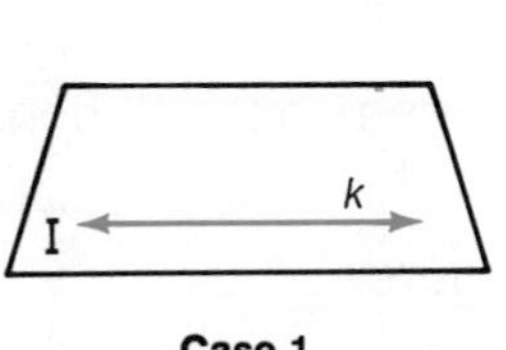

Case 1

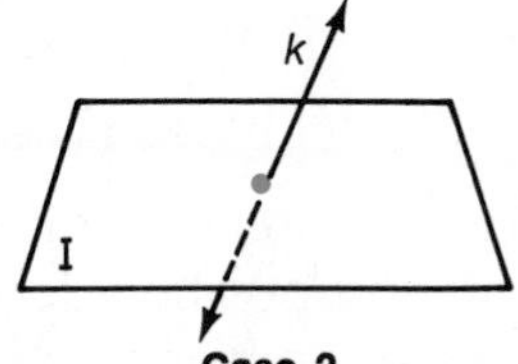

Case 2

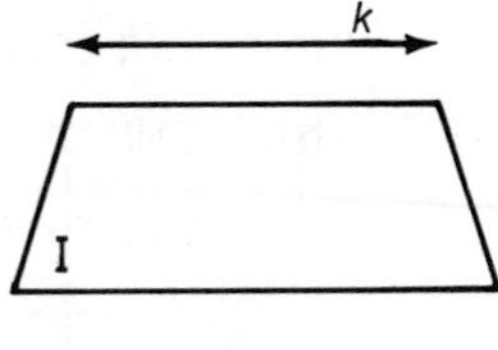

Case 3

NOTE: Each case gives you a different solution.

Try These

Write a description of each locus in space. A sketch of the figure may help you to visualize the locus.

1. The locus of points equidistant from two given parallel lines.
2. The locus of points whose distance from a given point is less than a given distance d.
3. The locus of points equidistant from two concentric spheres whose radii are 2 cm and 2.75 cm, respectively.
4. The locus of points on each of two given planes (There are three cases to consider.)

Exercises

Write a description of each locus in space. A sketch of the figure may help you to visualize the locus.

a

1. The locus of lines perpendicular to a given line p at a given point on p
2. The locus of points 1 centimeter from the closest point of a given segment XY
3. The locus of the centers of spheres of given radius r that are tangent to a given plane
4. The locus of the centers of spheres tangent to both faces of a given dihedral angle
5. The locus of the centers of spheres that are tangent to a given plane at a given point of the plane
6. The locus of the center of a sphere whose radius is s if the sphere passes through a given point Q
7. The locus of points on two spheres (There are three cases to consider.)
8. The locus of side RS in square $RSTU$ if side UT remains fixed in length and position (Let the figure revolve around side UT as an axis.)
9. The locus of side UR in square $RSTU$ if side TS remains fixed in length and position

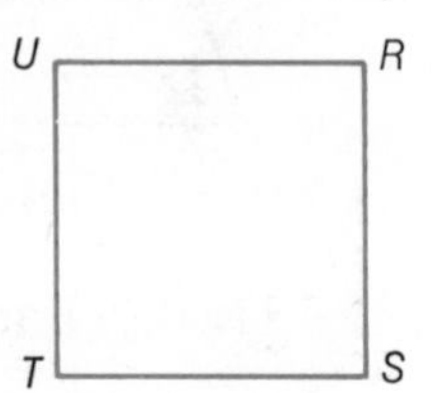

10. The locus of side UR in square $RSTU$ if side UT remains fixed in length and position

Find the locus of points for each given rotation of right triangle ABC.

11. Around $\overline{AB}$ as an axis
12. Around $\overline{AC}$ as an axis
13. Around $\overline{BC}$ as an axis

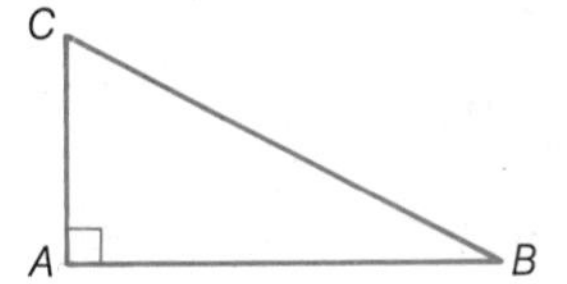

Write a description for each locus in space. Begin by sketching the locus.

14. The locus of points equidistant from two given points and on a given line (There are three cases to consider.)
15. The locus of a point at a given distance from a given point and equidistant from two given parallel planes
16. The locus of points equidistant from two given points and equidistant from two given parallel planes
17. The locus of lines tangent to a given sphere at a given point of the sphere
18. The locus of planes tangent to a given sphere at each point of a great circle of the sphere

PUZZLE

On base AB of the parallelogram, trapezoid, and quadrilateral, construct a triangle having an area equal to that of the figure. No measuring is allowed!

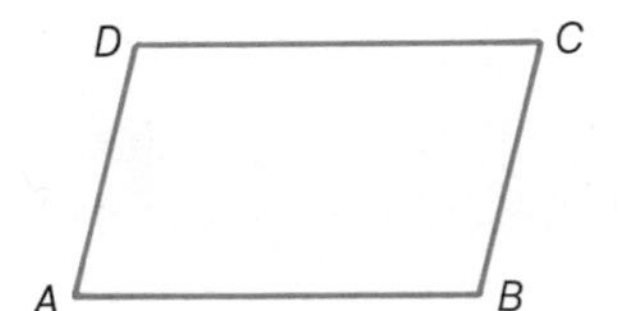

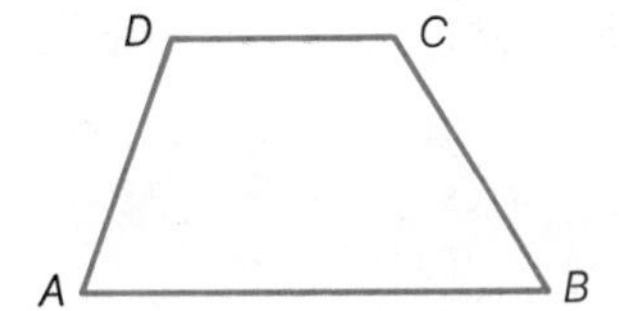

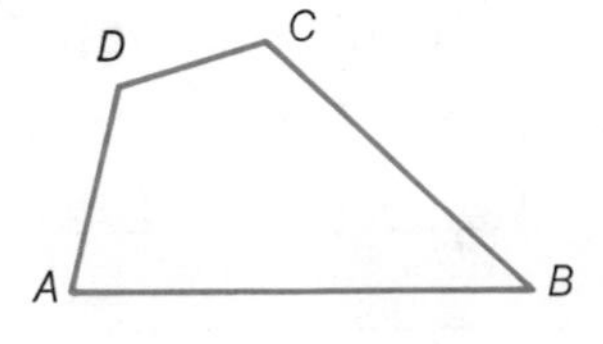

Area and Constructions

You can construct a triangle with area equal to that of <u>any</u> given polygon.

Construct a triangle with area equal to that of trapezoid $ABCD$.

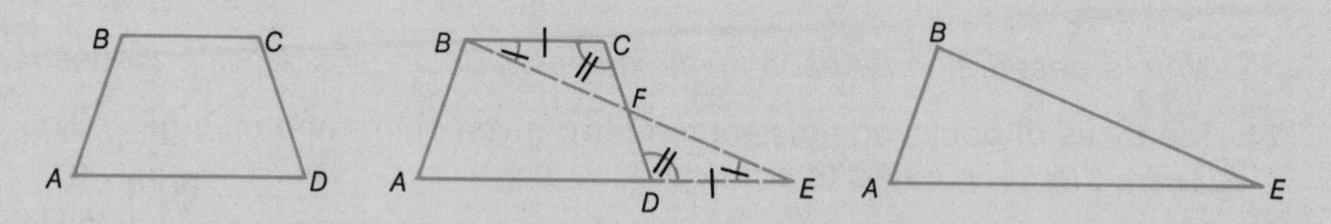

Extend side AD to a point E such that $DE = BC$. Draw $\overline{BE}$, and label the point of intersection of $\overline{BE}$ and $\overline{CD}$ as F.
Since $\overline{DE} \cong \overline{CB}$, $\angle CBF \cong \angle DEF$ (Why?), and $\angle BCF \cong \angle EDF$ (Why?), $\triangle CFB \cong \triangle DFE$, and Area $\triangle CFB =$ Area $\triangle DFE$ (Why?).
$\therefore$ Area of $\triangle ABE =$ Area of trapezoid $ABCD$.

For a polygon of n sides ($n > 4$), first construct a polygon of equal area but with $(n - 1)$ sides. Then construct a polygon with area equal to that of the new polygon but with $(n - 1) - 1$ sides, and so on, until a triangle equal in area to the original polygon is reached.

Construct a triangle with area equal to the area of polygon $ABCDE$.

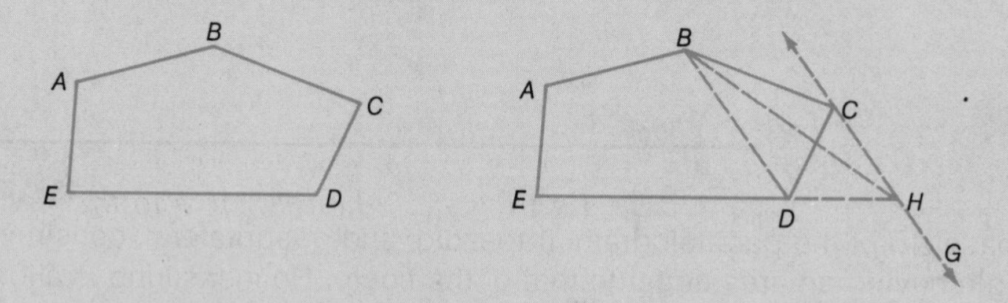

Draw $\overline{BD}$. Through C, construct $\overleftrightarrow{CG} \parallel \overline{BD}$.
Extend side ED until it intersects $\overleftrightarrow{FG}$, and label the point of intersection H. Draw $\overline{BH}$.

Since $\triangle BCD$ and $\triangle BDH$ have the same base, $\overline{BD}$, and equal altitudes, they are equal in area (Corollary 8-4, page 377).

$\therefore$ Area of polygon $ABHE$ = Area of polygon $ABCDE$

Now construct a triangle equal in area to the area of polygon $ABHE$.

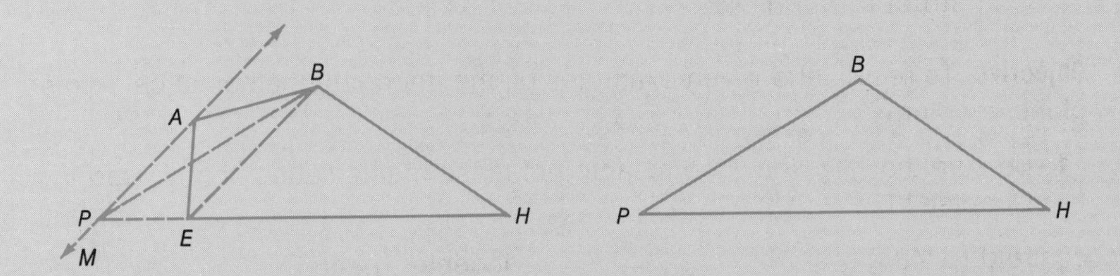

Draw $\overline{BE}$. Through A construct $\overleftrightarrow{AM} \parallel \overline{BE}$.
Extend side HE until it intersects $\overleftrightarrow{AM}$, and label the point of intersection P. Draw $\overline{BP}$.
Since $\triangle ABE$ and $\triangle PBE$ have the same base, $\overline{EB}$, and equal altitudes, they are equal in area.

$\therefore$ Area of $\triangle PBH$ = Area of polygon $ABHE$ = Area of polygon $ABCDE$

Can You Solve These?

*For Exercises **1–4**, construct a triangle with area equal to that of the given polygon.*

1. Square $ABCD$ with $AB = 3$ cm
2. Rectangle $PQRS$ with $PQ = 4$ cm and $QR = 3$ cm
3. Parallelogram $ABCD$ with $AB = 3$ cm, $BC = 5$ cm, and $m\angle A = 65$
4. Regular pentagon $TQRSW$ with $TQ = 2$ cm

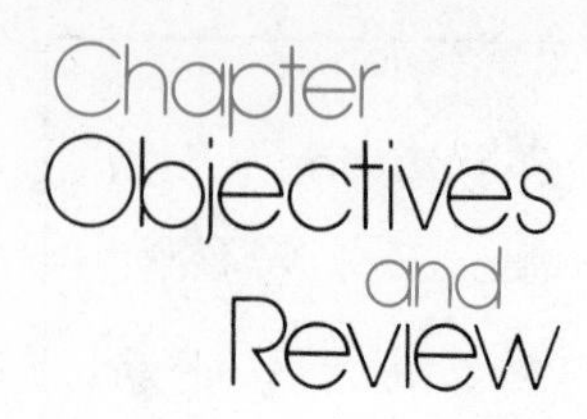

Objective: To recall, and given examples of, the important mathematical terms of the chapter.

1. Be sure that you know the meaning of these mathematical terms used in Chapter 11.

centroid (p. 484)
circumcenter (p. 482)
concurrent lines (p. 482)
incenter (p. 483)
locus (p. 474)
orthocenter (p. 484)

Objective: To draw the locus of points in a plane that satisfy a given condition. (Section 11-1)

Locate at least five points that satisfy the given condition. Then draw the locus.

2. The locus of points within a given circle that are equidistant from the ends of a given chord
3. The locus of centers of circles that are tangent to two or more sides of a given square

Objective: To describe a locus of points that satisfy a given condition. (Section 11-1)

Draw each locus. Then write its description.

4. The locus of centers of circles of radius 3 that are tangent to a given circle of radius 4
5. The locus of a point A if $\overline{AD}$ is the median to a fixed base $\overline{BC}$ in a triangle ABC and if $AD = 2$ centimeters

Objective: To describe a locus that is the intersection of two loci. (Section 11-2)

6. Point P is 2 inches from line m. Find the locus of points 5 inches from P and 3 inches from m.

7. Lines r and s intersect at Q. Find the locus of points 2 centimeters from Q and equidistant from r and s.

Objective: To recognize four points of concurrency in a triangle. (Section 11-3)

*In Exercises **8–10,** select the word or phrase that best completes each statement. (perpendicular bisectors of the sides, angle bisectors, altitudes, medians)*

8. The __?__ of a triangle intersect in one point that is equidistant from the three vertices.
9. The __?__ of a triangle intersect in one point that is two-thirds of the distance from each vertex to the endpoint on the opposite side.
10. The __?__ of a triangle intersect in one point that is equidistant from the three sides.

Objective: To describe a locus in space. (Section 11-4)

Describe the required locus in space.

11. The locus of points 2 meters from a fixed plane
12. The locus of points 10 centimeters from A and 10 centimeters from B if $AB = 12$ centimeters

*Each of the Exercises **1–10** describes a locus in a plane. State whether the locus is a circle, 1 or 2 lines, or 1, 2, 3, or 4 points.*

1. The locus of points 1 cm from a given line q
2. The locus of points 2 cm from a given point T
3. The locus of points equidistant from two parallel lines, p and q
4. The locus of points equidistant from two intersecting lines, r and s
5. The locus of points 2 cm from line t and 3 cm from point P on line t
6. The locus of points 5 inches from D and 7 inches from F for $DF = 9$

7. The locus of points equidistant from the sides of an angle and 2 cm from its vertex
8. The locus of points 3 cm from a circle of radius 7 cm and also equidistant from the endpoints of a diameter *FG*
9. The locus of the centers of circles of radius 2 that are tangent to line *q*
10. The locus of vertex *T* in triangle *RST* if side *RS* is fixed in position and the altitude to *RS* is 1.5 centimeters

Draw each locus. Then write its description.

11. The locus of the vertex *C* in isosceles triangle *ABC*, with fixed base *AB*
12. The locus of vertex *B* in rectangle *ABCD* if diagonal *AC* is fixed in position and has a length of 10
13. The locus of the centers of circles tangent to a given circle *Q* at point *D* on the circle

Describe each locus in space.

14. The locus of points 5 inches from a given plane
15. The locus of points 1 meter from a given point *T*
16. The locus of points equidistant from two points *R* and *S*
17. The locus of points equidistant from two intersecting planes

For Exercises ***18–20,*** *classify each statement as* *True* *or* *False.*

18. The angle bisectors of a triangle are concurrent at a point equidistant from the three vertices.
19. The perpendicular bisectors of the sides of a triangle are concurrent at a point equidistant from the three vertices.
20. The altitudes of a right triangle are concurrent at a point on the triangle.

Chapter 12
Introduction to Trigonometry

12-1 The Tangent Ratio

These three triangles are similar.

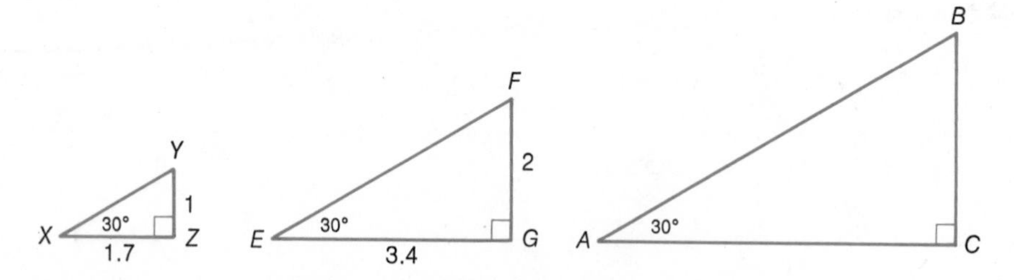

Thus, you can write the following statement.

$$\frac{1}{1.7} = \frac{2}{3.4} = \frac{BC}{AC}$$

The ratio $\frac{BC}{AC}$ in any right triangle ABC, where C is a right angle, is the tangent of angle A.

Definition: In a right triangle, the **tangent of an acute angle** is the ratio

$$\frac{\textbf{length of the opposite leg}}{\textbf{length of the adjacent leg}}.$$

Thus, the tangent of angle B, or $\tan B$, is written as follows.

$$\tan B = \frac{AC}{BC} \longleftarrow \frac{\text{length of opposite leg}}{\text{length of adjacent leg}}$$

Example 1

Use right triangle ABC to find each ratio.

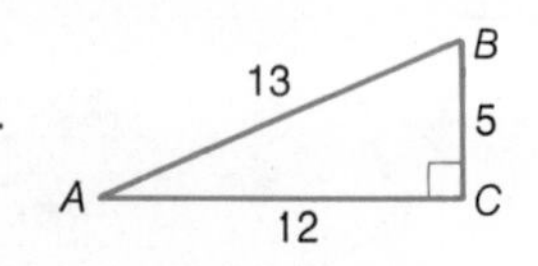

a. $\tan A$ **b.** $\tan B$

Solutions: **a.** $\tan A = \frac{BC}{AC}$ ⟵ $\frac{\overline{BC} \text{ is opposite } \angle A}{\overline{AC} \text{ is adjacent to } \angle A}$

$\tan A = \frac{5}{12}$

$\tan A \approx .4167$ ⟵ Write as a four-place decimal.

b. $\tan B = \frac{AC}{BC}$ ⟵ $\frac{\overline{AC} \text{ is opposite } \angle B}{\overline{BC} \text{ is adjacent to } \angle B}$

$\tan B = \frac{12}{5}$

$\tan B = 2.4$

A ratio of the lengths of two sides of a right triangle is a **trigonometric ratio.** Such ratios are the basis for trigonometry, the study of triangles.

A trigonometric ratio depends only on the measure of an acute angle, not on the size of the right triangle. The **Table of Sine, Cosine, and Tangent Values** on page 581 gives these values for acute angles. Although most values are approximations for the ratios, the "=" symbol is used, because it is more convenient. Thus, in Example 1, write $\tan A = .4167$ instead of $\tan A \approx .4167$.

Example 2

Find the tangent of 67° (tan 67°).

Angle	Sine	Cosine	Tangent
66	.9135	.4067	2.2460
67	.9205	.3907	2.3559
68	.9272	.3746	2.4751

⟵ Find 67 in the **Angle**-column. Move directly right to the **Tangent**-column.

$\tan 67° = 2.3559$

When the value of the tangent of an angle is known, you can use the table to find the angle.

Example 3

Find the measure of the angle whose tangent is .4245.

Angle	Sine	Cosine	Tangent
22	.3746	.9272	.4040
23	.3907	.9205	.4245
24	.4067	.9135	.4452

Find .4245 in the **Tangent**-column. Move directly left to the **Angle**-column.

The measure of the angle whose tangent is .4245 is 23°.

Try These

Use the right triangles below for Exercises ***1–3.***

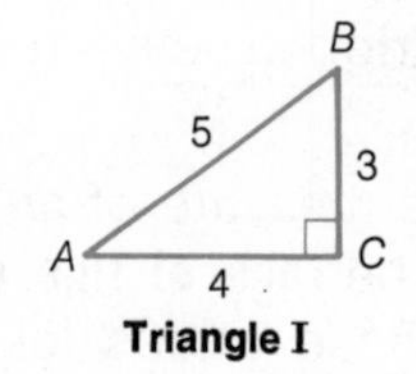

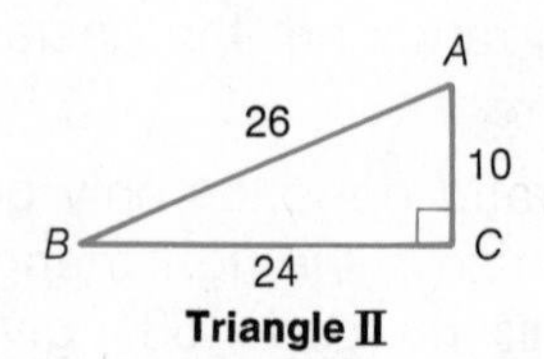

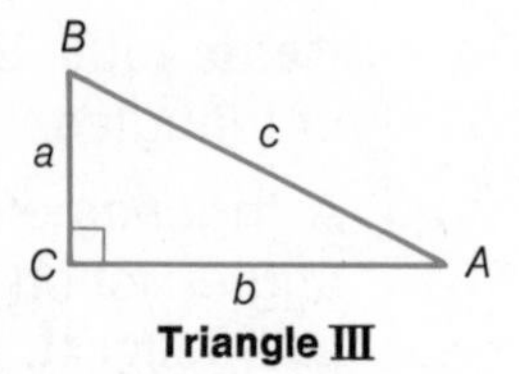

1. Write the length of the leg opposite $\angle A$.
2. Write the length of the leg adjacent to $\angle B$.
3. Find tan A and tan B for each triangle.

Use the table on page 581 to find x.

4. $\tan 73° = x$ **5.** $\tan 8° = x$ **6.** $\tan x = .5095$

Exercises

Use the right triangles below for Exercises ***1–3.***

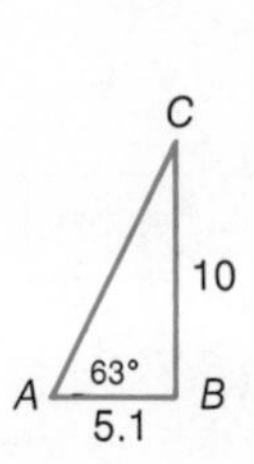

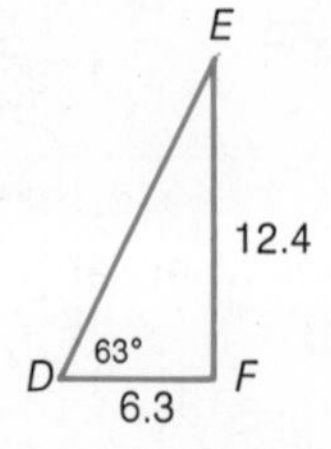

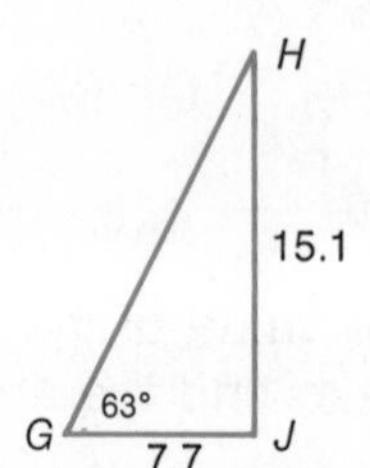

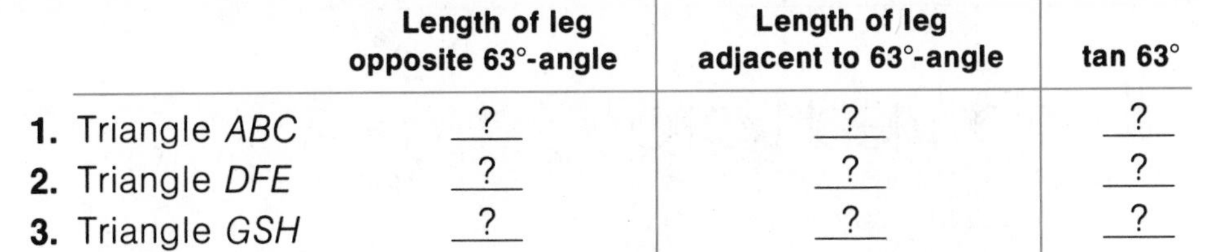

	Length of leg opposite 63°-angle	Length of leg adjacent to 63°-angle	tan 63°
1. Triangle *ABC*	?	?	?
2. Triangle *DFE*	?	?	?
3. Triangle *GSH*	?	?	?

4. Compare the values of tan 63° found in Exercises **1–3** with the value from the table on page 581. Do they agree to two decimal places?

In Exercises **5–7,** *find tan A and tan B as a four-place decimal.*

5.

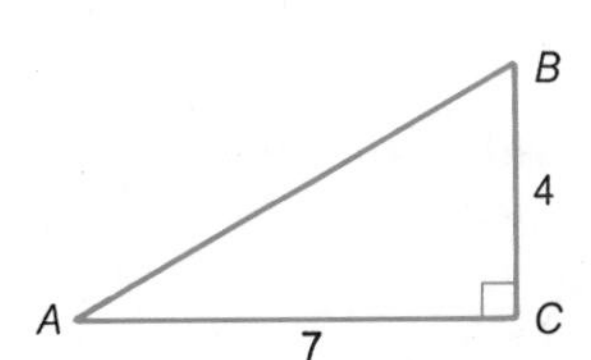

6.

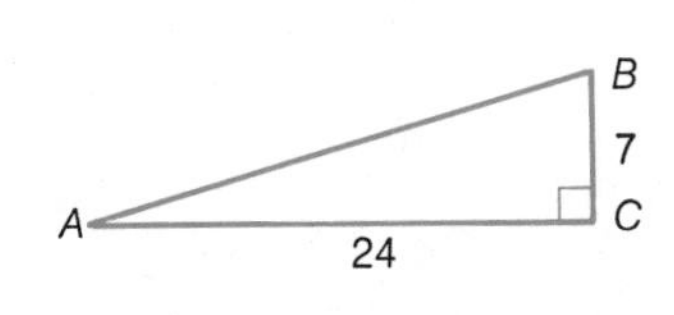

7.

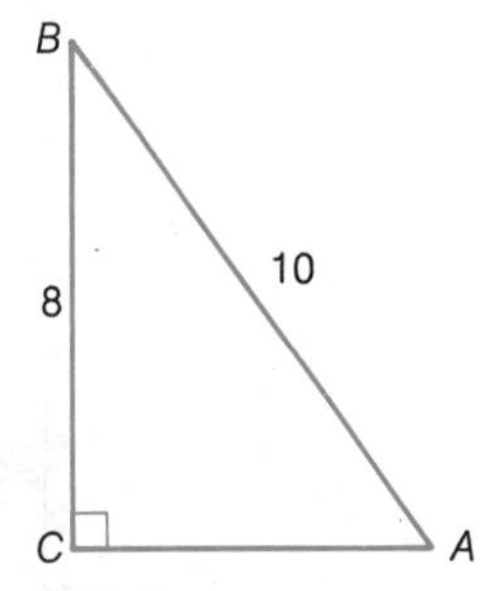

Use the table on page 581 to find each ratio.

8. tan 25° **9.** tan 29° **10.** tan 38°

11. tan 14° **12.** tan 28° **13.** tan 62°

Find x.

14. $\tan x = .1228$ **15.** $\tan x = .5774$ **16.** $\tan x = 11.4301$

17. $\tan x = 57.2900$ **18.** $\tan x = .9657$ **19.** $\tan x = 2.2460$

Remember

Solve for x.

1. $\frac{3}{2} = \frac{27}{x}$ **2.** $\frac{x}{4} = \frac{6}{12}$ **3.** $\frac{5}{x} = \frac{10}{24}$

4. $\frac{21}{5} = \frac{x}{2.5}$ **5.** $\frac{x}{65} = \frac{5}{13}$ **6.** $\frac{4}{20} = \frac{x}{16}$

The answers are on page 514. If you need help, see pages 250 and 251.

12-2 Using the Tangent Ratio

The equation $\tan A = \frac{BC}{AC}$ has three variables. If you know the value of any two of them, you can find the value of the third.

Example 1

Find the height of the flagpole to the nearest meter.

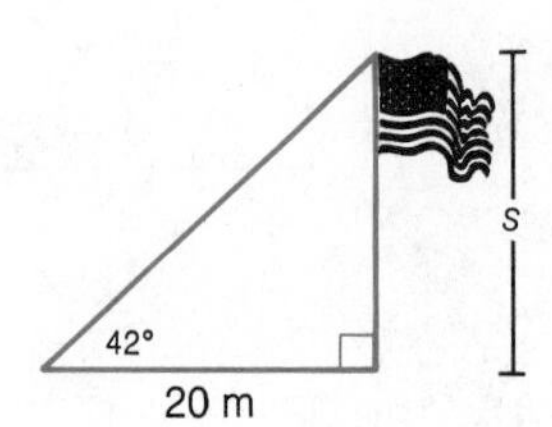

$$\tan 42° = \frac{s}{20}$$

$$.9004 = \frac{s}{20} \quad \longleftarrow \text{ Replace tan 42° with .9004.}$$

$$20(.9004) = s$$

$$18.08 = s \quad \longleftarrow \text{ The height is about 18 meters.}$$

Example 2

In $\triangle PQR$, $PQ = 95$ cm and $m\angle R = 17$. Find QR to the nearest centimeter.

$$\tan 17° = \frac{95}{QR}$$

$$.3057 = \frac{95}{QR}$$

$$QR = \frac{95}{.3057}$$

$$= 310.7 \quad \longleftarrow \text{ } QR \text{ is about 311 centimeters.}$$

Try These

*For Exercises **1–3,** $m\angle B$ and a, the length of side BC, in right triangle ABC are given. Find b to the nearest whole number.*

1. $a = 142$, $m\angle B = 36$

2. $a = 385$, $m\angle B = 24$

3. $a = 556$, $m\angle B = 62$

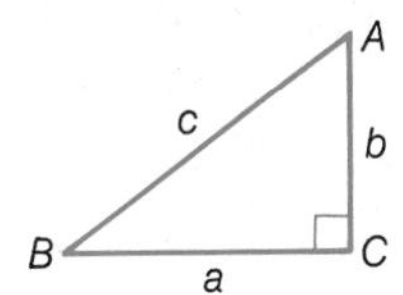

Exercises

*For Exercises **1–3,** $m\angle A$ and b, the length of side AC in right triangle ABC are given. Find a to the nearest tenth.*

a

1. $b = 16.5$, $m\angle A = 32$

2. $b = 98.3$, $m\angle A = 70$

3. $b = 19.7$, $m\angle A = 38$

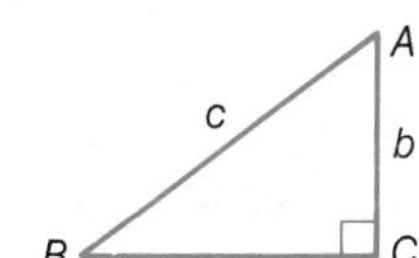

*For Exercises **4–6,** $m\angle B$ and b, the length of side AC in right triangle ABC, are given. Find a to the nearest hundredth. (HINT: Use tan B.)*

4. $b = 3.24$, $m\angle B = 25$

5. $b = 8.62$, $m\angle B = 60$

6. $b = 5.91$, $m\angle B = 72$

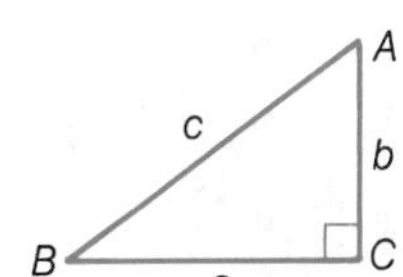

b

7. In order to find the width of a river, a base line *AC* of 216 meters is measured along the bank. Point *B* is located on the opposite bank such that $\angle ACB$ is a right angle and $m\angle A = 55$. Find the width of the river to the nearest meter.

8. A ladder leaning against a wall meets the ground at a point 4 meters from the foot of the wall and makes an angle of 70° with the ground. To the nearest meter, find how far up the wall the ladder reaches.

9. A guy wire is anchored 3.5 meters from the foot of a pole. The wire makes an angle of 63° with the ground. To the nearest tenth, find how far up the pole the wire is fastened.

12-3 The Sine and Cosine Ratios

You cannot use the tangent ratio to find BC and AB in the figures below, because you do not know the values of two of the variables in the equation $\tan A = \frac{BC}{AC}$.

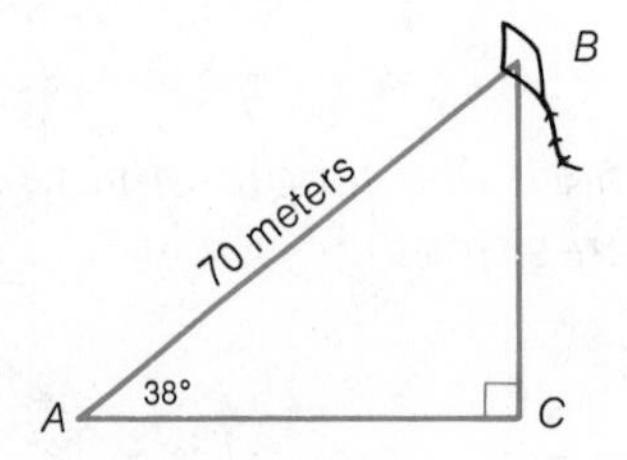

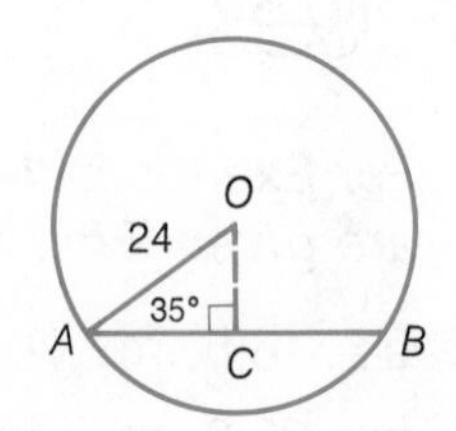

There are two other ratios that you can use, the sine (abbreviated: sin) and the cosine (abbreviated: cos).

Definitions:

In a right triangle, the **sine of an acute angle** is the ratio

$$\frac{\text{length of the opposite leg}}{\text{length of the hypotenuse}}.$$

In a right triangle, the **cosine of an acute angle** is the ratio

$$\frac{\text{length of the adjacent side}}{\text{length of the hypotenuse}}.$$

Example 1

A kite has 70 meters of string out. The string makes an angle of 38° with the ground. Find, to the nearest meter, how far above the ground the kite is flying.

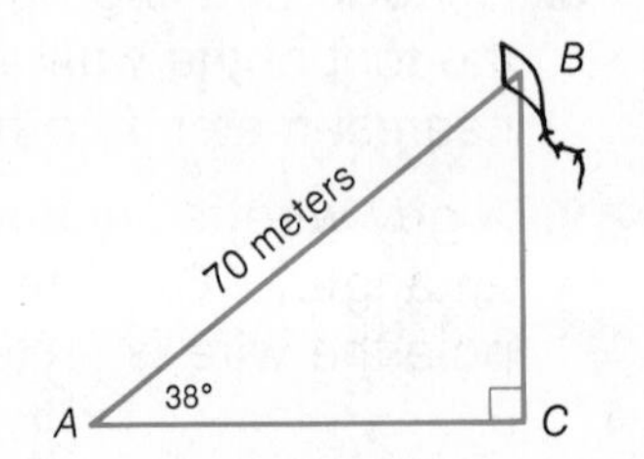

Solution:

$$\sin A = \frac{BC}{BA}$$ ⟵ Since you know m∠A and the length of the hypotenuse AB, and you want to find the length of the side opposite ∠A, BC, use sin A.

$$\sin 38° = \frac{BC}{70}$$

$$.6157 = \frac{BC}{70}$$ ⟵ Replace sin 38° with .6157.

$$70(.6157) = BC$$

$$43.099 = BC$$ ⟵ The height of the kite is about 43 meters.

Example 2

In the figure, circle O has radius OA, $\overline{OC} \perp \overline{AB}$, $OA = 24$, and m∠$A = 35$. Find AB to the nearest whole number.

By Theorem 7-5, $AB = 2AC$, or $AC = \frac{1}{2}AB$.

$$\cos A = \frac{AC}{AO}$$ ⟵ Since you know m∠A and the length of the hypotenuse, AO, and you want to find the length of the side adjacent to ∠A, use cos A.

$$\cos 35° = \frac{AC}{24}$$

$$.8192 = \frac{AC}{24}$$ ⟵ Replace cos 35 with .8192.

$$24(.8192) = AC$$

$$19.6608 = AC$$ ⟵ $AC = \frac{1}{2}AB$

$$39.3216 = 2AC$$ ⟵ The length of $\overline{AB}$ is about 39.

To decide which trigonometric ratio you should use to solve for an unknown length, first make a drawing. Label the parts of the right triangle with what is known and what is to be found. Use the ratio that involves a known part and the unknown part.

Known and Unknown Sides of the Right Triangle	**Ratio to Use**
opposite and adjacent	tangent
opposite and hypotenuse	sine
adjacent and hypotenuse	cosine

Try These

*Use the figures at the right to write each ratio in Exercises **1–6** as a fraction.*

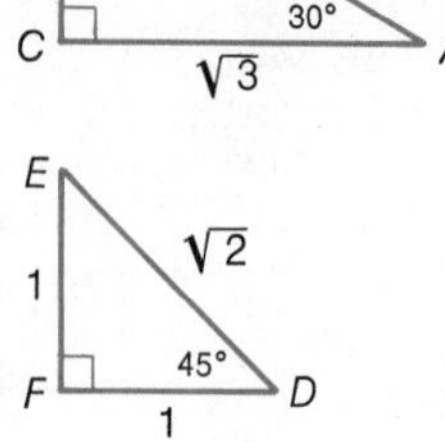

1. sin 30° **2.** cos 30° **3.** sin 60°

4. cos 60° **5.** sin 45° **6.** cos 45°

7. Write each of the answers to Exercises **1–6** as four-place decimals. Then compare these decimals with the values found in the table.

Name the trigonometric ratio that you would use to solve for the unknown measure.

8.

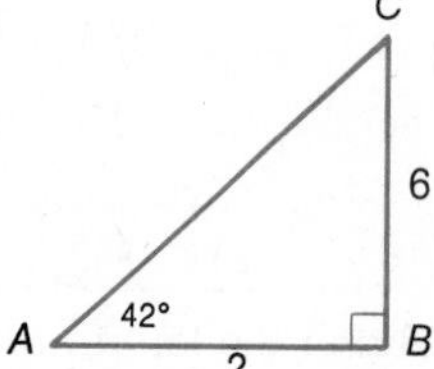

9.

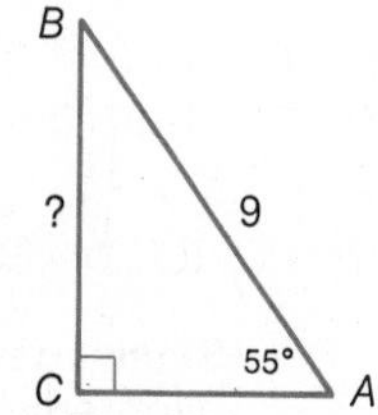

10.

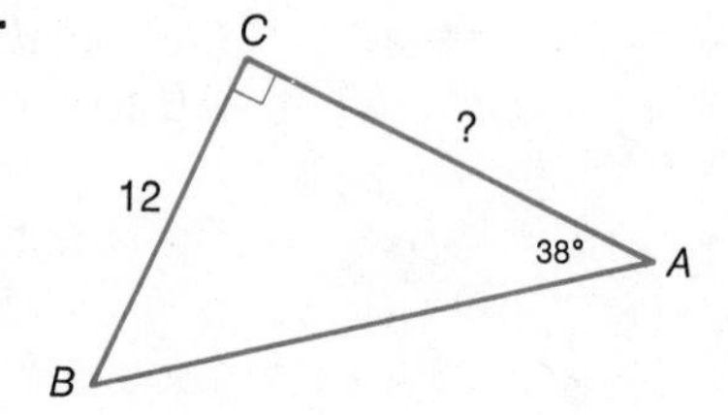

Exercises

*Use right triangle ABC for Exercises **1–8**.*

*For Exercises **1–2**, m∠B and c, the length of AB are given. Find b to the nearest whole number.*

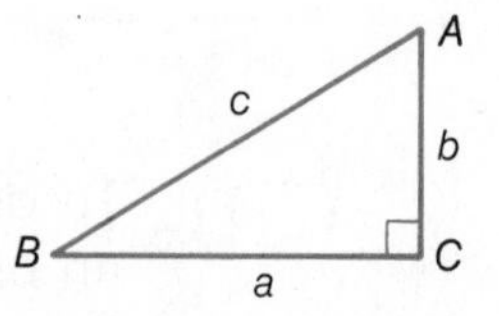

a

1. $c = 462$, $m\angle B = 49$

2. $c = 215$, $m\angle B = 57$

*For Exercises **3–4**, c and m∠B are given. Find a to the nearest whole number.*

3. $c = 485$, $m\angle B = 62$

4. $c = 12.3$, $m\angle B = 55$

*For Exercises **5–6,** c and m∠A are given. Find a to the nearest tenth.*

5. $c = 21.2$, $m\angle A = 18$

6. $c = 93.2$, $m\angle A = 68$

*For Exercises **7–8,** c and m∠A are given. Find b to the nearest tenth.*

7. $c = 200$, $m\angle A = 14$

8. $c = 12\frac{1}{2}$, $m\angle A = 60$

9. A guy wire 40 meters long runs from the ground to the top of a pole. (See the figure at the left below.) It makes a 64° angle with the line drawn to the foot of the pole. Find the height of the pole.

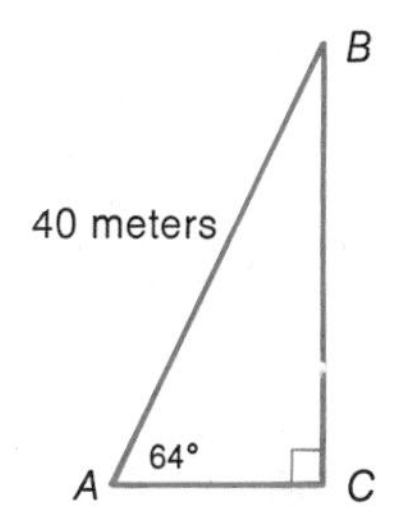

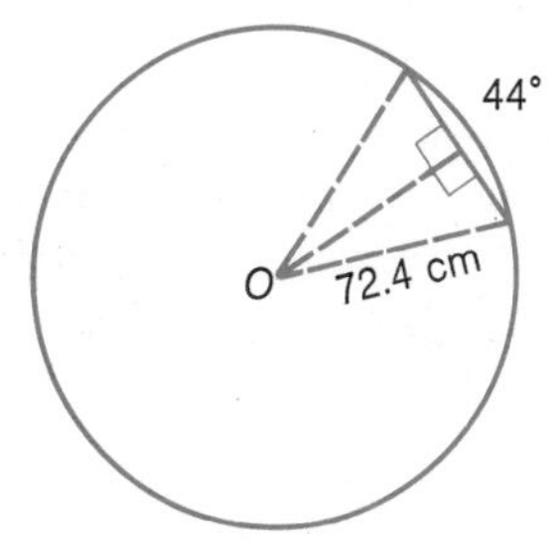

10. The radius of a circle is 72.4 cm. (See the figure at the right above.) Find the length of a chord whose arc measures 44°.

11. The congruent sides of a roof are $\overline{AC}$ and $\overline{BC}$ as shown below. Find the length of $\overline{AB}$, the <u>span</u> of the roof.

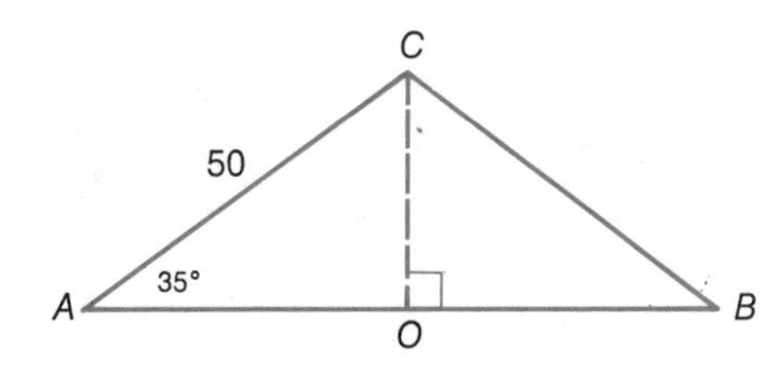

12. The measure of each base angle of an isosceles triangle is 70. The length of each of the legs is 5.2. Find the length of the base.

b

13. Two legs of a right triangle have lengths of 12 and 16. Find the sine and cosine of the smaller acute angle. (HINT: Use the Pythagorean theorem first.)

14. Two legs of a right triangle have lengths of $\frac{1}{2}$ and $\frac{6}{5}$. Find the sine and cosine of the larger acute angle. (HINT: Use the Pythagorean theorem first.)

15. A chord in a circle is 52 meters long. Radii drawn to the endpoints of the chord form an angle of 110°. Find the length of a radius of the circle.

16. A flagpole is broken and the top has fallen over so that it touches the ground. The two parts form a right triangle with the ground. The upper part forms a 32° angle with the ground and touches it at a point 23 meters from the foot of the pole. Find the original height of the pole.

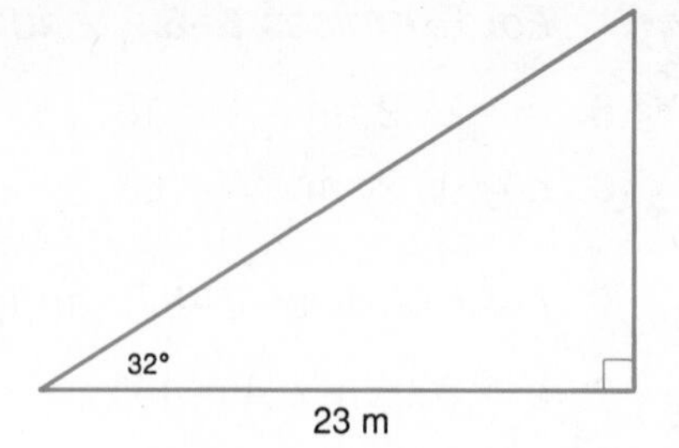

17. In a right triangle ABC, angle C is a right angle and $\overline{CD}$ is perpendicular to $\overline{AB}$. If tan A is $\frac{3}{4}$ and the length of $\overline{AC}$ is 10, find BC, CD, and AD.

18. A ladder 10 meters long is resting against a vertical wall. The ladder makes an angle of 60° with the horizontal ground. If the foot of the ladder is drawn away 1 meter, how far down the wall will the top of the ladder descend? Give your answer to the nearest meter.

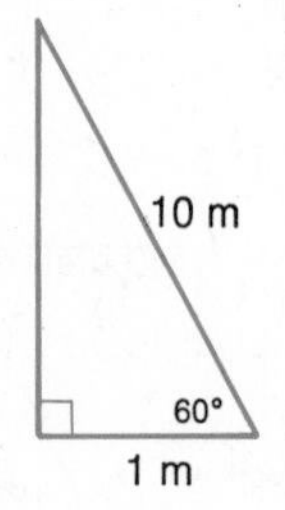

C **19.** $\overline{AC}$ is a diameter of a circle and $\overleftrightarrow{AD}$ is a tangent. $\overline{BC}$ is drawn from one end of the diameter to a point B on $\overleftrightarrow{AD}$. Angle CBA measures 40. $\overline{BC}$ intersects the circle at E and $\overline{CE}$ measures 10 centimeters. Find the length of the radius of the circle to the nearest tenth.

PUZZLE

Find the area of the smallest square in each figure. Each square has a horizontal side or a side inclined at 45° to the horizontal.

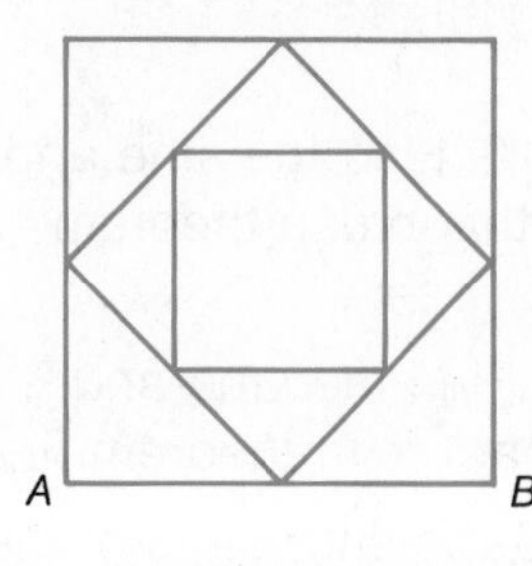

$AB = 12$

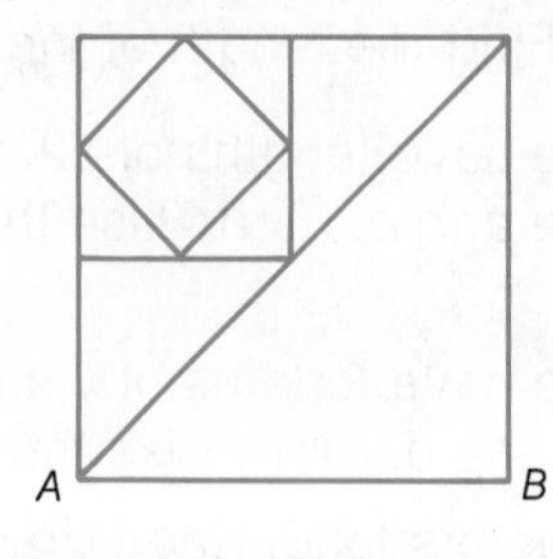

$AB = 12$

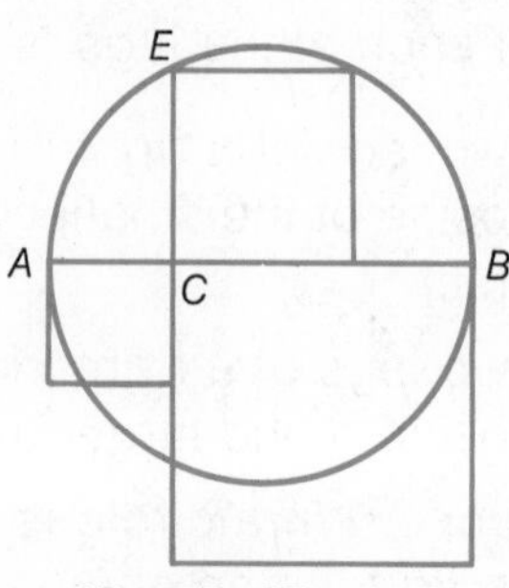

$AB = 13$; $CE = 6$

12-4 Solving Problems

Example 1

A road rises 350 meters in a distance of 3000 meters along the road. Find the measure, to the nearest degree, of the angle that the road makes with the horizontal.

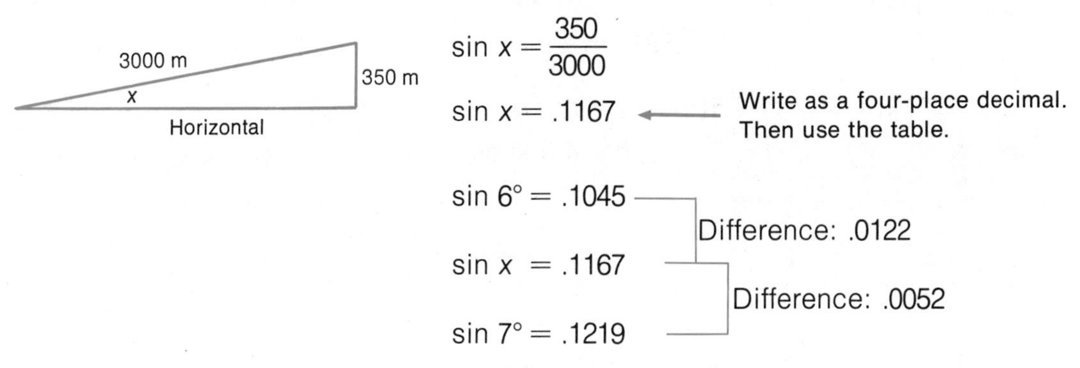

$$\sin x = \frac{350}{3000}$$

$$\sin x = .1167$$ ← Write as a four-place decimal. Then use the table.

$\sin 6° = .1045$
Difference: .0122
$\sin x = .1167$
Difference: .0052
$\sin 7° = .1219$

Since .1167 is closer to sin 7°, angle x measures about 7 degrees.

When you look up toward an object, your line of sight forms an **angle of elevation** with a horizontal line in the same vertical plane. (See angle x in Example 1.)

Example 2

Find, to the nearest degree, the angle of elevation of the top of a tower 56 meters high from a point 90 meters from C.

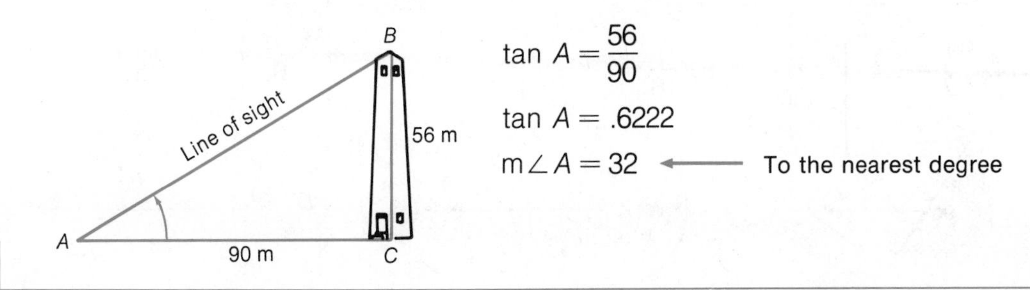

$$\tan A = \frac{56}{90}$$

$$\tan A = .6222$$

$$m\angle A = 32$$ ← To the nearest degree

If a viewed object is below, rather than above, the observer, an **angle of depression** is formed.

Example 3

An airplane pilot notes that the angle of depression to an airport measures 28° when the plane is above a point 7.5 kilometers from the airport. Find the altitude of the plane to the nearest tenth.

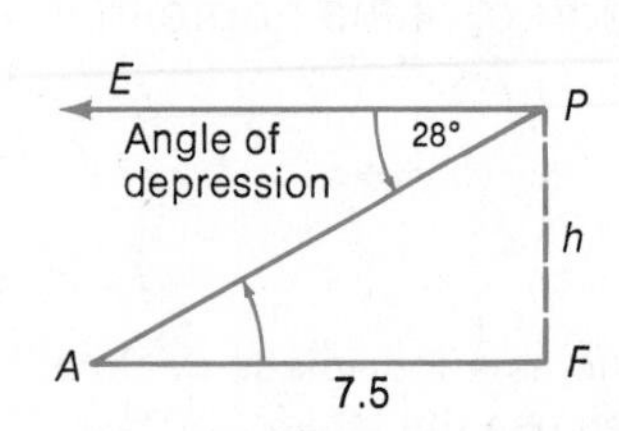

$$\tan 28° = \frac{h}{7.5}$$ ← $\angle EPA$ and $\angle A$ are alternate interior angles. Thus, $m\angle A = 28$.

$$.5317 = \frac{h}{7.5}$$

$$7.5(.5317) = h$$

$$h = 4.0 \text{ kilometers}$$ ← To the nearest tenth

Try These

For Exercises **1–6,** *express each ratio as the sine, cosine, or tangent of an angle measure. Then find x to the nearest whole number or to the nearest degree.*

1. $\frac{x}{100} = \underline{\ ?\ }$

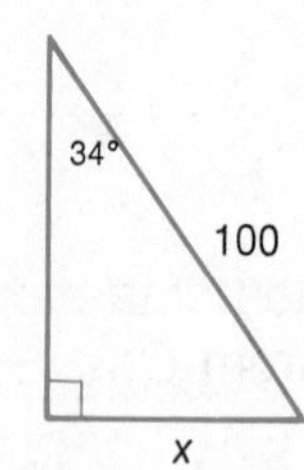

2. $\frac{20}{x} = \underline{\ ?\ }$; $\frac{x}{20} = \underline{\ ?\ }$

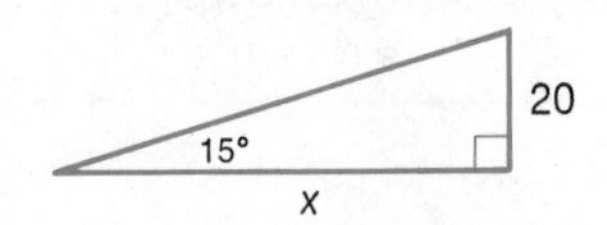

3. $\frac{x}{162} = \underline{\ ?\ }$

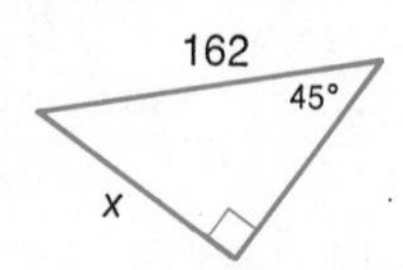

4. $\frac{90}{50} = \underline{\ ?\ }$

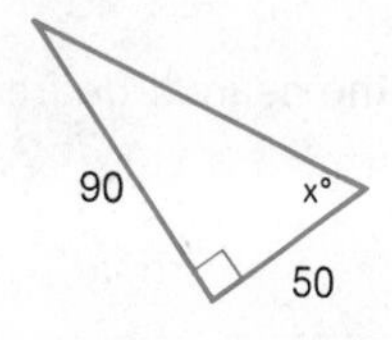

5. 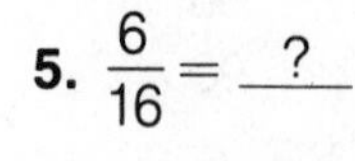 $\frac{6}{16} = \underline{\ ?\ }$

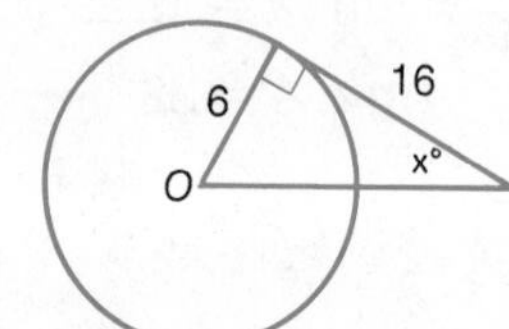

6. 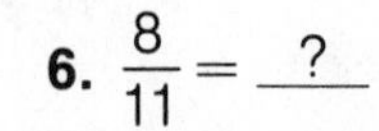 $\frac{8}{11} = \underline{\ ?\ }$

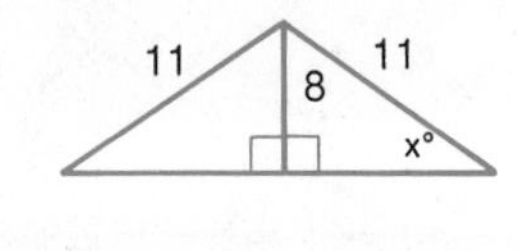

Exercises

In Exercises **1–12,** *give each answer to the nearest whole number or to the nearest degree.*

a

1. The angle of elevation of a monument is 53° from a point on level ground that is 35 meters from the base. Find the height of the monument.

2. A ladder 5.2 meters long leans against a building and makes an angle of 68° with the ground. How far up the building does the ladder reach?

3. In isosceles triangle ABC, sides AB and BC are congruent. The measure of $\angle ABC$ is 48° and $AB = 32$. Find the length of $\overline{BD}$, the altitude to $\overline{AC}$.

4. A ladder 13 meters long resting upon the ground reaches a point 11 meters high upon a vertical wall. Find the measure of the angle of elevation formed by the ladder and a horizontal line that includes the foot of the ladder and that is perpendicular to the wall.

5. Two 120-meter high towers are 800 meters apart. Find the measure of the angle of elevation from the base of one to the top of the other.

6. The angle of elevation of the top of a tree from a point 17 meters from its foot is 42°. Find the height of the tree.

7. From a plane flying at an altitude of 2000 meters, the measure of the angle of depression of a control tower is 38°. Find the distance along the ground from a point directly below the plane to the tower.

8. The regular polygon below is inscribed in circle O whose radius is 12. Find the measure of central angle AOB and of side AB.

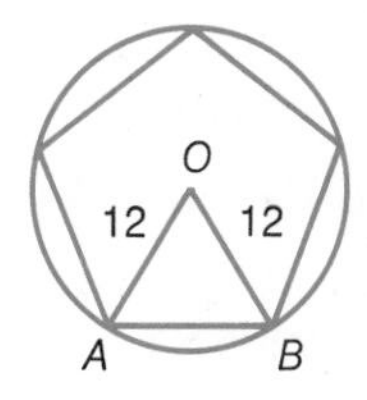

9. From the top of a building whose base is 2000 meters from a lake, the angle of depression to the lake measures 14°. Find the height of the building to the nearest meter.

10. Find the radius of a circle circumscribed about a square whose side measures 7.5 centimeters.

11. Find your own height in meters. Then calculate the length of the shadow you would cast when the angle of elevation of the sun is 47°.

12. The diagonal of a rectangle measures 12 centimeters. It makes an angle of 67° with the shorter side of the rectangle. Find the length of the longer side of the rectangle.

13. In the figure at the right, $\triangle EAC$ is inscribed in circle O, $\overline{OB} \perp \overline{AC}$, $m\angle OAB = 25$, and $OA = 12.6$ centimeters. Find AC.

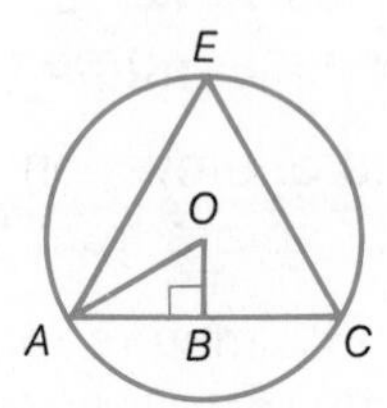

14. In $\triangle DAC$, $\overline{DB}$ is the perpendicular bisector of $\overline{AC}$, $m\angle A = 73$, and $DA = 35$ meters. Find AC.

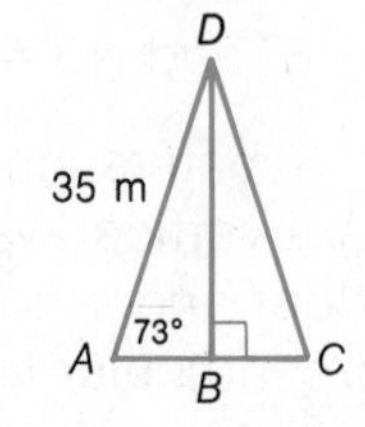

b

15. A tree 66 meters high casts a 44-meter shadow. Find the measure of the angle of elevation of the sun to the nearest degree.

16. A helicopter pilot flying at an altitude of 500 meters finds that the angle of depression of a buoy on the ocean is 52°. Find the number of meters it is from the buoy to a point directly below the helicopter.

17. The angle of elevation of C from point A measures 18°, and the angle of elevation of C from point B measures 24°. If C is at an altitude of 1000 meters, find the distance between points A and B.

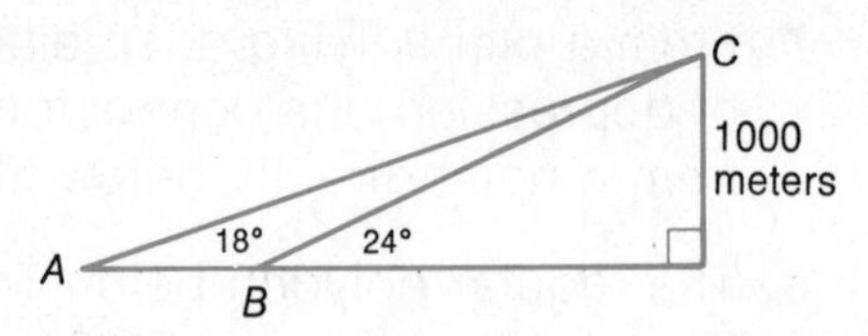

C

18. Each edge of a cube measures 10 centimeters. Find the smallest angle formed by the intersection of two diagonals of the cube. Express your answer to the nearest degree.

19. An acute angle of a right triangle measures y. Prove that $(\sin y)^2 + (\cos y)^2 = 1$.

20. Use $\triangle ABC$ at the right to show that $\frac{\sin A}{\sin B} = \frac{a}{b}$. (HINT: Draw the altitude to $\overline{AB}$ from C.)

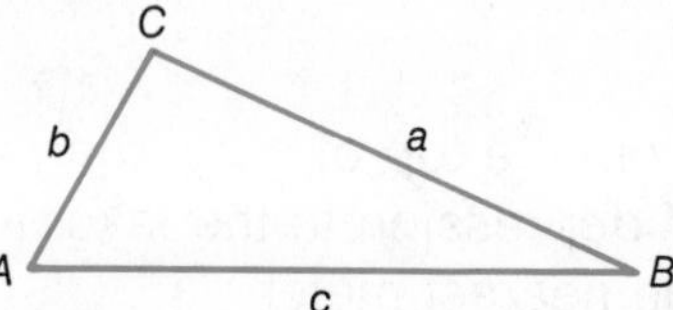

Mathematics and Astronomy

Astronomers—sometimes called astrophysicists—collect and analyze data on the sun, moon, planets, stars, and so on. Although having a degree in astronomy may be the easiest way to enter this field, students with a bachelor's degree in mathematics or physics can qualify for graduate work in astronomy. Courses in computer science and statistics are growing in importance.

One problem faced in the study of outer space is the identification of elements in the universe. The **spectroscope** is used to help in this identification. A prism (usually made of glass) is used in a spectroscope to separate a beam of light, say from the sun, into a spectrum of colors—from red to violet—like a rainbow.

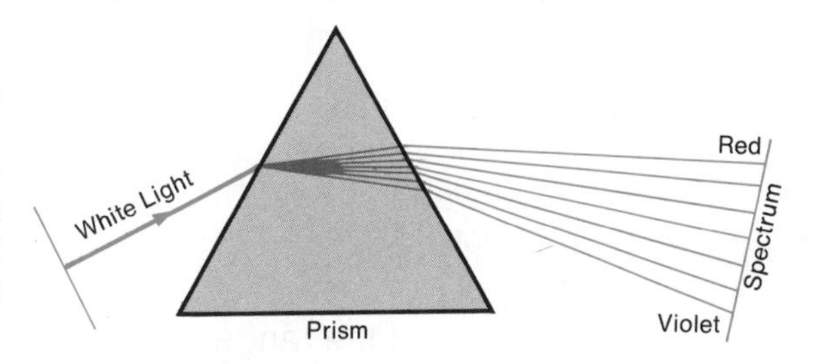

The parallel lines of a spectrum are then recorded on photographic film to produce a **spectrogram** of the substance being analyzed. Each element has a unique spectrogram. To identify an unknown element, its spectrogram is compared with spectrograms of known elements. This involves comparing the parallel lines for a "match." The photograph below shows the spectra (plural of spectrum) of the sun and of iron. It indicates that there is iron in the sun.

These photographs show other ways that prisms can be used to "bend" light.

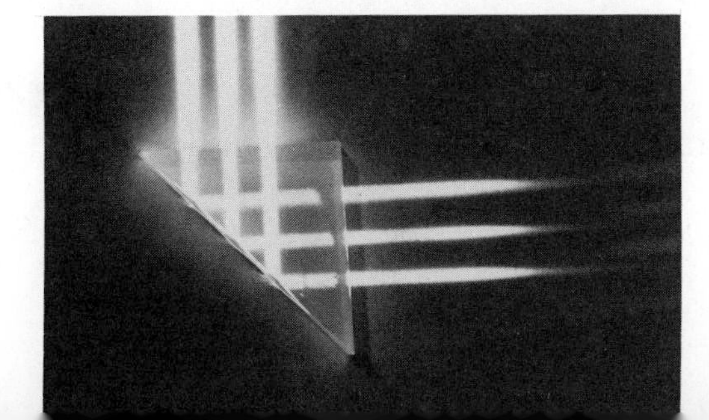

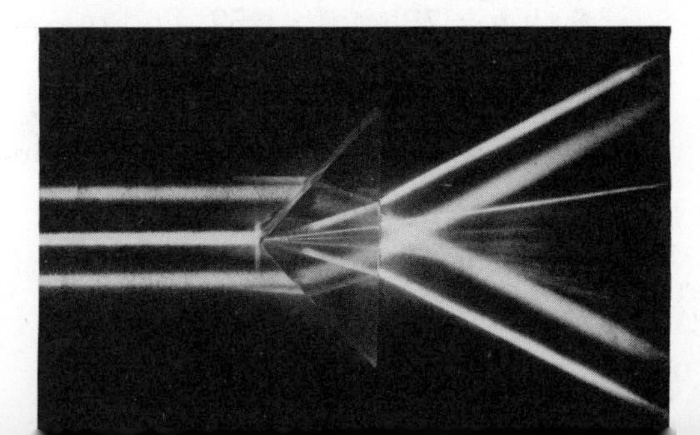

Chapter Objectives and Review

Objective: To recall, and give examples of, the important mathematical terms of the chapter.

1. Be sure that you know the meaning of these mathematical terms used in Chapter 12.

adjacent leg (p. 496)
angle of depression (p. 508)
angle of elevation (p. 507)
cosine ratio (p. 502)
opposite leg (p. 496)
sine ratio (p. 502)
tangent ratio (p. 496)
trigonometric ratio (p. 497)

Objective: To find the tangent of an acute angle. (Section 12-1)

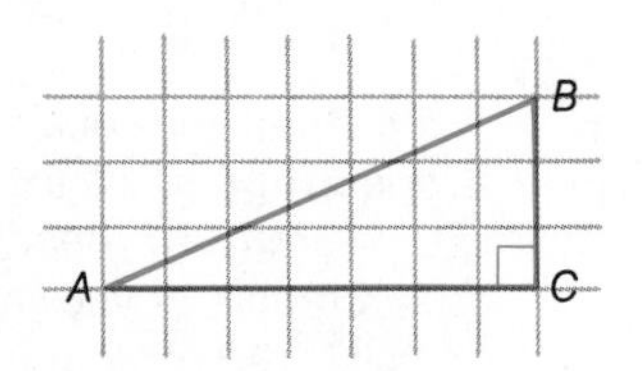

2. For $\triangle ABC$ at the right, find tan A and tan B. Express each answer in fraction form and in decimal form to four decimal places.

Objective: To use a table of Sines, Cosines, and Tangents. (Sections 12-1, 12-2, 12-3, 12-4)

Use the table on page 581 to find x.

3. $\sin 27° = x$

4. $\cos 88° = x$

5. $\tan x = 1.8040$

Objective: To use the tangent ratio to solve problems with right triangles. (Section 12-2)

Refer to $\triangle ABC$ below. Give answers to the nearest whole number.

6. If $m\angle A = 28$ and $b = 82$, find a.

7. If $m\angle B = 65$ and $b = 104$, find a.

8. If $a = 75$ and $b = 52$, find $m\angle A$ and $m\angle B$.

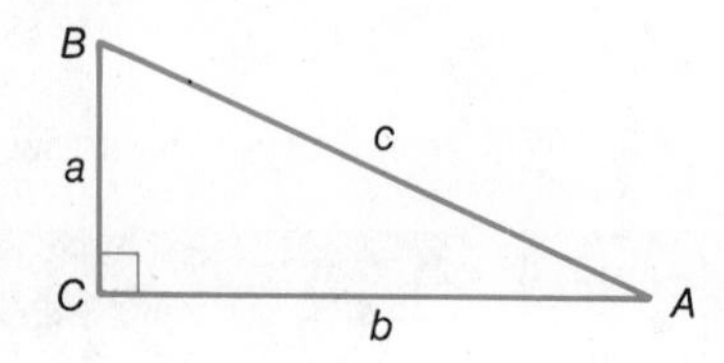

Objective: To use the sine and cosine ratios to solve problems with right triangles. (Section 12-3)

9. In right triangle ABC, the hypotenuse AB is 15 centimeters long and $m\angle A = 37$. Find AC and BC to the nearest centimeter.

10. In isosceles triangle RST, the length of the altitude to base RS is 18 and the length of each leg is 26. Find $m\angle R$ to the nearest degree.

*For Exercises **11–13,** express each ratio as the sine, cosine, or tangent of an angle measure.*

11. $\frac{a}{8} = \underline{\ ?\ }$

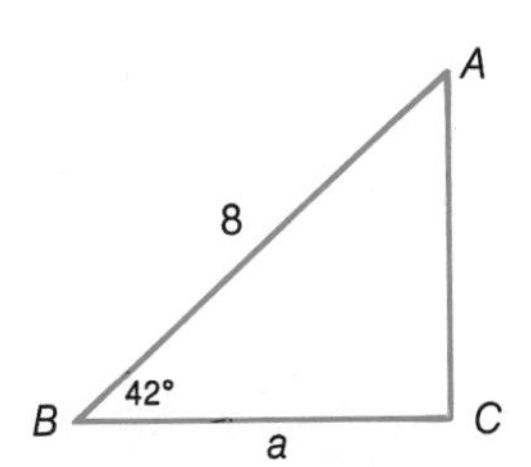

12. $\frac{7}{12} = \underline{\ ?\ }$

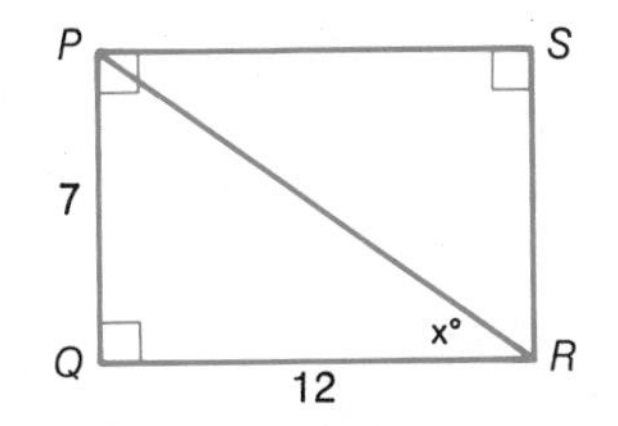

13. $\frac{h}{15} = \underline{\ ?\ }$

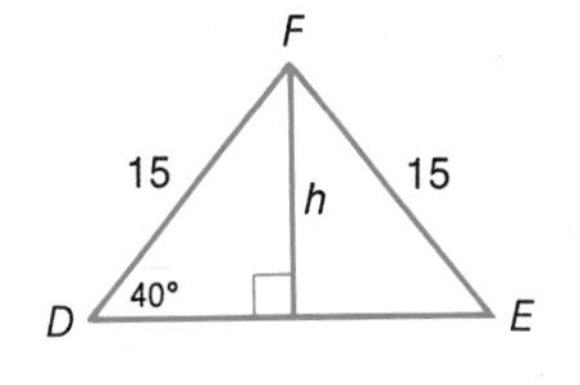

14. The base of an isosceles triangle is 26 and one of the base angles has a measure of 28°. Find the length of the altitude to the base.

Objective: To use the angle of elevation or the angle of depression in solving problems. (Section 12-4)

15. The angle of elevation of the top of a tower from a point 150 meters from its base is 8°. Find the height of the tower to the nearest meter.

Chapter Test

*Use $\triangle RST$ for Exercises **1–6**.*
Write each ratio as a fraction.

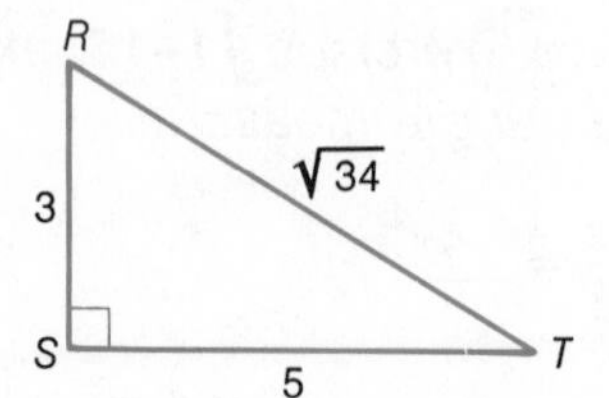

1. $\tan R = \underline{\ ?\ }$ **2.** $\sin R = \underline{\ ?\ }$

3. $\tan T = \underline{\ ?\ }$ **4.** $\cos T = \underline{\ ?\ }$

5. $\cos R = \underline{\ ?\ }$ **6.** $\sin T = \underline{\ ?\ }$

*For Exercises **7–9,** write an equation you can use to find x. Then find x to the nearest whole number.*

7.

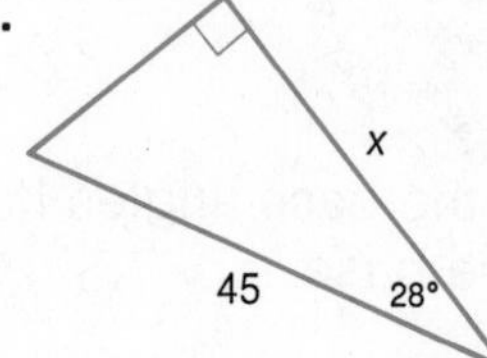

8.

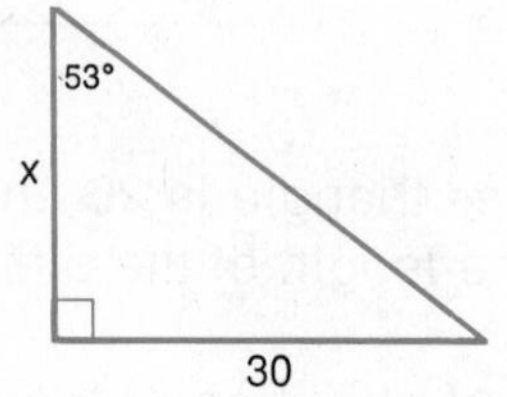

9.

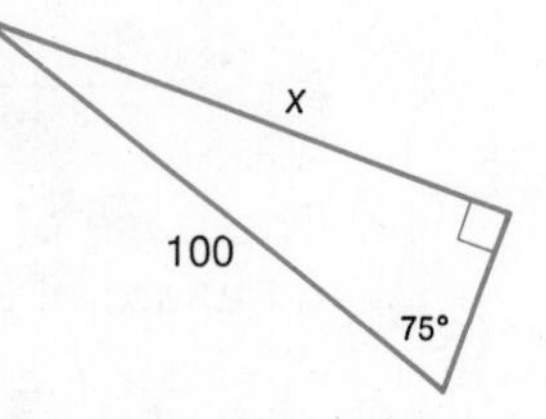

10. The length of each of the congruent sides of an isosceles triangle is 48 and the measure of each base angle is 72°. Find the length of the altitude to the base.

11. Triangle DAC is inscribed in circle O, $m\angle AOB = 30$, $\overline{OB} \perp \overline{AC}$, and $OA = 6.3$. Find AC.

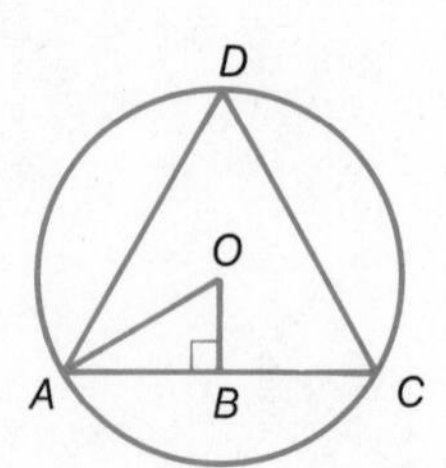

Answers to Remember

Page 499: **1.** 18 **2.** 2 **3.** 12 **4.** 10.5 **5.** 25 **6.** 3.2

Chapter 13

Introduction to Transformations

13-1 Reflections over a Line

A **transformation** is a relation in which a point P is paired with exactly one point P' (P prime) called its **image.** One such transformation is a **reflection.**

Example 1

Find the image of points A, B, C, and D where k is the reflecting line, or **line of reflection.** Note that D is on line k.

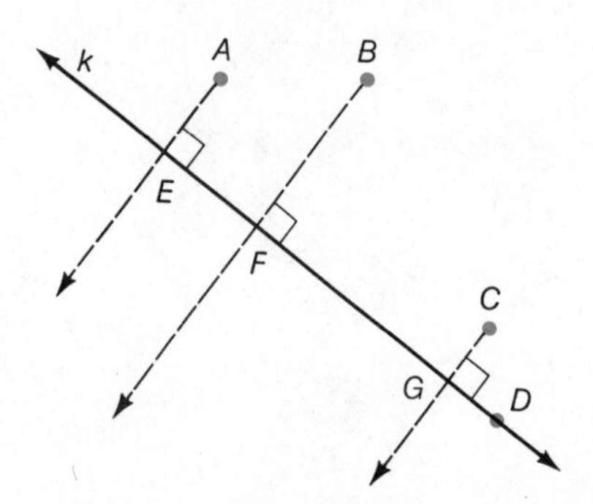

Draw perpendiculars from A, B, and C to line k. Since D is on line k, this cannot be done for point D.

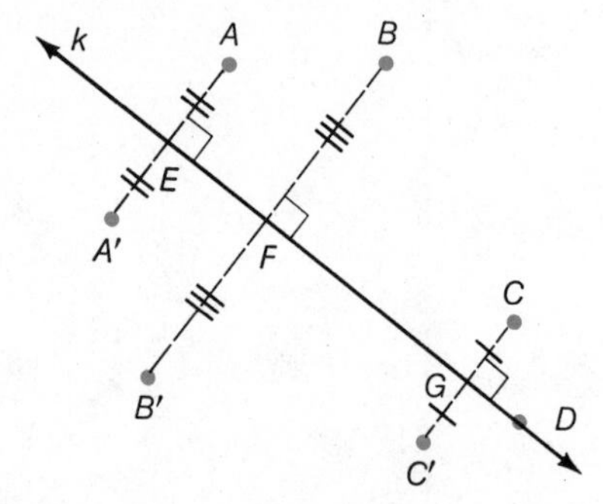

Measure $\overline{AE}$. Locate A' such that $AE = A'E$. Repeat this to find B' and C'. Since D is on line k, it is its own image.

Thus, the reflection of a point P over a line k maps P, called the **preimage,** onto its image, P'. If P is on k, then P is its own image.

Note that line k is the perpendicular bisector of $\overline{AA'}$, $\overline{BB'}$, and $\overline{CC'}$.

You can find the image of a geometric figure without finding the image of every point.

Since two points determine a ray or a line, you can find the image of a ray or line by reflecting two of its points. However, three points will be used in Example 2. Since three noncollinear points determine an angle or a triangle, you can find the image of an angle or triangle by reflecting three points.

Example 2

Find the image of $\overleftrightarrow{MP}$ and of $\angle ABC$.

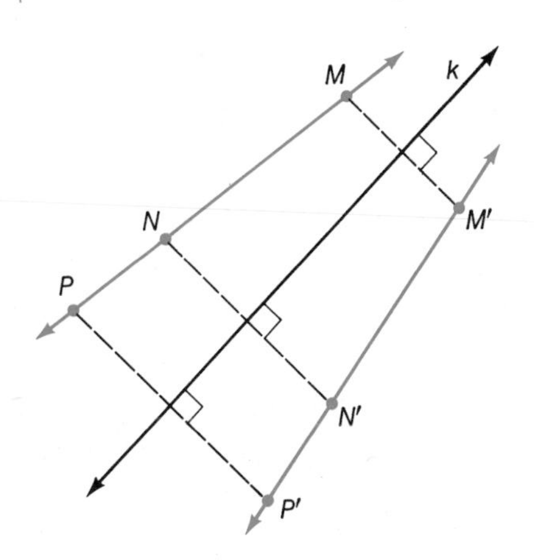

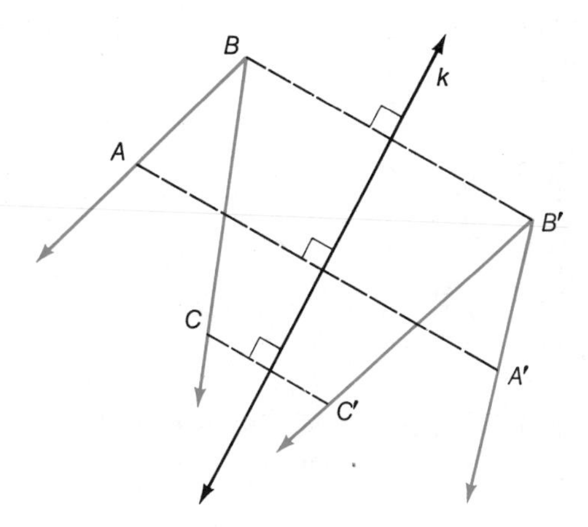

Find M', N', and P'.
Then draw $\overleftrightarrow{M'P'}$.

Find A', B', and C'.
Then draw $\overrightarrow{B'A'}$ and $\overrightarrow{B'C'}$.

By measuring $\overline{MN}$, $\overline{NP}$, $\overline{M'N'}$, and $\overline{N'P'}$, you will find that $MN = M'N'$ and $NP = N'P'$. Similarly, $m\angle ABC = m\angle A'B'C'$. Thus, segments map onto congruent segments, and angles map onto congruent angles. Since polygons are composed of segments and angles, it follows that a line reflection of a polygon will result in a congruent polygon. Thus, a reflection is a congruence mapping.

Try These

Name the least number of points needed to reflect each of the figures in Exercises ***1–8.***

1. Line
2. Ray
3. Segment
4. Angle
5. Triangle
6. Rectangle
7. Hexagon
8. Pentagon

Exercises

Copy each figure in Exercises **1–6.** *Find the reflection over line k for each figure.*

a

1.

2.

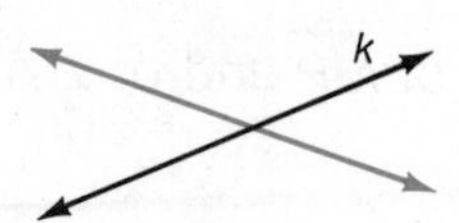

3.

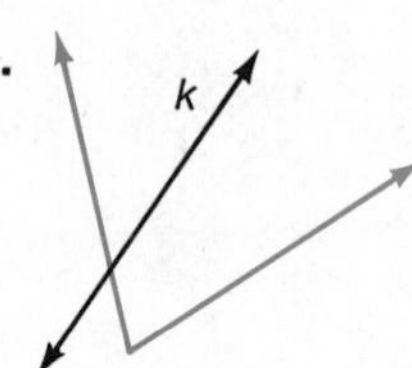

4.

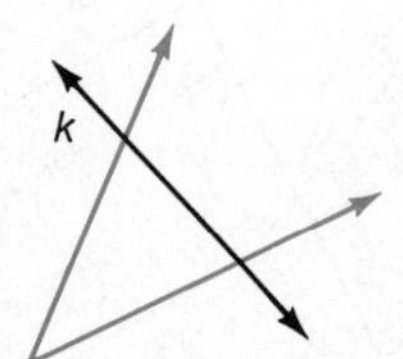

5.

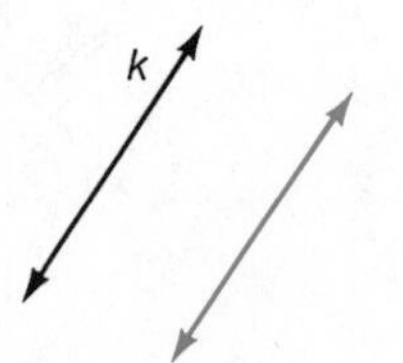

6.

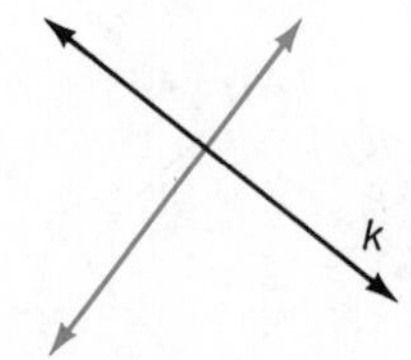

b

7. You are given lines r and s at the left below such that r is the image of s over a reflecting line k that is not shown. Copy this figure and find k.

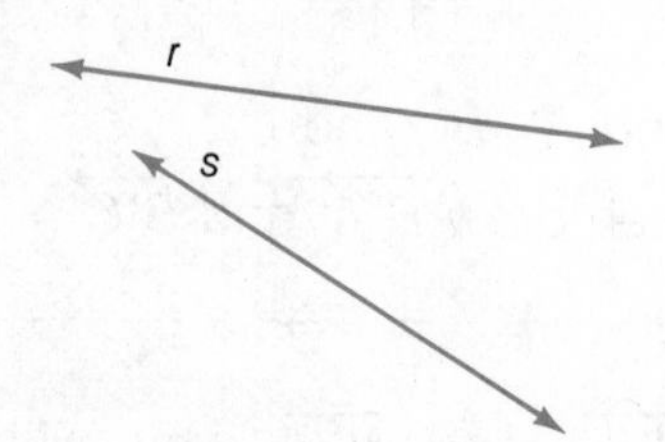

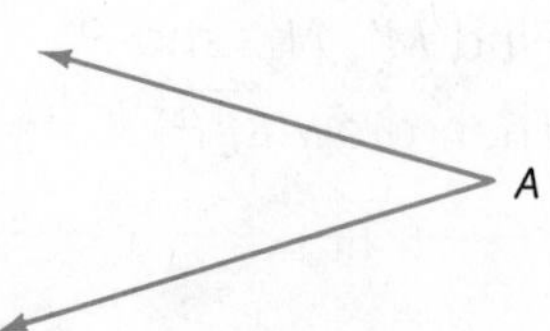

8. Copy the figure at the right above in which A' is the image of A. Find the image of $\angle A$.

9. Copy the figure at the right in which H' is the image of the midpoint of $\overline{AB}$. Construct the reflecting line.

10. Copy the figure at the right. Reflect the midpoints of each side of $\triangle ABC$ over line m. Then use the midpoints to find the image of $\triangle ABC$.

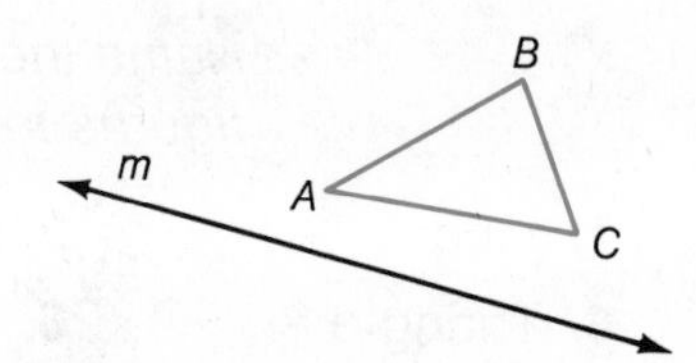

11. A surveyor wishes to find a point C on line m such that the distance from A to C to B is a minimum. Where on m should the surveyor place C?

Consider points P and A at the right.
To reflect A over P, draw $\overleftrightarrow{AP}$. The image of A over P is the point A′ on $\overleftrightarrow{PA}$, such that P is the midpoint of $\overline{AA'}$.
This is a ***point reflection.***
A is also the image of A′ over P.

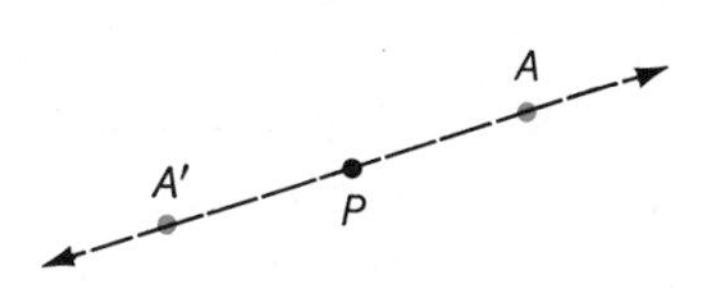

12. Copy the figure at the left below. Reflect points A, B, and C over P. Draw $\triangle ABC$ and its image $\triangle A'B'C'$. Compare the corresponding sides and angles of the two triangles.

13. Copy the figure at the right above. Reflect $\overline{AB}$ through P. Then reflect that image through Q. Label the image $A'B'$. What kind of figure does quadrilateral $AA'B'B$ appear to be?

14. In trapezoid $ABCD$ below, S and T are the midpoints of the nonparallel sides. Copy the trapezoid. Then show by a point reflection over point S that the area of the trapezoid equals the area of the rectangle whose height equals the height of the trapezoid, and whose base has the measure ST.

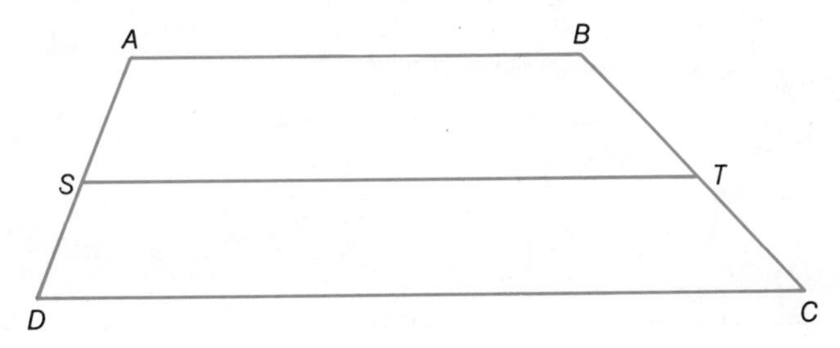

13-2 Special Reflections

If a line can be drawn through a geometric figure such that the figure on one side of the line is the reflection of the figure on the opposite side, the line is a **line of symmetry,** or axis of symmetry. The geometric figure is symmetrical with respect to the line. Some geometric figures, such as a square, are symmetrical with respect to more than one line.

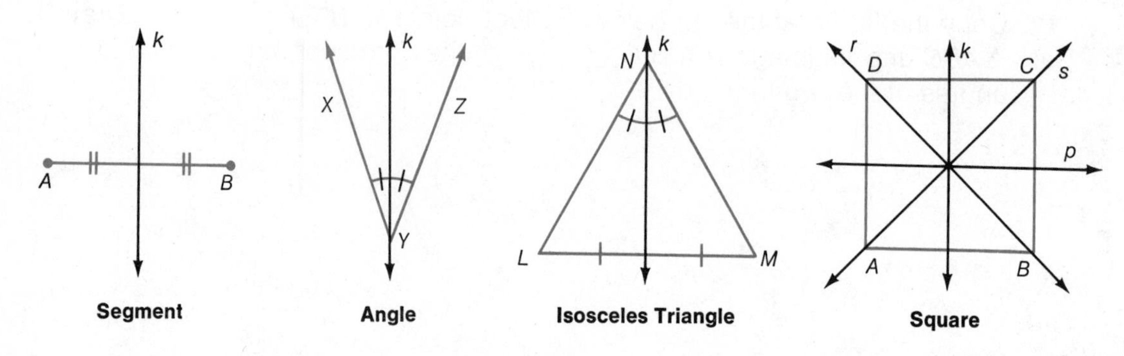

A reflection over a line produces a "mirror" effect. The image is the opposite of the geometric figure being reflected.

Example 1

Find the image of $\triangle EFG$ over k. Then find the image when $\triangle E'F'G'$ is reflected over line m, where $k \parallel m$.

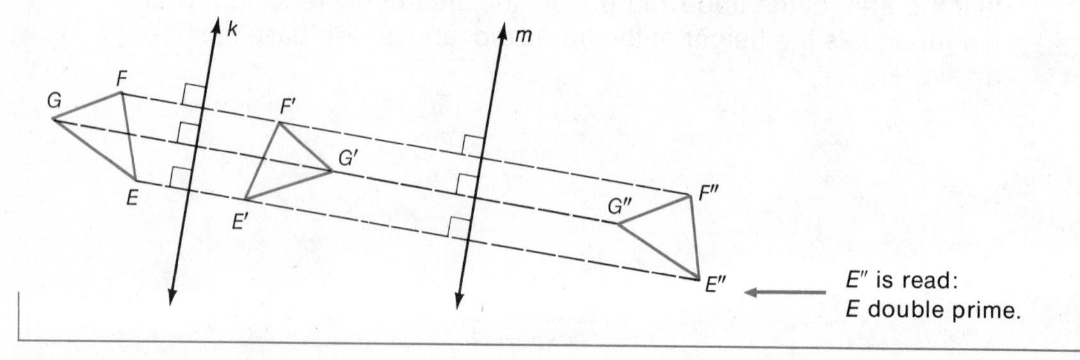

Example 1 illustrates a composition of two reflections over two parallel lines. This type of mapping of points is a **translation.** In Example 1, $\triangle E''F''G''$ is the image of $\triangle EFG$ under the translation. Since the image under a reflection is a congruence mapping, a composition of reflections is also a congruence mapping. Thus,

$$\triangle EFG \cong \triangle E''F''G''$$

It can be shown that a segment and its image are parallel under a translation. Thus, in Example 1,

$$\overline{FG} \parallel \overline{F''G''},\ \overline{FE} \parallel \overline{F''E''},\ \text{and}\ \overline{EG} \parallel \overline{E''G''}.$$

Example 2

Find the image of $\triangle EFG$ by reflecting $\triangle E''F''G''$ (the image of $\triangle EFG$ under the translation in Example 1) over line r, where $r \perp m$. Draw $\overline{FF'''}$ and label the intersection of $\overline{FF'''}$ and r as O. Compare FO with FF'''.

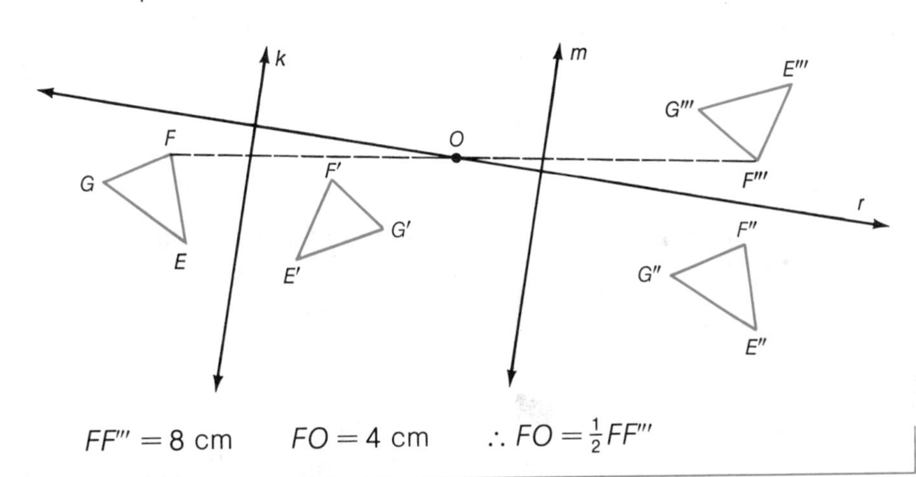

$FF''' = 8$ cm $\qquad FO = 4$ cm $\qquad \therefore FO = \frac{1}{2}FF'''$

Example 2 illustrates a composition of reflections called a glide reflection. A **glide reflection** maps every point P of a given geometric figure onto its image P''' by a translation followed by a reflection over a line that is perpendicular to the lines of translation.

It can be shown that the line of reflection bisects every such segment PP''', as is suggested by Example 2.

Try These

*In Exercises **1–8,** state the number of lines of symmetry for each figure. Make a sketch to help you.*

1. Scalene triangle
2. Right (not isosceles) triangle
3. Equiangular triangle
4. Isosceles triangle
5. Rhombus
6. Isosceles trapezoid
7. Kite
8. Rectangle

*For Exercises **9–10,** state whether the indicated composition of reflections is a translation.*

9.

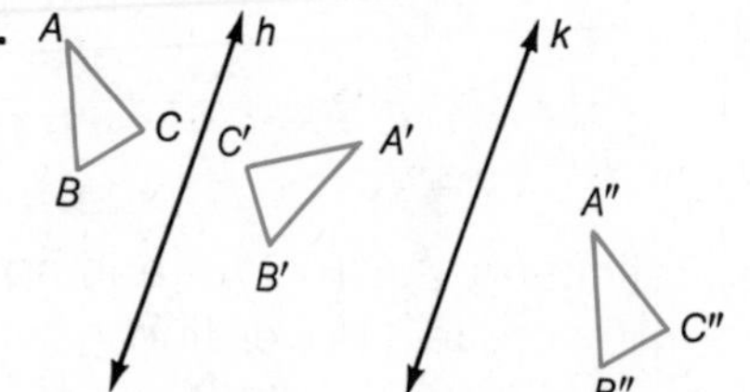

10.

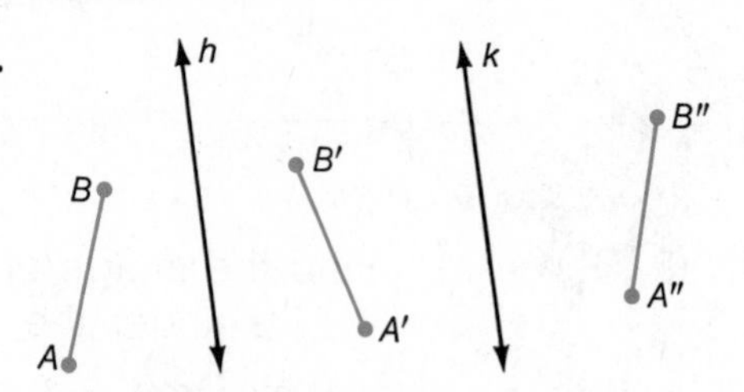

Exercises

a

1. State the number of lines of symmetry for each letter.

A B C D E H I J

2. In the figure below, $m \parallel k$. Copy the figure. Draw the image of $\triangle ABC$ over k. Then reflect the image, $\triangle A'B'C'$, over m. Measure $\overline{AA''}$, $\overline{BB''}$, and $\overline{CC''}$. Compare each of these measures with the distance between m and k.

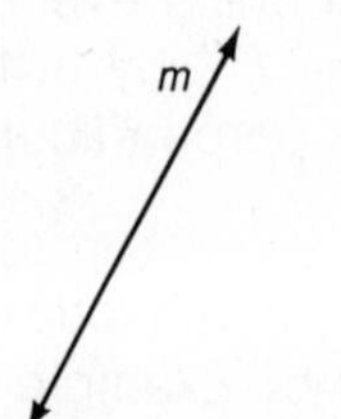

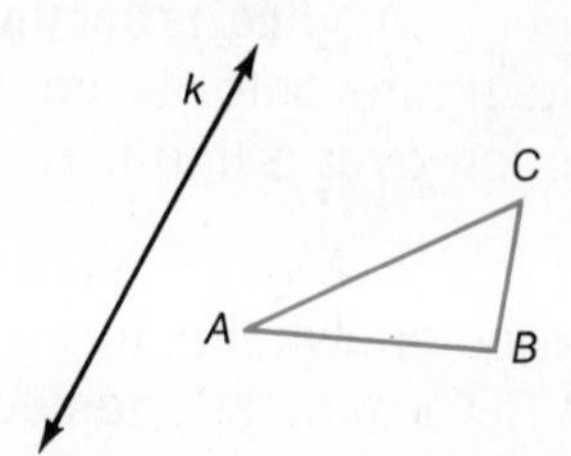

Copy each figure below. In each case $h \parallel k$. Translate $\overline{PQ}$ by reflecting it first over line h and then by reflecting the image over k.

3.

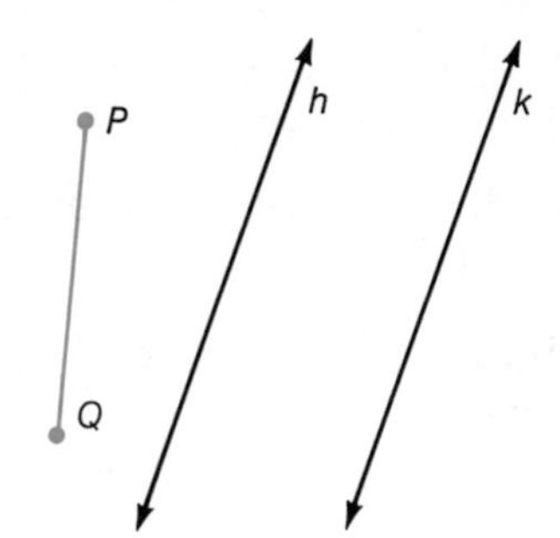

4.

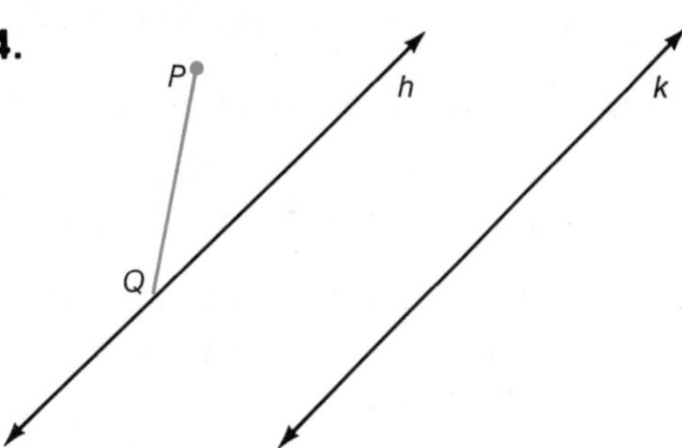

*In Exercises **5–6,** copy the figure. Then find an image under a glide reflection over k.*

5.

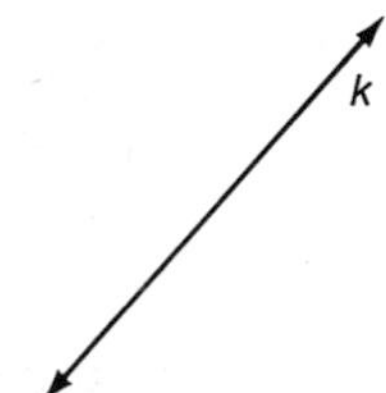

6.

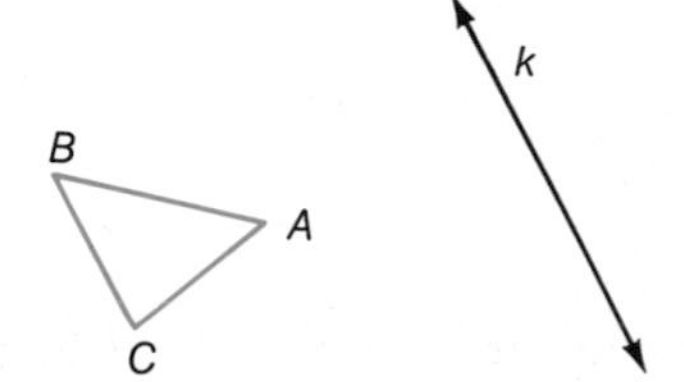

*In Exercises **7–10,** P', P'', P''' are all images of P under glide reflections over line k.*

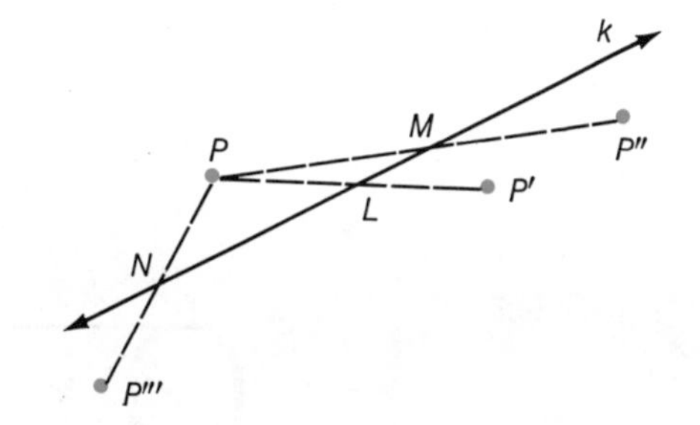

7. If $PL = 3$, find $P'L$.

8. If $PM = 4\frac{1}{2}$, find PP''.

9. If $PP''' = 5$, find NP'''.

10. If $PM = a$, find PP''.

11. Repeat Exercises **3–4** but reflect $\overline{PQ}$ over line k first. In what way are the two results different? In what way are the results alike?

12. Point P is mapped onto P' under a glide reflection. P is two centimeters from the reflecting line. The translation portion of the glide is a distance of three centimeters. Find PP'.

In each case $\overline{AB}$ is translated to its image of $\overline{A'B'}$. Find the coordinates of the missing endpoint.

13. $A(-1, 5)$, $B(4, 3)$; $A'(1, 2)$, $B'(?, ?)$

14. $A(1, -3)$, $B(4, -2)$; $B'(-2, 2)$, $A'(?, ?)$

15. The image of $A(-3, 2)$ under a glide reflection is $A'(5, -2)$ and the line of reflection is the x axis. Find the coordinates of the intersection of $\overline{AA'}$ with the line of reflection.

16. The line of reflection for a glide reflection is the graph of $y = x$. Point B is the image of point $A(2, 5)$ under this glide reflection and $\overline{AB}$ intersects the graph of $y = x$ in $(6, 6)$. Find the coordinates of B.

17. Points P and P' at the left below are two centimeters apart and P' is the image of P under a translation. Copy the figure and find two parallel lines for the translation.

18. In the figure at the right above, $\overline{A'B'}$ is the image of $\overline{AB}$ under a translation. Copy the figure and find two parallel lines for the translation.

PUZZLE

Two poles, a and b meters high, are perpendicular to the ground. Wires are stretched from the top of one pole to the foot of the other and they cross at a point h feet from the ground.

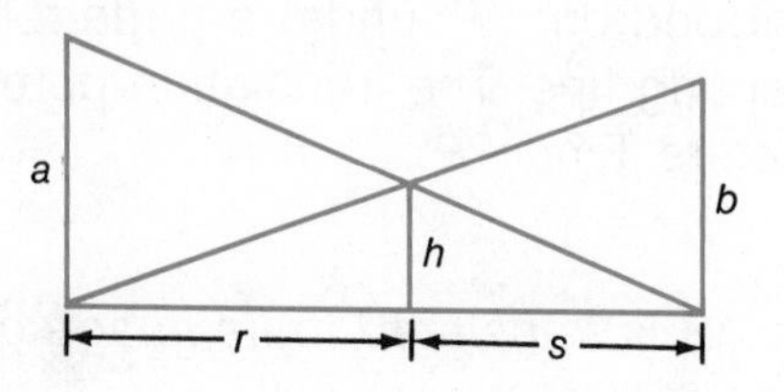

Prove that $\frac{1}{a} + \frac{1}{b} = \frac{1}{h}$.

13-3 Rotations

A composition of two reflections over two intersecting lines is a **rotation.**

Example 1

a. Find the image of $\triangle ABC$ by reflecting it over line s and then over line r, where s and r intersect in Q and $m\angle Q = 45$.

b. Find $m\angle BQB''$ and $m\angle CQC''$. Compare them with $m\angle Q$. Compare BQ and $B'Q$. Compare CQ and $C'Q$.

a.

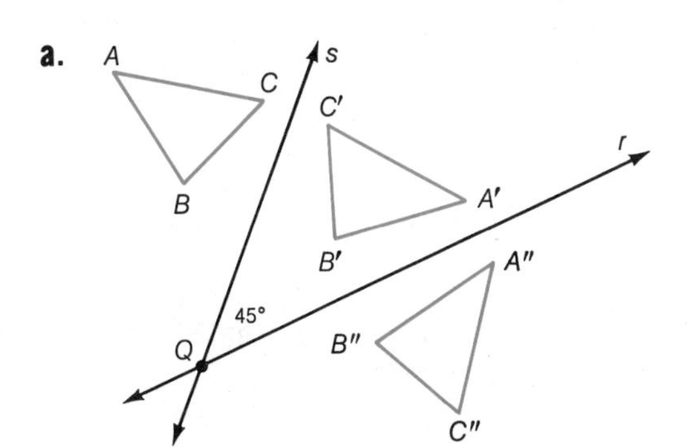

b.

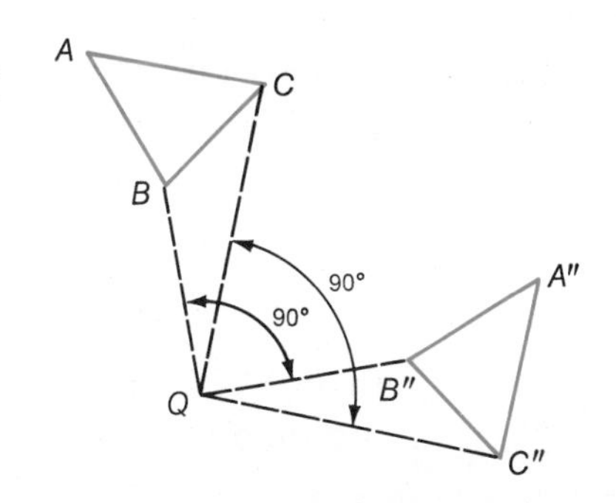

$m\angle BQB'' = 90$; $m\angle CQC'' = 90$
Since $m\angle Q = 45$, $2m\angle Q = m\angle BQB''$
and $2m\angle Q = m\angle CQC''$.
$BQ = B'Q$; $CQ = C'Q$

In Example 1, Q is the center of rotation. As Example 1 suggests, the angle determined by a preimage point, the center of rotation, and the image is twice the measure of the angle formed by the intersection of the reflecting lines. Further, the segment determined by the preimage and the center of rotation is congruent to the segment determined by the image and the center of rotation.

Example 2

Find the image of $\triangle EFG$ under a rotation for each measure of $\angle Q$.

a. $m\angle Q = 43$

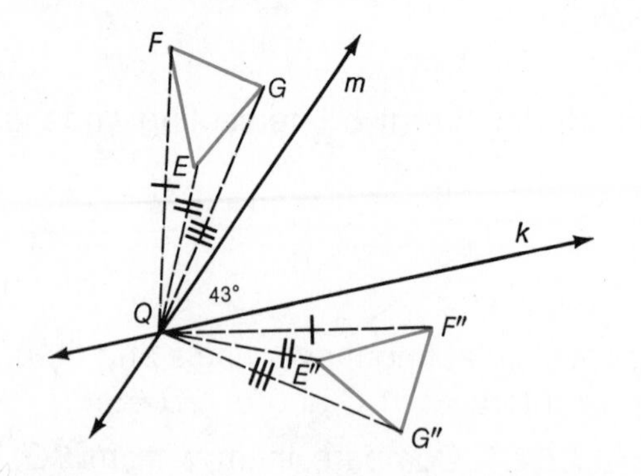

Draw $\angle EQE''$, $\angle FQF''$, and $\angle GQG''$, where each equals $2m\angle Q$, or 86. Since $EQ = QE''$, $FQ = QF''$, and $GQ = QG''$, locate E'', F'', and G''.

b. $m\angle Q = 90$

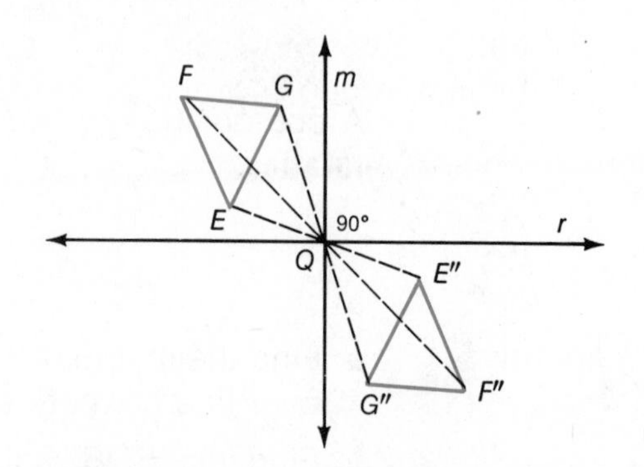

Draw $\angle EQE''$, $\angle FQF''$, and $\angle GQG''$, where each equals $2m\angle Q$, or 180. Since $EQ = QE''$, $FQ = QF''$, and $GQ = QG''$, locate E'', F'', and G''.

Thus, a rotation can be performed by using an **angle of rotation,** which is $2m\angle Q$.

Example 2b illustrates a special rotation called a **half-turn,** since the measure of the angle of rotation is 180.

Exercises

*In Exercises **1–3,** first reflect the figure in red over h, then over k.*

a

1.

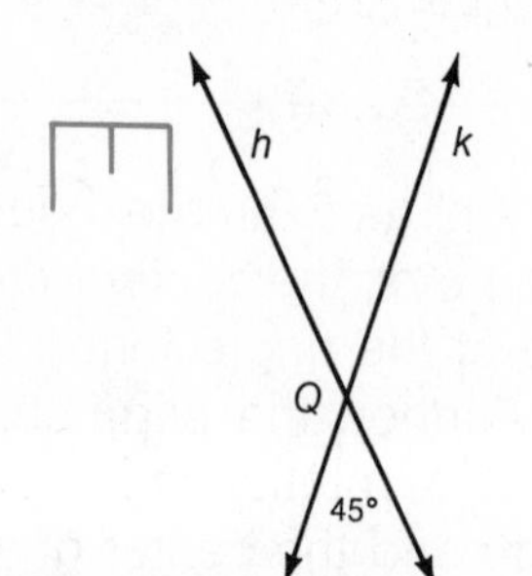

2.

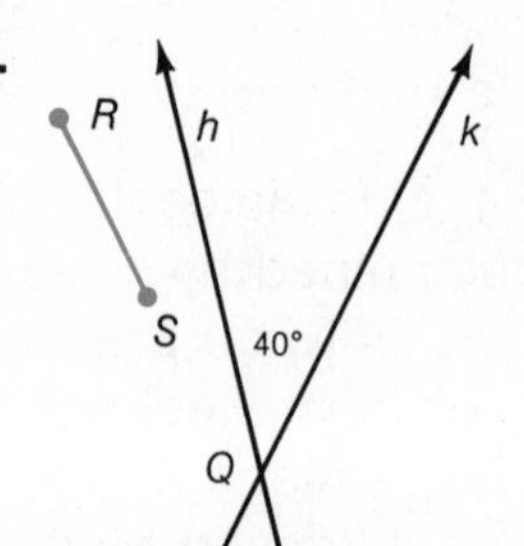

3.

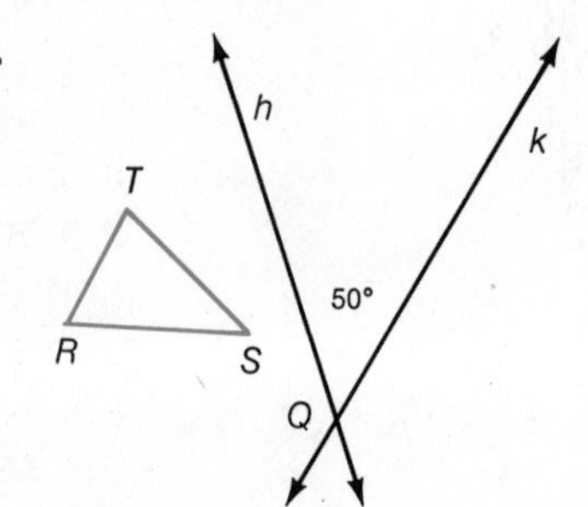

4. Reflect the figure in Exercise 1 first over k and then over h.
5. Reflect the figure in Exercise 2 first over k and then over h.
6. Reflect the figure in Exercise 3 first over k and then over h.
7. In Exercise 2, find the measures of $\overline{RS}$ and $\overline{R'S'}$.
8. Use a protractor to find the measures of $\angle RQR'$ and $\angle SQS'$ in Exercise 2.
9. In the figure at the left below, point A is mapped onto point B under a rotation through angle Q. Find the measure of $\angle AQB$.

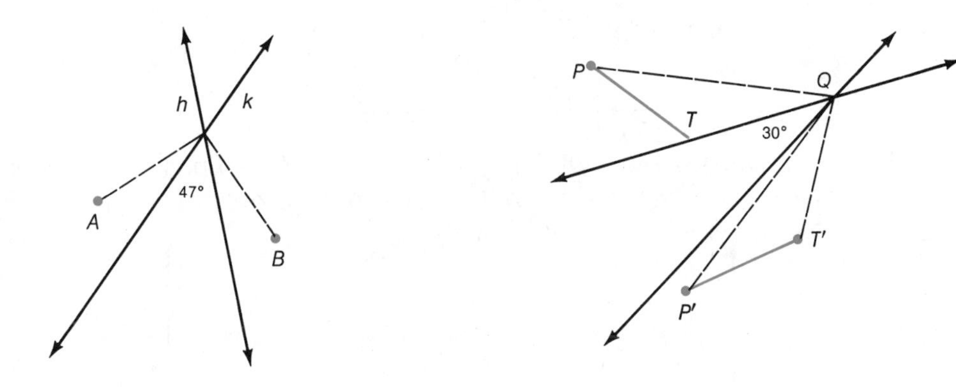

10. In the figure at the right above, $\overline{PT}$ is mapped onto $\overline{P'T'}$ under a rotation through angle Q. Find the measure of $\angle PQP'$ and $\angle TQT'$.
11. Point X is mapped onto point Y by a rotation whose center is A and $m\angle XAY = 164$. Find the measure of the acute angle formed by the reflecting lines of the rotation.
12. In the figure at the left below, Q is the center of rotation. Find the image of $\overline{ST}$ under a rotation of 72° clockwise.

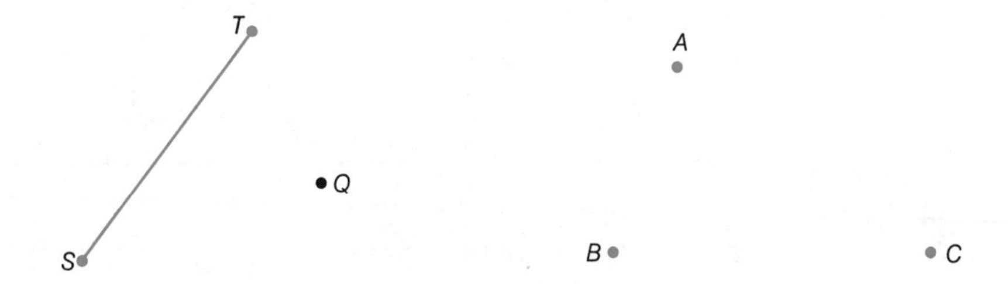

13. In the figure at the right above, A is mapped onto C by a counterclockwise rotation with center P. By the first reflection of the rotation, A is mapped onto B. Then B is then mapped onto C by a second reflection. Find the two reflecting lines and find their intersection P.

14. Copy $\triangle ABC$ and point P below and rotate $\triangle ABC$ through $50°$ using P as the center of rotation. (HINT: Find B' and A' in a manner similar to that shown for finding C'.)

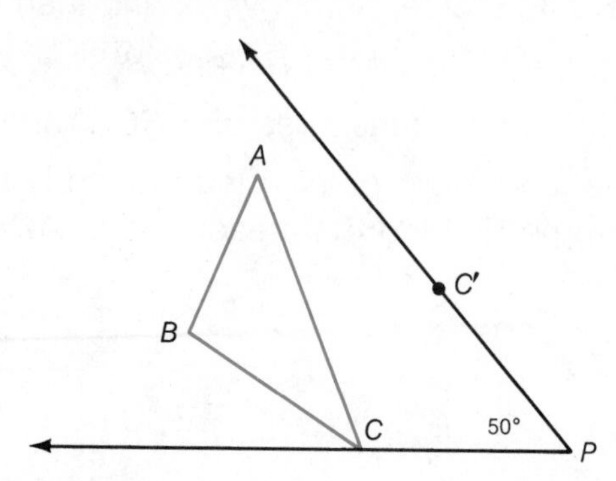

For Exercises ***15–16,*** *copy the given figure and the lines of reflection q and r ($q \perp r$). Reflect the figure first over q, then over r.*

15.

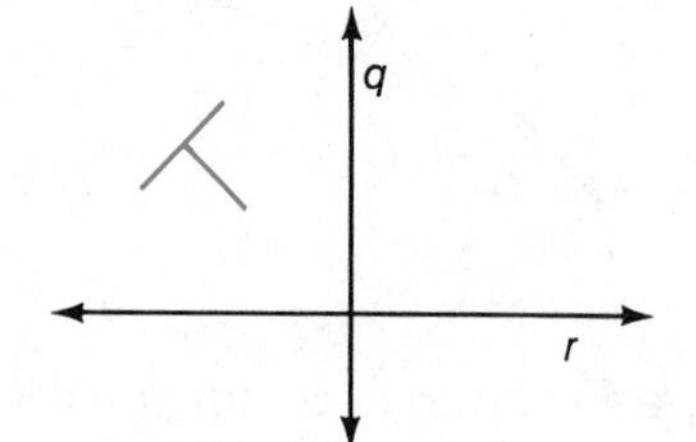

16.

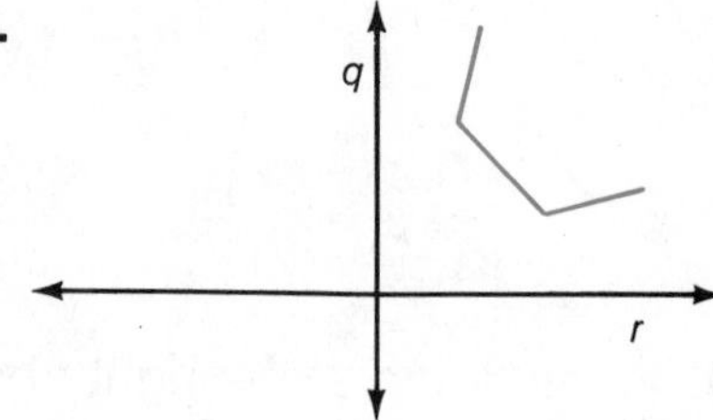

Write the coordinates of the image of each point under a rotation of 90° with the origin as center.

17. (5, 0) **18.** (3, 1) **19.** (−3, 1) **20.** (−2, −3)

PUZZLE

The lanes on the running track shown at the right are one meter wide and are numbered from smallest to largest. How many meters headstart should a runner in Lane 2 have over a runner in Lane 1 so that each will cover 800 meters at the finish line?

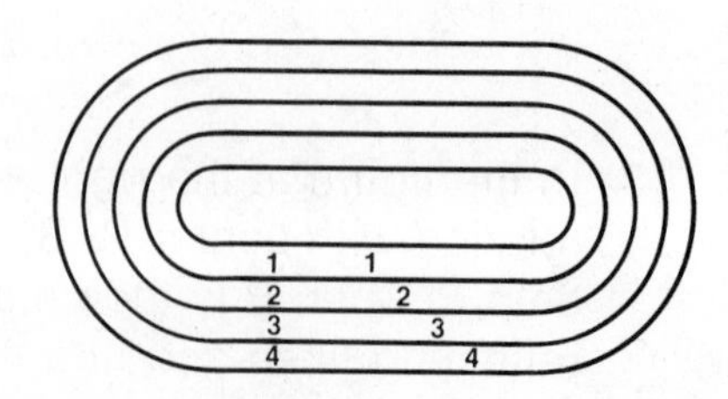

13-4 Dilations

Reflections, translations, glide reflections, and rotations are transformations that preserve distance, betweenness, collinearity, and angle measure. Such transformations are **isometries** (congruence mappings).

Example 1

Transform $\overline{AC}$ such that $OA' = 2\frac{1}{2}OA$, $OB' = 2\frac{1}{2}OB$, and $OC' = 2\frac{1}{2}OC$.

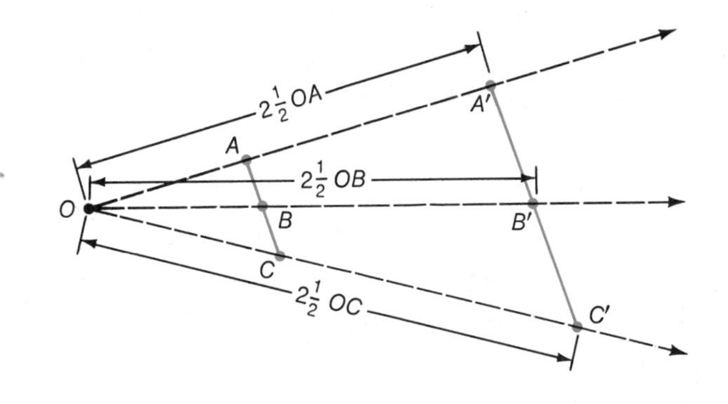

Draw rays OA, OB, and OC.

Measure $\overline{OA}$. Multiply by $2\frac{1}{2}$ to find A' on $\overrightarrow{OA}$.

Measure $\overline{OB}$. Multiply by $2\frac{1}{2}$ to find B' on $\overrightarrow{OB}$.

Measure $\overline{OC}$. Multiply by $2\frac{1}{2}$ to find C' on $\overrightarrow{OC}$.

Draw $\overline{A'C'}$.

Note that A', B', and C' are collinear and that B' is between A' and C'.

Under this transformation, $\overline{AC}$ is not congruent to $\overline{A'C'}$. Since distance is not preserved, this is not an isometry. However, collinearity and betweenness are preserved.

Example 2

Transform $\triangle XYZ$ such that $OX' = 2OX$, $OY' = 2OY$, and $OZ' = 2OZ$. Compare the measure of each angle in $\triangle XYZ$ with the measure of its image.

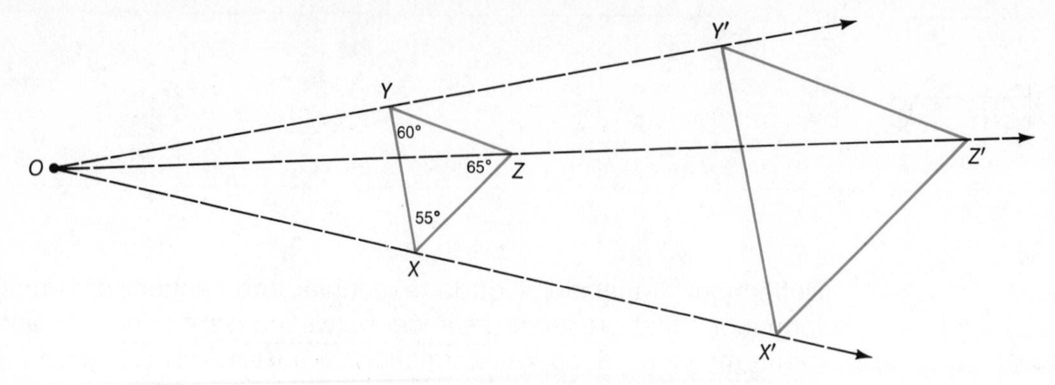

$m\angle X' = 55 \qquad \therefore m\angle X = m\angle X'$
$m\angle Y' = 60 \qquad \therefore m\angle Y = m\angle Y'$
$m\angle Z' = 65 \qquad \therefore m\angle Z = m\angle Z'$

Thus, angle measure is preserved under this transformation.

Examples 1 and 2 each illustrate a **dilation** (or **size transformation**), where O is the <u>center of the dilation</u>. The **magnitude,** k, of the dilation in Example 1 is $2\frac{1}{2}$. In Example 2, $k = 2$.

Example 3

a. Find the image of square $ABCD$ where $k = \frac{1}{2}$.
b. Compare the measure of each side and angle in square $ABCD$ with that of both sides and angles of its image.

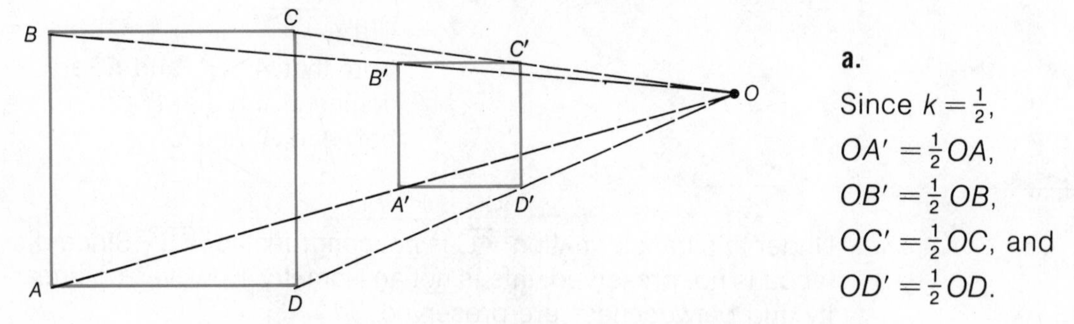

a.
Since $k = \frac{1}{2}$,
$OA' = \frac{1}{2}OA$,
$OB' = \frac{1}{2}OB$,
$OC' = \frac{1}{2}OC$, and
$OD' = \frac{1}{2}OD$.

b. $A'B' = \frac{1}{2}AB$; $B'C' = \frac{1}{2}BC$; $C'D' = \frac{1}{2}CD$; $D'A' = \frac{1}{2}DA$
$m\angle A = m\angle A'$; $m\angle B = m\angle B'$; $m\angle C = m\angle C'$; $m\angle D = m\angle D'$
$\therefore$ Square $ABCD$ and its image are similar.

Examples 2 and 3 illustrate that angle measure is preserved in a dilation.

In Example 3, the dilatation is a **contraction,** since $0 < k < 1$. In Examples 1 and 2, the dilation is an **expansion** since $k > 1$. If $k = 1$, the dilation is an **identity mapping,** since each image point is its own preimage.

Try These

In Exercises 1 and 2 use a ruler to find QA′, QA, QB′, and QB. Then find k, the ratio of QA′ to QA and the ratio of QB′ to QB.

1.

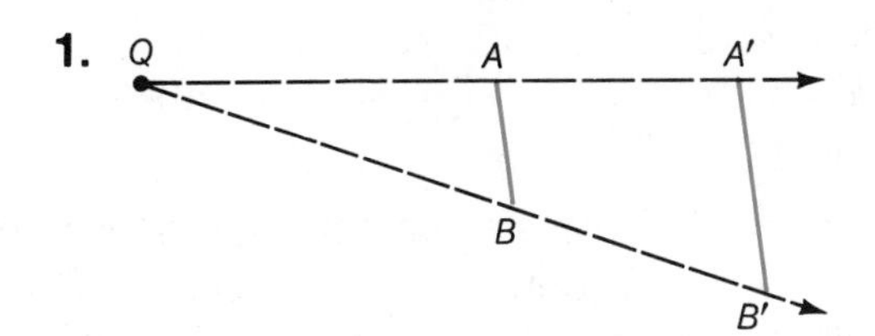

2.

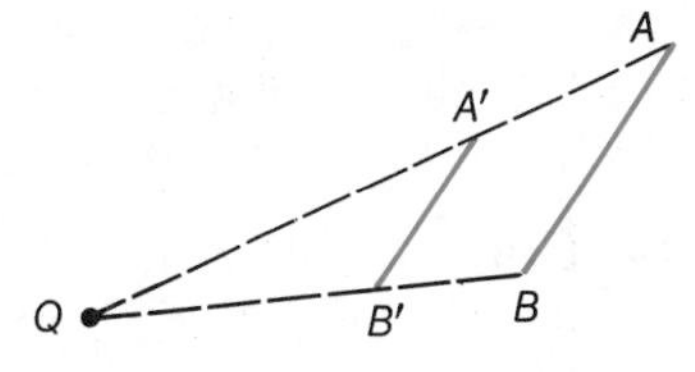

3. In Exercise 1, $A'B' = \underline{\ ?\ }\ AB$.

4. In Exercise 2, $A'B' = \underline{\ ?\ }\ AB$.

Exercises

Refer to the figure below for Exercises ***1–10.***

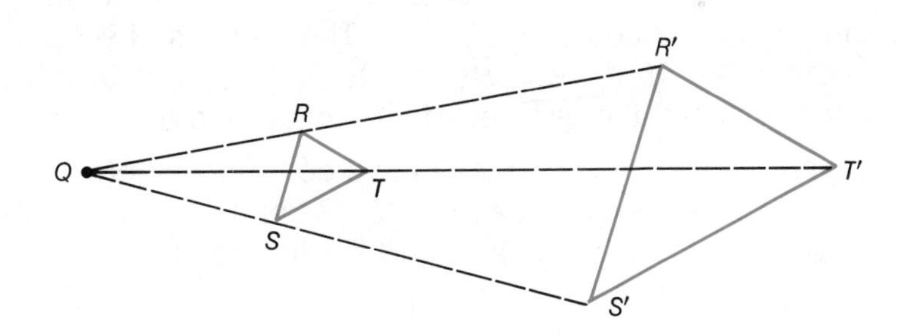

a

1. If $QS' = 12$ and $QS = 3$, then $k = \underline{\ ?\ }$.
2. If $k = 5$ and $QR = 8$, then $QR' = \underline{\ ?\ }$.
3. If $QR = 3$ and $RR' = 2$, then $k = \underline{\ ?\ }$.
4. If $k = 3$ and $QR = 2$, then $RR' = \underline{\ ?\ }$.
5. If $k = 2$ and $SR = 7$, then $S'R' = \underline{\ ?\ }$.
6. If $k = 4$ and $ST = \frac{3}{4}$, then $S'T' = \underline{\ ?\ }$.
7. If $QS':QS = 5:3$, then $R'T':RT = \underline{\ ?\ }$.

8. If R' is between Q and R, then k __?__ 1. $(>, =, <)$

9. If $m\angle R = 94$, then $m\angle R' =$ __?__.

10. If $m\angle S = 20$ and $m\angle T = 80$, then $m\angle R' =$ __?__.

11. If three points of a line are mapped onto their images under a dilation, will their images be collinear?

12. Name a property not preserved under a dilation that is preserved under a reflection.

13. Draw isosceles triangle ABC with base AB of 1 cm and each leg 2 cm in length. Select any point on the exterior of $\triangle ABC$, and call it O. Let O be the center of a dilation in which $k = 2$. Find the image triangle $A'B'C'$. Then find $A'B'$, $A'C'$, and $B'C'$.

14. Draw $\triangle ABC$ with sides of 3, $3\frac{1}{2}$, and 4 centimeters. Select any point in the interior of $\triangle ABC$, and call it O. Let O be the center of a dilation with $k = 3$. Find the image triangle $A'B'C'$. What are the lengths of the sides of $\triangle A'B'C'$?

b

15. If the measure of each side of polygon $ABCD$ is $\frac{2}{3}$ of the corresponding side of a polygon $EFGH$ under a dilation in which $k = \frac{3}{2}$, which polygon is the preimage?

16. Draw two parallel segments AB and CD. Find the images of $\overline{AB}$ and $\overline{CD}$ under a dilation in which $k = 2\frac{1}{2}$. Are the images parallel?

17. Draw two perpendicular segments RS and PQ. Find the images of $\overline{RS}$ and $\overline{PQ}$ under a dilation in which $k = \frac{1}{2}$. Are the images perpendicular?

c

18. Square $ABCD$ is mapped onto its image by a dilation in which $k = \frac{1}{2}$. The center O has coordinates (1, 1). The vertices of square $ABCD$ have coordinates $A(-1, -3)$, $B(-1, 3)$, $C(5, 3)$, and $D(5, -3)$. Find the coordinates of the vertices of the image and the area of the image.

19. Given $\triangle ABC$ whose vertices have coordinates $A(-3, 0)$, $B(-1, 3)$, and $C(4, 0)$, what is the area of $\triangle ABC$? Let the origin be the center of a dilation in which $k = 2$, and find the image of $\triangle ABC$. What is the area of the image of $\triangle ABC$?

Mathematics and Mineralogy

A **geologist** is an environmental scientist who studies the structure and composition of the earth's crust. Persons planning to become geologists study mathematics, physics, chemistry, and engineering in college. Courses in statistics and computer programming are also becoming important.

A geologist who specializes in the analysis and classification of minerals and precious stones is called a **mineralogist.** This analysis and classification is done according to the composition and structure of the substance. For example, similarities between crystals are revealed by their *symmetry*.

For the three crystals in the top row, the *axis of rotation* is indicated by the dashed line. A rotation of 120° causes each crystal to coincide with itself. Since there are three positions in which the crystal will coincide with itself, this is called a *threefold axis*. For these crystals, there are four threefold axes, three *fourfold axes*, and six *twofold axes*.

The *symmetric property of reflection in a plane* is exhibited by the crystals in the second and third rows. For each of these crystals, there are nine such planes.

These crystals also have a *point of symmetry*.

A crystal such as galena *(a principal ore of lead) with all of these symmetry elements has a* cubic unit cell *as its basic building block. This cell structure is suggested by the rectangular shape of the fragments shown in the photograph of galena* above.

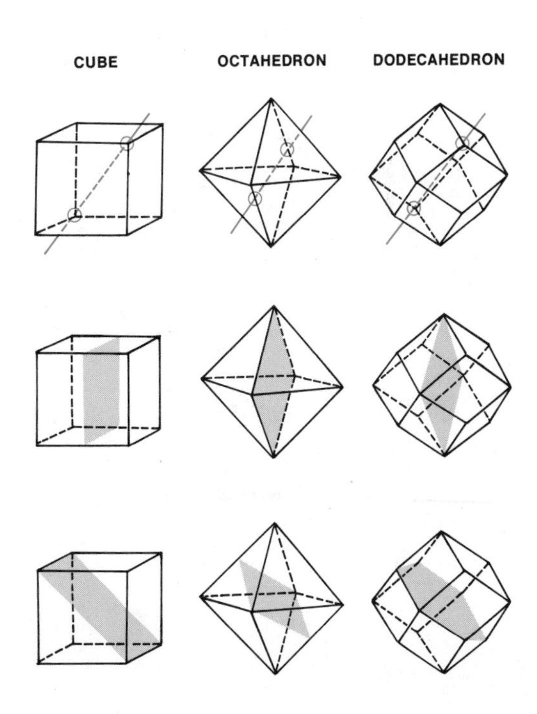

Chapter Objectives and Review

Objective: To recall, and give examples of, the important mathematical terms of the chapter.

1. Be sure that you know the meaning of these mathematical terms used in Chapter 13.

angle of rotation (p. 526)
contraction (p. 531)
dilation (p. 530)
expansion (p. 531)
glide reflection (p. 521)
identity mapping (p. 531)
image (p. 516)
isometry (p. 529)
line of reflection (p. 516)
line of symmetry (p. 520)
magnitude of dilation (p. 530)
preimage (p. 516)
reflection (p. 516)
rotation (p. 525)
translation (p. 521)
transformation (p. 516)

Objective: To find the reflection of a set of points over a given line. (Section 13-1)

Copy each figure. Find the reflection over line k for each figure.

2. 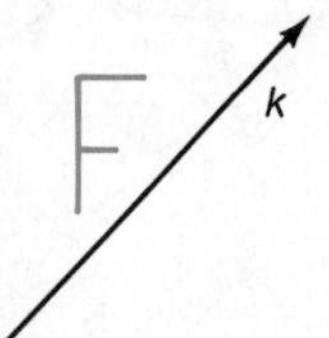

3. 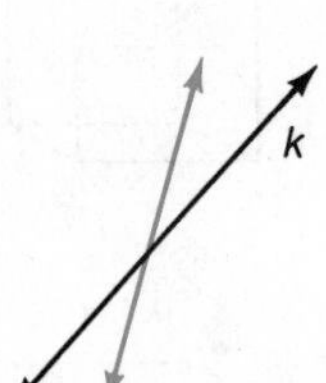

4. 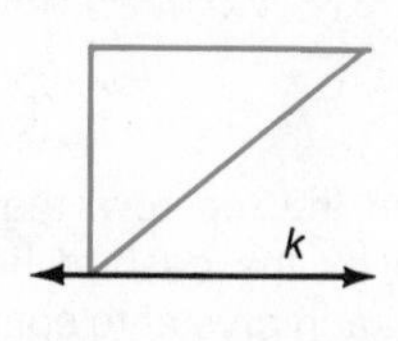

5. 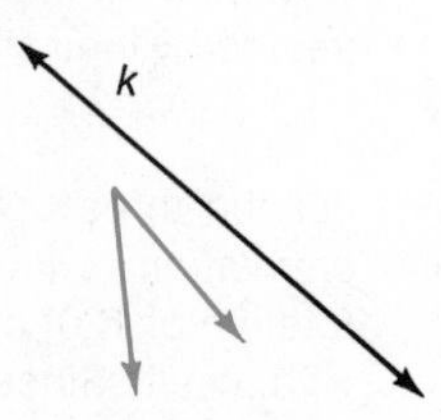

Objective: To identify lines of symmetry in a plane geometric figure. (Section 13-2)

In Exercises **6–9,** *state the number of lines of symmetry for each figure.*

6. 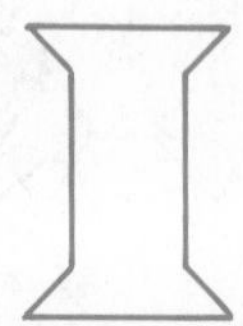

7. 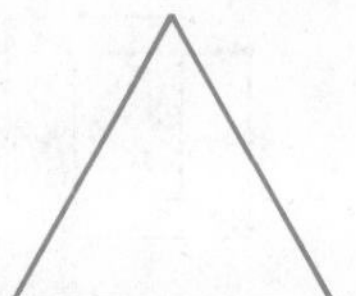

8. 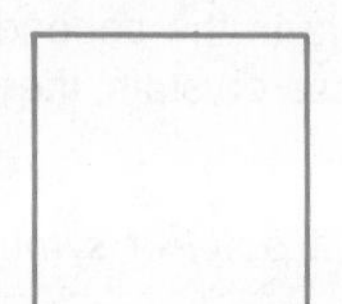

9. 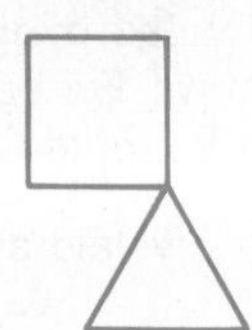

Objective: To translate a given figure. (Section 13-2)

Copy the figure. Translate $\overline{RS}$ by reflecting it first over line h, then over line k.

10.

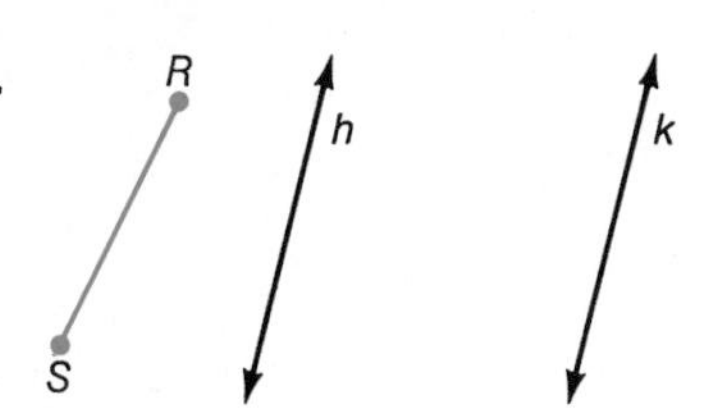

11.

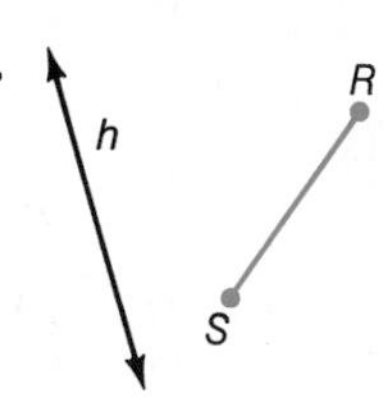

Objective: To transform a given figure in a glide reflection. (Section 13-2)

Copy the figure. Then find an image under a glide reflection over k.

12.

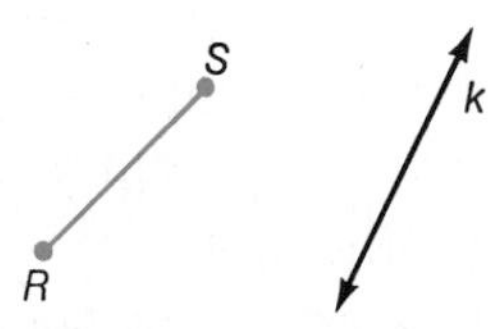

13.

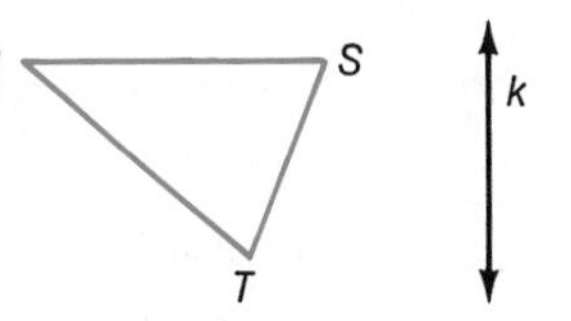

Objective: To rotate a given figure. (Section 13-3)

14. Copy the figure at the left below. Rotate $\overline{PQ}$ by reflecting it over h and then reflecting that image over k.

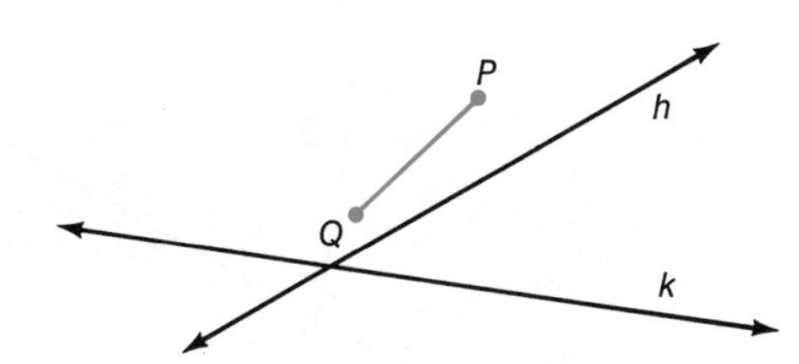

A

• T

B

15. Copy the figure at the right above. Find the image of $\overline{AB}$ under a clockwise rotation of 80°. Use T as the center of rotation.

Objective: To apply dilations to geometric figures. (Section 13-4)

Exercises ***16–19*** *refer to a dilation that maps $\overline{AB}$ onto $\overline{A'B'}$. The center of the transformation is Q and the magnitude is k.*

16. If $k = 3$ and $QA = 9$, then $QA' =$ _?_.
17. If $k = \frac{1}{2}$ and $QA = 7$, then $QA' =$ _?_.
18. If $k = 4$ and $AB = 8$, then $A'B' =$ _?_.
19. If $QA : QA' = 2 : 3$, then $AB : A'B' =$ _?_.

Chapter Test

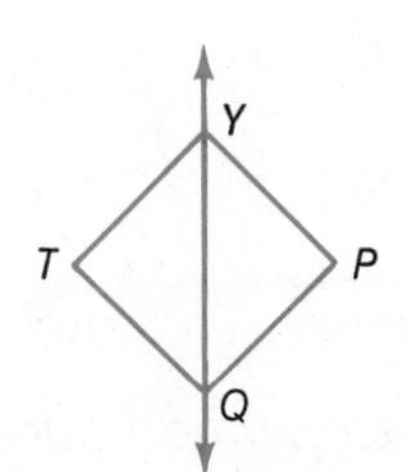

In the rhombus at the right, YQ is the line of reflection. Name the image of each of the following.

1. T **2.** Y **3.** $\overline{TY}$

4. $\overline{YQ}$ **5.** $\angle P$ **6.** $\angle YQT$

7. Two parallel lines of reflection are five centimeters apart. Point P is one centimeter from one of the given lines. P is reflected over that line and then over the second line. Find the distance from P to its final image.

8. Under a rotation with center Q that maps P onto P', the angle PQP' has a measure of 154. Find the measure of the acute angle formed by two intersecting lines that reflect P onto P'.

For Exercises ***9–10,*** *copy the given figure and the lines q and r. Then reflect the given figure over q and reflect that image over r. State whether the composition of the reflections is a rotation or translation.*

9.

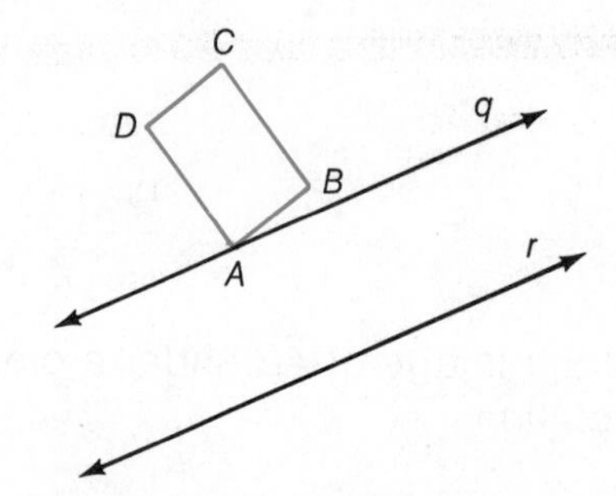

10.

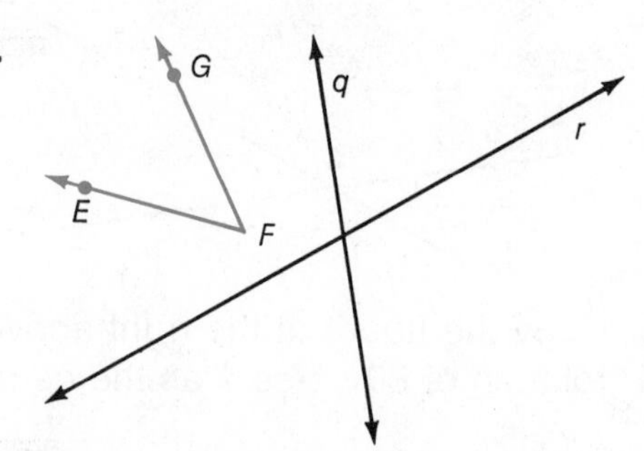

11. How many lines of symmetry does a regular hexagon have?

In Exercises ***12–14,*** *point Q is the center of a size transformation that maps A, B, and C onto A′, B′, and C′.*

12. If $QA' : QA = 4 : 1$, then the magnitude $k =$ __?__.

13. If $k = \frac{3}{2}$ and $QA = 12$, then $QA' =$ __?__.

14. If $k = 3$ and $BC = 1.5$, then $B'C' =$ __?__.

Chapter 14
Introduction to Vectors

14-1 Vectors

14-2 Addition of Vectors

14-3 Vector Theorems

14-4 More Vector Theorems

14-1 Vectors

A **vector** *AB* ($\overrightarrow{AB}$) is an ordered pair of real numbers (a, b), where a is the **horizontal component** and b is the **vertical component.** $A(x_A, y_A)$ is the **initial point** and $B(x_B, y_B)$ is the **terminal point.** Thus,

$$\overrightarrow{AB} = (a, b) = (x_B - x_A, y_B - y_A)$$

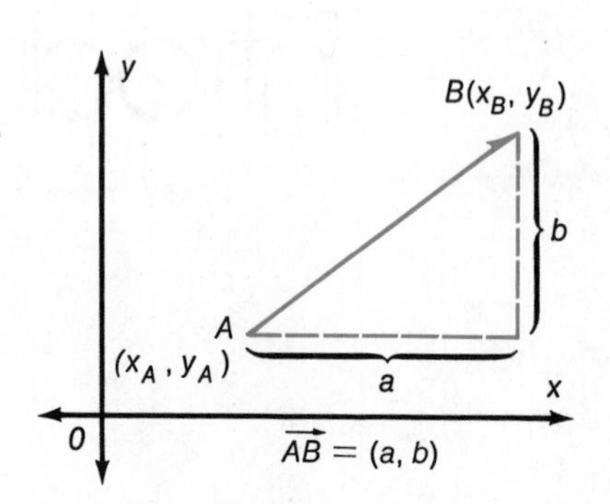

Example 1

Write the ordered pair that describes each vector.

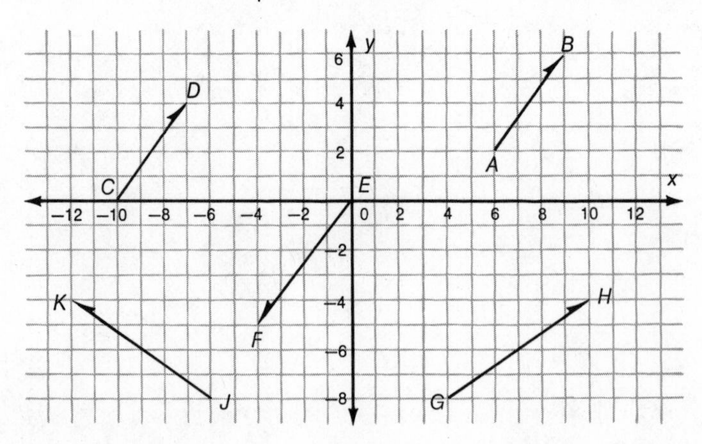

Vector	Initial Point	Terminal Point	Horizontal Component	Vertical Component	Ordered Pair
$\overrightarrow{AB}$	(6, 2)	(9, 6)	$9 - 6 = 3$	$6 - 2 = 4$	(3, 4)
$\overrightarrow{CD}$	(−10, 0)	(−7, 4)	$-7 - (-10) = 3$	$4 - 0 = 4$	(3, 4)
$\overrightarrow{EF}$	(0, 0)	(−4, −5)	$-4 - 0 = -4$	$-5 - 0 = -5$	(−4, −5)
$\overrightarrow{GH}$	(4, −8)	(10, −4)	$10 - 4 = 6$	$-4 - (-8) = 4$	(6, 4)
$\overrightarrow{JK}$	(−6, −8)	(−12, −4)	$-12 - (-6) = -6$	$-4 - (-8) = 4$	(−6, 4)

Vectors AB and CD each equal $(3, 4)$. Such vectors are **equivalent vectors.** Note that $\overrightarrow{AB}$ and $\overrightarrow{CD}$ have the same direction.

You can find the length or **magnitude** of a vector AB, symbolized as $|\overrightarrow{AB}|$, by using the distance formula.

$$\text{If } \overrightarrow{AB} = (a, b), \text{ then } |\overrightarrow{AB}| = \sqrt{a^2 + b^2}.$$

Example 2

Find the magnitude of each vector in Example 1.

Vector	Magnitude
$\overrightarrow{AB} = (3, 4)$	$\sqrt{3^2 + 4^2} = \sqrt{9 + 16} = \sqrt{25} = 5$
$\overrightarrow{CD} = (3, 4)$	$\sqrt{3^2 + 4^2} = \sqrt{9 + 16} = \sqrt{25} = 5$
$\overrightarrow{EF} = (-4, -5)$	$\sqrt{(-4)^2 + (-5)^2} = \sqrt{16 + 25} = \sqrt{41}$
$\overrightarrow{GH} = (6, 4)$	$\sqrt{6^2 + 4^2} = \sqrt{36 + 16} = \sqrt{52} = \sqrt{4 \cdot 13} = 2\sqrt{13}$
$\overrightarrow{JK} = (-6, 4)$	$\sqrt{(-6)^2 + 4^2} = \sqrt{36 + 16} = \sqrt{52} = \sqrt{4 \cdot 13} = 2\sqrt{13}$

NOTE: Although $|\overrightarrow{GH}| = |\overrightarrow{JK}|$, $\overrightarrow{GH} \neq \overrightarrow{JK}$ because $(6, 4) \neq (-6, 4)$, and they do not have the same direction.

A vector is sometimes called a directed segment.

Try These

*In Exercises **1–10,** name the ordered pair that describes each vector AB.*

1. $A(2, 0)$; $B(3, 3)$

2. $A(1, 2)$; $B(-1, 4)$

3. $A(0, 2)$; $B(-2, -1)$

4. $A(-1, -1)$; $B(3, -2)$

5. $A(-2, -1)$; $B(-6, -9)$

6. $A(-7, -5)$; $B(-2, -1)$

7. $A(0, 0)$; $B(-4, 5)$

8. $A(0, 0)$; $B(9, -3)$

9. $A(-1, -2)$; $B(0, 0)$

10. $A(3, 3)$; $B(5, -5)$

11. Find the magnitude of each vector AB in Exercises ***1–4.***

Exercises

*In Exercises **1–8**, give the components and the magnitude of each vector.*

1. 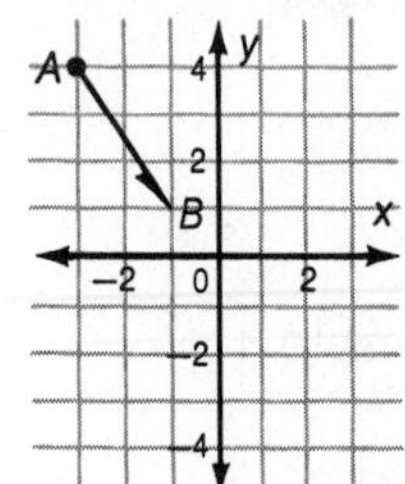

2. 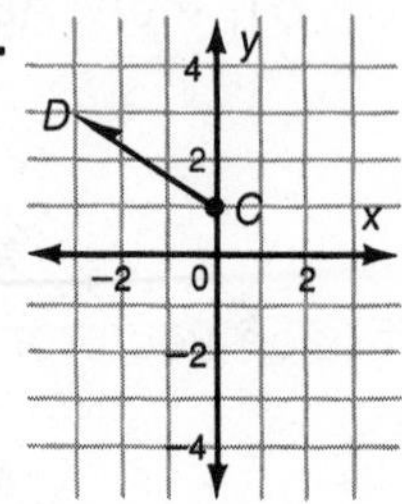

3. 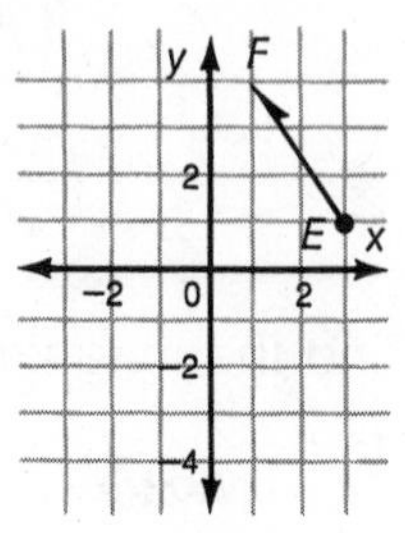

4. 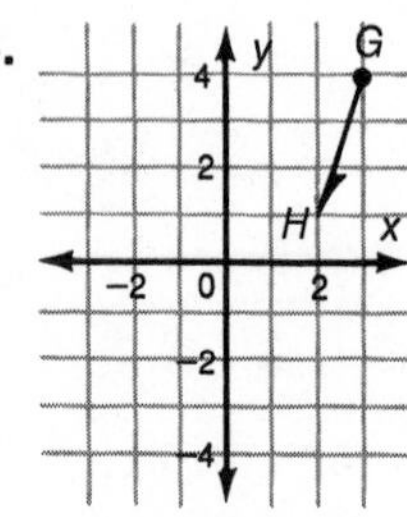

5. 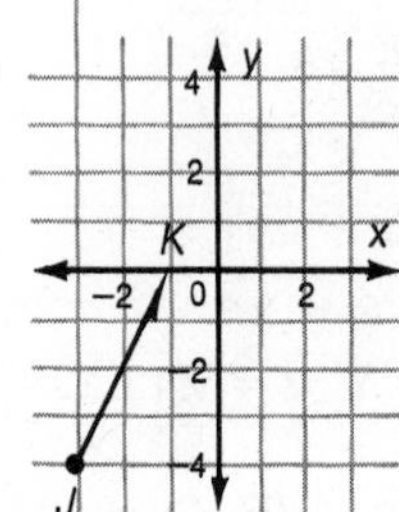

6. 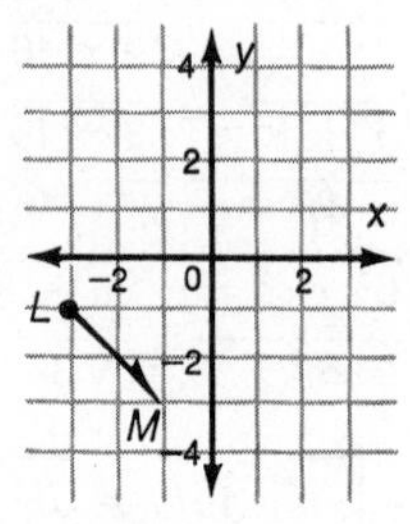

7. 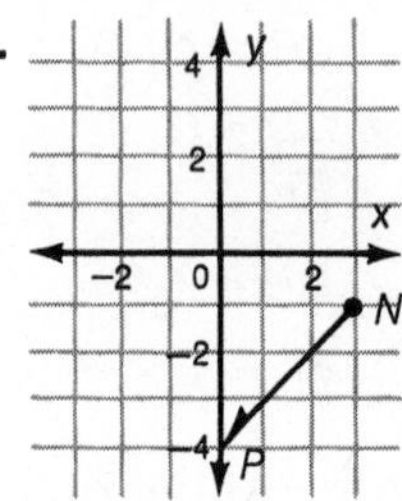

8. 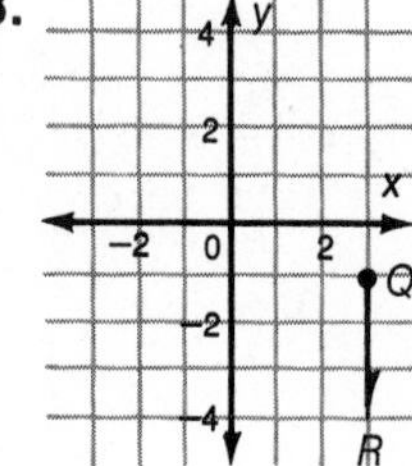

9. Which vectors in Exercises **1–8** have the same magnitude?

Find the components and the magnitude of each vector AB.

10. $A(1, 0)$; $B(4, 2)$

11. $A(1, 6)$; $B(2, 2)$

12. $A(0, 0)$; $B(2, -2)$

13. $A(3, -2)$; $B(-1, 2)$

14. $(x_A, y_A) = (1, 4)$
$(x_B, y_B) = (-2, 0)$

15. $(x_A, y_A) = (-2, -2)$
$(x_B, y_B) = (-1, -1)$

16. $(x_A, y_A) = (3, 1)$
$(x_B, y_B) = (0, -3)$

17. $(x_A, y_A) = (-4, -1)$
$(x_B, y_B) = (0, 0)$

*In Exercises **18–21**, $\overrightarrow{AB} = (4, 2)$. Find the coordinates of B when the coordinates of A are as given.*

18. $(0, 0)$ **19.** $(3, -1)$ **20.** $(-3, 4)$ **21.** $(5, -4)$

*In Exercises **22–25**, $\overrightarrow{CD} = (-3, 5)$. Find the coordinates of C when the coordinates of D are as given.*

22. $(0, 0)$ **23.** $(-2, 5)$ **24.** $(-3, 5)$ **25.** $(3, -5)$

14-2 Addition of Vectors

You can add vectors by graphing.

Example 1

Find the sum of $\overrightarrow{AB} = (5, 3)$ and $\overrightarrow{CD} = (-2, 1)$ by graphing. Use the origin as the initial point for $\overrightarrow{AB}$.

Graph (5, 3). Draw $\overrightarrow{AB}$. Start at B. This is the initial point for $\overrightarrow{CD}$. Move 2 units to the left and 1 unit up. This locates D. Draw $\overrightarrow{CD}$. Draw $\overrightarrow{AD}$. $\overrightarrow{AD}$ is the sum vector or **resultant.**

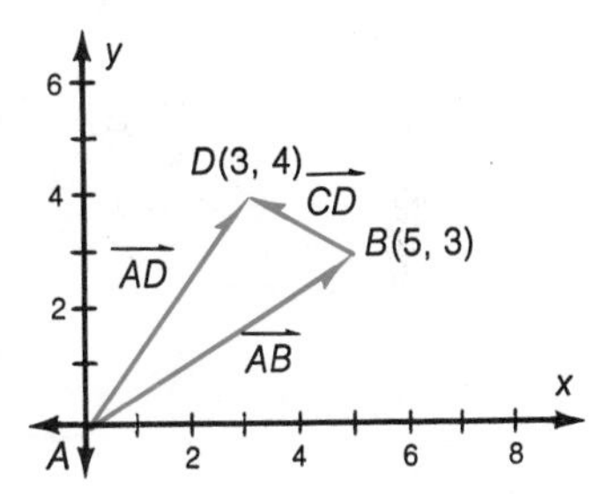

Thus, $\overrightarrow{AB} + \overrightarrow{CD} = \overrightarrow{AD}$

$(5, 3) + (-2, 1) = (3, 4)$

Example 1 suggests the following definition for addition.

$$\overrightarrow{AB} + \overrightarrow{CD} = (a, b) + (c, d) = (a + c, b + d)$$

Vector Theorem 1 follows from the definition of vector addition.

Vector Theorem 1: $\overrightarrow{AB} + \overrightarrow{BC} = \overrightarrow{AC}$

Example 2

Add: $(-3, 4) + (3, -4)$

$$(-3, 4) + (3, -4) = (-3 + 3, 4 + (-4))$$
$$= (0, 4 - 4) = (0, 0)$$

The vector (0, 0) is the **zero vector,** $\overrightarrow{0}$.

Since the resultant in Example 2 is (0, 0), (−3, 4) and (3, −4) are opposite vectors. In general, if $\overrightarrow{AB} + \overrightarrow{CD} = 0$, then $\overrightarrow{AB}$ and $\overrightarrow{CD}$ are **opposite vectors.**

If $\overrightarrow{CD}$ is the opposite of $\overrightarrow{AB}$, then $\overrightarrow{AB} = -\overrightarrow{CD}$ or $\overrightarrow{CD} = -\overrightarrow{AB}$.

The definition of subtraction of vectors resembles subtraction of real numbers.

$$\overrightarrow{AB} - \overrightarrow{CD} = \overrightarrow{AB} + (-\overrightarrow{CD}) \longleftarrow \text{Add the opposite of } \overrightarrow{CD}.$$

Example 3

Subtract: (2, 3) − (1, 1)

$$\begin{aligned}(2, 3) - (1, 1) &= (2, 3) + (-(1, 1)) \\ &= (2, 3) + (-1, -1) \\ &= (2 + (-1), 3 + (-1)) \\ &= (2 - 1, 3 - 1) = (1, 2)\end{aligned}$$

Try These

Perform the vector operations indicated.

1. (2, 3) + (7, 8)
2. (4, 5) + (−3, 4)
3. (8, 2) + (−8, −2)
4. (8, 2) − (−8, −2)

Classify each statement as True or False. Use a sketch to help you.

5. $\overrightarrow{AB} + \overrightarrow{BC} = \overrightarrow{AC}$
6. $\overrightarrow{AB} + \overrightarrow{BA} = \overrightarrow{AB}$
7. $\overrightarrow{AB} + \overrightarrow{BC} = \overrightarrow{CA}$
8. $\overrightarrow{AB} - \overrightarrow{AB} = \vec{0}$

Exercises

Perform the vector operations indicated.

a

1. (4, 6) + (−3, 8)
2. (−2, 5) + (−17, −3)
3. (9, −12) + (18, −22)
4. (−26, 16) + (−35, 41)

5. (12, 22) − (9, 18)

6. (−13, 15) − (−20, −9)

7. (−16, 23) − (−11, 11)

8. (17, −28) − (25, −34)

Classify each statement as True or False. Use a sketch to help you if necessary.

9. $\vec{AB} + \vec{BA} = \vec{0}$

10. $\vec{AB} - \vec{BC} = \vec{AB} + \vec{CB}$

11. $\vec{AC} + \vec{BC} = \vec{AB}$

12. $\vec{AB} + \vec{CB} = \vec{AC}$

13. $\vec{AC} - \vec{BC} = \vec{AB}$

14. $\vec{AC} + \vec{AB} = \vec{BC}$

15. $\vec{DE} + \vec{FE} = \vec{DF}$

16. $\vec{DF} - \vec{DE} = \vec{EF}$

17. $\vec{DF} + \vec{FE} = \vec{DE}$

*In Exercises **18–23** use parallelogram ABCD shown below. You may wish to make a separate figure for each exercise to help visualize the vector relationships. Complete each statement.*

18. $\vec{AB} + \vec{BC} =$ __?__

19. $\vec{BC} +$ __?__ $= \vec{BD}$

20. __?__ $+ \vec{AB} = \vec{DB}$

21. $\vec{AB} - \vec{CB} =$ __?__

22. $\vec{BD} +$ __?__ $= \vec{BC}$

23. $\vec{AD} -$ __?__ $= \vec{AC}$

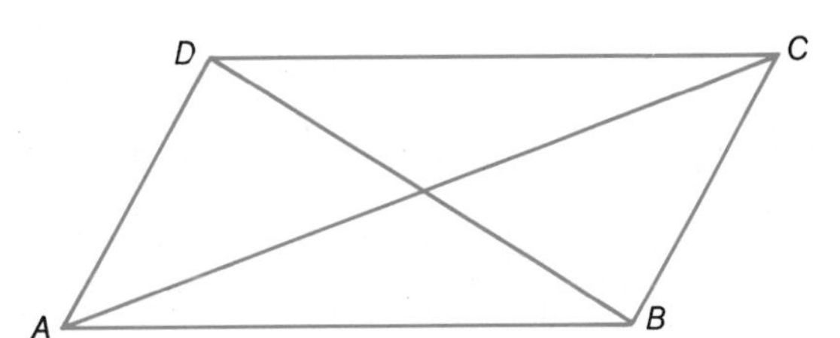

24. Prove Vector Theorem 1. (HINT: Let triangle ABC have vertices $A(x_A, y_A)$, $B(x_B, y_B)$, and $C(x_C, y_C)$. Then $\vec{AB} = (x_B - x_A, y_B - y_A)$, $\vec{BC} = (x_C - x_B, y_C - y_B)$, and $\vec{AC} = (x_C - x_A, y_C - y_A)$.)

25. Triangle ABC has vertices $A(0, 0)$, $B(5, 2)$, and $C(4, 6)$. Plot these points and draw vectors AB, BC, and CA. Find the components of $\vec{AB}$, $\vec{BC}$, $\vec{CA}$ and also find $(\vec{AB} + \vec{BC}) + \vec{CA}$.

26. Triangle DEF has vertices $D(0, 0)$, $E(4, 7)$, and $F(-5, 3)$. Plot these points and draw vectors DF, FE, and ED. Find the components of $\vec{DF}$, $\vec{FE}$, $\vec{ED}$, and find $(\vec{DF} + \vec{FE}) + \vec{ED}$.

27. Triangle ABC has vertices $A(0, 0)$, $B(3, -2)$, and $C(2, 5)$. Find $\vec{AC} - \vec{AB}$.

28. Triangle ABC has vertices $A(-3, -3)$, $B(3, -1)$, and $C(-5, 3)$. Find $\vec{AC} - \vec{AB}$.

29. Given vectors $\vec{AB} = (a, b)$ and $\vec{CD} = (c, d)$, under what conditions do $\vec{AB}$ and $\vec{CD}$ lie on parallel lines?

30. Under what conditions do the vectors in Exercise 29 lie on perpendicular lines?

14-3 Vector Theorems

Many proofs of vector theorems rely upon the ideas of coordinate geometry, such as slope.

Vector Theorem 2: If $\overrightarrow{AB} = (a, b)$ and $a \neq 0$, then the slope of $\overleftrightarrow{AB}$ is $\frac{b}{a}$.

Proof: Since $\overrightarrow{AB} = (a, b)$, $a = x_B - x_A$ and $b = y_B - y_A$. By the definition of the slope of a line, $\frac{y_B - y_A}{x_B - x_A}$ is the slope of $\overleftrightarrow{AB}$. So the slope of $\overleftrightarrow{AB}$ is $\frac{b}{a}$.

Vector Theorem 3: For the nonzero vectors AB and CD, if $\overrightarrow{AB} = \overrightarrow{CD}$, then $\overleftrightarrow{AB} \parallel \overleftrightarrow{CD}$ and $AB = CD$.

Proof: You are given that $\overrightarrow{AB} = \overrightarrow{CD} = (a, b)$. Thus, since the slope of $\overleftrightarrow{AB}$ is $\frac{b}{a}$ (Vector Theorem 2), the slope of $\overleftrightarrow{CD}$ is also $\frac{b}{a}$. Therefore, $\overleftrightarrow{AB} \parallel \overleftrightarrow{CD}$ by Theorem 10-2 on page 456. Also, $|\overrightarrow{AB}| = \sqrt{a^2 + b^2}$ and $|\overrightarrow{CD}| = \sqrt{a^2 + b^2}$. $\therefore AB = CD$.

Some theorems that were proved earlier can be proved using vectors. Vector Theorem 4 corresponds to Theorem 5-8 on page 211.

Vector Theorem 4: If $\overrightarrow{AB} = \overrightarrow{DC}$ and $ABCD$ is a quadrilateral, then $ABCD$ is a parallelogram.

Proof: Since $\overrightarrow{AB} = \overrightarrow{DC}$, then $\overrightarrow{AB} \parallel \overrightarrow{DC}$ and $AB = DC$ by Vector Theorem 3. Since these two opposite sides of quadrilateral $ABCD$ are parallel and congruent, $ABCD$ is a parallelogram.

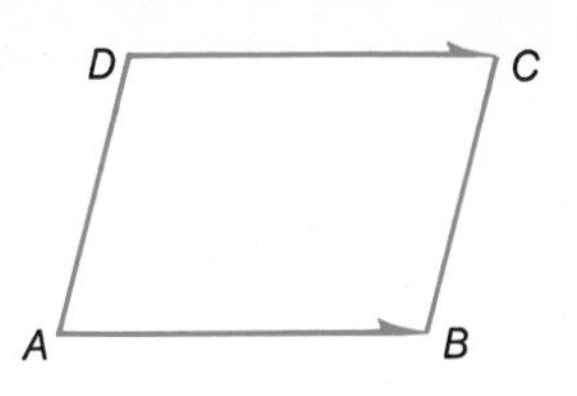

Vector Theorem 5: $\overrightarrow{AM} = \overrightarrow{MB}$ if and only if M is the midpoint of $\overrightarrow{AB}$.

Since this is a biconditional there are two parts to prove.

Part 1 **Given:** $\overrightarrow{AM} = \overrightarrow{MB}$

Prove: M is the midpoint of $\overrightarrow{AB}$.

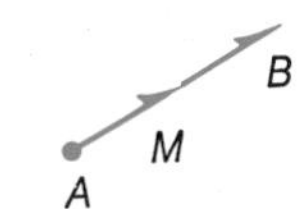

Proof: Since $\overrightarrow{AM} = \overrightarrow{MB}$, $x_M - x_A = x_B - x_M$

$$2x_M = x_A + x_B$$

$$x_M = \frac{x_A + x_B}{2}$$

Similarly, $y_M = \dfrac{y_A + y_B}{2}$. Thus, M is the midpoint of $\overrightarrow{AB}$. (See the midpoint formula on page 448.)

The proof of Part 2 is asked for in the Exercises.

Vector Theorem 6 corresponds to Theorem 5-5 on page 208: "The diagonals of a parallelogram bisect each other." The proof is asked for in the Exercises.

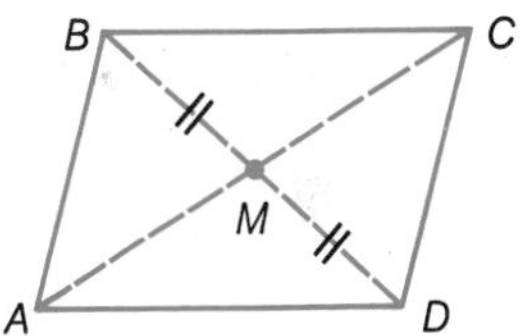

Vector Theorem 6: If $\overrightarrow{AB} = \overrightarrow{DC}$ in quadrilateral $ABCD$ and M is the midpoint of $\overline{BD}$, then $\overrightarrow{AM} = \overrightarrow{MC}$.

Try These

Draw a diagram to show each vector. Then find the slope and magnitude of each.

1. (5, 1) **2.** (−1, 5) **3.** (1, 1) **4.** (−3, −3)

5. (−3, 6) **6.** $(3\sqrt{2}, 0)$ **7.** (7 − 2, 8 − 7) **8.** (1 − 6, 2 − 3)

Exercises

a

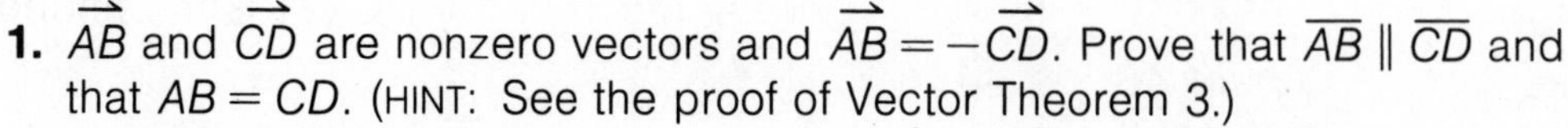

1. $\overrightarrow{AB}$ and $\overrightarrow{CD}$ are nonzero vectors and $\overrightarrow{AB} = -\overrightarrow{CD}$. Prove that $\overline{AB} \parallel \overline{CD}$ and that $AB = CD$. (HINT: See the proof of Vector Theorem 3.)
2. Given quadrilateral $ABCD$, prove that $(\overrightarrow{AB} + \overrightarrow{BC}) + \overrightarrow{CD} = \overrightarrow{AD}$. (HINT: Use Vector Theorem 1.)
3. In pentagon $ABCDE$, prove that $(\overrightarrow{AB} + \overrightarrow{BC}) + \overrightarrow{CD} = \overrightarrow{AE} + \overrightarrow{ED}$.
4. Prove Part 2 of Vector Theorem 5. That is, given that M is the midpoint of $\overrightarrow{AB}$, prove that $\overrightarrow{AM} = \overrightarrow{MB}$. (HINT: Reverse the steps in the proof of Part 1.)
5. In the figure, $\overrightarrow{AB} = \overrightarrow{DC}$ and $\overrightarrow{BM} = \overrightarrow{MD}$. Prove that $\overrightarrow{AM} = \overrightarrow{MC}$.

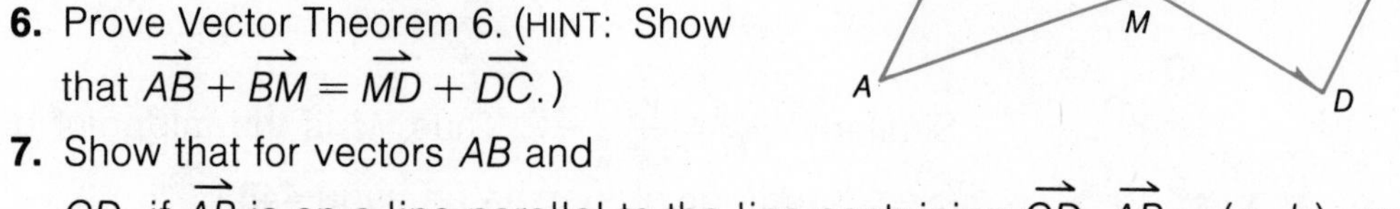

6. Prove Vector Theorem 6. (HINT: Show that $\overrightarrow{AB} + \overrightarrow{BM} = \overrightarrow{MD} + \overrightarrow{DC}$.)
7. Show that for vectors AB and CD, if $\overrightarrow{AB}$ is on a line parallel to the line containing $\overrightarrow{CD}$, $\overrightarrow{AB} = (a, b)$, and $\overrightarrow{CD} = (c, d)$, then $bc - ad = 0$.
8. Vectors AB and CD lie on parallel lines k_1 and k_2, and $\overline{AB} \cong \overline{CD}$. Prove that $\overrightarrow{AB} = \overrightarrow{CD}$ or $\overrightarrow{AB} = -\overrightarrow{CD}$.

Use the figure below for Exercises ***9–19.***

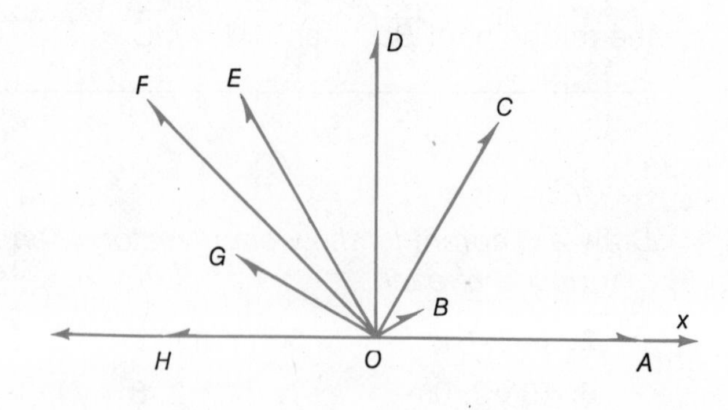

9. Find the components of each of the vectors OA through OH. Use the figure at the bottom of page 546 and the following measures.

$OA = \frac{5}{2}$	$OE = \frac{5}{2}$	$m\angle BOA = 30$	$m\angle EOA = 120$
$OB = \frac{1}{2}$	$OF = 3$	$m\angle COA = 60$	$m\angle FOA = 135$
$OC = \frac{9}{4}$	$OG = \frac{3}{2}$	$m\angle DOA = 90$	$m\angle GOA = 150$
$OD = \frac{11}{4}$	$OH = 2$		

Find each sum or difference. Use the measures given in Exercise 9 and the figure at the bottom of page 546.

10. $\overrightarrow{OA} + \overrightarrow{OB}$
11. $\overrightarrow{OB} + \overrightarrow{OA}$
12. $\overrightarrow{OF} - \overrightarrow{OG}$
13. $\overrightarrow{OG} - \overrightarrow{OF}$
14. $(\overrightarrow{OC} + \overrightarrow{OD}) + \overrightarrow{OH}$
15. $\overrightarrow{OC} + (\overrightarrow{OD} + \overrightarrow{OH})$
16. $(\overrightarrow{OF} - \overrightarrow{OH}) + \overrightarrow{OE}$
17. $\overrightarrow{OF} + ((-\overrightarrow{OH}) + \overrightarrow{OE})$
18. $(\overrightarrow{OD} - \overrightarrow{OC}) - \overrightarrow{OB}$
19. $(-\overrightarrow{OB}) + (\overrightarrow{OD} - \overrightarrow{OC})$

b

20. A car is traveling from O towards A at 80 kilometers per hour. A second car starts at the same time from O and travels towards B at the same speed. How far apart are the cars after 5 hours?

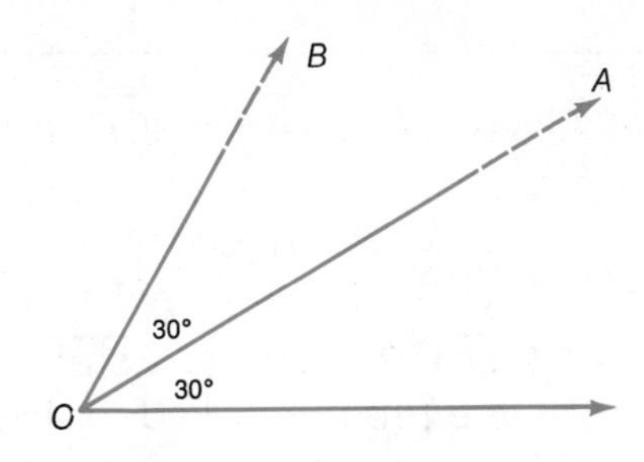

C

21. Prove: If $\overrightarrow{AB} = (a, b)$ and $\overrightarrow{CD} = (c, d)$, and $\overrightarrow{AB} \perp \overrightarrow{CD}$, then $ac + bd = 0$.
22. If $\overrightarrow{AB} \perp \overrightarrow{CD}$ and $\overrightarrow{AB} = (a, 4)$ and $\overrightarrow{CD} = (2, 7)$, find a.
23. If $\overrightarrow{EF} \perp \overrightarrow{GH}$ and $\overrightarrow{EF} = (5, f)$ and $\overrightarrow{GH} = (-2, 3)$, find f.
24. If $\overrightarrow{AB} \perp \overrightarrow{JK}$ and $\overrightarrow{AB} = (-7, 8)$ and $\overrightarrow{JK} = (9, -k)$, find k.

14-4 More Vector Theorems

You can stretch a vector $AB = (a, b)$ by multiplying the vector by a real number s, where $|s| > 1$. You shrink a vector when $0 \leq s < 1$. Multiplication of a real number by a vector is defined as follows.

$$s\overrightarrow{AB} = s(a, b) = (sa, sb)$$

The real number s is a scalar number or a **scalar.** You can use the definition given above to prove additional vector theorems.

Vector Theorem 7: For the nonzero vectors AB and CD, if $\overrightarrow{AB} = s\overrightarrow{CD}$, then $\overrightarrow{AB}$ and $\overrightarrow{CD}$ lie on parallel lines.

Proof: Let $\overrightarrow{CD} = (a, b)$. Then, since it is given that $\overrightarrow{AB} = s\overrightarrow{CD}$, $\overrightarrow{AB} = (sa, sb)$. The slope of $\overleftrightarrow{CD}$ is $\frac{b}{a}$ by Vector Theorem 2. Also, the slope of $\overleftrightarrow{AB}$ is $\frac{sb}{sa}$, or $\frac{b}{a}$. Since the slopes are the same, $\overrightarrow{AB}$ and $\overrightarrow{CD}$ lie in parallel lines.

Vector Theorem 8: If $\overrightarrow{AB} = s\overrightarrow{CD}$, then $|\overrightarrow{AB}| = |s| \cdot |\overrightarrow{CD}|$.

Outline of Proof: Let $\overrightarrow{CD} = (a, b)$. Then $\overrightarrow{AB} = (sa, sb)$ and $|\overrightarrow{AB}| = \sqrt{(sa)^2 + (sb)^2} = \sqrt{s^2a^2 + s^2b^2}$. Also, $|\overrightarrow{CD}| = \sqrt{a^2 + b^2}$. The complete proof is asked for in the exercises.

Theorem 5-12 can be proved using vectors.

Vector Theorem 9: If a segment joins the midpoints of two sides of a triangle, it is parallel to the third side and is one half as long as the third side.

Given: D and E are midpoints of $\overline{AC}$ and $\overline{BC}$, respectively, in $\triangle ABC$.

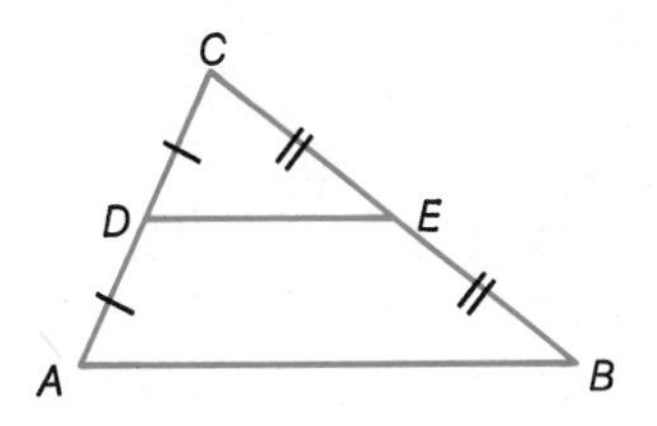

Prove: $\overrightarrow{DE} = \frac{1}{2}\overrightarrow{AB}$ and $\overrightarrow{DE} \parallel \overrightarrow{AB}$

Statements	Reasons
1. D and E are midpoints of $\overline{AC}$ and $\overline{BC}$, respectively.	1. Given
2. $\overrightarrow{AD} = \overrightarrow{DC}$; $\overrightarrow{EB} = \overrightarrow{CE}$	2. (1). Vector Theorem 5
3. $\overrightarrow{AD} + \overrightarrow{DC} = \overrightarrow{DC} + \overrightarrow{DC}$ $\overrightarrow{CE} + \overrightarrow{EB} = \overrightarrow{CE} + \overrightarrow{CE}$	3. (2). If $x = y$, then $x + a = y + a$.
4. $\overrightarrow{AC} = 2\overrightarrow{DC}$; $\overrightarrow{CB} = 2\overrightarrow{CE}$	4. (3). Vector Theorem 1
5. $\overrightarrow{AC} + \overrightarrow{CB} = 2\overrightarrow{DC} + 2\overrightarrow{CE}$	5. Addition Postulate for Equations
6. $\overrightarrow{AB} = 2(\overrightarrow{DC} + \overrightarrow{CE})$, or $\overrightarrow{AB} = 2\overrightarrow{DE}$, or $\overrightarrow{DE} = \frac{1}{2}\overrightarrow{AB}$	6. (5). Vector Theorem 1
7. $\overrightarrow{DE} \parallel \overrightarrow{AB}$	7. (6). Vector Theorem 7

Try These

In Exercises **1–12,** $\overrightarrow{AB} = (-2, 3)$ *and* $\overrightarrow{CD} = (3, 1)$*. Find the components of each of the following.*

1. $1\overrightarrow{AB}$

2. $-1\overrightarrow{AB}$

3. $3\overrightarrow{AB}$

4. $\frac{1}{2}\overrightarrow{AB}$

5. $2(3\overrightarrow{AB})$

6. $(2 \cdot 3)\overrightarrow{AB}$

7. $0\overrightarrow{AB}$

8. $2\overrightarrow{CD}$

9. $2\overrightarrow{CD} + 3\overrightarrow{CD}$

10. $2\overrightarrow{CD} + 3\overrightarrow{AB}$

11. $2(\overrightarrow{AB} + \overrightarrow{CD})$

12. $2\overrightarrow{AB} + 2\overrightarrow{CD}$

Exercises

a

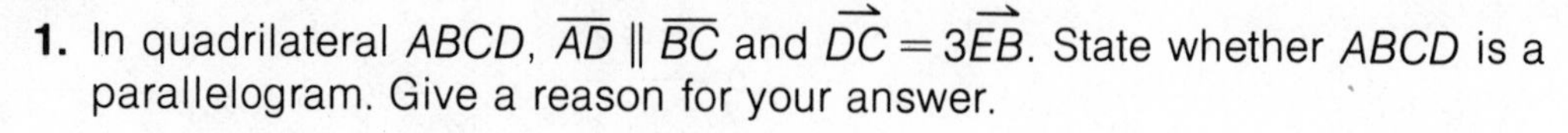

1. In quadrilateral $ABCD$, $\overline{AD} \parallel \overline{BC}$ and $\overrightarrow{DC} = 3\overrightarrow{EB}$. State whether $ABCD$ is a parallelogram. Give a reason for your answer.

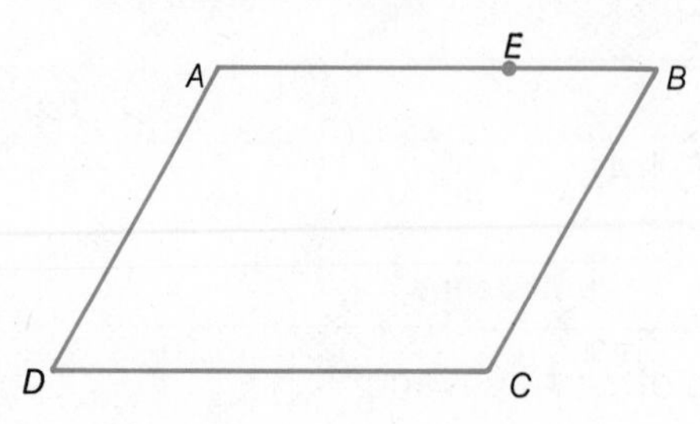

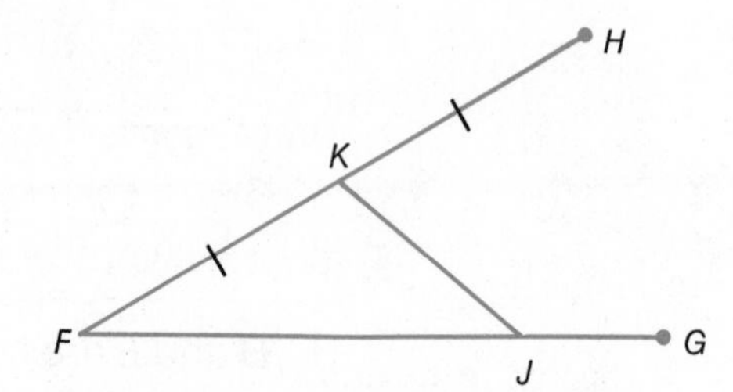

2. In the figure at the right above, $JG = \frac{1}{3}FG$ and K is the midpoint of $\overline{FH}$. Express $\overrightarrow{JK}$ in terms of $\overrightarrow{FH}$ and $\overrightarrow{FG}$.

3. Use the figure and given conditions of Exercise 2 to express $\overrightarrow{KJ}$ in terms of $\overrightarrow{HK}$ and $\overrightarrow{GJ}$.

4. In parallelogram $ABCD$, E is a point on $\overline{BC}$, $CE = \frac{1}{3}CB$, and F is the midpoint of $\overline{CD}$. Express $\overrightarrow{EF}$ in terms of $\overrightarrow{AB}$ and $\overrightarrow{AD}$.

5. Write a complete proof for Vector Theorem 8.

6. Prove: If $\overrightarrow{AB}$ is a vector and s is a real number, then $s\overrightarrow{AB} = \overrightarrow{0}$ if and only if $s = 0$ or $\overrightarrow{AB} = \overrightarrow{0}$.

b

7. Use vectors to prove that the median of a trapezoid is parallel to the bases and that its length is one half the sum of the lengths of the bases.

8. Use vectors to prove that the quadrilateral formed by joining the midpoints of the sides of a given quadrilateral in order is a parallelogram.

9. Use vectors to prove that the segment joining the midpoints of the diagonals of a trapezoid is parallel to the bases and that its length is one half the difference in the lengths of the bases.

10. Use vectors to prove that the medians of a triangle intersect at a point that is two-thirds of the distance from each vertex to the midpoint of the opposite side.

Chapter Objectives and Review

Objective: To recall, and give examples of, the important mathematical terms of the chapter.

1. Be sure that you know the meaning of these mathematical terms used in Chapter 14.

equivalent vectors (p. 539)
horizontal component (p. 538)
initial point (p. 538)
magnitude of a vector (p. 539)
opposite vectors (p. 542)
resultant (p. 541)
scalar (p. 548)
terminal point (p. 538)
vector (p. 538)
vertical component (p. 538)
zero vector (p. 541)

Objective: To represent vectors graphically and as ordered pairs of real numbers. (Section 14-1)

Graph each vector AB in Exercises **2–5.** *Then find the horizontal and vertical components of each vector.*

2. $A(2, 0)$; $B(3, 1)$
3. $A(-1, 6)$; $B(4, 3)$
4. $(x_A, y_A) = (4, 1)$; $(x_B, y_B) = (-3, 2)$
5. $(x_A, y_A) = (-6, 7)$; $(x_B, y_B) = (0, 1)$
6. Find the magnitude of each vector AB in Exercises **2–5.**

Objective: To add and subtract vectors. (Section 14-2)

Represent graphically the sum of $\overrightarrow{AB}$ *and* $\overrightarrow{CD}$.

7. $\overrightarrow{AB} = (3, 4)$; $\overrightarrow{CD} = (2, -2)$
8. $\overrightarrow{AB} = (-2, 0)$; $\overrightarrow{CD} = (3, 1)$
9. $\overrightarrow{AB} = (8, 4)$; $\overrightarrow{CD} = (-6, -6)$
10. $\overrightarrow{AB} = (-4, -4)$; $\overrightarrow{CD} = (1, 2)$

Perform the vector operations indicated.

11. $(2, 7) + (-1, 5)$
12. $(8, 1) + (6, 0)$
13. $(10, 1) + (-(4, 1))$
14. $(8, 2) + (-(-6, 1))$
15. $(9, 6) - (4, 2)$
16. $(-8, -3) - (-(5, 8))$

Objective: To use vector theorems in proofs. (Sections 14-3 and 14-4)

17. Given hexagon $ABCDEF$ at the left below, prove that

$$(\overrightarrow{AB} + \overrightarrow{BC}) + \overrightarrow{CD} = (\overrightarrow{AF} + \overrightarrow{FE}) + \overrightarrow{ED}.$$

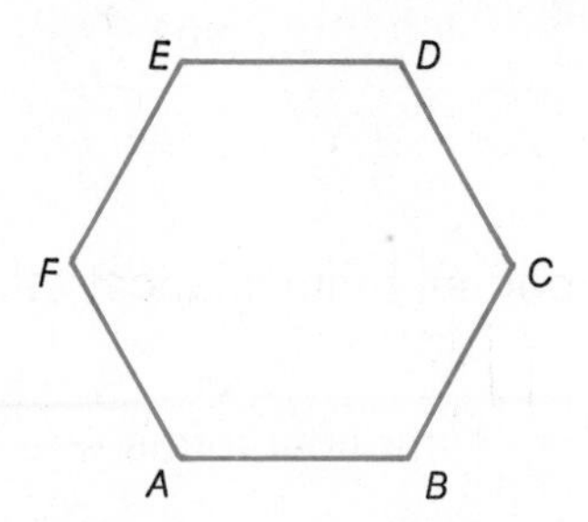

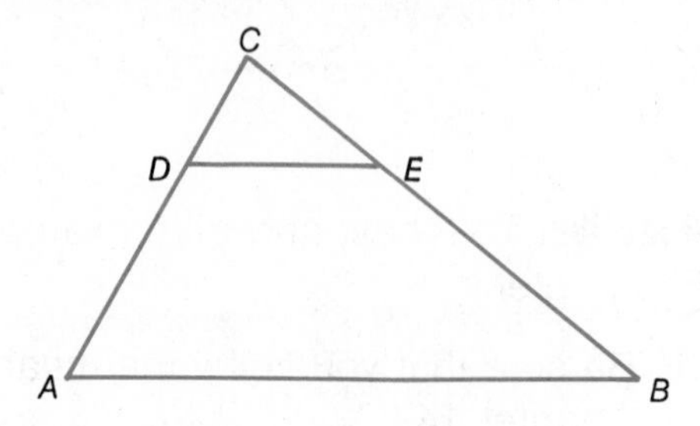

18. In $\triangle ABC$ at the right above, points D and E are chosen such that $\overrightarrow{AD} = 2\overrightarrow{DC}$ and $\overrightarrow{EB} = 2\overrightarrow{CE}$. Prove that $\overrightarrow{AB} = 3\overrightarrow{DE}$.

Chapter Test

Graph each vector $\overrightarrow{AB}$. Then find the horizontal and vertical components of each vector.

1. $A(0, 2)$; $B(1, -3)$

2. $A(-2, 5)$; $B(3, -4)$

3. $(x_A, y_A) = (9, 4)$
$(x_B, y_B) = (6, -2)$

4. $(x_A, y_A) = (4, -5)$
$(x_B, y_B) = (2, 0)$

5. Find the magnitude of each vector AB in Exercises **1–4.**

Represent graphically the sum of $\overrightarrow{AB}$ and $\overrightarrow{CD}$.

6. $\overrightarrow{AB} = (5, 1)$; $\overrightarrow{CD} = (-6, 4)$

7. $\overrightarrow{AB} = (-4, 4)$; $\overrightarrow{CD} = (3, 0)$

Perform the indicated vector operations.

8. $(-4, 0) + (4, 0)$

9. $(7, 3) + (-5, -2)$

10. $(12, 1) - (8, 2)$

11. $(-8, 5) - (-2, -9)$

12. In $\triangle ABC$, points D and E are chosen on $\overline{AC}$ and $\overline{BC}$, respectively, such that $\overrightarrow{AD} = 3\overrightarrow{DC}$ and $\overrightarrow{EB} = 3\overrightarrow{CE}$. Prove that $\overrightarrow{AB} = 4\overrightarrow{DE}$.

Cumulative Review

Write the letter of the response that best answers each question.

1. In a plane containing point P, find the locus of points one centimeter from P.

a. A line **b.** A sphere **c.** A circle **d.** A square

2. Points A and B are in plane I. Describe the locus of points in plane I equidistant from A and B.

a. A line parallel to $\overleftrightarrow{AB}$ **b.** A line perpendicular to $\overleftrightarrow{AB}$
c. Two parallel lines **d.** A plane

3. In plane II, point X is two centimeters from line m. Describe the locus of points in plane II one centimeter from X and three centimeters from m.

a. A point **b.** Two points **c.** A line **d.** Two lines

4. Given triangle ABC, tell how to locate the center of the circle that contains points A, B, and C.

a. Construct the bisectors of two angles of $\triangle ABC$.
b. Construct the medians to two sides of $\triangle ABC$.
c. Construct the perpendicular bisectors of two sides of $\triangle ABC$.
d. There is no such circle unless $\triangle ABC$ is equilateral.

5. Find the locus of points in space two meters from P and three meters from Q if the distance from P to Q is four meters.

a. A point **b.** A circle **c.** A sphere **d.** Two points

6. Find the tangent of 45°.

a. $\frac{\sqrt{2}}{2}$ **b.** $\sqrt{2}$ **c.** $\frac{\sqrt{3}}{3}$ **d.** 1

7. In $\triangle ABC$, $m\angle C = 90$ and $\tan A = \frac{3}{4}$. Find $\tan B$.

a. $\frac{3}{4}$ **b.** $\frac{3}{5}$ **c.** $\frac{4}{3}$ **d.** $\frac{5}{3}$

8. Find the sine of 30°.

a. 0.5 **b.** 1 **c.** $\frac{\sqrt{2}}{2}$ **d.** $\frac{\sqrt{3}}{2}$

9. In $\triangle PQR$, $PQ = 6$, $QR = 8$, and $m\angle Q = 90$. Find $\cos P$.

a. 0.8 **b.** 0.75 **c.** 0.6 **d.** 1.4

10. The top of a ladder 13 meters long rests against a vertical wall, and the bottom of the ladder is 5 meters from the wall on level ground. Find the sine of the angle of elevation formed by the ladder and the horizontal ground.

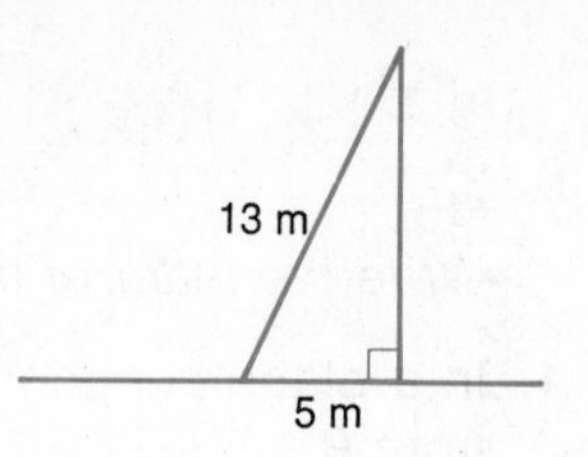

a. $\frac{5}{13}$ b. $\frac{13}{5}$ c. $\frac{12}{5}$ d. $\frac{12}{13}$

11. Triangle ABC, shown at the right, is reflected over line m. Choose the diagram that illustrates this transformation.

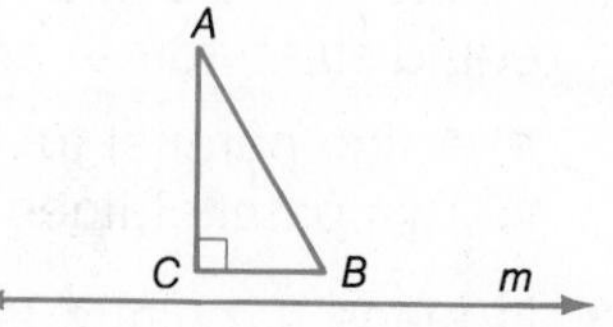

a.
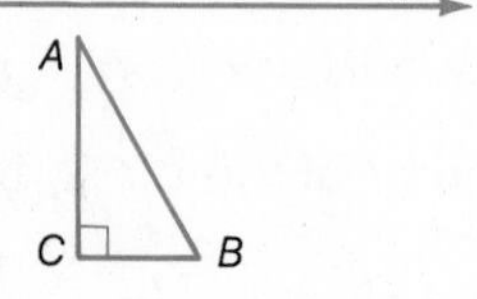

b.

c. 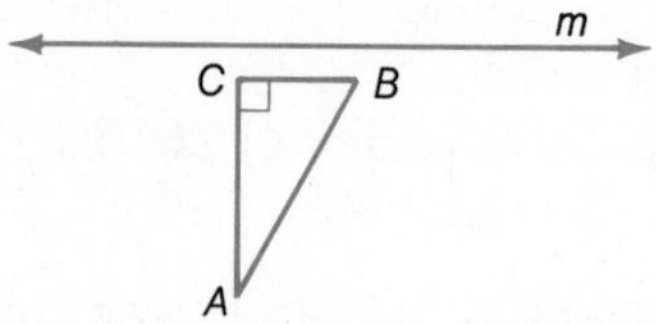
d.
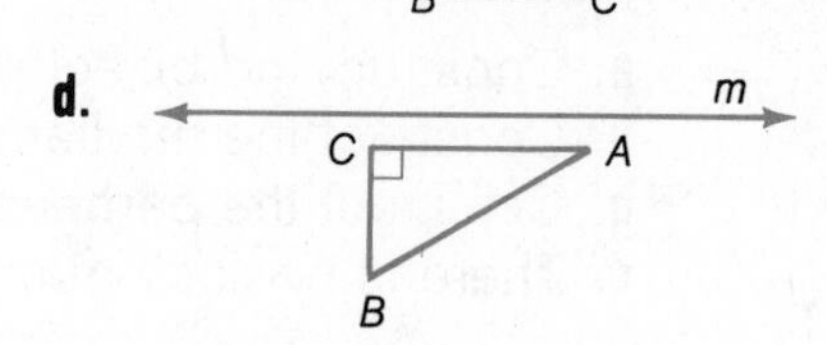

12. Tell which of the following geometric figures has exactly one axis of symmetry.

a. A rectangle b. An angle c. A circle d. A point

13. The measure of a line segment is preserved under each of the following transformations except one. Name the exception.

a. Reflection b. Translation c. Rotation d. Dilation

14. Given that $A = (2, -1)$ and $B = (3, 7)$, write the ordered pair that describes vector AB.

a. (1, 8) b. (1, 6) c. (8, 1) d. (6, 1)

15. Find the magnitude of $\overrightarrow{VW}$ if $V = (1, 5)$ and $W = (-5, -3)$.

a. 10 b. $\sqrt{38}$ c. $4\sqrt{5}$ d. 14

16. Let $\overrightarrow{AB} = (2, -1)$ and $\overrightarrow{CD} = (0, 3)$. Find $2\overrightarrow{AB} + \overrightarrow{CD}$.

a. (2, 2) b. (4, 1) c. (2, 5) d. (4, −5)

Review Topics From Algebra One

The Review: Topics From Algebra One contains additional help and practice on those topics from first-year algebra that are used in the study of geometry. These topics are listed in the Contents below. Each of the Remember exercise sets that reviews an algebraic topic is referenced to one of these. (See, for example, page 317.) Thus, the Review: Topics From Algebra One, when used in this manner, is a supplement to those Remember exercise sets that review algebraic topics. Of course, it can also be used as a separate unit of study.

Contents

A-1 Subtraction/Distance on the Number Line

To subtract a real number b from a real number a, add the opposite of b to a.

$$a - b = a + (-b)$$

Example 1 Subtract: **a.** $8 - (-3)$ **b.** $7 - 5$ **c.** $9 - (-4)$

a. $-8 - (-3) = -8 + 3 = -5$ ⟵ 3 is the opposite of -3.

b. $7 - 5 = 7 + (-5) = 2$ ⟵ -5 is the opposite of 5.

c. $9 - (-4) = 9 + 4 = 13$ ⟵ 4 is the opposite of -4.

To find the distance between two points on the number line, find the absolute value of the difference of their coordinates. The symbol AB represents the distance between A and B.

Example 2 Use the number line below to find DE, BD, CE, and AB.

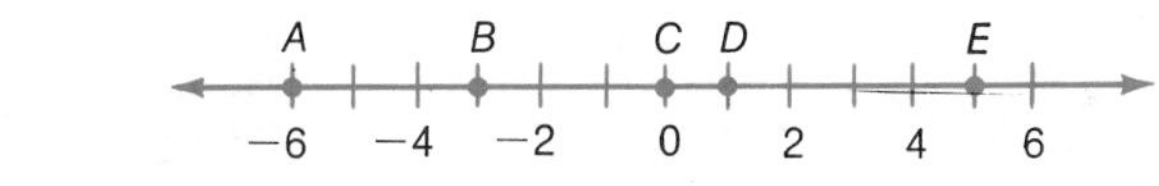

$DE = |5 - 1| = |4| = 4$ $BD = |1 - (-3)| = |1 + 3| = 4$

$CE = |5 - 0| = |5| = 5$ $AB = |-3 - (-6)| = |-3 + 6| = 3$

Exercises

Subtract.

1. $5 - 6$ **2.** $5 - (-6)$ **3.** $-5 - (-6)$ **4.** $3 - (-1)$ **5.** $0 - (-5)$

6. $0 - (-1)$ **7.** $10 - (-10)$ **8.** $-6 - (-7)$ **9.** $4 - (-6)$ **10.** $16 - (-15)$

Two points on the number line have the coordinates given. Find the distance between the points.

11. 10; 5 **12.** 9; 0 **13.** 17; 12 **14.** 17; -1 **15.** 3; -9

16. 5; -5 **17.** 0; -5 **18.** -1; -4 **19.** -1; -10 **20.** -5; 0

21. -3; -7 **22.** -2; -9 **23.** 0; -15 **24.** 3; -10 **25.** 15; -8

A-2 Solving Equations

Equivalent equations are equations that have the same solution set. You use this idea and these postulates to solve equations.

Addition Postulate for Equations

If the same number is added to both sides of an equation, the result is an equivalent equation.

Multiplication Postulate for Equations

If both sides of an equation are multiplied by the same nonzero number, the result is an equivalent equation.

Example 1

Solve: $-6x + 9 = -8$

$-6x + 9 = -8$

$-6x + 9 + (-9) = -8 + (-9)$ ⟵ Add -9, the opposite of 9, to both sides of the equation.

$-6x = 17$

$-\frac{1}{6}(-6x) = -\frac{1}{6}(-17)$ ⟵ Multiply both sides by $-\frac{1}{6}$, the reciprocal of -6.

$x = \frac{17}{6}$ ⟵ The solution set is $\left\{\frac{17}{6}\right\}$.

Example 2

Solve: $3m - 5 = m + 1$

$3m - 5 = m + 1$

$3m - m - 5 = m - m + 1$ ⟵ Addition Postulate for Equations

$2m - 5 = 1$ ⟵ Add 5 to both sides.

$2m = 6$ ⟵ Multiply both sides by $\frac{1}{2}$.

$m = 3$ ⟵ The solution set is $\{3\}$.

To solve an equation containing parentheses, first write an equivalent equation without parentheses.

Example 3 Solve: $5(2x + 3) = 28 - 3x$

$5(2x + 3) = 28 - 3x$

$5(2x) + 5(3) = 28 - 3x$ ← Distributive Postulate

$10x + 15 = 28 - 3x$ ← Add $3x$ to both sides.

$13x + 15 = 28$ ← Add -15 to both sides.

$13x = 13$ ← Multiply both sides by $\frac{1}{13}$.

$x = 1$ ← Check in the original equation.

Solution set: $\{1\}$

Exercises

Solve each equation.

1. $x + 4 = -8$

2. $\frac{1}{5}y = 12$

3. $9x = 11$

4. $3y = y - 12$

5. $-9x - 11 = 32$

6. $5x + x = 1$

7. $9x - 11x = 14$

8. $2m = 18 - m$

9. $17 - 6a = 11$

10. $7y + 16 = 2$

11. $9z - 3 = 25$

12. $-5 - 3b = 16$

13. $5n - 2 = 8 + 2n$

14. $\frac{4}{3}z + 10 = 2$

15. $3y - 5 = 8 + 2y$

16. $5(3 - 2n) = 5n$

17. $4(3x - 2) + 2x = 6$

18. $5(2y - 3) = -2(3y + 4)$

19. $3(5z - 2) = 4(7 + z) - 1$

20. $3(1 - 2x) + 10 = -4(2x - 3)$

21. $2(3x - 4) = 2(20 + 7x)$

22. $10(0.6 - m) = 2(7m + 0.6)$

23. $3r(2r + 3) + 2(r - 3) = r(6r + 1 - 7)$

24. $2(3y - 4) - y(2y + 3) = 2y(5 - y) + 8$

A-3 Solving Inequalities

You can solve inequalities by using postulates similar to those you use to solve equations.

Addition Postulate for Inequalities

If the same number is added to both sides of an inequality, the result is an equivalent inequality.

Example 1

Solve: $x + 7 > 12$

$$x + 7 > 12 \longleftarrow \text{Add } -7 \text{ to both sides.}$$
$$x + 7 + (-7) > 12 + (-7)$$
$$x > 5$$

Solution set: $\{x: x > 5\}$

Multiplication Postulates for Inequalities

Multiplying both sides of an inequality by the same positive number gives an equivalent inequality.

Multiplying both sides of an inequality by the same negative number gives an equivalent inequality when the inequality is reversed.

Example 2

Solve: $2x + 9 < 7$

$$2x + 9 < 7 \longleftarrow \text{Add } -9 \text{ to both sides.}$$
$$2x < -2 \longleftarrow \text{Multiply both sides by } \tfrac{1}{2}.$$
$$x < -1$$

Solution set: $\{x: x < -1\}$

Example 3 Solve: $5 - 3x > 8$

$5 - 3x > 8$ ⟵ Add -5 to both sides.

$-3x > 3$ ⟵ Multiply both sides by $-\frac{1}{3}$ and reverse the inequality.

$x < -1$

Solution set: $\{x: x < -1\}$

Exercises

Solve each inequality.

1. $n + 5 < 22$

2. $z + 4 > 6$

3. $z - 4 > 6$

4. $x - 7 < 13$

5. $x - 15 > -22$

6. $7 < 2x + 9$

7. $5x > 50$

8. $-7x < 14$

9. $2n < n + 5$

10. $5 + 2z < 17$

11. $3n + 4 < 2n + 8$

12. $5n + 12 < 7 + 6n$

13. $n + 5 > 2n$

14. $4x - 8 < 5x - 2.5$

15. $2x + 2 < -4$

16. $\frac{1}{2}y + 1 < y - 2$

17. $2x < 10$

18. $3y - 1 > 17$

19. $3m + 3 > 15 - 5m$

20. $t > 2t - 7$

21. $-3x + 5 > 10$

22. $5 - 6x < 17$

23. $-2x + 5 < 10$

24. $-4x + 2 < x + 9$

25. $-x + 4 > 3(x + 2)$

26. $-7(3x + 4) > 0$

27. $-2x - 5 < -x + 10$

28. $-2(z - 3) < 6z - 7(z - 4)$

A-4 Exponents

If exponential expressions have the same base, their product can be expressed using the base and a single exponent.

Multiplication Theorem for Exponents

If x is a real number and m and n are integers, then

$$x^m \cdot x^n = x^{m+n}.$$

Power Theorem for Exponents

If x is a real number and m and n are integers, then

$$(x^m)^n = x^{mn}.$$

Example 1 a. $(-3x^2)(2x^3) = \underline{\ ?\ }$ **b.** $(y^5)^{10} = \underline{\ ?\ }$

a. $(-3x^2)(2x^3) = (-3 \cdot 2)(x^2 \cdot x^3)$ ⟵ Associative Postulate for Multiplication

$= -6x^{2+3}$ ⟵ Multiplication Theorem for Exponents

$= -6x^5$

b. $(y^5)^{10} = y^{5 \cdot 10}$ ⟵ Power Theorem for Exponents

$= y^{50}$

If exponential expressions have the same base, their quotient can be expressed using a single exponent.

Division Theorem for Exponents

If x is a real number, $x \neq 0$, and m and n are positive integers such that $m > n$, then

$$\frac{x^m}{x^n} = x^{m-n}.$$

If $m = n$, then $\frac{x^m}{x^n} = m^{m-n} = x^0 = 1$.

Example 2 Divide: $\frac{x^4y^3}{xy^2}$

$$\frac{x^4y^3}{xy^2} = \left(\frac{x^4}{x}\right)\left(\frac{y^3}{y^2}\right)$$
$$= x^{4-1}y^{3-2} \longleftarrow \text{Division Theorem for Exponents}$$
$$= x^3y$$

Exercises

Multiply.

1. $x^8 \cdot x^8$
2. $-a^3 \cdot a^6$
3. $x \cdot x^{12}$
4. $(3x)(2x^2)$
5. $3 \cdot 3^2$
6. $x(-x^2)$
7. $-y(-y^3)$
8. $b^2 \cdot b^3$
9. $(-4x^2y)(5xy^2)$
10. $(2z)(3z^4)$
11. $(ab)(-9a^2b^3)$
12. $(4c^2d)(5c^5d)$

Simplify. No denominator is zero.

13. $(a^3)^4$
14. $(y^3)^3$
15. $(x^5)^2$
16. $(x^4)^3$
17. $(b^4)^6$
18. $(ab^2)^3$
19. $\left(\frac{a}{b}\right)^3$
20. $(x^2)^6$
21. $(3a^2b)^2$
22. $(4x^2y^3)^2$
23. $(x^2y)^4$
24. $\left(\frac{a^2}{b^2}\right)^3$

Divide. No denominator is zero.

25. $\frac{a^5}{a}$
26. $\frac{x^8}{x^6}$
27. $\frac{y^{11}}{y^{10}}$
28. $\frac{x^5}{x^3}$
29. $\frac{y^9}{y^9}$
30. $\frac{a^3b^5}{ab^2}$
31. $\frac{xyz}{xyz}$
32. $\frac{z^8}{z^7}$
33. $\frac{a^5c^3}{a^3c^2}$
34. $\frac{-27r^5s^8}{-3r^4s^7}$
35. $\frac{-36a^2b^2c^4}{4abc^2}$
36. $\frac{7^9}{7^5}$
37. $\frac{9^{100}}{9^{100}}$
38. $\frac{(-6)^{12}}{(-6)^5}$
39. $\frac{(-1)^9}{(-1)^8}$
40. $\frac{x^{98}}{x^4}$

A-5 Squaring and Taking the Square Root

To square a number you multiply it by itself.

Example Simplify.

a. $\left(\frac{2}{3}\right)^2$ **b.** $(\sqrt{3})^2$ **c.** $(2\sqrt{7})^2$ **d.** $\left(\frac{\sqrt{2}}{5}\right)^2$

Solutions: **a.** $\left(\frac{2}{3}\right)^2 = \frac{2}{3} \cdot \frac{2}{3} = \frac{4}{9}$

b. $(\sqrt{3})^2 = \sqrt{3} \cdot \sqrt{3} = (\sqrt{3})^2 = 3$

c. $(2\sqrt{7})^2 = (2\sqrt{7})(2\sqrt{7}) = (2 \cdot 2 \cdot \sqrt{7} \cdot \sqrt{7}) = 4 \cdot 7$, or 28

d. $\left(\frac{\sqrt{2}}{5}\right)^2 = \frac{\sqrt{2}}{5} \cdot \frac{\sqrt{2}}{5} = \frac{2}{25}$

Taking the square root is the reverse operation of squaring. A radical, such as $\sqrt{}$, names just one number, the principal root. A negative square root is associated with the symbol, $-\sqrt{}$.

$$\sqrt{49} = 7 \qquad -\sqrt{49} = -7 \qquad \pm\sqrt{49} = \pm 7$$

Exercises

Simplify.

1. $\left(\frac{2}{5}\right)^2$ **2.** $(\sqrt{3})^2$ **3.** $(\sqrt{5})^2$ **4.** $\left(\frac{\sqrt{5}}{2}\right)^2$

5. $\left(\frac{\sqrt{3}}{5}\right)^2$ **6.** $\left(\frac{\sqrt{9}}{7}\right)^2$ **7.** $\left(\frac{\sqrt{3}}{3}\right)^2$ **8.** $\left(\frac{\sqrt{2}}{3}\right)^2$

9. $(3\sqrt{3})^2$ **10.** $(5\sqrt{2})^2$ **11.** $(6\sqrt{5})^2$ **12.** $(10\sqrt{3})^2$

13. $(9\sqrt{2})^2$ **14.** $(2\sqrt{7})^2$ **15.** $(2\sqrt{6})^2$ **16.** $(3\sqrt{10})^2$

17. $\sqrt{36}$ **18.** $-\sqrt{36}$ **19.** $-\sqrt{81}$ **20.** $\sqrt{100}$

21. $\pm\sqrt{25}$ **22.** $\sqrt{144}$ **23.** $\sqrt{400}$ **24.** $\sqrt{169}$

A-6 Taking Square Roots to Solve Equations

Taking the square root of both sides of an equation produces an equivalent equation. **Equivalent equations** have the same solution set.

Example 1 Solve: $x^2 = 144$

$x^2 = 144$ ← Take the square root of both sides of the equation.

$x = 12$ or $x = -12$

Solution set: $\{12, -12\}$

Example 2 Solve: $y^2 - 8 = 0$

$y^2 - 8 = 0$ ← Add 8 to both sides of the equation.

$y^2 = 8$ ← Take the square root of both sides.

$y = \sqrt{8}$ or $-\sqrt{8}$ ← Simplify.

$y = 2\sqrt{2}$ or $-2\sqrt{2}$

Solution set: $\{2\sqrt{2}, -2\sqrt{2}\}$

Exercises

Solve.

1. $x^2 = 36$
2. $y^2 = 81$
3. $x^2 = 100$
4. $y^2 = 400$
5. $x^2 = 243$
6. $x^2 = \frac{4}{9}$
7. $2x^2 = 20$
8. $x^2 = 5\sqrt{16}$
9. $x^2 = 12$
10. $x^2 = 133$
11. $x^2 = 4\sqrt{36}$
12. $y^2 = ab$, $a > 0$, $b > 0$
13. $y^2 = 36a^2$, $a > 0$
14. $\frac{1}{2}x^2 = 100$
15. $6x^2 = 432$

A-7 Simplifying Radicals

The square root of the product of two nonnegative numbers is the product of their square roots.

$$\sqrt{36} = \sqrt{9} \cdot \sqrt{4} = 3 \cdot 2 = 6$$
$$\sqrt{16} = \sqrt{4} \cdot \sqrt{4} = 2 \cdot 2 = 4$$

You use this property to simplify radicals. A radical is simplified when the radicand does not contain a perfect square factor.

$\sqrt{200}$ ← 200 is the radicand.

Example Simplify.

a. $\sqrt{50}$ **b.** $\sqrt{96}$ **c.** $6\sqrt{72}$

Solutions: **a.** $\sqrt{50} = \sqrt{25} \cdot \sqrt{2} = 5\sqrt{2}$ ← Simplest form

b. $\sqrt{96} = \sqrt{16} \cdot \sqrt{6} = 4\sqrt{6}$

c. $6\sqrt{72} = 6\sqrt{36} \cdot \sqrt{2} = 6 \cdot 6\sqrt{2} = 36\sqrt{2}$

Exercises

Simplify.

1. $\sqrt{8}$ **2.** $\sqrt{75}$ **3.** $\sqrt{300}$ **4.** $\sqrt{72}$

5. $\sqrt{32}$ **6.** $\sqrt{98}$ **7.** $\sqrt{128}$ **8.** $\sqrt{243}$

9. $2\sqrt{9}$ **10.** $5\sqrt{4}$ **11.** $16\sqrt{81}$ **12.** $3\sqrt{100}$

13. $3\sqrt{27}$ **14.** $2\sqrt{32}$ **15.** $9\sqrt{8}$ **16.** $7\sqrt{18}$

17. $5\sqrt{125}$ **18.** $3\sqrt{288}$ **19.** $2\sqrt{363}$ **20.** $10\sqrt{250}$

21. $16\sqrt{64}$ **22.** $9\sqrt{40}$ **23.** $7\sqrt{75}$ **24.** $4\sqrt{12}$

25. $11\sqrt{125}$ **26.** $13\sqrt{32}$ **27.** $5\sqrt{44}$ **28.** $9\sqrt{20}$

29. $10\sqrt{50}$ **30.** $6\sqrt{72}$ **31.** $3\sqrt{28}$ **32.** $6\sqrt{250}$

A-8 Rationalizing Denominatiors

Sometimes a fraction has a square root radical in the denominator. When you multiply both numerator and denominator of the fraction by a number that makes the denominator a perfect square, you are **rationalizing the denominator** of the fraction.

Example 1 Rationalize the denominator and simplify: $\frac{3}{\sqrt{3}}$

$\frac{3}{\sqrt{3}} = \frac{3}{\sqrt{3}} \cdot \frac{\sqrt{3}}{\sqrt{3}}$ ⟵ Multiply by $\frac{\sqrt{3}}{\sqrt{3}}$ to make the denominator a perfect square.

$= \frac{3\sqrt{3}}{3}$, or $\sqrt{3}$ ⟵ $\sqrt{3} \cdot \sqrt{3} = 3$ and $\frac{3}{3} = 1$.

Example 2 Rationalize the denominator and simplify: $\frac{5}{\sqrt{8}}$

$\frac{5}{\sqrt{8}} = \frac{5}{\sqrt{8}} \cdot \frac{\sqrt{2}}{\sqrt{2}}$ ⟵ Multiply by $\frac{\sqrt{2}}{\sqrt{2}}$ to make the denominator a perfect square.

$= \frac{5\sqrt{2}}{\sqrt{16}}$, or $\frac{5\sqrt{2}}{4}$ ⟵ $\sqrt{8} \cdot \sqrt{2} = \sqrt{16} = 4$

Exercises

Rationalize the denominator and simplify.

1. $\frac{1}{\sqrt{2}}$ **2.** $\frac{1}{\sqrt{5}}$ **3.** $\frac{1}{\sqrt{3}}$ **4.** $\frac{2}{\sqrt{7}}$ **5.** $\frac{3}{\sqrt{5}}$

6. $\frac{2}{\sqrt{3}}$ **7.** $\frac{3}{\sqrt{2}}$ **8.** $\frac{2}{\sqrt{2}}$ **9.** $\frac{1}{\sqrt{8}}$ **10.** $\frac{2}{\sqrt{8}}$

11. $\frac{36\sqrt{2}}{\sqrt{6}}$ **12.** $\frac{5\sqrt{3}}{\sqrt{18}}$ **13.** $\frac{8\sqrt{5}}{\sqrt{15}}$ **14.** $\frac{5\sqrt{3}}{\sqrt{15}}$ **15.** $\frac{2\sqrt{4}}{\sqrt{3}}$

16. $\frac{3\sqrt{9}}{\sqrt{2}}$ **17.** $\frac{3\sqrt{6}}{2\sqrt{2}}$ **18.** $\frac{2\sqrt{7}}{5\sqrt{3}}$ **19.** $\frac{5\sqrt{8}}{\sqrt{2}}$ **20.** $\frac{4\sqrt{2}}{\sqrt{20}}$

A-9 Solving for a Variable

To solve for y in the equation

$$3x - 5y = 19$$

you find y in terms of x.

Example 1 Solve for y: $3x - 5y = 19$

$3x - 5y = 19$ ⟵ Add $-3x$ to both sides.

$-5y = 19 - 3x$ ⟵ Multiply both sides by $-\frac{1}{5}$.

$$y = -\frac{19}{5} + \frac{3}{5}x, \text{ or } y = \frac{1}{5}(-19 + 3x)$$

You can use the same procedure to solve for one of the variables in a formula in terms of the others.

Example 2 Solve $T = 2\pi rh + 2\pi r^2$ for h.

$T = 2\pi rh + 2\pi r^2$ ⟵ Add $(-2\pi r^2)$ to both sides.

$T - 2\pi r^2 = 2\pi rh$ ⟵ Multiply both sides by $\frac{1}{2\pi r}$.

$$\frac{T - 2\pi r^2}{2\pi r} = h, \text{ or } h = \frac{T}{2\pi r} - r$$

Exercises

Solve each equation for y.

1. $y - 2x = 12$ **2.** $by + bx = a$ **3.** $-x - y = 9$

4. $3x - 2y = 4$ **5.** $2x - 3y = -7$ **6.** $3x - 2y = 0$

7. $7y - 5x = 12$ **8.** $11 - 5y = 6x$ **9.** $2y = 13x + 8$

Solve each formula for the given variable.

10. $P = 2l + 2w$, for w

11. $a^2 + b^2 = c^2$, for a^2

12. $C = \pi d$, for d

13. $A = bh$, for h

14. $A = \frac{1}{2}by$, for b

15. $A = \frac{1}{2}ap$, for p

16. $L = 2\pi rh$, for r

17. $A = \frac{1}{2}abn$, for b

18. $P = bn$, for n

19. $V = \frac{1}{3}\pi r^2 h$, for h

20. $A = \pi r^2$, for r

21. $A = 4\pi r^2$, for r

22. $V = e^2$, for e

23. $A = s^2$, for s

24. $S = (n - 2)180$, for n

25. $a^2 + b^2 = c^2$, for b

26. $e = \dfrac{360}{n}$, for n

27. $V = \frac{1}{3}\pi r^2 h$, for r

Answers to Review: Topics from Algebra One

Section A-1

Page 557 **1.** −1 **2.** 11 **3.** 1 **4.** 4 **5.** 5 **6.** 1 **7.** 20 **8.** 1 **9.** 10 **10.** 31 **11.** 5 **12.** 9 **13.** 5 **14.** 18 **15.** 12 **16.** 10 **17.** 5 **18.** 3 **19.** 9 **20.** 5 **21.** 4 **22.** 7 **23.** 15 **24.** 13 **25.** 23

Section A-2

Page 559 **1.** $\{-12\}$ **2.** $\{60\}$ **3.** $\left\{\frac{11}{9}\right\}$ **4.** $\{-6\}$ **5.** $\left\{-\frac{43}{9}\right\}$ **6.** $\left\{\frac{1}{6}\right\}$ **7.** $\{-7\}$ **8.** $\{6\}$ **9.** $\{1\}$ **10.** $\{-2\}$ **11.** $\left\{\frac{28}{9}\right\}$ **12.** $\{-7\}$ **13.** $\left\{\frac{10}{3}\right\}$ **14.** $\{-6\}$ **15.** $\{13\}$ **16.** $\{1\}$ **17.** $\{1\}$ **18.** $\left\{\frac{7}{16}\right\}$ **19.** $\{3\}$ **20.** $\left\{-\frac{1}{2}\right\}$ **21.** $\{-6\}$ **22.** $\{0.2\}$ **23.** $\left\{\frac{6}{17}\right\}$ **24.** $\left\{-\frac{16}{7}\right\}$

Section A-3

Page 561 **1.** $\{n: n < 17\}$ **2.** $\{z: z > 2\}$ **3.** $\{z: z > 10\}$ **4.** $\{x: x < 20\}$ **5.** $\{x: x > -7\}$ **6.** $\{x: x > -1\}$ **7.** $\{x: x > 10\}$ **8.** $\{x: x > -2\}$ **9.** $\{n: n < 5\}$ **10.** $\{z: z < 6\}$ **11.** $\{n: n < 4\}$ **12.** $\{n: n > 5\}$ **13.** $\{n: n < 5\}$ **14.** $\{x: x > -5.5\}$ **15.** $\{x: x < -3\}$ **16.** $\{y: y > 6\}$ **17.** $\{x: x < 5\}$ **18.** $\{y: y > 6\}$ **19.** $\left\{m: m > \frac{3}{2}\right\}$ **20.** $\{t: t < 7\}$ **21.** $\left\{x: x < -\frac{5}{3}\right\}$ **22.** $\{x: x > -2\}$ **23.** $\left\{x: x > -\frac{5}{2}\right\}$ **24.** $\left\{x: x > -\frac{7}{5}\right\}$ **25.** $\left\{x: x < -\frac{1}{2}\right\}$ **26.** $\left\{x: x < -\frac{4}{3}\right\}$ **27.** $\{x: x > -15\}$ **28.** $\{z: z > -22\}$

Section A-4

Page 563 **1.** x^{16} **2.** $-a^9$ **3.** x^{13} **4.** $6x^3$ **5.** 3^3 or 27 **6.** $-x^3$ **7.** y^4 **8.** b^5 **9.** $-20x^3y^3$ **10.** $6z^5$ **11.** $-9a^3b^4$ **12.** $20c^7d^2$ **13.** a^{12} **14.** y^9 **15.** x^{10} **16.** x^{12} **17.** b^{24} **18.** a^3b^6 **19.** $\frac{a^3}{b^3}$ **20.** x^{12} **21.** $9a^4b^2$ **22.** $16x^4y^6$ **23.** x^8y^4 **24.** $\frac{a^6}{b^6}$ **25.** a^4 **26.** x^2 **27.** y **28.** x^2 **29.** 1 **30.** a^2b^3 **31.** 1 **32.** z **33.** a^2c **34.** $9rs$ **35.** $-9abc^2$ **36.** 7^4 or 2401 **37.** 1 **38.** $(-6)^7$ **39.** -1 **40.** x^{94}

Section A-5

Page 564 **1.** $\frac{4}{25}$ **2.** 3 **3.** 5 **4.** $\frac{5}{4}$ **5.** $\frac{3}{25}$ **6.** $\frac{9}{49}$ **7.** $\frac{3}{9}$ **8.** $\frac{2}{9}$ **9.** 27 **10.** 50 **11.** 180 **12.** 300 **13.** 162 **14.** 28 **15.** 24 **16.** 90 **17.** 6 **18.** -6 **19.** -9 **20.** 10 **21.** ± 5 **22.** 12 **23.** 20 **24.** 13

Section A-6

Page 565 **1.** $\{6, -6\}$ **2.** $\{9, -9\}$ **3.** $\{10, -10\}$ **4.** $\{20, -20\}$ **5.** $\{9\sqrt{3}, -9\sqrt{3}\}$ **6.** $\left\{\frac{2}{3}, -\frac{2}{3}\right\}$ **7.** $\{\sqrt{10}, -\sqrt{10}\}$ **8.** $\{2\sqrt{5}, -2\sqrt{5}\}$ **9.** $\{2\sqrt{3}, -2\sqrt{3}\}$ **10.** $\{\sqrt{133}, -\sqrt{133}\}$ **11.** $\{2\sqrt{6}, -2\sqrt{6}\}$ **12.** $\{\sqrt{ab}, -\sqrt{ab}\}$ **13.** $\{6a, -6a\}$ **14.** $\{10\sqrt{2}, -10\sqrt{2}\}$ **15.** $\{6\sqrt{2}, -6\sqrt{2}\}$

Section A-7

Page 566 **1.** $2\sqrt{2}$ **2.** $5\sqrt{3}$ **3.** $10\sqrt{3}$ **4.** $6\sqrt{2}$ **5.** $4\sqrt{2}$ **6.** $7\sqrt{2}$ **7.** $8\sqrt{2}$ **8.** $9\sqrt{3}$ **9.** 6 **10.** 10 **11.** 144 **12.** 30 **13.** $9\sqrt{3}$ **14.** $8\sqrt{2}$ **15.** $18\sqrt{2}$ **16.** $21\sqrt{2}$ **17.** $25\sqrt{5}$ **18.** $36\sqrt{2}$ **19.** $22\sqrt{3}$ **20.** $50\sqrt{10}$ **21.** 128 **22.** $18\sqrt{10}$ **23.** $35\sqrt{3}$ **24.** $8\sqrt{3}$ **25.** $55\sqrt{5}$ **26.** $52\sqrt{2}$ **27.** $10\sqrt{11}$ **28.** $18\sqrt{5}$ **29.** $50\sqrt{2}$ **30.** $36\sqrt{2}$ **31.** $6\sqrt{7}$ **32.** $30\sqrt{10}$

Section A-8

Page 567 **1.** $\frac{\sqrt{2}}{2}$ **2.** $\frac{\sqrt{5}}{5}$ **3.** $\frac{\sqrt{3}}{3}$ **4.** $\frac{2\sqrt{7}}{7}$ **5.** $\frac{3\sqrt{5}}{5}$ **6.** $\frac{2\sqrt{3}}{3}$ **7.** $\frac{3\sqrt{2}}{2}$ **8.** $\sqrt{2}$ **9.** $\frac{\sqrt{2}}{4}$ **10.** $\frac{\sqrt{2}}{2}$ **11.** $12\sqrt{3}$ **12.** $\frac{5\sqrt{6}}{6}$ **13.** $\frac{8\sqrt{3}}{3}$ **14.** $\sqrt{5}$ **15.** $\frac{4\sqrt{3}}{3}$ **16.** $\frac{9\sqrt{2}}{2}$ **17.** $\frac{3\sqrt{3}}{2}$ **18.** $\frac{2\sqrt{21}}{15}$ **19.** 10 **20.** $\frac{2\sqrt{10}}{5}$

Section A-9

Page 568 **1.** $y = 2x + 12$ **2.** $y = \frac{a}{b} - x$ **3.** $y = -x - 9$ **4.** $y = \frac{3}{2}x - 2$ **5.** $y = \frac{2}{3}x + \frac{7}{3}$ **6.** $y = \frac{3}{2}x$ **7.** $y = \frac{5}{7}x + \frac{12}{7}$ **8.** $y = -\frac{6}{5}x + \frac{11}{5}$ **9.** $y = \frac{13}{2}x + 4$ **10.** $w = \frac{P}{2} - \ell$ **11.** $a^2 = c^2 - b^2$ **12.** $d = \frac{C}{\pi}$ **13.** $h = \frac{A}{b}$ **14.** $b = \frac{2A}{y}$ **15.** $p = \frac{2A}{a}$ **16.** $r = \frac{L}{2\pi h}$ **17.** $b = \frac{2A}{an}$ **18.** $m = \frac{P}{b}$ **19.** $h = \frac{3V}{\pi r^2}$ **20.** $r = \sqrt{\frac{A}{\pi}}$ **21.** $r = \sqrt{\frac{A}{4\pi}}$ or $r = \frac{1}{2}\sqrt{\frac{A}{\pi}}$ **22.** $e = \sqrt{V}$ **23.** $s = \sqrt{A}$ **24.** $n = \frac{s}{180} + 2$ **25.** $b = \sqrt{c^2 - a^2}$ **26.** $n = \frac{360}{e}$ **27.** $r = \sqrt{\frac{3V}{\pi h}}$

Answers to Try These and Chapter Tests

Chapter 1

Page 3 **1.** Ray *TU* **2.** $\triangle HAP$ **3.** Angle *WHY* **4.** Line *GH*, line *GH*, line *JG* (Line *HG* is also a possible answer.) **5.** $\overrightarrow{HG}$, $\overrightarrow{HJ}$ **6.** $\overline{GH}$ or $\overline{HG}$, $\overline{GJ}$ or $\overline{JG}$, $\overline{HJ}$ or $\overline{JH}$ **7.** $\overrightarrow{GH}$

Page 7 **1.** True **2.** False **3.** False **4.** True **5.** False **6.** True **7.** False **8.** True **9.** True

Page 11 **1.** Right **2.** Obtuse **3.** Acute **4.** True **5.** False **6.** False **7.** True **8.** True **9.** True

Page 15 **1.** $\overline{CB}$, $\overline{AB}$; $CB = 8.3$, $AB = 8.3$ **2.** $\angle B$; $m\angle B = 28$ **3.** $\angle A$, $\angle C$; $m\angle A = 76$, $m\angle C = 76$ **4.** $\angle R$; $m\angle R = 90$ **5.** $\overline{HT}$; $HT = 13$ **6.** $\overline{HR}$, $\overline{TR}$; $HR = 12$, $TR = 5$ **7.** 2 **8.** 0 **9.** 3 **10.** Acute **11.** Acute **12.** Right **13.** Right isosceles **14.** Acute or right scalene **15.** Obtuse isosceles

Page 20 **1.** Angle, measure of an angle, congruent angles **2.** Triangle, isosceles triangle, legs of an isosceles triangle **3.** Angle, obtuse angle, obtuse triangle **4.** A triangle with three congruent sides is an equilateral triangle. True **5.** The side opposite the right angle is the hypotenuse of a right triangle. True

Page 25 **1.** Postulate 5 **2.** Postulate 4 **3.** Postulate 6 **4.** $\overleftrightarrow{AC}$ **5.** *B*

Page 29 **1.** Two planes intersect; Their intersection is a line. **2.** Three sides of a triangle are congruent; The three angles of the triangle are congruent. **3.** $\overline{AC}$, $\overline{CB}$, $\overline{AB}$ **4.** $\angle A$, $\angle B$, $\angle C$ **5.** Statement 2, Statement 1

Chapter Test Page 38 **1.** $\overline{DE}$ **2.** $\overleftrightarrow{DE}$ **3.** $\overrightarrow{DE}$ **4.** $\triangle WXY$ **5.** True **6.** True **7.** False **8.** True **9.** False **10.** True **11.** False **12.** False **13.** True **14.** Right isosceles **15.** Acute isosceles **16.** Obtuse scalene **17.** Theorem **18.** Line **19.** Plane **20.** Three angles of a triangle are congruent; The three sides of the triangle are congruent. **21.** Given: $\triangle ABC$ in which $\angle A \cong \angle B \cong \angle C$; Prove: $\overline{AB} \cong \overline{BC} \cong \overline{AC}$

Chapter 2

Page 43 **1.** 5 **2.** *B* **3.** 3 **4.** *A*, *C* **5.** 2 **6.** $\overline{BD}$

Page 51 **1.** 30 **2.** 50 **3.** 80 **4.** 55 **5.** 90 **6.** 25 **7.** 20 **8.** 105 **9.** 70

Page 60 **1.** $\angle AEC$, $\angle DEB$ **2.** $\angle FED$, $\angle FEC$ **3.** 90 **4.** 20 **5.** $\angle FEB$ **6.** $\angle FED$ **7.** $\angle AEF$ **8.** $\angle AEC$, $\angle AEF$ **9.** 110 **10.** $\angle FEB$

Page 66 **1.** $\overline{EF}$ **2.** $\overline{SK}$ **3.** $\angle A$ **4.** $\angle T$, $\angle G$ **5.** $\overline{PQ}$ **6.** Commutative Postulate for Addition **7.** Associative Postulate for Multiplication **8.** Associative Postulate for Addition **9.** Substitution Principle

Page 71 **1.** They are vertical angles and vertical angles are congruent. **2.** $\angle DAC$, $\angle CAE$, $\angle BAF$, $\angle GAF$ **3.** If two angles are complements of the same angle, then they are congruent. **4.** *Reason 1:* Given; *Reason 2:* Definition of linear pair; *Reason 3:* If two angles form a linear pair, then they are supplementary; *Reason 4:* Given; *Reason 5:* If two angles are supplements of the same angle, then they are congruent.

Page 78 **1.** True **2.** False; $m\angle 2 = 90$ **3.** False; they are vertical angles since they do not have a common side. **4.** False; $\angle TER$ and $\angle TES$ form a linear pair and points R, E, and S are collinear. **5.** False; both angles measure 45. **6.** True **7.** If a triangle is equilateral, then it is equiangular. If a triangle is equiangular, then it is equilateral. **8.** A triangle has two congruent angles if and only if it has two congruent sides. **9.** Two angles are complementary if and only if the sum of their measures is 90. **10.** An angle is a right angle if and only if its measure is 90.

Page 83 **1.** b **2.** a **3.** a **4.** a **5.** a **6.** b

Chapter Test Pages 91–92 **1.** True **2.** False **3.** True **4.** False **5.** False **6.** True **7.** False **8.** True **9.** False **10.** False **11.** 18 **12.** $m\angle R = 48\frac{3}{4}$, $m\angle S = 116\frac{1}{4}$ **13.** 45 **14.** 144 **15.** 43 **16.** 1. $\overleftrightarrow{EF}$ intersects $\overleftrightarrow{AB}$ and $\overleftrightarrow{CD}$; Given 2. $\angle 1 \cong \angle 3$; Given 3. $\angle 2$ and $\angle 3$ are vertical angles; (1). Definition of vertical angles 4. $\angle 3 \cong \angle 2$; (3). Vertical angles are congruent. 5. $\angle 1 \cong \angle 2$; (2). (4). Transitive Property of Congruence 6. $\angle 2 \cong \angle 1$; (5). Symmetric Property of Congruence **17.** 1. $\angle BCA$ is a right angle; $\angle 1$ and $\angle 2$ are complementary; Given 2. $\angle 3$ and $\angle 2$ are complementary; (1). Definition of complementary angles 3. $\angle 3 \cong \angle 1$; (1). (2). Complements of the same angle are congruent.

Chapter 3

Page 95 **1.** $\angle A \leftrightarrow \angle D$, $\angle B \leftrightarrow \angle E$, $\angle C \leftrightarrow \angle F$, $\overline{AB} \leftrightarrow \overline{DE}$, $\overline{BC} \leftrightarrow \overline{EF}$, $\overline{AC} \leftrightarrow \overline{DF}$ **2.** $\overline{YZ}$ **3.** $\angle J$ **4.** $\overline{TR}$ **5.** K **6–8.** Exercises 7 and 8 are not congruences. **9.** $RTS \leftrightarrow HKG$ **10.** GKH **11.** $TSR \leftrightarrow KGH$ **12.** KHG

Page 102 **1–6.** The pairs of triangles in Exercises 2, 3, and 5 are congruent by the S.A.S. Postulate. **7.** Yes **8.** No **9.** Yes **10.** Yes **11.** No **12.** No **13.** Yes **14.** No

Page 109 **1.** 10, 9, 4 **2.** 23, 38 **3.** A.S.A. **4.** S.A.S **5.** S.S.S.

Page 117 **1.** Corollary 3-2 **2.** Theorem 3-1 **3.** Corollary 3-4 **4.** Two sides of a triangle are congruent if and only if the angles opposite these sides are congruent, or The angles opposite two sides of a triangle are congruent if and only if the two sides are congruent. **5.** All three sides of a triangle are congruent if and only if all three angles are also congruent, or All three angles of a triangle are congruent if and only if all three sides are also congruent. **6.** $AC = 8$, $BC = 8$ **7.** $EF = 4$ **8.** $KL = 2$, $m\angle KML = 30$, $m\angle JMK = 70$, $m\angle JKL = 100$

Page 122 **1.** No **2.** Yes **3.** Yes **4.** Yes **5.** No **6.** No **7.** Yes **8.** Yes **9.** No **10.** Yes **11.** Yes **12.** No

Page 132 **1.** $\overline{SP}$ **2.** S **3.** $\overline{TS}$ **4.** TPS **5.** BCD **6.** $\overline{CE}$ **7.** CDB **8.** $\overline{AE}$ **9.** $\overline{HG}$ **10.** FHG **11.** F **12.** GHK

Page 137 **1.** $\angle 1$ is not congruent to $\angle 2$. **2.** $\overline{AB}$ is not perpendicular to $\overline{CD}$. **3.** $m\angle C = m\angle D$ **4.** Angles 3 and 4 are complementary. **5.** Angles A and B are not supplementary. **6.** Segments AB and CD are congruent.

Page 142 **1.** Yes, by the H.L. Theorem **2.** Yes, by the H.L. Theorem **3.** Yes, by the H.A. Postulate **4.** A point is on the bisector of an angle if and only if it is equidistant from the sides of the angle, or A point is equidistant from the sides of an angle if and only if it is on the bisector of the angle.

Chapter Test Pages 151–152 **1.** $\overline{TN}$ **2.** $\angle TSN$ **3.** $\angle STN$ **4.** $\overline{ST}$ **5.** S.S.S. **6.** S.S.S., S.A.S. **7.** A.S.A. **8.** False **9.** True **10.** False **11.** True **12.** True **13.** $\triangle PSR \cong \triangle QRS$, H.L. Theorem **14.** $\triangle ACF \cong \triangle DBE$, S.A.S. Post. **15.** $\triangle CBA \cong \triangle BCD$, A.S.A. Post.; $\triangle AEB \cong \triangle DEC$, A.S.A. Post. **16.** *Reason 1:* Given; *Reason 2:* (1). Theorem 3-3; *Reason 3:* (1). A triangle having a right angle is a right triangle; *Reason 4:* (1). (2). (3). H.L. Theorem; *Reason 5:* (4). C.P.C.T.C.

Chapter 4

Page 157 **1.** *ABD* **2.** *A, C* **3.** > **4.** > **5.** c **6.** e **7.** b **8.** d **9.** a

Page 162 **1.** $p \parallel t$ **2.** $\overleftrightarrow{BA} \parallel \overleftrightarrow{CD}$ **3.** $\overleftrightarrow{BC} \parallel k$ **4.** $\angle 4$ and $\angle 2$, $\angle 1$ and $\angle 3$ **5.** $\angle 1$ and $\angle 4$ **6.** $\angle 1$ and $\angle 4$, $\angle 5$ and $\angle 6$ **7.** Two lines are cut by a transversal so that two alternate interior angles are congruent if and only if the lines are parallel, or Two lines cut by a transversal are parallel if and only if the alternate interior angles are congruent.

Page 167 **1.** 117 **2.** 93 **3.** $m\angle 6 = 135$, $m\angle 7 = 45$ **4.** $180 - x$ **5.** Theorem 4-7: In a plane, if two lines are both perpendicular to a third line, then the two lines are parallel. **6.** Theorem 4-8: In a plane, if a line is perpendicular to one of two parallel lines, it is perpendicular to the other line also.

Page 174 **1.** 5 and 10, 6 and 9; 1 and 9, 5 and 13, 2 and 10, 6 and 14 **2.** 7 and 12, 8 and 11; 3 and 11, 7 and 15, 4 and 12, 8 and 16 **3.** 3 and 6, 2 and 7; 4 and 2, 3 and 1, 8 and 6, 7 and 5 **4.** 11 and 14, 10 and 15; 12 and 10, 11 and 9, 16 and 14, 15 and 13

Page 181 **1.** f **2.** d **3.** a **4.** c **5.** g **6.** c **7.** Corollary 4-13 **8.** Corollary 4-13

Page 186 **1.** b **2.** c **3.** b **4.** a **5.** b **6.** Corollary 4-15 **7.** Corollary 4-18 **8.** Theorem 4-12 **9.** Postulate 10

Page 192 **1.** False **2.** True **3.** True **4.** False **5.** True

Page 196 **1.** 180 **2.** 360 **3.** 360 **4.** 72 **5.** 40

Chapter Test Page 202 **1.** $\overline{AB} \parallel \overline{DC}$ **2.** $\overline{HE} \parallel \overline{GF}$ **3.** $\overrightarrow{KH} \parallel \overrightarrow{MP}$ **4.** $m\angle 1 = 68$, $m\angle 2 = 43$ **5.** $m\angle 1 = 100$, $m\angle 2 = 120$ **6.** $m\angle 1 = 75$, $m\angle 2 = 30$ **7.** 180 **8.** $\angle C$, $\angle EBC$ **9.** 140 **10.** 2. $\overline{BA} \parallel \overrightarrow{CD}$; Theorem 4-7 3. Theorem 4-3 **11.** 61 **12.** $m\angle A = 50$, $m\angle B = 65$, $m\angle C = 65$ **13.** 720 **14.** 108 **15.** 24

Chapter 5

Page 209 **1.** $\overline{BC}$ **2.** $\overline{AB}$ **3.** $\angle CBA$ **4.** *CDA* **5.** $\overline{QA}$ **6.** *CBQ* **7.** 40 **8.** 60 **9.** *QD* or *QB* **10.** *AC*

Page 211 **1.** Yes, by Theorem 5-7 **2.** Yes, opposite sides are parallel by Theorem 4-2. **3.** No, $\overline{LK} \parallel \overline{NJ}$ by Theorem 4-4 but there is no way of proving that $\overline{LN} \parallel \overline{KJ}$. **4.** No, $\overline{PO} \parallel \overline{MN}$ by Theorem 4-9 and $\overline{MP} \cong \overline{NO}$, but to use Theorem 5-8, the same pair of sides must be congruent and parallel. **5.** Yes, $\overline{XW} \cong \overline{UV}$ and $\overline{XW} \parallel \overline{UV}$ by Theorem 4-2. Therefore, Theorem 5-8 can be used to prove *XWVU* is a parallelogram. **6.** No, opposite angles in a parallelogram must be congruent by Theorem 5-3.

Page 216 **1.** Parallelogram **2.** Parallelogram **3.** Rectangle, rhombus, parallelogram **4.** Square, rectangle **5.** Rhombus, square **6.** Rhombus, square **7.** $DS = 5.6$, $AP = 2.8$, $PH = 2.8$, $AH = 5.6$

Page 220 **1.** 4, 3, and $2\frac{1}{2}$ **2.** Yes **3.** $EF = \frac{1}{2}BD$ **4.** $GH = \frac{1}{2}BD$ **5.** $EF = GH$ **6.** Yes, $\overline{EF} \parallel \overline{BD}$ and $\overline{GH} \parallel \overline{BD}$ by Theorem 5-12, and $\overline{EF} \parallel \overline{GH}$ by Theorem 4-11.

Page 224 **1.** $7\frac{1}{2}$ units **2.** $AE = EC = 9$ **3.** $DB = 10$, $AB = 20$ **4.** 4 **5.** $QO = 8$, $VO = 16$ **6.** 17

Page 231 **1.** $\angle 4$ **2.** $m\angle 4 > m\angle 1$ **3.** $m\angle 4 > m\angle A$ **4.** $m\angle 3 > m\angle 2$ **5.** $m\angle A = m\angle 3$ **6.** $m\angle 3 > m\angle B$ **7.** $m\angle A > m\angle B$ **8.** $BC > AC$

Page 236 **1.** b **2.** a **3.** b **4.** c **5.** c

Page 240 **1.** *A-CQ-B* **2.** *A-CB-Q* **3.** *C-AB-Q* **4.** *A-CQ-B* **5.** *A-QB-C* **6.** *B-AQ-C*

Chapter Test Page 248 **1.** True **2.** True **3.** False **4.** False **5.** False **6.** $\overline{AB} \parallel \overline{CD}$ **7.** *CBA* **8.** $\overline{AD} \cong \overline{DC}$ **9.** $4\frac{1}{2}$ **10.** $11\frac{1}{2}$ **11.** $\overline{PR}$ **12.** $\angle M$ **13.** 1. In rectangle *RSTW*, *Q* is the midpoint of $\overline{RW}$; Given 2. Angles *R*, *S*, *T*, and *W* are right angles; (1). Definition of rectangle 3. $\overline{RW} \perp \overline{WT}$ and $\overline{ST} \perp \overline{WT}$, $\overline{RS} \perp \overline{ST}$ and $\overline{WT} \perp \overline{ST}$; (2). Definition of perpendicular lines 4. $\overline{RW} \parallel \overline{ST}$, $\overline{RS} \parallel \overline{WT}$; (3). Theorem 4-7 5. Quadrilateral *RSTW* is a parallelogram; (4). Definition of parallelogram 6. $\overline{RS} \cong \overline{WT}$; (5). Corollary 5-2 7. $\angle R \cong \angle W$; (2). Corollary 2-14 8. $RQ = QW$; (1). Definition of midpoint of a segment 9. $\overline{RQ} \cong \overline{QW}$; (8). Definition of congruent segments 10. $\therefore \triangle QWT \cong \triangle QRS$; (6). (7). (9). S.A.S. Postulate

Chapter 6

Page 252 **1.** $\frac{2}{3}$ **2.** $\frac{1}{3}$ **3.** $\frac{4}{5}$ **4.** $\frac{5x}{2}$ **5.** $\frac{1}{3}$ **6.** $\frac{1}{4}$ **7.** $\frac{5}{1}$ **8.** $\frac{1}{10}$ **9.** 8 **10.** If $\frac{a}{b} = \frac{c}{d}$ then $ad = bc$. If $ad = bc$ then $\frac{a}{b} = \frac{c}{d}$. $(b \neq 0, d \neq 0)$

Page 255 **1.** 6 **2.** 6 **3.** $6a$ **4.** $9\frac{1}{3}$ **5.** $7\frac{1}{2}$ **6.** $2\frac{1}{2}$

Page 260 **1.** *BD* **2.** $\frac{ED}{BD}$ **3.** $\frac{EA}{AC}$ **4.** $\frac{EA + AC}{EA}$ **5.** 32 **6.** 30

Page 263 **1.** False **2.** False **3.** 5 **4.** $5\frac{1}{3}$ **5.** 16 **6.** 4 **7.** A line intersecting the interior of a triangle is parallel to one side if and only if it divides the other two sides proportionally, or A line divides two sides of a triangle proportionally if and only if it is parallel to the third side.

Page 268 **1.** Yes, corresponding angles are congruent because both triangles are equiangular and corresponding sides have the same ratio because both triangles are equilateral. **2.** No, corresponding angles are not congruent. **3.** No, corresponding angles are not congruent.

Page 273 **1.** Yes, Corollary 6-10 **2.** Yes, Corollary 6-12 **3.** Yes, Corollary 6-11 **4.** Yes, by Theorem 4-10, $\angle T \cong \angle CKM$, $\angle S \cong \angle CMK$; and by Corollary 6-10, $\triangle CKM \sim \triangle CTS$. **5.** No, because only one pair of angles is congruent. **6.** Yes, by Theorem 2-10, $\angle ACB \cong \angle DCE$; by Theorem 4-12, $m\angle B = 89$, $\angle B \cong \angle D$; and by Corollary 6-10, $\triangle ABC \sim \triangle EDC$.

Page 278 **1.** 15 **2.** $7\frac{1}{5}$ **3.** $4\frac{2}{7}$

Page 283 **1.** $5\sqrt{2}$ **2.** $3\sqrt{3}$ **3.** $5\frac{1}{3}$ **4.** 4 or 9 **5.** 6 **6.** 16

Page 288 **1.** 20 **2.** $4\sqrt{3}$ **3.** $7\sqrt{2}$ **4.** $x = 6$, $y = 10$ **5.** $\sqrt{39}$ **6.** 13 **7.** Yes **8.** No **9.** Yes **10.** The square of the length of one side of a triangle equals the sum of the squares of the lengths of the other two sides if and only if the triangle is a right triangle.

Page 293 **1.** $8\sqrt{2}$ **2.** $15\sqrt{2}$ **3.** $\frac{3}{4}\sqrt{2}$ **4.** 12 **5.** $5\sqrt{2}$ **6.** $6\sqrt{2}$ **7.** $\frac{21}{8}\sqrt{2}$ **8.** 18

Chapter Test Pages 301–302 **1.** $9\frac{1}{3}$ **2.** 18 **3.** 10 **4.** 21 **5.** 21 **6.** $6\frac{3}{4}$ **7.** 2 **8.** $AD = 4$, $DB = 6$ **9.** False **10.** True **11.** False **12.** True **13.** True **14.** $\triangle ACE$ and $\triangle DCB$ **15.** $\triangle ACB$ and $\triangle ABD$ **16.** 1. In parallelogram $ABCD$, $\overline{DE} \perp \overline{AB}$, and $\overline{DF} \perp \overline{BC}$; Given 2. $\angle AED$ and $\angle CFD$ are right angles; (1). Corollary 2-13 3. $\triangle AED$ and $\triangle CFD$ are right triangles; (2). Definition of right triangles 4. $\angle A \cong \angle C$; (1). Corollary 5-3 5. $\triangle AED \sim \triangle CFD$; (3). (4). Corollary 6-11 **17.** 13 units **18.** $3\sqrt{5}$ centimeters **19.** $5\sqrt{2}$ units **20.** 6 units

Chapter 7

Page 305 **1.** O **2.** $\overline{OC}$, $\overline{OD}$ **3.** $\overline{CD}$ **4.** $\overline{AB}$, $\overline{EF}$, and $\overline{CD}$ **5.** $\overleftrightarrow{BK}$ **6.** $\overleftrightarrow{EF}$ **7.** 2 points **8.** 1 point **9.** 0 points **10.** 2 points

Page 310 **1.** $\angle APD$, $\angle DPB$, $\angle BPC$, $\angle CPA$ **2.** $\overline{CD}$, or $\overline{AB}$ **3.** $\overset{\frown}{AD}$ and $\overset{\frown}{CB}$, $\overset{\frown}{AC}$ and $\overset{\frown}{DB}$ **4.** $\overset{\frown}{CAD}$, $\overset{\frown}{ADB}$, $\overset{\frown}{DBC}$, $\overset{\frown}{BCA}$ **5.** $\overset{\frown}{ADC}$, $\overset{\frown}{CAB}$, $\overset{\frown}{BAD}$ **6.** 65, 115, 65, 115, 180 **7.** 120, 90, 70, 80, 200, 240 **8.** In the same or in congruent circles, if two arcs are congruent then their central angles are congruent; In the same or in congruent circles, if two central angles are congruent then their arcs are congruent.

Page 315 **1.** Theorem 7-4 **2.** Theorem 7-3 **3.** Theorem 7-2 **4.** Theorem 7-2 **5.** Theorem 7-5 **6.** Theorem 7-5 **7.** Theorem 6-21 **8.** Theorem 6-21 **9-10.** Theorem 7-6 **11.** In the same or in congruent circles, two chords are congruent if and only if their arcs are congruent.

Page 320 **1.** a **2.** b **3.** c **4.** a **5.** b **6.** In the same or in congruent circles, if two chords are congruent, then they are equidistant from the center; In the same or in congruent circles, if two chords are equidistant from the center, then they are congruent.

Page 325 **1.** Right triangle **2.** $\overline{BC}$ is tangent to the circle at B, Theorem 7-11 **3.** In the plane of a given circle O, if a line is perpendicular to radius OC at C, then the line is tangent to the circle at C; In the plane of a given circle O, if a line is tangent to the circle at C, then it is perpendicular to radius OC. **4.** Isosceles triangle **5.** 50

Page 331 **1.** 44 **2.** 44 **3.** $\angle CBA$ **4.** 30, 30 **5.** 44, 22 **6.** $42\frac{1}{2}$, $42\frac{1}{2}$ **7.** $2a$, a

Page 337 **1.** True, by Theorem 7-16. **2.** False, by Theorem 7-16, $\angle XRZ$ is a right angle and therefore $\triangle XRZ$ is a right triangle. **3.** True, by Corollary 7-17 **4.** True, by Theorem 4-3 since $\overline{YZ} \parallel \overline{XR}$. **5.** False since $(m\angle YXZ + m\angle 2) + (m\angle RZX + m\angle 1) = 180$, by Corollary 7-18. **6.** True, by Corollary 7-18. **7.** True, by Corollary 7-18. **8.** True, by Corollary 4-13. **9.** If an inscribed angle is a right angle, then it is inscribed in a semicircle; If an angle is inscribed in a semicircle, then it is a right angle.

Page 343 **1.** 118 **2.** 79 **3.** 79 **4.** $131\frac{1}{2}$ **5.** 41 **6.** 74 **7.** 67

Page 348 **1.** 33 **2.** 51 **3.** 41 **4.** 260, 80 **5.** 110, 70 **6.** 90, 270, 90

Page 353 **1.** 8 **2.** $2\frac{1}{2}$ **3.** 4, 4, 8 **4.** 2 **5.** $3\frac{1}{2}$ **6.** 13 **7.** 10 **8.** 8 **9.** 5

Page 357 **1.** A, B, P, S, R, N, E, and G **2.** D and F **3.** Q **4.** $\overline{QP}$, $\overline{QS}$, and $\overline{QR}$ **5.** $\overline{RP}$ **6.** $\overline{AB}$, $\overline{RP}$, and $\overline{NG}$ **7.** $\overleftrightarrow{AB}$ **8.** $\overleftrightarrow{DF}$ **9.** Circle Q **10.** $\overparen{RS}$ and $\overparen{PS}$ **11.** $\angle RQS$ and $\angle SQP$

Chapter Test Pages 364–365 **1.** 75 **2.** $8\sqrt{3}$ **3.** Chord ST **4.** 12 **5.** $\angle ZYX$ and $\angle ZWX$ **6.** 95 **7.** $2\sqrt{14.04}$ **8.** 106 **9.** 4, 9 **10.** 100 **11.** $15\frac{1}{2}$ **12.** 8 **13.** $m\angle R = 95$, $m\angle S = 80$ **14.** Circle with radius less than 5 centimeters.

Chapter 8

Page 372 **1.** Yes **2.** Yes **3.** Yes **4.** 62 sq. units **5.** 60 sq. cm **6.** $7\frac{1}{5}$

Page 378 **1.** 60 sq. cm **2.** 4 **3.** 45 sq. cm **4.** 12 **5.** 84 sq. cm **6.** $36\sqrt{3}$ sq. m

Page 383 **1.** 320 sq. cm **2.** 8 **3.** 500 sq. m **4.** 7 **5.** 30 sq. cm

Page 388 **1.** n **2.** 40 **3.** 8 **4.** Octagon **5.** Congruent **6.** Consecutive radii **7.** 9 **8.** $\perp$, $\overline{AB}$

Page 393 **1.** Perimeter = 60 cm, area = $150\sqrt{3}$ sq. cm **2.** Area = $288\sqrt{3}$ **3.** Area = $100\sqrt{3}$ **4.** Perimeter = $5x$, area = $\frac{5}{2}xy$ **5.** Side = 20 dm, perimeter = 80 dm, area = 400 sq. dm **6.** Apothem = $2\sqrt{3}$ mm, perimeter = 36 mm, area = $36\sqrt{3}$ sq. mm

Page 396 **1.** $\frac{3}{7}$ **2.** $\frac{4}{9}$ **3.** $\frac{8}{9}$ **4.** $2:\sqrt{7}$

Page 400 **1.** 28π cm **2.** 17 units **3.** $\frac{4}{3}\pi$ **4.** 72

Page 405 **1.** 36π sq. cm **2.** $\frac{4}{9}$ **3.** 5 units **4.** 3π sq. cm

Chapter Test Pages 411–412 **1.** 96 **2.** $18\sqrt{3}$ **3.** $\frac{3}{7}$ **4.** $\frac{9\sqrt{3}}{4}$ sq. units **5.** 30 **6.** 7 cm **7.** 32 sq. cm **8.** 30 **9.** 9 **10.** $4\sqrt{3}$ cm **11.** 52 sq. mm **12.** $\frac{2}{7}$ **13.** 43.96 m **14.** $\frac{28\pi}{45}$ m **15.** 25π sq. cm **16.** $\frac{9}{8}\pi$ **17.** $(24\pi - 36\sqrt{3})$ sq. cm

Chapter 9

Page 416 **1.** 48 **2.** 480 **3.** $96\sqrt{3}$ **4.** $480 + 192\sqrt{3}$ **5.** 17 m **6.** 102 sq. m

Page 420 **1.** 252 sq. m **2.** $36\sqrt{3}$ sq. m **3.** $252 + 36\sqrt{3}$ sq. m

Page 425 **1.** $L = 240\pi$, $T = 440\pi$ **2.** $L = 320\pi$, $T = 576\pi$ **3.** $L = 64\pi$, $T = 96\pi$ **4.** $L = 120\pi$, $T = 156\pi$

Page 431 **1.** 60 cu. cm **2.** 216 cu. cm **3.** 480 cu. cm **4.** 192 cu. cm **5.** 1152π cu. cm **6.** 256π cu. cm

Page 436 **1.** 100π sq. cm **2.** 3 units **3.** 288π cu. cm

Chapter Test Page 442 **1.** True **2.** True **3.** False **4.** False **5.** True **6.** 121.5 cu. cm **7.** $90 + 9\sqrt{3}$ sq. m **8.** 88π **9.** $160\sqrt{3}$ cu. cm **10.** 576 cu. m **11.** $\frac{200}{3}\pi$ cu. cm **12.** 4500π cu. m

Chapter 10

Page 445 **1.** III **2.** IV **3.** II **4.** 5 units **5.** Parallel; perpendicular **6.** Parallel **7.** Perpendicular

Page 449 **1.** (4, 8) **2.** $(-\frac{1}{2}, 4)$ **3.** (1, 8)

Page 451 **1.** 4 **2.** $-\frac{2}{7}$ **3.** $\frac{4}{5}$ **4.** 0 **5.** 0 **6.** Vertical

Page 454 **1.** A line passing through the points (−7, 0) and (1, 4). **2.** $y = 3x + 5$ **3.** $y = -\frac{3}{5}x + \frac{1}{5}$ **4.** $y = 2x - 3$ **5.** $y = -\frac{1}{2}x + \frac{5}{2}$; slope: $-\frac{1}{2}$; y intercept: $(0, \frac{5}{2})$ **6.** $y = \frac{1}{3}x - \frac{1}{3}$; y intercept: $(0, -\frac{1}{3})$ **7.** $y = 3x - 5$; slope: 3; y intercept: (0, −5)

Page 458 **1.** $-\frac{2}{3}; \frac{3}{2}$ **2.** $-\frac{5}{3}; \frac{3}{5}$ **3.** 3 **4.** 2 **5.** Parallel **6.** Perpendicular

Page 461 **1.** 5 **2.** 10 **3.** $10\sqrt{2}$ **4.** $\sqrt{(3-a)^2 + (3-b)^2}$, or $\sqrt{a^2 + b^2 - 6(a+b) + 18}$

Page 464 Answers will vary. **1.** $(0, 0), (a, 0), (a, a), (0, a)$ **2.** $(0, 0), (a, 0), (a, b), (0, b)$ **3.** $(0, 0), (a, 0), (a + b, c), (b, c)$ **4.** $(0, 0), (a, 0), (0, b)$ **5.** $(0, 0), (2a, 0), (a, b)$ **6.** $(0, 0), (a, 0), \left(\frac{a}{2}, \frac{a}{2}\sqrt{3}\right)$

Chapter Test Page 469 **1.** IV **2.** Parallel **3.** −4, (0, 7) **4.** −1 **5.** (−1, 4) **6.** $4\sqrt{5}$ **7.** 2 **8.** $\frac{2}{3}$ **9.** $y + 3 = \frac{1}{2}(x - 2)$, or $2y = x - 8$ **10.** $y = 2x + 2$ **11.** Perpendicular **12.** Parallel **13.** $AB = 3\sqrt{10}$, $BC = 3\sqrt{5}$, and $AC = 3\sqrt{5}$ so that $BC = AC$, $\overline{BC} \cong \overline{AC}$ and $\triangle ABC$ is an isosceles triangle. **14.** Let the slope of $\overline{DE} = m$, and the slope of $\overline{DF} = m_2$; $m_1 = \frac{5}{9}$, $m_2 = -\frac{9}{5}$ so that $m_1 \cdot m_2 = -1$. Therefore the slopes of $\overline{DE}$ and $\overline{DF}$ are negative reciprocals and by Theorem 10-3, $\overline{DE} \perp \overline{DF}$; $\therefore \angle D$ is a right angle and $\triangle DEF$ is a right triangle. **15.** Let $A(0, 0)$, $B(a, 0)$, $C(a - b, c)$, and $D(b, c)$ be the vertices of the isosceles trapezoid with diagonals DB and AC. $DB = \sqrt{(a-b)^2 + (0-c)^2} = \sqrt{(a-b)^2 + c^2}$; $AC = \sqrt{(a-b-0)^2 + (c-0)^2} = \sqrt{(a-b)^2 + c^2}$; $\therefore DB = AC$ and $\overline{DB} \cong \overline{AC}$.

Chapter 11

Page 476 **1.** True **2.** False **3.** True **4.** False **5.** True **6.** True **7.** False **8.** False **9.** True

Page 480 **1.** 0, 1, 2, 3, or 4 **2.** 1 or 2 **3.** 0, 1, 2, 3, or 4 **4.** 0, 1, or 2 **5.** 0 or 2

Page 484 **1.** False **2.** False **3.** True **4.** True **5.** True

Page 488 **1.** A plane which is the perpendicular bisector of a line segment between the two given lines. **2.** The interior of a sphere with center at the given point and radius d. **3.** A sphere concentric to the given spheres, with radius 2.375 cm. **4.** If the planes are parallel, no points; if the planes intersect, a line; if the planes coincide, the plane.

Chapter Test Page 493 **1.** 2 lines **2.** A circle **3.** 1 line **4.** 2 lines **5.** 4 points **6.** 2 points **7.** 1 point **8.** 4 points **9.** 2 lines **10.** 2 lines **11.** The perpendicular bisector of the base excluding the midpoint **12.** A semicircle with diameter AC, excluding points A and C **13.** $\overline{QD}$, excluding points Q and D **14.** Two planes, parallel to the given plane and 5 in. from it on either side **15.** A sphere with center T and radius 1 meter **16.** The plane perpendicular to $\overline{RS}$ at the midpoint of $\overline{RS}$ **17.** Two perpendicular planes which bisect the angles formed by the two intersecting planes **18.** False **19.** True **20.** True

Chapter 12

Page 498 **1.** 3; 24; a **2.** 3; 24; a **3.** $\tan A = 0.75$; $\tan A = 2.4$; $\tan A = \frac{a}{b}$; $\tan B \approx 1.333$; $\tan B \approx 0.4167$; $\tan B = \frac{b}{a}$ **4.** 3.2709 **5.** 0.1405 **6.** 27°

Page 501 **1.** 103 **2.** 171 **3.** 1046

Page 504 **1.** $\frac{1}{2}$ **2.** $\frac{\sqrt{3}}{2}$ **3.** $\frac{\sqrt{3}}{2}$ **4.** $\frac{1}{2}$ **5.** $\frac{\sqrt{2}}{2}$ **6.** $\frac{\sqrt{2}}{2}$ **7.** 1. 0.5000; 0.5000; 2. 0.8660; 0.8660; 3. 0.8660; 0.8660; 4. 0.5000; 0.5000; 5. 0.7071; 0.7071; 6. 0.7071; 0.7071. Therefore, the four-place decimals are the same as the values found in the table. **8.** tan 42° **9.** sin 55° **10.** tan 38°

Page 508 **1.** sin 34°, 56 **2.** tan 15°, 75; tan 75°, 75 **3.** sin 45°, 115 **4.** tan x°, 61° **5.** tan x°, 21° **6.** tan x°, 36°

Chapter Test Page 514 **1.** $\frac{5}{3}$ **2.** $\frac{5}{\sqrt{34}}$ or $\frac{5\sqrt{34}}{34}$ **3.** $\frac{3}{5}$ **4.** $\frac{5}{\sqrt{34}}$ or $\frac{5\sqrt{34}}{34}$ **5.** $\frac{3}{\sqrt{34}}$ or $\frac{3\sqrt{34}}{34}$ **6.** $\frac{3}{\sqrt{34}}$ or $\frac{3\sqrt{34}}{34}$ **7.** $\cos 28° = \frac{x}{45}$; 40 **8.** $\tan 53° = \frac{30}{x}$; 23 **9.** $\sin 75° = \frac{x}{100}$; 97 **10.** 45.6528 or 46 **11.** 10.9116 or 11

Chapter 13

Page 517 **1.** 2 **2.** 2 **3.** 2 **4.** 3 **5.** 3 **6.** 4 **7.** 6 **8.** 5

Page 522 **1.** None **2.** None **3.** Three **4.** One **5.** Two **6.** One **7.** One **8.** Two **9.** Yes **10.** Yes

Page 531 **1.** $QA' \approx 5$ cm, $QA \approx 3$ cm, $\frac{QA'}{QA} \approx \frac{5}{3}$; $QB' \approx 5.5$ cm, $QB \approx 3.3$ cm, $\frac{QB'}{QB} \approx \frac{5}{3}$
2. $QA' \approx 2.8$ cm, $QA \approx 4.2$ cm, $\frac{QA'}{QA} \approx \frac{2}{3}$; $QB' \approx 2$ cm, $QB \approx 3$ cm, $\frac{QB'}{QB} \approx \frac{2}{3}$ **3.** $\frac{5}{3}$ **4.** $\frac{2}{3}$

Chapter Test Page 536 **1.** P **2.** Y **3.** $\overline{PY}$ **4.** $\overline{YQ}$ **5.** $\angle T$ **6.** $\angle YQP$ **7.** 10 cm **8.** 77 **9.** Translation **10.** Rotation **11.** 6 **12.** 4 **13.** 18 **14.** 4.5

Chapter 14

Page 539 **1.** (1, 3) **2.** (−2, 2) **3.** (−2, −3) **4.** (4, −1) **5.** (−4, −8) **6.** (5, 4) **7.** (−4, 5) **8.** (9, −3) **9.** (1, 2) **10.** (2, −8) **11.** (1). $\sqrt{10}$, (2). $2\sqrt{2}$, (3). $\sqrt{13}$, (4). $\sqrt{17}$

Page 542 **1.** (9, 11) **2.** (1, 9) **3.** (0, 0) **4.** (16, 4) **5.** True **6.** False **7.** False **8.** True

Page 545 **1.** $\frac{1}{5}$; $\sqrt{26}$ **2.** −5; $\sqrt{26}$ **3.** 1; $\sqrt{2}$ **4.** (−3, −3) **5.** −2; $3\sqrt{5}$ **6.** 0, $3\sqrt{2}$ **7.** $\frac{1}{5}$; $\sqrt{26}$ **8.** $\frac{1}{5}$; $\sqrt{26}$

Page 549 **1.** (−2, 3) **2.** (2, −3) **3.** (−6, 9) **4.** $(-1, \frac{3}{2})$ **5.** (−12, 18) **6.** (−12, 18) **7.** (0, 0) **8.** (6, 2) **9.** (15, 5) **10.** (0, 11) **11.** (2, 8) **12.** (2, 8)

Chapter Test Page 552 **1.** $\overrightarrow{AB} = (1, -5)$ **2.** $\overrightarrow{AB} = (5, -9)$ **3.** $\overrightarrow{AB} = (-3, -6)$ **4.** $\overrightarrow{AB} = (-2, 5)$ **5.** (1). $\sqrt{26}$; (2). $\sqrt{106}$; (3). $3\sqrt{5}$; (4). $\sqrt{29}$ **6.** $\overrightarrow{AD} = (-1, 5)$ **7.** $\overrightarrow{AD} = (-1, 4)$ **8.** (0, 0) **9.** (2, 1) **10.** (4, −1) **11.** (−6, 14) **12.** 1. $\overrightarrow{AD} = 3\overrightarrow{DC}$, $\overrightarrow{EB} = 3\overrightarrow{CE}$, Given; 2. $\overrightarrow{AC} = \overrightarrow{AD} + \overrightarrow{DC} = 3\overrightarrow{DC} + \overrightarrow{DC} = 4\overrightarrow{DC}$, $\overrightarrow{CB} = \overrightarrow{CE} + \overrightarrow{EB} = \overrightarrow{CE} + 3\overrightarrow{CE} = 4\overrightarrow{CE}$; (1). Vector Theorem 1, Substitution Principle 3. $\overrightarrow{AB} = \overrightarrow{AC} + \overrightarrow{CB}$; Vector Theorem 1 4. $\overrightarrow{AB} = 4\overrightarrow{DC} + 4\overrightarrow{CE}$; (2). (3). Substitution Principle 5. $\overrightarrow{AB} = 4(\overrightarrow{DC} + \overrightarrow{CE})$; (4). Distributive Property 6. $\overrightarrow{AB} = 4\overrightarrow{DE}$; (5). Vector Theorem 1

Table of Squares and Square Roots

No.	Square	Square Root	No.	Square	Square Root	No.	Square	Square Root
1	1	1.000	**51**	2601	7.141	**101**	10,201	10.050
2	4	1.414	**52**	2704	7.211	**102**	10,404	10.100
3	9	1.732	**53**	2809	7.280	**103**	10,609	10.149
4	16	2.000	**54**	2916	7.348	**104**	10,816	10.198
5	25	2.236	**55**	3025	7.416	**105**	11,025	10.247
6	36	2.449	**56**	3136	7.483	**106**	11,236	10.296
7	49	2.646	**57**	3249	7.550	**107**	11,449	10.344
8	64	2.828	**58**	3364	7.616	**108**	11,664	10.392
9	81	3.000	**59**	3481	7.681	**109**	11,881	10.440
10	100	3.162	**60**	3600	7.746	**110**	12,100	10.488
11	121	3.317	**61**	3721	7.810	**111**	12,321	10.536
12	144	3.464	**62**	3844	7.874	**112**	12,544	10.583
13	169	3.606	**63**	3969	7.937	**113**	12,769	10.630
14	196	3.742	**64**	4096	8.000	**114**	12,996	10.677
15	225	3.873	**65**	4225	8.062	**115**	13,225	10.724
16	256	4.000	**66**	4356	8.124	**116**	13,456	10.770
17	289	4.123	**67**	4489	8.185	**117**	13,689	10.817
18	324	4.243	**68**	4624	8.246	**118**	13,924	10.863
19	361	4.359	**69**	4761	8.307	**119**	14,161	10.909
20	400	4.472	**70**	4900	8.367	**120**	14,400	10.954
21	441	4.583	**71**	5041	8.426	**121**	14,641	11.000
22	484	4.690	**72**	5184	8.485	**122**	14,884	11.045
23	529	4.796	**73**	5329	8.544	**123**	15,129	11.091
24	576	4.899	**74**	5476	8.602	**124**	15,376	11.136
25	625	5.000	**75**	5625	8.660	**125**	15,625	11.180
26	676	5.099	**76**	5776	8.718	**126**	15,876	11.225
27	729	5.196	**77**	5929	8.775	**127**	16,129	11.269
28	784	5.292	**78**	6084	8.832	**128**	16,384	11.314
29	841	5.385	**79**	6241	8.888	**129**	16,641	11.358
30	900	5.477	**80**	6400	8.944	**130**	16,900	11.402
31	961	5.568	**81**	6561	9.000	**131**	17,161	11.446
32	1024	5.657	**82**	6724	9.055	**132**	17,424	11.489
33	1089	5.745	**83**	6889	9.110	**133**	17,689	11.533
34	1156	5.831	**84**	7056	9.165	**134**	17,956	11.576
35	1225	5.916	**85**	7225	9.220	**135**	18,225	11.619
36	1296	6.000	**86**	7396	9.274	**136**	18,496	11.662
37	1369	6.083	**87**	7569	9.327	**137**	18,769	11.705
38	1444	6.164	**88**	7744	9.381	**138**	19,044	11.747
39	1521	6.245	**89**	7921	9.434	**139**	19,321	11.790
40	1600	6.325	**90**	8100	9.487	**140**	19,600	11.832
41	1681	6.403	**91**	8281	9.539	**141**	19,881	11.874
42	1764	6.481	**92**	8464	9.592	**142**	20,164	11.916
43	1849	6.557	**93**	8649	9.644	**143**	20,449	11.958
44	1936	6.633	**94**	8836	9.695	**144**	20,736	12.000
45	2025	6.708	**95**	9025	9.747	**145**	21,025	12.042
46	2116	6.782	**96**	9216	9.798	**146**	21,316	12.083
47	2209	6.856	**97**	9409	9.849	**147**	21,609	12.124
48	2304	6.928	**98**	9604	9.899	**148**	21,904	12.166
49	2401	7.000	**99**	9801	9.950	**149**	22,201	12.207
50	2500	7.071	**100**	10,000	10.000	**150**	22,500	12.247

Table of Sines, Cosines, and Tangents

Angle	Sin	Cos	Tan	Angle	Sin	Cos	Tan
0°	.0000	1.0000	.0000	45°	.7071	.7071	1.0000
1	.0175	.9998	.0175	46	.7193	.6947	1.0355
2	.0349	.9994	.0349	47	.7314	.6820	1.0724
3	.0523	.9986	.0524	48	.7431	.6691	1.1106
4	.0698	.9976	.0699	49	.7547	.6561	1.1504
5	.0872	.9962	.0875	50	.7660	.6428	1.1918
6	.1045	.9945	.1051	51	.7771	.6293	1.2349
7	.1219	.9925	.1228	52	.7880	.6157	1.2799
8	.1392	.9903	.1405	53	.7986	.6018	1.3270
9	.1564	.9877	.1584	54	.8090	.5878	1.3764
10	.1736	.9848	.1763	55	.8192	.5736	1.4281
11	.1908	.9816	.1944	56	.8290	.5592	1.4826
12	.2079	.9781	.2126	57	.8387	.5446	1.5399
13	.2250	.9744	.2309	58	.8480	.5299	1.6003
14	.2419	.9703	.2493	59	.8572	.5150	1.6643
15	.2588	.9659	.2679	60	.8660	.5000	1.7321
16	.2756	.9613	.2867	61	.8746	.4848	1.8040
17	.2924	.9563	.3057	62	.8829	.4695	1.8807
18	.3090	.9511	.3249	63	.8910	.4540	1.9626
19	.3256	.9455	.3443	64	.8988	.4384	2.0503
20	.3420	.9397	.3640	65	.9063	.4226	2.1445
21	.3584	.9336	.3839	66	.9135	.4067	2.2460
22	.3746	.9272	.4040	67	.9205	.3907	2.3559
23	.3907	.9205	.4245	68	.9272	.3746	2.4751
24	.4067	.9135	.4452	69	.9336	.3584	2.6051
25	.4226	.9063	.4663	70	.9397	.3420	2.7475
26	.4384	.8988	.4877	71	.9455	.3256	2.9042
27	.4540	.8910	.5095	72	.9511	.3090	3.0777
28	.4695	.8829	.5317	73	.9563	.2924	3.2709
29	.4848	.8746	.5543	74	.9613	.2756	3.4874
30	.5000	.8660	.5774	75	.9659	.2588	3.7321
31	.5150	.8572	.6009	76	.9703	.2419	4.0108
32	.5299	.8480	.6249	77	.9744	.2250	4.3315
33	.5446	.8387	.6494	78	.9781	.2079	4.7046
34	.5592	.8290	.6745	79	.9816	.1908	5.1446
35	.5736	.8192	.7002	80	.9848	.1736	5.6713
36	.5878	.8090	.7265	81	.9877	.1564	6.3138
37	.6018	.7986	.7536	82	.9903	.1392	7.1154
38	.6157	.7880	.7813	83	.9925	.1219	8.1443
39	.6293	.7771	.8098	84	.9945	.1045	9.5144
40	.6428	.7660	.8391	85	.9962	.0872	11.4301
41	.6561	.7547	.8693	86	.9976	.0698	14.3007
42	.6691	.7431	.9004	87	.9986	.0523	19.0811
43	.6820	.7314	.9325	88	.9994	.0349	28.6363
44	.6947	.7193	.9657	89	.9998	.0175	57.2900
45	.7071	.7071	1.0000	90	1.0000	.0000	

Postulates

Postulate 1 Every line contains at least two distinct points.

Postulate 2 Every plane contains at least three different noncollinear points.

Postulate 3 Space contains at least four noncoplanar points.

Postulate 4 For any two distinct points, there is exactly one line containing them.

Postulate 5 For any three distinct noncollinear points, there is exactly one plane containing them.

Postulate 6 If any two distinct points lie in a plane, the line containing these points lies in the plane.

Postulate 7 If two distinct planes have one point in common, they have at least two points in common.

Postulate 8 **The Ruler Postulate**

a. To every distinct pair of points there corresponds exactly one positive number. This number is the distance between the two points.

b. To every real number there corresponds a point on the number line. To every point on the number line there corresponds a real number.

Postulate 9 **The Protractor Postulate**

a. To every angle there corresponds exactly one real number between 0 and 180. This number is the measure of the angle.

b. For half-plane H and the point Q on its edge, p, the rays in H or p with vertex Q can be placed in one-to-one correspondence with the real numbers n, $0 < n < 180$, such that a coordinate system for rays is established.

Postulate 10 **Linear Pair Postulate**

If two angles form a linear pair, then they are supplementary.

Postulate 11 **S.A.S. Postulate**

If two triangles have two sides and the included angle of one triangle congruent respectively to two sides and the included angle of the other triangle, then the triangles are congruent.

Postulate 12 **A.S.A. Postulate**

If two triangles have two angles and the included side of one triangle congruent respectively to two angles and the included side of the other triangle, then the triangles are congruent.

Postulate 13 S.S.S. **Postulate**

If two triangles have three sides of one triangle congruent respectively to the three sides of the other triangle, then the triangles are congruent.

Postulate 14 H.A. **Postulate**

If two right triangles have the hypotenuse and an acute angle of one triangle congruent respectively to the hypotenuse and an acute angle of the other triangle, then the triangles are congruent.

Postulate 15 Through a point not on a given line, there is exactly one line parallel to the given line.

Area Postulates

Postulate 16 To each polygon (polygonal region) there corresponds a positive number which is its area.

Postulate 17 Regions of congruent triangles have the same area.

Postulate 18 The area of a polygon is the sum of the areas of the triangular regions into which it is separated.

Postulate 19 The area A of a rectangle is the product of its length, ℓ, and its width, w. That is, $A = \ell w$.

Volume Postulates

Postulate 20 Every geometric solid corresponds to a positive number which is its volume.

Postulate 21 The volume of a solid figure is the sum of the volumes of a finite number of nonoverlapping figures of which it is composed.

Postulate 22 The volume V of a rectangular prism is the product of its altitude h, the length of its base, ℓ, and the width of its base, w. That is, $V = \ell wh$.

Theorems

Theorem 1-1 If two distinct planes intersect, then their intersection is a line.

Theorem 1-2 If two distinct lines intersect, then their intersection is a point.

Theorem 1-3 If a line and a plane intersect and the plane does not contain the line, then their intersection is a point.

Theorem 1-4 If a point is not on a line, then the point and the line determine exactly one plane.

Theorem 1-5 If two distinct lines intersect, then they determine exactly one plane.

Theorem 2-1 A segment has exactly one midpoint.

Theorem 2-2 An angle has exactly one bisector.

Theorem 2-3 Through a given point on a line in a plane, there is exactly one line in that plane perpendicular to the given line.

Theorem 2-4 For a given segment in a plane, the segment has exactly one perpendicular bisector in the plane.

Theorem 2-5 Congruence is an equivalence relation.

Theorem 2-6 If two angles are supplements of the same angle, then they are congruent.

Theorem 2-7 If two angles are complements of the same angle, then they are congruent.

Theorem 2-8 If two angles are supplements of congruent angles, then they are congruent.

Theorem 2-9 If two angles are complements of congruent angles, then they are congruent.

Theorem 2-10 Vertical angles are congruent.

Theorem 2-11 If one angle of a linear pair is a right angle, then the other is also a right angle.

Theorem 2-12 If two intersecting lines form one right angle, then they form four right angles.

Corollary 2-13 Perpendicular lines form four right angles.

Corollary 2-14 All right angles are congruent.

Theorem 2-15 If congruent adjacent angles are formed by two intersecting lines, then the lines are perpendicular.

Theorem 2-16 If two lines are perpendicular, then they form congruent adjacent angles.

Theorem 3-1 **Isosceles Triangle Theorem**

If two sides of a triangle are congruent, then the angles opposite these sides are congruent.

Corollary 3-2 If the three sides of a triangle are congruent, then the three angles are also congruent.

Theorem 3-3 If two angles of a triangle are congruent, then the sides opposite these angles are congruent.

Corollary 3-4 If the three angles of a triangle are congruent, then the three sides are congruent.

Theorem 3-5 The bisector of the vertex angle of an isosceles triangle is the perpendicular bisector of the base.

Theorem 3-6 The median from the vertex angle of an isosceles triangle is perpendicular to the base and bisects the vertex angle.

Theorem 3-7 Any point on the perpendicular bisector of a segment is equidistant from the endpoints of the segment.

Theorem 3-8 In a plane, a line is the perpendicular bisector of a given segment if and only if it is determined by two points equidistant from the endpoints of the segment.

Theorem 3-9 **H.L. Theorem**

If two right triangles have the hypotenuse and one leg of one triangle congruent respectively to the hypotenuse and one leg of the other triangle, then the triangles are congruent.

Corollary 3-10 In an isosceles triangle, the altitude to the base bisects the base and bisects the vertex angle.

Theorem 3-11 Through a point not on a line, there is exactly one line perpendicular to a given line.

Theorem 3-12 If a point is on the bisector of an angle, it is equidistant from the sides of angle.

Theorem 3-13 If a point in the interior of an angle is equidistant from the sides of an angle, then it is on the bisector of the angle.

Theorem 4-1 **Exterior Angle Inequality Theorem**

The measure of an exterior angle of a triangle is greater than the measure of either of its remote interior angles.

Theorem 4-2 If two lines are cut by a transversal so that alternate interior angles are congruent, then the lines are parallel.

Theorem 4-3 If two parallel lines are cut by a transversal, then alternate interior angles are congruent.

Theorem 4-4 If two lines are cut by a transversal so that interior angles on the same side of the transversal are supplementary, then the lines are parallel.

Theorem 4-5 If two lines are cut by a transversal, then interior angles on the same side of the transversal are supplementary.

Theorem 4-6 Two parallel lines determine exactly one plane.

Theorem 4-7 In a plane, if two lines are both perpendicular to a third line, then the two lines are parallel.

Theorem 4-8 In a plane, if a line is perpendicular to one of two parallel lines, then it is perpendicular to the other line also.

Theorem 4-9 If two lines are cut by a transversal so that corresponding angles are congruent, then the lines are parallel.

Theorem 4-10 If two parallel lines are cut by a transversal, then corresponding angles are congruent.

Theorem 4-11 Two distinct lines parallel to the same line are parallel to each other.

Theorem 4-12 **Triangle-Sum Theorem**

The sum of the measures of the angles of a triangle is 180.

Corollary 4-13 If two angles of one triangle are congruent to two angles of another triangle, then the third angles are congruent.

Corollary 4-14 A triangle can have no more than one right angle or one obtuse angle.

Corollary 4-15 The acute angles of a right triangle are complementary.

Corollary 4-16 The measure of each angle of an equilateral triangle is 60.

Corollary 4-17 **S.A.A. Corollary**

If two triangles have a side and two angles of one congruent respectively to a side and two angles of the other, then the triangles are congruent.

Corollary 4-18 **Exterior Angle-Sum Corollary for Triangles**

The measure of one exterior angle of a triangle equals the sum of the measures of its remote interior angles.

Theorem 4-19 **Angle-Sum Theorem for Polygons**

The formula for the sum, S, of the measures of the angles of a polygon of n sides is $S = (n - 2)180$.

Corollary 4-20 If a polygon has n sides and if all of its angles are congruent, then the formula for the measure of one of its angles, a, is $a = \frac{(n-2)180}{n}$.

Corollary 4-21 **Exterior Angle-Sum Corollary**

The sum, E, of the measures of the exterior angles of a polygon, taking one exterior angle at each vertex, is 360.

Corollary 4-22 If a polygon of n sides is equiangular, then the measure e of one of its exterior angles is $e = \frac{360}{n}$.

Theorem 5-1 A diagonal of a parallelogram forms two congruent triangles.

Corollary 5-2 The opposite sides of a parallelogram are congruent.

Corollary 5-3 The opposite angles of a parallelogram are congruent.

Corollary 5-4 If two lines are parallel, then any two points on one of the lines are equidistant from the other line.

Theorem 5-5 The diagonals of a parallelogram bisect each other.

Theorem 5-6 Any two consecutive angles of a parallelogram are supplementary.

Theorem 5-7 If both pairs of opposite sides of a quadrilateral are congruent, then the quadrilateral is a parallelogram.

Theorem 5-8 If two sides of a quadrilateral are parallel and congruent, then the quadrilateral is a parallelogram.

Theorem 5-9 The diagonals of a rectangle are congruent.

Theorem 5-10 The diagonals of a rhombus are perpendicular to each other.

Theorem 5-11 The diagonals of a rhombus bisect the angles of the rhombus.

Theorem 5-12 If a segment joins the midpoints of two sides of a triangle, then it is parallel to the third side and its length is one half the length of the third side.

Theorem 5-13 The median of a trapezoid is parallel to the bases and its length is one half the sum of the lengths of the bases.

Theorem 5-14 If three or more parallel lines cut off congruent segments on one transversal, then they cut off congruent segments on any transversal.

Corollary 5-15 If a line is parallel to one side of a triangle and bisects a second side, then it bisects the third side also.

Corollary 5-16 If a line is parallel to the bases of a trapezoid and bisects one of the nonparallel sides, then it bisects the other side also.

Theorem 5-17 If two sides of a triangle are not congruent, then the angles opposite these sides are not congruent, and the smaller angle is opposite the smaller side.

Theorem 5-18 If two angles of a triangle are not congruent, then the sides opposite these angles are not congruent, and the smaller side is opposite the smaller angle.

Theorem 5-19 The perpendicular segment from a point to a line is the shortest distance from the point to the line.

Theorem 5-20 **Triangle Inequality Theorem**

The sum of the lengths of two sides of a triangle is greater than the length of the third side.

Theorem 5-21 If two sides of one triangle are congruent to two sides of another triangle and if the included angles are not congruent, then the remaining sides are also not congruent, and the smaller side is opposite the smaller angle.

Theorem 5-22 If two sides of one triangle are congruent to two sides of another triangle and if the third sides are not congruent, then the angles opposite the third sides are also not congruent, and the smaller angle is opposite the smaller side.

Theorem 5-23 All plane angles of the same dihedral angle are congruent.

Theorem 6-1 $\frac{a}{b} = \frac{c}{d}$ if and only if $ad = bc$. $(b \neq 0, d \neq 0)$

Theorem 6-2 If $\frac{a}{b} = \frac{c}{d}$, then $\frac{a+b}{b} = \frac{c+d}{d}$ and $\frac{a-b}{b} = \frac{c-d}{d}$.

Theorem 6-3 If three parallel lines intersect two transversals, then the lines divide the transversals proportionally.

Corollary 6-4 If a line intersecting the interior of a triangle is parallel to one side, then the line divides the other two sides proportionally.

Corollary 6-5 If a line intersecting the interior of a triangle is parallel to one side, then either side intersected by the line is to one of its segments as the other side is to its corresponding segment.

Corollary 6-6 If a line divides two sides of a triangle proportionally, then the line is parallel to the third side.

Corollary 6-7 The bisector of an angle of a triangle divides the opposite side into segments that are proportional to the adjacent sides of the triangle.

Corollary 6-8 If two lines are cut by three parallel planes, the corresponding segments are proportional.

Theorem 6-9 **A.A.A. Theorem**

If the angles of one triangle are congruent to the angles of another triangle, then the triangles are similar.

Corollary 6-10 **A.A. Corollary**

If two angles of one triangle are congruent to two angles of a second triangle, then the triangles are similar.

Corollary 6-11 If two right triangles have an acute angle of one congruent to an acute angle of the other, then the triangles are similar.

Corollary 6-12 If a line parallel to one side of a triangle determines a second triangle, then the second triangle will be similar to the original triangle.

Theorem 6-13 **S.A.S. Similarity Theorem**

If an angle of one triangle is congruent to an angle of another, and the sides including these angles are proportional, then the triangles are similar.

Theorem 6-14 **S.S.S. Similarity Theorem**

If the corresponding sides of two triangles are proportional, then the triangles are similar.

Corollary 6-15 The perimeters of two similar triangles are proportional to any pair of corresponding sides.

Corollary 6-16 The altitudes of similar triangles are proportional to any pair of corresponding sides.

Corollary 6-17 The medians of similar triangles are proportional to any pair of corresponding sides.

Theorem 6-18 The altitude to the hypotenuse of a right triangle determines two triangles that are similar to each other and to the original triangle.

Theorem 6-19 The altitude to the hypotenuse of a right triangle is the geometric mean between the two segments of the hypotenuse.

Corollary 6-20 If the altitude to the hypotenuse of a right triangle is drawn, either leg of the triangle is the geometric mean between the hypotenuse and the segment of the hypotenuse adjacent to the leg.

Theorem 6-21 **Pythagorean Theorem**

In any right triangle, the square of the length of the hypotenuse equals the sum of the squares of the lengths of the other two sides.

Theorem 6-22 If the square of the length of one side of a triangle equals the sum of the squares of the lengths of the other two sides, then the triangle is a right triangle.

Theorem 6-23 **Isosceles Right Triangle Theorem**

In an isosceles right triangle with legs of length a and hypotenuse of length c, $a = \frac{c\sqrt{2}}{2}$ and $c = a\sqrt{2}$.

Theorem 6-24 **30-60-90 Triangle Theorem**

In any right triangle with acute angle measures of 30 and 60 and with hypotenuse s, the length of the shorter leg (opposite the 30°-angle) is $\frac{s}{2}$, and the length of the longer leg (opposite the 60°-angle) is $\frac{s\sqrt{3}}{2}$.

Theorem 7-1 **Arc-Addition Theorem**

If B is a point on $\widehat{AC}$, then $m\widehat{AB} + m\widehat{BC} = m\widehat{AC}$.

Theorem 7-2 In the same circle or in congruent circles, two arcs are congruent if and only if their central angles are congruent.

Theorem 7-3 In the same or in congruent circles, two chords are congruent if their arcs are congruent.

Theorem 7-4 In the same or in congruent circles, two arcs are congruent if their chords are congruent.

Theorem 7-5 If a diameter of a circle is perpendicular to a chord, then it bisects the chord and its arc.

Theorem 7-6 If one chord of a circle intersects a second chord so that it bisects both the second chord and its arc, then the first chord is a diameter and is perpendicular to the second chord.

Theorem 7-7 If a diameter bisects a chord that is not a diameter, then it is perpendicular to the chord and bisects its arc.

Theorem 7-8 In the same circle or in congruent circles, two chords are congruent if and only if they are equidistant from the center.

Theorem 7-9 In the same or in congruent circles, if two chords are not congruent then their distances from the center of the circle are not equal, and the longer chord is closer to the center of the circle.

Theorem 7-10 In the same or in congruent circles, if the distances of two chords from the center of the circle are not equal, then the chords are not congruent, and the chord that is closer to the center of the circle is the longer chord.

Theorem 7-11 In the plane of a given circle O, a line is perpendicular to radius OC at C if and only if the line is tangent to the circle at C.

Theorem 7-12 The two tangent segments from the same exterior point of a circle are congruent.

Corollary 7-13 The two tangents to a circle from a given point in the exterior of the circle determine an angle that is bisected by the segment joining the given point to the center of the circle.

Theorem 7-14 The measure of an inscribed angle is one half the measure of its intercepted arc.

Theorem 7-15 If inscribed angles intercept the same arc or congruent arcs, the angles are congruent.

Corollary 7-16 An inscribed angle is a right angle if and only if it is inscribed in a semicircle.

Corollary 7-17 If two secants of the same circle are parallel, then the arcs between them are congruent.

Corollary 7-18 The opposite angles of an inscribed quadrilateral are supplementary.

Theorem 7-19 If a tangent and a secant (or chord) intersect in a point on a circle, the measure of the angle formed is one half the measure of the intercepted arc.

Theorem 7-20 If two secants (or chords) intersect in the interior of a circle, the measure of an angle formed is one half the sum of the measures of the arcs intercepted by the angle and its vertical angle.

Theorem 7-21 If two secants intersect in the exterior of a circle, the measure of the angle formed by the secants is one half the difference of the measures of the intercepted arcs.

Theorem 7-22 If a tangent and a secant intersect in the exterior of a circle, the measure of the angle formed is one half the difference of the measures of the intercepted arcs.

Theorem 7-23 If two tangents intersect in the exterior of a circle, the measure of the angle formed is one half the difference of the intercepted arcs.

Theorem 7-24 If two chords of a circle intersect in the interior of a circle, the product of the lengths of the segments of the first chord equals the product of the lengths of the segments of the second chord.

Theorem 7-25 If two secant segments are drawn to a circle from the same exterior point, the product of the lengths of one secant segment and its external segment equals the product of the lengths of the other secant segment and its external segment.

Theorem 7-26 If a tangent and a secant are drawn to a circle from the same exterior point, the tangent segment is the geometric mean between the secant segment and its external segment.

Theorem 7-27 If a plane intersects a sphere, the intersection is either a point or a circle.

Theorem 8-1 The area A of a parallelogram is the product of a base b and its corresponding altitude h. That is, $A = bh$.

Corollary 8-2 Parallelograms with equal bases and equal altitudes have equal areas.

Theorem 8-3 The area A os a triangle is one half the product of a base b and its corresponding altitude h. That is, $A = \frac{1}{2}bh$.

Corollary 8-4 Triangles with equal bases and equal altitudes have equal areas.

Corollary 8-5 The area A of an equilateral triangle with side of length s is $\frac{s^2\sqrt{3}}{4}$. That is,

$$A = \frac{s^2\sqrt{3}}{4}.$$

Corollary 8-6 The area A of a rhombus is one half the product of the lengths of its diagonals, d_1 and d_2. That is,

$$A = \frac{1}{2}d_1d_2.$$

Theorem 8-7 The area A of a trapezoid is one half the product of its altitude and the sum of its bases b and b'. That is,

$$A = \frac{1}{2}h(b + b').$$

Theorem 8-8 A polygon is regular if and only if a circle with a common center can be inscribed in and circumscribed about it.

Corollary 8-9 The measure of each central angle of a regular polygon of n sides is $\frac{360}{n}$.

Corollary 8-10 A radius of a regular polygon bisects an angle of the polygon.

Corollary 8-11 The apothem of a regular polygon is the perpendicular bisector of a side of the polygon.

Theorem 8-12 The area A of a regular polygon is one half the product of its perimeter, P, and the length, a, of the apothem. That is,

$$A = \frac{1}{2}aP.$$

Theorem 8-13 Regular polygons of the same number of sides are similar.

Corollary 8-14 The perimeters of similar polygons have the same ratio as the measures of any two corresponding sides.

Corollary 8-15 The perimeters of two regular polygons of the same number of sides have the same ratio as their radii or as their apothems.

Theorem 8-16 The areas of two similar polygons have the same ratio as the squares of the measures of any two corresponding sides.

Corollary 8-17 The areas of two regular polygons of the same number of sides have the same ratio as the squares of their radii or as the squares of their apothems.

Theorem 8-18 The ratio $\frac{C}{d}$ of the circumference, C, of a circle to the measure of the diameter, d, is the same for all circles.

Corollary 8-19 The circumferences of two circles have the same ratio as their radii.

Corollary 8-20 In a circle, the ratio of the length ℓ of an arc to the circumference C is equal to the ratio of the degree measure m of the arc to 360. That is,

$$\frac{\ell}{C} = \frac{m}{360}, \text{ or } \frac{\ell}{2\pi r} = \frac{m}{360}.$$

Theorem 8-21 The area A of a circle of radius r is πr^2. That is, $A = \pi r^2$.

Corollary 8-22 The areas of two circles have the same ratio as the squares of their radii.

Corollary 8-23 In a circle with radius r, the ratio of the area, A, of a sector to the area of the circle equals the ratio of the degree measure, m, of its arc to 360. That is,

$$\frac{A}{\pi r^2} = \frac{m}{360}, \text{ or } A = \frac{m}{360}\pi r^2.$$

Theorem 9-1 The lateral surface area L of a right prism is the product of the perimeter P of its base and its lateral edge e. That is, $L = Pe$.

Theorem 9-2 The lateral area L of a regular pyramid is one half the product of its slant height s and the perimeter P of its base. That is,

$$L = \tfrac{1}{2}sP.$$

Theorem 9-3 The lateral area L of a right circular cylinder with altitude h and base radius r is $2\pi rh$. The total area T is $2\pi rh + 2\pi r^2$. That is,

$$L = 2\pi rh \text{ and } T = 2\pi r(h + r).$$

Theorem 9-4 The lateral area L of a right circular cone is one half the product of its slant height s and the circumference $2\pi r$ of its base. The total area T is $\pi rs + \pi r^2$. That is,

$$L = \pi rs \text{ and } T = \pi r(s + r).$$

Theorem 10-1 **The Midpoint Formula**

The coordinates (x_m, y_m) of the midpoint M of the segment whose endpoints are $P_1(x_1, y_1)$ and $P_2(x_2, y_2)$ are

$$x_m = \frac{x_1 + x_2}{2} \text{ and } y_m = \frac{y_1 + y_2}{2}.$$

Theorem 10-2 Two nonvertical lines are parallel if and only if they have the same slope.

Theorem 10-3 Two nonvertical lines are perpendicular if and only if their slopes are negative reciprocals.

Theorem 10-4 **The Distance Formula**

The distance, d, between two points $P_1(x_1, y_1)$ and $P_2(x_2, y_2)$ is

$$d = \sqrt{(x_2 - x_1)^2 + (y_2 - y_1)^2}.$$

Theorem 11-1 The perpendicular bisectors of the sides of a triangle are concurrent in a point that is equidistant from the vertices of the triangle.

Theorem 11-2 The bisectors of the angles of a triangle are concurrent in a point that is equidistant from the sides of the triangle.

Theorem 11-3 The altitudes of a triangle are concurrent.

Theorem 11-4 The medians of a triangle are concurrent in a point that is two thirds of the distance from each vertex to the midpoint of the opposite side.

Vector Theorem 1 $\overrightarrow{AB} + \overrightarrow{BC} = \overrightarrow{AC}$

Vector Theorem 2 If $\overrightarrow{AB} = (a, b)$ and $a \neq 0$, then the slope of $\overleftrightarrow{AB}$ is $\frac{b}{a}$.

Vector Theorem 3 For the nonzero vectors AB and CD, if $\overrightarrow{AB} = \overrightarrow{CD}$, then $\overleftrightarrow{AB} \parallel \overleftrightarrow{CD}$ and $AB = CD$.

Vector Theorem 4 If $\overrightarrow{AB} = \overrightarrow{DC}$ and $ABCD$ is a quadrilateral, then $ABCD$ is a parallelogram.

Vector Theorem 5 $\overrightarrow{AM} = \overrightarrow{MB}$ if and only if M is the midpoint of $\overrightarrow{AB}$.

Vector Theorem 6 If $\overrightarrow{AB} = \overrightarrow{DC}$ in quadrilateral $ABCD$ and M is the midpoint of $\overline{BD}$, then $\overrightarrow{AM} = \overrightarrow{MC}$.

Vector Theorem 7 For the nonzero vectors AB and CD, if $\overrightarrow{AB} = s\overrightarrow{CD}$, then $\overrightarrow{AB}$ and $\overrightarrow{CD}$ lie on parallel lines.

Vector Theorem 8 If $\overrightarrow{AB} = s\overrightarrow{CD}$, then $|\overrightarrow{AB}| = |s| \cdot |\overrightarrow{CD}|$.

Vector Theorem 9 If a segment joins the midpoints of two sides of a triangle, it is parallel to the third side and is one half as long as the third side.

Boldfaced numerals indicate the pages that contain formal or informal definitions.

D 0
E 1
F 2
G 3
H 4
I 5
J 6